CALCULUS

Concepts and Applications

Solutions Manual

Paul A. Foerster

Editors: Sarah Block and Bill Medigovich
Mathematics Reviewers: Cavan Fang, Leslie Nielsen, and Loyce Collenback
Copyeditor: Judith Abrahms
Production Manager: Luis Shein
Layout: Kirk Mills
Production Coordinator: Susan Parini
Production Assistant: Carrye De Mers

Cover Design: Maryann Ohki
Cover Photograph: Images ©1995 PhotoDisc, Inc.

Publisher: Steven Rasmussen
Editorial Director: John Bergez

Key Curriculum Press
1150 65th Street
Emeryville, CA 94608
(510) 595-7000
editorial@keypress.com
http://www.keypress.com

Printed in the United States of America

10 9 8 7 6 5 4 02 01 00 99

ISBN 1-55953-118-5

The graphs in this text were created using PSMathGraphs II. PSMathGraphs is a trademark of MaryAnn Software.

Contents

Overview

This *Solutions Manual* contains the answers to all problems in *Calculus: Concepts and Applications*. Solutions or key steps in the solutions are presented for all but the simplest problems.

In most cases the solutions are presented in the form your students would be expected to use. For instance, decimal approximations are displayed as *exact* answers using ellipsis format for a mathematical world answer, then rounded to an appropriate number of decimal places with units of measurement applied for the corresponding real-world answer. An answer such as $f(3) = 13.7569\ldots \approx 13.8$ cm indicates that the precise answer, 13.7569 . . . , has been retained in memory in the student's calculator without round-off for possible use in subsequent computations. The ellipses indicate that the student chooses not to write all the digits on his or her paper.

Because the problems applying to the real world may be somewhat unfamiliar to both you and your students, fairly complete solutions are presented for these. Often commentary is included over and above what the student would be expected to write to further guide your evaluation of students' solutions, and in some cases reference is provided to later sections in which more sophisticated solutions appear. Later in the text, the details of computing definite integrals by the fundamental theorem are omitted because students are usually expected to do these numerically. However, exact answers such as $V = 8\pi/3$ are presented where possible in case you choose to have your students do the algebraic integration.

Solutions are not presented for journal entries because these are highly individual for each student. The "prompts" in most problems calling for journal entries should be sufficient to guide students in making their own responses.

Where programs are called for, you may use as a model the programs in the *Instructor's Resource Book*. Check the publisher's Web page (see the address on the copyright page of this manual) for further information on programs for specific models of the graphing calculator.

As the author of this manual, I assume full responsibility for the correctness of the solutions. If you or your students find any mistakes, please report them to Key Curriculum Press by sending in the Correction/Comment Form in the back of this book. Wrong answers are more important than typographical errors.

Paul A. Foerster

Chapter 1

Problem Set 1-1, page 5 — The Concept of Instantaneous Rate

1. Pendulum Problem
   a. 95 cm, Q.E.D.
   b. t = 5.1, rate ≈ 26.34 cm/sec
      t = 5.01, rate ≈ 27.12 cm/sec
      t = 5.001, rate ≈ 27.20 cm/sec
      So the instantaneous rate of change at t = 5 is about 27.20 or 27.21 cm/sec
   c. Instantaneous rate would involve division by zero.
   d. For t = 1.5 to 1.501, rate ≈ −31.42 cm/sec The pendulum is approaching the wall. Since the rate of change is negative, the distance is decreasing.
   e. The instantaneous rate of change is the limit of the average rates as the time interval approaches zero. It is called the derivative.
   f. Before t = 0 the pendulum was not yet moving. For large values of t, the pendulum's motion will die out due to friction.

2. Board Price Problem
   a. x = 5: y = 305, price is $3.05
      x = 10: y = 520, price is $5.20
      x = 20: y = 1280, price is $12.80
   b. x = 5.1, rate ≈ 46.822 ¢/ft
      x = 5.01, rate ≈ 46.9820... ¢/ft
      x = 5.001, rate ≈ 46.9982... ¢/ft
   c. 47 ¢/ft It is called the derivative.
   d. x = 10: 44 ¢/ft x = 20: 128 ¢/ft
   e. The 20-ft board costs more per foot than the 10-ft board. The reason is that longer boards require taller trees, which are harder to find.

Problem Set 1-2, pages 10 to 13 — Rate of Change by Equation, Graph, or Table

Q1. Power (polynomial) fn. Q2. f(2) = 8
Q3. Exponential function Q4. g(2) = 9
Q5. Graph Q6. h(5) = 25

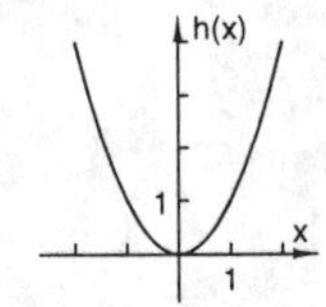

Q7. $y = ax^2 + bx + c$, $a \neq 0$ Q8. y = x
Q9. y = |x| Q10. Derivative

1. a. Increasing slowly.
   b. Increasing fast.
2. a. Increasing fast.
   b. Decreasing slowly.
3. a. Decreasing fast.
   b. Decreasing slowly.
4. a. Decreasing slowly.
   b. Increasing slowly.
5. a. Increasing fast.
   b. Increasing slowly.
   c. Decreasing slowly.
   d. Increasing fast.
6. a. Decreasing fast.
   b. Increasing slowly.
   c. Increasing fast.
   d. Decreasing fast.
7. a. Increasing slowly.
   b. Increasing slowly.
   c. Increasing slowly.
8. a. Decreasing fast.
   b. Decreasing fast.
   c. Decreasing fast.
9. a. Increasing fast.
   b. Neither increasing nor decreasing.
   c. Increasing fast.
   d. Increasing slowly.
10. a. Decreasing slowly.
    b. Decreasing fast.
    c. Decreasing fast.
    d. Neither increasing nor decreasing.
11. a. x = 1.5: rate ≈ 6.0 cm/min Increasing.
    b. x = 3.0: rate ≈ 6.8 cm/min Increasing.
    c. x = 4.0: rate ≈ −0.3 cm/min Decreasing.
12. a. x = 1.0: rate ≈ 0.02 cm/min Increasing.
    b. x = 3.0: rate ≈ 0.42 cm/min Increasing.
    c. x = 4.5: rate ≈ 2.3 cm/min Increasing.
13. Rolling Tire Problem
    a. i. −1.0 in/sec ii. 0.0 in/sec iii. 1.15 in/sec
    b. 1.7 sec, since y = 0 at that time.
14. Flat Tire Problem
    a. i. t = 2: rate ≈ −0.395 in/min
       ii. t = 8: rate ≈ −0.14 in/min
       iii. t = 14: rate ≈ −0.105 in/min
    b. The rate is negative, because y is decreasing as the tire goes down.
15. a. Quadratic (or polynomial).
    b. f(3) = 30
    c. Increasing at about 11.0 (2.99 to 3.01)
16. a. Quadratic (or polynomial).
    b. f(1) = 12.
    c. Increasing at about 6.0 (0.99 to 1.01)
17. a. Exponential.
    b. f(2) = 9
    c. Increasing at about 9.89 (1.99 to 2.01)
18. a. Exponential.
    b. $f(-3) = 2^{-3} = 0.125$
    c. Increasing at about 0.0866 (−3.01 to −2.99)
19. a. Rational algebraic.
    b. f(4) = −1
    c. Decreasing at about 1.00 (3.99 to 4.01)
20. a. Rational algebraic.
    b. f(−2) = −1/(−2) = 0.5
    c. Increasing at about 0.2500 (−2.01 to −1.99)
21. a. Linear (or polynomial).
    b. f(5) = −8
    c. Decreasing at 3 (Exact)
22. a. Linear (or polynomial).
    b. f(8) = −3.4
    c. Increasing at 0.2 (Exact)
23. a. Circular (or trigonometric).
    b. f(2) = 0.90929...
    c. Decreasing at about 0.416 (1.99 to 2.01)
24. a. Circular (or trigonometric).
    b. f(1) = 0.54030...
    c. Decreasing at about 0.8414 (0.99 to 1.01).

25. Accurate Graph of a Cubic Function Problem

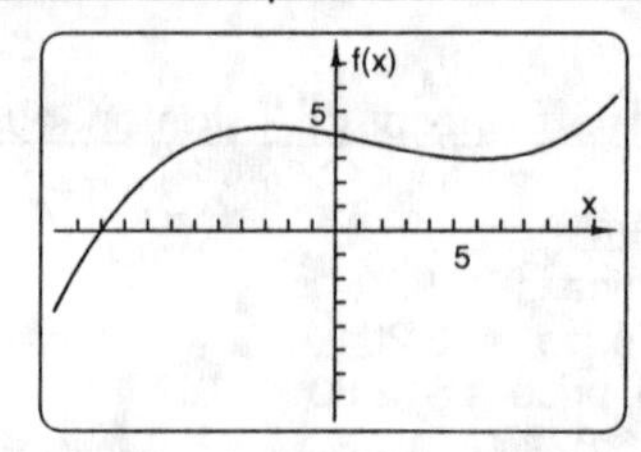

a. f(x) is increasing fast when the graph slopes steeply upward.
b. f(x) is decreasing for about $-3 < x < 6$.
c. False. f(x) is positive, but decreasing between $x = -3$ and $x = 6$.
d. f(x) is decreasing fastest at about $x = 1$ or 2.

26. Accurate Graph of a Rational Function Problem

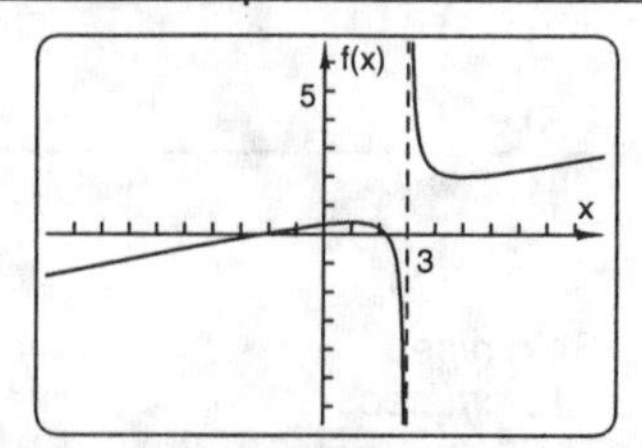

a. f(x) is increasing slowly when x is far from 3.
b. f(x) is decreasing fast when x is close to 3.
c. f(x) stops increasing and starts decreasing at about $x = 1$.
d. f(x) stops decreasing and starts increasing at about $x = 5$.
e. f(x) is a real number for all $x \neq 3$.
f. By tracing on the graph, the high point $f(1) = 0.4$ and the low point $f(5) = 2$. So the range is $y \leq 0.4$ or $y \geq 2$.

27. See definition in text.

28. Discussion Problem: Meaning of Limit
The ratio can be kept within a certain number of units of the limit just by keeping the change in x close enough to zero, but not equal to zero.

Problem Set 1-3, pages 16 to 18 — One Type of Integral of a Function

Q1. $f(5) = 4$
Q2. Area = 72 ft^2
Q3. Graph.

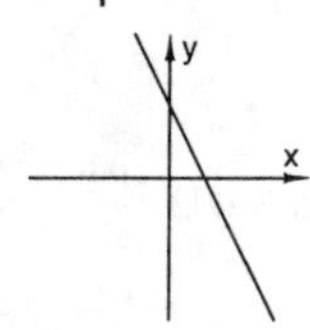

Q4. Graph.

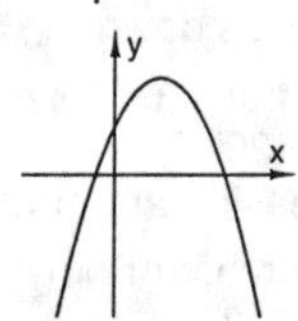

Q5. Graph.

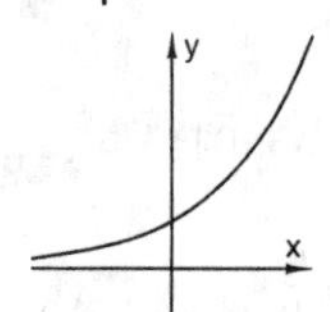

Q6. Undefined at $x = 3$

Q7. $y = \cos x$
Q8. $y = 2^x$
Q9. $y = 1/x$
Q10. $y = x^2$

1. $f(x) = -0.1x^2 + 7$
   a. Approx. 30.8
   b. Approx. 41.8

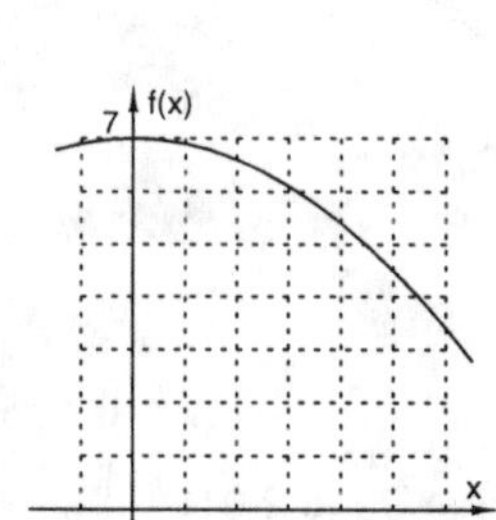

2. $f(x) = -0.2x^2 + 8$
   a. Approx. 22.2
   b. Approx. 47.1

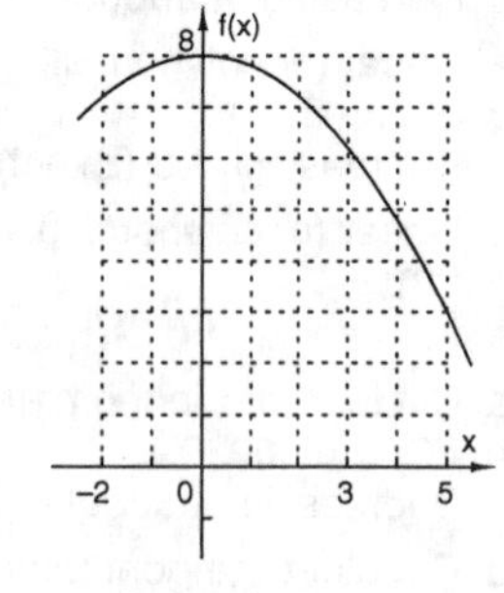

3. $h(x) = \sin x$
   a. Approx. 2.0
   b. Approx. 1.0

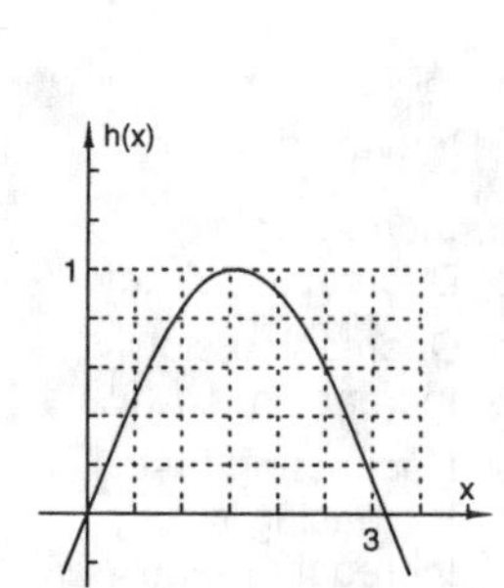

4. $g(x) = 2^x + 5$
   a. Approx. 7.9
   b. Approx. 12.2

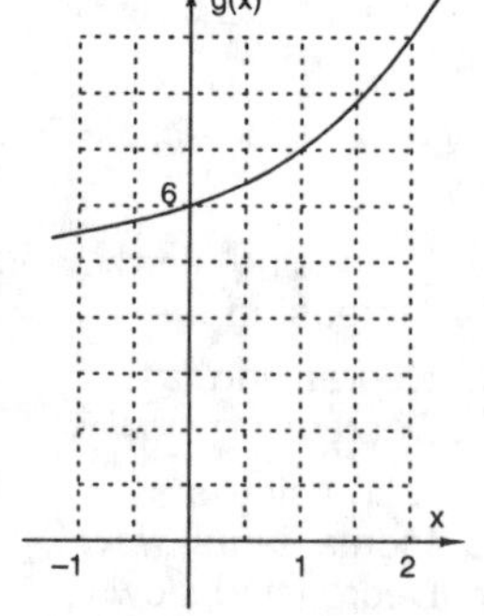

5. There are approximately 6.8 squares. Each square represents (5)(20) = 100 feet. So the distance is about 680 feet.

6. There are approximately 53.3 squares. Each square represents (0.5)(10) = 5 miles. So the distance is about 266 miles.

7. Derivative $\approx \dfrac{\tan 1.01 - \tan 0.99}{1.01 - 0.99} = 3.42...$

8. Derivative = -7 (exactly, since that is the slope of the linear function).

9. Sports Car Problem

a. Graph.

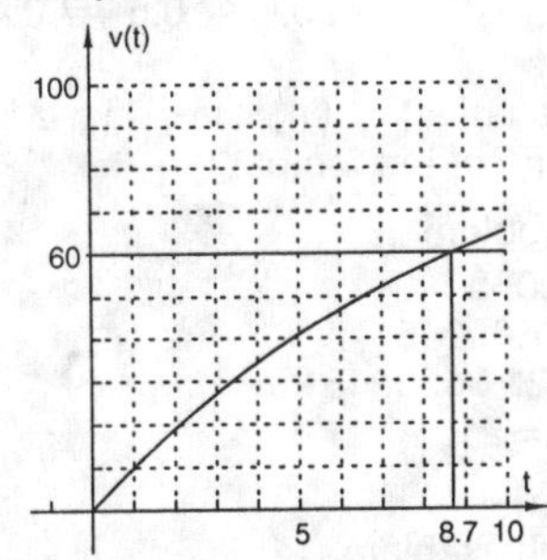

b. Range is $0 \le y < 100$.

c. Using SOLVE, x = 8.6967... ≈ 8.7 sec

d. By counting squares, distance ≈ 300 ft

e. Rate $\approx \dfrac{v(5.01) - v(4.99)}{5.01 - 4.99} = 6.2214...$

About 6.2 (ft/sec)/sec

f. The rate of change of speed is called acceleration.

10. Slide Problem

a. Graph.

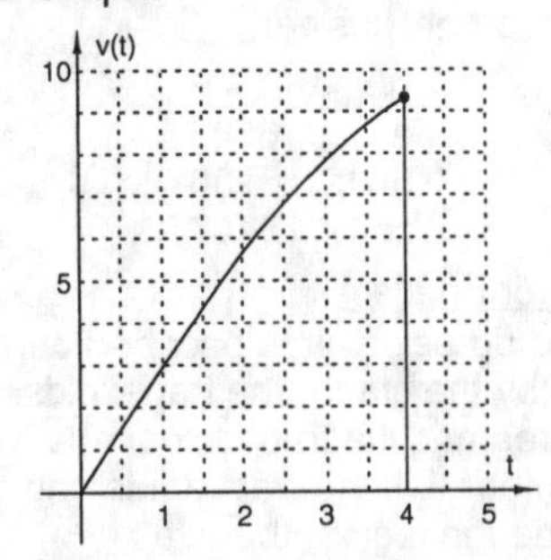

b. Domain: $0 \le t \le 4$. Range: $0 \le v(t) \le 9.32...$

c. v(4) = 9.3203... ≈ 9.3 ft/sec

d. By counting squares, slide is about 21.3 ft

e. Rate $\approx \dfrac{v(3.01) - v(2.99)}{3.01 - 2.99} = 1.8648...$

About 1.86 (ft/sec)/sec

f. Rate of change of speed is acceleration.

11. Negative Velocity Problem

From t = 0 to t = 5, object goes about 11.4 cm.
From t = 5 to t = 9, object goes back about 4.3 cm.
Object is about 11.4 – 4.3 = 7.1 cm from start.

12. The derivative of a function is the instantaneous rate of change of the dependent variable with respect to the independent variable.

13. See text definition of definite integral.

14. See text definition of limit.

Problem Set 1-4, pages 21 to 25 — Definite Integrals by Trapezoids, from Equations and Data

Q1. y changes at 30
Q2. Derivative ≈ –500
Q3. Graph
Q4. f(3) = 9

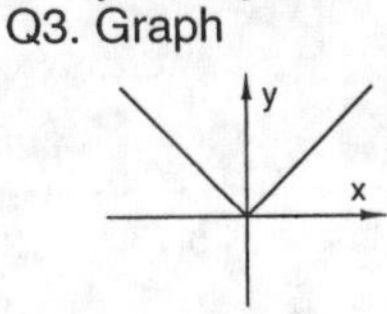

Q5. 100
Q6. sin (π/2) = 1
Q7. 366 days
Q8. derivative
Q9. definite integral
Q10. f(x) = 0 at x = 4

1. Spaceship Problem

a. $v(t) = 1600 \times 1.1^t$. Graph.

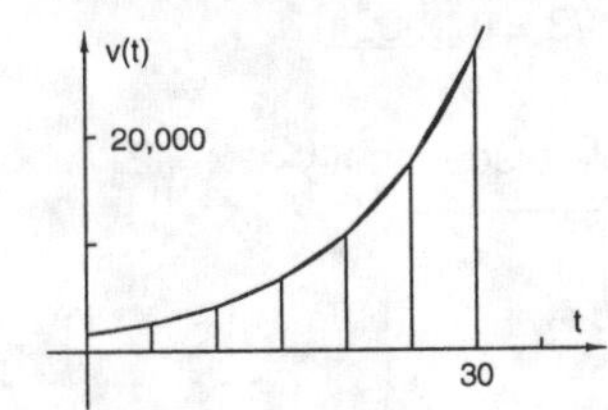

b. Distance = rate × time. Since the vertical axis represents distance and the horizontal axis represents time, their product (i.e., the area) represents distance.

c. Graph.

Distance ≈ 5(0.5v(0) + v(5) + v(10) + v(15) + v(20) + v(25) + 0.5v(30))
= 5(56269.45...) = 281347.26... ≈ 281,000 ft

d. Definite integral.

e. Yes, it will be going fast enough.
v(30) = 27,919.04... > 27,000

2. Walking Problem

a. v(t) = 4 + sin 1.4t

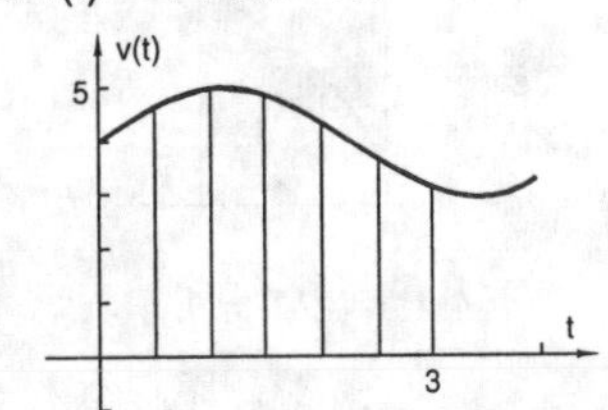

b. A definite integral has the units of the x-variable times the y-variable. Distance = rate × time. Since v(t) is distance/time and t is time, their product is expressed in units of distance.

c. Distance ≈ 0.5(0.5v(0) + v(0.5) + v(1) + v(1.5) + v(2) + v(2.5) + 0.5v(3))
= 0.5(26.041...) = 13.02064... ≈ 13.0 ft
Graph, part (a).

d. v(3) = 3.128... ≈ 3.1 mph
Maximum speed was 5 mph at about 1.12 hr.

3. Aircraft Carrier Landing Problem

Distance ≈ 0.6(150 + 230 + 150 + 90 + 40 + 0)
= 396 ft No danger of running off!

4. Water Over the Dam Problem

Volume ≈ 3(2500 + 8000 + 12000 + 13000 + 11000 + 7000 + 4000 + 6000 + 4500)
= 204,000 ft^3

5. Integral ≈ 70.8

6. Integral ≈ 9.0

7. Program for Trapezoidal Rule Problem
   Programs will vary depending on calculator.
8. The program gives the right answer.
9. $f(x) = -0.1x^2 + 7$
   a. 30.8125
   b. 41.7095
   c. 41.766095
10. $g(x) = 2^x + 5$
   a. 7.996545...
   b. 12.167507...
   c. 12.164077...
11. Trapezoidal Rule Error Problem
   If the trapezoids end up being circumscribed outside the region bounded by the graph, the trapezoids enclose too much area and the trapezoidal rule overestimates the integral. If the trapezoids end up being inscribed inside the region, the rule underestimates the integral. Thus, for Problem 9 the rule underestimates and for Problem 10 it overestimates.
12. Elliptical Table Problem
   From the given equation, $y = \pm(40/110)\sqrt{110^2 - x^2}$.
   Using the trapezoidal rule program on the positive branch with n = 100 increments gives 6904.190... for the top half of the ellipse. Doubling this gives an area of 13,808.38... cm^2.
   The estimate is too low, because the trapezoids end up being inscribed within the ellipse.
   The area of an ellipse is πab, where a and b are the x- and y-radii, respectively. So the exact area is $\pi(110)(40) = 4400\pi =$ 13,823.007... cm^2, which agrees both with the answer itself and with the conclusion that the trapezoidal rule underestimates the area.
13. Football Problem
   Integral $\approx (1)(0 + 7.0 + 10.5 + 23.0 + 27.2 + 30.3 + 31.8 + 30.3 + 27.2 + 23.0 + 10.5 + 7.0 + 0)$
   $= 227.8\ in^3$
   The integral will have units $(in^2)(in) = in^3$, so the integral represents the volume of the football.
14. Integral as a Limit Problem
   n = 10: Integral ≈ 21.045
   n = 100: Integral ≈ 21.00045
   n = 1000: Integral ≈ 21.0000045
   Conjecture: Integral = 21.
   The word is limit.
15. Derivative from Graph Problem
   a. Derivative ≈ −5.6
   b. Derivative ≈ 5.6
   Note the different scales on the two axes.
16. Exact Integral Conjecture Problem
   n = 100: Integral ≈ 156.0096.
   Conjecture: Integral = 156.
17. Meaning of Limits Problem
   a. f(5) is undefined because it would involve division by zero.
   b. $f(x) = \dfrac{2x^2 - 50}{x - 5} = \dfrac{2(x-5)(x+5)}{x - 5} = 2(x + 5),\ x \neq 5$
   $f(4.9) = 19.8$, $f(5.1) = 20.2$
   c. Both are close to 20.
   d. $f(4.99) = 19.98$, $f(5.01) = 20.02$
   Both are close to 20.
   e. "If x is within 0.01 unit of 5, then f(x) is within 0.02 unit of L."

Problem Set 1-5, pages 28 to 31 — Limit of a Function

Q1. Graph

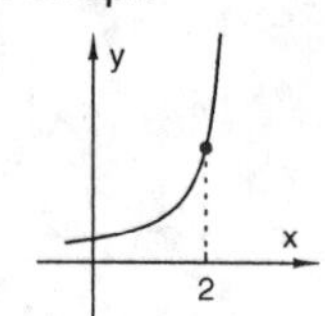

Q2. Graph

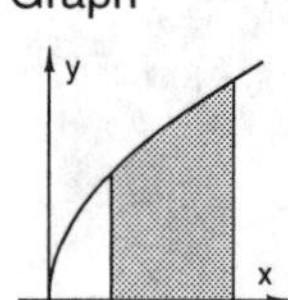

Q3. Graph

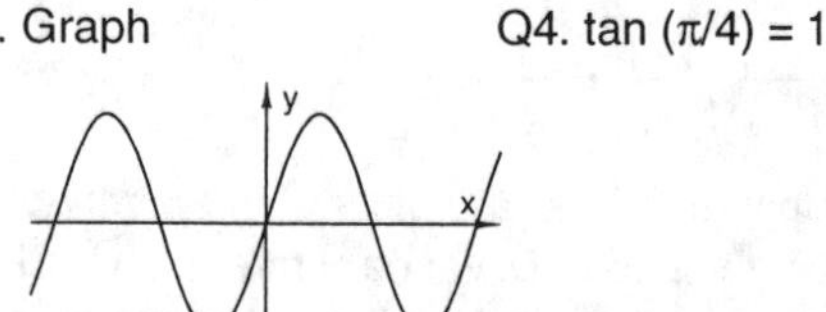

Q4. $\tan(\pi/4) = 1$

Q5. $3^{-2} = 1/9$
Q6. $24/36 = 2/3$
Q7. $0.3(600) = 180$
Q8. 52 weeks
Q9. Exponential function
Q10. Derivative

1. Has a limit, 3
2. Has a limit, 2
3. Has a limit, 3
4. Has a limit, 5
5. Has no limit
6. Has no limit
7. Has a limit, 7
8. Has a limit, 20
9. Has no limit
10. Has no limit
11. Definition of Limit I
   a. See text definition of limit.
   b. $f(4) = 3(4) - 7 = 5$, Q.E.D.
   c. Keep x within 0.2 units of 4.
   d. Graph

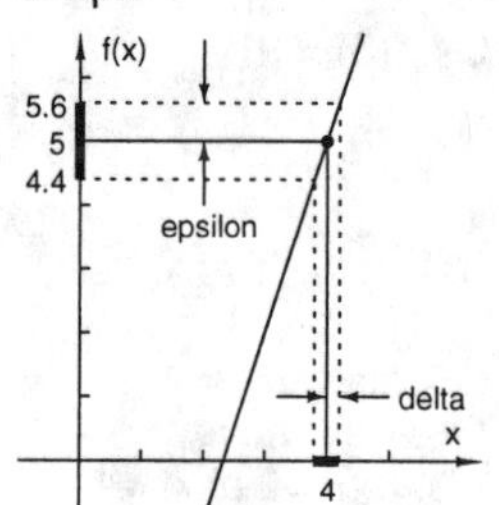

   e. For example, let x = 4.1. Then f(4.1) = 5.3, which is within 0.6 units of 5.
   f. $\delta = \varepsilon/3 = (0.00012)/3 = 0.00004$
12. Definition of Limit II
   a. Graph. Removable discontinuity at x = 2.

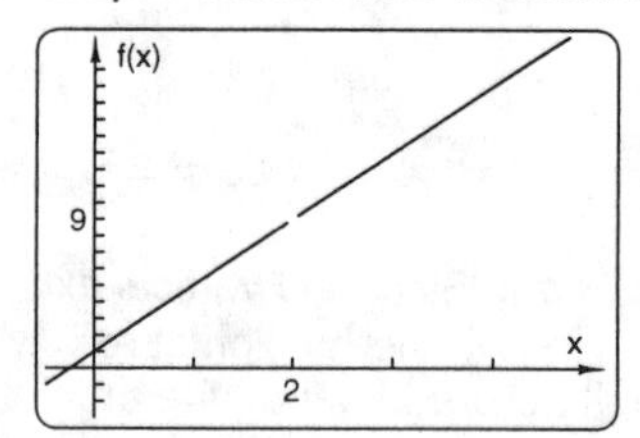

   b. Limit = 9.
   c. The answer takes the indeterminate form 0/0.
   d. $f(x) = \dfrac{(4x + 1)(x - 2)}{x - 2} = 4x + 1,\ x \neq 2.$
   Substituting 2 for x gives 4(2) + 1 = 9, which is the limit.

e. $4x + 1 = 8.9 \Rightarrow x = 1.975$
$4x + 1 = 9.1 \Rightarrow x = 2.025$
x must be within 0.025 units of 2.
(True because f(x) is monotone increasing.)
f. x must be within 0.00025 unit of 2.
g. L = 9, c = 2, epsilon = 0.001, delta = 0.00025
h. Let delta be 1/4 of epsilon. 1/4 of a positive number is always positive, so there is a positive value of delta for any positive value of epsilon.
i. f(c) may be undefined, so $x \neq c$ is specified.

13. Definition of Limit III
a. $f(x) = \dfrac{(x^2 - 6x + 13)(x - 2)}{(x - 2)}$
$f(2) = \dfrac{(5)(0)}{(0)} = \dfrac{0}{0}$, Q.E.D.
The limit is 5. Substitute 2 for x into the simplified expression, $f(x) = x^2 - 6x + 13$, $x \neq 2$

b.

	x	f(x)	x	f(x)
	1.990	5.0201	2.001	4.998001
	1.991	5.018081	2.002	4.996004
	1.992	5.016064	2.003	4.994009
	1.993	5.014049	2.004	4.992016
	1.994	5.012036	→ 2.005	4.990025
	1.995	5.010025	2.006	4.988036
→	1.996	5.008016	2.007	4.986049
	1.997	5.006009	2.008	4.984064
	1.998	5.004004	2.009	4.982081
	1.999	5.002001	2.010	4.9801
	2.000	(none)		

If x is within 0.004 units of 2, then . . . . (Any positive number less than 0.004 would also be a correct answer.) You must use the value of x that is closer to 2.

c. $x^2 - 6x + 13 = 4.99$:
x = 3.994987... or 2.00501256...
$x^2 - 6x + 13 = 5.01$:
x = 4.004987... or 1.99501243...
Pick the two values in the neighborhood of x = 2.
1.99501243... < x < 2.00501256...
(Uses the fact that f(x) is monotone decreasing in a neighborhood of x = 2.)

d. Graph (exaggerated to show concept).

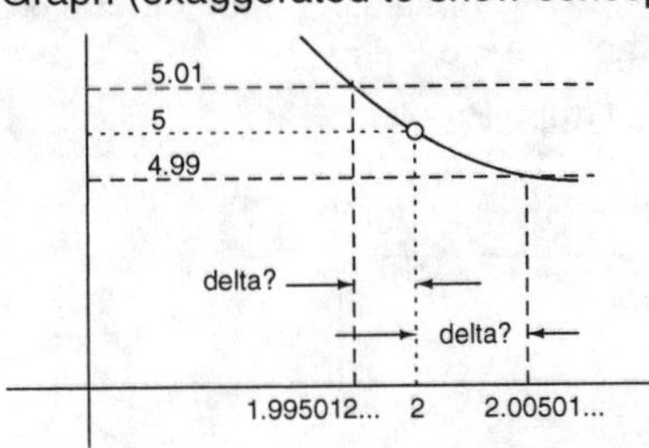

e. The largest allowable delta is the smaller of the two possible values in the diagram. Since the graph slopes more steeply on the negative side of x = 2, that value of delta is smaller.
Delta = 2 − 1.99501243... = 0.00498756...
f. L = 5, c = 2, epsilon = 0.01, delta = 0.00498756...

14. Definition of Limit IV
a. $f(x) = x - \dfrac{x - 2}{|x - 2|}$. Graph:

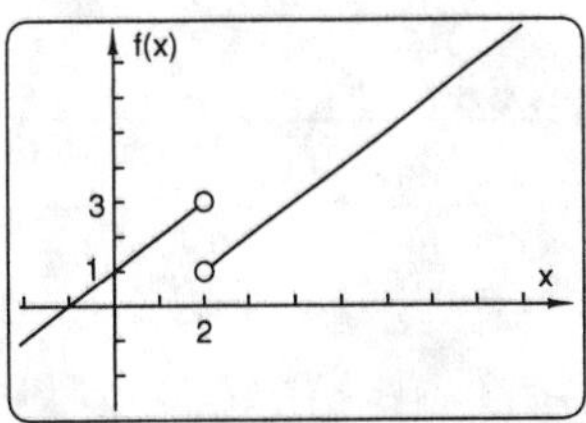

b. f(1.99) = 2.99, f(2.01) = 1.01.
f(x) jumps from 3 down to 1 at x = 2, so there is no *one* number L that f(x) stays close to when x is close to 2.

15. One-Sided Limit Problem
a. The quantity $|x - 2|/(x - 2)$ changes from −1 to 1 at x = 2, thus causing the jump.
b. From the left, the limit is 3.
c. From the right, the limit is 5.
d. Pick any value of epsilon less than 1. No matter what number you claim as the limit, there are values of x on one side of 2 or the other that make f(x) come out more than epsilon units away from that number.

16. Piecewise-Defined Function Problem
a. Graph.

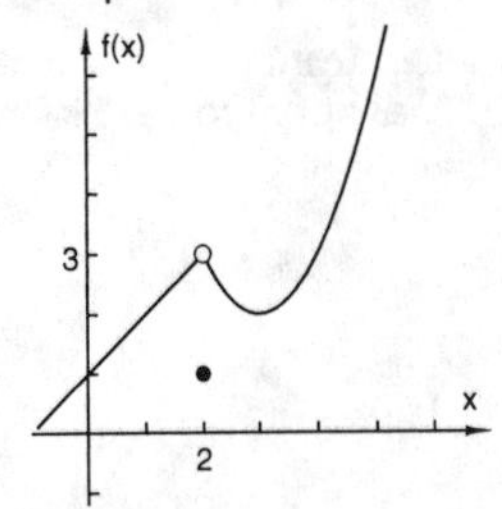

b. Both discontinuities are at (2, 3).
c. Yes. The limit is 3.
d. No. f(2) is defined to be 1, not 3.
e. f(2) would have to be defined to equal 3.
(This definition "removes" the discontinuity.)

17. $r(x) = 1/x$
Derivative ≈ −0.1111 using r(−3.01) and r(−2.99).

18. $j(x) = 10 - 2^x$
Integral ≈ 19.90077... using 100 trapezoids.

19. Don't Believe Everything You See Problem!
"Look, Ima. The two curves are so close together that the grapher can't tell the difference. But you should realize that by using TRACE on the two graphs, you will see a slight difference in the y-values at the same x-value. Or you could use a wider window, thus showing the curve of the sine graph away from the straight line of the linear graph."

1. Answers will vary.

Review Problems

R1. Bungee Problem

a. $d = 90 - 80 \sin 1.2(t - 3)$
$t = 4$: $d \approx 15.4$ ft

b. From 3.9 to 4, avg. rate ≈ -40.1 ft/sec
From 4 to 4.1, avg. rate ≈ -29.3 ft/sec
Instantaneous rate ≈ -34.7 ft/sec
Going down. Distance from water is decreasing.

c. Instantaneous rate ≈ 70.8

d. Going up at about 70.8 ft/sec

e. Derivative.

R2. a. Instantaneous rate of change of a function.

b. $x = -4$: Decreasing fast.
$x = 1$: Increasing slowly.
$x = 3$: Increasing fast.
$x = 5$: Neither increasing nor decreasing.

c. $f(x) = 5^x \Rightarrow f(2) = 25$
Derivative ≈ 40.2 using $f(1.99)$ and $f(2.01)$

d. $t = 2$: 3.25 m/sec
$t = 18$: 8.75 m/sec
$t = 24$: 11.5 m/sec
Speed is constant, 7 m/sec, from $t = 6$ to 16 sec
At $t = 24$, Mary is in her final sprint toward the finish line.

R3. a. $v(t) = (5t)(0.8)^t$ Graph.

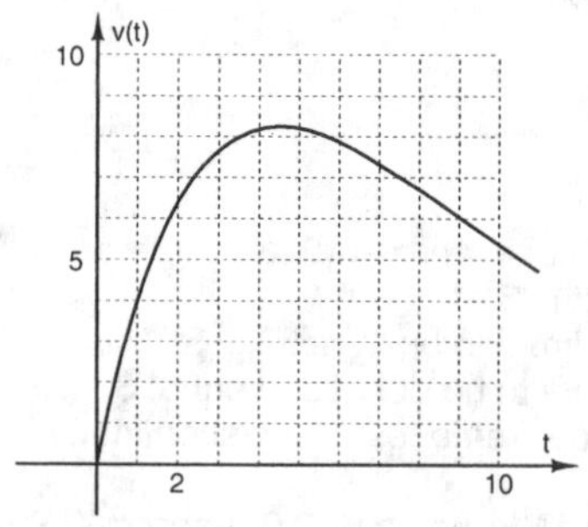

b. Distance ≈ 58.1 ft by counting squares.

c. Definite integral.

R4. a. $f(x) = -0.5x^2 + 1.8x + 4$. Graph is correct.

b. Integral ≈ 15.0

c.

x	f(x)
1.0	5.3
1.5	5.575
2.0	5.6
2.5	5.375
3.0	4.9
3.5	4.175
4.0	3.2

Integral $\approx 0.5(2.65 + 5.575 + 5.6 + 5.375 + 4.9 + 4.175 + 1.6)$
$= \underline{14.9375}$

R5. a. See definition of limit in text.

b. $f(x) = \dfrac{(x^2 - 8x + 5)(x - 3)}{x - 3} = x^2 - 8x + 5,\ x \neq 3$
Limit $= 3^2 - 8(3) + 5 = -10$

c. $x^2 - 8x + 5 = -9.99$:
$x = 5.00498756...$ or $x = 2.99501243...$
$x^2 - 8x + 5 = -10.01$:
$x = 4.99498743...$ or $x = 3.00501256...$
Pick the two values in the neighborhood of $x = 3$.
Delta $= 3 - 2.99501243... = 0.00498756...$, or
delta $= 3.00501256... - 3 = 0.00501256...$.
Pick the smaller of these, delta $= \underline{0.00498756...}$
(Relies on the fact that $f(x)$ is monotone in a neighborhood of $x = 3$.)

d. For example, let $x = 3.004$.
$f(3.004) = -10.007984$, which is within 0.01 unit of -10.

e. Graph.

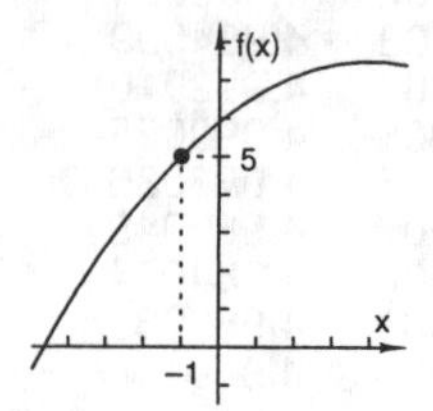

R6. The journal gives you a chance to summarize things you have learned and condense the class notes you have taken. It also gives you a chance to write down unanswered questions. You do *not* have to know the answers to everything you write.

Concepts Problems

C1. Exact Value of a Derivative Problem

a. $f(x) = x^2 - 7x + 11 \Rightarrow f(3) = -1$

b. $f(x) - f(3) = x^2 - 7x + 11 + 1 = x^2 - 7x + 12$

c. $\dfrac{f(x) - f(3)}{x - 3} = \dfrac{x^2 - 7x + 12}{x - 3} = \dfrac{(x - 4)(x - 3)}{x - 3}$
$= x - 4$, if $x \neq 3$

d. Limit is found by substituting 3 for x in $x - 4$.
Limit = exact rate $= 3 - 4 = \underline{-1}$.

C2. Tangent to a Graph Problem
$f(x) = x^2 - 7x + 11$. Graph.
The line is tangent to the graph.

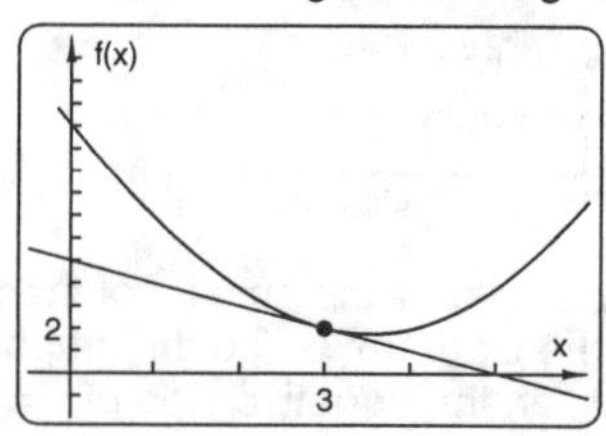

Zooming in by a factor of 10 on the point (3, 2) shows that the graph becomes straighter, and looks almost like the tangent line. (Soon students will learn that this property is called *local linearity*.)

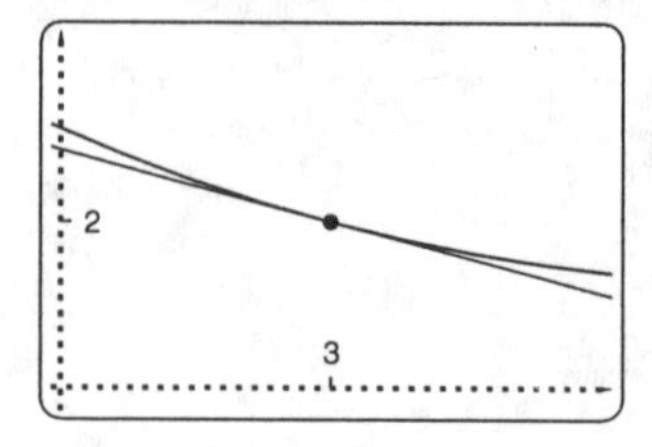

Chapter Test

T1. Graph.

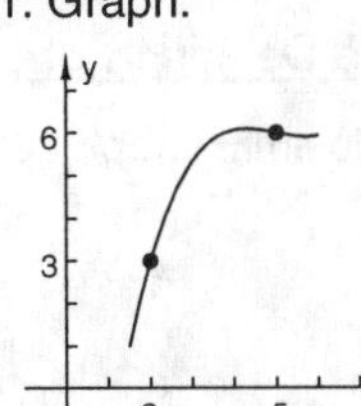

T2. Graph.

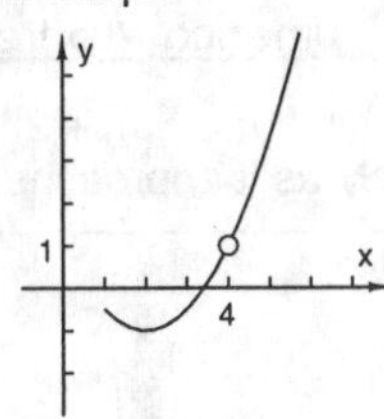

T3. $f(x) = 2 \cos x$

Rate $\approx \dfrac{f(1.01) - f(0.99)}{1.01 - 0.99} = \underline{-1.6829...}$

The concept is the derivative.

T4. $f(x) = 1.2^x$

Integral $\approx 0.5[0.5f(1) + f(1.5) + f(2) + f(2.5) + f(3) + f(3.5) + f(4) + f(4.5) + 0.5f(5)]$

$= \underline{7.071...}$

T5. a. $g(x) = \dfrac{5x^2 + 17x + 14}{x + 2}$ Graph.

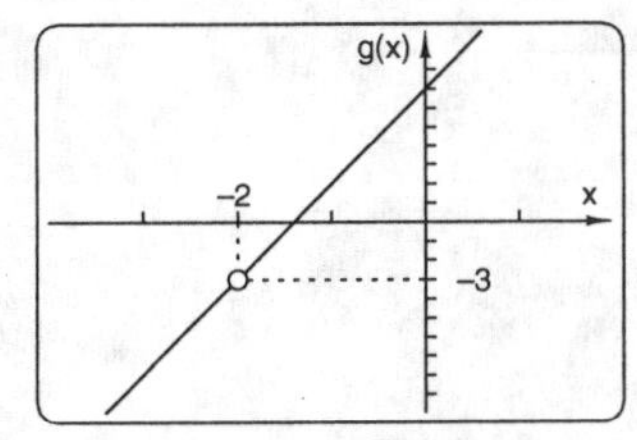

b. $g(x) = \dfrac{(5x + 7)(x + 2)}{x + 2} = 5x + 7,\ x \neq -2$

Limit $= 5(-2) + 7 = \underline{-3}$. Graph, part a.

c. $g(x) = -3.4 \Rightarrow 5x + 7 = -3.4 \Rightarrow x = -2.08$

$g(x) = -2.6 \Rightarrow 5x + 7 = -2.6 \Rightarrow x = -1.92$

Interval is $-2.08 < x < -1.92$. Graph.

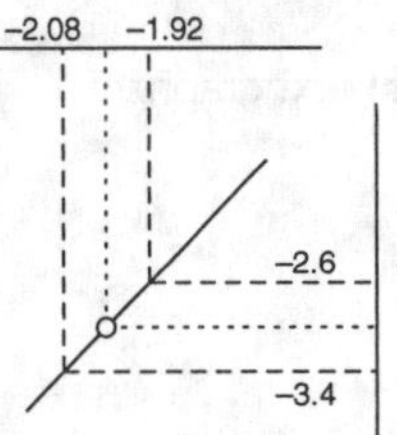

(Answer relies on the fact that g(x) is monotone.)

d. c = −2, L = −3, epsilon = 0.4, delta = 0.08

e. In this problem, g(−2) takes the form 0/0, which is indeterminate. Limits handle the behavior of such a function when x is close to c, but where f(c) itself is undefined. What happens *at* x = c is not important for the concept of limit.

T6. a. $v(t) = 2.718^t$

$v(1) = 2.718^1 = \underline{2.718 \text{ in/min}}$

b. Rate of change $\approx \dfrac{v(1.01) - v(0.99)}{1.01 - 0.99}$

$= \underline{2.71776...}$

c. The distance is the definite integral of v(t) with respect to t from t = 0 to t = 1. Using the trapezoidal rule program with n = 100, the integral is approximately 1.718... So the distance is about 1.7 inches.

T7. Distance = integral from 0 to 28. By trapezoids,

dist. $\approx 4(8 + 26 + 30 + 34 + 37 + 36 + 32 + 12.5)$

$= \underline{862 \text{ ft}}$

Chapter 2

Problem Set 2-1, page 39 — Numerical Approach to the Definition of Limit

1. a. $f(x) = (x - 2)^{1/3} + 3$
   Grapher graph agrees with text graph.

   b.

x	f(x)
1.9995	2.920629947...
1.9996	2.926319370...
1.9997	2.933056704...
1.9998	2.941519645...
1.9999	2.953584111...
2	3
2.0001	3.046415888...
2.0002	3.058480354...
2.0003	3.066943295...
2.0004	3.073680629...
2.0005	3.079370052...

   c. f(x) is within 0.07 unit of 3 for all x in the interval $1.9997 \le x \le 2.0003$.

   d. f(x) is within 0.05 unit of 3 for all x in the interval $1.9999 \le x \le 2.0001$.

   e. Yes. To make $3 - 0.01 < f(x) < 3 + 0.01$, keep x in the interval $2 - 0.01^3 < x < 2 + 0.01^3$. That is, $1.999999 < x < 2.000001$ (but $x \ne 2$).

   f. L = 3, c = 2, epsilon = 0.07, and delta = 0.0003.

   g. Keep x in the interval $2 - \text{epsilon}^3 < x < 2 + \text{epsilon}^3$.

2. $g(x) = (x - 3) \sin [1/(x - 3)] + 2$
   Graphs. The limit seems to be 2.

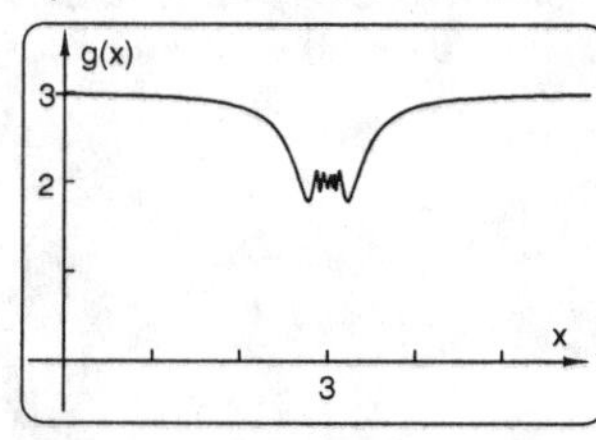

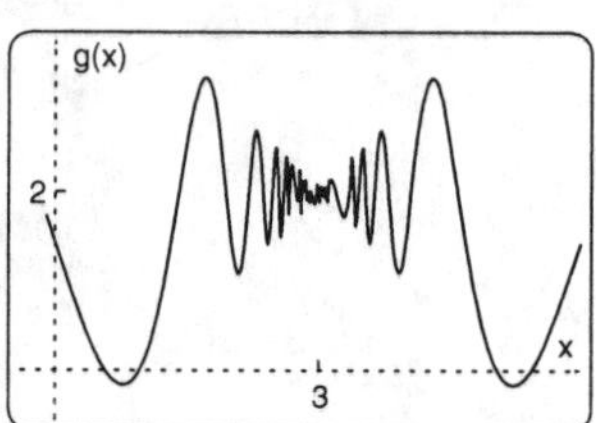

3. $h(x) = \sin [1/(x - 3)] + 2$. Graphs. No limit. Graph cycles infinitely as it approaches x = 3.

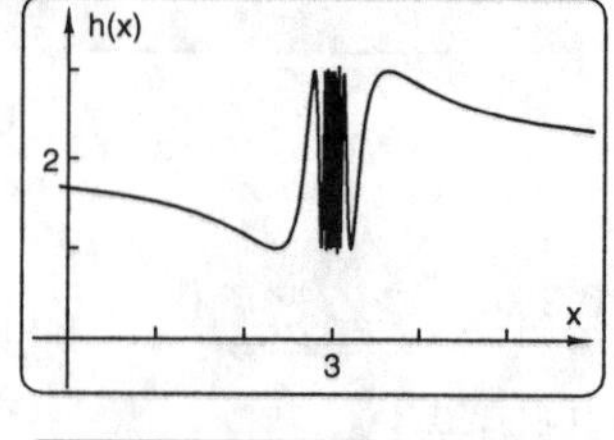

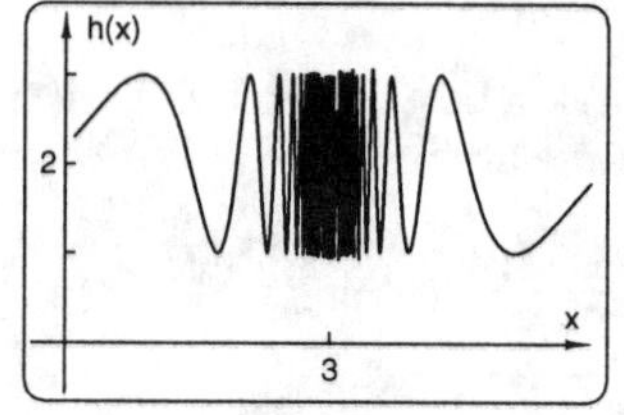

Problem Set 2-2, pages 44 and 45 — Graphical and Algebraic Approaches to the Definition of Limit

Q1. Graph (ellipse)

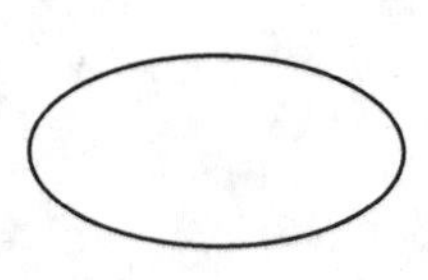

Q2. Graph (at (2, 5))

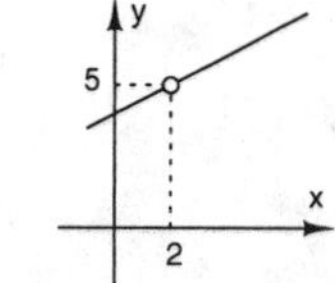

Q3. $|-49| = 49$

Q4. $\sqrt{-25} = 5i$

Q5. $|7 - 3| = 4$

Q6. +

Q7. 3.

Q8. Commutative, addition

Q9. $60/0.3 = 200$

Q10. Decreasing. Graph

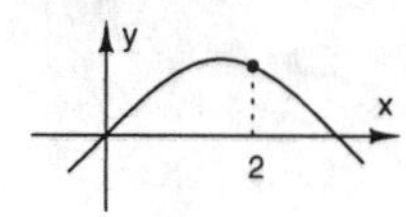

1. $\lim_{x\to 3} f(x) = 5$. For $\varepsilon = 0.5$, $\delta \approx 0.2$ or 0.3
2. $\lim_{x\to 2} f(x) = 3$. For $\varepsilon = 0.5$, $\delta \approx 0.8$
3. $\lim_{x\to 6} f(x) = 4$. For $\varepsilon = 0.7$, $\delta \approx 0.5$ or 0.6
   (The right side is the more restrictive.)
4. $\lim_{x\to 4} f(x) = 2$. For $\varepsilon = 0.8$, $\delta \approx 0.7$ or 0.8
   (The left side is the more restrictive.)
5. $\lim_{x\to 5} f(x) = 2$. For $\varepsilon = 0.3$, $\delta \approx 0.5$ or 0.6
   (The right side is more restrictive.)
6. $\lim_{x\to 3} f(x) = 6$. For $\varepsilon = 0.4$, $\delta \approx 0.1$
7. a. Graph. (Same as Problem 1.)
   b. $\lim_{x\to 3} f(x) = 5$

c. Graph is symmetrical about x = 3
Let $5 - 2\sin(x - 3) = 5 + 0.5 = 5.5$.
$\therefore \sin(x - 3) = -0.25$
$x = 3 + \sin^{-1}(-0.25)$
Max. $\delta = 3 - (3 + \sin^{-1}(-0.25)) = \underline{0.25268...}$

d. Let $5 - 2\sin(x - 3) = 5 + \varepsilon$.
$\therefore \sin(x - 3) = -\varepsilon/2$
$x = 3 + \sin^{-1}(-\varepsilon/2)$
Max. $\delta = 3 - (3 + \sin^{-1}(-\varepsilon/2))$
$= -\sin^{-1}(-\varepsilon/2) = \sin^{-1}(\varepsilon/2)$,
which is positive for any positive value of ε.

8. a. Graph. (Same as Problem 2.)
b. $\lim_{x\to 2} f(x) = 3$
c. Graph is symmetrical about x = 2.
Let $(x - 2)^3 + 3 = 3 + 0.5 = 3.5$.
$\therefore x = 2 + \sqrt[3]{0.5}$
Max. $\delta = 2 + \sqrt[3]{0.5} - 2 = \sqrt[3]{0.5} = \underline{0.7937...}$
d. Let $(x - 2)^3 + 3 = 3 + \varepsilon$.
$\therefore x = 2 + \varepsilon^{1/3}$
Max. $\delta = 2 + \varepsilon^{1/3} - 2 = \varepsilon^{1/3}$,
which is positive for any positive value of ε.

9. a. Graph. (Same as Problem 3.)
b. $\lim_{x\to 6} f(x) = 4$
c. The right side is more restrictive.
Let $1 + 3(7 - x)^{1/3} = 4 - 0.7 = 3.3$.
$\therefore x = 7 - (2.3/3)^3$
Max. $\delta = (7 - (2.3/3)^3) - 6 = \underline{0.5493...}$
d. Since the right side is more restrictive, set
$1 + 3\sqrt[3]{7 - x} = 4 - \varepsilon$
$\therefore x = 7 - ((3 - \varepsilon)/3)^3$
Max. $\delta = (7 - ((3 - \varepsilon)/3)^3) - 6 = 1 - ((3 - \varepsilon)/3)^3$,
which is positive for all positive values of ε.

10. a. Graph. (Same as Problem 4.)
b. $\lim_{x\to 4} f(x) = 2$
c. The left side is more restrictive.
Let $1 + 2^{4-x} = 2 + 0.8 = 2.8$.
$\therefore 2^{4-x} = 1.8$
$x = 4 - (\log 1.8)/(\log 2)$
Max. $\delta = 4 - (4 - (\log 1.8)/(\log 2)) = \underline{0.84799...}$.
d. Since the left side is more restrictive, set
$1 + 2^{4-x} = 2 + \varepsilon$.
$\therefore 2^{4-x} = 1 + \varepsilon$
$x = 4 - (\log(1 + \varepsilon))/(\log 2)$
Max. $\delta = 4 - (4 - (\log(1 + \varepsilon))/(\log 2))$
$= \log(1 + \varepsilon)/\log 2$, which is positive for all $\varepsilon > 0$.

11. a. Graph. (Same as Problem 5.)
b. $\lim_{x\to 5} f(x) = 2$
c. The right side is more restrictive.
Let $(x - 5)^2 + 2 = 2 + 0.3 = 2.3$.
$\therefore x = 5 + \sqrt{0.3}$
Max. $\delta = (5 + \sqrt{0.3}) - 5 = \underline{0.54772...}$
d. Since the right side is more restrictive, set
$(x - 5)^2 + 2 = 2 + \varepsilon$
$\therefore x = 5 + \sqrt{\varepsilon}$
Max. $\delta = (5 + \sqrt{\varepsilon}) - 5 = \sqrt{\varepsilon}$, which is positive for all $\varepsilon > 0$.

12. a. Graph. (Same as Problem 6.)
b. $\lim_{x\to 3} f(x) = 6$.
c. Graph is symmetrical about x = 3.
Let $6 - 2(x - 3)^{2/3} = 6 - 0.4 = 5.6$.
$\therefore x = 3 + 0.2^{3/2}$
Max. $\delta = (3 + 0.2^{3/2}) - 3 = \underline{0.08944...}$
d. Let $6 - 2(x - 3)^{2/3} = 6 - \varepsilon$.
$\therefore x = 3 + (\varepsilon/2)^{3/2}$
Max. $\delta = (3 + (\varepsilon/2)^{3/2}) - 3 = (\varepsilon/2)^{3/2}$, which is positive for all $\varepsilon > 0$.

13. Limits Applied to Derivatives Problem
a. $m(t) = \dfrac{3t^2 - 48}{t - 4}$
b. Graph. Removable discontinuity at x = 4.

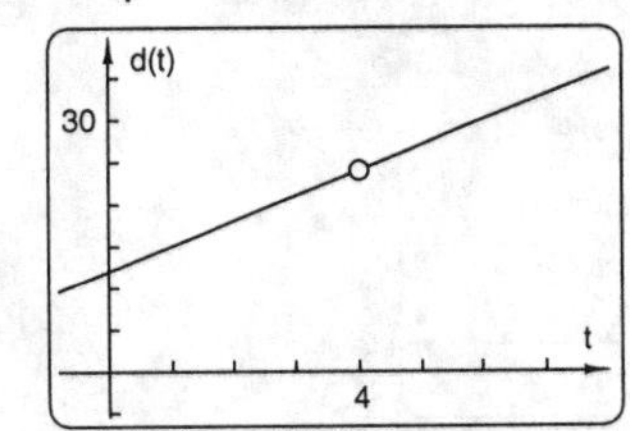

c. Limit = 24 ft/sec
d. $m(t) = \dfrac{3(t - 4)(t + 4)}{t - 4} = 3t + 12$, if $t \neq 4$
$3t + 12 = 24.12 \Rightarrow t = 4.04$
$3t + 12 = 23.88 \Rightarrow t = 3.96$
Keep t within 0.04 sec of 4 sec.
e. The limit of the average velocity is the exact velocity.

Problem Set 2-3, pages 49 to 52 — The Limit Theorems

Q1. $\lim_{x\to 4} (13x)/(x) = 13$
Q2. Limit, but f(2) undef.:

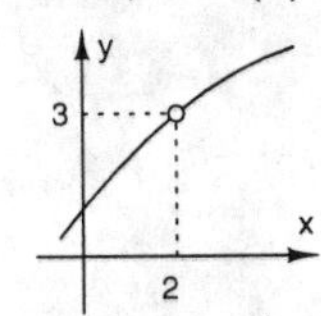

Q3. Decr. slowly at x = −4

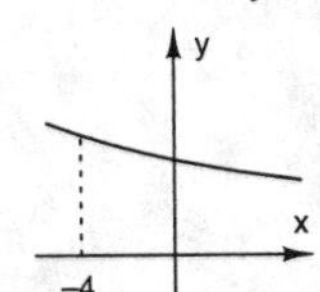

Q4. Quadratic

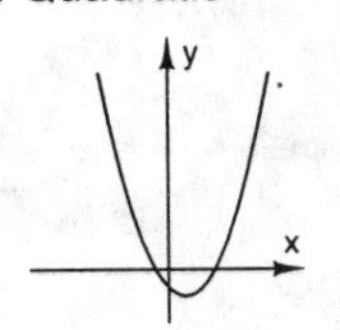

Q5. $y = x^3$

Q6. $(x - 10)(x + 10)$
Q7. 75%
Q8. 10 mi
Q9. $4x^{20}$
Q10. Product of x and y, where y can vary.

1. Limit of a Function Plus a Function Problem

Graph. $g(x) = x^2$ and $h(x) = 12/x$.

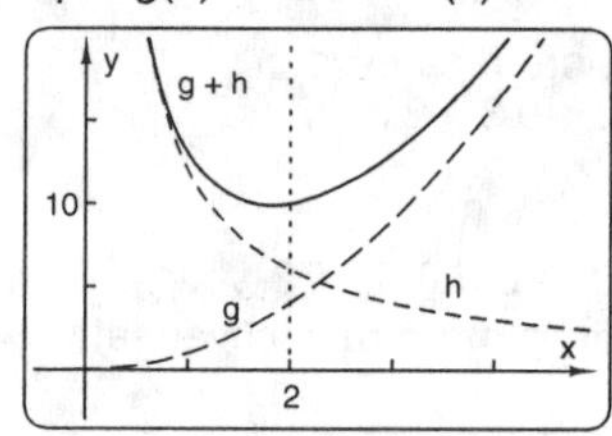

$\lim_{x\to2} f(x) = 10$, $\lim_{x\to2} g(x) = 4$, and $\lim_{x\to2} h(x) = 6$.

$\therefore \lim_{x\to2} f(x) = \lim_{x\to2} g(x) + \lim_{x\to2} h(x)$, Q.E.D.

Example: Use each 0.01 from x = 1.96 to 2.04.

x	f(x)
1.96	9.9640...
1.97	9.9722...
1.98	9.9810...
1.99	9.9902...
2.00	10
2.01	10.0102...
2.02	10.0209...
2.03	10.0322...
2.04	10.0439...

All these f(x) values are close to 10.

2. Limit of a Constant Times a Function Problem

Graph. $g(x) = x^2$, $f(x) = 0.2x^2$

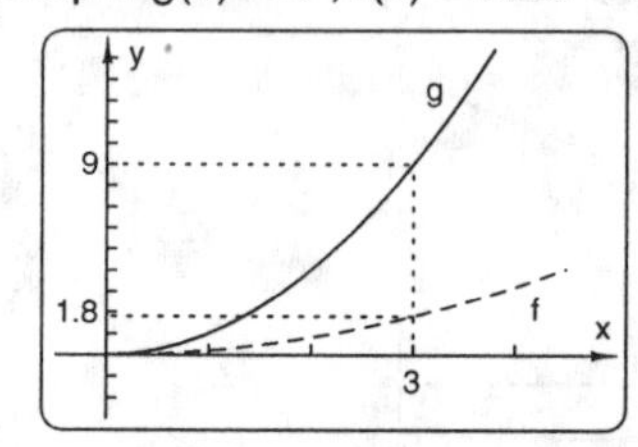

$\lim_{x\to3} f(x) = 1.8$ and $\lim_{x\to3} g(x) = 9$

$\therefore \lim_{x\to3} f(x) = 0.2 \lim_{x\to3} g(x)$, Q.E.D.

Example: Use each 0.01 from x = 2.96 to 3.04.

x	f(x)
2.96	1.75232
2.97	1.76418
2.98	1.77608
2.99	1.78802
3.00	1.8
3.01	1.81202
3.02	1.82408
3.03	1.83618
3.04	1.84832

All of these f(x) values are close to 1.8.

3. Limit of a Constant Problem

Graph. $f(x) = 7$

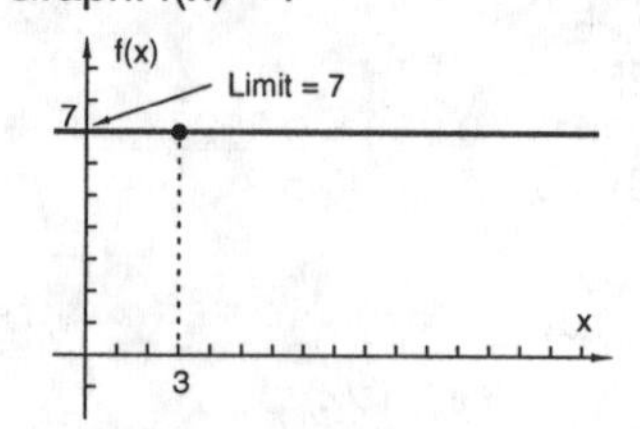

The limit is 7 because f(x) is *always* close to 7, no matter what value x takes on. (It shouldn't bother you that $f(x) = 7$ for $x \neq 3$ if you think of the definition of limit for a while.)

4. Limit of x Problem

Graph. $f(x) = x$

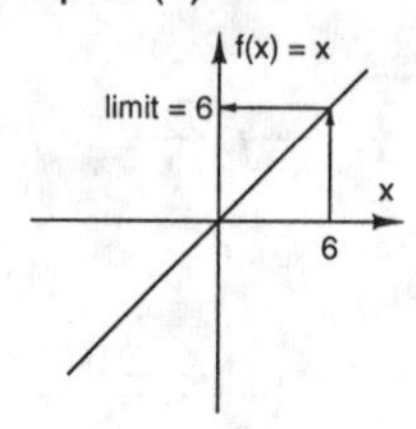

$\lim_{x\to6} f(x) = 6$. The y-value equals the x-value.

5. Limit of a Product Problem

$1.5^2 = 2.25$ and $\tan 1.5 = 14.101419...$

$\therefore f(1.5) = (2.25)(14.10...) = \underline{31.72819...}$

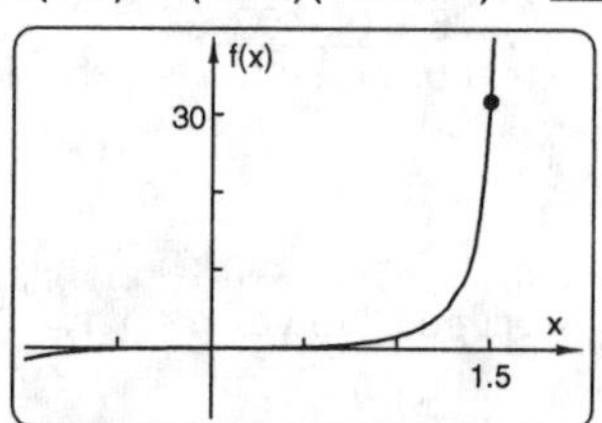

By tracing on the graph or by using the calculator to make a table of values of f(x) close to x = 1.5, with an increment of 0.000001,

$f(1.499980) = 31.71835...$

$f(1.500020) = 31.73803...$

Since both of these are within 0.01 of the limit, and the next increment of 0.000001 gives values farther away, let $\delta = 0.000020$.

If $x = 1.5 + \delta$, x^2 is within 0.0000600004 of 1.5^2 and tan x is within 0.0039981... of tan 1.5.

6. Limit of a Quotient Problem

$r(x) = 2^x/\sin x$

$2^3 = 8$ and $\sin 3 = 0.141120008...$

$\therefore\ r(3) = (8)/(0.141120008...) = \underline{56.68933...}$

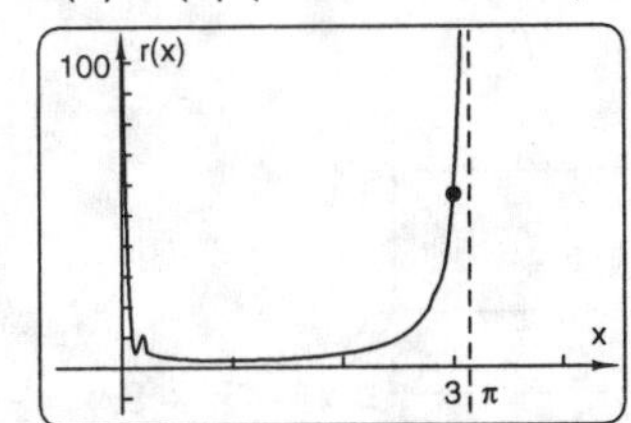

By TRACE or TABLE with x close to 3,

$r(2.99978) = 56.59335...$

$r(3.00022) = 56.78562...$

Since both of these are within 0.1 unit of the limit, and the next increment of 0.00001 gives values farther away, let $\delta = 0.00022$.

If $x = 3 + \delta$, 2^x is within 0.00122... of 2^3 and sin x is within 0.000217... of sin 3.

7. a. Graph. $f(x) = 3x - 7$

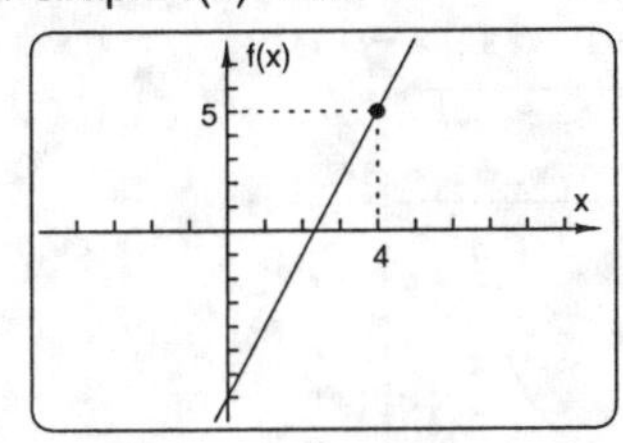

b. $\lim_{x\to4} f(x) = 3(4) - 7 = \underline{5}$

c. Proof:

$\lim_{x\to4} f(x) = \lim_{x\to4} (3x - 7)$

$= \lim_{x\to4} 3x + \lim_{x\to4} (-7)$ . . . . Limit of a sum.

$= 3 \lim_{x\to4} x - 7$ . . . . Limit of a constant times a fn., and limit of a constant.

$= 3\cdot4 - 7 = 5$, Q.E.D. . . . . Limit of x.

8. a. Graph. $h(x) = -5x + 23$

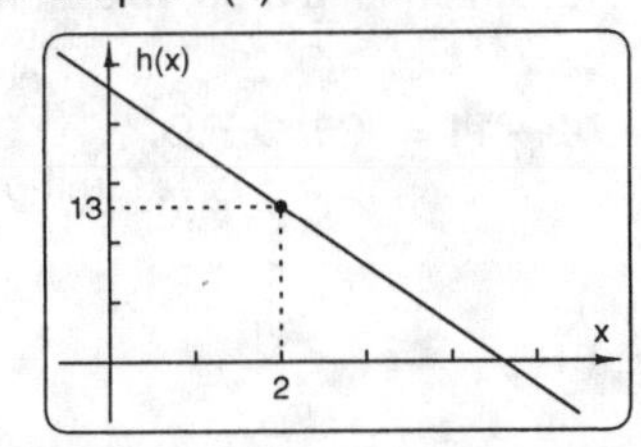

b. $\lim_{x\to2} h(x) = -5(2) + 23 = \underline{13}$

c. Proof:

$\lim_{x\to2} h(x) = \lim_{x\to2} (-5x + 23)$

$= \lim_{x\to2} (-5x) + \lim_{x\to2} 23 = -5 \lim_{x\to2} x + 23$

$= -5\cdot2 + 23 = 13$, Q.E.D.

9. a. Graph. $f(x) = x^2 - 9x + 5$

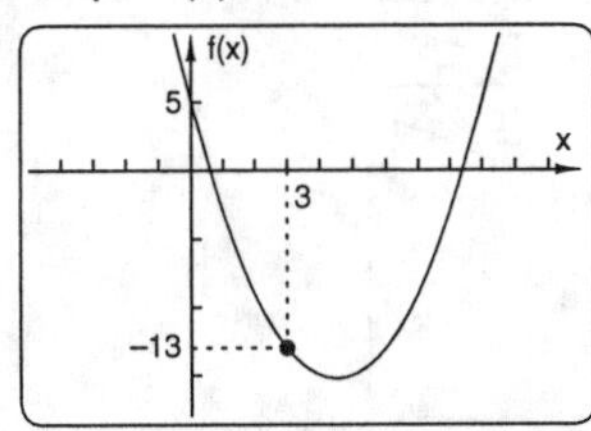

b. $\lim_{x\to3} f(x) = 3^2 - 9(3) + 5 = \underline{-13}$

c. Proof:

$\lim_{x\to3} f(x) = \lim_{x\to3} (x^2 - 9x + 5)$

$= \lim_{x\to3} x^2 + \lim_{x\to3} (-9x) + \lim_{x\to3} 5$

. . . . Limit of a sum.

$= \lim_{x\to3} x \cdot \lim_{x\to3} x + (-9) \lim_{x\to3} x + 5$

. . Limit of a product, const. times fn., and const.

$= 3\cdot3 + (-9)(3) + 5 = -13$, Q.E.D. . . . . . Limit of x.

10. a. Graph. $p(x) = x^2 + 3x - 6$

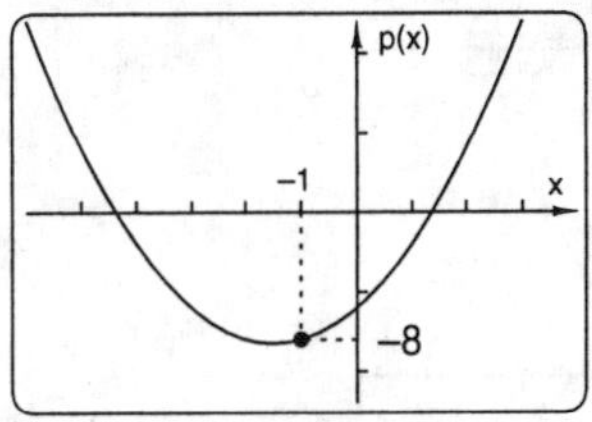

b. $\lim_{x\to-1} p(x) = (-1)^2 + 3(-1) - 6 = \underline{-8}$

c. Proof:

$\lim_{x\to-1} p(x) = \lim_{x\to-1} (x^2 + 3x - 6)$

. . . . Limit of a sum.

$= \lim_{x\to-1} x^2 + \lim_{x\to-1} 3x + \lim_{x\to-1} (-6)$

$= \lim_{x\to-1} x \cdot \lim_{x\to-1} x + 3 \lim_{x\to-1} x - 6$

. . Limit of a product, const. times fn., and const.

$= (-1)(-1) + 3(-1) - 6 = -8$, Q.E.D. . . . Limit of x.

11. a. Graph. $r(x) = \dfrac{x^2 - 4x - 12}{x + 2}$

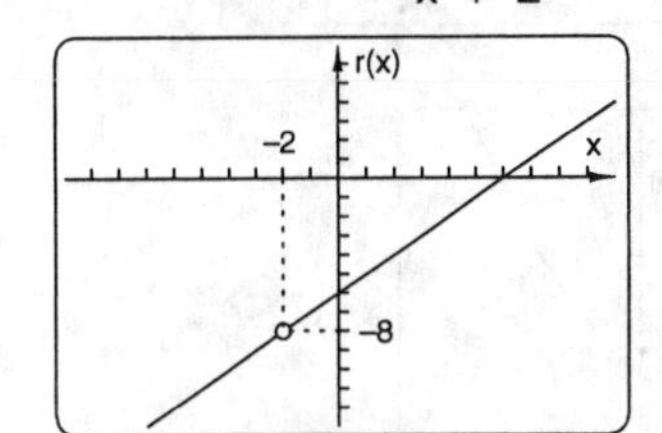

b. $r(x) = \dfrac{(x - 6)(x + 2)}{x + 2} = x - 6,\ x \ne -2$

$\lim_{x\to-2} r(x) = -2 - 6 = -8$

c. Proof:

$\lim_{x\to-2} r(x) = \lim_{x\to-2} (x - 6)$ . . . . Since $x \ne -2$

$= \lim_{x\to-2} x + \lim_{x\to-2} (-6)$ . . . . Limit of a sum

$= -2 - 6 = -8$, Q.E.D. . . . . Limit of x

12. a. Graph. $f(x) = \dfrac{x^2 + 3x - 40}{x - 5}$

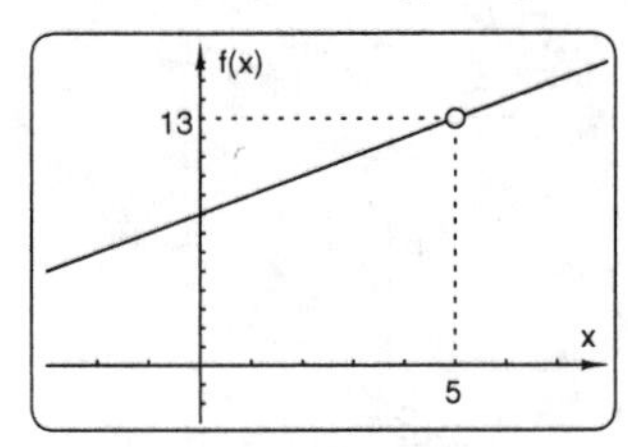

b. $f(x) = \dfrac{(x + 8)(x - 5)}{x - 5} = x + 8,\ x \neq 5$

$\lim_{x \to 5} f(x) = 5 + 8 = \underline{13}$

c. <u>Proof</u>:

$\lim_{x \to 5} f(x) = \lim_{x \to 5} (x + 8)$ . . . . Since $x \neq 5$

$= \lim_{x \to 5} x + \lim_{x \to 5} 8$ . . . . Limit of a sum

$= 5 + 8 = 13$, Q.E.D. . . . . Limit of x

13. a. Graph. $f(x) = \dfrac{x^3 - 3x^2 - 4x - 30}{x - 5}$

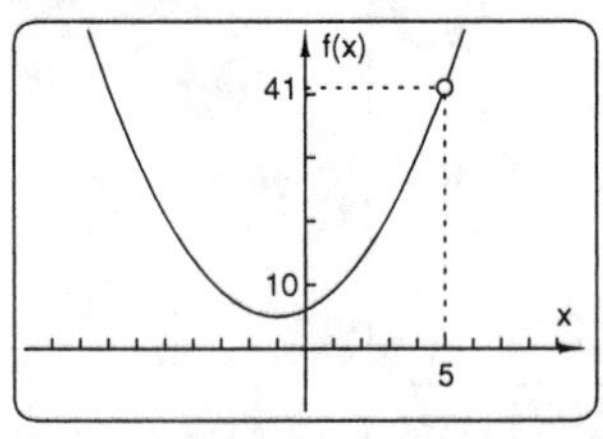

b. $f(x) = \dfrac{(x^2 + 2x + 6)(x - 5)}{x - 5} = x^2 + 2x + 6,\ x \neq 5$

$\lim_{x \to 5} f(x) = 5^2 + 2(5) + 6 = \underline{41}$

c. <u>Proof</u>:

$\lim_{x \to 5} f(x) = \lim_{x \to 5} (x^2 + 2x + 6)$ . . . . . . Since $x \neq 5$

$= \lim_{x \to 5} x^2 + \lim_{x \to 5} (2x) + \lim_{x \to 5} 6$ . . . Limit of a sum

$= \lim_{x \to 5} x \cdot \lim_{x \to 5} x + 2 \lim_{x \to 5} x + 6$ Limit of a prod. limit of a const.

$= 5 \cdot 5 + 2 \cdot 5 + 6 = 41$, Q.E.D. . . . . Limit of x

14. a. Graph. $f(x) = \dfrac{x^3 + x^2 - 5x - 21}{x - 3}$

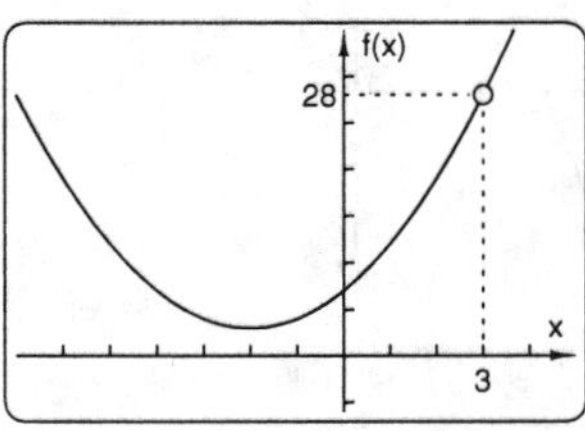

b. $f(x) = \dfrac{(x^2 + 4x + 7)(x - 3)}{x - 3} = x^2 + 4x + 7,\ x \neq 3$

$\lim_{x \to 3} f(x) = 3^2 + 4(3) + 7 = \underline{28}$

c. <u>Proof</u>:

$\lim_{x \to 3} f(x) = \lim_{x \to 3} (x^2 + 4x + 7)$ . . . . Since $x \neq 3$

$= \lim_{x \to 3} x^2 + \lim_{x \to 3} 4x + \lim_{x \to 3} 7$ . . . . . . Limit of a sum

$= \lim_{x \to 3} x \cdot \lim_{x \to 3} x + 4 \lim_{x \to 3} x + 7$ Limit of a prod.

Limit of a const.

$= 3 \cdot 3 + 4 \cdot 3 + 7 = 28$, Q.E.D. . . . . Limit of x

15. a. Graph. $f(x) = \dfrac{x^3 - 4x^2 - 2x + 3}{x + 1}$

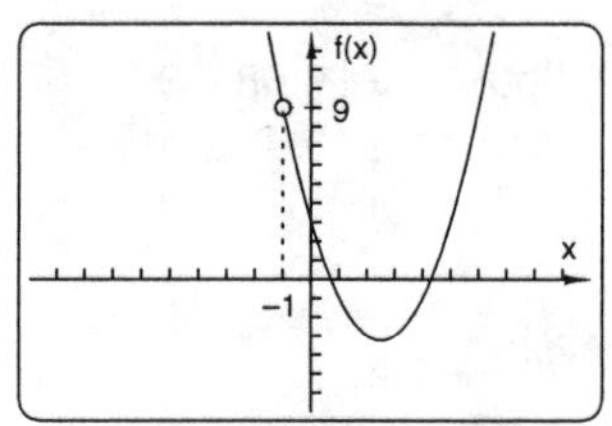

b. $f(x) = \dfrac{(x^2 - 5x + 3)(x + 1)}{x + 1} = x^2 - 5x + 3,\ x \neq -1$

$\lim_{x \to -1} f(x) = (-1)^2 - 5(-1) + 3 = 9$

c. <u>Proof</u>:

$\lim_{x \to -1} f(x) = \lim_{x \to -1} (x^2 - 5x + 3)$ . . . . . Since $x \neq -1$

$= \lim_{x \to -1} x^2 + \lim_{x \to -1} (-5x) + \lim_{x \to -1} 3$ . . Lim. of a sum

$= \lim_{x \to -1} x \cdot \lim_{x \to -1} x + (-5) \lim_{x \to -1} x + 3$ Lim. of a prod. and of a const.

$= (-1)(-1) + (-5)(-1) + 3 = 9$, Q.E.D. . . . Lim. of x

16. a. Graph. $f(x) = x^3 - 10x^2 + 7x - 11$

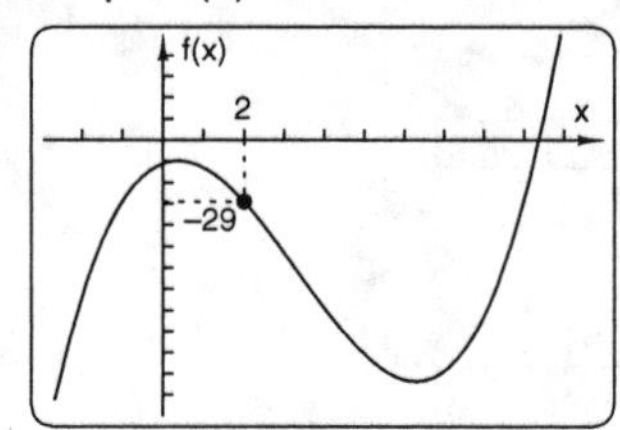

b. $\lim_{x \to 2} f(x) = 2^3 - 10(2^2) + 7(2) - 11 = \underline{-29}$

c. <u>Proof</u>:

$\lim_{x \to 2} f(x) = \lim_{x \to 2} (x^3 - 10x^2 + 7x - 11)$ . . . Since $x \neq 2$

$= \lim_{x \to 2} x^3 + \lim_{x \to 2} (-10x^2) + \lim_{x \to 2} 7x + \lim_{x \to 2} (-11)$

. . . . Limit of a sum

$= \lim_{x \to 2} x \cdot \lim_{x \to 2} x \cdot \lim_{x \to 2} x + (-10) \lim_{x \to 2} x \cdot \lim_{x \to 2} x$
$+ 7 \lim_{x \to 2} x - 11$. . . . Lim. of a prod, and lim. of a const.

$= 2 \cdot 2 \cdot 2 - 10 \cdot 2 \cdot 2 + 7 \cdot 2 - 11 = -29$, Q.E.D.

. . . . Limit of x

17. a. Graph. $f(x) = \frac{x^4 - 11x^3 + 21x^2 - x - 10}{x - 2}$

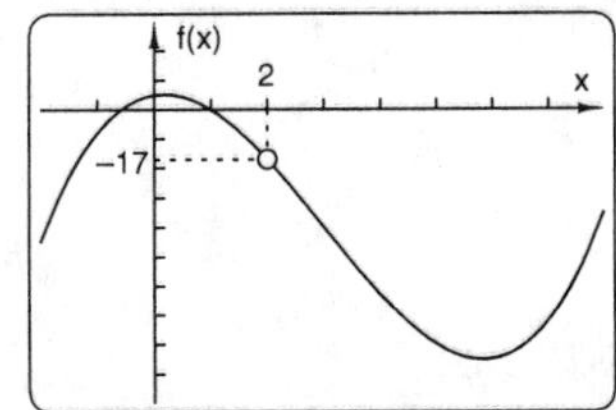

b. $f(x) = \frac{(x^3 - 9x^2 + 3x + 5)(x - 2)}{x - 2}$

$= x^3 - 9x^2 + 3x + 5,\ x \neq 2$

$\lim_{x\to2} f(x) = 2^3 - 9(2^2) + 3(2) + 5 = \underline{-17}$

c. Proof:

$\lim_{x\to2} f(x) = \lim_{x\to2} (x^3 - 9x^2 + 3x + 5)$ . . . Since $x \neq 2$

$= \lim_{x\to2} x^3 + \lim_{x\to2} (-9x^2) + \lim_{x\to2} 3x + \lim_{x\to2} 5$

. . . . Limit of a sum

$= \lim_{x\to2} x \cdot \lim_{x\to2} x \cdot \lim_{x\to2} x + (-9) \lim_{x\to2} x \cdot \lim_{x\to2} x$

$+ 3 \lim_{x\to2} x + 5$ . . Lim. of a prod, and lim. of a const.

$= 2{\cdot}2{\cdot}2 + (-9)(2{\cdot}2) + 3{\cdot}2 + 5 = -17$, Q.E.D.

. . . . Limit of x

18. Check the Answer by Table Problem

From the graph in Problem 13, the right side is more restrictive. Let f(x) = 41.1.

$x^2 + 2x + 6 = 41.1$

$x^2 + 2x - 35.1 = 0$

$x = \frac{-2 \pm \sqrt{144.4}}{2} = 5.008327...$ (or $-7.008327...$)

Let $\delta = 0.0083$. Use TABLE starting at x = 4.992 with increment 0.003.

x	f(x)
4.992	40.904064
4.995	40.940025
4.998	40.976004
5.001	41.012001
5.004	41.048016
5.007	41.084049

All these x-values are within 0.0083 of 5 and all the values of f(x) are within 0.1 unit of 41, Q.E.D.

19. Limit of a Composite Function Problem

a. Graph. y = cos x

y is close to 1 when x is close to 0.

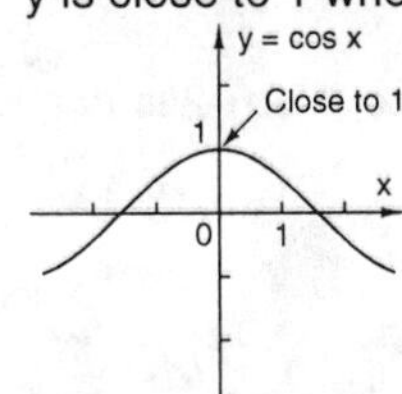

b. Graph. y = tan x

y is close to tan 1 = 1.557... when x is close to 1.

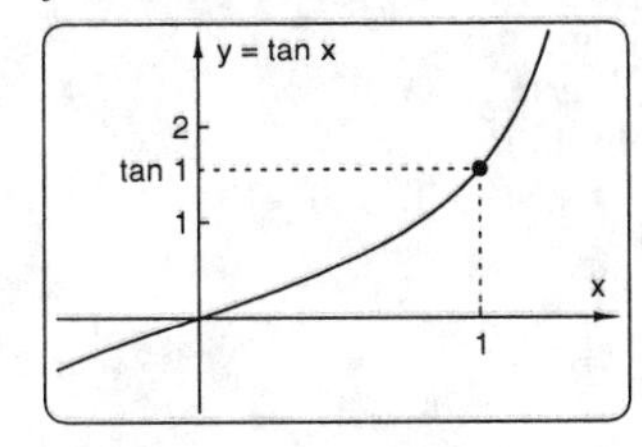

c. Graph. y = tan (cos x)

y stays close to tan 1 = 1.557... when x is close to 0.

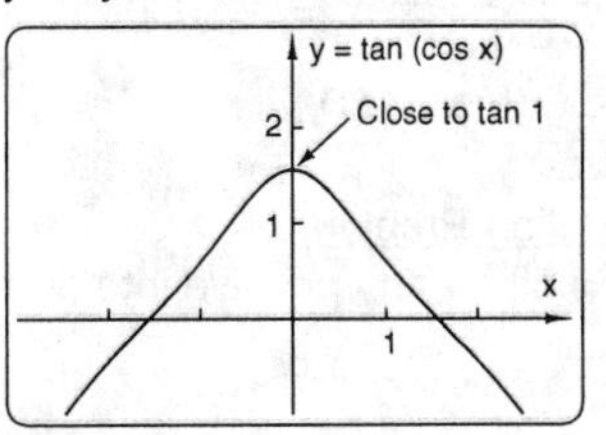

d. $\lim_{x\to0} \cos x = \underline{1}$. $\lim_{u\to1} \tan u = \underline{1.55...}$

$\lim_{x\to0} \tan(\cos x) = \underline{1.55...}$

20. Pizza Delivery Problem

a. $5(0)^{1/2} = 0 = v(0)$ (checks)

$5(1)^{1/2} = 5 = v(1)$ (checks)

$5(4)^{1/2} = 10 = v(4)$ (checks)

$5(9)^{1/2} = 15 = v(9)$ (checks)

$5(16)^{1/2} = 20 = v(16)$ (checks)

b. $a(9) \approx \frac{v(9.001) - v(9)}{9.001 - 9} = 0.8333101...$

Conjecture: a(9) = 0.8333... repeating = 5/6

Units of a(t): mph/sec

c. $a(9) = \lim_{t\to9} \frac{v(t) - v(9)}{t - 9} = \lim_{t\to9} \frac{5t^{1/2} - 15}{t - 9}$

$= \lim_{t\to9} \frac{5(t^{1/2} - 3)}{(t^{1/2} - 3)(t^{1/2} + 3)}$

$= \lim_{t\to9} \frac{5}{t^{1/2} + 3}$

= 5/6, which agrees with the conjecture.

d. Distance = integral of v(t) from 1 to 9.

By trapezoidal rule with n = 100 increments, integral ≈ 86.6657... . The units are mph·sec For ft, multiply by 5280 and divide by 3600, getting 127.1098... . (Exact: $127\frac{1}{9}$)

The truck went about 127 ft

21. Exact Derivative Problem

a. Derivative $\approx \frac{2.1^3 - 2^3}{2.1 - 2} = 12.61$

b. $\frac{x^3 - 8}{x - 2} = \frac{(x - 2)(x^2 + 2x + 4)}{x - 2}$

$= x^2 + 2x + 4$, provided $x \neq 2$.

This expression approaches $\underline{12}$.

Proof:

$\lim_{x\to2} \frac{x^3 - 8}{x - 2} = \lim_{x\to2} (x^2 + 2x + 4)$ . . . . Since $x \neq 2$

$= \lim_{x\to2} x^2 + \lim_{x\to2} 2x + \lim_{x\to2} 4$ . . . . . Limit of a sum

$= \lim_{x\to2} x \cdot \lim_{x\to2} x + 2 \lim_{x\to2} x + 4$

. . . . . Limit of a product and limit of a constant

$= 2{\cdot}2 + 2{\cdot}2 + 4 = 12$, Q.E.D. . . . . Limit of x.

c. Graph. The line appears to be tangent to the graph of f at (2, 8).

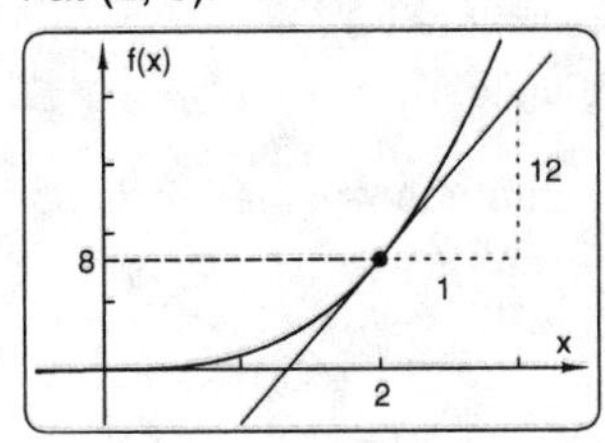

22. By symmetric difference quotient,
derivative $\approx \dfrac{0.7^{5.01} - 0.7^{4.99}}{2(0.01)} = \underline{-0.05994...}$

23. By trapezoidal rule with n = 100,
integral $\approx$ $\underline{11.8235...}$

24. Mathematical Induction Problem
Prove that $\lim_{x\to c} x^n = c^n$ for any positive integer n.
Proof:
Anchor:
If n = 1, $\lim_{x\to c} x^1 = c = c^1$ by the limit of x
Induction Hypothesis:
Assume that the property is true for n = k.
$\therefore \lim_{x\to c} x^k = c^k$
Verification for n = k + 1:
$\lim_{x\to c} x^{k+1} = \lim_{x\to c} (x^k \cdot x)$
$= \lim_{x\to c} x^k \cdot \lim_{x\to c} x = c^k \cdot c$ . . . . By the induction hyp.
$= c^{k+1}$
Conclusion:
$\therefore \lim_{x\to c} x^n = c^n$ for *all* integers n ≥ 1, Q.E.D.

25. Journal Problem
Answers will vary. See solutions in Section 1–6.

Problem Set 2-4, pages 56 to 60 — Continuity

Q1. Derivative: Instantaneous rate of change.
Q2. Definite integral: Product of x and y, y variable.
Q3. $\delta = 0.1/200 = 0.0005$
Q4. Graph. Alt. int. angles

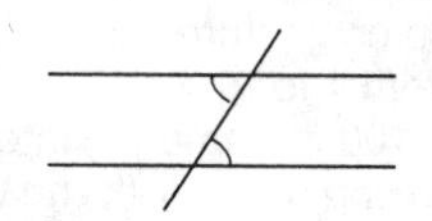

Q6. Graph. y = cos x

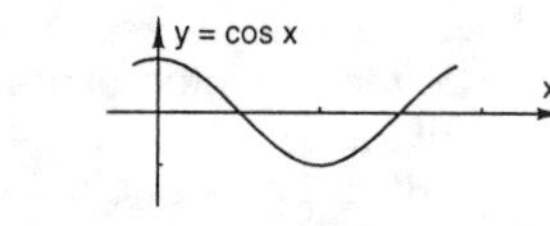

Q5. Exponential function.
Q7. (x + 6)(x – 1)
Q8. $53^{2001}/53^{2000} = 53$
Q9. 5! = 120
Q10. 103 (*Not* 28!)

1. a. Has right and left limits.
 b. Has no limit.
 c. Discontinuous. Has no limit.
2. a. Has right and left limits.
 b. Has a limit.
 c. Discontinuous. No f(3).
3. a. Has right and left limits.
 b. Has a limit.
 c. Continuous.
4. a. Has right and left limits.
 b. Has a limit.
 c. Continuous.
5. a. Has right and left limits.
 b. Has a limit.
 c. Continuous.
6. a. Has no right and left limits.
 b. Has no limit.
 c. Discontinuous. No limit or f(2).
7. a. Has right and left limits.
 b. Has a limit.
 c. Continuous. (Note that the x-value, –3, is *not* at the asymptote.)
8. a. Has no right and left limits.
 b. Has no limit.
 c. Discontinuous. No limit or f(–π/2).
9. a. Has right and left limits.
 b. Has a limit.
 c. Discontinuous. No value for f(–6).
10. a. Has right and left limits.
 b. Has a limit.
 c. Continuous.
11. a. Has no right and left limits.
 b. Has no limit.
 c. Discontinuous. No limit. No value for f(–2).
12. a. Has no right and left limits.
 b. Has no limit.
 c. Discontinuous. Not a function.
 (Note: Technically, f(x) is improper on the axis.)
13. a. Has right and left limits.
 b. Has a limit.
 c. Continuous. (Note that the x-value 5 is *not* at the discontinuity.)
14. a. Has right and left limits.
 b. Has a limit.
 c. Continuous. (Note that the x-value –2 is *not* at the asymptote.)
15. a. Has right and left limits.
 b. Has a limit.
 c. Discontinuous. f(1) ≠ limit.
16. a. Has left limit but no right limit.
 b. Has no limit.
 c. Discontinuous. No limit or f(10).
17. a. Has right and left limits.
 b. Has no limit.
 c. Discontinuous. No limit.

18. a. Has right and left limits.
    b. Has a limit, 7.
    c. Continuous.
19. a. Has right and left limits.
    b. Has a limit.
    c. Discontinuous. No f(c).
20. a. Has right and left limits.
    b. Has no limit.
    c. Discontinuous. No limit, no f(c).

21. Graph (example).

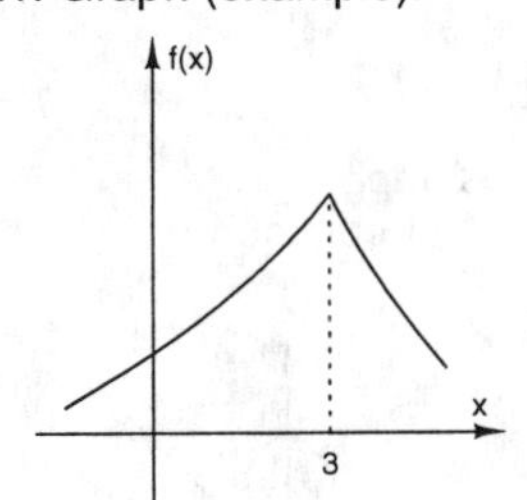

22. Graph (example).

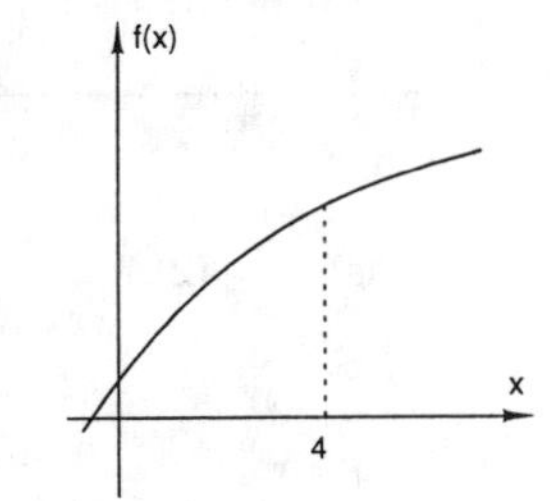

23. Graph (example).

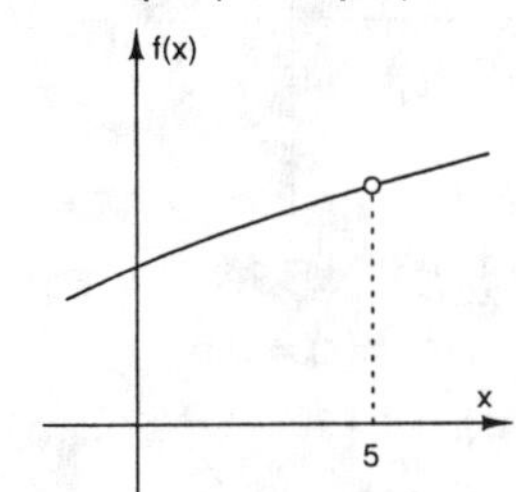

24. Graph (example).

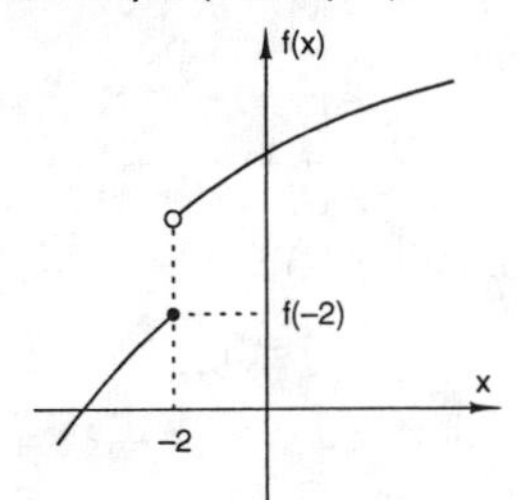

25. Graph (example).

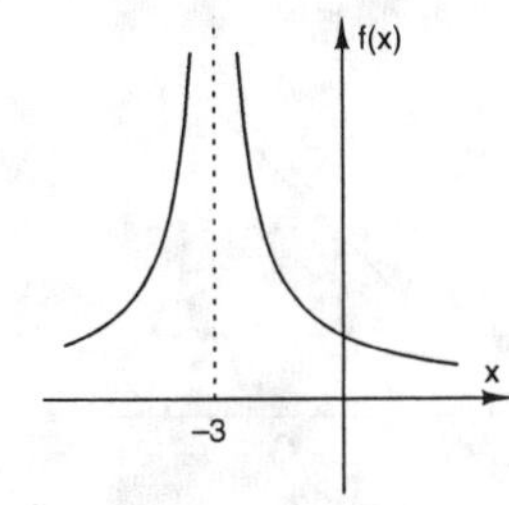

26. Graph (example).

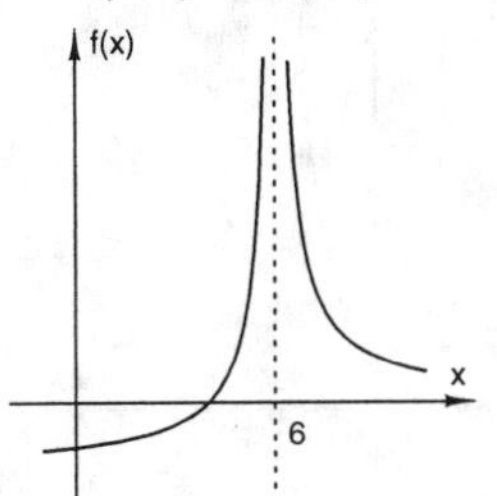

27. Graph (example).

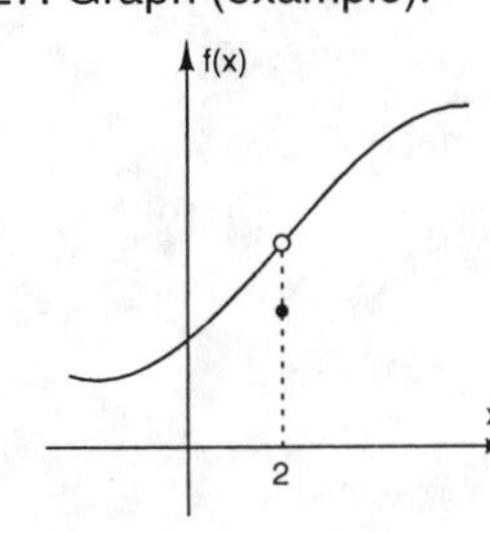

28. Graph (example).

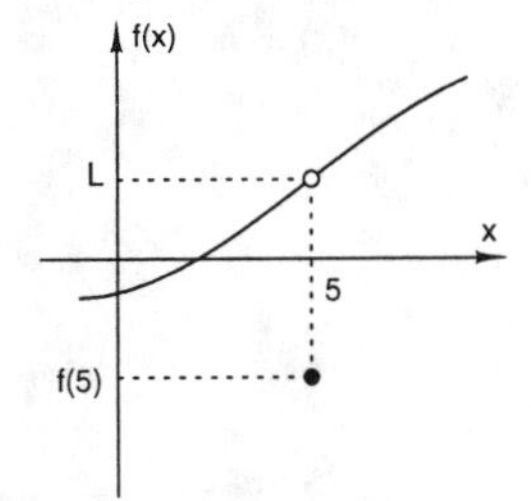

29. Graph (example).

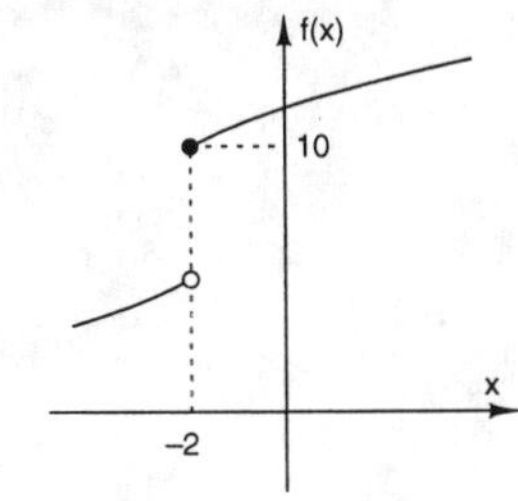

30. Graph (example).

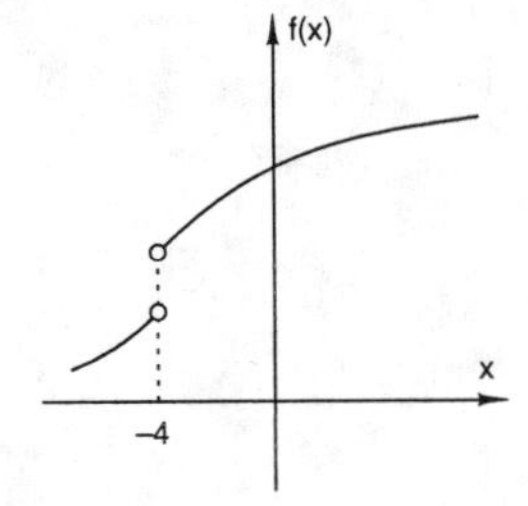

31. Graph (example).

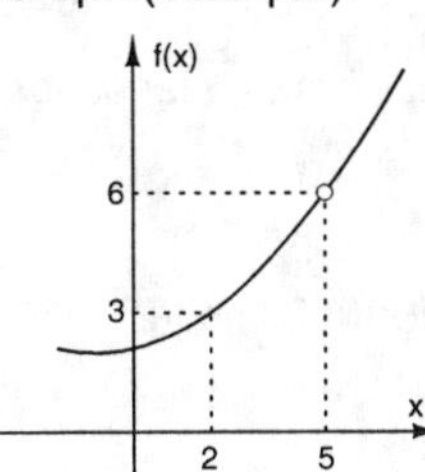

32. Graph (example).

33. Graph (example).

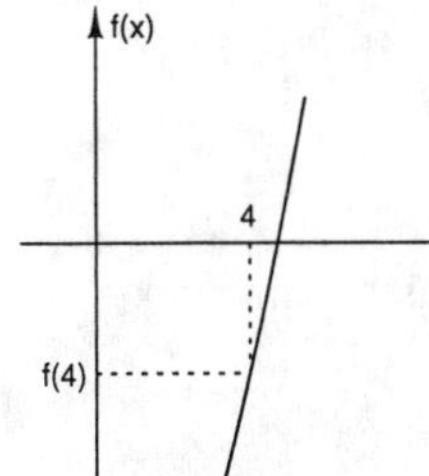

34. Graph (example).

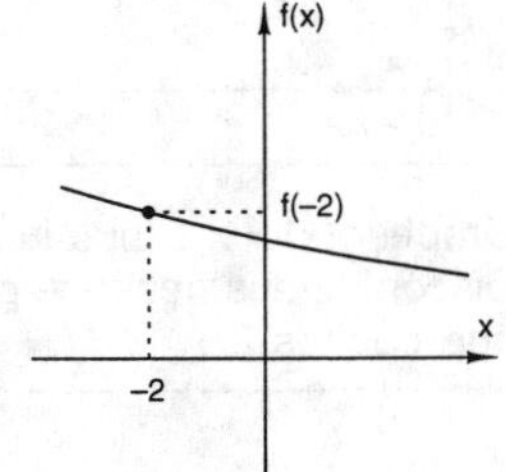

35. Graph (example).

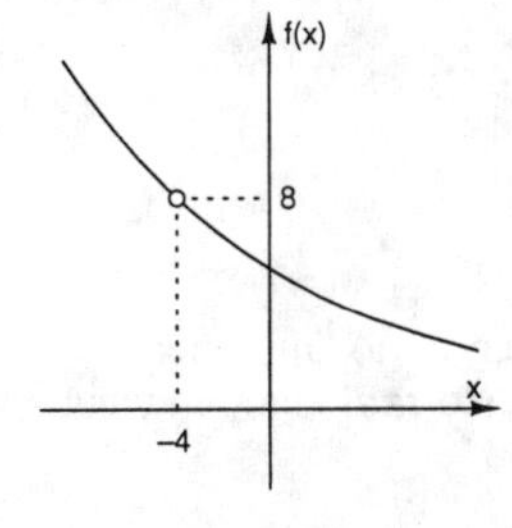

36. Graph (example).

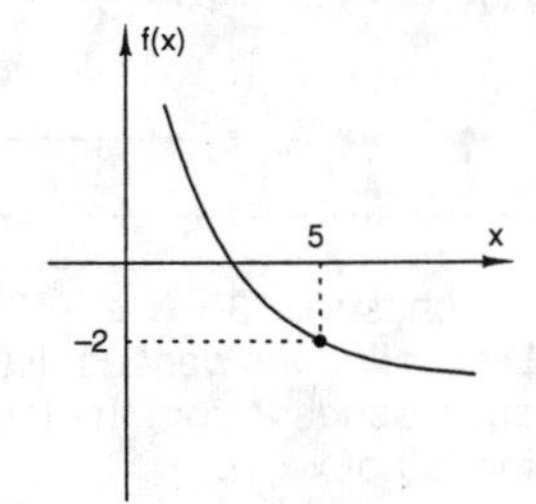

37. Graph (example).

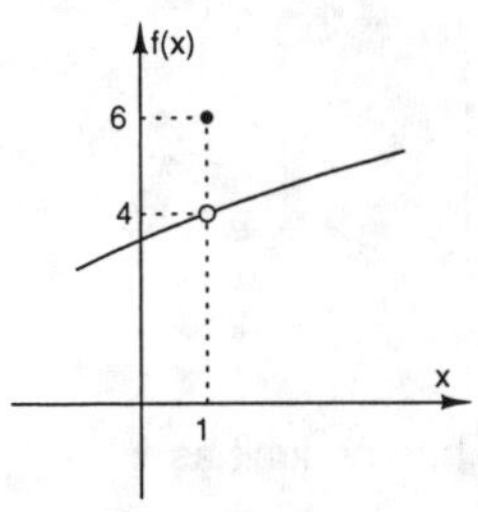

38. Graph (example).

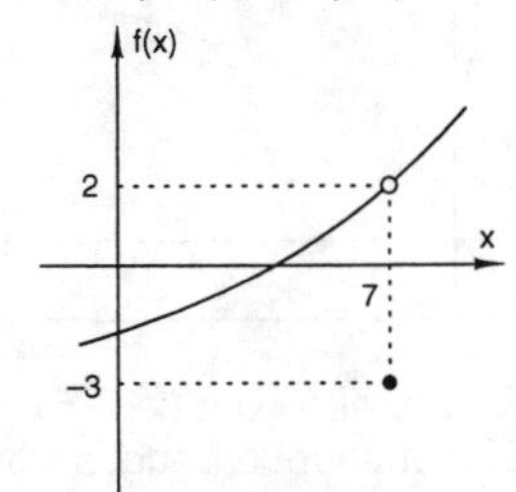

39. Graph (example).

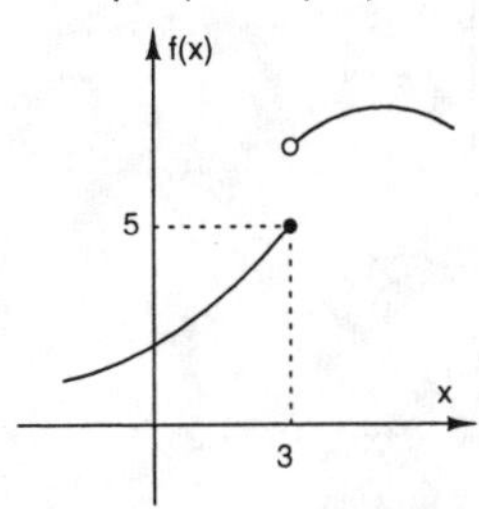

40. Graph (example).

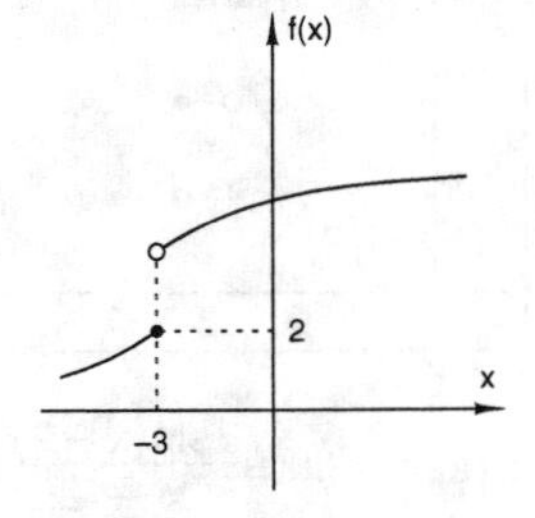

41. Graph (example).

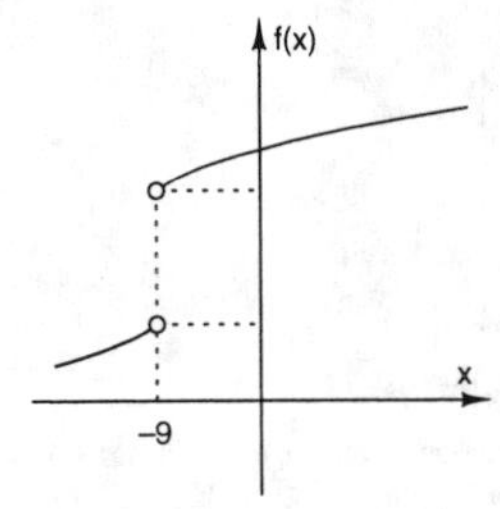

42. Graph (example).

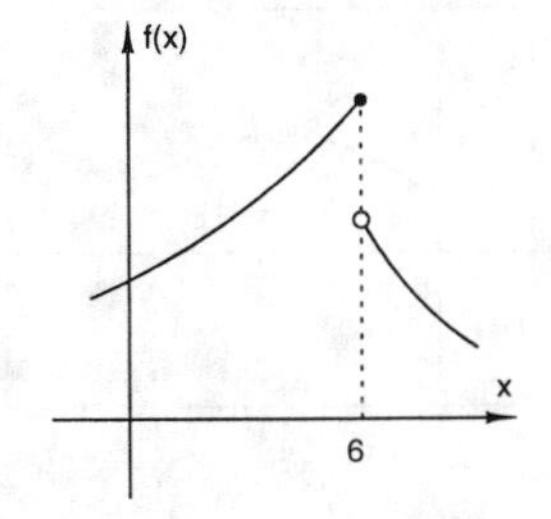

43. Discontinuous at $x = -3$
44. Discontinuous at $x = 11$
45. Discontinuous at $x = \pi/2 + \pi n$, where n stands for an integer.
46. Nowhere discontinuous.
47. Graph. $f(x) = x + \text{int}(\cos \pi x)$
Discontinuous because $\lim_{x \to 2} f(x) = 2$ and $f(2) = 3$.

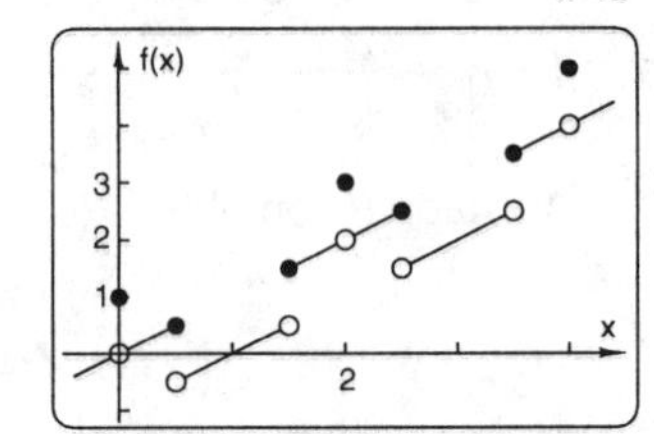

48. Graph. $g(x) = x + \text{int}(\sin \pi x)$
Discontinuous because g(x) has no limit as x approaches 2.

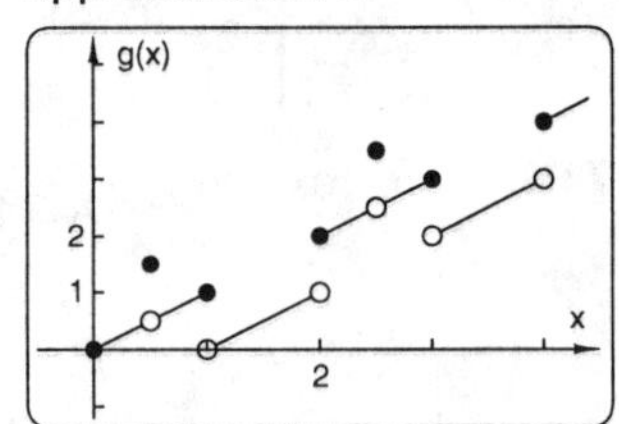

49. Graph. $s(x) = 3 + \sqrt{x - 2}$
Discontinuous because s(x) has no limit as x approaches 2 from the left. (No real function values to the left of $x = 2$.)

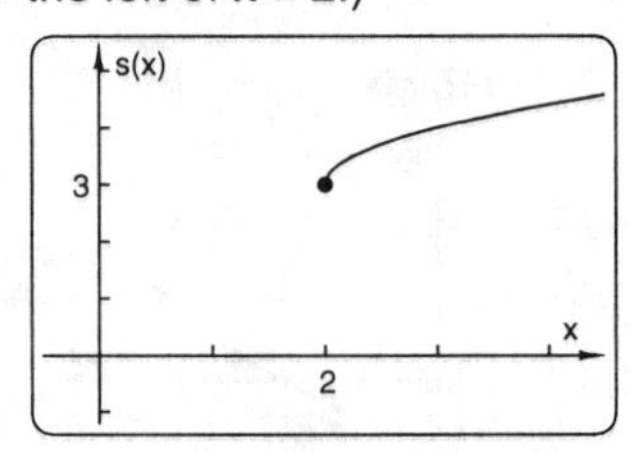

50. Graph. $p(x) = \text{int}(x^2 - 6x + 9)$
Discontinuous because p(x) has no limit as x approaches 2.

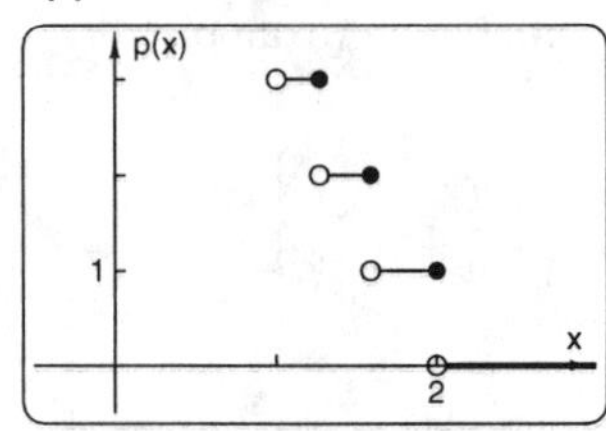

51. Graph. $h(x) = \dfrac{\sin(x - 2)}{x - 2}$
Discontinuous because there is no value of h(2).

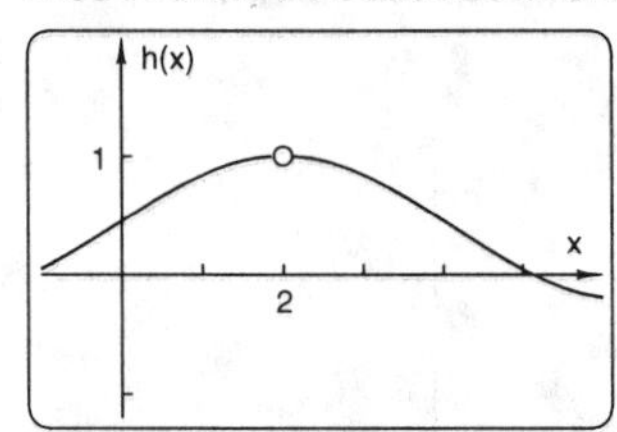

52. Graph. $f(x) = \begin{cases} x + (2 - x)^{-1}, & \text{if } x \neq 2 \\ 3, & \text{if } x = 2 \end{cases}$
Discontinuous because there is no limit of f(x) as x approaches 2.

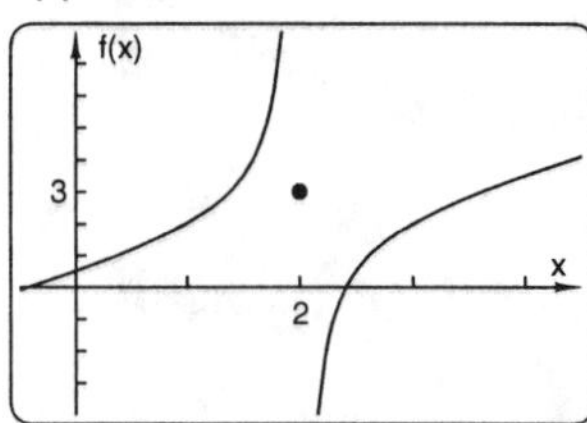

53. a. Graph.
Not continuous.
(No value for f(2).)

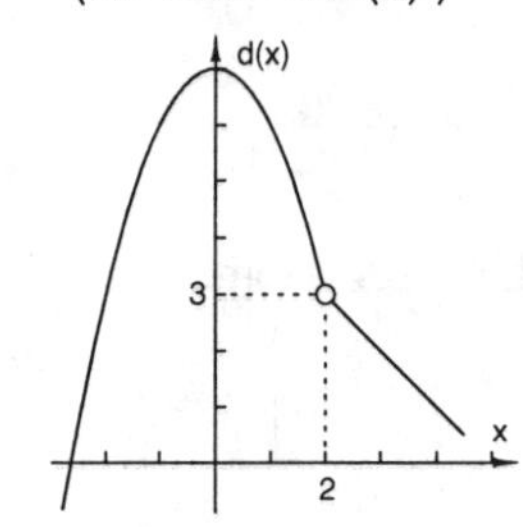

b. $\lim_{x \to 2^-} d(x) = 3$,
$\lim_{x \to 2^+} d(x) = 3$,
Limit = 3

54. a. Graph.
Not continuous.

b. $\lim_{x \to 1^-} h(x) = 3$
$\lim_{x \to 1^+} h(x) = 2$,
No limit

55. a. Graph.
Not continuous.

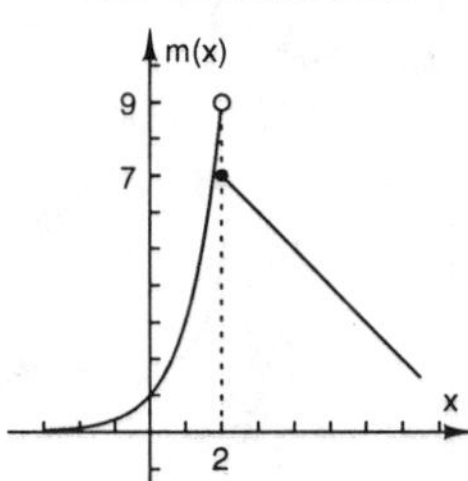

b. $\lim_{x \to 2^-} m(x) = 9$,
$\lim_{x \to 2^+} m(x) = 7$,
No limit

56. a. Graph.
Continuous.

b. $\lim_{x \to -1^-} q(x) = 2$,
$\lim_{x \to -1^+} q(x) = 2$,
Limit = 2

57. a. Graph.
Not continuous.

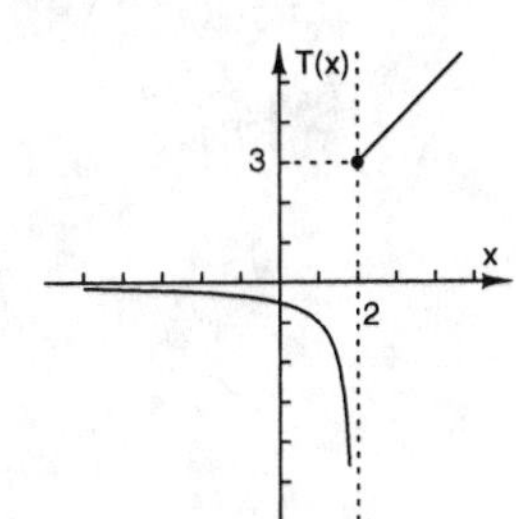

b. $\lim_{x\to2^-} T(x)$: none.
$\lim_{x\to2^+} T(x) = 3$,
No limit.

58. a. Graph.

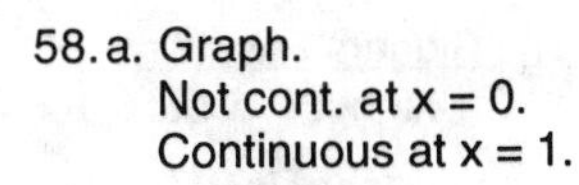

Not cont. at x = 0.
Continuous at x = 1.

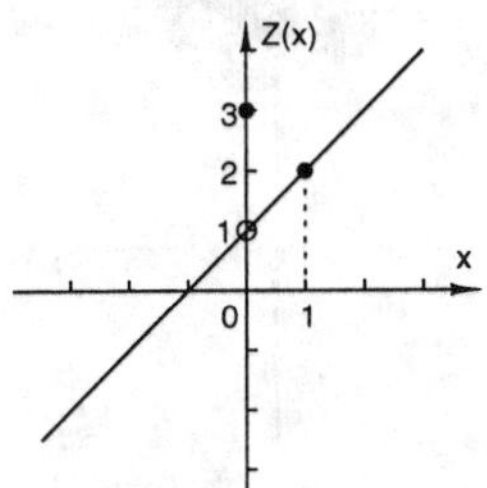

b. $\lim_{x\to0^-} Z(x) = 1$,
$\lim_{x\to0^+} Z(x) = 1$,
Limit = 1 as $x\to0$
$\lim_{x\to1^-} Z(x) = 2$,
$\lim_{x\to1^+} Z(x) = 2$,
Limit = 2 as $x\to1$

59. $-0.4(1) + 2 = 1.6$.
Make $0.3(1) + k = 1.6$.
$\therefore$ <u>k = 1.3</u>.
Graph

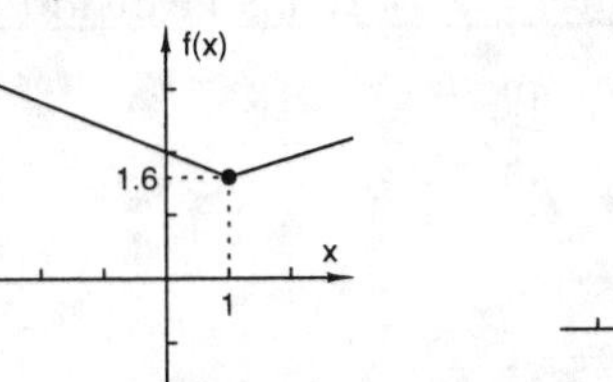

60. $2^2 = 4$
Make $k - 2 = 4$.
$\therefore$ <u>k = 6</u>
Graph

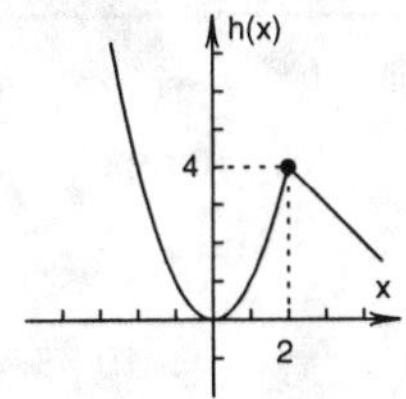

61. $9 - 2^2 = 5$.
Make $2k = 5$.
$\therefore$ <u>k = 2.5</u>.
Graph

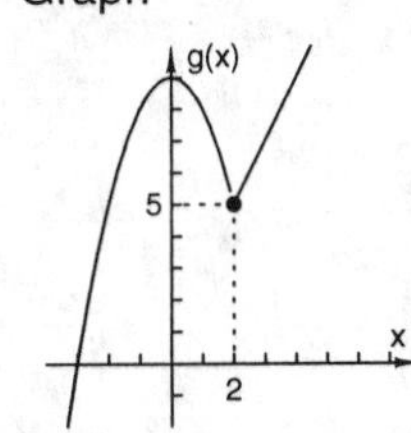

62. $0.4(1) + 1 = 1.4$
Make $k(1) + 2 = 1.4$
$\therefore$ <u>k = −0.6</u>
Graph

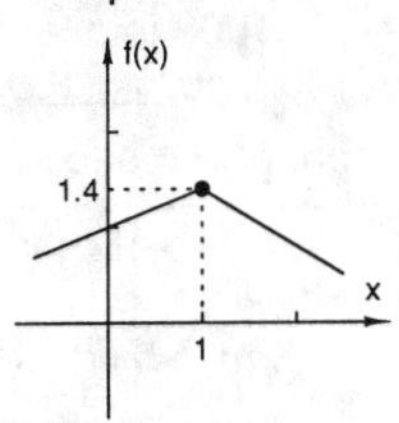

63. Make $9k = 3k - 3$.
$\therefore$ <u>k= −1/2</u>.
Graph

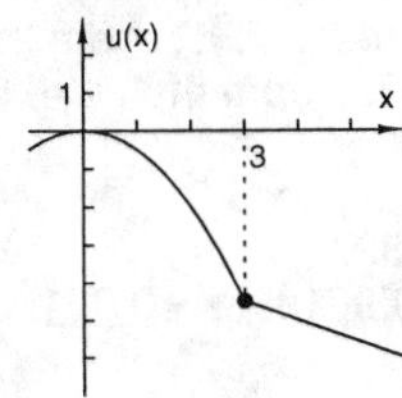

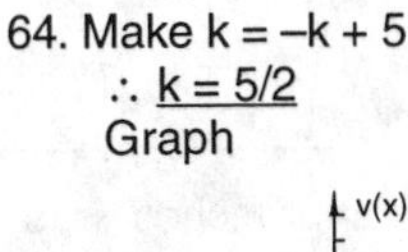

64. Make $k = -k + 5$
$\therefore$ <u>k = 5/2</u>
Graph

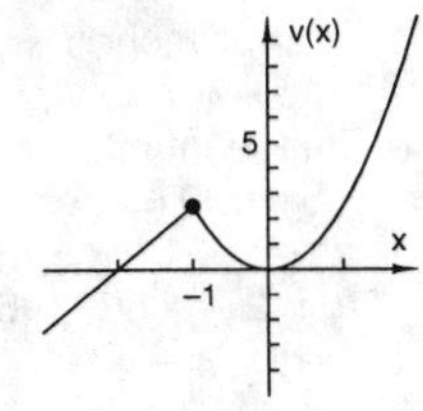

65. Make $0.4(1) + k^2 = k(1) + 2.4$
$\therefore k^2 - k - 2 = 0 \Rightarrow (k + 1)(k - 2) = 0 \Rightarrow k = -1$ or 2
Graphs

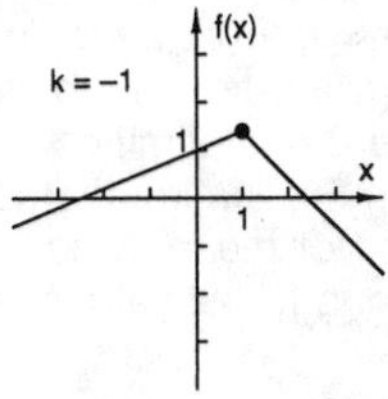

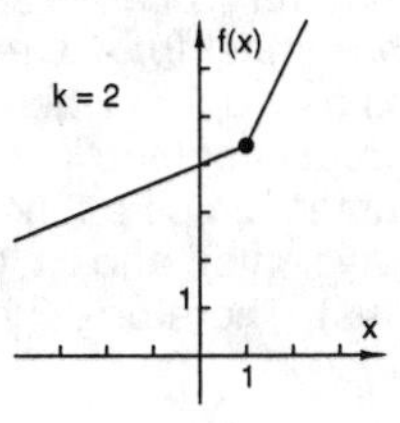

66. Make $k^2 - 2^2 = 1.5k(2)$.
$\therefore k^2 - 3k - 4 = 0 \Rightarrow (k - 4)(k + 1) = 0 \Rightarrow k = 4$ or -1
Graphs

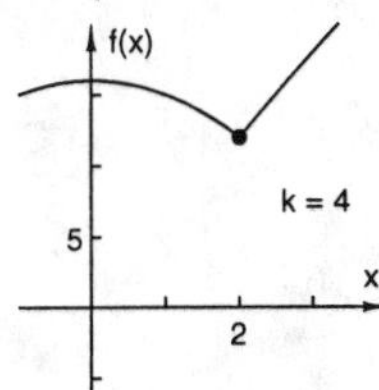

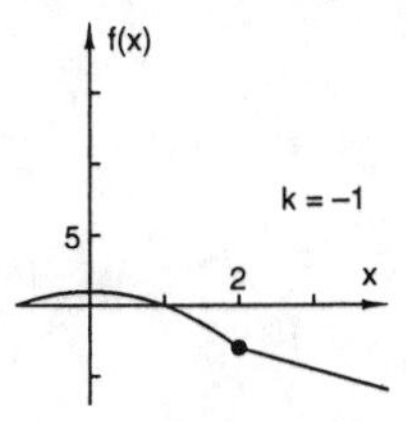

67. <u>Two Constants Problem</u>

$$f(x) = \begin{cases} b - x, & \text{if } x \le 1 \\ a(x - 2)^2, & \text{if } x > 1 \end{cases}$$

a. $b - 1 = a(1 - 2)^2 \Rightarrow b - 1 = a$
b. $a = -1 \Rightarrow b = 0$. Graph. Continuous at x = 1.

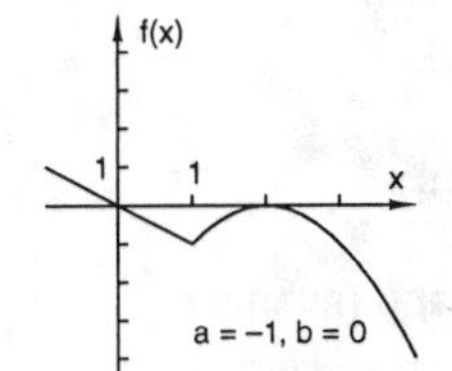

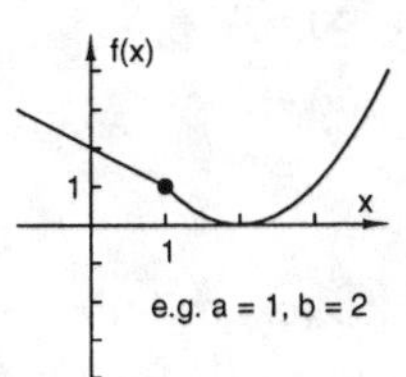

c. For example, $a = 1 \Rightarrow b = 2$. Graph, above.
Continuous at x = 1.

68. <u>Surprise Function Problem!</u>
a. $f(x) = x + 3 + \dfrac{10^{-20}}{x - 1}$. Graph

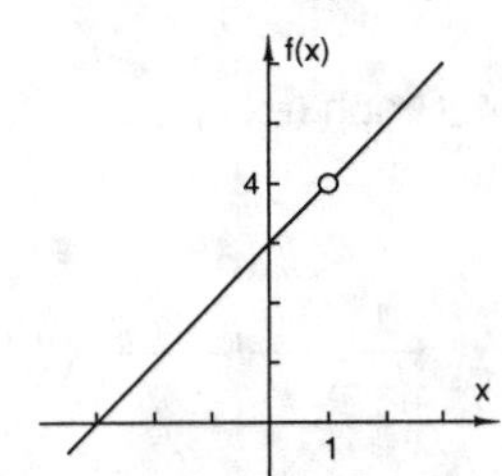

b. f(x) seems to approach 4 as x approaches 1.
c. $f(1.0000001) = 1.0000001 + 3 + 10^{-13}$
≈ 4.0000001, which is close to 4.
d. There is a vertical asymptote at x = 0. You must get x much closer to 1 than x = 1.0000001 for the discontinuity to show up.

69. Continuity of Polynomial Functions

For any value of c, P(c) is determined by addition and multiplication. Since the set of real numbers is closed under multiplication and addition, P(c) will be a *unique, real* number for any real value x = c. P(c) is the *limit* of P(x) as x approaches c by the properties of the limit of a product of functions (for powers of x), limit of a constant times a function (for multiplication by the coefficients), and limit of a sum (for the individual terms). Therefore, P is continuous for all values of x.

70. The Signum Function

a. $\lim_{x\to 4} |\text{sgn } x| = 1$ but f(0) = 0. Discontinuous.

b. g(x) = 3 sgn (x – 2)

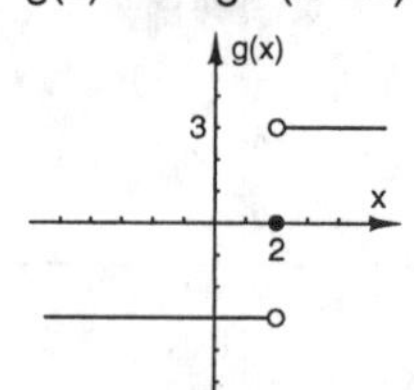

c. h(x) = – sgn x

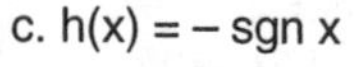

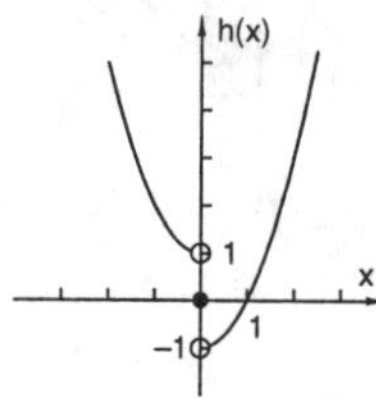

d. For x > 0, a(x) = x/x = 1 = sgn x
For x < 0, a(x) = (–x)/x = –1 = sgn x.
For x = 0, a(0) is not defined.
∴ a(x) = sgn x for all x ≠ 0, Q.E.D.

e. f(x) = cos x + sgn x

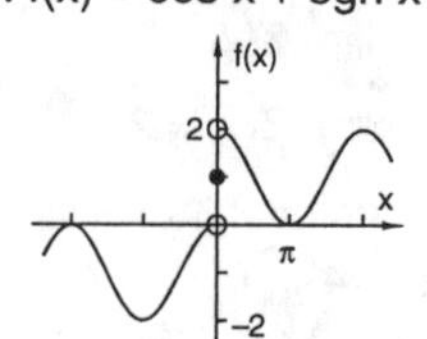

f. $p(x) = \text{sgn}(x)\cdot|x|^{3/7}$

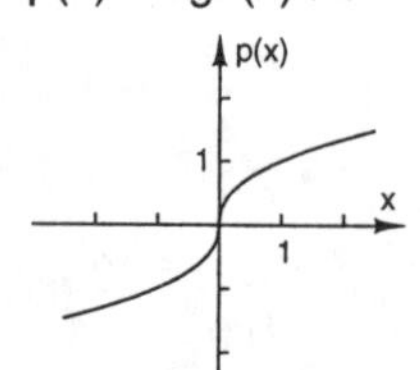

Problem Set 2-5, pages 64 to 66 — Limits Involving Infinity

Q1. No limit.

Q2. $\lim_{x\to 2} f(x) = 3$

Q3. $\lim_{x\to 3} f(x) = 4$

Q4. $\lim_{x\to 4} f(x) = 3$

Q5. $\lim_{x\to 5} f(x) = 2$

Q6. No.

Q7. No.

Q8. Yes.

Q9. No.

Q10. Yes.

1. Graph (example)

2. Graph (example)

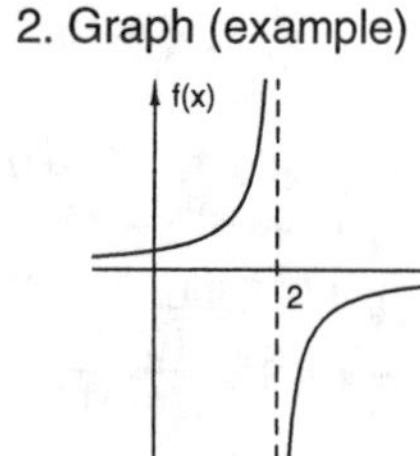

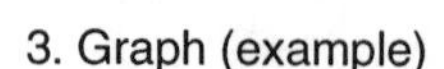

3. Graph (example)

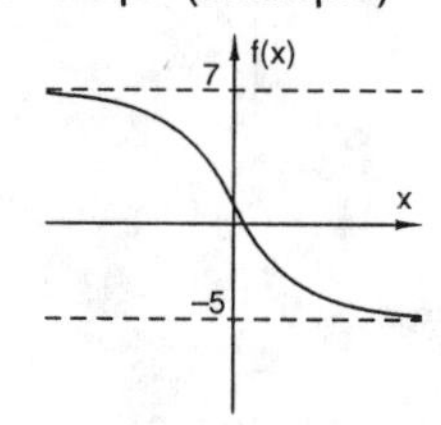

4. Graph (example)

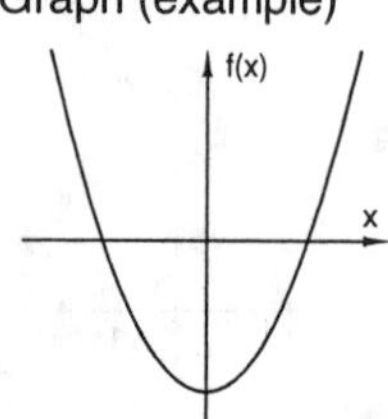

5. a. Graph. $f(x) = 2 + \dfrac{1}{x - 3}$

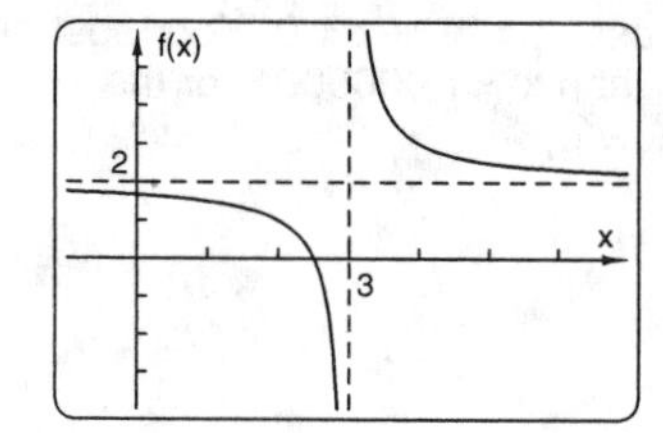

b. $\lim_{x\to 3^+} f(x) = \infty$, $\lim_{x\to 3^-} f(x) = -\infty$,
$\lim_{x\to 3} f(x)$, none, $\lim_{x\to\infty} f(x) = 2$,
$\lim_{x\to -\infty} f(x) = 2$.

c. $2 + \dfrac{1}{x-3} > 100 \Rightarrow \dfrac{1}{x-3} > 98$
x – 3 < 1/98 (since x – 3 is *positive*)
δ = 1/98.

d. $2 + \dfrac{1}{x-3} < 2.001 \Rightarrow \dfrac{1}{x-3} < 0.01$
x – 3 > 1000 (since x – 3 is *positive*)
x > 1003, so D = 1003.

6. a. Graph. g(x) = sec x

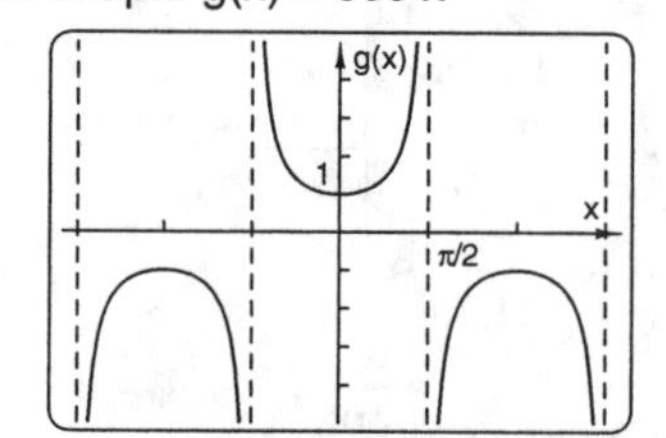

b. Sec x approaches ∞ as x approaches π/2 from the left, and – ∞ as x approaches π/2 from the right. So the limit is infinite.

c. sec x > 1000 ⇒ cos x < 0.001 (cos x > 0)
cos x = 0.001 if x = 1.56979632...
∴ δ = π/2 – 1.56979632... = 0.00100... ≈ 0.001.

d. $\lim_{x\to \pi/2^+} g(x) = -\infty$
By symmetry, g(x) < –1000 if x is within 0.001 unit of π/2 on the right side.

7. a. Graph. $r(x) = 2 + \frac{\sin x}{x}$

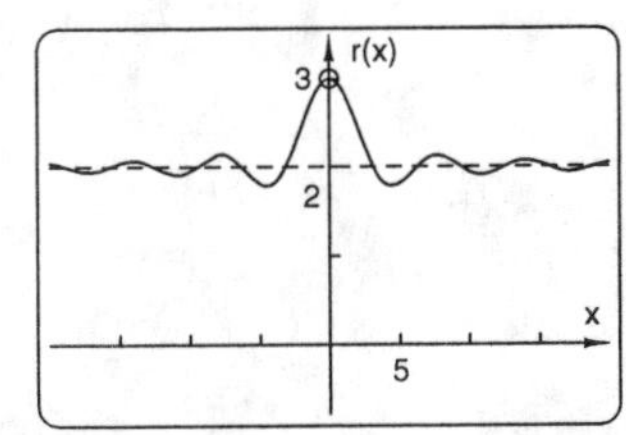

b. $\lim_{x\to\infty} r(x) = 2$ because (sin x)/(x) approaches 0.

c. $1.999 < 2 + \frac{\sin x}{x} < 2.001$

$-0.001 < \frac{\sin x}{x} < 0.001$

Since $|\sin x| \le 1$, make $1/x < 0.001$.
Thus $x > 1000$. So D = 1000.

d. The line y = 2 is *not* an asymptote, because the graph crosses this line an infinite number of times as x increases. ("Asymptote" comes from the Greek *asymptotus*, meaning "not falling together." "Asymmetry" comes from a similar root.)

e. $\lim_{x\to 0} r(x) = 3$. By zooming in on the graph around x = 0, you can see that r(x) is very close to 3 when x is close to, but not equal to, zero.

8. a. Graph. $h(x) = (1 + 1/x)^x$

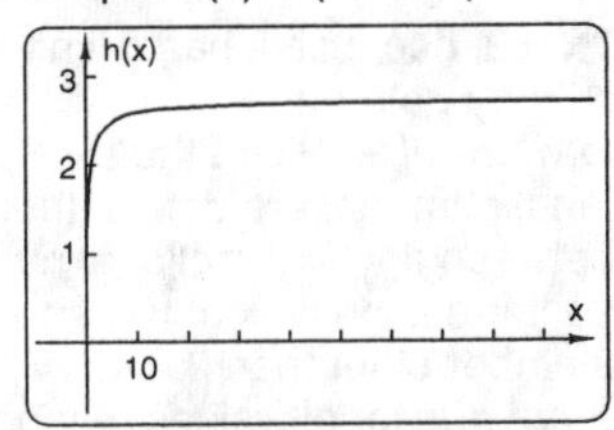

b. Neither phenomenon "wins". (The "compromise" is a number called *e*, approximately 2.718..., which you will encounter in your study of natural logarithms in Chapter 6.

9. The limit is infinite. Y is unbounded as x approaches infinity. If there were a number E such that log x < E for all x > 0, then you could let $x = 10^{2E}$, so that log x $= \log 10^{2E} = 2E$, which is greater than E, which was assumed to be an upper bound.

10. "Look, Wanda. Here's what happens to a fraction when the denominator gets close to zero.

$\frac{1}{0.1} = 10, \frac{1}{.0001} = 10{,}000, \frac{1}{.00001} = 100{,}000.$

The answers just keep getting bigger and bigger. When the denominators get bigger and bigger, the fraction gets closer and closer to zero, like this:

$\frac{1}{10} = 0.1, \frac{1}{100} = .01, \frac{1}{1000} = .001.$"

11. Limits Applied to Integrals Problem

a. The definite integral is the product of the independent and the dependent variable. Since distance = (rate)(time), the integral represents distance in this case.

b. $T_9 = 17.8060052...$
$T_{45} = 17.9819616...$
$T_{90} = 17.9935649...$
$T_{450} = 17.9994175...$

c. The exact answer is 18. It is a limit because the sums can be made as close to it as you like, just by making the number of trapezoids large enough (and thus their widths close to zero). The sums are smaller than the integral because each trapezoid is inscribed under the graph, and thus leaves out a part of its respective strip of the region.

d. T_n is 0.01 unit from 18 when it equals 17.99. From part a., this occurs between n = 45 and n = 90. By experimentation,
$T_{66} = 17.9897900...$
$T_{67} = 17.9900158...$
Therefore, the approximation is within 0.01 units of 18 for any value of $n \ge 67$.
An alternative solution is to plot the graph of the difference between 18 and T_n as a function of the number of increments, n, or to do a regression analysis to find an equation. The best-fitting elementary function is an inverse power variation function,
$y = (5.01004...)(x^{-1.48482...})$
The graph of this function and three of the four data points are shown below. Use the TRACE or SOLVE feature of your grapher to find $n \approx 67$.

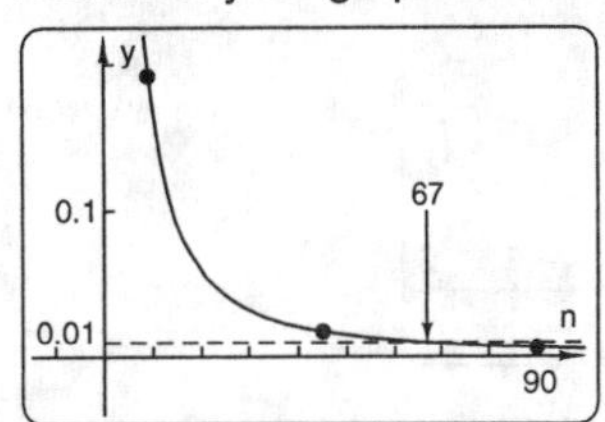

12. Work Problem

a. Work = force × distance. Since a definite integral measures the y-variable times the x-variable, it represents work in this case.

b. By the trapezoidal rule,
$T_{10} = 24.147775...$
$T_{100} = 24.004889...$.
The units are foot-pounds.

c. The integer is 24.

d. By experimentation,
$T_{289} = 24.001003...$
$T_{290} = 24.000998...$
$\therefore D = 290$

13. Searchlight Problem

Length = 100 sec x = 100/cos x
Length > 1000 ⇒ 100/cos x > 1000
cos x < 0.1 (because cos x is *positive*)
$x > \cos^{-1} 0.1$ (because cos is *decreasing*)
x > 1.4706289...
$\pi/2 - 1.4706289... = 0.100167...$
x must be within 0.100167... radian of $\pi/2$.

14. Zero Times Infinity Problem

a. $f(2) = 5 \cdot 2 \cdot 0 \cdot (1/0)$, which has the form $0 \cdot \infty$.
$g(2) = 5 \cdot 2 \cdot 0 \cdot (1/0)^2$, which has the form $0 \cdot \infty$.
$h(2) = 5 \cdot 2 \cdot 0^2 \cdot (1/0)$, which has the form $0 \cdot \infty$.

b. $f(x) = 5x(x-2)\dfrac{1}{x-2} = 5x,\ x \neq 2.$

$\therefore \lim_{x \to 2} f(x) = 10.$

$g(x) = 5x(x-2)\dfrac{1}{(x-2)^2} = \dfrac{5x}{x-2},\ x \neq 2.$

$\therefore \lim_{x \to 2} g(x)$ is infinite.

$h(x) = 5x(x-2)^2\dfrac{1}{x-2} = 5x(x-2),\ x \neq 2.$

$\therefore \lim_{x \to 2} h(x) = 0.$

c. The indeterminate form $0 \cdot \infty$ could approach zero, infinity, or some finite number.

Problem Set 2-6, pages 68 to 70

The Intermediate Value Theorem and Its Consequences

Q1. $f(2) = 53$	Q2. Limit = 53
Q3. $h(3)$ is undefined	Q4. Limit = 5
Q5. $s(0)$ is undefined	Q6. Limit does not exist
Q7. $\sin(\pi/2) = 1$	Q8. $\lvert 13 - 7 \rvert = 6$
Q9. +	Q10. $x > -4$

1. $f(x) = (x-3)^4 + 2$, $[1, 4]$, $y = 8$.
f is continuous because it is a polynomial function.
$f(1) = 18$, $f(4) = 3$
Since 8 is between 18 and 3, there is a number $x = c$ between 1 and 4 for which $f(c) = 8$, Q.E.D.
$(c-3)^4 + 2 = 8$ if $c = 3 \pm 6^{1/4}$
$= 4.5650...$ or $1.4349...$.
$1.4349...$ is between 0 and 4.
Graph

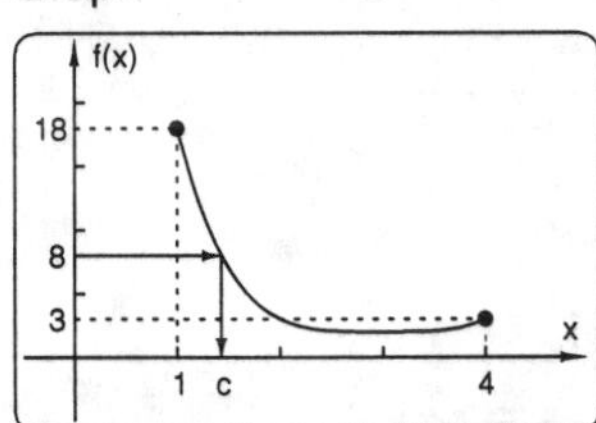

2. $f(x) = 0.001x^5 - 8$, $[0, 6]$, $y = -1$.
f is continuous because it is a polynomial function.
$f(0) = -8$, $f(6) = -0.224$.
Since -1 is between -8 and -0.224, there is a number $x = c$ between 0 and 6 for which $f(c) = -1$, Q.E.D.
$0.001c^5 - 8 = -1$ if $c = 7000^{1/5} = 5.8751...$, which is between 0 and 6.
Graph

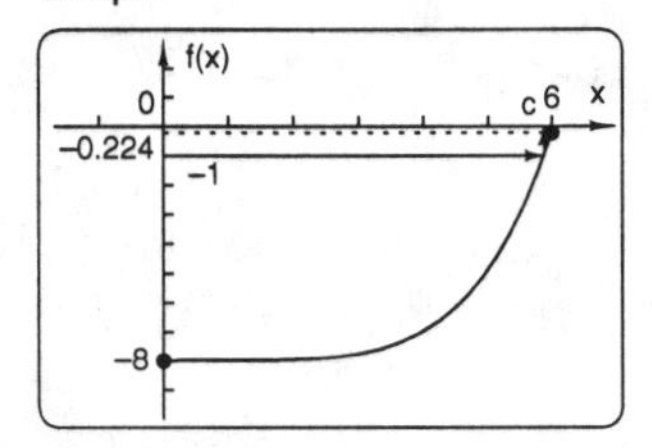

3. Converse of the Intermediate Value Theorem?
a. For $1 \leq y < 2$ or for $5 < y \leq 8$, the conclusion would be true. But for $2 \leq y \leq 5$, it would be false because there are no values of x in $[1, 5]$ that give these values for $f(x)$.
b. The conclusion of the theorem is true because every number y in $[4, 6]$ is a value of $g(x)$ for some value of x in $[1, 5]$.

4. a. $f(2) = 4$, $f(3) = 8$, $f(0.5) = \sqrt{2} = 1.414...$,
$f(\sqrt{5}) = 8$.
b. f *is* continuous at $x = 3$, because it has a limit and a function value and they both equal 8.
c. f is continuous *nowhere else.* Since the sets of rational and irrational numbers are dense, there is a rational number between any two irrational numbers and vice versa. So there is no limit of $f(x)$ as x approaches any number other than 2.
d. The conclusion is *not true* for all values of y between 1 and 4. For instance, if $y = 3$, then c would equal $\log_2 3$, which is irrational. So $f(c) = 8$, which is not between 1 and 4.

5. Let $f(x) = x^2$.
Since f is a polynomial function, it is continuous and thus the intermediate value theorem applies.
Since $f(1) = 1$ and $f(2) = 4$, there is a number c between 1 and 2 such that $f(c) = 3$.
By the definition of square root, $c = \sqrt{3}$, Q.E.D.

6. Prove that if f is continuous, and if $f(a)$ is positive and $f(b)$ is negative, then there is at least one zero of $f(x)$ between $x = a$ and $x = b$.
Proof: Since f is continuous, the intermediate value theorem applies. Since $f(a)$ is positive and $f(b)$ is negative, there is a number $x = c$ between a and b for which $f(c) = 0$. Therefore f has at least one zero between $x = a$ and $x = b$, Q.E.D.

7. The intermediate value theorem is called an existence theorem because it tells you that a number such as $\sqrt{3}$ *exists.* It does not tell you how to *calculate* that number.

8. Sweetheart Problem
Telephone your sweetheart's house. An answer to the call tells you the "existence" of the sweetheart at home. The call doesn't tell such things as how to get there, and so on. Also, getting no answer does not necessarily mean that your sweetheart is out.

9. Foot Race Problem
Let f(t) = Jesse's speed – Kay's speed.
$f(1) = 20 - 15 = 5$, which is *positive.*
$f(3) = 17 - 19 = -2$, which is *negative.*
Since the speeds are assumed to be continuous, f is also continuous and the intermediate value theorem applies.
Thus, there is a value of t between 1 and 3 for which $f(t) = 0$, meaning that Jesse and Kay are going at exactly the same speed at that time.
The *existence* of the time tells you neither what that time is nor what the speed is. An existence theorem, such as the intermediate value theorem, does not tell these things.

10. Postage Stamp Problem
The function does *not* meet the hypotheses of the intermediate value theorem because it is not continuous. There is *no* letter weight that requires exactly $1.00, since a 3-ounce letter costs $0.78 and a 4-ounce letter costs $1.01.

11. Cosine Function Problem
The intermediate value theorem *cannot* be used on the cosine function until it has been proved that cos is *continuous.* Once it has been proved (Chapter 3), you can conclude that there is a number $c = \cos^{-1} 0.6 = 0.92729521...$.

12. Exponential Function Problem
The intermediate value theorem *cannot* be used in the exponential function until it has been proved that the function is *continuous.* Once it has been proved (Chapter 5), you can conclude that there is a number $c = \log_2 3 = 1.58496250...$ between 0 and 2 for which $2^c = 3$.

13. The Extreme Value Theorem
This means that a function graph has a high point and a low point on any interval in which the function is continuous. Graph.

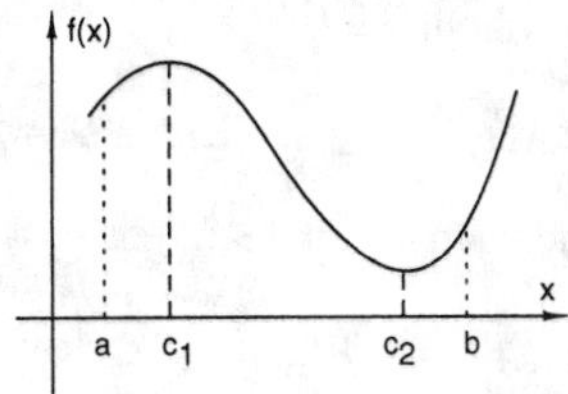

If the function is *not* continuous, there may be a point missing where the maximum or minimum would have been. Graph.

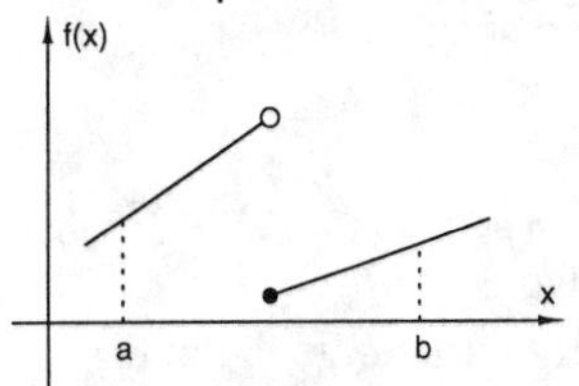

Another possibility would be a graph with a vertical asymptote somewhere between a and b.

14. The Image Theorem
Prove that if f is continuous on [a, b], the image of f is all real numbers between the minimum and the maximum values of f(x), inclusive.
Proof:
By the extreme value theorem, there are numbers x_1 and x_2 in [a, b] such that $f(x_1)$ and $f(x_2)$ are the minimum and maximum values of f(x) on [a, b]. Since x_1 and x_2 are in [a, b], f is continuous on the interval whose endpoints are x_1 and x_2. Thus, the intermediate value theorem applies on the latter interval. Thus, for any number y between $f(x_1)$ and $f(x_2)$ there is a number $x = c$ between x_1 and x_2 for which $f(c) = y$, implying that the image of f is all real numbers between the minimum and the maximum values of f(x), inclusive, Q.E.D.

Problem Set 2-7, pages 71 to 76 — Chapter Review and Test

Review Problems

R0. (Journal update problem)
R1. a. See text definition of limit.
b. Graph. $f(2) = 0^{1/5} + 3 = 3$, Q.E.D.

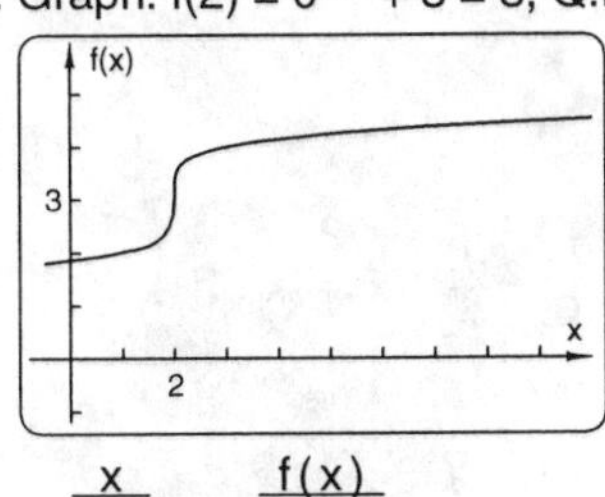

x	f(x)
1.9995	2.78132...
1.9996	2.79087...
1.9997	2.80256...
1.9998	2.81794...
1.9999	2.84151...
2	3
2.0001	3.15848...
2.0002	3.18205...
2.0003	3.19743...
2.0004	3.20912...
2.0005	3.21867...

Keep x within 0.0003 units of 2.

c. Graph. Graph has a cusp and a minimum point.
There is a limit.

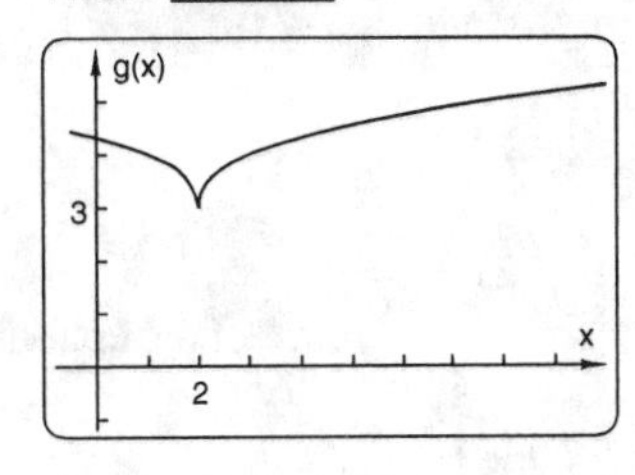

R2. a. Graph is symmetrically steep about $x = 2$.
Let $(x-2)^{1/5} + 3 = 3.2$.
$\therefore x = 2 + 0.2^5 = 2.00032$
$\therefore$ Maximum value of δ is 0.00032.
b. Graph is symmetrical about $x = 2$.
Let $f(x) = 3 + \varepsilon$.
$(x-2)^{1/5} + 3 = 3 + \varepsilon$
$(x-2) = \varepsilon^5$
Let $\delta = \varepsilon^5$, which is positive for all $\delta > 0$.
c. $\lim_{x\to 2} f(x) = 3$.
Maximum δ is 0.6 or 0.7.
d. Left side of $x = 2$ is more restrictive.
Let $2 + \sqrt{x-1} = 3 - 0.4 = 2.6$.
$\therefore x = 1 + 0.6^2 = 1.36$
$\therefore$ max. value of δ is $2 - 1.36 = 0.64$.
e. Let $f(x) = 3 - \varepsilon$.
$2 + \sqrt{x-1} = 3 - \varepsilon$
$x = (1-\varepsilon)^2 + 1$
Let $\delta = 2 - ((1-\varepsilon)^2 + 1) = 1 - (1-\varepsilon)^2$, which is positive for all positive $\varepsilon < 1$.

R3. a. See the limit property statements in the text.
b. Graph. $g(x) = \dfrac{x^3 - 13x^2 + 32x - 6}{x - 3}$

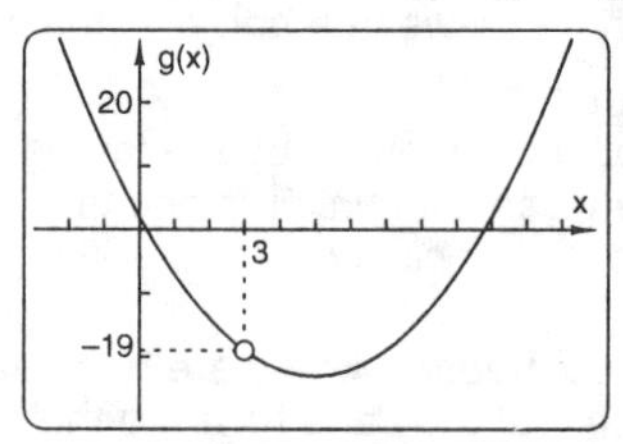

$g(x) = \dfrac{(x-3)(x^2 - 10x + 2)}{x - 3}$
$g(x) = x^2 - 10x + 2,\ x \ne 3$
$\lim_{x\to 3} g(x) = 3^2 - 10(3) + 2 = -19$,
which agrees with the graph.
c. The part of the definition is "..., but not equal to c, ..." Since the definition restricts x away from 3, the quantity $(x - 3)$ in the denominator cannot equal zero, so you are allowed to cancel.
d. $m(x) = \dfrac{(x+3)(x-2)}{x-4}$
$\lim_{x\to 6} m(x) = (6+3)(6-2)/(6-4) = 18$.
Proof:
$\lim_{x\to 6} m(x)$
$= \dfrac{\lim_{x\to 6}(x+3)(x-2)}{\lim_{x\to 6}(x-4)}$ Lim. of a quotient.
$= \dfrac{\lim_{x\to 6}(x+3)\cdot\lim_{x\to 6}(x-2)}{\lim_{x\to 6}(x-4)}$ Lim. of prod.
$= \dfrac{9\cdot 4}{3}$ Lim. of a linear function (3 times).
$= 18$, Q.E.D.
For limit as x approaches 4, the property cannot be used because the denominator goes to zero. The property specifically excludes the denominator function having zero as its limit.

e. Chuck's Rock Problem
From 5 to 5.1 sec, av. vel. = −15.5 m/sec
avg. vel. $= \dfrac{f(t) - f(5)}{t - 5} = \dfrac{35t - 5t^2 - 50}{t - 5}$
$= \dfrac{-5(t-2)(t-5)}{t-5} = -5(t-2)$, for $t \ne 5$.
Inst. vel. = limit $= -5(5-2) = -15$ m/sec
Rate is negative, so distance above starting point is getting smaller, which means the rock is going down.
Instantaneous velocity is a derivative.

R4. a. See text definition of continuity at a point.
b. i. Graph (example).

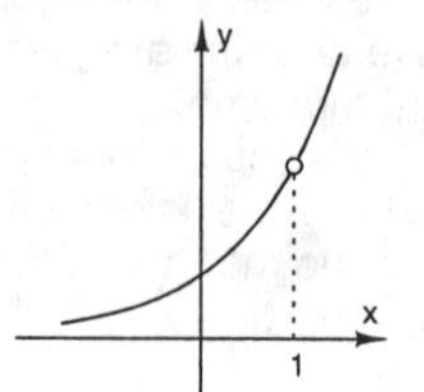

ii. Graph (example).

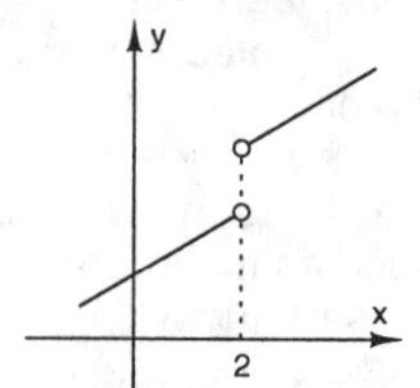

iii. Graph (example).

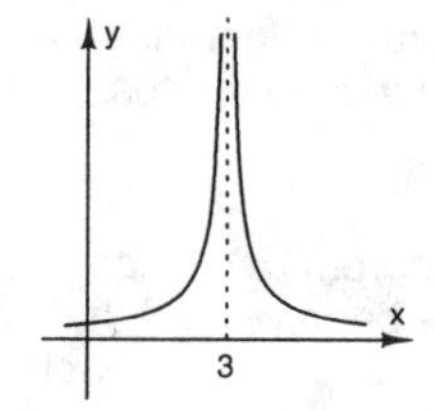

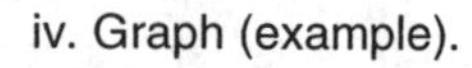
iv. Graph (example).

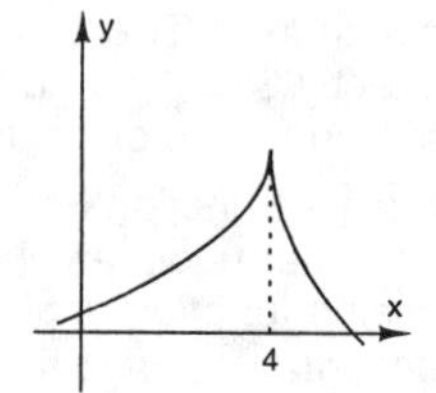

v. Graph (example).

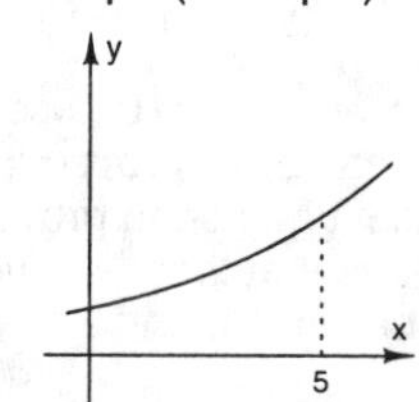

vi. Graph (example).

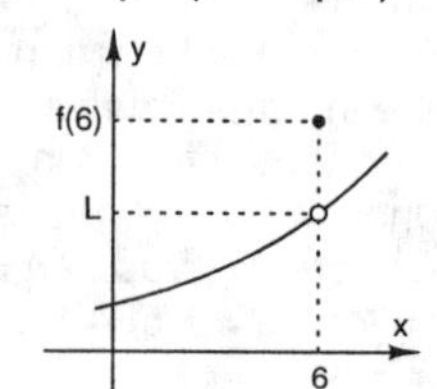

vii. Graph (example).

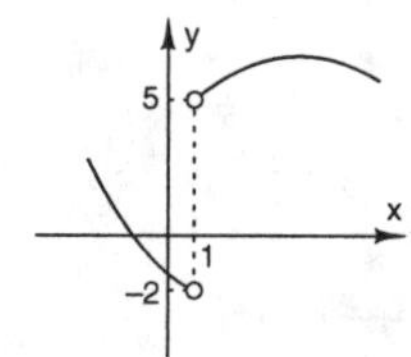

c. i. Graph. $f(x) = \begin{cases} x^2, & \text{if } x \le 2 \\ x^2 - 6x + k, & \text{if } x > 2 \end{cases}$

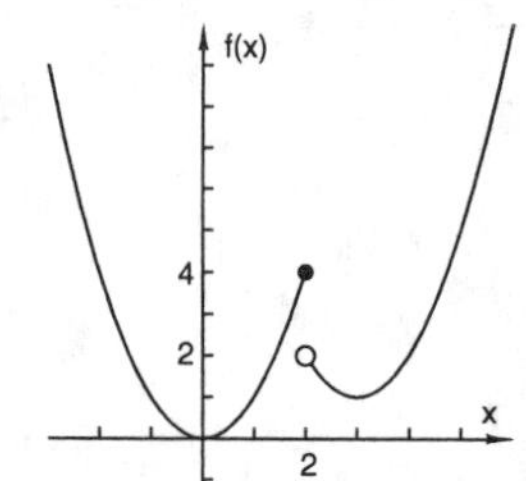

ii. The left limit is 4 and the right limit is 2. So f is discontinuous at $x = 2$, Q.E.D.
iii. Let $2^2 = 2^2 - 6(2) + k$.
$\therefore k = 12$.

R5. a. See the text definition of infinite limit.

b. Graph (example).

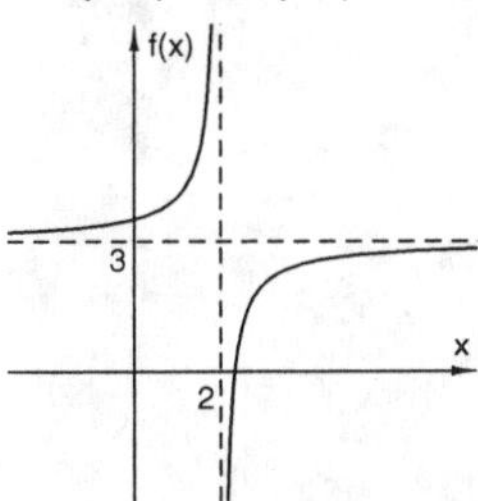

c. $f(x) = 6 - 2^{-x}$.

$\lim_{x\to\infty} f(x) = \underline{6}$, since 2^{-x} approaches zero.

Graph.

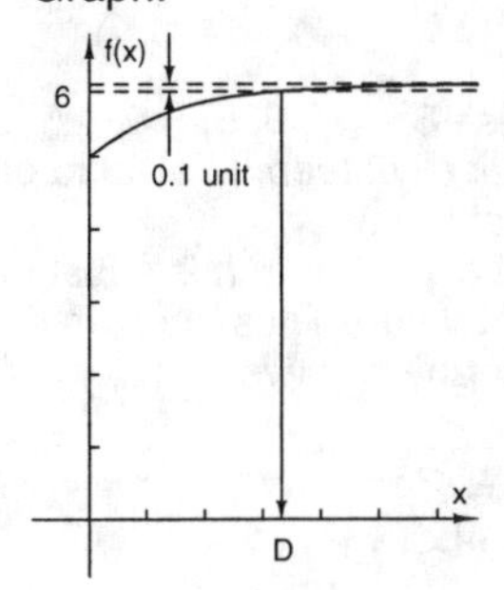

$6 - 2^{-x} = 5.999 \Rightarrow 2^{-x} = 0.001 \Rightarrow 2^x = 1000 \Rightarrow$
$x = 9.9657...$

Let D = 9.97. If x > D, f(x) is within 0.001 unit of 6.

d. $v(t) = 40 + 6\sqrt{t}$

n	Trap. Rule
50	467.9074...
100	467.9669...
200	467.9882...
400	467.9958...

The limit of these sums seems to be 468.

By exploration,

$T_{222} = 467.98995...$

$T_{223} = 467.99002...$

$\therefore$ D = <u>223</u>.

R6. a. See text statement of intermediate value theorem.

The Basis is the completeness axiom.

See text statement of extreme value theorem.

The word is <u>corollary</u>.

b. $f(x) = -x^3 + 5x^2 - 10x + 20$

$f(3) = 8$, $f(4) = -4$.

So f(x) = 0 for some x between 3 and 4 by the intermediate value theorem.

The property is <u>continuity</u>.

The value of x is approximately 3.7553.

c. Graph.

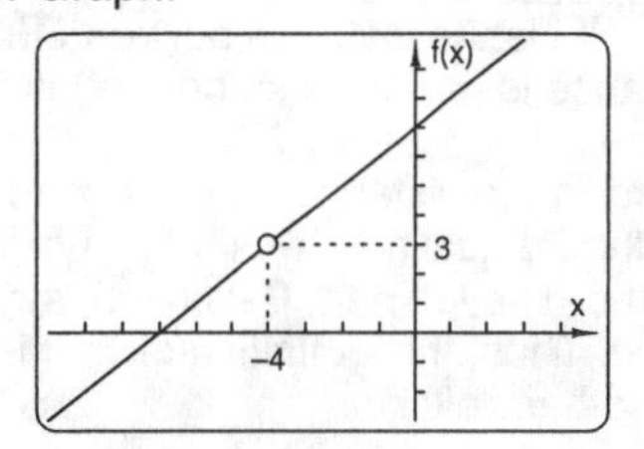

$f(-6) = 1$ and $f(-2) = 5$ by tracing on the graph or by simplifying the fraction to get $f(x) = x + 7$.

You will <u>not</u> always get a value of x if y is between 1 and 5. Pick y = 3, and there is no value of x. This fact does not contradict the intermediate value theorem. Function f does not meet the continuity hypothesis of the theorem.

<u>Concepts Problems</u>

C1. <u>Squeeze Theorem Introduction Problem</u>

Graph. Conjecture: $\lim_{x\to 4} f(x) = 7$.

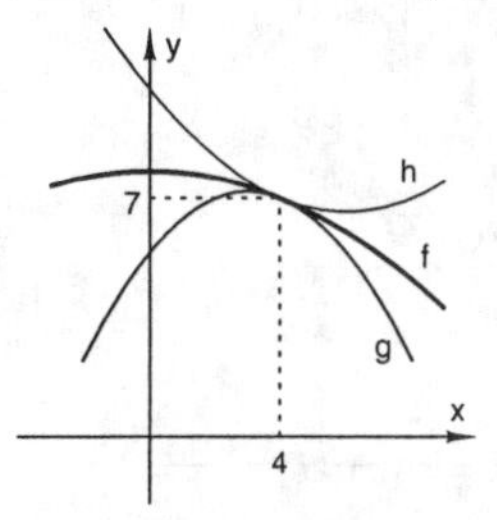

C2. <u>Derivatives and Continuity Problem</u>

$f(1) = 1^2 - 6\cdot 1 + 9 = 4$

As $x \to 1$ from the left, $f(x) \to 1^2 + 3 = 4$.

As $x \to 1$ from the right, $f(x) \to 1^2 - 6 + 9 = 4$.

$\therefore \lim_{x\to 1} f(x) = 4 = f(1)$

$\therefore$ f is continuous at x = 4, Q.E.D.

For the derivative, from the left side,

$$\frac{f(x) - f(1)}{x - 1} = \frac{x^2 + 3 - 4}{x - 1} = \frac{(x - 1)(x + 1)}{x - 1}$$

$= x + 1, x \neq 1.$

$\therefore \lim_{x\to 1^-} f(x) = 1 + 1 = 2.$

For the derivative, from the right side,

$$\frac{f(x) - f(1)}{x - 1} = \frac{x^2 - 6x + 9 - 4}{x - 1} = \frac{(x - 1)(x - 5)}{x - 1}$$

$= x - 5, x \neq 1.$

$\therefore \lim_{x\to 1^+} f(x) = 1 - 5 = -4.$

So f is continuous at x = 1, but does not have a value for the derivative there because the rate of change jumps abruptly from 2 to –4 at x = 1. In general, if a function has a cusp at a point, then the derivative does not exist.

C3. <u>Equation from Graph Problem</u>

The graph is a $y = x^2$ parabola with a step discontinuity at x = 1. (Use the "rise-run" property. Start at the vertex. Then run 1, rise 1; run 1, rise 3; run 1, rise 5, ... Ignore the discontinuity at first.) To create the discontinuity, use the signum function with argument (x – 1). Since there is no value for f(1), the absolute value form of the signum function can be used.

$$y = x^2 + 2 - \frac{|x - 1|}{x - 1}$$

C4. <u>Absolute Value Definition of Limit</u>
The quantity $|f(x) - L|$ is the distance between f(x) and L. If this distance is less than ε, then f(x) is within ε units of L.
The quantity $|x - c|$ is the distance between x and c. The right part of the inequality, $|x - c| < \delta$, says that x is within δ units of c. The left part, $0 < |x - c|$, says that x does not equal c. Thus, this definition of limit is equivalent to the other definition.

Chapter Test

T1. See text statement of quotient prop., Section 2-3.

T2. a. Left: –4; right: –4
b. Limit: –4
c. Discontinuous

T3. a. Left: none; right: none
b. Limit: none
c. Discontinuous

T4. a. Left: 6; right: 6
b. Limit: 6
c. Continuous.

T5. a. Left: –2; right: 3
b. Limit: none
c. Discontinuous

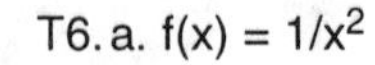
T6. a. $f(x) = 1/x^2$

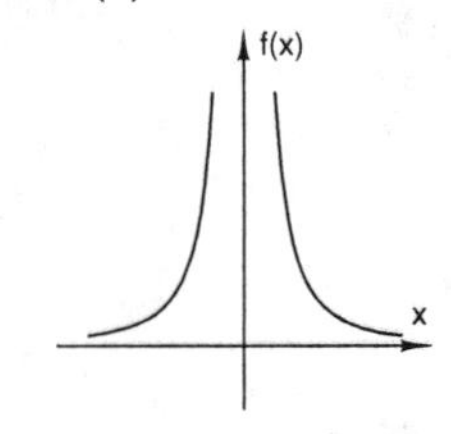

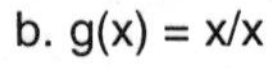
b. $g(x) = x/x$

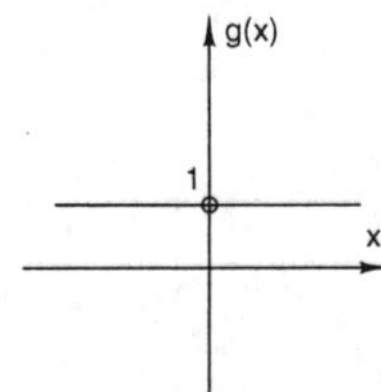

c. $h(x) = |x|/x$

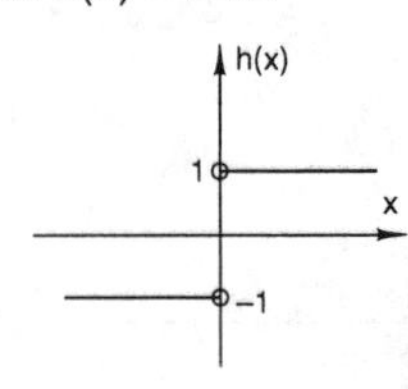

d. $s(x) = \sin(1/x)$

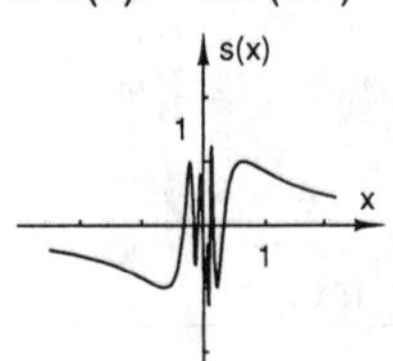

T7. a. $g(x) = \dfrac{4x^2 + 17x + 15}{x + 3}$. Graph

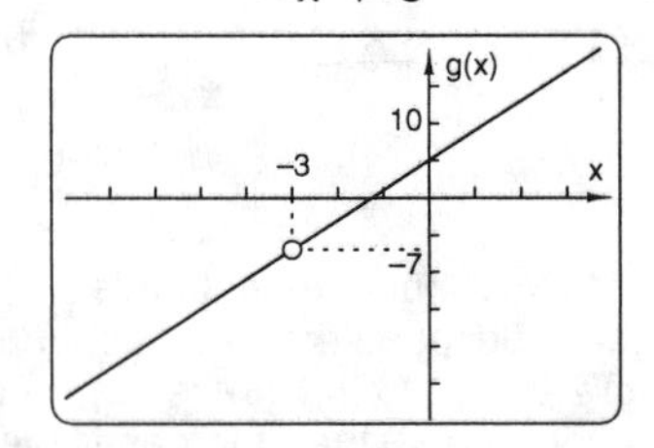

b. $\lim_{x \to -3} g(x) = -7$. Graph in part a.

c.

x	g(x)
–3.05	–7.2
–3.04	–7.16
–3.03	–7.12
–3.02	–7.08
–3.01	–7.04
–3	none
–2.99	–6.96
–2.98	–6.92
–2.97	–6.88
–2.96	–6.84
–2.95	–6.8

d. Based on the table, g(x) is within 0.1 units of –7 whenever x is within 0.2 units of –3.

e. $g(x) = \dfrac{(x + 3)(4x + 5)}{x + 3} = 4x + 5,\ x \neq -3.$
Let $4x + 5 = -7.1$.
$\therefore x = -3.025$
Maximum value of δ is $-3 - (-3.025) = \underline{0.025}$. Since the graph is symmetrically steep, this value of δ works on both sides of x = 3.

f. For any value of ε, let $\delta = \varepsilon/4$, which is equal to $\varepsilon/|\text{slope}|$ for a linear function. Thus, there is a positive value of δ for any positive number ε.

T8. a. $h(x) = x^3 - 10x^2 + 3x + 31$
$h(2) = 8 - 40 + 6 + 31 = 5.$
Prove that $h(2) = \lim_{x \to 2} h(x)$.

<u>Proof</u>:
$\lim_{x \to 2} h(x) = \lim_{x \to 2} (x^3 - 10x^2 + 3x + 31)$
$= \lim_{x \to 2} x^3 + \lim_{x \to 2} (-10x^2) + \lim_{x \to 2} 3x + \lim_{x \to 2} 31$
. . . . Limit of a sum.
$= \lim_{x \to 2} x \cdot \lim_{x \to 2} x \cdot \lim_{x \to 2} x - 10 \lim_{x \to 2} x \cdot \lim_{x \to 2} x$
$+ 3 \lim_{x \to 2} x + 31$
. . . . . Limit of a product and limit of a constant.
$= 2 \cdot 2 \cdot 2 - 10 \cdot 2 \cdot 2 + 3 \cdot 2 + 31$
. . . . Limit of a constant.
$= 5 = h(2)$, Q.E.D.

b. h is continuous at x = 2 becasue the limit of h(x) as x approaches 2 is equal to h(2).

c. $h(3) = 3^3 - 10 \cdot 3^2 + 3 \cdot 3 + 31 = -23$, which has sign opposite that of h(2).
Since h is a polynomial function, it is continuous for all values of x. Thus, the intermediate value theorem applies on the interval [2, 3], and there is a number x = c between 2 and 3 for which h(c) = 0, Q.E.D.

T9. Glacier Problem

a. $d(t) = 0.01t^2 + 0.5t$
Store this in the grapher, then use either the TRACE or the TABLE feature to show
$d(0) = 0$ (checks)
$d(10) = 6$ (checks)
$d(20) = 14$ (checks)
$d(30) = 24$ (checks)
$d(40) = 36$ (checks)
$d(50) = 50$ (checks)

b. Average rate $= \dfrac{14.0901 - 14}{20.1 - 20} = \underline{0.901 \text{ cm/day}}$

c. Average rate $= \dfrac{0.01t^2 + 0.5t - 14}{t - 20}$
$= \dfrac{0.01(t + 70)(t - 20)}{t - 20} = 0.01t + 0.7,\ t \neq 20.$
The limit as t approaches 20 is $0.01(20) + 0.7$, which equals 0.9 cm/day. This instantaneous rate is called the derivative.

d. The glacier seems to be speeding up, because each 10-day period it moved farther than it had in the preceding 10-day period.

T10. Calvin and Phoebe's Acceleration Problem

$c(t) = 16 - 6(2^{-t})$, $p(t) = 10 + \sqrt{t}$
$c(0) = p(0) = 10$, so each has the same speed at $t = 0$.
$\lim_{t\to\infty} c(t) = 16$. $\lim_{t\to\infty} p(t) = \infty$. Surprise for Phoebe!

T11. $f(x) = \begin{cases} kx^2, & \text{if } x \le 2 \\ 10 - kx, & \text{if } x > 2 \end{cases}$

$\lim_{x\to 2^-} f(x) = k\cdot 2^2 = 4k$
$\lim_{x\to 2^+} f(x) = 10 - 2k$
Make $4k = 10 - 2k \Rightarrow k = \frac{5}{3}$
Graph, showing cusp at $x = 2$.

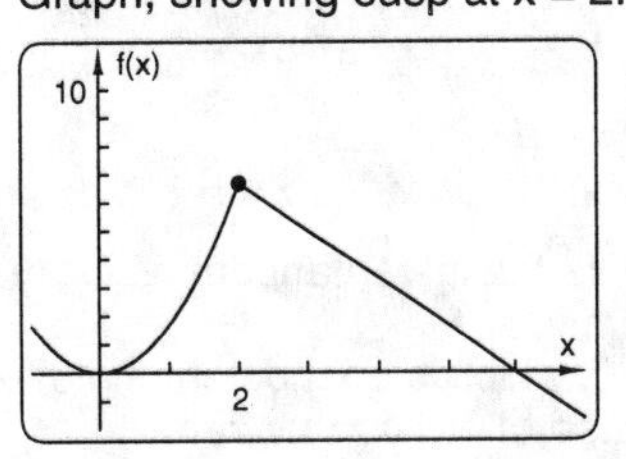

T12. $h(x) = x^3$
$h(1) = 1$ and $h(2) = 8$, so 7 is between $h(1)$ and $h(2)$. The intermediate value theorem allows you to conclude that there is a real number between 1 and 8 equal to the cube root of 7.

Chapter 3

Problem Set 3-1, page 79 — Graphical Interpretation of Derivative

1. Graph is correct.
2. Avg. rate $= \dfrac{f(5.1) - f(5)}{0.1} = \dfrac{3.21 - 3}{0.1}$
   $= 2.1$ km/min
3. $m(x) = \dfrac{x^2 - 8x + 18 - 3}{x - 5} = \dfrac{x^2 - 8x + 15}{x - 5}$
   $= \dfrac{(x - 5)(x - 3)}{x - 5} = x - 3$, provided $x \neq 5$
4. Limit = 2. It represents the instantaneous velocity of the spaceship in km/min
5. m(5) has the form 0/0, which is an indeterminate form. It is undefined because of division by zero.
6. Graph

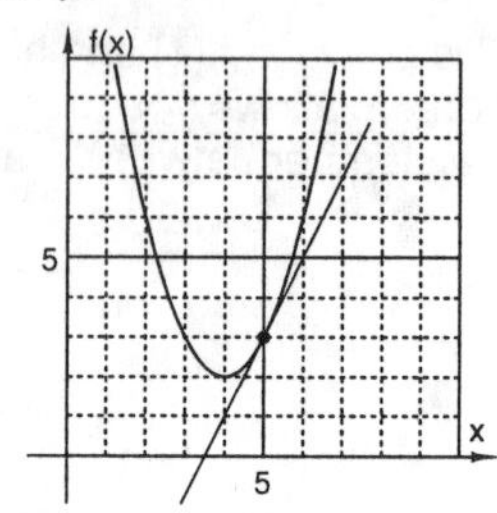

7. The line is <u>tangent</u> to the graph.
8. The line has slope 2 and point (5, 3).
   $\therefore y - 3 = 2(x - 5) \Rightarrow y = 2x - 7$
   The diagram below shows this line and the graph of f with a zoom by a factor of 10 in both the x- and y-directions. The graph looks more and more like a line the closer you zoom. The phenomenon is known as *local linearity*.

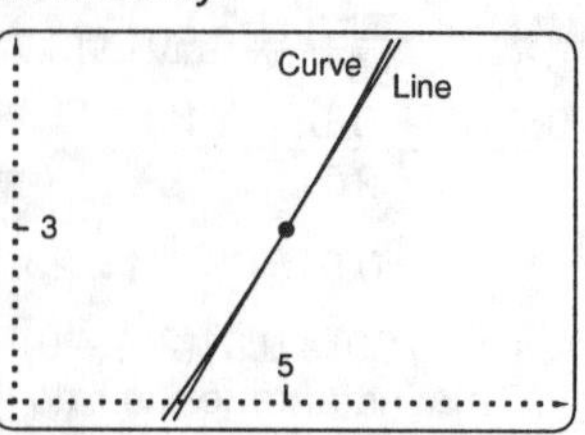

9. The journal entry should include the insight that an exact derivative can be calculated *algebraically* by writing an equation for the difference quotient (i.e., the slope of the secant line) in terms of x, canceling to "remove" the factor in the denominator that causes the discontinuity, and finding the limit of the simplified expression by direct substitution. The journal entry could also include the observation about local linearity from Problem 8.

Problem Set 3-2, pages 81 to 84 — Difference Quotients and One Definition of Derivative

Q1. Derivative: Instantaneous rate of change
Q2. $x + 9$
Q3. Limit = 18
Q4. Graph. $y = 2^x$

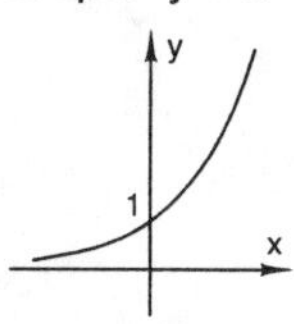

Q5. $9x^2 - 42x + 49$
Q6. "–" sign
Q7. Graph (example)

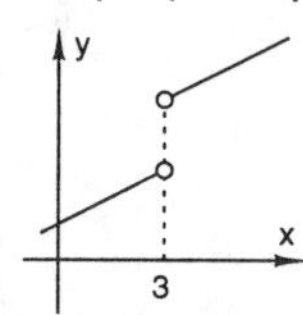

Q8. Graph (example)

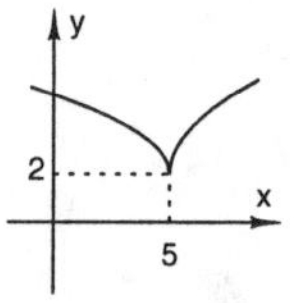

Q9. Graph

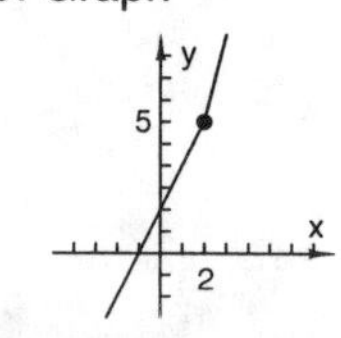

Q10. Newton and Leibniz

1. See text definition of *derivative.*
2. Physical: Instantaneous rate of change of the dependent variable with respect to the independent variable
   Geometrical: Slope of the tangent line to the graph of the function at that point
3. a. $f(x) = 0.6x^2$, $f'(3) = \lim_{x \to 3} \dfrac{0.6x^2 - 5.4}{x - 3}$
   $= \lim_{x \to 3} \dfrac{0.6(x - 3)(x + 3)}{x - 3} = \underline{3.6}$

   b. Graph of the difference quotient m(x)

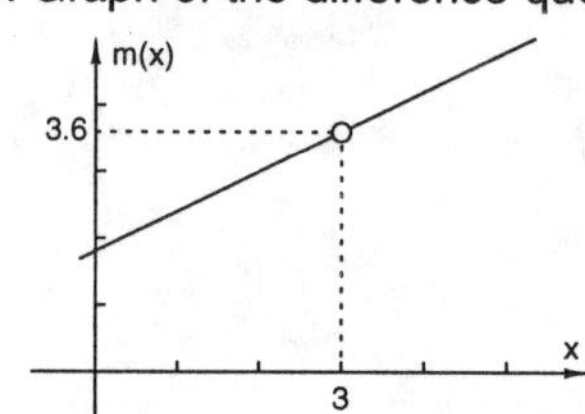

   c and d. Graph. Tangent line: $y = 3.6x - 5.4$

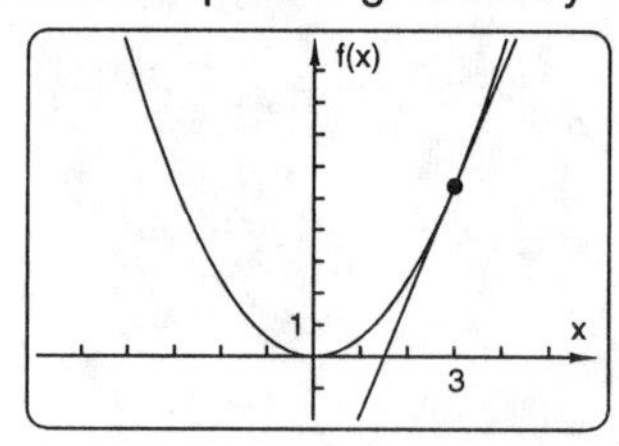

4. a. $f(x) = -0.2x^2$, $f'(6) = \lim_{x\to 6} \frac{-0.2x^2 + 7.2}{x - 6}$

$= \lim_{x\to 6} \frac{-0.2(x-6)(x+6)}{x-6} = \underline{-2.4}$

b. Graph of the difference quotient

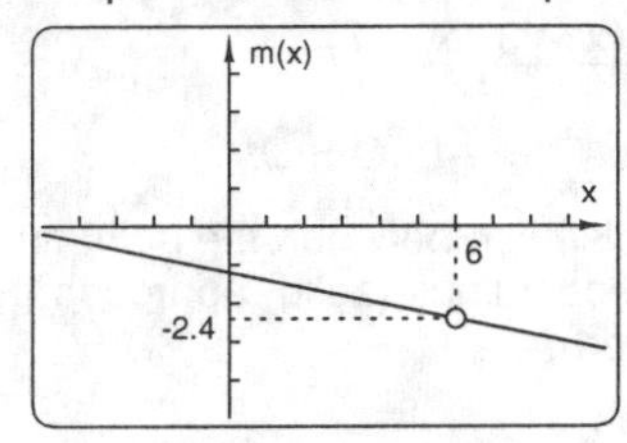

c. and d. Graph. Tangent line: $y = -2.4x + 7.2$

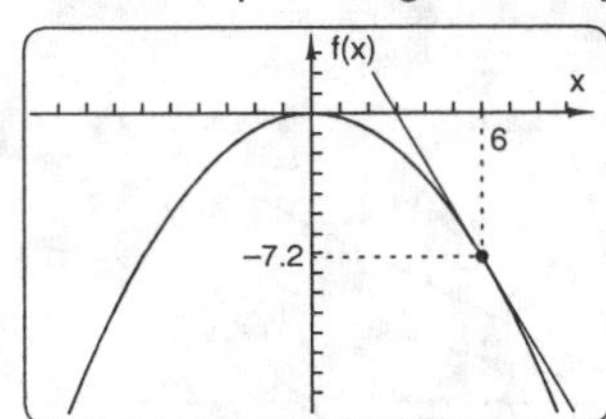

5. $f'(-2) = \lim_{x\to -2} \frac{x^2 + 5x + 1 + 5}{x + 2}$

$= \lim_{x\to -2} \frac{(x+2)(x+3)}{x+2} = \underline{1}$

6. $f'(-4) = \lim_{x\to -4} \frac{x^2 + 6x - 2 + 10}{x + 4}$

$= \lim_{x\to -4} \frac{(x+4)(x+2)}{x+4} = \underline{-2}$

7. $f'(1) = \lim_{x\to 1} \frac{x^3 - 4x^2 + x + 8 - 6}{x - 1}$

$= \lim_{x\to 1} \frac{(x-1)(x^2 - 3x - 2)}{x - 1} = \underline{-4}$

8. $f'(-1) = \lim_{x\to -1} \frac{x^3 - x^2 - 4x + 6 - 8}{x + 1}$

$= \lim_{x\to -1} \frac{(x+1)(x^2 - 2x - 2)}{x + 1} = \underline{1}$

9. $f'(3) = \lim_{x\to 3} \frac{-0.7x + 2 + 0.1}{x - 3}$

$= \lim_{x\to 3} \frac{-0.7(x-3)}{x - 3} = \underline{-0.7}$

10. $f'(4) = \lim_{x\to 4} \frac{1.3x - 3 - 2.2}{x - 4}$

$= \lim_{x\to 4} \frac{1.3(x-4)}{x - 4} = \underline{1.3}$

11. $f'(-1) = \lim_{x\to -1} \frac{5 - 5}{x + 1} = \underline{0}$

12. $f'(3) = \lim_{x\to 3} \frac{-2 + 2}{x - 3} = \underline{0}$

13. The derivative of a linear function equals the slope. The tangent line coincides with the graph.

14. The derivative of a constant function is zero. Constant functions don't change! The tangent line coincides with the graph.

15. Local Linearity Problem

a. First find f'(1), then plot a straight line through point (1, f(1)) using f'(1) as the slope.
b. Near the point (1, f(1)), which is (1, 1), the tangent line and the curve appear coincidental.
c. The curve appears to get closer and closer to the line and finally touch it at the point (1, f(1)).
d. Near point (1,1) the curve looks linear.
e. If a graph has local linearity, the graph near that point looks like the tangent line. Therefore, the derivative at that point could be said to equal the slope of the graph at that point.

16. Local Nonlinearity Problem

a. $f(x) = x^2 + 0.1(\sqrt[3]{x - 1})^2$
$f(1) = 1^2 + 0.1(1 - 1)^{2/3} = 1 + 0 = 1$, Q.E.D.
b. Zoom by a factor of 10,000. Graph

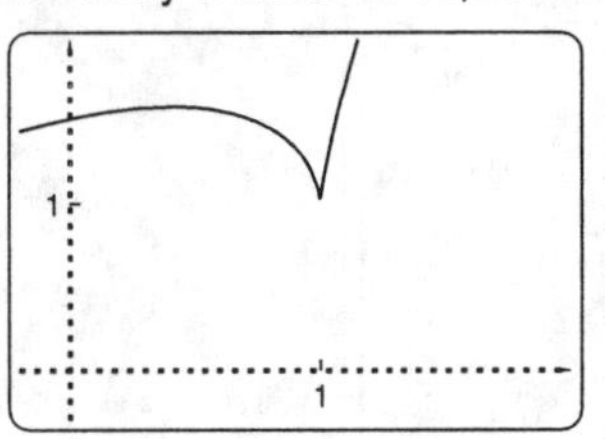

c. The graph has a cusp at x = 1. It changes direction abruptly, not smoothly.
d. If you draw a secant line through (1,1) from a point just to the left of x = 1, it has a large negative slope. If you draw one from a point just to the right, it has a large positive slope. In both cases, the secant line becomes vertical as x approaches 1, and a vertical line has infinite slope. So there is no real number equal to the derivative.

17. a. $f(x) = \begin{cases} \dfrac{x^2 - x - 6}{x - 3}, \text{ if } x \neq 3 \\ 7, \text{ if } x = 3 \end{cases}$

Graph.

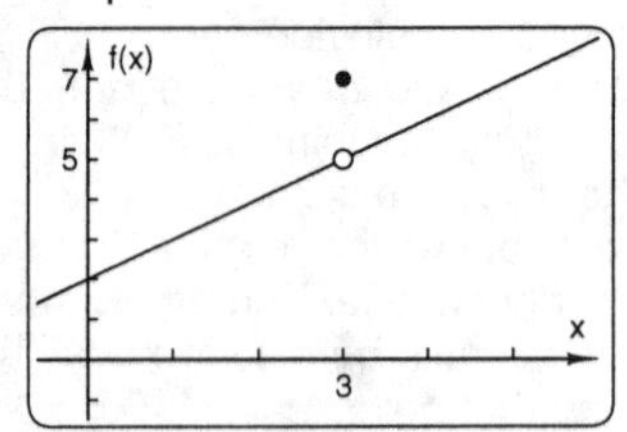

b. First simplify the equation.

$f(x) = \begin{cases} x + 2, \text{ if } x \neq 3 \\ 7, \text{ if } x = 3 \end{cases}$

Difference quotient is

$m(x) = \dfrac{(x + 2) - 7}{x - 3} = \dfrac{x - 5}{x - 3}$

Graph.

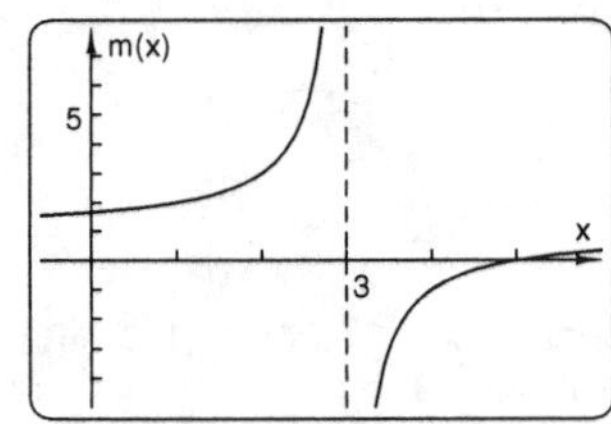

c.

x	*f(x)*
2.997	667.66...
2.998	1001
2.999	2001
3.000	error
3.001	–1999
3.002	–999
3.003	–665.66...

The difference quotients are all large positive numbers on the left side of 3. On the right side, they are large negative numbers. For a derivative to exist, the difference quotient must approach the *same* number as x gets closer to 3.

18. a. Graph. $s(x) = 2 + |\sin (x - 1)|$

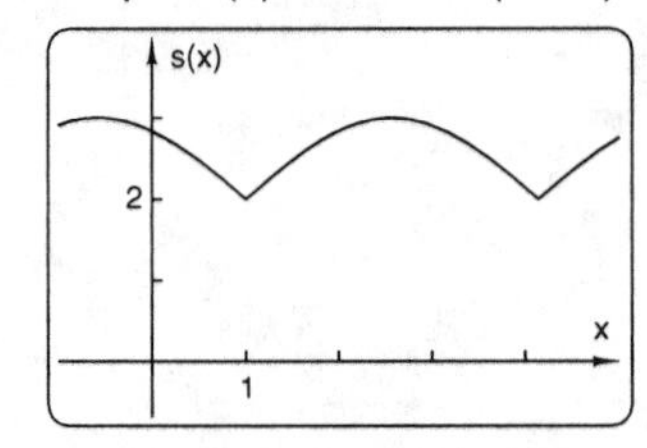

b. $m(x) = \dfrac{|\sin (x - 1)|}{x - 1}$. Graph.

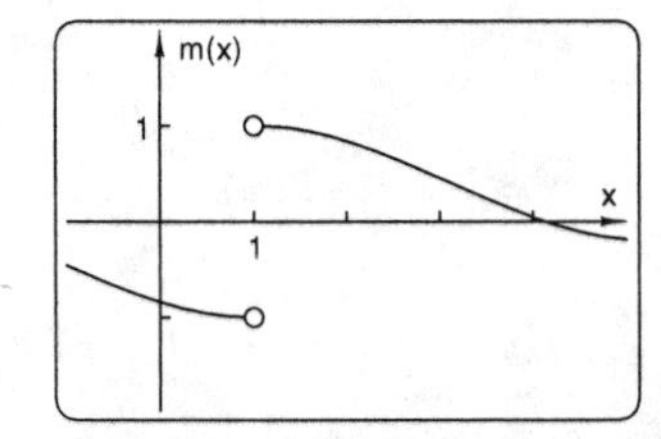

c. As x approaches 1 from the left, m(x) approaches –1. As x approaches 1 from the right, m(x) approaches 1. Since the left and right limits are unequal, there is no derivative at x = 1.

19. Tangent Lines as Limits of Secant Lines

$f(x) = 0.25x^2 - 2.5x + 7.25$

a. The tangent line on the graph has a slope of –1.

$$f'(x) = \lim_{x \to 3} \frac{0.25x^2 - 2.5x + 7.25 - 2}{x - 3}$$
$$= \lim_{x \to 3} \frac{0.25(x - 3)(x - 7)}{x - 3}$$
$$= \lim_{x \to 3} 0.25(x - 7) = -1, \text{ Q.E.D.}$$

b. Graph. As the x-distance between the point and 3 decreases, the secant lines (solid) approach the tangent line (dotted).

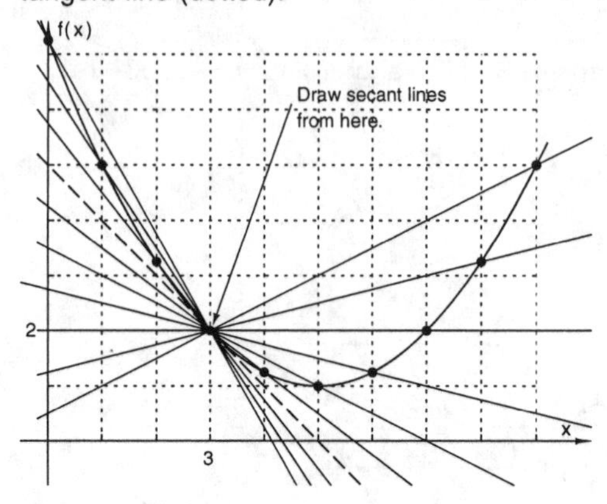

c. The same thing happens with secant lines from the left of x = 3. See graph, above.

d. Graph. $g(x) = 4 - 6\left|\cos \frac{\pi}{6}x\right|$

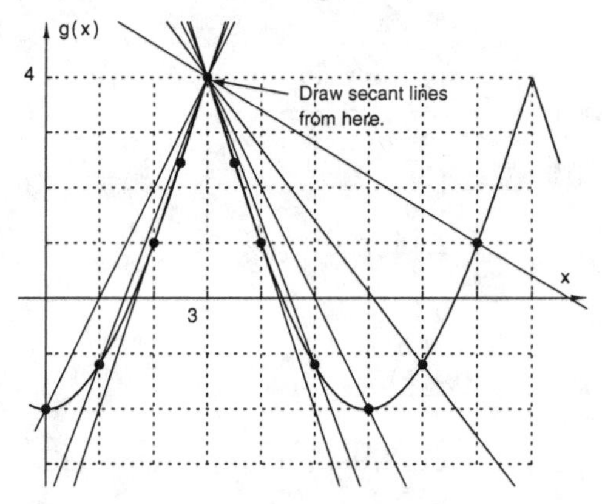

e. A derivative is a limit. Since the left and right limits are unequal, there is no derivative at x = 3.

f. $m(x) = \dfrac{-6\left|\cos \frac{\pi}{6}x\right|}{x - 3}$. By table,

x	m(x)
2.9	3.1401...
2.99	3.1415...
3	ERROR
3.01	–3.1415...
3.1	–3.1401...

Conjecture: The numbers are π and $-\pi$.

20. From Problem 19, parts b. and c., the tangent line is the limit of the secant line as x approaches c. Since the slope of the secant line is the average rate of change of f(x) for the interval from x to c (or c to x) and the derivative, f'(c), is the limit of this average rate, the slope of the tangent line equals f'(c).

Q1. Limit = 3

Q2. Graph (example)

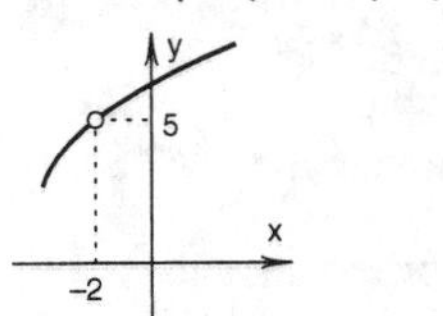

Q3. Graph. y = tan x

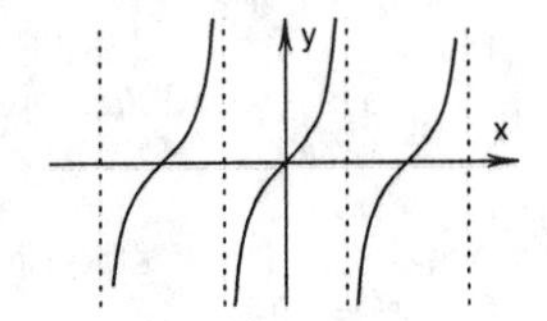

Q4. 20%

Q5. $3x^2 - 2x - 8$

Q6. $25x^2 - 70x + 49$

Q7. log 6

Q8. $(x - 2)(x^2 + 2x + 4)$

Q9. Graph (tangent)

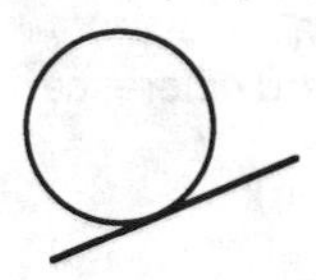

Q10. Graph (secant)

1. Cubic Function Problem I

a. Graph. $f(x) = -x^3 + 12x + 25$, and f'

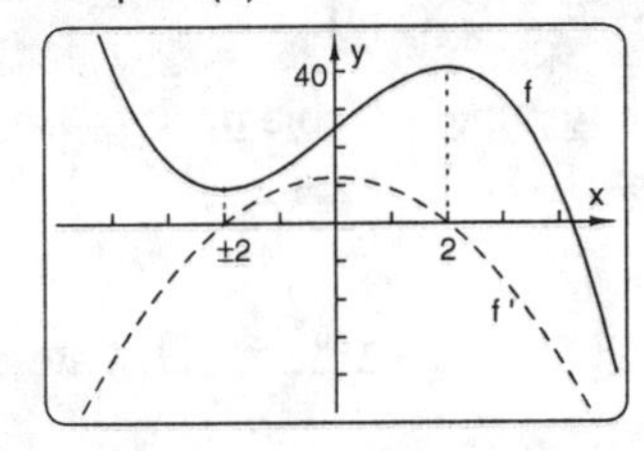

b. f'(x) is positive for $-2 < x < 2$.
The graph of f is increasing for these x-values.

c. f(x) is decreasing for x satisfying $|x| > 2$. $f'(x) < 0$ for these values of x.

d. Where the f' graph crosses the x-axis, the f graph has a high point or a low point.

e. See the graph in part a.

f. Conjecture: f' is quadratic.

2. Cubic Function Problem II

Graph. $f(x) = x^3 - 2x^2 + 2x - 15$

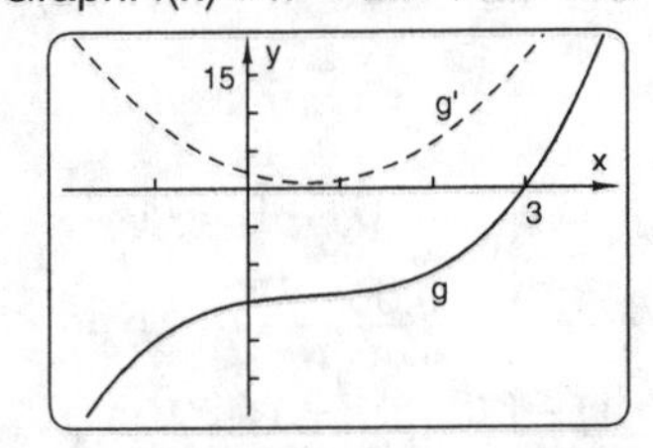

The graph does not have the high and low points that are typical of a cubic function. As x increases, the graph starts to roll over and form a high point, but it starts going back up again before that happens. This behavior is revealed by the fact that the derivative is positive everywhere. Between x = 0 and x = 1 the derivative reaches a low point, indicating that the slope is a minimum, but the slope is still positive and the graph of g is still going up.

3. Quartic Function Problem I

a. Graph. $h(x) = x^4 - 2x^3 - 9x^2 + 20x + 80$

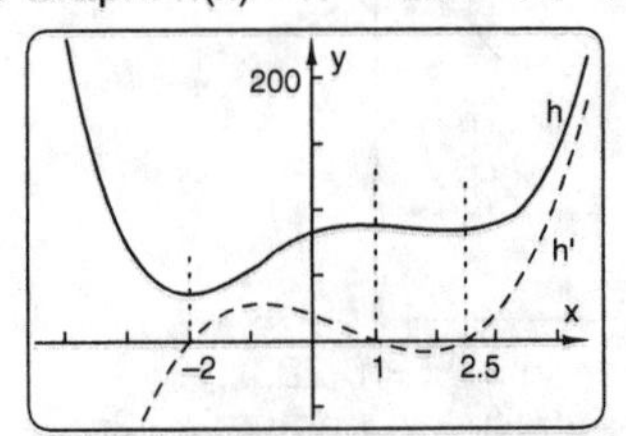

b. The h' graph looks like a cubic function graph.
Conjecture: Seventh-degree function has a sixth-degree function for its derivative.

c. By plotting the graph using a friendly window, then tracing, the zeros of h' are −2, 1, 2.5.

d. If h'(x) = 0, the h graph has a high point or a low point. This is reasonable because if h'(x) = 0, the rate of change of h(x) is zero, which would happen when the graph stops going up and starts going down, or vice versa.

e. See graph in part a.

4. Quartic Function Problem II

Graph. $q(x) = -x^4 + 8x^3 - 24x^2 + 32x - 25$

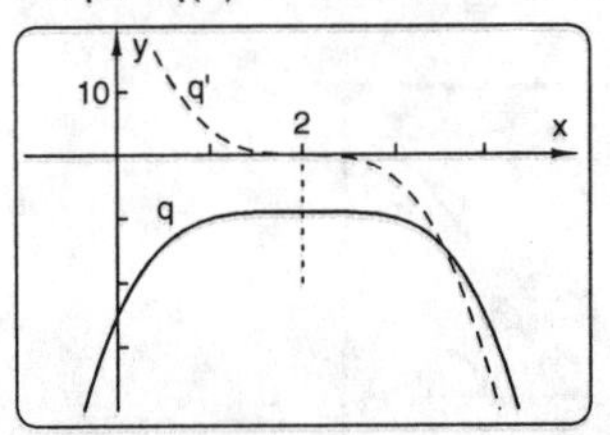

The graph does not have the expected shape for a quartic function. The two high points and the low point all appear to occur as a high point at x = 2. The derivative graph crosses the x-axis just once, at x = 2, indicating that this is the only place where the function graph is horizontal.

5. <u>Sinusoid Problem I</u>

a. Graph. $f(x) = 4 + \sin x$

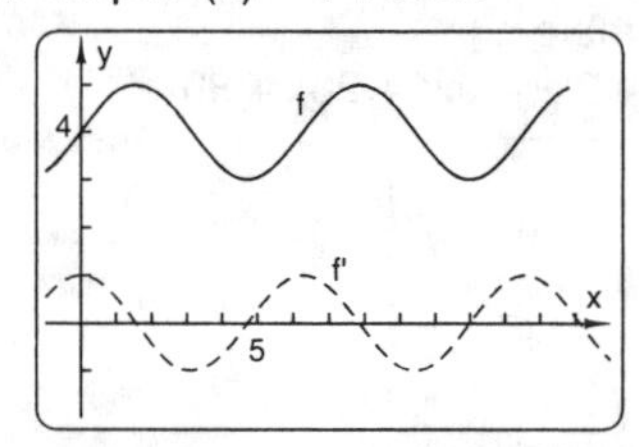

b. Amplitude = 1, period = $2\pi = 6.283...$

c. The f' graph has amplitude 1 and period 2π.

d. Graph.

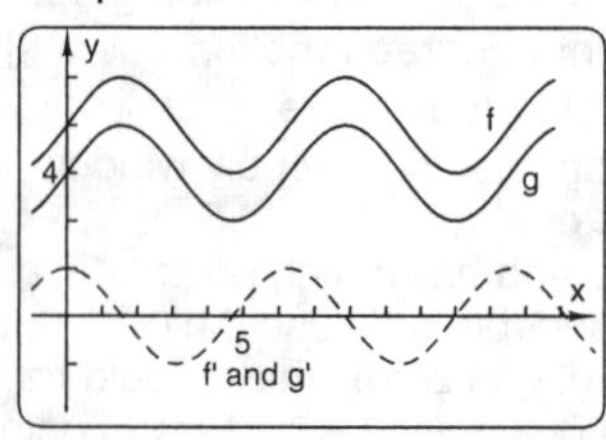

The graphs of f and g are the same shape, spaced 1 unit apart vertically. The graphs of f' and g' are identical! This is to be expected, because the shapes of the f and g graphs are the same.

6. <u>Sinusoid Problem II</u>

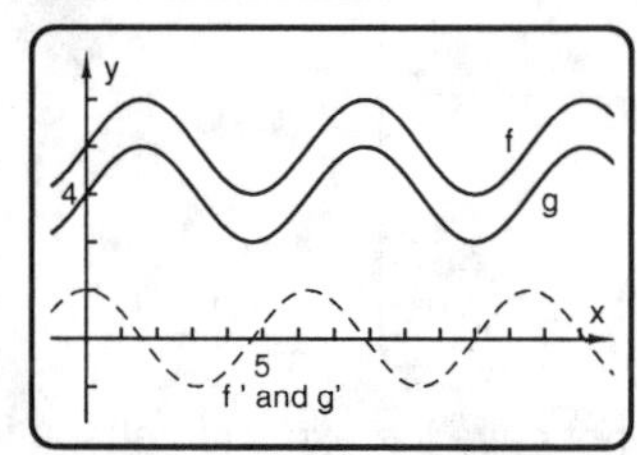

The function available on the grapher is $y = \cos x$. The amplitude is 1, the period is 2π, and the shape is sinusoidal. Cos 0 = 1, and the graph is at a high point, y = 1, when x = 0.

7. <u>Exponential Function Problem</u>

The derivative for $f(x) = 2^x$ is consistently below that of the function itself. This fact implies that f(x) does not increase rapidly enough to make the derivative equal the function value. So the base must be greater than 2. By experimenting, 3 is too large, but not by much. You can use trial and error with bases between 2 and 3, checking the results either by plotting the graph and the numerical derivative or by constructing tables. An ingenious method that some students come up with uses the numerical derivative and numerical solve features to solve this equation at x = 1:

nDeriv(b^x, x, 1) = b^1

The answer is about 2.718281... . (In Chapter 6, the student will learn that this number is e, the base of natural logarithms). The graph of $y = 2.781...^x$ and its numerical derivative are shown in the diagram.

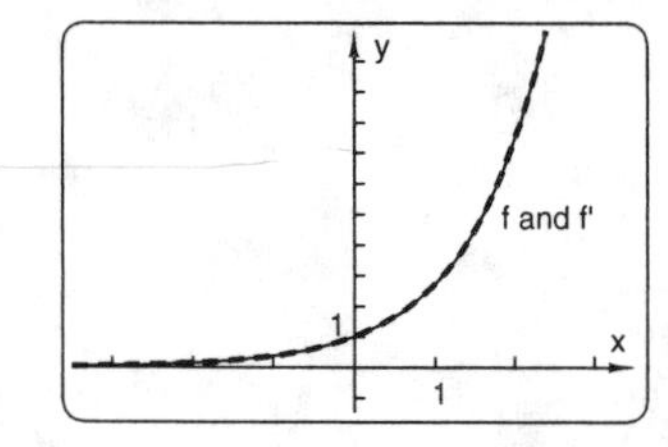

8. <u>How the Grapher Works Problem</u>

Answer will vary depending on calculator.

9. <u>Tolerance Problem (Epsilon and Delta)</u>

a. Maximum area = $(12.01)^2 = 144.2401$ in^2
Minimum area = $(11.99)^2 = 143.7601$ in^2
Range is $143.7601 \le \text{area} \le 144.2401$
Area is within 0.2401 in^2 of the nominal

b. Let x be the number of inches
Area = x^2. Right side of 12 is more restrictive
Set $x^2 = 144.02$
$\therefore x = 144.02^{1/2} = 12.000833...$
Keep x within 0.0008 in. of 12 in.

c. The 0.02 in part b. corresponds to ε and the 0.0008 corresponds to δ.

10. <u>Symmetric Difference Quotient Problem</u>

The average of the forward and backward difference quotients equals

$$\frac{1}{2}\left(\frac{f(x+h)-f(x)}{h} + \frac{f(x)-f(x-h)}{h}\right)$$
$$= \frac{1}{2}\left(\frac{f(x+h)-f(x-h)}{h}\right)$$
$$= \frac{f(x+h)-f(x-h)}{2h}, \text{ Q.E.D.}$$

11. <u>Difference Quotient Accuracy Problem</u>

a. $f(x) = x^3 - x + 1 \Rightarrow f(1) = 1$

$$f'(1) = \lim_{x\to 1} \frac{(x^3 - x + 1) - 1}{x - 1}$$
$$= \lim_{x\to 1} \frac{x^3 - x}{x - 1} = \lim_{x\to 1} \frac{x(x+1)(x-1)}{x-1}$$
$$= \lim_{x\to 1} x(x+1) = \underline{2}.$$

b. Forward: $\frac{f(1.1)-f(1)}{0.1} = \frac{1.231-1}{0.1} = \underline{2.31}$

Backward: $\frac{f(1)-f(0.9)}{0.1} = \frac{1-0.829}{0.1} = \underline{1.71}$

Symm.: $\frac{f(1.1)-f(0.9)}{2(0.1)} = \frac{1.231-0.829}{0.2} = \underline{2.01}$

The symmetric difference quotient is closer to the actual because it is the average of the other two, and the other two span the actual derivative.

c. $f(0) = 1$

$$f'(0) = \lim_{x\to 0} \frac{(x^3 - x + 1) - 1}{x - 0}$$
$$= \lim_{x\to 0} \frac{x^3 - x}{x} = \lim_{x\to 0} (x^2 - 1) = \underline{-1}.$$

d. Forward: $\frac{f(0.1)-f(0)}{0.1} = \frac{0.901-1}{0.1} = \underline{-0.99}$

Backward: $\frac{f(-0.1)-f(0)}{0.1} = \frac{1-1.099}{0.1} = \underline{-0.99}$

Symmetric: $\frac{f(0.1)-f(-0.1)}{2(0.1)} = \frac{0.901-1.099}{0.2}$
$= \underline{-0.99}$.

All three difference quotients are equal, because f(x) changes just as much from –0.1 to 0 as it does from 0 to 0.1.

e. The journal entry should note that in general the symmetric difference quotient is more accurate than either the forward or backward one, except when the function is increasing or decreasing at the same rate on both sides of x = c.

12. Numerical Derivative Error Problem!

$f(x) = (\sqrt[3]{x-2})^2 + x - 1$

h	backward	forward	symmetric
0.1	−1.1154...	3.1544...	1
0.01	−3.6415...	5.6415...	1
0.001	−9	11	1

The backward difference quotients are becoming large and negative while the forward difference quotients are becoming large and positive. Their average, the symmetric difference quotient, is always equal to 1. For the journal entry, students should put in some kind of caution that at a cusp the symmetric difference quotient may give an answer, but that answer has no relationship to the derivative.

13. Journal Problem

Appropriate entries should include the fact that the derivative *function* is the function whose values are the derivatives at each value of x. Students should also include the extent to which they have mastered the numerical derivative function on the grapher. The more observant students should have noticed that:

- The derivative of a polynomial function seems to be a polynomial function of degree 1 less than the parent function.
- The derivative of an exponential function seems to be another exponential function.
- The derivative of the sine function seems to be the cosine function.
- The grapher will give a wrong answer for a numerical derivative at a point where the graph has a cusp or a vertical asymptote.

Problem Set 3-4, pages 95 to 98 — Derivative of the Power Function and Another Definition of Derivative

Q1. $9x^2 - 24x + 16$

Q2. $a^3 + 3a^2b + 3ab^2 + b^3$

Q3. See text def. of deriv.

Q4. $\dfrac{f(x+h) - f(x-h)}{2h}$

Q5. Infinite

Q6. $\log 7^3$

Q7. $\sqrt{3}$

Q8. Pythagorean theorem

Q9. 10

Q10. Graph (example)

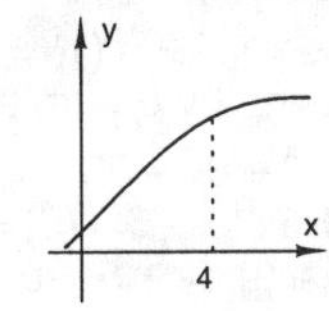

1. $f(x) = 5x^4 \Rightarrow f'(x) = 20x^3$
2. $y = 11x^8 \Rightarrow dy/dx = 88x^7$
3. $v = 0.007t^{-83} \Rightarrow dv/dt = -0.581t^{-84}$
4. $v(x) = \dfrac{x^{-9}}{18} \Rightarrow v'(x) = -\frac{1}{2}x^{-10}$
5. $M(x) = 1215 \Rightarrow M'(x) = 0$ (Deriv. of a constant)
6. $f(x) = 4.77^{23} \Rightarrow f'(x) = 0$ (Deriv. of a constant)
7. $y = 0.3x^2 - 8x + 4 \Rightarrow dy/dx = 0.6x - 8$
8. $r = 0.2x^2 + 6x - 1 \Rightarrow dr/dx = 0.4x + 6$
9. $\dfrac{d}{dx}(13 - x) = -1$
10. $f(x) = 4.5x^2 - x \Rightarrow f'(x) = 9x - 1$
11. $y = x^{2.3} + 5x^{-2} - 100x + 4 \Rightarrow$
    $dy/dx = 2.3x^{1.3} - 10x^{-3} - 100$
12. $\dfrac{d}{dx}(x^{2/5} - 4x^2 - 3x^{-1} + 14) = \frac{2}{5}x^{-3/5} - 8x + 3x^{-2}$
13. $v = (3x - 4)^2 = 9x^2 - 24x + 16 \Rightarrow dv/dx = 18x - 24$
14. $u = (5x - 7)^2 = 25x^2 - 70x + 49 \Rightarrow du/dx = 50x - 70$
15. $f(x) = (2x + 5)^3 = 8x^3 + 60x^2 + 150x + 125 \Rightarrow$
    $f'(x) = 24x^2 + 120x + 150$
16. $f(x) = (4x - 1)^3 = 64x^3 - 48x^2 + 12x - 1 \Rightarrow$
    $f'(x) = 192x^2 - 96x + 12$
17. $P(x) = \dfrac{x^2}{2} - x + 4 \Rightarrow P'(x) = x - 1$
18. $Q(x) = \dfrac{x^3}{3} + \dfrac{x^2}{2} - x + 1 \Rightarrow Q'(x) = x^2 + x - 1$
19. $f(x) = 7x^4$
    $f'(x) = \lim_{h\to 0} \dfrac{7(x+h)^4 - 7x^4}{h}$
    $= \lim_{h\to 0} (28x^3 + 42x^2h + 28xh^2 + 7h^3) = 28x^3$
    By formula, $f'(x) = 7 \cdot 4x^3 = 28x^3$, which checks.
20. $g(x) = 5x^3$
    $g'(x) = \lim_{h\to 0} \dfrac{5(x+h)^3 - 5x^3}{h}$
    $= \lim_{h\to 0} (15x^2 + 15xh + 5h^2) = 15x^2$
    By formula, $g'(x) = 5 \cdot 3x^2 = 15x^2$, which checks.
21. $v(t) = 10t^2 - 5t + 7$
    $v'(t)$
    $= \lim_{h\to 0} \dfrac{[10(t+h)^2 - 5(t+h) + 7] - [10t^2 - 5t + 7]}{h}$
    $= \lim_{h\to 0} \dfrac{20th + 10h^2 - 5h}{h} = \lim_{h\to 0} (20t + 10h - 5)$
    $= 20t - 5$
    By formula, $v'(t) = 10 \cdot 2t - 5 = 20t - 5$, which checks.
22. $s(t) = t^4 - 6t^2 + 3.7$
    $s'(t)$
    $= \lim_{h\to 0} \dfrac{[(t+h)^4 - 6(t+h)^2 + 3.7] - [t^4 - 6t^2 + 3.7]}{h}$
    $= \lim_{h\to 0} \dfrac{4t^3h + 6t^2h^2 + 4th^3 + h^4 - 12th - 6h^2}{h}$
    $= \lim_{h\to 0} (4t^3 + 6t^2h + 4th^2 + h^3 - 12t - 6h) = 4t^3 - 12t$
    By formula, $s'(t) = 4t^3 - 6 \cdot 2t = 4t^3 - 12t$, which checks.
23. Misconception Problem
    Mae should realize that you differentiate *functions*, not values of functions. If you substitute a value for x into $f(x) = x^4$, you get $f(3) = 3^4 = 81$, which is a *new* function, $g(x) = 81$. It is the derivative of g that equals zero.
    Moral: Differentiate *before* you substitute for x.
24. Higher Math Problem
    a. $v(x) = h'(x) = -10x + 20$
    b. Book was going down at 10 m/sec.
    The velocity is −10, so h(x) is *decreasing*.
    c. The book was 15 m above where he threw it.
    d. 2 sec. Book is at its highest point when velocity is zero. $v(x) = 0$ if and only if $x = 2$.

25. Graph. Dashed line is the derivative.
(Equation is $f(x) = x^3/24 - x^2/8 - x + 2$.)

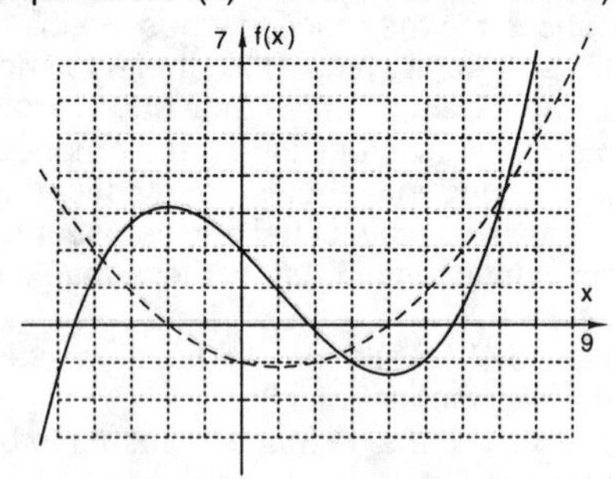

26. Graph. Dashed line is the derivative.
(Equation is $g(x) = -x^3/9 + 2^2/3 + x - 1$.)

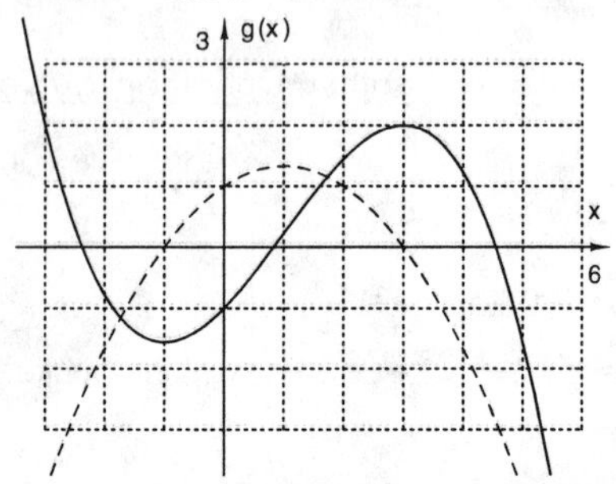

27. Numerical versus Exact Derivative Problem
a. Graph. $f(x) = 0.4x^3 - 7x + 4$

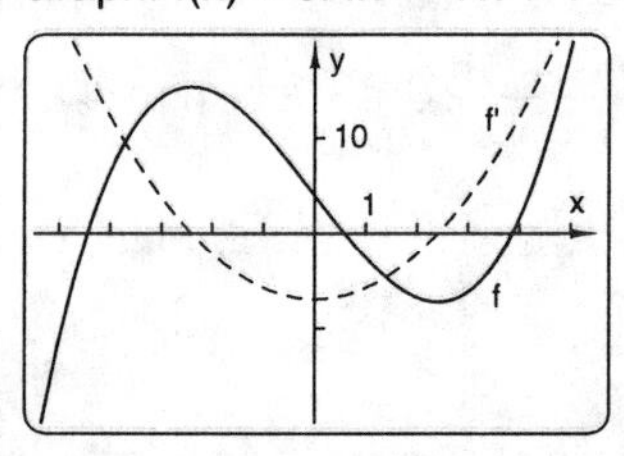

b. The graph of f' is shown dotted in part (a).
c. There appear to be only two graphs because the exact and the numerical derivative graphs almost coincide.
d. $f(3) = -6.2$
$f'(3) = 3.8$ (by formula)
$f'(3) \approx 3.8000004$ (depending on grapher)
The two values of f'(3) are almost identical!

28. Power Formula for Various Types of Exponents
a. $g(x) = x^{-1}$: Conjecture: $g'(x) = -1 \cdot x^{-2}$. Graph.
Conjecture is confirmed.

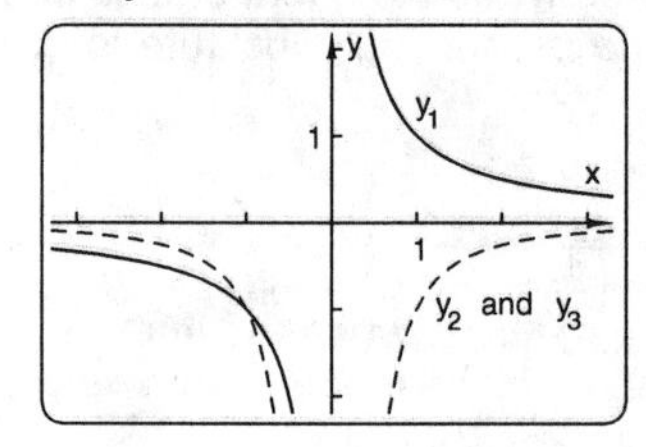

b. $h(x) = x^{1/2}$: Conjecture: $g'(x) = 0.5x^{-1/2}$. Graph.
Conjecture is confirmed.

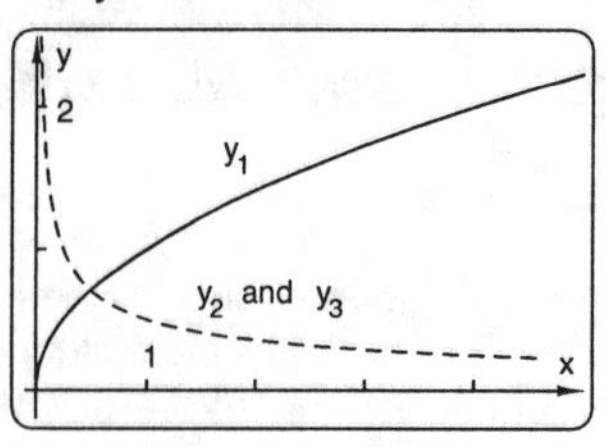

c. $e(x) = 2^x$: Conjecture: $e'(x) = x \cdot 2^{x-1}$. Graph.
Conjecture is refuted!

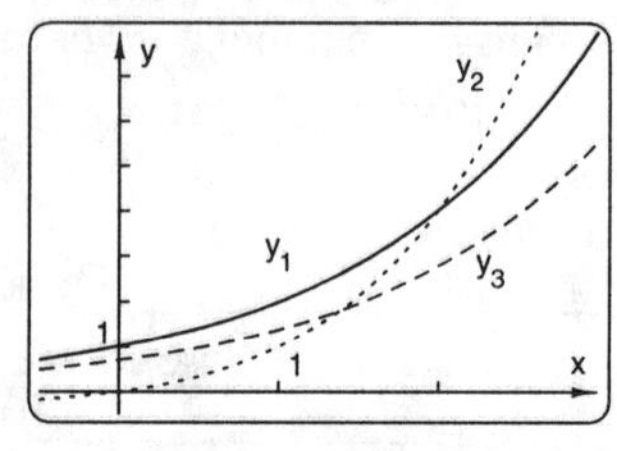

29. $f(x) = x^{1/2} + 2x - 13$
$f'(x) = \frac{1}{2}x^{-1/2} + 2$, $f'(4) = \frac{9}{4}$
Increasing by 9/4 y-units per x-unit at x = 4

30. $f(x) = x^{-2} - 3x + 11$
$f'(x) = -2x^{-3} - 3$, $f'(1) = -5$
Decreasing by 5 y-units per x-unit at x = 1

31. $f(x) = x^{1.5} - 6x + 30$
$f'(x) = 1.5x^{0.5} - 6$, $f'(9) = -1.5$
Decreasing by 1.5 y-units per x-unit at x = 9

32. $f(x) = -3\sqrt{x} + x + 1$
$f'(x) = -\frac{3}{2}x^{-1/2} + 1$, $f'(2) = -0.0607$
Decreasing by 0.0607 y-unit per x-unit at x = 2

33. $f(x) = \frac{x^3}{3} - x^2 - 3x + 5$, $f'(x) = x^2 - 2x - 3$, Graph.
High and low points of the f graph are at the x-intercepts of the f' graph.

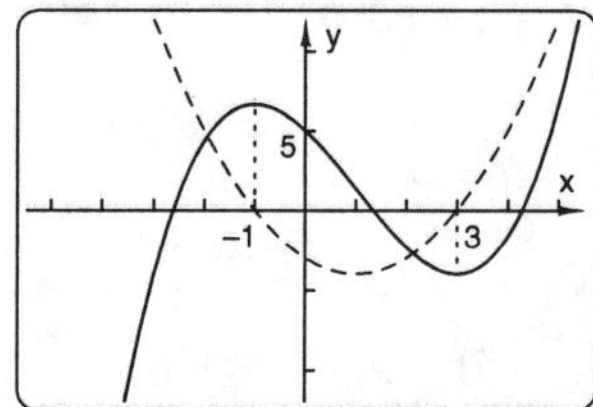

34. $f(x) = \frac{x^3}{3} - 2x^2 + 3x + 9$, $f'(x) = x^2 - 4x + 3$. Graph.
High and low points of the f graph are at the x-intercepts of the f' graph.

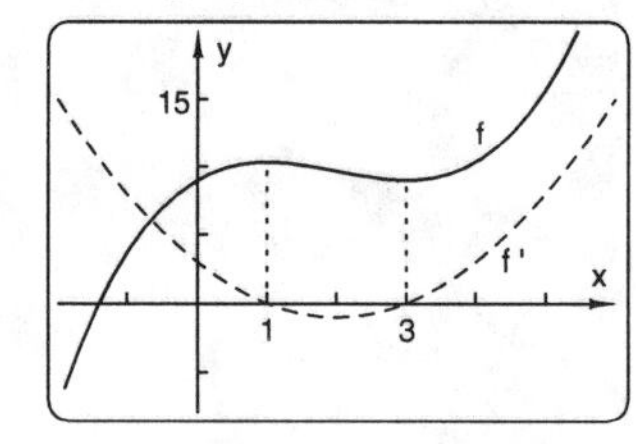

35. Formula Proof Problem I

If $f(x) = k \cdot g(x)$, then $f'(x) = k \cdot g'(x)$.

Proof:

$$f'(x) = \lim_{h \to 0} \frac{f(x + h) - f(x)}{h}$$
$$= \lim_{h \to 0} \frac{k \cdot g(x + h) - k \cdot g(x)}{h}$$
$$= \lim_{h \to 0} k \cdot \frac{g(x + h) - g(x)}{h}$$
$$= k \cdot \lim_{h \to 0} \frac{g(x + h) - g(x)}{h}$$
$$= k \cdot g'(x), \text{ Q.E.D.}$$

36. Formula Proof Problem II

If $f(x) = x^5$, then $f'(c) = 5c^4$.

Proof:

$$f'(c) = \lim_{x \to c} \frac{f(x) - f(c)}{x - c}$$
$$= \lim_{x \to c} \frac{x^5 - c^5}{x - c}$$
$$= \lim_{x \to c} \frac{(x - c)(x^4 + x^3c + x^2c^2 + xc^3 + c^4)}{x - c}$$
$$= \lim_{x \to c} (x^4 + x^3c + x^2c^2 + xc^3 + c^4)$$
$$= c^4 + c^4 + c^4 + c^4 + c^4$$
$$= 5c^4, \text{ Q.E.D.}$$

37. Derivative of a Power Formula

If $f(x) = x^n$, then $f'(x) = nx^{n-1}$.

Proof:

$$f'(x) = \lim_{h \to 0} \frac{(x+h)^n - x^n}{h}$$
$$= \lim_{h \to 0} \frac{x^n + nx^{n-1}h + \frac{1}{2}n(n-1)x^{n-2}h^2 + \ldots + h^n - x^n}{h}$$
$$= \lim_{h \to 0} (nx^{n-1} + \tfrac{1}{2}n(n-1)x^{n-2}h + \ldots + h^{n-1})$$
$$= nx^{n-1} + 0 + 0 + \ldots + 0$$

$= nx^{n-1}$, which is from the second term in the binomial expansion of $(x + h)^n$, Q.E.D.

38. Derivative of a Sum of n Functions Problem

If $y_n = u_1 + u_2 + u_3 + \ldots + u_n$, where the u_i are differentiable functions of x, prove that $y_n' = u_1' + u_2' + u_3' + \ldots + u_n'$ for *all* integers $n \geq 2$.

Proof:

Anchor: For $n = 2$, $y_2 = u_1 + u_2$.

$\therefore y_2' = u_1' + u_2'$ by the derivative of a sum of *two* functions property, thus anchoring the induction.

Induction Hypothesis:

Suppose that for $n = k > 2$,

$y_k' = u_1' + u_2' + u_3' + \ldots + u_k'$.

Verification for $n = k + 1$:

Let $y_{k+1} = u_1 + u_2 + u_3 + \ldots + u_k + u_{k+1}$.

Then $y_{k+1} = (u_1 + u_2 + u_3 + \ldots + u_k) + u_{k+1}$, which is a sum of *two* terms.

$\therefore y_{k+1}' = (u_1 + u_2 + u_3 + \ldots + u_k)' + u_{k+1}'$ by the anchor

$= u_1' + u_2' + u_3' + \ldots + u_k' + u_{k+1}'$,

which completes the induction.

$\therefore y_n' = u_1' + u_2' + u_3' + \ldots + u_n'$ for *all* integers $n \geq 2$, Q.E.D.

39. Introduction to Antiderivatives

a. $f'(x) = 3x^2 - 10x + 5 \Rightarrow f(x) = x^3 - 5x^2 + 5x$

b. $g(x) = f(x) + 13$ is also an answer to part a, because it has the same derivative as f(x). The derivative of a constant is zero.

c. The name *antiderivative* is chosen because it is an inverse operation of taking the derivative.

Problem Set 3-5, pages 102 to 104 — Displacement, Velocity, and Acceleration

Q1. No values of t

Q2. $dy/dx = 10x$

Q3. $y' = -51x^{-4}$

Q4. $f'(x) = 1.7x0.7$

Q5. $(d/dx)(3x + 5) = 3$

Q6. $f(3) = 45$

Q7. $f'(3) = 30$

Q8. Limit = 45

Q9. Epsilon

Q10. Definite integral

1. $y = 5t^4 - 3t^{2.4} + 7t$

$$v = \frac{dy}{dt} = 20t^3 - 7.2t^{1.4} + 7, \quad a = \frac{dv}{dt} = 60t^2 - 10.08t^{0.4}$$

2. $y = 0.3t^{-4} - 5t$

$$v = \frac{dy}{dt} = -1.2t^{-5} - 5, \quad a = \frac{dv}{dt} = 6t^{-6}$$

3. $x = -t^3 + 13t^2 - 35t + 27$. Graph.

The object starts out at x = 27 ft when t = 0 sec. It moves to the left to $x \approx 0.16$ ft when $t \approx 1.7$ sec. It turns there and goes to the right to x = 70 ft when t = 7 sec. It turns there and speeds up, going to the left for all higher values of t.

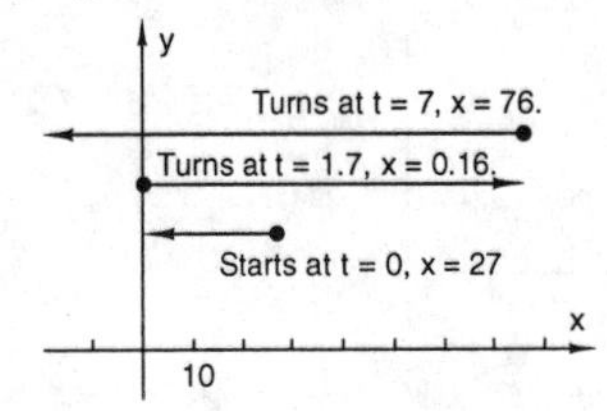

4. $x = t^4 - 11t^3 + 38t^2 - 48t + 50$. Graph.
The object starts out at x = 50 ft when t = 0 sec. It moves to the left to $x \approx 30$ ft when $t \approx 1.0$ sec. Then it moves to the right to $x \approx 34.8$ ft when $t \approx 2.4$ sec. The object moves to the left again, turning at $x \approx 9.4$ ft when $t \approx 4.8$ sec and then moving back to the right for higher values of t.

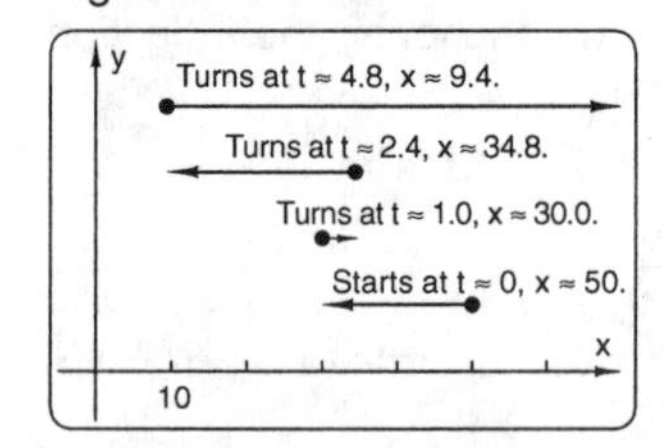

5. a. $x = -t^3 + 13t^2 - 35t + 27$ (See Problem 3.)
$v = -3t^2 + 26t - 35$, $a = -6t + 26$
b. $v(1) = -3 + 26 - 35 = -12$.
So x is <u>decreasing</u> at <u>12 ft/sec</u> at t = 1.
c. $a(1) = -6 + 26 = 20$ (ft/sec)/sec
So the object is <u>slowing down</u> at <u>20 (ft/sec)/sec,</u> since the velocity and acceleration are in opposite directions when t = 1.
d. At t = 7, x has a relative maximum, since v(7) = 0 at that point and is positive just before t = 7 and negative just after.
e. No, x is never negative for t in [0, 9]. It starts out at 27 ft, decreases to just above 0 around t = 1.7 sec, and does not become negative until some time between t = 9.6 and 9.7 sec.

6. a. $x = t^4 - 11t^3 + 38t^2 - 48t + 50$ (See Problem 4.)
$v = 4t^3 - 33t^2 + 76t - 48$, $a = 12t^2 - 66t + 76$
b. v = 0 when t = 1.0475..., 2.370..., or 4.831... .
c. Graph. The displacement is at a maximum or a minimum whenever v = 0.

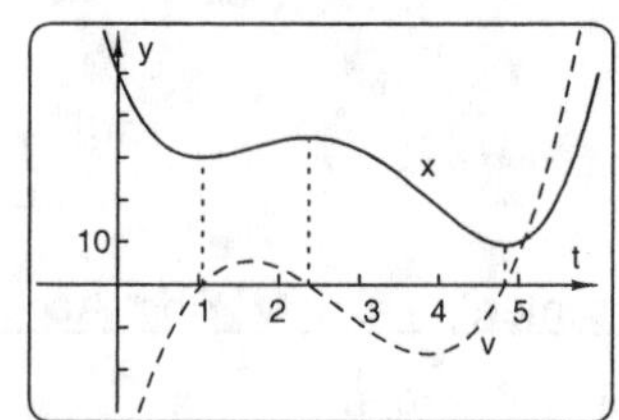

d. Graph. a = 0 when t = 1.641... or 3.858... .
When a = 0, v is at a maximum or minimum point, and the graph of x is at its steepest for times around these values.

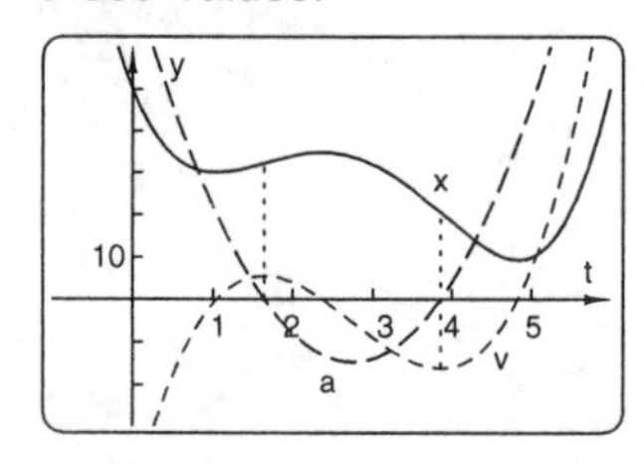

7. <u>Car Problem</u>
a. Graph. $d(t) = 99 + 30t - t^2$

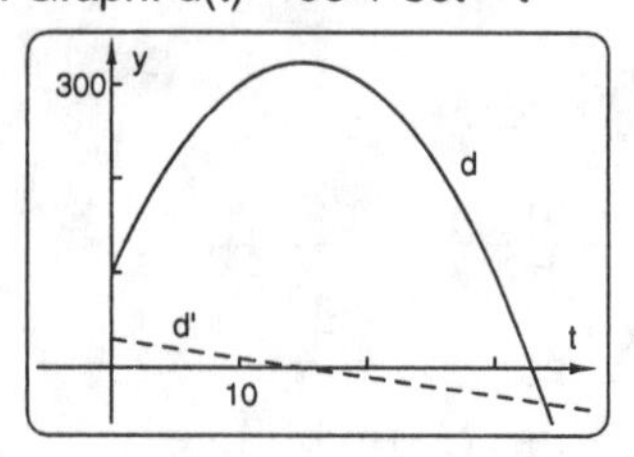

b. $v = d' = 30 - 2t$.
Velocity is positive for $0 \le t < 15$.
Calvin is going <u>up</u> the hill for the first 15 sec.
c. At 15 seconds his car stopped.
d(15) = 324, so distance is <u>324 feet</u>.
d. $99 + 30t - t^2 = 0 \Rightarrow (33 - t)(3 + t) = 0 \Rightarrow t = 33$ or $t = -3$.
He'll be back at the bottom when t = <u>33 sec</u>.
e. d(0) = 99. Car runs out of gas <u>99 ft</u> from the bottom.

8. <u>Sky Diver's Acceleration Problem</u>
a. Graph. $v(t) = 251(1 - 0.88^t)$

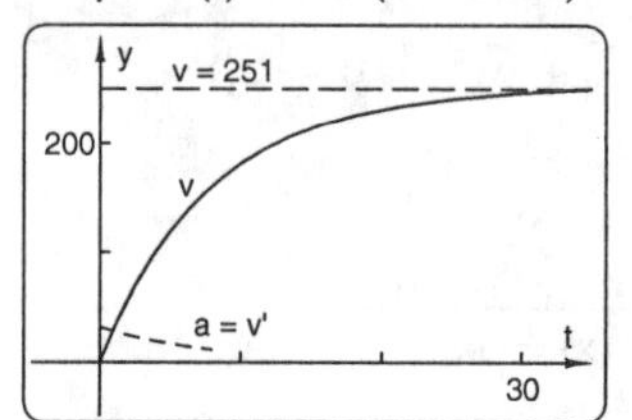

b. Trace the v' graph to find $a(0) \approx 32$. The acceleration decreases because the velocity is approaching a constant. In the real world, this occurs because the wind resistance increases as the velocity increases.
c. The limit is 251 ft/sec as t approaches infinity. The term 0.88^t approaches zero as t gets very large, leaving only 1 inside the parentheses.
d. 90% of terminal velocity is 0.9(251) = 225.9.
Algebraic solution:
$251(1 - 0.88^t) = 225.9 \Rightarrow -0.88^t = -0.1$
$t = \dfrac{\log 0.1}{\log 0.88} = 18.012394... \approx 18.0$ sec
Numerical solution gives the same answer.
Graphical solution: Trace to v(t) = 225.9.
T is between 18 and 18.5.
e. Find the numerical derivative.
$v'(18.0123...) \approx 3.2086...$, which *is* approximately 10% of the initial acceleration.

9. Velocity from Displacement Problem
   a. $d(t) = 18t - 4.9t^2 \Rightarrow d'(t) = 18 - 9.8t$
      $d'(1) = 18 - 9.8 = 8.2$
      $d'(3) = 18 - 9.8 \cdot 3 = -11.4$
      d' is called velocity in physics.
   b. At t = 1 the football is going up at 8.2 m/sec.
      At t = 3 the football is going down at 11.4 m/sec.
      The ball is going up when the derivative is positive and coming down when the derivative is negative.
      The ball is going up when the graph slopes up and coming down when the graph slopes down.
   c. $d'(4) = -21.2$, which suggests that the ball is going down at 41.2 m/sec. However, $d(4) = -6.4$, which reveals that the ball has gone underground. The function gives meaningful answers in the real world only if the domain of t is restricted to values that make d(t) nonnegative.

10. Displacement from Velocity Problem
    $v(t) = 15t^{0.6}$
    Since $v(t) = x'(t)$, x(t) must have had $t^{1.6}$ in it. The derivative of $t^{1.6}$ can be assumed to be $1.6t^{0.6}$. So the coefficient of $t^{1.6}$ must be 15/1.6, or 9.375. But x(0) was 50. Thus, $x(t) = 9.375t^{1.6} + 50$.
    The derivative x'(t) really does equal v(t).
    Using this equation,
    $x(10) = 9.375(10^{1.6}) + 50 = 423.225...$.
    So the distance traveled is 423.225... − 50 = 373.225..., or about 373 ft.
    The concept is antiderivative. (See Problem 39 in Problem Set 3-4.)
    By the trapezoidal rule, with n = 100 increments, distance ≈ 373.162... ≈ 373 ft.
    Concept: definite integral.

11. Average Versus Instantaneous Velocity Problem
    The average rate is defined to be the change in the dependent variable divided by the change in the independent variable (such as total distance divided by total time). Thus, the difference quotient is an average rate.
    The instantaneous rate is the limit of this average rate as the change in the independent variable approaches zero.

12. a. Graph of velocity is the dashed line.

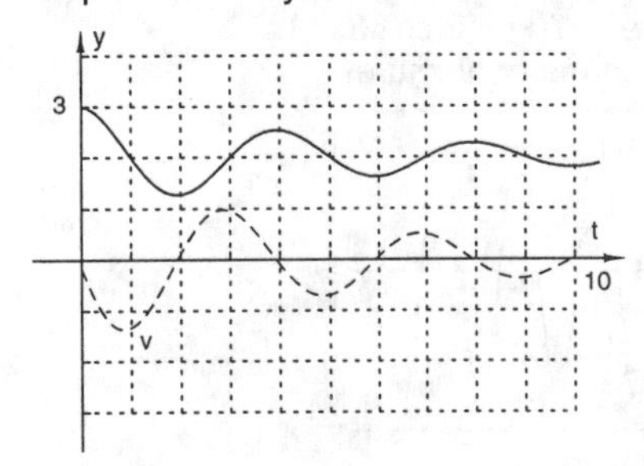

   b. Y is a relative maximum when t ≈ 0, 4, 8, ... sec.
      Y is a relative minimum when t ≈ 2, 6, 10, ... sec.
   c. The velocity is a relative maximum when is t ≈ 3 sec or 7 sec. The displacement graph at these times appears to be increasing the fastest.
   d. The equation used in the text is
      $$y = 2 + 0.85^t \cos \frac{\pi}{2}t$$
      The student could observe that the period is 4, leading to the coefficient of $\pi/2$. The amplitude decreases in a way that suggests an exponential function with base close to, but less than, 1. The additive 2 raises the graph up two units, as can be ascertained by the fact that the graph seems to converge to 2 as t gets larger. The graph shown above agrees with the numerical derivative. Note that the actual maximum and minimum values occur slightly before the values of t read from the graph in part (b). For instance, the maximum near t = 4 is actually at t = 3.9346... .

Problem Set 3-6, page 106 — Introduction to Sine, Cosine, and Composite Functions

1. Graph. f(x) = sin x

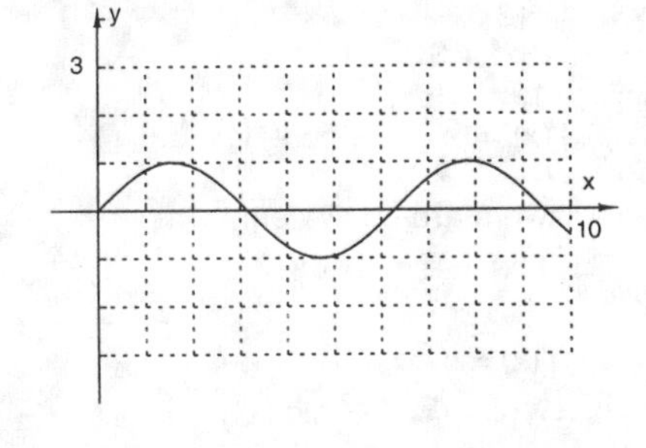

2. $f'(x) = \cos x$, so $f(2) = \cos 2 = -0.416...$.
   $y_2 = (\cos 2)x + (\sin 2 - 2\cos 2) = -0.41...x + 1.74...$
   Graph. The line appears to be tangent to the sine graph at x = 2. The sine function and the linear function have the same slope at x = 2, which means they have the same rate of change. The derivative is the rate of change of the function.

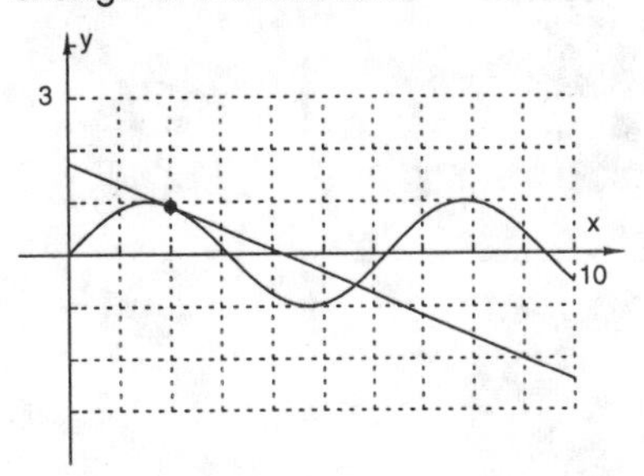

3. $g(x) = \sin 3x$
Conjecture: $g'(x) = 3 \cos 3x$
Graph confirms conjecture.

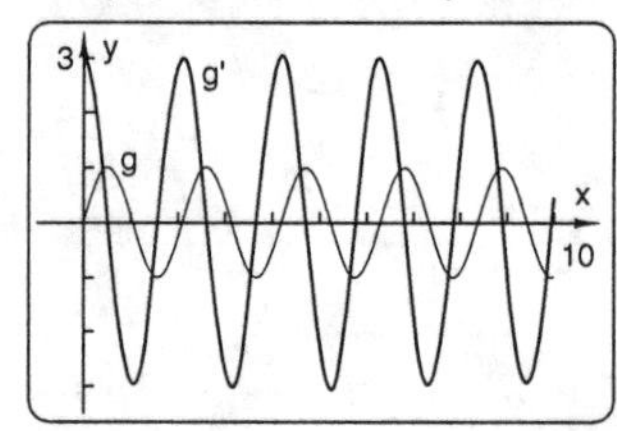

4. $h(x) = \sin x^2$
Conjecture: $h'(x) = 2x \cos x^2$
Graph confirms conjecture.

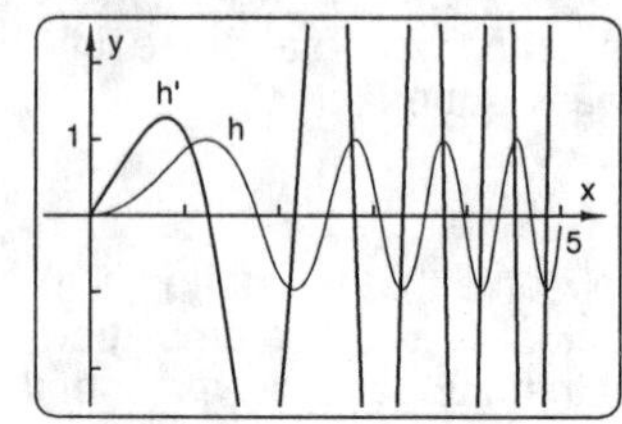

5. $t(x) = \sin x^{0.7}$
Conjecture: $t'(x) = 0.7x^{-0.3} \cos x^{0.7}$
Graph confirms conjecture!

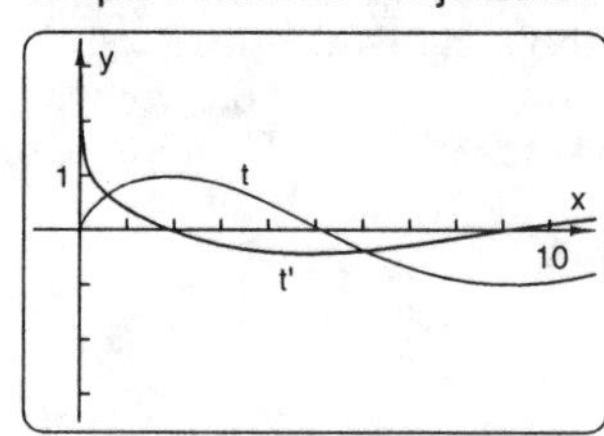

6. $f(x) = \sin [g(x)]$
f is a <u>composite function</u>.
g is the <u>inside function</u>.
sine is the <u>outside function</u>.
Differentiate the outside function with respect to the inside function. Then multiply the answer by the derivative of the inside function with respect to x.

7. a. $f(x) = \sin 3x$. Inside: 3x. Outside: sine.
b. $h(x) = \sin^3 x$. Inside: sine. Outside: cube.
c. $g(x) = \sin x^3$. Inside: cube. Outside: sine.
d. $r(x) = 2^{\cos x}$.
Inside: cosine. Outside: exponential.
e. $q(x) = 1/(\tan x)$.
Inside: tangent. Outside: reciprocal.
f. $L(x) = \log (\sec x)$.
Inside: secant. Outside: logarithm.

8. <u>Journal Problem</u>
The journal entry should mention the conjectures made, which ones were right, and what blind alleys were met on the way to the right conjectures.

Problem Set 3-7, pages 109 and 110 — Derivatives of Composite Functions—The Chain Rule

Q1. f(c) exists
Q2. $\lim_{x \to c} f(x)$ exists
Q3. $\lim_{x \to c} f(x) = f(c)$
(Any order is acceptable)

Q4. No (not continuous)
Q5. $dy/dx = 16x^{-1/5}$
Q6. $f(x) = -10x^{-3}$
Q7. Antiderivative
Q8. Graph. ($y = \sin x$)

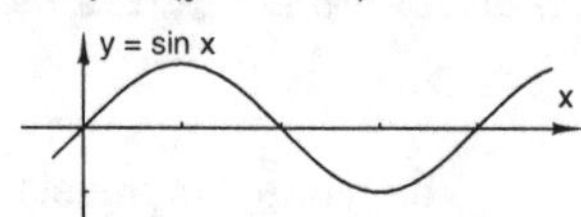

Q9. Graph. ($y = \cos x$)

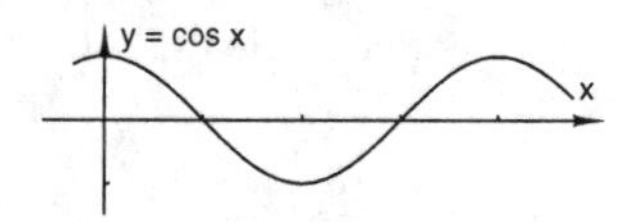

Q10. Graph. ($y = -\sin x$)

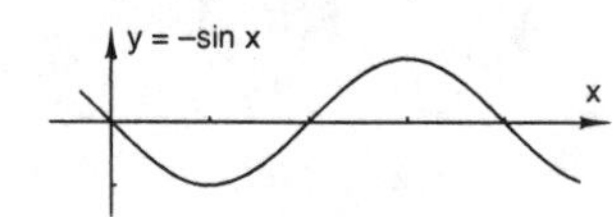

1. a. Let $y = f(u)$, $u = g(x)$.
$$\frac{dy}{dx} = \frac{dy}{du} \cdot \frac{du}{dx}$$
b. $y' = f'(g(x)) \cdot g'(x)$
c. To differentiate a composite function, differentiate the outside function with respect to the inside function, then multiply by the derivative of the inside function with respect to x.

2. $f(x) = (x^2 - 1)^3$
a. $f'(x) = 3(x^2 - 1)^2(2x)$
b. $(x^2 - 1)^3 = x^6 - 3x^4 + 3x^2 - 1$,
so $f'(x) = 6x^5 - 12x^3 + 6x$.
c. From part a., $f'(x) = 6x(x^4 - 2x^2 + 1)$
$= 6x^5 - 12x^3 + 6x$,
so the two answers are equivalent.

3. $f(x) = \cos 3x \Rightarrow f'(x) = -\sin 3x \cdot 3$
$= -3 \sin 3x$

4. $f(x) = \sin 5x \Rightarrow f'(x) = 5 \cos 5x$

5. $g(x) = \cos (x^3) \Rightarrow g'(x) = -3x^2 \sin (x^3)$

6. $h(x) = \sin (x^5) \Rightarrow h'(x) = 5x^4 \cos (x^5)$

7. $y = (\cos x)^3 \Rightarrow y' = 3(\cos x)^2 \cdot (-\sin x)$
$= -3 \cos^2 x \sin x$

8. $f(x) = (\sin x)^5 \Rightarrow f'(x) = 5(\sin x)^4 \cdot \cos x$
$= 5 \sin^4 x \cos x$

9. $y = \sin^6 x \Rightarrow y' = 6 \sin^5 x \cos x$

10. $f(x) = \cos^7 x \Rightarrow f'(x) = 7\cos^6 x \cdot (-\sin x)$
$= -7\cos^6 x \sin x$
11. $y = -6\sin 3x \Rightarrow y' = -18\cos 3x$
12. $f(x) = 4\cos(-5x) \Rightarrow f'(x) = 4(-\sin(-5x)) \cdot (-5)$
$= 20\sin(-5x)$
13. $\frac{d}{dx}(\cos^4 7x) = 4\cos^3 7x \cdot (-\sin 7x) \cdot 7$
$= -28\cos^3 7x \sin 7x$
14. $\frac{d}{dx}(\sin^9 13x) = 9\sin^8 13x \cos 13x \cdot 13$
$= 117\sin^8 13x \cos 13x$
15. $f(x) = 24\sin^{5/3} 4x \Rightarrow$
$f'(x) = 40\sin^{2/3} 4x \cdot \cos 4x \cdot 4$
$= 160\sin^{2/3} 4x \cos 4x$
16. $f(x) = -100\sin^{6/5}(-9x) \Rightarrow$
$f'(x) = -120\sin^{1/5}(-9x) \cdot \cos(-9x) \cdot (-9)$
$= 1080\sin^{1/5}(-9x)\cos(-9x)$
17. $f(x) = (5x+3)^7 \Rightarrow f'(x) = 7(5x+3)^6 \cdot 5 = 35(5x+3)^6$
18. $f(x) = (x^2+8)^9 \Rightarrow f'(x) = 9(x^2+8)^8 \cdot 2x$
$= 18x(x^2+8)^8$
19. $y = (4x^3-7)^{-6} \Rightarrow y' = -6(4x^3-7)^{-7} \cdot 12x^2$
$= -72x^2(4x^3-7)^{-7}$
20. $y = (x^2+3x-7)^{-5} \Rightarrow y' = -5(x^2+3x-7)^{-6} \cdot (2x+3)$
$= -5(2x+3)(x^2+3x-7)^{-6}$
21. $y = (\cos(x^2+3))^{100} \Rightarrow$
$y' = 100(\cos(x^2+3))^{99} \cdot (-\sin(x^2+3)) \cdot 2x$
$= -200x\cos^{99}(x^2+3)\sin(x^2+3)$
22. $y = (\cos(5x+3)^4)^5 \Rightarrow$
$y' = 5(\cos(5x+3)^4)^4 \cdot (-\sin(5x+3)^4) \cdot 4(5x+3)^3 \cdot 5$
$= -100(5x+3)^3\cos^4(5x+3)^4\sin(5x+3)^4$
23. Graphical Verification Problem
$f(x) = 5\cos 0.2x$
$f'(x) = -5\sin 0.2x \cdot 0.2 = -\sin 0.2x$
$f'(3) = -\sin 0.6 = -0.5646...$ and $f(3) = 4.126...$
Line has equation $y = -0.5646...x + 5.820....$
Graph. Line is tangent to graph.

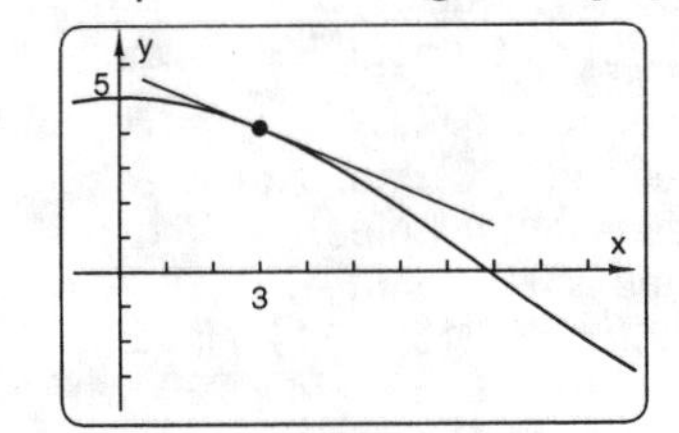

24. Beanstalk Problem
$y = 7\sin \pi t + 12t^{1.2}$
velocity $= \frac{dy}{dt} = 7\pi\cos \pi t + 14.4t^{0.2}$
Graph. Yes, there are times when the beanstalk is shrinking. The velocity graph is negative for brief intervals, and the y-graph is decreasing in these intervals.

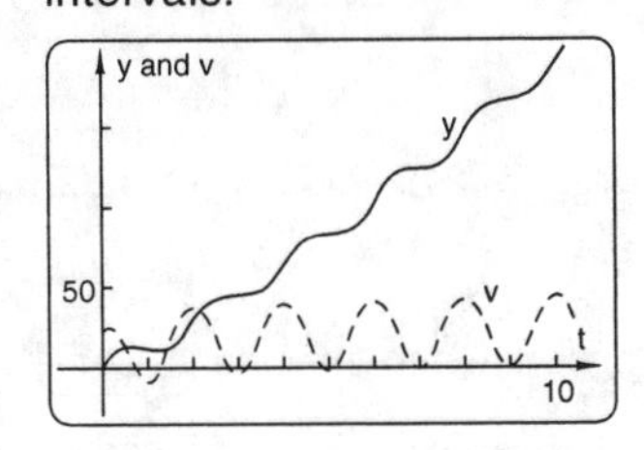

25. Balloon Volume Problem
a. $V = \frac{4\pi}{3}r^3 \Rightarrow \frac{dV}{dr} = 4\pi r^2$
dV/dr is in (cm^3/cm), or cm^2.
b. $r = 6t + 10$.
c. $\frac{dr}{dt} = 6$ (*not* surprising!). Units: cm/min
d. $\frac{dV}{dt} = \frac{dV}{dr} \cdot \frac{dr}{dt}$
When $t = 5$, $r = 40$. So
$\frac{dV}{dr} = 4\pi(40^2) = 6400\pi$.
$\therefore \frac{dV}{dt} = 6400\pi \cdot 6 = 38400\pi$ cm^3/min.
Since dV/dr has units cm^2, and dr/dt has units cm/min, dV/dt has units
$cm^2 \cdot \frac{cm}{min}$
which becomes cm^3/min, Q.E.D.
e. $V = \frac{4\pi}{3}(6t+10)^3$
$\therefore \frac{dV}{dt} = 4\pi(6t+10)^2(6) = 24\pi(6t+10)^2$
When $t = 5$,
$\frac{dV}{dt} = 24\pi(6(5)+10)^2 = 38400\pi$, which checks.
26. Δu and Δx Problem
a. Graph (example).
Δu does *not* approach zero as Δx approaches zero from the left side. (Δu *does* approach zero as Δx approaches zero from the left side.)

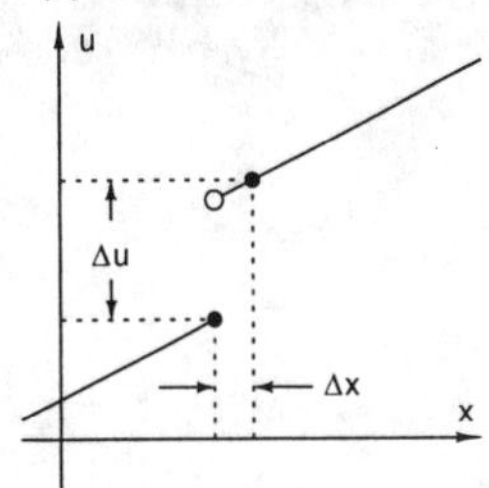

b. Δu *does* approach zero as Δx approaches zero from either side.

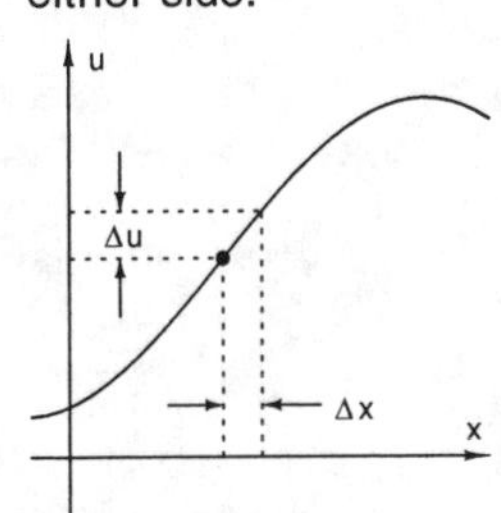

Q1. $f'(x) = 9x^8$
Q2. $dy/dx = -3 \sin x$
Q3. $y' = 72x^5(5x^6 + 11)^{1.4}$
Q4. $s' = 0$
Q5. Limit = 12
Q6. Limit = 1
Q7. Yes (continuous)
Q8. $f(x) = -\cos x^2$
Q9. 1
Q10. Graph

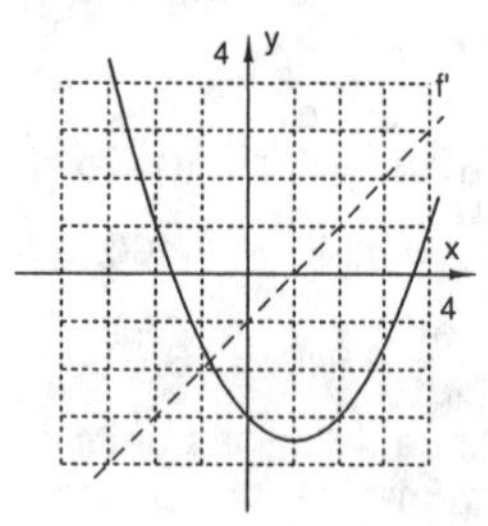

1. Ferris Wheel Problem
   a. Graph

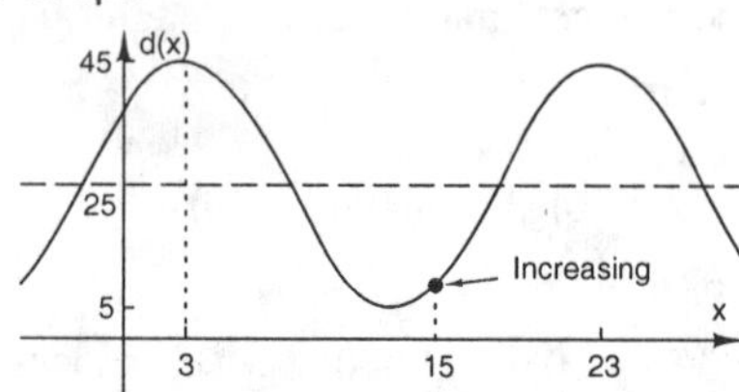

$y(t) = C + A \cos B(t - D)$
Vertical displacement = 25 = C
Amplitude = 0.5(40) = 20 = A
Phase disp. (for cosine) = 3 = D
Period = 60/3 = 20, so $B = 2\pi/20 = \pi/10$
(Note that B is the angular velocity in radians per second.)

$$y(t) = 25 + 20 \cos \frac{\pi}{10}(t - 3)$$

   b. $y'(t) = -2\pi \sin \frac{\pi}{10}(t - 3)$
   c. $y'(15) = -2\pi \sin \frac{\pi}{10}(15 - 3) = 3.69316...$
   y(t) is increasing at about 3.7 ft/sec.
   d. The fastest that y(t) changes is 2π, or 6.28... ft/sec. The seat is at y(t) = 25 ft above the ground then.
2. Pendulum Problem
   a. $y = C + A \cos B(x - D)$.
   $B = 2\pi/6 = \pi/3$ rad/sec
   D = phase displacement = 1.3 sec
   A = 0.5(110 − 50) = 30 cm.
   C = 110 − 30 or 50 + 30, which equals 80 cm.
   $\therefore d = 80 + 30 \cos \frac{\pi}{3}(t - 1.3)$
   b. $d' = -10\pi \sin \frac{\pi}{3}(t - 1.3)$
   c. $d'(5) = -10\pi \sin \frac{\pi}{3}(5 - 1.3) = 21.02135...$
   $d'(11) = -10\pi \sin \frac{\pi}{3}(11 - 1.3) = 21.02135...$
   At both times the pendulum is moving away from the wall at about 21.0 cm/sec. The answers are the same because the times are exactly one period apart.
   d. $d'(20) = -10\pi \sin \frac{\pi}{3}(20 - 1.3) = -21.02135...$
   The pendulum is moving toward the wall. Since the derivative is negative, d is decreasing, which in this problem implies motion toward the wall.
   e. The fastest is $10\pi \approx 31.4$ cm/sec, when d = 80.
   f. $0 = -10\pi \sin \frac{\pi}{3}(t - 1.3) \Rightarrow \sin \frac{\pi}{3}(t - 1.3) = 0 \Rightarrow$
   $= \frac{\pi}{3}(t - 1.3) = \sin^{-1} 0 \Rightarrow \frac{\pi}{3}(t - 1.3) = 0 + \pi n \Rightarrow$
   $t - 1.3 = 3n \Rightarrow t = 1.3 + 3n$.
   The first positive time occurs when n = 0. When the velocity is 0, the pendulum is at its maximum height t = 1.3 sec.
3. Playground Problem
   a. Curb has slope (3.25 − 0.75)/44 = 2.5/44.
   $\therefore$ equation is $f(x) = 0.75 + (2.5/44)x$
   b. Sinusoid has period 8 ft, so $B = 2\pi/8 = \pi/4$.
   Amplitude = 0.5(0.75 − 0.25) = 0.25 ft
   Low end of ramp is a low point on the sinusoid.
   $\therefore$ sinusoidal axis is at y = 0.25 when x = 0, and goes up with slope 2.5/44.
   Sinusoid is at a low point when x = 0. So phase displacement is 0 if the cosine is *subtracted.*
   $\therefore$ equation is
   $g(x) = 0.25 + \frac{2.5}{44}x - 0.25 \cos \frac{\pi}{4}(x)$
   (There are other correct forms.)
   c. $g'(x) = \frac{2.5}{44} + \frac{\pi}{16} \sin \frac{\pi}{4}(x)$
   $g'(9) = \frac{2.5}{44} + \frac{\pi}{16} \sin \frac{\pi}{4}(9) = 0.1956...$ ft/ft
   Going up at about 0.2 vertical ft per horizontal ft
   $g'(15) = \frac{2.5}{44} + \frac{\pi}{16} \sin \frac{\pi}{4}(15) = -0.0820...$ ft/ft
   Going down at about 0.08 vert. ft per horiz. ft
   Negative derivative implies g(x) is getting smaller and thus child is going down, and vice versa.
   d. By tracing the g' graph, maximum value of g'(x) is 0.2531... ft/ft (about 14.2° up).
   Minimum is −0.1395... ft/ft (about 7.9° down).
4. Daylight Problem
   a. Let d = day number and L(d) = no. of minutes.
   14 hours 3 minutes is 843 minutes.
   10 hours 15 minutes is 615 minutes.
   $\therefore$ Amplitude = (1/2)(843 − 615) = 114 minutes.
   Sinusoidal axis is at L(d) = 615 + 114 = 729 min
   Assuming a 365-day year, $B = 2\pi/365$.
   Phase displacement = 172.
   $\therefore L(d) = 729 + 114 \cos \frac{2\pi}{365}(d - 172)$
   On August 7, d = 219.
   $L(219) = 729 + 114 \cos \frac{2\pi}{365}(219 - 172) = 807.67...$
   or about 13 hours 28 minutes.
   b. $L'(d) = -\frac{228\pi}{365} \sin \frac{2\pi}{365}(d - 172)$
   On Aug. 7, d = 219.
   $L'(219) = -\frac{228\pi}{365} \sin \frac{2\pi}{365}(219 - 172) = -1.42009...$.
   Rate ≈ -1.42 min/day.
   (Decreasing at about 1.42 min/day.)
   c. The greatest rate occurs when the sine is 1 or −1.
   Rate is $228\pi/365 \approx 1.96$ min/day.
   1/4 year is about 91 days. So greatest rate occurs at day 172 ± 91, which is day 263 or day 81 (September 20 or March 22).

5. Pendulum Experiment

In general, the period for a pendulum formed by a weight suspended by a string of negligible mass is $2\pi\sqrt{L/g}$, where L is the length from the pivot point to the center of mass (actually, the center or percussion) of the weight, and g is the gravitational acceleration, about 9.8 m/sec^2. Consequently, if the pendulum is 1 meter long, its period will be $2\pi\sqrt{1/9.8} = 2.007...$, or about 2 sec. This is the period for a complete back-and-forth swing. You must quadruple the length of a pendulum to double its period. A pendulum hung from the ceiling will have a period slow enough to measure fairly precisely. A good way to get more accuracy is to count the total time for 10 swings, then divide by 10. The period is roughly constant for any (moderate) amplitude, as long as the amplitude is not too big. This fact is not obvious to the uninitiated student, and is worth spending time showing. It is quite dramatic to watch a pendulum take just as long to make 10 swings with an amplitude of 2 cm as it does with amplitude 20 or 30 cm.

6. Daylight Research Project

The following data were computed from actual sunrise and sunset times for San Antonio for each 10 days. You can get similar information for your locality from the local weather bureau, or newspaper office, or from the Nautical Almanac Office, U.S. Naval Observatory, Washington, DC 20390, or from the Internet.

Day	Min	Day	Min	Day	Min
0	617	120	797	240	772
10	623	130	811	250	755
20	632	140	823	260	738
30	645	150	833	270	720
40	660	160	840	280	703
50	676	170	842	290	686
60	693	180	842	300	669
70	711	190	836	310	653
80	729	200	828	320	639
90	747	210	816	330	628
100	764	220	803	340	620
110	780	230	789	350	615
				360	615

The graph shows a good fit to the data. But there is a noticeable deviation in the fall and winter, where the day is slightly longer than predicted. The main reason for the discrepancy, apparently, is the fact that in the fall and winter the earth is closer to the sun, and hence moves slightly more rapidly through its angle with the sun than during the spring and summer.

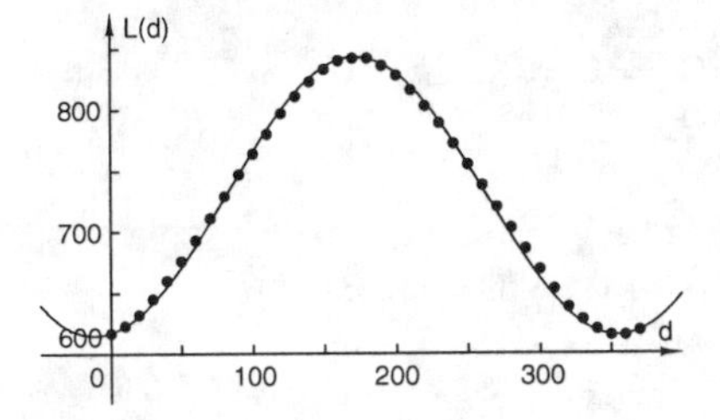

7. Squeeze Theorem, Numerically

a. Graph. $f(x) = -2x^2 + 8x - 2$, $g(x) = 2x^2 + 2$, $h(x) = 4x$. Limits are all equal to 4.

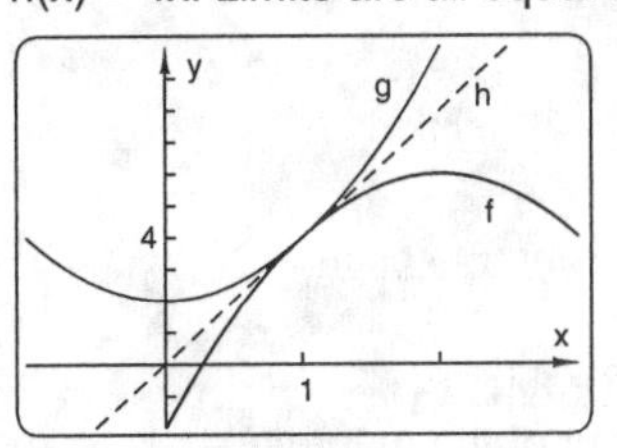

b. Each function is continuous because it is a polynomial function.
$f(x) \le h(x) \le g(x)$.

c.

x	f(x)	h(x)	g(x)
0.95	3.795	3.8	3.805
0.96	3.8368	3.84	3.8432
0.97	3.8782	3.88	3.8818
0.98	3.9192	3.92	3.9208
0.99	3.9598	3.96	3.9602
1.00	4	4	4
1.01	4.0398	4.04	4.0402
1.02	4.0792	4.08	4.0808
1.03	4.1182	4.12	4.1218
1.04	4.1568	4.16	4.1632
1.05	4.195	4.2	4.205

d. From the table, $\delta = 0.01$ or 0.02 will work, but 0.03 is too large.

e. All the values of h(x) are between the corresponding values of f(x) and g(x), and the three functions all approach 4 as a limit.

8. Limit of (sin x)/x, Numerically

a. The numbers are correct.

b.

x	(sin x)/x
0.05	0.99958338541...
0.04	0.99973335466...
0.03	0.99985000674...
0.02	0.99993333466...
0.01	0.99998333341...

Values *are* getting closer to 1, Q.E.D.

c. Answers will vary according to calculator. For the TI-82 in TABLE mode, starting x at 0 and using $\Delta x = 10^{-7}$ shows that all values round to 1 until x reaches 1.8×10^{-6}, which registers as 0.999999999999.

d. Answer will depend on calculator. For TI-82 in TABLE mode, (sin 0.001)/0.001 is 0.999999833333, which agrees exactly with the value published by NBS to 12 places.

e. If students have studied Taylor series (Chapter 12) before taking this course, they will be able to see the reason. The Taylor series for sin 0.001 is

$$0.001 - \frac{0.001^3}{3!} + \frac{0.001^5}{5!} - \frac{0.001^7}{7!} + \cdots$$

= 0.00100 00000 00000 00000 000...
− 0.00000 00001 66666 66666 666...
+ 0.00000 00000 00000 00833 333...
= 0.00099 99998 33333 34166 666...

9. Limit of (sin x)/x Problem

Prove that $\lim_{x\to 0} \frac{\sin x}{x} = 0$.

See text proof.

10. Derivative of the Sine Function

See text proof.

11. Derivative of the Cosine Function

See text proof.

12. Squeeze Theorem Problem

a. See text statement of the theorem.

b. See text proof of the theorem.

c. See Figure 3-8c or 3-8d.

13. Group Discussion Problem

$y = 2 + (x - 1)\sin\frac{1}{x - 1}$

a. Limit seems to equal 2.

b. Graph.

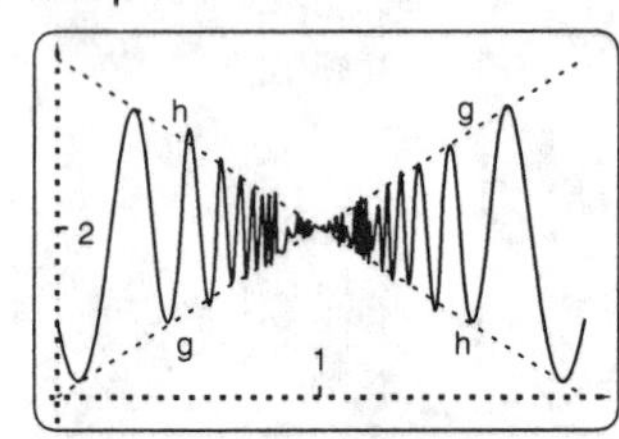

c. Graph in part (b). The lines have equations $g(x) = x + 1$ and $h(x) = 3 - x$.

d. Prove that $\lim_{x\to 1} y = 2$.

Proof:

$\lim_{x\to 1} (x + 1) = 1 + 1 = 2.$

$\lim_{x\to 1} (3 - x) = 3 - 1 = 2.$

For $x < 1$, $g(x) \le y \le h(x)$.

$\therefore$ the squeeze theorem applies, and

$\lim_{x\to 1^-} y = 2.$

For $x > 1$, $h(x) \le y \le g(x)$.

$\therefore$ the squeeze theorem applies, and

$\lim_{x\to 1^+} y = 2.$

Since both left- and right-hand limits equal 2,

$\lim_{x\to 1} y = 2$, Q.E.D.

e. The word *envelope* (a noun) is used because the small window formed by the two lines "envelops" (a verb) the graph of the function.

f. As $|x|$ becomes large, $(x - 1)\cdot\sin\frac{1}{x - 1}$

$= \frac{\sin(1/(x-1))}{1/(x-1)}$ takes on the form

$\frac{\sin(\text{argument})}{(\text{argument})}$ as the argument approaches zero.

Thus the limit is 1, and y approaches 2 + 1, which equals 3.

14. Journal Problem

Students should make the connection that they made a conjecture that the derivative of sine is cosine by examining the numerical derivative graph. Now they have *proved* it, using the definition of derivative and the limit properties.

Problem Set 3-9, pages 121 and 122 — Antiderivatives and Indefinite Integrals

Q1. Squeeze theorem

Q2. Limit = 1

Q3. $y' = -\sin x$

Q4. $y = \sin x + C$

Q5. No

Q6. x^8

Q7. x^{48}

Q8. $\log 32 = 5 \log 2$

Q9. Graph. ($y = |x|$)

Q10. Cube function

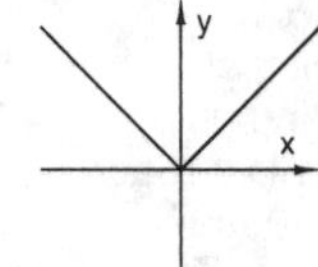

1. $f'(x) = 7x^6 \Rightarrow f(x) = x^7 + C$
2. $f'(x) = 10x^9 \Rightarrow f(x) = x^{10} + C$
3. $f'(x) = x^5 \Rightarrow f(x) = \frac{1}{6}x^6 + C$
4. $f'(x) = x^4 \Rightarrow f(x) = \frac{1}{5}x^5 + C$
5. $f'(x) = x^{-9} \Rightarrow f(x) = -\frac{1}{8}x^{-8} + C$
6. $f'(x) = x^{-1066} \Rightarrow f(x) = -\frac{1}{1065}x^{-1065} + C$
7. $f'(x) = \cos x \Rightarrow f(x) = \sin x + C$
8. $f'(x) = \sin x \Rightarrow f(x) = -\cos x + C$
9. $f'(x) = 36x^{7/2} \Rightarrow f(x) = 8x^{9/2} + C$
10. $f'(x) = 77x^{4/3} \Rightarrow f(x) = 33x^{7/3} + C$
11. $f'(x) = \sin 5x \Rightarrow f(x) = -0.2\cos 5x + C$
12. $f'(x) = \cos 4x \Rightarrow f(x) = \frac{1}{4}\sin 4x + C$
13. $f'(x) = (4x + 5)^7 \Rightarrow f(x) = \frac{1}{32}(4x + 5)^8 + C$
14. $f'(x) = (8x + 3)^5 \Rightarrow f(x) = \frac{1}{48}(8x + 3)^6 + C$
15. $f'(x) = x^2 + 6x - 5 \Rightarrow f(x) = \frac{1}{3}x^3 + 3x^2 - 5x + C$
16. $f'(x) = x^2 - 10x + 7 \Rightarrow f(x) = \frac{1}{3}x^3 - 5x^2 + 7x + C$
17. $f'(x) = x^4$ and $f(1) = 10$

    $f(x) = \frac{1}{5}x^5 + C$

    $10 = \frac{1}{5}\cdot 1^5 + C \Rightarrow C = 9.8$

    $f(x) = \frac{1}{5}x^5 + 9.8$
18. $f'(x) = x^7$ and $f(-1) = 100$

    $f(x) = \frac{1}{8}x^8 + C$

    $100 = \frac{1}{8}(-1)^8 + C \Rightarrow C = 99.875$

    $f(x) = 0.125x^8 + 99.875$
19. $f'(x) = \cos x$ and $f(\pi/2) = 5$

    $f(x) = \sin x + C$

    $5 = \sin(\pi/2) + C \Rightarrow C = 4$

    $f(x) = \sin x + 4$
20. $f'(x) = \sin x$ and $f(\pi) = 8$

    $f(x) = -\cos x + C$

    $8 = -\cos\pi + C \Rightarrow C = 7$

    $f(x) = -\cos x + 7$
21. $f'(x) = x^2 - 8x + 3$ and $f(-2) = 13$

    $f(x) = \frac{1}{3}x^3 - 4x^2 + 3x + C$

    $13 = -\frac{8}{3} - 16 - 6 + C \Rightarrow C = 113/3$

    $f(x) = x^3/3 - 4x^2 + 3x + 113/3$
22. $f'(x) = x^2 + 12x - 7$ and $f(3) = -10$

    $f(x) = \frac{1}{3}x^3 + 6x^2 - 7x + C$

    $-10 = 9 + 54 - 21 + C \Rightarrow C = -52$

    $f(x) = \frac{1}{3}x^3 + 6x^2 - 7x - 52$

23. Displacement Problem

a. $d'(t) = 70 - 9.8t$

$d(t) = 70t - 4.9t^2 + C$

b. $d(0) = 6 \Rightarrow C = 6$

$\therefore d(t) = 70t - 4.9t^2 + 6$

c. $d(5) = 233.5$ m

$d(6) = 249.6$ m

$d(9) = 239.1$ m

These three numbers show that d(t) has a high point somewhere between 5 and 9.

d. The high point occurs when $d'(t) = 0$.

$70 - 9.8t = 0 \Rightarrow t = 70/9.8 = 7.1428...$

$d(7.1428...) = 256$

The arrow was highest, 256 m, at about t = 7.1 sec.

24. Acceleration Problem

a. $v'(t) = 18 \sin 3t$

$v(t) = -6 \cos 3t + C$

b. $v(0) = -6 \Rightarrow -6 = -6 \cos 0 + C \Rightarrow C = 0$

$\therefore v(t) = -6 \cos 3t$

This negative velocity means that Calvin was swinging backwards at t = 0.

c.

t	v(t)
0	−6
0.2	−5
0.4	−2.2
0.6	1.4
0.8	4.4
1	5.9
1.2	5.4
1.4	2.9
1.6	−0.5
1.8	−3.8
2	−5.8

d. The maximum velocity is 6 ft/sec at $t = \pi/3$ and other times. The acceleration at this time is zero.

25. Derivative and Antiderivative Problem

a. $g'(x) = 0.6x$

$g(x) = 0.3x^2 + C$

b. i. $g(x) = 0.3x^2$

ii. $g(x) = 0.3x^2 + 3$

iii. $g(x) = 0.3x^2 + 5$

c. Graph. All the graphs are obtained by shifting the solution function vertically through some displacement C. So all the graphs are "related" and thus can be called a family.

Problem Set 3-10, pages 123 to 127

Chapter Review and Test

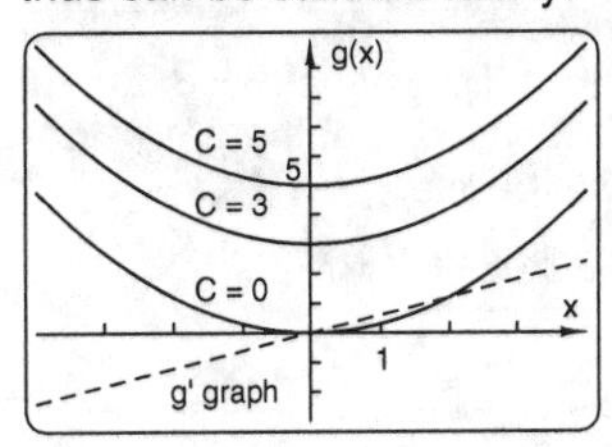

Review Problems

R0. Students should realize that the most important idea in Chapter 3 is the ability to find *exactly*, by *algebra*, the derivatives they had been able to find only approximately before. They should realize that the concept of limit has been applied to do this. Consequently, they can put a "check" in the "apply limits" box in the 4-by-4 matrix of concepts and techniques. By working the real-world problems that have appeared in most sections, students should realize that the algebraic techniques just provide another way to carry out the applications of derivatives they were doing graphically and numerically in the first two chapters.

R1. a. the numerical derivative $f'(2) \approx \underline{12}$.

b. $m(x) = \dfrac{x^3 - 8}{x - 2}$

m(2) takes the indeterminate form 0/0.

By tracing the graph or constructing a table, the limit of m(x) seems to be 12 as x approaches 2.

c. $m(x) = x^2 + 2x + 4$.

$\lim_{x \to 2} m(x) = 2^2 + 2 \cdot 2 + 4 = \underline{12}$.

d. The answer to part c. is exactly 12.

The answer to part a. is approximately 12.

R2. a. $f'(c) = \lim_{x \to c} \dfrac{f(x) - f(c)}{x - c}$

b. $f(x) = 0.4x^2 - x + 5$

$f'(3) = \lim_{x \to 3} \dfrac{0.4x^2 - x + 5 - 5.6}{x - 3}$

$= \lim_{x \to 3} \dfrac{(x - 3)(0.4x + 0.2)}{x - 3}$

$= \lim_{x \to 3} (0.4x + 0.2) = \underline{1.4}$

c. $m(x) = \dfrac{0.4x^2 - x - 0.6}{x - 3}$. Graph

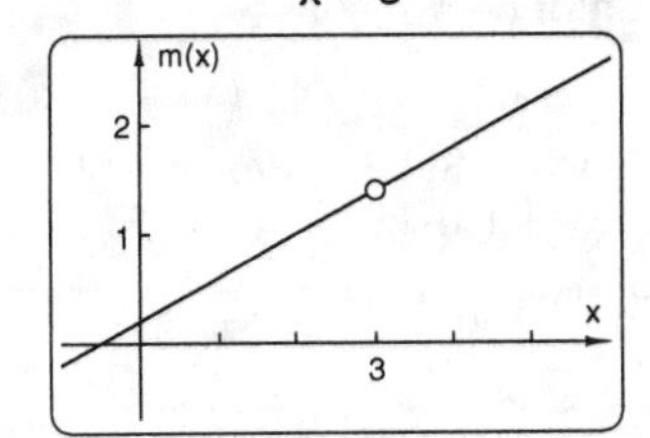

d. Line: $y = 1.4x + 1.4$. Graph

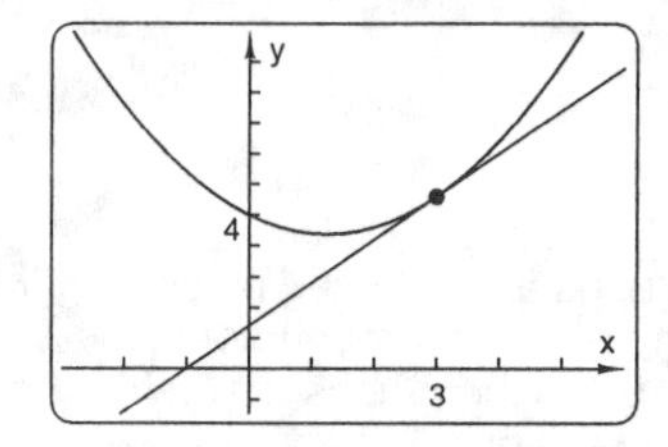

e. The line is tangent to the graph.

f. Yes, f does have local linearity at x = 3. Zooming in on the point (3, 5.6) shows that the graph looks more and more like the line.

R3. a. $y_1 = x^4 - 4x^3 - 7x^2 + 34x - 24$. Graph.

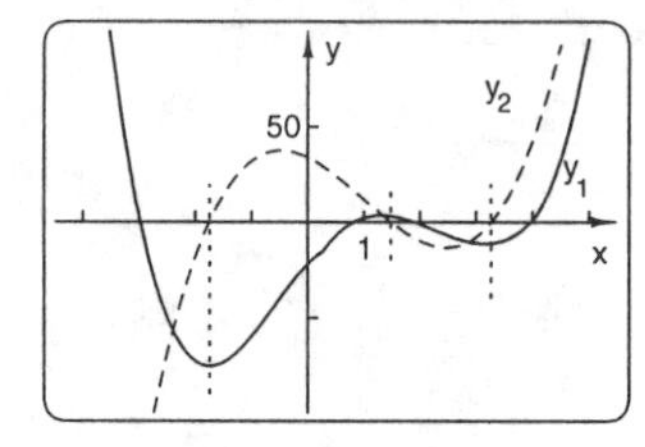

b. y_2 = numerical derivative. See graph in part a.

c. The y_1 graph has a high point or a low point at each x-value where the y_2 graph is zero.

d. Leaky Tire Problem

$p(t) = 35(0.9)^t$. Graph

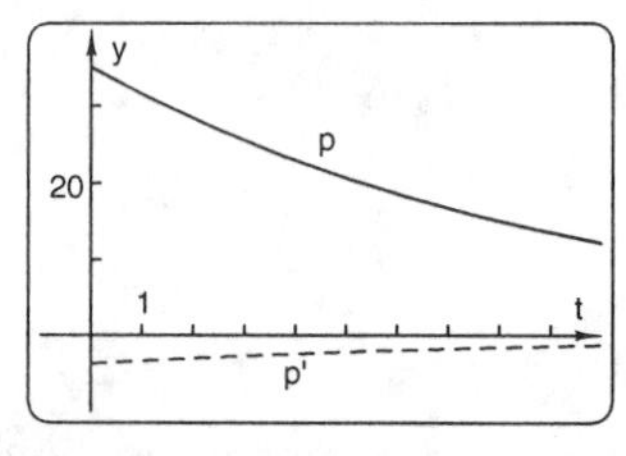

Take the numerical derivative at t = 3, 6, and 0.

$p'(3) \approx -2.688...$

Decreasing at about 2.69 psi/hr when t = 3.

$p'(6) \approx -1.959...$

Decreasing at about 1.96 psi/hr when t = 6.

$p'(0) \approx -3.687...$

Decreasing at about 3.69 psi/hr when t = 0.

The units are psi/hr.

The sign of the pressure change is negative because the pressure is decreasing.

Yes, the rate of pressure change is getting closer to zero.

R4. a. See text definition of derivative.

b. Differentiate.

c. If $y = x^n$, then $y' = nx^{n-1}$.

d. See solution to Problem Set 3-4, Problem 35.

e. See the proof in Section 3-4.

f. $\frac{dy}{dx}$ is pronounced "Dee y, dee x."

$\frac{d}{dx}(y)$ is pronounced "Dee, dee x, of y."

Both mean the derivative of y with respect to x.

g. i. $f(x) = 7x^{9/5} \Rightarrow f'(x) = \frac{63}{5}x^{4/5}$

ii. $g(x) = 7x^{-4} - \frac{x^2}{6} - x + 7 \Rightarrow g'(x) = -28x^{-5} - \frac{x}{3} - 1$

iii. $h(x) = 7^3 \Rightarrow h'(x) = 0$

h. $f'(32) = \frac{63}{5}(32)^{4/5} = 201.6$ exactly.

Numerical derivative is equal to or very close to 201.6.

i. Graph (Dotted line)

(Function is $y = 0.5x^2 - x + 4$.)

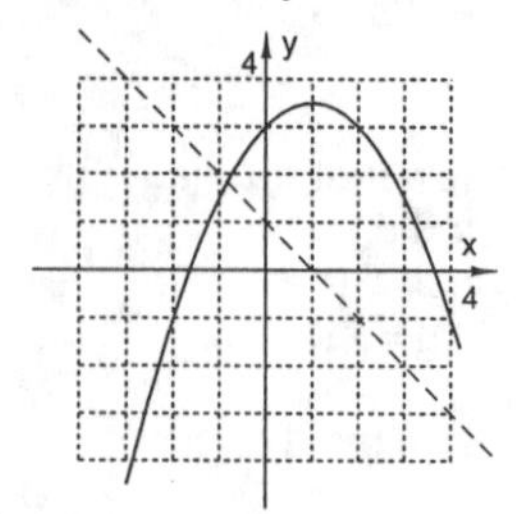

R5. a. $v = \frac{dx}{dt}$ or $x'(t)$.

$a = \frac{dv}{dt}$ or $v'(t)$, $a = \frac{d^2x}{dt^2}$ or $x''(t)$

b. Spaceship Problem

i. $y = -0.01t^3 + 0.9t^2 - 25t + 250$

$v = \frac{dy}{dt} = -0.03t^2 + 1.8t - 25$

$a = \frac{dv}{dt} = -0.06t + 1.8$

ii. $a(15) = -0.06(15) + 1.8 = 0.9$ (km/sec)/sec

$v(15) = -0.03(15^2) + 1.8(15) - 25$

$= -4.75$ km/sec

The spaceship is slowing down at t = 15 because the velocity and the acceleration have opposite signs.

iii. $v = -0.03t^2 + 1.8t - 25 = 0$

By SOLVE or quadratic formula,

t = 21.835... or t = 38.164... .

The spaceship is stopped at about 21.8 and 38.2 seconds.

iv. $y = -0.01t^3 + 0.9t^2 - 25t + 250 = 0$

By TRACE or SOLVE, t = 50.

$v(50) = -10$

Since the spaceship is moving at 10 km/sec when it reaches the surface, it is a crash landing!

R6. a. Graph.

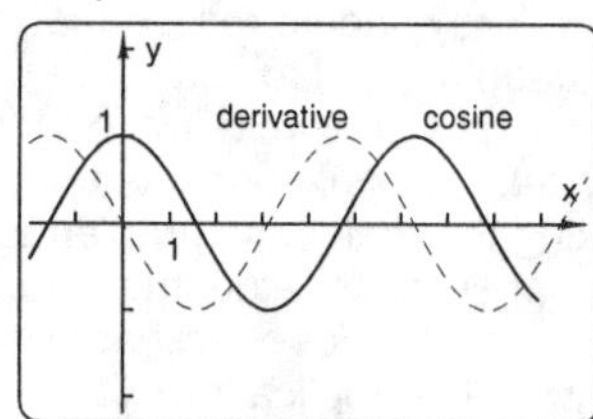

b. The graph of the derivative is the same as the sine graph, but inverted in the y-direction. Thus, $(\cos x)' = -\sin x$ is confirmed.

c. $\cos 1 = 0.540302305$

Numerical derivative ≈ 0.54030221

The two are very close!

d. Composite function.

$f'(x) = -2x \sin(x^2)$

R7. a. i. $\frac{dy}{dx} = \frac{dy}{du} \cdot \frac{du}{dx}$

ii. $f(x) = g(h(x)) \Rightarrow f'(x) = g'(h(x)) \cdot h'(x)$

iii. The derivative of a composite function is the derivative of the outside function with respect to the inside function, times the derivative of the inside function with respect to x.

b. See the derivation in the text. This derivation constitutes a proof.
Δu must be nonzero throughout the interval.

c. i. $f(x) = (x^2 - 4)^3$
$f'(x) = 3(x^2 - 4)^2 \cdot 2x = 6x(x^2 - 4)^2$

ii. $f(x) = x^6 - 12x^4 + 48x^2 - 64$
$f'(x) = 6x^5 - 48x^3 + 96x$
Expanding the answer to part (i) gives
$f'(x) = 6x^5 - 48x^3 + 96x$, which checks.

d. i. $f'(x) = -3x^2 \sin x^3$

ii. $g'(x) = 5 \cos 5x$

iii. $h'(x) = 6 \cos^5 x\,(-\sin x) = -6 \sin x \cos^5 x$

iv. $k'(x) = 0$

e. Shark Problem
$W = 0.6x^3$ and $dx/dt = 0.4$
$\frac{dW}{dt} = \frac{dW}{dx} \cdot \frac{dx}{dt} = 1.8x^2 \cdot 0.4 = 0.72x^2$
If $x = 2$, $W = 0.6 \cdot 2^3 = 4.8$ lb
$dW/dt = 0.72(2^2) = 2.88$
Shark is gaining about 2.88 lb/day.
If $x = 10$, $W = 0.6 \cdot 10^3 = 600$ lb.
$dW/dt = 0.72(10^2) = 72$
Shark is gaining about 72 lb/day.
The chain rule is used to get dW/dt from dW/dx by multiplying the latter by dx/dt.

R8. a. $\lim_{x \to 0} \frac{\sin x}{x} = 1.$

b.

x	(sin x)/x
−0.05	0.99958338541...
−0.04	0.99973335466...
−0.03	0.99985000674...
−0.02	0.99993333466...
−0.01	0.99998333341...
0.00	(No value)
0.01	0.99998333341...
0.02	0.99993333466...
0.03	0.99985000674...
0.04	0.99973335466...
0.05	0.99958338541...

The values approach 1 as x approaches 0.

c. See text statement of squeeze theorem.
Squeeze (sin x)/x between cos x and sec x.

d. See proof in text (Section 3-8).

e. $\cos x = \sin(\pi/2 - x)$
$\cos' x = \cos(\pi/2 - x)(-1) = -\sin x$, Q.E.D.

f. Clock Problem
$d(t) = C + A \cos B(t - D)$
$C = 180,\ A = 20$
$D = 0$ for cosine since hand starts at a high point.
$B = 2\pi/60 = \pi/30$ since period is 60 seconds.
$d(t) = 180 + 20 \cos \frac{\pi}{30} t$
$d'(t) = -\frac{2\pi}{3} \sin \frac{\pi}{30} t$
At 2, $t = 10$. $d'(10) \approx -1.81$ cm/sec
At 3, $t = 15$. $d'(15) \approx -2.09$ cm/sec
At 7, $t = 35$. $d'(35) \approx 1.05$ cm/sec
At the 2 and 3, the tip is going down, so the distance from the floor is decreasing, which is implied by the negative derivatives.
At the 7, the tip is going up, as implied by the positive derivative.

R9. a. $f(x) = 36x^5 \Rightarrow f(x) = 6x^6 + C$

b. $dy/dx = \sin 0.2x$ and $y(0) = 3$
$y = -5 \cos 0.2x + C$
$3 = -5 \cos 0 + C \Rightarrow C = 8$
$\therefore y = 5 \cos 0.2x + 8$

c. Distance Problem
$v(t) = 6t^{1/2}$
$y(t) = 4t^{3/2} + C$
$100 = 4(0^{3/2}) + C \Rightarrow C = 100$
$\therefore y(t) = 4t^{3/2} + 100$
$y(60) = 4(60)^{3/2} + 100 = 1959.03...$
$v(60) = 6(60^{1/2}) = 46.475...$
She is about 1959 feet away from the house, going about 46.5 ft/sec 1 minute after she starts.

d. An antiderivative and an indefinite integral are the same thing.

Concepts Problems

C1. Introduction to the Derivative of a Product

a. $f(x) = x^7$, $g(x) = x^9$. So $h(x) = f(x) \cdot g(x) = x^{16}$.

b. $h'(x) = 16x^{15}$.

c. $f'(x) = 7x^6$, $g'(x) = 9x^8$.
So $f'(x) \cdot g'(x) = 63x^{14} \neq h'(x)$.

d. $h'(x) = f'(x) \cdot g(x) + f(x) \cdot g'(x)$
$= 7x^6 \cdot x^9 + x^7 \cdot 9x^8 = 16x^{15}$, which checks.

C2. Graph of an Interesting Function

a. $f(x) = \frac{x - \sin 2x}{\sin x}$
f(0) has the form 0/0, which is indeterminate.
f is discontinuous at x = 0 because f(0) does not exist.

b. By graph (below) or by TABLE, f(x) seems to approach −1 as x approaches zero.
Define f(0) to be −1.

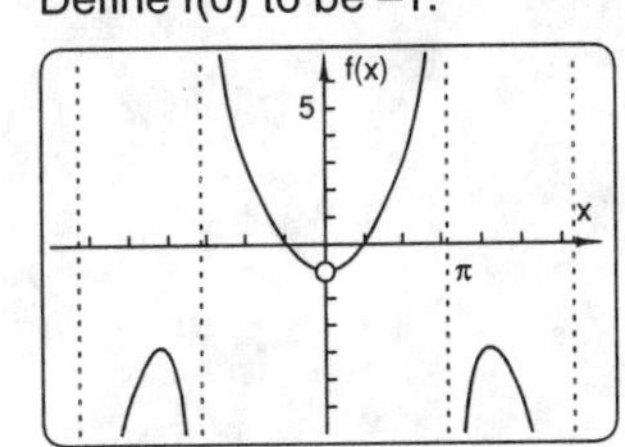

c. Conjecture: The function *is* differentiable at x = 0.
The derivative should equal zero because the graph is horizontal at x = 0.

d. $f'(0) = \lim_{h\to 0} \dfrac{f(x) - f(0)}{x - 0}$

$= \lim_{x\to 0} \dfrac{\dfrac{x - \sin 2x}{\sin x} - (-1)}{x}$

$= \lim_{x\to 0} \dfrac{x - \sin 2x + \sin x}{x \sin x}$

Using TABLE for numerator, denominator, and quotient shows that the numerator goes to zero faster than the denominator. For instance, if $x = 0.001$,

$\text{quotient} = \dfrac{1.1666... \times 10^{-9}}{9.999... \times 10^{-7}} = 0.00116...$.

Thus, the limit appears to be zero.
(The limit can be found algebraically to equal zero by l'Hospital's rule after students have studied Section 6-8.)

Chapter Test

T1. See definition of limit in Chapter 2.

T2. See definition of derivative in Section 3-2 or 3-4.

T3. Prove that if $f(x) = 3x^4$, then $f'(x) = 12x^3$.

Proof:

$f'(x) = \lim_{h\to 0} \dfrac{f(x+h) - f(x)}{h} = \lim_{h\to 0} \dfrac{3(x+h)^4 - 3x^4}{h}$

$= \lim_{h\to 0} \dfrac{3x^4 + 12x^3h + 18x^2h^2 + 12xh^3 + 3h^4 - 3x^4}{h}$

$= \lim_{h\to 0} (12x^3 + 18x^2h + 12xh^2 + 3h^3) = 12x^3$, Q.E.D.

T4. $t(x) = \cos 3x \Rightarrow t'(x) = -3 \sin 3x$.
$t'(5) = -3 \sin 15 = -1.95086...$
Decreasing at 1.95... y-units per x-unit.

T5. Graph (below). If you zoom in on the point where $x = 5$, the graph appears to get closer and closer to the tangent line. The name of this property is *local linearity*.

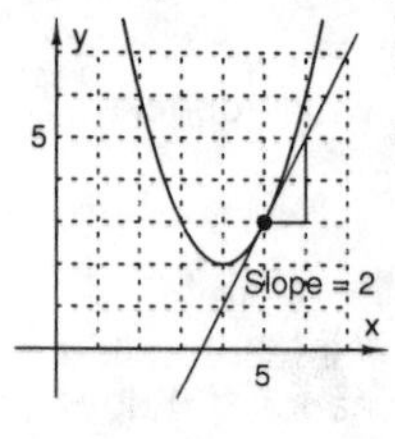

T6. Amos substituted *before* differentiating instead of after.
Correct solution is $f(x) = 7x \Rightarrow f'(x) = 7 \Rightarrow f'(5) = 7$.

T7. Graph. $f(x) = \dfrac{\sin x}{x}$

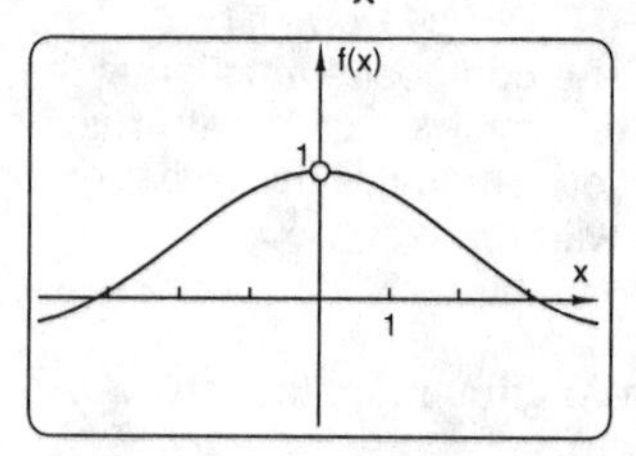

As x approaches 0, f(x) approaches 1.
The squeeze theorem. It states that:
If (1) $g(x) \le h(x)$ for all x in a neighborhood of c,
(2) $\lim_{x\to c} g(x) = \lim_{x\to c} h(x) = L$, and
(3) f is a function for which $g(x) \le f(x) \le h(x)$ for all x in that neighborhood of c,
Then $\lim_{x\to c} f(x) = L$.

T8. $f(x) = (7x + 3)^{15} \Rightarrow f'(x) = 105(7x + 3)^{14}$

T9. $g(x) = \cos(x^5) \Rightarrow g'(x) = -5x^4 \sin x^5$

T10. $\dfrac{d}{dx}(\sin 5x) = 5 \cos 5x$

T11. $y = 60x^{2/3} - x + 2^5 \Rightarrow y' = 40x^{-1/3} - 1$

T12. $f(x) = \cos(\sin^5 7x) \Rightarrow$
$f'(x) = -\sin(\sin^5 7x) \cdot 5 \sin^4 7x \cdot \cos 7x \cdot 7$
$= -35 \sin(\sin^5 7x) \sin^4 7x \cos 7x$

T13. $y' \approx 0.6$
(Function is $y = -3 + 1.5^x$, for which the numerical derivative is 0.6081... .)

T14. $y = 3 + 5x^{-1.6}$
$v = y' = -8x^{-2.6}$
$a = v' = 20.8x^{-3.6}$

T15. $f'(x) = 72x^{5/4} \Rightarrow f(x) = 32x^{9/4}$

T16. $f'(x) = 5 \sin x$ and $f(0) = 13$
$f(x) = -5 \cos x + C$
$13 = -5 \cos 0 + C \Rightarrow C = 18$
$f(x) = -5 \cos x + 18$

T17. Carbon Dioxide Problem

$c(t) = 300 + 2 \cos \dfrac{2\pi}{365} t$

a. $c'(t) = -\dfrac{4\pi}{365} \sin \dfrac{2\pi}{365} t$

b. $c'(273) = -\dfrac{4\pi}{365} \sin (\dfrac{2\pi}{365} \cdot 273)$
$= 0.03442...$ ppm/day

c. Rate is $\dfrac{6\times 10^{15}}{1{,}000{,}000} \times \dfrac{0.03442...}{24 \cdot 60 \cdot 60} = 2390.66...$,
which is approximately 2390 tons per second!

Chapter 4

Exploratory Problem Set 4-1, page 131

1. $f(x) = 3 \cos x \Rightarrow f'(x) = -3 \sin x$
   $g(x) = 2 \sin x \Rightarrow g'(x) = 2 \cos x$
2. Derivative of a Product of Two Functions
   Graph. $p(x) = f(x) \cdot g(x) = 6 \cos x \sin x$

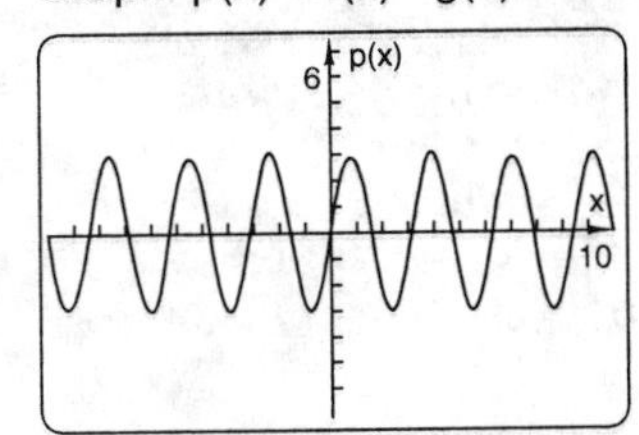

   $p'(2) \approx -3.9218...$ (numerically)
   p(x) is decreasing at x = 2 because $p'(2) < 0$. This fact corresponds with the graph, which slopes steeply in the negative direction at x = 2.
   $f'(2) \cdot g'(2) = (-3 \sin 2)(2 \cos 2) = 2.2704...$
   So $p'(2) \neq f'(2) \cdot g'(2)$.
3. Derivative of a Quotient of Two Functions
   Graph. $q(x) = f(x)/g(x) = (3 \cos x)/(2 \sin x)$

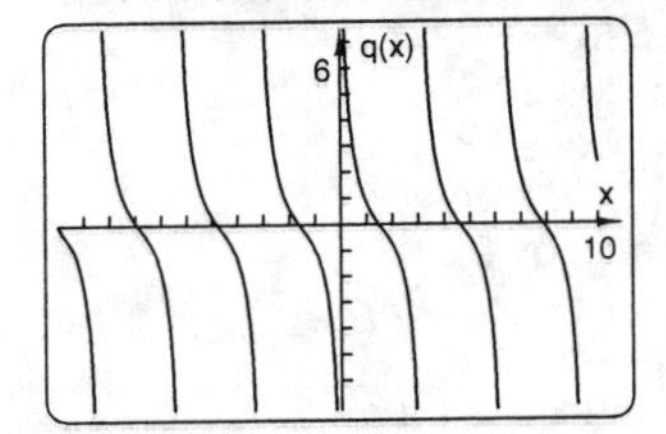

   q is the cotangent function.
   $q'(2) = -1.8141...$
   q(x) is decreasing at x = 2.
   $f'(2)/g'(2) = (-3 \sin 2)/(2 \cos 2) = 3.2775...$
   So $q'(2) \neq f'(2)/g'(2)$.
4. Parametric Function
   Graph. $x = 3 \cos t$, $y = 2 \sin t$

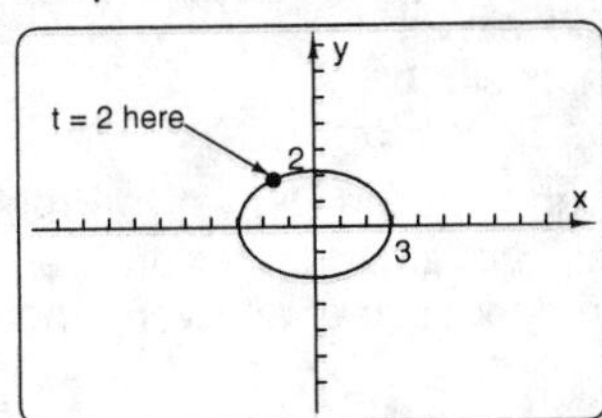

   The geometric figure seems to be an ellipse.
5. Derivative of a Parametric Function
   See graph in Problem 4.
   $\Delta x = 3 \cos 2.1 - 3 \cos 1.9 = -0.54466...$
   $\Delta y = 2 \sin 2.1 - 2 \sin 1.9 = -0.16618...$
   $\dfrac{dy}{dx} \approx \dfrac{\Delta y}{\Delta x} = \dfrac{-0.16618...}{-0.54466...} = 0.3051...$
   At t = 2, $\dfrac{dy/dt}{dx/dt} = \dfrac{2 \cos 2}{-3 \sin 2} = 0.3051...$,
   which agrees with the difference quotient.
   Also, from the graph in Problem 4, the slope of a line tangent to the graph at the point where t = 2 would be positive and less than 1, which agrees with the value of 0.3051... for the difference quotient.
   Note that the difference quotient is *exactly* equal to the ratio of the derivatives in this case. The sum and product properties from trigonometry show why.
   $$\frac{\sin 2.1 - \sin 1.9}{\cos 2.1 - \cos 1.9}$$
   $$= \frac{2 \cos [0.5(2.1 + 1.9)] \sin [0.5(2.1 - 1.9)]}{-2 \sin [0.5(2.1 + 1.9)] \sin [0.5(2.1 - 1.9)]}$$
   $$= \frac{\cos 2 \sin 0.1}{-\sin 2 \sin 0.1} = \frac{\cos 2}{-\sin 2}$$
   Multiplying this fraction by 2/3 gives the derivative!
6. *Conjectures?* From Section 4-2, $p'(x) = f'(x)\,g(x) + f(x)\,g'(x)$.
   $\therefore p'(2) = (-3 \sin 2)(2 \sin 2) + (3 \cos 2)(2 \cos 2)$
   $= -3.9218...$, which agrees with Problem 2.
   From Section 4-3, $q'(x) = \dfrac{f'(x)\,g(x) - f(x)\,g'(x)}{[g(x)]^2}$
   $\therefore q'(2) =$
   $$\frac{(-3 \sin 2)(2 \sin 2) - (3 \cos 2)(2 \cos 2)}{(2 \sin 2)^2}$$
   $= -1.8141...$, which agrees with Problem 3.

Problem Set 4-2, pages 134 to 136

Q1. $y' = \frac{3}{4}x^{-1/4}$
Q2. $y' = 17$
Q3. $\dfrac{dy}{dx} = -30(5x - 7)^{-7}$
Q4. $\dfrac{d}{dx}(\sin 2x) = 2 \cos 2x$
Q5. $v' = -3 \cos^2 t \sin t$
Q6. $L' = 2m + 5$
Q7. $y = \sin x^3 + C$
Q8. $y' \approx -3$*
Q9. Graph
Q10. 4 ft/sec

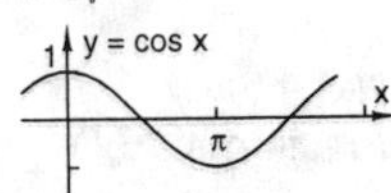

* Function is $y = 0.5x^2 - x - 3$.

1. $f(x) = x^3 \cos x \Rightarrow f'(x) = 3x^2 \cos x - x^3 \sin x$
2. $f(x) = x^4 \sin x \Rightarrow f'(x) = 4x^3 \sin x + x^4 \cos x$
3. $g(x) = x^{1.5} \sin 7x \Rightarrow$
   $g'(x) = 1.5x^{0.5} \sin 7x + 7x^{1.5} \cos 7x$
4. $h(x) = x^{-6.3} \cos 10x \Rightarrow$
   $h'(x) = -6.3x^{-7.3} \cos 10x - 10x^{-6.3} \sin 10x$
5. $y = x^7(2x + 5)^{10} \Rightarrow$
   $dy/dx = 7x^6(2x + 5)^{10} + x^7(10)(2x + 5)^9 \cdot 2$
   $= x^6(2x + 5)^9 (34x + 35)$
6. $y = x^8(3x + 7)^9 \Rightarrow$
   $dy/dx = 8x^7(3x + 7)^9 + x^8(9)(3x + 7)^8 (3)$
   $= x^7(3x + 7)^8 (51x + 56)$
7. $z = x^4 \cos^5 3x \Rightarrow$
   $z' = 4x^3 \cos^5 3x + x^4 (5 \cos^4 3x)(-\sin 3x)(3)$
   $= 4x^3 \cos^5 3x - 15x^4 \cos^4 3x \sin 3x$

8. $v = x^5 \sin^3 6x \Rightarrow$
$v' = 5x^4 \sin^3 6x + x^5 (3 \sin^2 6x)(\cos 6x)(6)$
$= 5x^4 \sin^3 6x + 18x^5 \sin^2 6x \cos 6x$

9. $(d/dx)[(4x-3)^6 \sin 5x]$
$= 6(4x-3)^5 (4) \sin 5x + (4x-6)^6 (5 \cos 5x)$
$= 24(4x-3)^5 \sin 5x + 5(4x-3)^6 \cos 5x$

10. $p = (7x-4)^9 \cos 2x \Rightarrow$
$(d/dx)(p) = 9(7x-4)^8 (7) \cos 2x$
$+ (7x-4)^9 (-2 \sin 2x)$
$= 63(7x-4)^8 \cos 2x - 2(7x-4)^9 \sin 2x$

11. $y = (6x+11)^4(5x-9)^7 \Rightarrow$
$y' = 4(6x+11)^3(6)(5x-9)^7$
$+ (6x+11)^4(7)(5x-9)^6(5)$
$= (6x+11)^3(5x-9)^6(330x+169)$

12. $y = (7x-3)^9(6x-1)^5 \Rightarrow$
$y' = 9(7x-3)^8(7)(6x-1)^5 + (7x-3)^9(5)(6x-1)^4(6)$
$= (7x-3)^8(6x-1)^4(588x-153)$

13. $P = (x^2-1)^{10} (x^2+1)^{15} \Rightarrow$
$P' = 10(x^2-1)^9 (2x)(x^2+1)^{15}$
$+ (x^2-1)^{10} (15)(x^2+1)^{14} (2x)$
$= 10x(x^2-1)^9 (x^2+1)^{14} [2(x^2+1) + 3(x^2-1)]$
$= 10x(x^2-1)^9 (x^2+1)^{14} (5x^2-1)$

14. $P(x) = (x^3+6)^4 (x^3+4)^6 \Rightarrow$
$P'(x) = 4(x^3+6)^3(3x^2)(x^3+4)^6$
$+ (x^3+6)^4 \cdot 6(x^3+4)^5 \cdot 3x^2$
$= 6x^2 (x^3+6)^3 (x^3+4)^5 [2(x^3+4) + 3(x^3+6)]$
$= 6x^2 (x^3+6)^3 (x^3+4)^5 (5x^3+26)$

15. $a(t) = 4 \sin 3t \cos 5t \Rightarrow$
$a'(t) = 12 \cos 3t \cos 5t + 4 \sin 3t (-5 \sin 5t)$
$= 12 \cos 3t \cos 5t - 20 \sin 3t \sin 5t$

16. $v = 7 \cos 2t \sin 6t \Rightarrow$
$v' = -14 \sin 2t \sin 6t + 7 \cos 2t (6 \cos 6t)$
$= -14 \sin 2t \sin 6t + 42 \cos 2t \cos 6t$

17. $y = 10 \cos^8 5x \sin^5 8x \Rightarrow$
$y' = 80 \cos^7 5x (-5 \sin 5x) \cdot \sin^5 8x$
$+ 10 \cos^8 5x \cdot (5 \sin^4 8x)(8 \cos 8x)$
$= -400 \cos^7 5x \sin 5x \sin^5 8x$
$+ 400 \cos^8 5x \sin^4 8x \cos 8x$

18. $y = 7 \sin^3 4x \cos^4 3x \Rightarrow$
$y' = 21 \sin^2 4x (4 \cos 4x) \cdot \cos^4 3x$
$+ 7 \sin^3 4x \cdot (4 \cos^3 3x)(-3 \sin 3x)$
$= 84 \sin^2 4x \cos 4x \cos^4 3x$
$- 84 \sin^3 4x \cos^3 3x \sin 3x$

19. $z = x^3 (5x-2)^4 \sin 6x \Rightarrow$
$z' = 3x^2 \cdot (5x-2)^4 \sin 6x + x^3 \cdot (4)(5x-2)^3 (5) \cdot \sin 6x$
$+ x^3 (5x-2)^4 \cdot (6 \cos 6x)$
$= 3x^2 (5x-2)^4 \sin 6x + 20x^3 (5x-2)^3 \sin 6x$
$+ 6x^3 (5x-2)^4 \cos 6x$

20. $u = 3x^5 (x^2-4) \cos 10x$
$u' = 15x^4 \cdot (x^2-4) \cos 10x + 3x^5 \cdot 2x \cdot \cos 10x$
$+ 3x^5 (x^2-4) \cdot (-10 \sin 10x)$
$= 15x^4 \cdot (x^2-4) \cos 10x + 6x^6 \cos 10x$
$- 30x^5 (x^2-4) \sin 10x$

21. $y = \cos (3 \sin x) \Rightarrow$
$y' = -\sin (3 \sin x) \cdot 3 \cos x = -3 \sin (3 \sin x) \cos x$

22. $y = \sin (5 \cos x) \Rightarrow$
$y' = \cos (5 \cos x) \cdot (-5 \sin x)$
$= -5 \cos (5 \cos x) \sin x$

23. Product of Three Functions Problem
If $y = uvw$, where u, v, and w are differentiable functions of x, then $y' = u'vw + uv'w + uvw'$.
Proof:
$y = uvw = (uv)w$
$\therefore y' = (uv)'w + (uv)w' = (u'v + uv')w + (uv)w'$
$= u'vw + uv'w + uvw'$, Q.E.D.

24. Product of n Functions Conjecture Problem
If $y_n = u_1u_2u_3 \ldots u_n$ where $u_1, \ldots, u_n$ are differentiable functions of x, then
$y_n' = u_1'u_2u_3 \ldots u_n + u_1u_2'u_3 \ldots$
$u_n + u_1u_2u_3' \ldots u_n$
$+ \ldots + u_1u_2u_3 \ldots u_n' \ldots$

25. $z = x^5 \cos^6 x \sin 7x \Rightarrow$
$z' = 5x^4 \cdot \cos^6 x \sin 7x$
$+ x^5 \cdot 6 \cos^5 x (-\sin x) \cdot \sin 7x$
$+ x^5 \cos^6 x \cdot 7 \cos 7x$
$= 5x^4 \cos^6 x \sin 7x - 6x^5 \cos^5 x \sin x \sin 7x$
$+ 7x^5 \cos^6 x \cos 7x$

26. $y = 4x^6 \sin^3 x \cos 5x \Rightarrow$
$y' = 24x^5 \cdot \sin^3 x \cos 5x$
$+ 4x^6 \cdot 3 \sin^2 x \cos x \cdot \cos 5x$
$+ 4x^6 \sin^3 x \cdot (-5 \sin 5x)$
$= 24x^5 \sin^3 x \cos 5x + 12x^6 \sin^2 x \cos x \cos 5x$
$- 20x^6 \sin^3 x \sin 5x$

27. $y = x^4(2x-3)^5 \sin x \cos 2x \Rightarrow$
$y' = 4x^3(2x-3)^5 \sin x \cos 2x$
$+ x^4 \cdot 5(2x-3)^4(2) \sin x \cos 2x$
$+ x^4(2x-3)^5 \cos x \cos 2x$
$+ x^4(2x-3)^5 \sin x \cdot (-2 \sin 2x)$
$= 4x^3(2x-3)^5 \sin x \cos 2x$
$+ 10x^4(2x-3)^4 \sin x \cos 2x$
$+ x^4(2x-3)^5 \cos x \cos 2x$
$- 2x^4(2x-3)^5 \sin x \sin 2x$

28. $u = x^5(3x-1)^2 \cos 2x \sin 3x \Rightarrow$
$u' = 5x^4(3x-1)^2 \cos 2x \sin 3x$
$+ x^5 \cdot 2(3x-1)(3) \cdot \cos 2x \sin 3x$
$+ x^5(3x-1)^2 (-2 \sin 2x) \sin 3x$
$+ x^5(3x-1)^2 \cos 2x \cdot 3 \cos 3x$
$= 5x^4(3x-1)^2 \cos 2x \sin 3x$
$+ 6x^5(3x-1) \cos 2x \sin 3x$
$- 2x^5(3x-1)^2 \sin 2x \sin 3x$
$+ 3x^5(3x-1)^2 \cos 2x \cos 3x$

29. Odd Function and Even Function Derivative Problem
Prove that the derivative of an odd function is an even function, and that the derivative of an even function is an odd function.
Proof:
For any function, the chain rule gives
$\frac{d}{dx} f(-x) = f'(-x) \cdot (-1) = -f'(-x)$.
For an odd function,
$\frac{d}{dx} f(-x) = \frac{d}{dx} (-f(x)) = -f'(x)$.
$\therefore -f'(-x) = -f'(x)$ or $f'(-x) = f'(x)$,
and the derivative is an even function.
For an even function,
$\frac{d}{dx} f(-x) = \frac{d}{dx} f(x) = f'(x)$.
$\therefore -f'(-x) = f'(x)$ or $f'(-x) = -f'(x)$,
and the derivative is an odd function, Q.E.D.

30. Double Argument Properties Problem
$f(x) = 2 \sin x \cos x \Rightarrow$
$f'(x) = 2 \cos x \cdot \cos x + 2 \sin x(-\sin x)$
$= 2 \cos^2 x - 2 \sin^2 x = 2 \cos 2x.$
$g(x) = \sin 2x \Rightarrow g'(x) = 2 \cos 2x = f'(x)$, Q.E.D.
$f(0) = 0$ and $g(0) = 0$
$\therefore f(x) = 2 \sin x \cos x = \sin 2x = g(x)$, by the uniqueness theorem for derivatives, Q.E.D.
$f(x) = \cos^2 x - \sin^2 x \Rightarrow$
$f'(x) = 2 \cos x \cdot (-\sin x) - 2 \sin x \cos x$
$= -4 \sin x \cos x = -\sin 2x.$
$g(x) = \cos 2x \Rightarrow$
$g'(x) = (-2 \sin 2x) = -\sin 2x = f'(x)$, Q.E.D.
$f(0) = 1$ and $g(0) = 1$.
$\therefore f(x) = \cos^2 x - \sin^2 x = \cos 2x = g(x)$ by the uniqueness theorem, Q.E.D.

31. Derivative of a Power Induction Problem
Prove that if $f_n(x) = x^n$, then $f_n'(x) = nx^{n-1}$ for all integers ≥ 1.
Proof (by induction on n):
If $n = 1$, then $f_1(x) = x^1$, which implies that $f_1'(x) = 1 = 1x^0$, which anchors the induction.
Assume that for some integer $n = k > 1$, $f_k'(x) = kx^{k-1}$.
For $n = k + 1$, $f_{k+1}(x) = x^{k+1} = (x^k)(x)$.
By the derivative of a product property,
$f_{k+1}'(x) = (x^k)'(x) + (x^k)(x)' = (x^k)'(x) + x^k$.
Substituting for $(x^k)'$ from the induction hypothesis,
$f_{k+1}'(x) = (kx^{k-1})(x) + x^k = kx^k + x^k$
$= (k + 1)x^k = (k + 1)x^{(k+1)-1}$, completing the induction.
$\therefore f_n'(x) = nx^{n-1}$ for all integers ≥ 1, Q.E.D.

32. Derivative Two Ways Problem
Way 1: $y = (x + 3)^8(x - 4)^8$
$y' = 8(x + 3)^7 \cdot (x - 4)^8 + (x + 3)^8 \cdot 8(x - 4)^7$
$= 8(x + 3)^7(x - 4)^7(x + 3 + x - 4)$
$= 8(x + 3)^7(x - 4)^7(2x - 1)$
Way 2: $y = (x^2 - x - 12)^8$
$y' = 8(x^2 - x - 12)^7(2x - 1)$
$= 8(x + 3)^7(x - 4)^7(2x - 1)$, which checks.

33. Confirmation of the Product Property
a. Graph. $f(x) = x^3 \sin x$, with the graph of f' sketched.

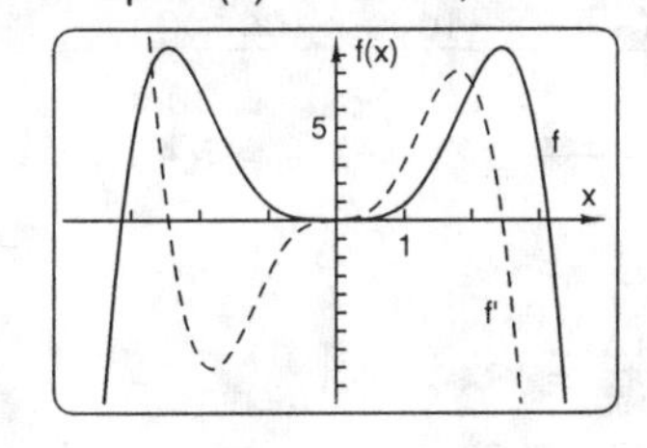

b. $f'(x) = 3x^2 \sin x + x^3 \cos x$
Graph in part a. is correct.
c. The numerical derivative graph duplicates the algebraic derivative graph, as in part a., thus showing that the algebraic derivative is right.

34. Repeated Roots Problem
a. Graph. $f(x) = (5x - 7)^4 (2x + 3)^5$

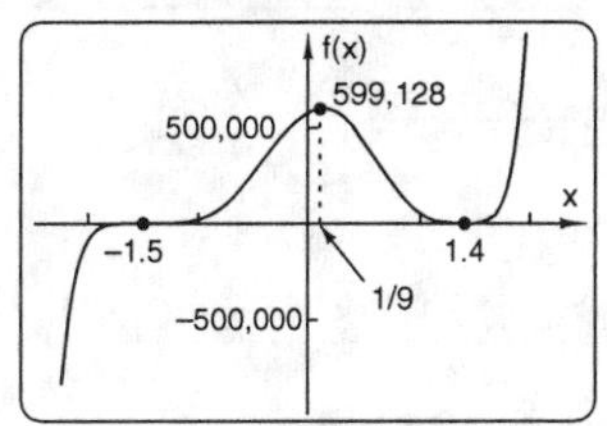

b. $f'(x) = 4(5x - 7)^3 (5) \cdot (2x + 3)^5$
$+ (5x - 7)^4 \cdot (5)(2x + 3)^4 (2)$
$= 10(5x - 7)^3 (2x + 3)^4[2(2x + 3) + 5x - 7]$
$= 10(5x - 7)^3 (2x + 3)^4(9x - 1)$

c. $f'(x) = 0 \Leftrightarrow 5x - 7 = 0$ or $2x + 3 = 0$ or $9x - 1 = 0$.
$\therefore x = 7/5 = 1.4$, or $x = -3/2 = -1.5$, or $x = 1/9$.
Graph, part a.
d. $f(1.4) = 0$, $f(-1.5) = 0$, $f(1/9) = 599{,}127.6\ldots$.
Graph, part a.
e. False. The graph may have a point where it levels off and then continues changing in the *same* direction, as at $x = -1.5$ in part a.

35. Pole Dance Problem
a. $A = LW$
$$\frac{dA}{dt} = \frac{dL}{dt} \cdot W + L \cdot \frac{dW}{dt}$$
b. $W = 2 + 2 \cos t \Rightarrow \frac{dW}{dt} = -2 \sin t$
$L = 3 + 2 \sin 2t \Rightarrow \frac{dL}{dt} = 4 \cos 2t$
$$\frac{dA}{dt} = (4 \cos 2t)(2 + 2 \cos t) + (3 + 2 \sin 2t)(-2 \sin t)$$
At $t = 4$, $dA/dt = 7.132\ldots$, so A is increasing.
At $t = 5$, $dA/dt = -4.949\ldots$, so A is decreasing.

Problem Set 4-3, pages 138 to 141 — Derivative of a Quotient of Two Functions

Q1. $(d/dx)\, x^{1066} = 1066x^{1065}$
Q2. $f(x) = 12x^5 + C$
Q3. $y' = 3x^2 \sin x + x^3 \cos x$
Q4. $dy/dx = -\sin (x^7) \cdot 7x^6 = -7x^6 \sin (x^7)$
Q5. $f'(x) = 0$ (derivative of a constant)
Q6. $a'(t) = 9 \cos 9t$
Q7. See text definition of derivative
Q8. Instantaneous rate of change at a given x
Q9. $(x - 3)^4 (x - 3 + 2x) = 3(x - 3)^4 (x - 1)$
Q10. Graph. $[y = -0.5(\cos 0.5(x + 2) + x + 1)^2 + 3]$

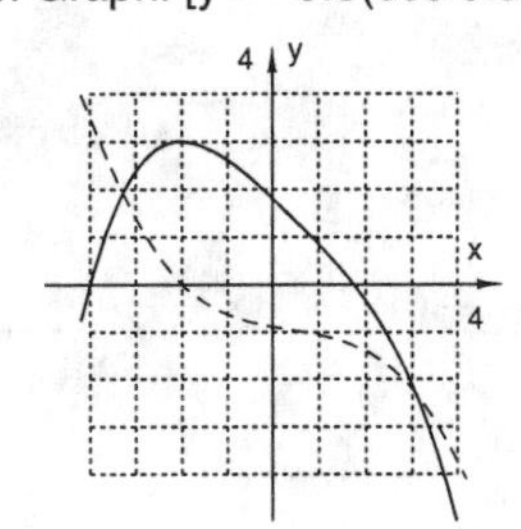

1. $f(x) = \frac{x^3}{\sin x} \Rightarrow f'(x) = \frac{3x^2 \sin x - x^3 \cos x}{\sin^2 x}$

2. $f(x) = \frac{x^4}{\cos x} \Rightarrow f'(x) = \frac{4x^3 \cos x + x^4 \sin x}{\cos^2 x}$

3. $g(x) = \frac{\cos^3 x}{x^5} \Rightarrow$

$g'(x) = \frac{3 \cos^2 x (-\sin x) \cdot x^5 - \cos^3 x \cdot 5x^4}{x^{10}}$

$= \frac{-3x \cos^2 x \sin x - 5 \cos^3 x}{x^6}$

4. $h(x) = \frac{\sin^5 x}{x^3} \Rightarrow$

$h'(x) = \frac{5 \sin^4 x \cos x \cdot x^3 - \sin^5 x \cdot 3x^2}{x^6}$

$= \frac{5x \sin^4 x \cos x - 3 \sin^5 x}{x^4}$

5. $y = \frac{\sin 10x}{\cos 20x} \Rightarrow$

$y' = \frac{10\cos 10x \cos 20x + 20 \sin 20x \sin 10x}{\cos^2 20x}$

6. $y = \frac{\cos 12x}{\sin 18x} \Rightarrow$

$y' = \frac{-12 \sin 12x \sin 18x - 18 \cos 12x \cos 18x}{\sin^2 18x}$

7. $y = \frac{3x + 7}{6x + 5} \Rightarrow y' = \frac{3(6x + 5) - (3x + 7)(6)}{(6x + 5)^2}$

$= \frac{-27}{(6x + 5)^2}$

8. $y = \frac{10x + 9}{5x - 3} \Rightarrow y' = \frac{10 \cdot (5x - 3) - (10x + 9) \cdot 5}{(5x - 3)^2}$

$= \frac{-75}{(5x - 3)^2}$

9. $z = \frac{(8x + 1)^6}{(5x - 2)^9} \Rightarrow$

$\frac{dz}{dx} = \frac{6(8x + 1)^5(8) \cdot (5x - 2)^9 - (8x + 1)^6 \cdot (9)(5x - 2)^8(5)}{(5x-2)^{18}}$

$= -\frac{(8x + 1)^5(120x + 141)}{(5x - 2)^{10}}$

10. $A = \frac{(4x - 1)^7}{(7x + 2)^4} \Rightarrow$

$\frac{dA}{dx} = \frac{7(4x-1)^6(4) \cdot (7x+2)^4 - (4x-1)^7 \cdot 4(7x+2)^3(7)}{(7x + 2)^8}$

$= \frac{28(4x - 1)^6(7x + 2)^3[(7x + 2) - (4x - 1)]}{(7x + 2)^8}$

$= \frac{28(4x - 1)^6(7x + 2)^3[(3x + 3)]}{(7x + 2)^8}$

$= \frac{84(4x - 1)^6(x + 1)}{(7x + 2)^5}$

11. $P = \frac{5x^2 - 10x + 3}{3x^2 + 6x - 8} \Rightarrow$

$P' = \frac{(10x - 10) \cdot (3x^2 + 6x - 8) - (5x^2 - 10x + 3) \cdot (6x + 6)}{(3x^2 + 6x - 8)^2}$

$= \frac{60x^2 - 98x + 62}{(3x^2 + 6x - 8)^2}$

12. $r = \frac{4x^2 + 8x + 1}{4x^2 - 8x + 3} \Rightarrow$

$r' = \frac{(8x + 8)(4x^2 - 8x + 3) - (4x^2 + 8x + 1) \cdot (8x - 8)}{(4x^2 - 8x + 3)^2}$

$= \frac{16(-4x^2 + x + 2)}{(4x^2 - 8x + 3)^2}$

13. $\frac{d}{dx}(60x^{-4/3}) = -80x^{-7/3}$

14. $\frac{d}{dx}(24x^{-7/3}) = -56x^{-10/3}$

15. $r(x) = \frac{12}{x^3} \Rightarrow r'(x) = \frac{0 \cdot x^3 - 12 \cdot 3x^2}{x^6} = \frac{-36}{x^4} = -36x^{-4}$

16. $t(x) = \frac{51}{x^{17}} \Rightarrow t'(x) = \frac{-867}{x^{18}} = -867x^{-18}$

17. $v(x) = \frac{14}{\cos 0.5x} \Rightarrow$

$v'(x) = \frac{0 \cdot \cos 0.5x - 14(-0.5) \sin 0.5x}{\cos^2 0.5x}$

$= \frac{7 \sin 0.5x}{\cos^2 0.5x}$

18. $a(x) = \frac{20}{\sin^2 x} \Rightarrow$

$a'(x) = \frac{0 \cdot \sin^2 x - 20 \cdot 2 \sin x \cos x}{\sin^4 x}$

$= \frac{-40 \cos x}{\sin^3 x}$

19. $e(x) = \frac{1}{x} \Rightarrow e'(x) = \frac{-1}{x^2} = -x^{-2}$

20. $s(x) = \frac{1}{x^2} \Rightarrow s'(x) = \frac{-2x}{x^4} = \frac{-2}{x^3} = -2x^{-3}$

21. $W(x) = \frac{10}{(x^3 - 1)^{-5}} = 10(x^3 - 1)^5 \Rightarrow$

$W'(x) = 150x^2 (x^3 - 1)^4$

22. $T(x) = \frac{1}{\cos x \sin x} \Rightarrow$

$T'(x) = \frac{0 - 1(-\sin x \sin x + \cos x \cos x)}{\cos^2 x \sin^2 x}$

$= \frac{\sin^2 x - \cos^2 x}{\cos^2 x \sin^2 x}$, which transforms to

$T'(x) = \frac{-\cos 2x}{\frac{1}{4} \sin^2 2x} = -4 \csc 2x \cot 2x$

23. $T(x) = \frac{\sin x}{\cos x} \Rightarrow$

$T'(x) = \frac{(\cos x)(\cos x) - (\sin x)(-\sin x)}{\cos^2 x}$

$= \frac{\cos^2 x + \sin^2 x}{\cos^2 x} = \frac{1}{\cos^2 x} = \sec^2 x$

(*T* is for *tangent function.*)

24. $C(x) = \frac{\cos x}{\sin x} \Rightarrow$

$C'(x) = \frac{(-\sin x)(\sin x) - (\cos x)(\cos x)}{\sin^2 x}$

$= \frac{-\sin^2 x - \cos^2 x}{\sin^2 x} = \frac{-1}{\sin^2 x} = -\csc^2 x$

25. $C(x) = \frac{1}{\sin x} \Rightarrow C'(x) = \frac{0 - \cos x}{\sin^2 x}$

$= -\frac{1}{\sin x} \cdot \frac{\cos x}{\sin x} = -\csc x \cot x$

(*C* is for *cosecant function.*)

26. $S(x) = \frac{1}{\cos x} \Rightarrow S'(x) = \frac{0 - (-\sin x)}{\cos^2 x}$

$= \frac{1}{\cos x} \cdot \frac{\sin x}{\cos x} = \sec x \tan x$

(*S* is for *secant.*)

27. Black Hole Problem

a. $v(t) = \dfrac{1000}{3 - t}$

$v(1) = \dfrac{1000}{3 - 1} = 500$ mph

$v(2) = \dfrac{1000}{3 - 2} = 1000$ mph

$v(3) = \dfrac{1000}{3 - 3} = \dfrac{1000}{0}$. No value for v(3).

b. $a(t) = \dfrac{0 - 1000(-1)}{(3 - t)^2} = \dfrac{1000}{(3 - t)^2}$

c. $a(1) = \dfrac{1000}{(3 - 1)^2} = 250$ mph/hr

$a(2) = \dfrac{1000}{(3 - 2)^2} = 1000$ mph/hr

$a(3) = \dfrac{1000}{(3 - 3)^2} = \dfrac{1000}{0}$. No value for a(3).

d. Graph.

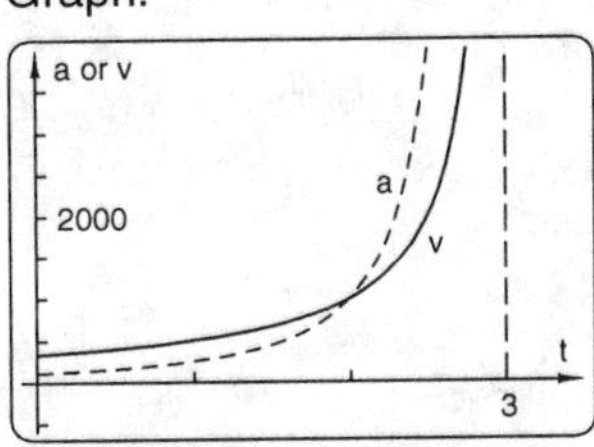

e. $\dfrac{1000}{(3 - t)^2} = 500 \Rightarrow 2 = (3 - t)^2 \Rightarrow 3 - t = \pm\sqrt{2} \Rightarrow$

$t = 3 \pm \sqrt{2} \Rightarrow t = 3 - \sqrt{2} = 1.585...$ in the domain.

Range is $0 \le t < 1.585...$.

28. Catch-Up Rate Problem

a. Since they are walking in the same direction, their relative rate is the difference $(x - 5)$.

b. $t(x) = \dfrac{300}{x - 5}$, assuming Willie's rate is constant.

c. t(6) = 300 sec, t(8) = 100 sec, t(10) = 60 sec, t(5) = 300/0, which is infinite, t(4) = –300, which is not reasonable in the real world, and t(5.1) = 3000 sec. A reasonable domain is $x > 5$.

d. $t'(x) = \dfrac{0 - 300(1)}{(x - 5)^2}$

$t'(6) = -300$ sec/(ft/sec)

e. t'(5) does not exist because of division by zero. More fundamentally, t'(5) does not exist because t(5) does not exist.

29. Confirmation of Quotient Formula Problem

$f(x) = \dfrac{3x + 7}{2x + 5} \Rightarrow$

$f'(x) = \dfrac{3\cdot(2x + 5) - (3x + 7)\cdot 2}{(2x + 5)^2} = \dfrac{1}{(2x + 5)^2}$

$f'(4) = \dfrac{1}{169} = 0.005917159...$

For 4.1, f'(4) ≈ 0.005827505...
For 4.01, f'(4) ≈ 0.005908070...
For 4.001, f'(4) ≈ 0.005916249...
f'(4) (exact) = 0.005917159...
Difference quotients are approaching f'(4).

30. Derivative Graph and Table Problem

a. Sketch. See accurate plot in part c.

b. $f(x) = \dfrac{x^2 - 8}{x - 3} \Rightarrow$

$f'(x) = \dfrac{2x(x - 3) - (x^2 - 8)(1)}{(x - 3)^2}$

$f'(x) = \dfrac{x^2 - 6x + 8}{(x - 3)^2} = \dfrac{(x - 4)(x - 2)}{(x - 3)^2}$

x	f(x)	f'(x)
2.95	–14.05	–399
2.96	–19.04	–624
2.97	–27.363...	–1110.11...
2.98	–44.02	–2499
2.99	–94.01	–9999
3.00	none	none
3.01	106.01	–9999
3.02	56.02	–2499
3.03	39.363...	–1110.11...
3.04	31.04	–624
3.05	26.05	–399

c. Graph of f and f'.

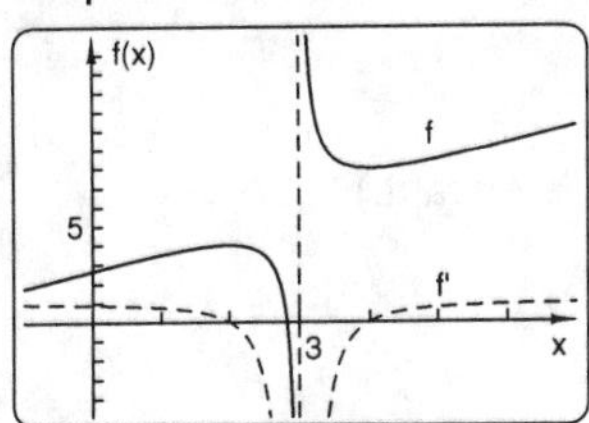

d. f(x) changes faster and faster as x approaches 3, shooting off to negative infinity as x approaches 3 from the negative side, and to positive infinity as x approaches 3 from the positive side. Note that the rates are symmetrical about x = 3.

e. f(x) stops increasing and starts decreasing at a point where f'(x) changes sign. Set f'(x) = 0.

$\dfrac{x^2 - 6x + 8}{(x - 3)^2} = 0 \Rightarrow x^2 - 6x + 8 = 0 \Rightarrow$

$(x - 2)(x - 4) = 0 \Rightarrow x = 2$ or 4.

At x = 2, f(x) stops increasing and starts decreasing.

f. At x = 4 (part e.), f(x) stops decreasing and starts increasing.

g. f: Domain: all real numbers, $x \ne 3$.
Range: $f(x) \le 4$ or $f(x) \ge 8$.
f': Domain: all real numbers, $x \ne 3$.
Range: $f'(x) < 1$.

31. Proof of the Power Rule for Negative Exponents

If $y = x^n$, where n is a negative integer, then $y' = nx^{n-1}$.

Proof:

Let $n = -p$, where p is a positive integer.

$\therefore y = x^{-p} = \dfrac{1}{x^p}$.

$\therefore y' = \dfrac{0\cdot x^p - 1\cdot px^{p-1}}{x^{2p}}$ since p is a positive integer.

$= -\dfrac{px^{p-1}}{x^{2p}} = -px^{p-1-2p} = -px^{-p-1}$.

Replacing –p with n gives

$y' = nx^{n-1}$, Q.E.D.

32. Graph, $y = \sec x$. Graph, $y = \tan x$.

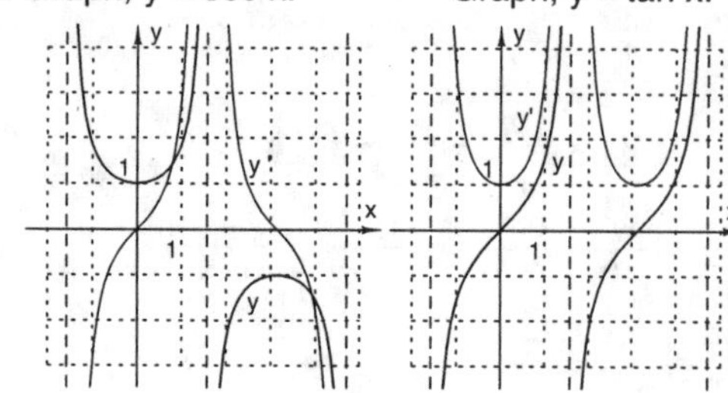

33. Journal Problem

Journal entries should reflect the fact that students can now do by algebra what they had only been able to do numerically and graphically. Specifically, they should see that they can differentiate products and quotients, neither of which has an intuitively obvious property such as the derivative of a sum or difference. They would also be well advised to include the difference between the way one finds a *derivative* of a product and the way one finds a *limit* of a product.

Problem Set 4-4, pages 143 to 145 — Derivatives of the Other Trigonometric Functions

Q1. $(\sin x)/(\tan x) = \cos x$.

Q2. $1/(\sec x) = \cos x$.

Q3. $\sin^2 3 + \cos^2 3 = 1$.

Q4. $f'(x) = \sin x + x \cos x$.

Q5. $g'(x) = \dfrac{\cos x + x \sin x}{\cos^2 x}$.

Q6. $h'(x) = -(15/7)(3x)^{-12/7}$.

Q7. $dy/dx = 3(\cos x)^{-4} \sin x$.

Q8. Limit $= -3$.

Q9. Limit $= \dfrac{dj}{dp}$.

Q10. Graph. (Function is secant.)

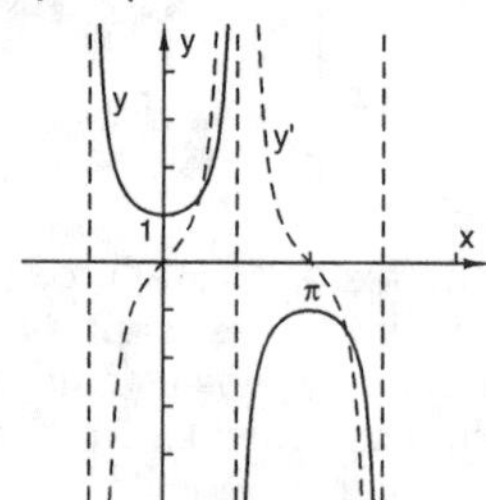

1. $f(x) = \tan 5x \Rightarrow f'(x) = 5 \sec^2 5x$
2. $f(x) = \sec 3x \Rightarrow f'(x) = 3 \sec x \tan x$
3. $y = \sec 7x \Rightarrow y' = 7 \sec 7x \tan 7x$
4. $z = \tan 9x \Rightarrow z' = 9 \sec^2 9x$
5. $g(x) = \cot 11x \Rightarrow g'(x) = -11 \csc^2 11x$
6. $h(x) = \csc 10x \Rightarrow h'(x) = -10 \csc 10x \cot 10x$
7. $r(x) = \csc 20x \Rightarrow r'(x) = -20 \csc 20x \cot 20x$
8. $p(x) = \cot 31x \Rightarrow p'(x) = -31 \csc^2 31x$
9. $y = \tan^5 4x \Rightarrow$
   $(d/dx)(y) = 5 \tan^4 4x \cdot \sec^2 4x \cdot 4$
   $= 20 \tan^4 4x \sec^2 4x$
10. $y = \tan^7 9x \Rightarrow$
    $(d/dx)(y) = 7 \tan^6 9x \cdot \sec^2 9x \cdot 9$
    $= 63 \tan^6 9x \sec^2 9x$
11. $(d/dx)(3 \cot^6 8x) = 18 \cot^5 8x \cdot (-\csc^2 8x) \cdot 8$
    $= -144 \cot^5 8x \csc^2 8x$
12. $(d/dx)(5 \sec^7 9x) = 35 \sec^6 9x \cdot \sec 9x \tan 9x \cdot 9$
    $= 315 \sec^7 9x \tan 9x$
13. $y = 8 \sec^{5/4} 4x \Rightarrow$
    $y' = 10 \sec^{1/4} 4x \cdot \sec 4x \tan 4x \cdot 4$
    $= 40 \sec^{5/4} 4x \tan 4x$
14. $y = 88 \csc^{11/8} 2x \Rightarrow$
    $y' = 121 \csc^{3/8} 2x \cdot (-\csc 2x \cot 2x) \cdot 2$
    $= -242 \csc^{11/8} 2x \cot 2x$
15. $v = \csc (x^{-7}) \Rightarrow$
    $v' = -\csc (x^{-7}) \cot (x^{-7}) \cdot (-7)x^{-8}$
    $= 7x^{-8} \csc (x^{-7}) \cot (x^{-7})$
16. $u = \cot (3x^{-5}) \Rightarrow$
    $u' = -\csc^2 (3x^{-5}) \cdot (-15)x^{-6}$
    $= 15x^{-6} \csc^2 (3x^{-5})$
17. $p = \sec x \tan x \Rightarrow$
    $dp/dx = \sec x \tan x \cdot \tan x + \sec x \cdot \sec^2 x$
    $= \sec x \tan^2 x + \sec^3 x$
18. $m = \csc x \cot x \Rightarrow$
    $dm/dx = -\csc x \cot x \cdot \cot x + \csc x \cdot (-\csc^2 x)$
    $= -\csc x \cot^2 x - \csc^3 x$
19. $y = x^{-3} \cot x \Rightarrow$
    $y' = -3x^{-4} \cdot \cot x + x^{-3} \cdot (-\csc^2 x)$
    $= -3x^{-4} \cot x - x^{-3} \csc^2 x$
20. $y = x^{5/2} \sec x \Rightarrow$
    $y' = 2.5x^{3/2} \cdot \sec x + x^{5/2} \cdot \sec x \tan x$
21. $y = \sec x \csc x \Rightarrow$
    $y' = \sec x \tan x \cdot \csc x + \sec x \cdot (-\csc x \cot x)$
    $= \sec^2 x - \csc^2 x$
22. $y = \tan x \cot x = 1$, for all x, $\Rightarrow y' = 0$
23. $y = \dfrac{\tan x}{\sin x} = \sec x \Rightarrow y' = \sec x \tan x$
24. $y = \dfrac{\cot x}{\cos x} = \csc x \Rightarrow y' = -\csc x \cot x$
25. $y = \dfrac{5x^7}{\cot 14x} \Rightarrow$
    $y' = \dfrac{35x^6 \cdot \cot 14x - 5x^7 \cdot (-\csc^2 14x) \cdot 14}{\cot^2 14x}$
    $= \dfrac{35x^6 \cot 14x + 70x^7 \csc^2 14x}{\cot^2 14x}$
26. $y = \dfrac{4 \csc 10x}{x^{40}} \Rightarrow$
    $y' = \dfrac{-40 \csc 10x \cot 10x \cdot x^{40} - 4 \csc 10x \cdot 40x^{39}}{x^{80}}$
    $= \dfrac{-40\, x \csc 10x \cot 10x - 160 \csc 10x}{x^{41}}$
27. $w = \tan (\sin 3x) \Rightarrow$
    $w' = \sec^2 (\sin 3x) \cdot 3 \cos 3x$
    $= 3 \sec^2 (\sin 3x) \cdot \cos 3x$
28. $t = \sec (\cos 4x) \Rightarrow$
    $t' = \sec (\cos 4x) \tan (\cos 4x) \cdot (-4 \sin 4x)$
    $= -4 \sec (\cos 4x) \tan (\cos 4x) \sin 4x$
29. $S(x) = \sec^2 x - \tan^2 x = 1 \Rightarrow S'(x) = 0$
    (The differentiation formulas give the same.)
30. $m(x) = \cot^2 x - \csc^2 x = -1 \Rightarrow m'(x) = 0$
    (The differentiation formulas give the same.)
31. $A(x) = \sin x^2 \Rightarrow A'(x) = \cos x^2 \cdot 2x$
    $= 2x \cos x^2$
32. $f(x) = \cos x^3 \Rightarrow f'(x) = -\sin x^3 \cdot 3x^2$
    $= -3x^2 \sin x^3$

33. $F(x) = \sin^2 x \Rightarrow F'(x) = 2 \sin x \cos x$

34. $g(x) = \cos^3 x \Rightarrow$
$g'(x) = 3 \cos^2 x \cdot (-\sin x) = -3 \cos^2 x \sin x$

35. $C(x) = \sin(\sin x) \Rightarrow C'(x) = \cos(\sin x) \cdot \cos x$

36. $h(x) = \cos(\cos x) \Rightarrow$
$h'(x) = -\sin(\cos x) \cdot (-\cos x)$
$= \sin(\cos x) \sin x$

37. Derivative of Cotangent Problem

$y = \cot x = \dfrac{\cos x}{\sin x} \Rightarrow$

$y' = \dfrac{-\sin x \cdot \sin x - \cos x \cdot \cos x}{\sin^2 x}$

$= \dfrac{-1}{\sin^2 x} = -\csc^2 x$ or:

$y = \dfrac{1}{\tan x} = (\tan x)^{-1} \Rightarrow$

$y' = -1 \cdot (\tan x)^{-2} \cdot \sec^2 x = -\csc^2 x$

38. Derivative of Cosecant Problem

$y = \csc x = \dfrac{1}{\sin x} \Rightarrow$

$y' = \dfrac{0 - \cos x}{\sin^2 x} = -\csc x \cot x$

39. Confirmation of Tangent Derivative Formula
a. See graph in part b.
b. $f(x) = \tan x \Rightarrow f'(x) = \sec^2 x$. Graph.
Predicted graph should be close to actual one.

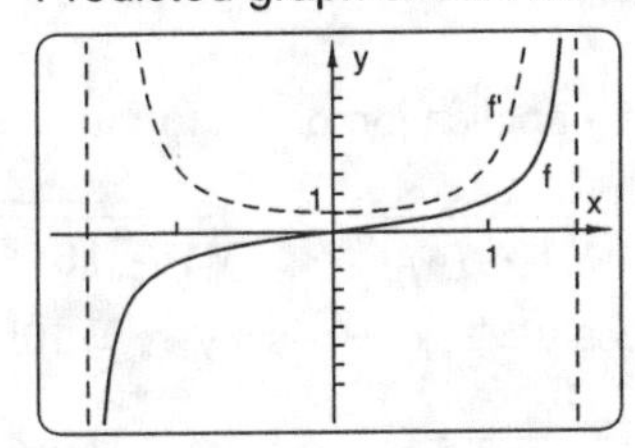

c. $\dfrac{\tan 1.01 - \tan 0.99}{2(0.01)} = 3.42646416...$
$\tan' 1 = \sec^2 1 = (1/\cos 1)^2 = 3.42551882...$
Difference quotient is within 0.001 of actual.

40. Confirmation of Secant Derivative Formula
a. $f(x) = \sec x \Rightarrow f'(x) = \sec x \tan x \Rightarrow$
$f'(1) = \sec 1 \tan 1 = 2.8824...$
b. Graph. Slope of line is about 2.88... .

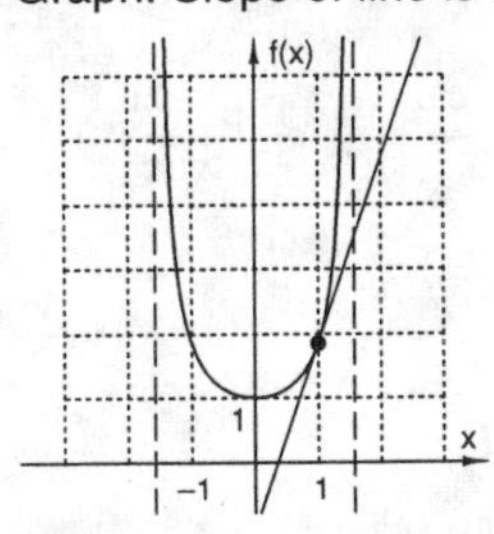

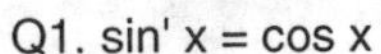

c. The formula is confirmed by the fact that the line is tangent to the graph.
d. Graph.

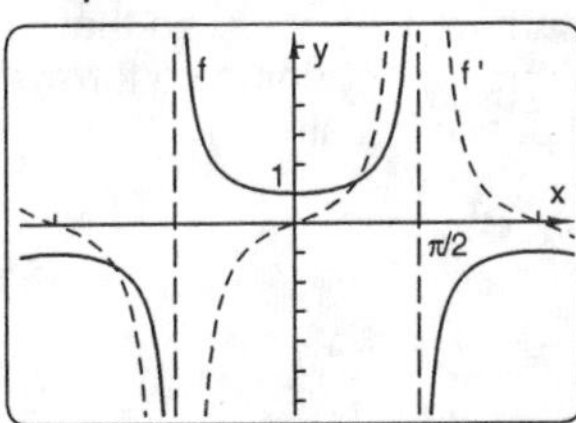

e. If $f'(x)$ is negative, the graph of f is decreasing.

41. Light on the Monument Problem
a. $y/10 = \tan x \Rightarrow y = 10 \tan x$, Q.E.D.
b. $y' = 10 \sec^2 x$.
At $x = 1$, $y' = 10 \sec^2 1 = 34.2551...$
y is increasing at about 34.3 ft/radian.
$(34.2551...)\dfrac{\pi}{180} = 0.5978...$ ft/degree
c. $y = 535 \Rightarrow x = \tan^{-1} 53.5 = 1.55210...$
$\therefore y' = 10 \sec^2 1.55210... = 28632.5$
y is increasing at about 28,632.5 ft/radian.

42. Point of Light Problem
a. $\tan x = \dfrac{\text{opposite side}}{\text{adjacent side}} = \dfrac{y}{500}$
$\therefore y = 500 \tan x$, Q.E.D.
b. $dy/dt = 500 \sec^2 x \cdot dx/dt$
c. At $y = 300$, $x = \tan^{-1}(300/500) = 0.5404...$
$\therefore dy/dt = 500 \sec^2 (0.5404...)(0.3)$
$= 500(1.36)(0.3) = 204$ ft/sec

43. Antiderivative Problem
a. $y = \sin x + C$
b. $y = -\frac{1}{2} \cos 2x + C$
c. $y = \frac{1}{3} \tan 3x + C$
d. $y = -\frac{1}{4} \cot 4x + C$
e. $y = 5 \sec x + C$

44. Journal Problem
Probably the most important thing students have learned is the proof that the derivative of a power formula works for negative and rational exponents, confirming previous conjectures. Another thing students may have picked as most important is the ability to differentiate the other four trigonometry functions.

Problem Set 4-5, pages 151 to 153 — Derivatives of Inverse Trigonometric Functions

Q1. $\sin' x = \cos x$
Q2. $\cos' x = -\sin x$
Q3. $\tan' x = \sec^2 x$
Q4. $\cot' x = -\csc^2 x$
Q5. $\sec' x = \sec x \tan x$
Q6. $\csc' x = -\csc x \cot x$
Q7. $f'(1)$ is infinite
Q8. $f'(3)$ is undefined
Q9. $f'(4) = -1$
Q10. $f'(6) = 0$

For Problems 1 through 4, see Figure 4-5d.
1. Graph, $y = \cos^{-1} x$.
2. Graph, $y = \sin^{-1} x$.
3. Graph, $y = \csc^{-1} x$.
4. Graph, $y = \cot^{-1} x$.
5. The principal branch of the inverse cotangent function goes from 0 to π so that the function will be continuous.

6. There are no values of the inverse secant for x between −1 and 1, so the inverse secant function cannot be continuous. (Some texts restrict the range of the inverse cosecant to $0 \le y \le \pi/2$ so that the function will be continuous, but doing so throws away the other half of the possible values.)
7. $\sin(\sin^{-1} 0.3) = 0.3$
8. $\cos^{-1}(\cos 0.8) = 0.8$
9. $y = \sin^{-1} x \Rightarrow \sin y = x \Rightarrow \cos y \cdot y' = 1 \Rightarrow$

   $y' = \dfrac{1}{\cos y} = \dfrac{1}{\sqrt{1 - x^2}}$, Q.E.D.

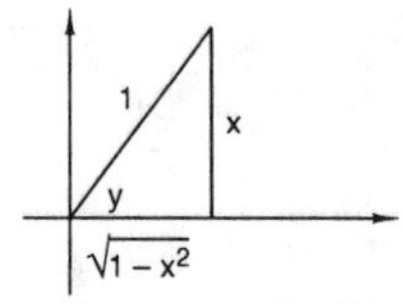

   [Since sin y = (opposite leg)/(hypotenuse), put x on the opposite leg and 1 on the hypotenuse.

   Adjacent leg = $\sqrt{1 - x^2}$, and
   cos y = (adjacent)/(hypotenuse).]

10. $y = \cos^{-1} x \Rightarrow \cos y = x \Rightarrow -\sin y \cdot y' = 1 \Rightarrow$

   $y' = -\dfrac{1}{\sin y} = -\dfrac{1}{\sqrt{1 - x^2}}$, Q.E.D.

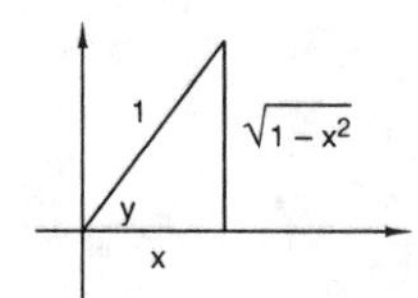

   [Since cos y = (adjacent leg)/(hypotenuse), put x on the adjacent leg and 1 on the hypotenuse.

   Opposite leg = $\sqrt{1 - x^2}$, and
   sin y = (opposite)/(hypotenuse).]

11. $y = \csc^{-1} x \Rightarrow \csc y = x \Rightarrow -\csc y \cot y \cdot y' \Rightarrow$

   $y' = -\dfrac{1}{\csc y \cot y} = -\dfrac{1}{x\sqrt{x^2 - 1}}$ if $x > 0$

   If $x < 0$, then y is in QIV. So both csc y and cot y are negative, and thus their product is positive.

   $\therefore y' = -\dfrac{1}{|x|\sqrt{x^2 - 1}}$, Q.E.D.

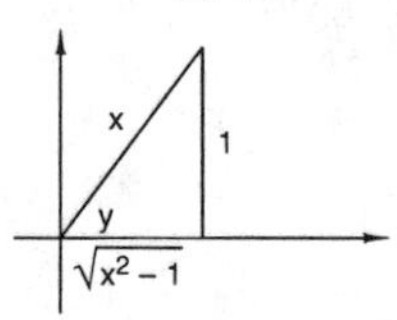

   [Since csc y = (hypotenuse)/(opposite leg), put x on the hypotenuse and 1 on the opposite leg.

   Adjacent leg = $\sqrt{x^2 - 1}$, and
   csc y = x and cot y = (adjacent)/(opposite).]

12. $y = \cot^{-1} x \Rightarrow \cot y = x \Rightarrow -\csc^2 y \cdot y' = 1 \Rightarrow$

   $y' = -\dfrac{1}{\csc^2 y} = -\dfrac{1}{(\sqrt{1 + x^2})^2} = -\dfrac{1}{1 + x^2}$, Q.E.D.

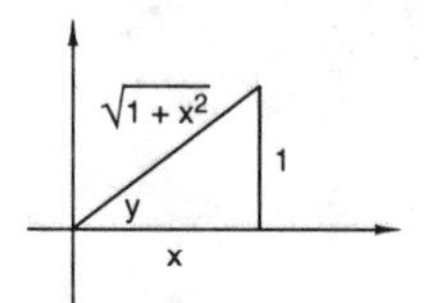

   [Since cot y = (adjacent leg)/(opposite leg), put x on the adjacent leg and 1 on the opposite leg.

   Hypotenuse = $\sqrt{1 + x^2}$, and
   csc y = (hypotenuse)/(opposite).]

Problems 13 through 18 are shown done "from scratch," as in Example 3. If students practice doing them this way, they will not be dependent on memorized formulas. Problem 13 shows how an alternate solution using the formulas and the chain rule could be reached.

13. $y = \sin^{-1} 4x \Rightarrow \sin y = 4x \Rightarrow \cos y \cdot y' = 4 \Rightarrow$

   $y' = \dfrac{4}{\cos y} = \dfrac{4}{\sqrt{1 - 16x^2}}$

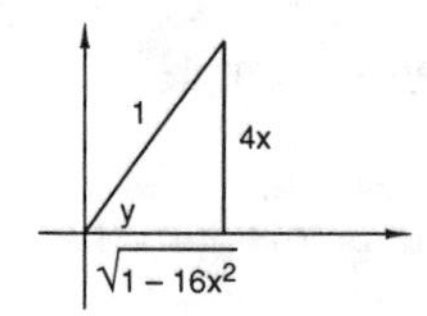

   Alternate solution by application of the formula:

   $y = \sin^{-1} 4x \Rightarrow y' = \dfrac{1}{\sqrt{1 - (4x)^2}} \cdot 4 = \dfrac{4}{\sqrt{1 - 16x^2}}$

14. $y = \cos^{-1} 10x \Rightarrow \cos y = 10x \Rightarrow -\sin y \cdot y' = 10 \Rightarrow$

   $y' = -\dfrac{10}{\sin y} = -\dfrac{10}{\sqrt{1 - 100x^2}}$

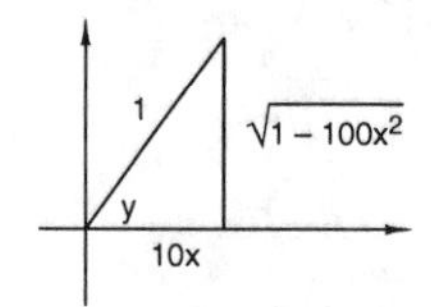

15. $y = \cot^{-1} x^{0.5} \Rightarrow \cot y = x^{0.5} \Rightarrow$

   $-\csc^2 y \cdot y' = 0.5x^{-0.5} \Rightarrow$

   $y' = -\dfrac{0.5x^{-0.5}}{\csc^2 y} = -\dfrac{0.5x^{-0.5}}{(\sqrt{1 + x})^2} = -\dfrac{0.5x^{-0.5}}{1 + x}$

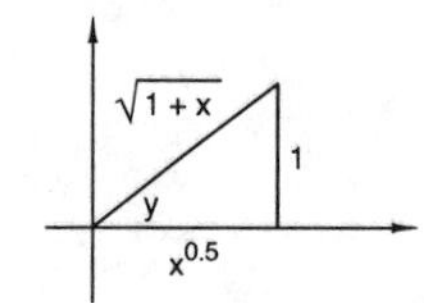

16. $y = \tan^{-1} x^{0.5} \Rightarrow \tan y = x^{0.5} \Rightarrow$

   $\sec^2 y \cdot y' = 0.5x^{-0.5} \Rightarrow$

   $y' = \dfrac{0.5x^{-0.5}}{\sec^2 y} = \dfrac{0.5x^{-0.5}}{(\sqrt{1 + x})^2} = \dfrac{0.5x^{-0.5}}{1 + x}$

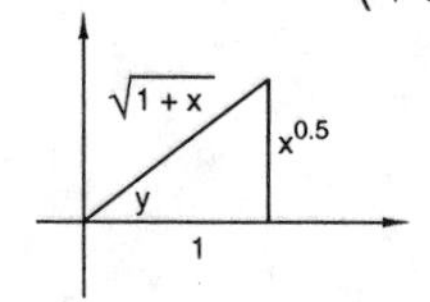

17. $y = \sec^{-1}\frac{x}{3} \Rightarrow \sec y = \frac{x}{3} \Rightarrow \sec y \tan y \cdot y' = \frac{1}{3} \Rightarrow$

$$y' = \frac{1}{3 \sec y \tan y} = \frac{1}{3\cdot\frac{x}{3}\sqrt{x^2 - 9}}, \text{ if } x > 0$$

If $x < 0$, then y is in Quadrant II, where both sec y and tan y are negative. So their product is positive.

$$\therefore y' = \frac{1}{|x|\sqrt{x^2 - 9}}$$

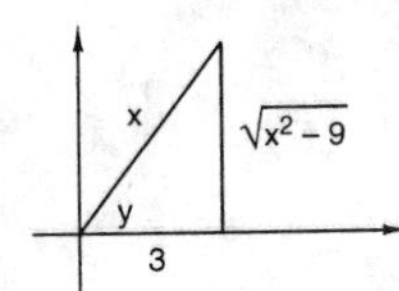

18. $y = \csc^{-1}\frac{x}{10} \Rightarrow \csc y = \frac{x}{10} \Rightarrow -\csc y \cot y \cdot y' = \frac{1}{10} \Rightarrow$

$$y' = -\frac{1}{10 \csc y \cot y} = -\frac{1}{10\cdot\frac{x}{10}\sqrt{\frac{x^2 - 100}{100}}}$$

If $x < 0$, then y is in Quadrant IV, where both csc y and cot y are negative. So their product is positive.

$$\therefore y' = -\frac{10}{|x|\sqrt{x^2 - 100}}$$

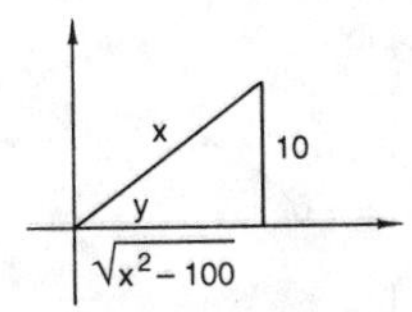

For Problems 19 through 24 a solution is shown using the appropriate formula.

19. $y = \cos^{-1} 5x^2$

$$y' = -\frac{1}{\sqrt{1 - (5x^2)^2}} \cdot 10x = -\frac{10x}{\sqrt{1 - 25x^4}}$$

20. $f(x) = \tan^{-1} x^3$

$$f'(x) = \frac{1}{1 + (x^3)^2} \cdot 3x^2 = \frac{3x^2}{1 + x^6}$$

21. $g(x) = (\sin^{-1} x)^2$

$$g'(x) = 2 \sin^{-1} x \cdot \frac{1}{\sqrt{1 - x^2}}$$

22. $u = (\sec^{-1} x)^2$

$$u' = 2 \sec^{-1} x \cdot \frac{1}{|x|\sqrt{x^2 - 1}}$$

23. $v = x \sin^{-1} x + (1 - x^2)^{1/2}$

$$v' = 1\cdot\sin^{-1} x + x\cdot\frac{1}{\sqrt{1 - x^2}} + \tfrac{1}{2}(1 - x^2)^{-1/2}\cdot(-2x)$$

$$= \sin^{-1} x + \frac{x}{\sqrt{1 - x^2}} - \frac{x}{\sqrt{1 - x^2}} = \sin^{-1} x$$

The surprise is that you now have seen a formula for the antiderivative of the inverse sine function.

24. $f(x) = \cot^{-1} (\cot x) = x \Rightarrow f'(x) = 1$ (Surprise!!)
Application of the formulas gives the same result.

25. Radar Problem

a. $\tan \theta = x/100$, so $\theta = \tan^{-1} (x/100)$, Q.E.D.

b. $\frac{d\theta}{dx} = \frac{1}{1 + (x/100)^2} \cdot \frac{1}{100} = \frac{100}{10000 + x^2}$

$$\frac{d\theta}{dt} = \frac{d\theta}{dx} \cdot \frac{dx}{dt} = \frac{100}{10000 + x^2} \cdot \frac{dx}{dt}$$

c. If $x = 500$ ft and $d\theta/dt = -0.04$ rad/sec, then

$$-0.04 = \frac{100}{10000 + 500^2} \cdot \frac{dx}{dt}$$

$$\frac{dx}{dt} = \frac{(-0.04)(260000)}{100} = -104$$

Truck is going 104 ft/sec.
$104(3600/5280) = 70.909... \approx 71$ mph

26. Exit Sign Problem

a. $\theta = \tan^{-1} (50/x) - \tan^{-1} (30/x)$ or
$\theta = \cot^{-1} (x/50) - \cot^{-1} (x/30)$
(The inverse tangent equation has the advantage that the function appears on the calculator. The inverse cotangent equation has the advantage that x is in the numerator of the argument, which makes the chain rule less complicated to use.)

b. $\frac{d\theta}{dx} = \frac{-50x^{-2}}{1 + (50/x)^2} - \frac{-30x^{-2}}{1 + (30/x)^2}$

$$= \frac{-50}{x^2 + 2500} - \frac{-30}{x^2 + 900}$$

$$= \frac{-20x^2 + 30000}{(x^2 + 2500)(x^2 + 900)}$$

c. $d\theta/dx = 0 \Leftrightarrow 20x^2 = 30000$

$x = \pm\sqrt{1500} = \pm 38.729...$
About 38.7 ft.

d. Graph. Maximum is between $x = 38$ and 39.

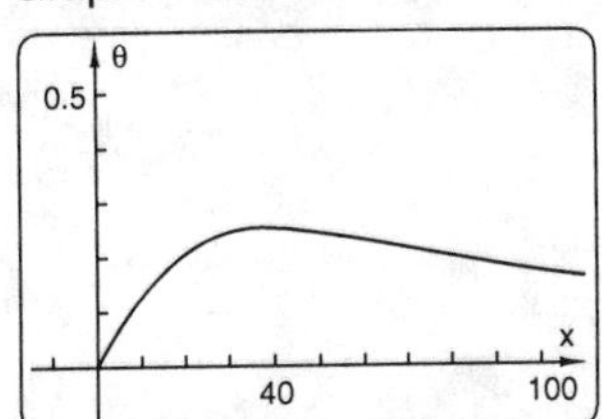

27. Numerical Answer Check Problem

x	Num. Deriv.*	Alg. Deriv.
−0.8	−1.666671...	−1.666666...
−0.6	−1.250000...	−1.25
−0.4	−1.091089...	−1.091089...
−0.2	−1.020620...	−1.020620...
0	−1.000000...	−1
0.2	−1.020620...	−1.020620...
0.4	−1.091089...	−1.091089...
0.6	−1.250000...	−1.25
0.8	−1.666671...	−1.666666...

*The precise value for the numerical derivative will depend on the tolerance to which the grapher is set.

28. Graphical Analysis Problem

a. $y = \sec^{-1} x \Rightarrow \dfrac{dy}{dx} = \dfrac{1}{|x|\sqrt{x^2 - 1}}$

At $x = 2$, $\dfrac{dy}{dx} = \dfrac{1}{|2|\sqrt{3}} = 0.288675...$

The answer is reasonable because the graph slopes up at x = 2 with slope significantly less than 1.

b. At x = 2, $y = \sec^{-1} 2 = \cos^{-1} (1/2) = 1.04719...$

$\dfrac{d}{dy} \sec y = \sec y \tan y$

At y = 1.047...,

$\dfrac{d}{dy} \sec y = (\sec 1.047...)(\tan 1.047...)$

$= 3.464101...$

c. The answer to part b. is the reciprocal of the answer to part a. That is,

$\dfrac{1}{3.464101...} = 0.288675...$

Thus, the derivative of the inverse secant at x = c is the reciprocal of the derivative of the derivative of the secant at $y = \sec^{-1} c$.

29. General Derivative of the Inverse of a Function

a. $y = \sin^{-1} x \Rightarrow \sin y = x \Rightarrow \cos y \cdot y' = 1 \Rightarrow$

$y' = \dfrac{1}{\cos y}$, Q.E.D.

b. $y' = \dfrac{1}{\cos(\sin^{-1} x)} = \dfrac{1}{\cos(\sin^{-1} 0.6)} = 1.25$

$y' = \dfrac{1}{\sqrt{1 - x^2}} = \dfrac{1}{\sqrt{1 - 0.6^2}} = \dfrac{1}{0.8} = 1.25$, Q.E.D.

c. $y = f^{-1}(x) \Rightarrow f(y) = x \Rightarrow f'(y) \cdot \dfrac{d}{dx}(y) = 1 \Rightarrow$

$\dfrac{d}{dx}(y) = \dfrac{1}{f'(y)} \Rightarrow \dfrac{d}{dx}(f^{-1}(x)) = \dfrac{1}{f'(f^{-1}(x))}$, Q.E.D.

d. $f(x) = x^3 + x = 10$

$(x - 2)(x^2 + 2x + 5) = 0$

$x = 2$ (only)

$\therefore h(10) = 2.$

Since $h(x) = f^{-1}(x)$ and $f'(x) = 3x^2 + 1$,

$h'(10) = \dfrac{1}{f'(h(10))} = \dfrac{1}{f'(2)} = \dfrac{1}{3 \cdot 2^2 + 1} = 1/13.$

30. The inverse trig cofunctions, $\cos^{-1}$, $\cot^{-1}$, and $\csc^{-1}$, are the ones preceded by a minus sign.

Problem Set 4-6, pages 157 to 160 — Differentiability and Continuity

Q1. See text definition of *continuity.*

Q2. See text definition of *derivative.*

Q3. $y' = -6x^{-2} + C$.

Q4. $\cos' x = -\sin x$.

Q5. $dy/dx = \sec^2 x$

Q6. $1/(|x|\sqrt{x^2 - 1})$

Q7. $f'(x) = 4x^3$; $f'(2) = 32$

Q8. $dy/dx = 15x^2(x^3 + 1)^4$.

Q9. Integral ≈ 5.4 (Function is $y = 2^{-x}$.)

Q10. Graph. (Function is $y = 2^{-x}$.)

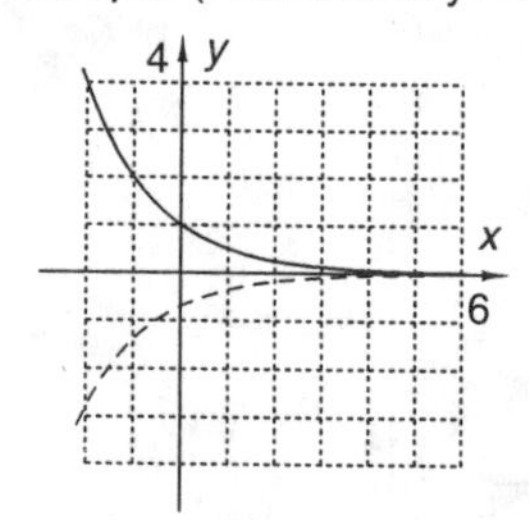

1. Continuous.
2. Neither.
3. Neither.
4. Both.
5. Neither.
6. Neither.
7. Both.
8. Neither.
9. Neither.
10. Neither.
11. Continuous
12. Both.

13. a. Graph (example).
b. (Eqns. will vary.)

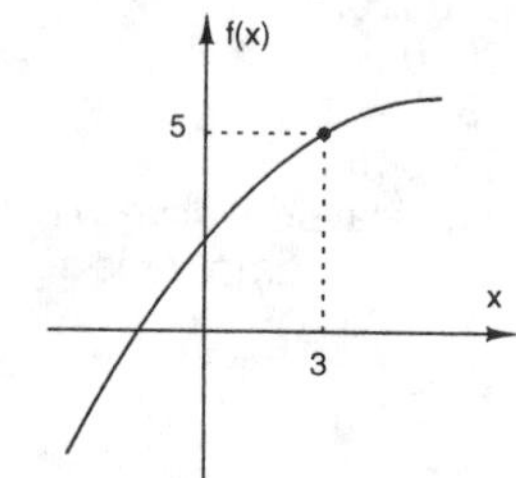

14. a. Graph (example).
b. (Eqns. will vary.)

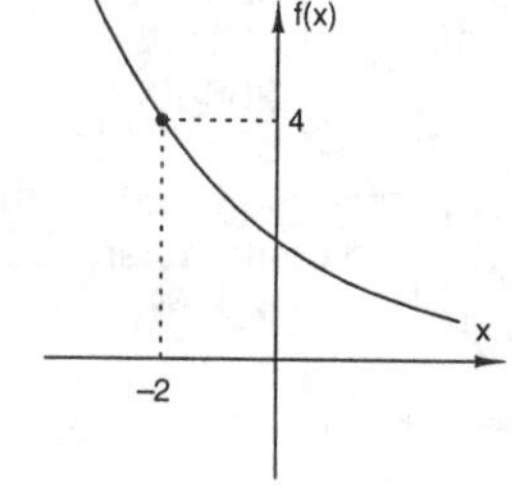

15. a. Graph (example).
b. (Eqns. will vary.)

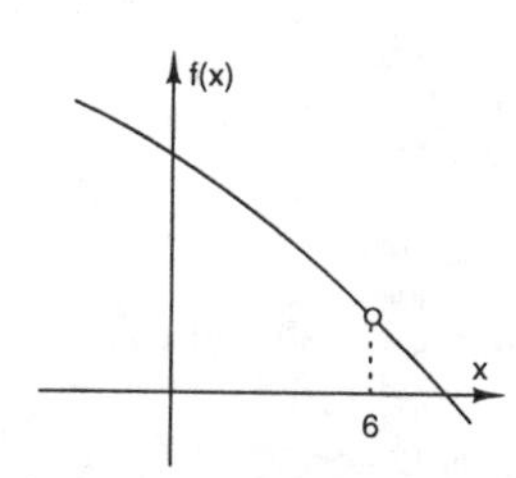

16. a. Graph (example).
b. (Eqns. will vary.)

17. a. Graph (example).
b. (Eqns. will vary.)

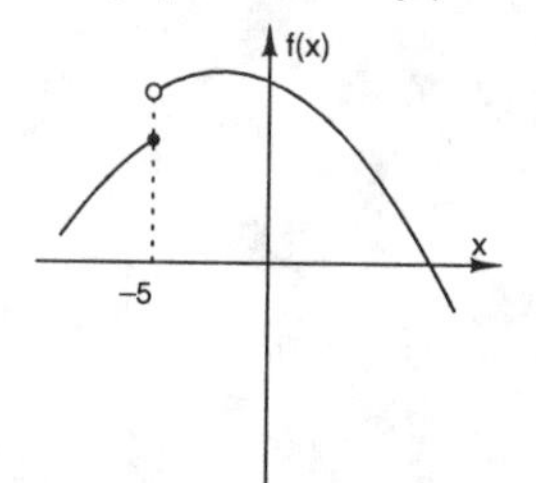

18. a. Graph (example).
b. (Eqns. will vary.)

19. a. Graph (example).
b. (Eqns. will vary.)

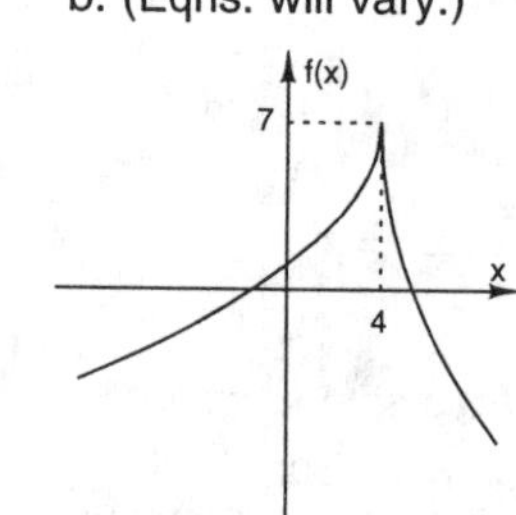

20. a. No such function.
b. No such function.

Not possible. Differentiability implies continuity.

21. Graph. Continuous.

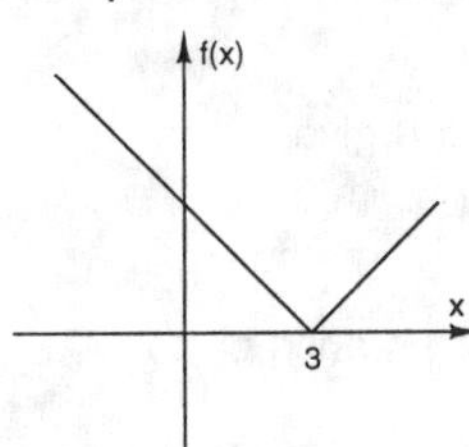

22. Graph. Both.

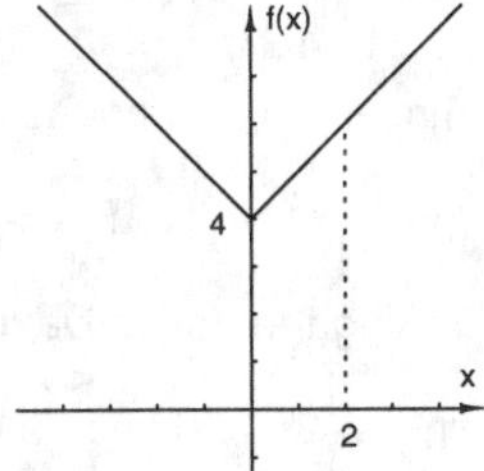

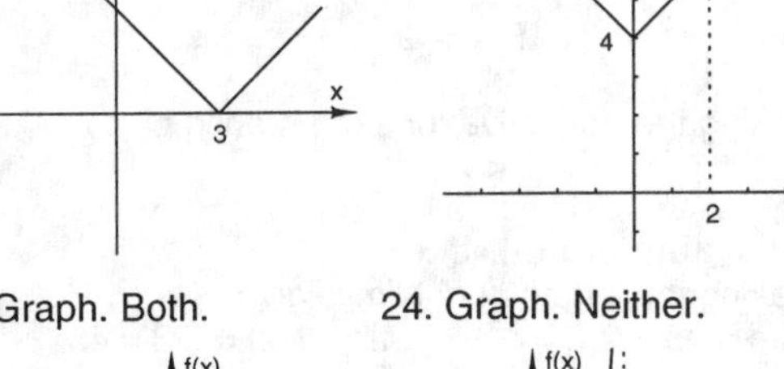

23. Graph. Both.

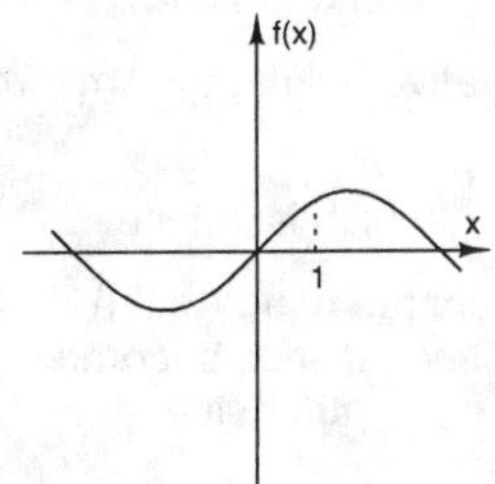

24. Graph. Neither.

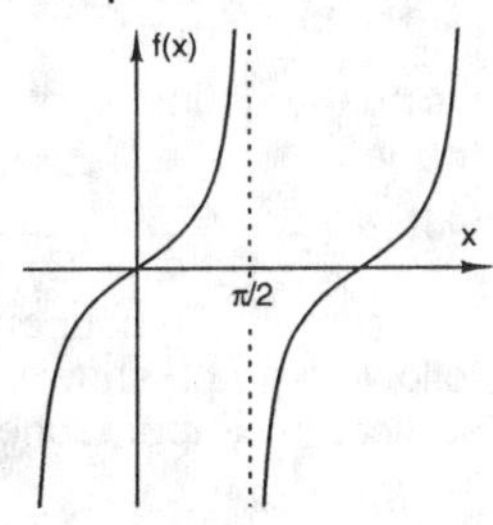

25. Graph. Neither.

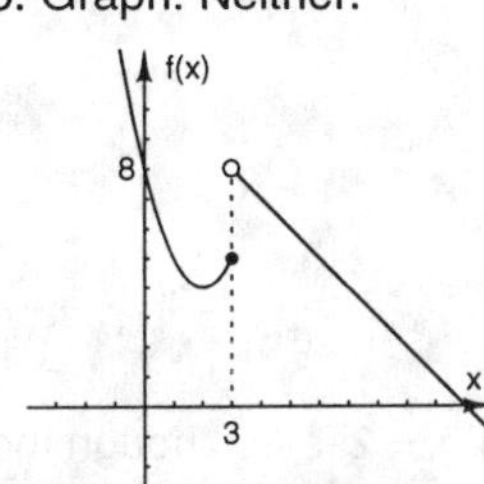

26. Graph. Both.

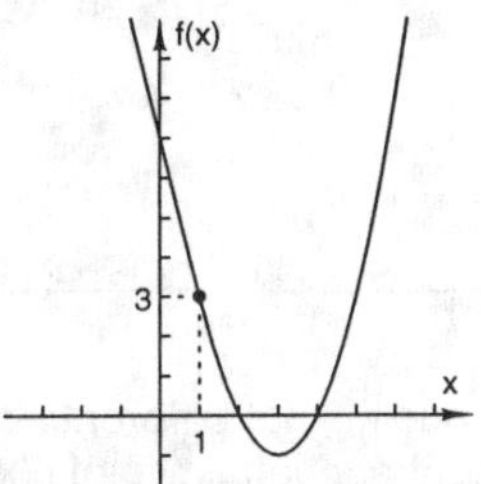

27. Graph. Neither.

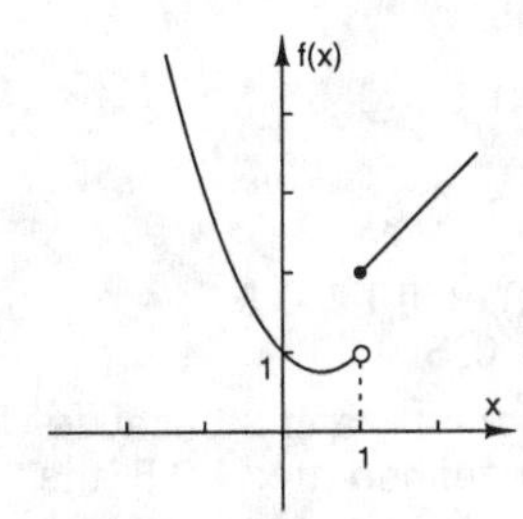

28. Not differentiable, but continuous.

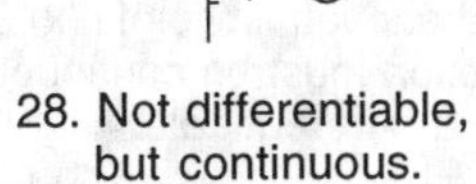

29. Graph. Neither.

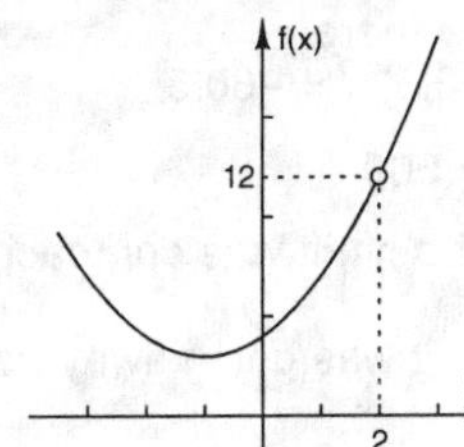

30. Graph. Neither.

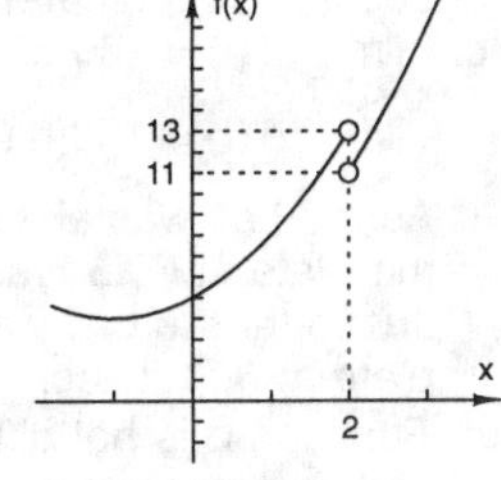

31. $f(x) = \begin{cases} x^3, \text{ if } x < 1 \\ a(x-2)^2 + b, \text{ if } x \geq 1 \end{cases}$

For f to be continuous at x = 1,
f(1) must equal $1^3 = 1$.
$\therefore a(1-2)^2 + b = 1 \Rightarrow a + b = 1$
For f to be differentiable at x = 1,
f′(1) must equal $3 \cdot 1^2 = 3$.
$\therefore 2a(1-2)^1 = 3 \Rightarrow \underline{a = -1.5}$
$b = 1 - a = 1 - (-1.5) \Rightarrow \underline{b = 2.5}$
Graph. f is differentiable at x = 1.

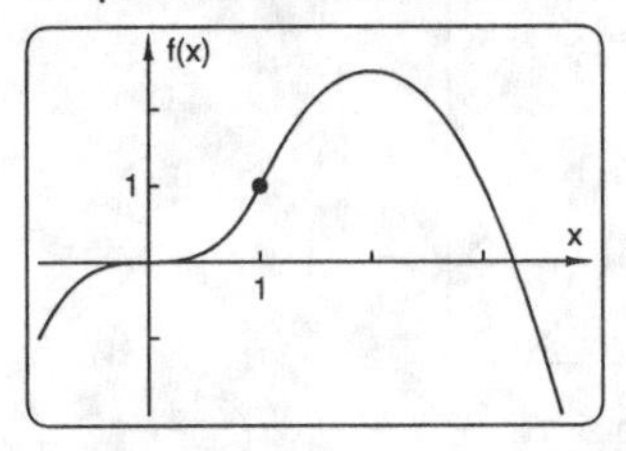

32. $f(x) = \begin{cases} -(x-3)^2 + 7, \text{ if } x \geq 2 \\ ax^3 + b, \text{ if } x < 2 \end{cases}$

For f to be continuous at x = 2,
f(2) must equal $-(2-3)^2 + 7 = 6$.
$\therefore a \cdot 2^3 + b = 6 \Rightarrow 8a + b = 6$
For f to be differentiable at x = 2,
f′(x) must equal $-2(2-3)^1 = 2$.
$\therefore 3a \cdot 2^2 = 2 \Rightarrow \underline{a = 1/6}$
$b = 6 - 8(1/6) \Rightarrow \underline{b = 14/3}$
Graph. f is differentiable at x = 2.

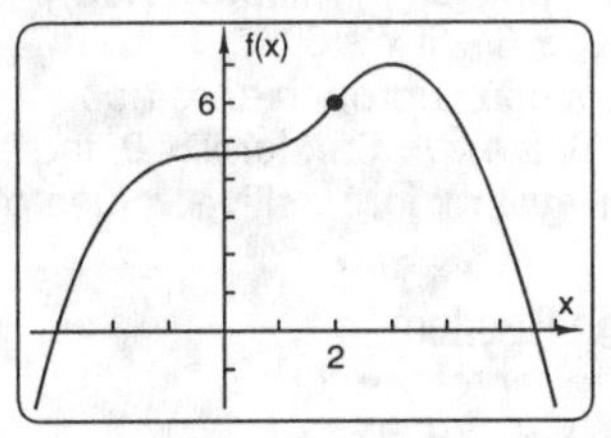

33. $f(x) = \begin{cases} ax^2 + 10, \text{ if } x < 2 \\ x^2 - 6x + b, \text{ if } x \geq 2 \end{cases}$

For f to be continuous at x = 2,
$4a + 10 = 4 - 12 + b \Rightarrow b = 4a + 18$
For f to be differentiable at x= 2,
$2a \cdot 2 = 2 \cdot 2 - 6 \Rightarrow \underline{a = -0.5}$
$b = 4(-0.5) + 18 \Rightarrow \underline{b = 16}$
Graph. f is differentiable at x = 2.

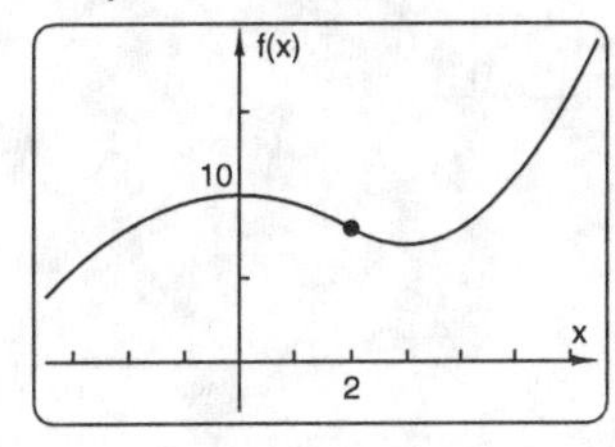

34. $f(x) = \begin{cases} a/x, \text{ if } x \le 1 \\ 12 - bx^2, \text{ if } x > 1 \end{cases}$

For f to be continuous at x = 1,
$a/1 = 12 - b \cdot 1^2 \Rightarrow a + b = 12$
For f to be differentiable at x = 1,
$-a \cdot 1^{-2} = -2b \cdot 1 \Rightarrow a = 2b$
$\therefore 2b + b = 12 \Rightarrow \underline{b = 4}$
$a = 2 \cdot 4 \Rightarrow \underline{a = 8}$
Graph. f is differentiable at x = 1.

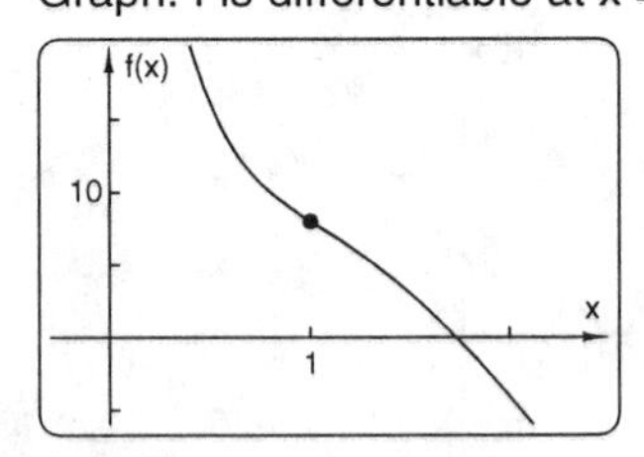

35. Railroad Curve Problem

a. $y = \begin{cases} 0, \text{ if } x < 0 \\ ax^3, \text{ if } 0 \le x \le 100 \\ x + b, \text{ if } x > 100 \end{cases}$

For y to be continuous at x = 100,
$a \cdot 100^3 = 100 + b \Rightarrow b = 1{,}000{,}000a - 100$
For y to be differentiable at x = 100,
$3a \cdot 100^2 = 1 \Rightarrow \underline{a = 1/30000}$
$b = 1{,}000{,}000/30{,}000 - 100 \Rightarrow \underline{b = -200/3}$
Check: Graph shows that y is differentiable at x = 100 with these values of a and b.

b. Rate of change of slope is (y')', abbreviated y".
y" = 0 if x < 0 and y" = 6ax if x > 0.
Both of these quantities approach zero as x approaches zero. Since y" = 6ax for x > 0, the slope increases uniformly with x for positive values of x, Q.E.D.

36. Bicycle Frame Design Problem

Equation of the linear part of the fork is
$y - 20 = 5(x - 10) \Rightarrow y = 5x - 30$

$\therefore y = \begin{cases} ax^3 + bx, \text{ if } x < 10 \\ 5x - 30, \text{ if } x \ge 10 \end{cases}$

For y to be continuous at x = 10,
$a \cdot 10^3 + b \cdot 10 = 5 \cdot 10 - 30$
$1000a + 10b = 20 \Rightarrow b = 2 - 100a$
For y to be differentiable at x = 10,
$3a \cdot 10^2 + b = 5$
$300a + (2 - 100a) = 5$
$200a = 3 \Rightarrow \underline{a = 3/200}$
$b = 2 - 100(3/200) \Rightarrow \underline{b = 0.5}$

37. $f(x) = \begin{cases} x^2 - \dfrac{|x - 2|}{x - 2}, \text{ if } x \ne 2 \\ 4, \text{ if } x = 2 \end{cases}$

Simplifying the equation for f(x) gives

$f(x) = \begin{cases} x^2 + 1, \text{ if } x < 2 \\ x^2 - 1, \text{ if } x > 2 \\ 4, \text{ if } x = 2 \end{cases}$

Taking the derivative for each branch gives

$f'(x) = \begin{cases} 2x, \text{ if } x < 2 \\ 2x, \text{ if } x > 2 \\ \text{undefined, if } x = 2 \end{cases}$

Taking the left and right limits gives
$\lim_{x \to 2^-} f'(x) = 2 \cdot 2 = 4 \qquad \lim_{x \to 2^+} f'(x) = 2 \cdot 2 = 4$
Using the definition of derivative, taking the limit from the left,
$f'(x) = \lim_{x \to 2^-} \dfrac{x^2 + 1 - 4}{x - 2} \to \dfrac{1}{0}$, which is infinite.
The same thing happens from the right. As the following graph shows, the secant lines become vertical as x approaches 2 from either side.

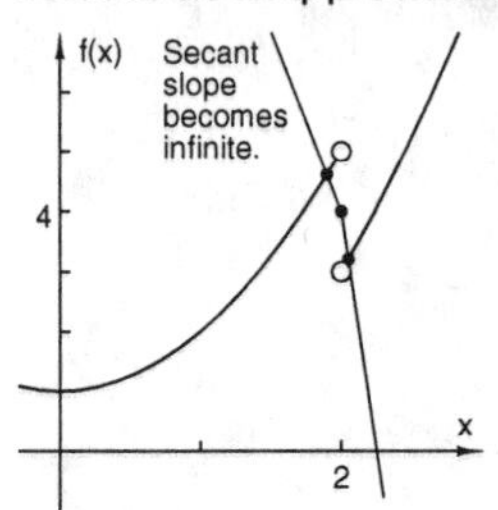

Thus f is not differentiable at x = 2, even though the right and left limits of f'(x) are equal to each other. The function must be continuous if it is to have a chance of being differentiable.

38. Baseball Line Drive Problem

a. $d(t) = \begin{cases} 60.5\left(\dfrac{0.5 - t}{0.5 + t}\right), \text{ if } t \le 0.5 \\ 150\left(2 - \dfrac{1}{t}\right), \text{ if } t \ge 0.5 \end{cases}$

$d'(t) = \begin{cases} -60.5(0.5 + t)^{-2}, \text{ if } t < 0.5 \\ 150t^{-2}, \text{ if } t > 0.5 \end{cases}$

The inequality signs must be < and > because although the function is defined at x = 0.5, the derivative is not.

b. $d'(1) = 150 \cdot 1^{-2} = 150 \Rightarrow$ d is continuous at x = 1 because it is differentiable there.

c. $\lim_{x \to 0.5^-} d'(t) = -60.5(0.5 + 0.5)^{-2} = -60.5$
$\lim_{x \to 0.5^+} d'(t) = 150(0.5)^{-2} = 600$
As the ball was about to be hit, it was approaching the plate at 60.5 ft/sec.
Just after the ball was hit, it was going away from the plate at 600 ft/sec.

d. Function d is not differentiable at t = 0.5 because d'(t) approaches different limits from both sides of x = 0.5.
Function d is continuous at t = 0.5 because you get zero as the limit of d(t) as t approaches zero from either left or right.

e. A regulation baseball diamond has the pitcher's mound 60.5 feet from home plate. Substituting zero for t gives d(0) = 60.5, confirming that the pitcher was on the mound at that time.

39. Continuity Proof Problem

a. $y = mx + b \Rightarrow y' = m$, which is independent of x.
$\therefore$ linear functions are differentiable for all x.
$\therefore$ linear functions are continuous for all x.

b. $y = ax^2 + bx + c \Rightarrow y' = 2ax + b$, which exists for all x by the closure axioms.
$\therefore$ quadratic functions are differentiable for all x.
$\therefore$ quadratic functions are continuous for all x.

c. $y = 1/x = x^{-1} \Rightarrow y' = -x^{-2}$, which exists for all $x \neq 0$ by closure and multiplicative inverse axioms.
$\therefore$ the reciprocal function is differentiable for all $x \neq 0$.
$\therefore$ the reciprocal function is continuous for all $x \neq 0$.

d. $y = x \Rightarrow y' = 1$, which is independent of x.
$\therefore$ the identity function is differentiable for all x.
$\therefore$ the identity function is continuous for all x.

e. $y = k \Rightarrow y' = 0$, which is independent of x.
$\therefore$ constant functions are differentiable for all x.
$\therefore$ constant functions are continuous for all x.

40. Differentiation Implies Continuity Proof
See text proof.

Problem Set 4-7, pages 163 to 167 — Derivative of a Parametric Function

Q1. $y' = 243x^{121}$.
Q2. $dy/dx = 2/(x-1)^2$.
Q3. $f'(x) = \cos x - x \sin x$.
Q4. $y'(x) = 5x^4 \cos x^5$.
Q5. $(d/dx)(y) = 3x^2,\ x \neq 0$.
Q6. $y' = 0$.
Q7. $\theta' = -1/\sqrt{1 - x^2}$.
Q8. Graph. ($y = \tan x$)

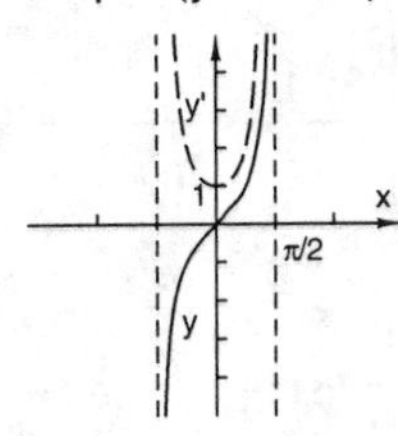

Q9. v(t) is decreasing at t = 5.
Q10. Nothing can be concluded about u(t) at t = 8.

1. Parabola Problem

a. $x = 2 + t$
$y = 3 - t^2$

t	x	y
−3	−1	−6
−2	0	−1
−1	1	2
0	2	3
1	3	2
2	4	−1
3	5	−6

b. Graph.

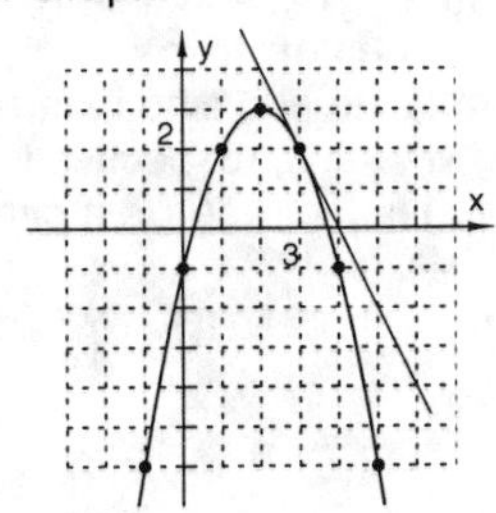

c. $\dfrac{dy}{dx} = \dfrac{dy/dt}{dx/dt} = \dfrac{-2t}{1} = -2t$
If t = 1, dy/dx = −2 and (x, y) = (3, 2).
Line through (3, 2) with slope −2 is tangent to the graph. See part b.

d. $x = 2 + t \Rightarrow t = x - 2 \Rightarrow y = 3 - (x - 2)^2$
This is the Cartesian equation of a parabola because only one of the variables is squared.

e. By direct differentiation, $dy/dx = -2(x - 2)$.
At (x, y) = (3, 2), $dy/dx = -2(3 - 2) = -2$, which agrees with part c.
$dy/dx = -2(x - 2) = -2(2 + t - 2) = -2t$, which agrees with part c.

2. Semicubical Parabola Problem

a. $x = t^2$
$y = t^3$

t	x	y
−3	9	−27
−2	4	−8
−1	1	−1
0	0	0
1	1	1
2	4	8
3	9	27

b. graph

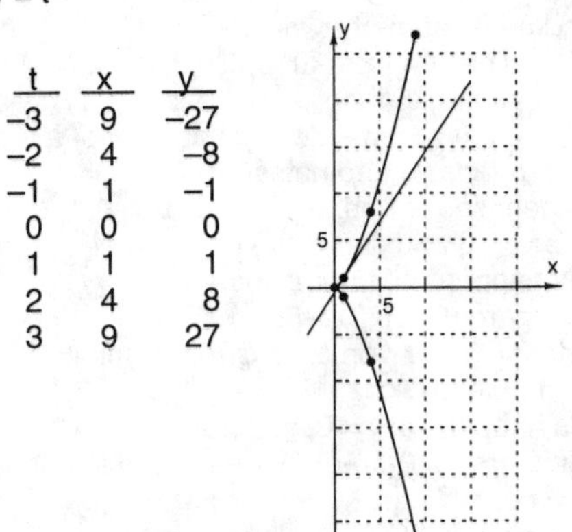

c. $\dfrac{dy}{dx} = \dfrac{dy/dt}{dx/dt} = \dfrac{3t^2}{2t} = 1.5t$
If t = 1, dy/dx = 1.5 and (x, y) = (1, 1).
Line through (1, 1) with slope 1.5 is tangent to the graph. See part b.

d. $x = t^2 \Rightarrow t = x^{1/2} \Rightarrow y = (x^{1/2})^3 \Rightarrow y = x^{1.5}$
The name *semicubical* is picked because 1.5 is half of 3, the exponent for a cubic function. The name *parabola* is used because the equation looks similar to $y = x^2$ for a parabola.

e. By direct differentiation,
$dy/dx = 1.5x^{0.5}$
At (x, y) = (1, 1), $dy/dx = 1.5 \cdot 1^{0.5} = 1.5$, which agrees with part c.

3. Ellipse Problem

a. Graph. $x = 3 \cos t$, $y = 5 \sin t$

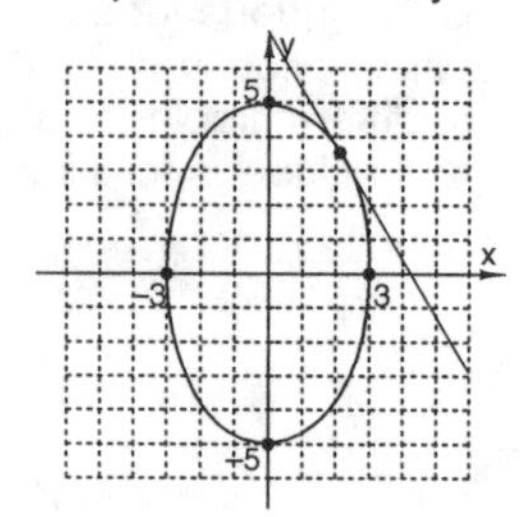

b. $\dfrac{dy}{dx} = \dfrac{5 \cos t}{-3 \sin t}$

c. If $t = \pi/4$, $x = 3\sqrt{2}/2$ and $y = 5\sqrt{2}/2$.

$(x, y) = (2.121..., 3.535...)$

$\dfrac{dy}{dx} = \dfrac{5 \cos (\pi/4)}{-3 \sin (\pi/4)} = -5/3$

Graph, part a.

The line is tangent to the graph.

d. False. The line from (0, 0) to (2.1..., 3.5...) does not make an angle of 45° with the x-axis. [This shows that the t in parametric functions is not the same as the θ in polar coordinates.]

e. Tangent line is horizontal if $dy/dx = 0$.

$\therefore \cos t = 0$ and $\sin t \neq 0$.

This happens at $t = \pi/2, 3\pi/2, \ldots$.

Points are (0, 5), (0, −5).

Tangent line is vertical if dy/dx is infinite.

$\therefore \sin t = 0$ and $\cos t \neq 0$.

This happens at $t = 0, \pi, 2\pi, \ldots$.

Points are (3, 0), (−3, 0). See graph in part a.

f. $x/3 = \cos t \Rightarrow (x/3)^2 = \cos^2 t$

$y/5 = \sin t \Rightarrow (y/5)^2 = \sin^2 t$

Adding left and right sides of the equations gives $(x/3)^2 + (y/5)^2 = \cos^2 t + \sin^2 t$.

$\therefore (x/3)^2 + (y/5)^2 = 1$, which is a standard form of the equation of an ellipse centered at the origin, with x-radius 3 and y-radius 5.

4. Astroid Problem

a. Graph. $x = 8 \cos^3 t$, $y = 8 \sin^3 t$

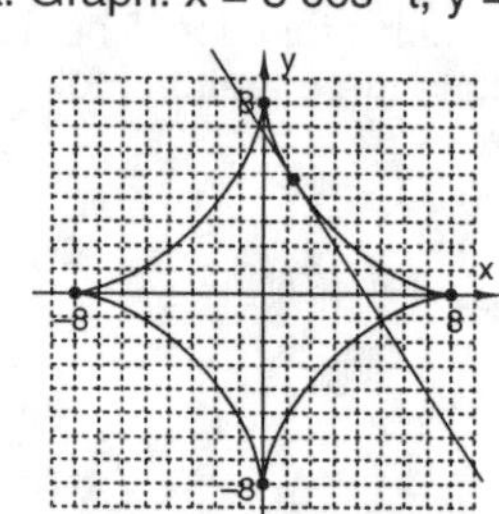

b. $\dfrac{dy}{dx} = \dfrac{24 \sin^2 t \cos t}{24 \cos^2 t (-\sin t)} = -\dfrac{\sin t}{\cos t} = -\tan t$

$\therefore dy/dx = -\tan t$

c. If $t = 1$, $x = 8 \cos^3 1 = 1.2618...$, and $y = 8 \sin^3 1 = 4.7665...$

$(x, y) = (1.2618..., 4.7665...)$

At $t = 1$, $dy/dx = -\tan 1 = -1.5574....$

Graph, part a.

The line is tangent to the graph.

d. $dx/dt = -24 \cos^2 t \sin t$

$dy/dt = 24 \sin^2 t \cos t$

The cusps occur where t is a multiple of $\pi/2$.

At each such value, dx/dt and dy/dt equal zero.

$t = 0$ gives the cusp at (8, 0).

$\lim_{t \to 0} (dy/dx) = \lim_{t \to 0} (-\tan t) = -\tan 0 = 0$

So the graph becomes horizontal at (8, 0).

$t = \pi/2$ gives the cusp at (0, 8).

$\lim_{t \to \pi/2} (dy/dx) = \lim_{t \to \pi/2} (-\tan t)$, which is infinite.

So the graph becomes vertical at (0, 8).

e. $x/8 = \cos^3 t \Rightarrow (x/8)^{2/3} = \cos^2 t$

$y/8 = \sin^3 t \Rightarrow (y/8)^{3/2} = \sin^2 t$

$\therefore (x/8)^{2/3} + (y/8)^{2/3} = \cos^2 t + \sin^2 t$

$x^{2/3} + y^{2/3} = 4$

5. Circle Problem

a. Graph. $x = 6 + 5 \cos t$, $y = 3 + 5 \sin t$

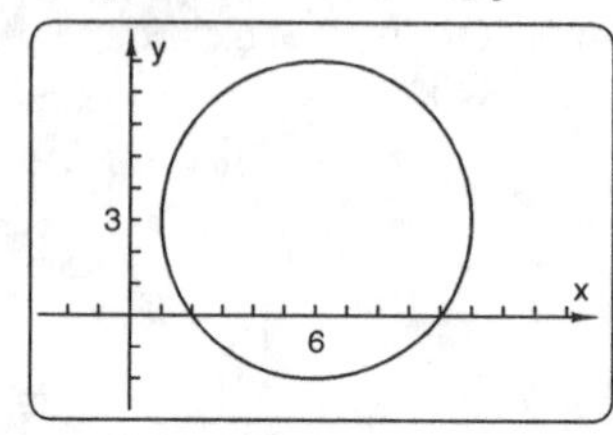

b. $\dfrac{dy}{dx} = \dfrac{5 \cos t}{-5 \sin t} \Rightarrow dy/dx = -\cot t$

c. $dy/dx = 0$ if $\cos t = 0$ and $\sin t \neq 0$.

$\therefore t = 0.5\pi, 1.5\pi, 2.5\pi, \ldots$

dy/dx is infinite if $\sin t = 0$ and $\cos t \neq 0$.

$\therefore t = 0, \pi, 2\pi, \ldots$

At a point where dy/dx is infinite, dx/dt must be 0. If $dy/dt \neq 0$, dy/dx is infinite. If $dy/dt = 0$, dy/dx is indeterminate, and could be infinite.

d. $\dfrac{x-6}{5} = \cos t$ and $\dfrac{y-3}{5} = \sin t$

$\left(\dfrac{x-6}{5}\right)^2 + \left(\dfrac{y-3}{5}\right)^2 = \cos^2 t + \sin^2 t$

$\left(\dfrac{x-6}{5}\right)^2 + \left(\dfrac{y-3}{5}\right)^2 = 1$

This is a standard form of the equation of a circle centered at (6, 3) with radius 5.

e. The 6 and 3 added in the original equations are the x- and y-coordinates of the center, respectively.

The coefficients, 5, for cosine and sine in the original equations are the x- and y-radii, respectively. Since the x- and y-radii are equal, the graph is a circle.

6. Line Segment Problem

$x = \cos^2 t$

$y = \sin^2 t$

$$\frac{dy}{dx} = \frac{2 \cos t (-\sin t)}{2 \sin t \cos t} = -1 \ (\cos t \neq 0, \sin t \neq 0)$$

Graph.

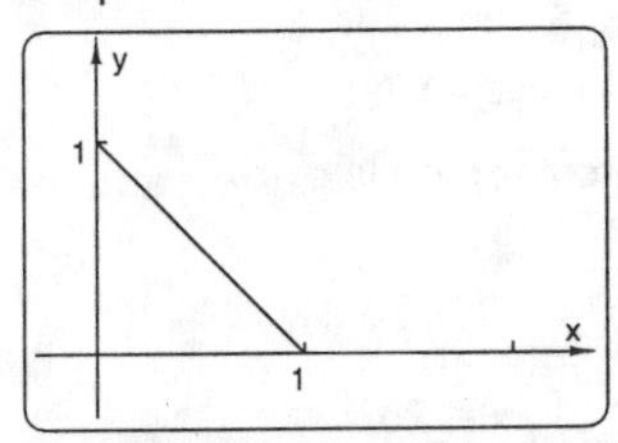

The graph is a line segment with a slope of −1.

$x + y = \cos^2 t + \sin^2 t \Rightarrow x + y = 1$

This is the equation of a line with slope −1, confirming what was observed on the graph.

The parametric equations restrict the ranges of x and y to the first quadrant, no matter what is the domain of t. This is true because $\cos^2 t$ and $\sin^2 t$ are never negative.

The Cartesian equation allows

$-\infty < x < \infty$ and $-\infty < y < \infty$.

7. Deltoid Problem

a. $x = 2 \cos t + \cos 2t$

$y = 2 \sin t - \sin 2t$

Grapher confirms figure in text.

b. $$\frac{dy}{dx} = \frac{2 \cos t - 2 \cos 2t}{-2 \sin t - 2 \sin 2t} = \frac{\cos t - \cos 2t}{-\sin t - \sin 2t}$$

c. Cusps occur where both dx/dt and dy/dt = 0.

Graphical solution shows that this occurs at $t = 0, t = 2\pi/3, t = 4\pi/3, t = 2\pi, \ldots$

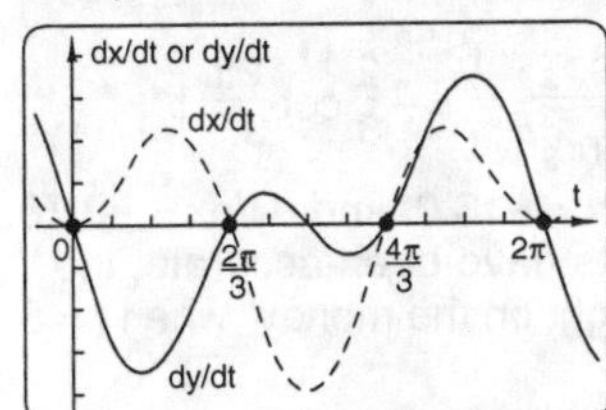

At t = 0, 2π, . . ., the tangent appears to be horizontal. At t = 2π/3, 4π/3, . . ., there appears to be a tangent line but not a horizontal one.

A numerical solution shows the following values as t approaches 2π/3:

t	dy/dx
2π/3 − 0.1	−1.547849...
2π/3 − 0.01	−1.712222...
2π/3 − 0.001	−1.730052...
2π/3	Indeterminate
2π/3 + 0.001	−1.734052...
2π/3 + 0.01	−1.752225...
2π/3 + 0.1	−1.951213...

dy/dx seems to be approaching about −1.732 as t approaches 2π/3.

[The exact answer is $-\sqrt{3}$, which students will be able to prove easily with l'Hospital's rule after they have studied Section 6-8. Joan Gell and Cavan Fang have shown clever trigonometric transformations that "remove" the removable discontinuity and lead to the same answer. These are:

1. Use the sum and product properties on dy/dx:

$$\frac{dy}{dx} = \frac{2 \sin 1.5t \sin 0.5t}{-2 \sin 1.5t \cos 0.5t} = -\tan 0.5t \text{ if } dx/dt \neq 0$$

As $t \to 2\pi/3$, $dy/dx \to -\tan(\pi/3) = -\sqrt{3}$.

2. Use the double argument properties on dy/dx:

$$\frac{dy}{dx} = \frac{\cos t - (2 \cos^2 t - 1)}{-(\sin t + 2 \sin t \cos t)}$$

$$= \frac{(1 - \cos t)(1 + 2 \cos t)}{-(\sin t)(1 + 2 \cos t)} = \frac{1 - \cos t}{-\sin t},$$

which approaches $-\sqrt{3}$ as $t \to 2\pi/3$.]

8. Witch of Agnesi Problem

a. $x = 2a \tan t = 6 \tan t$

$y = 2a \cos^2 t = 6 \cos^2 t$

Grapher confirms figure in text.

b. $$\frac{dy}{dx} = \frac{4a \cos t (-\sin t)}{2a \sec^2 t} = -2 \cos^3 t \sin t$$

(The answer is independent of a.)

c. $$x^2 = 4a^2 \tan^2 t = \frac{4a^2 \sin^2 t}{\cos^2 t} = \frac{4a^2(1 - \cos^2 t)}{\cos^2 t}$$

$y = 2a \cos^2 t \Rightarrow \cos^2 t = y/(2a)$

$$\therefore x^2 = \frac{4a^2(1 - y/(2a))}{y/(2a)} = \frac{4a^2(2a - y)}{y}$$

$x^2 y = 8a^3 - 4a^2 y \Rightarrow (x^2 + 4a^2)y = 8a^3$

$$y = \frac{8a^3}{x^2 + 4a^2}$$

$$a = 3 \Rightarrow y = \frac{216}{x^2 + 36}$$

d. $$\frac{dy}{dx} = \frac{0 - 8a^3(2x)}{(x^2 + 4a^2)^2} = \frac{-16a^3 x}{(x^2 + 4a^2)^2}$$

e. At $t = \pi/4$, $x = 2a \tan(\pi/4) = 2a$.

From part d.,

$$\frac{dy}{dx} = \frac{-16a^3(2a)}{((2a)^2 + 4a^2)^2} = \frac{-32a^4}{64a^4} = -1/2$$

From part b.

$$\frac{dy}{dx} = -2 \cos^3(\pi/4) \sin(\pi/4)$$

$= -2(\sqrt{2}/2)^3 (\sqrt{2}/2) = -1/2$, which agrees.

At $t = \pi/4$, $x = 2a \tan(\pi/4) = 2a = 6$

$y = 2a \cos^2(\pi/4) = 2a(1/2) = a = 3$

A line through (6, 3) with slope −1/2 is tangent to the graph at that point.

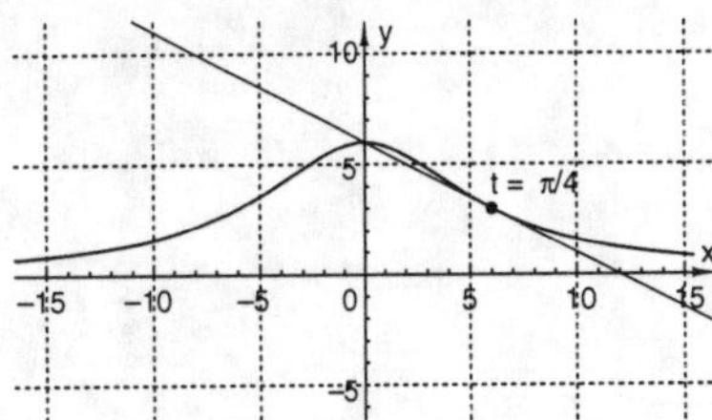

9. Involute Problem

a. $x = \cos t + t \sin t$
$y = \sin t - t \cos t$
Grapher confirms figure in text.
[Note: In the derivation of these equations from the geometric definition of *involute,*
$x = \cos t + t \cos (t - \pi/2)$
$y = \sin t + t \sin (t - \pi/2)$
$(\cos t, \sin t)$ is the point of tangency of the string.
Since the circle is a unit circle, the length of the string is also t, the central angle in radians.
The string makes an angle of $(t - \pi/2)$ with the positive x-axis, so that
$(t \cos (t - \pi/2), t \sin (t - \pi/2))$ is a vector representing the unwound string.
The cofunction properties and odd-even properties from trig are used to simplify the equations so that the calculus will be easier.]

b. $\dfrac{dy}{dx} = \dfrac{\cos t - [\cos t + t(-\sin t)]}{-\sin t + [\sin t + t \cos t]} = \dfrac{t \sin t}{t \cos t}$
$= \tan t$

c. At $t = \pi$, $dy/dt = \tan \pi = 0$.
The string will be pointing straight up from the x-axis.
The diagram shows that the tangent to the graph is horizontal at this point.

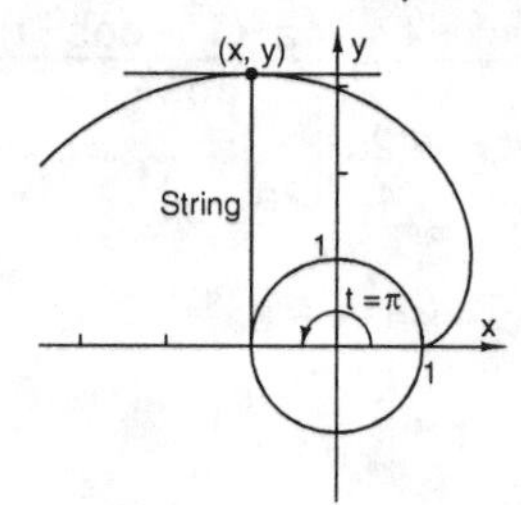

10. Clock Problem

a. x starts at a middle point and increases.
y starts at a high point and decreases.
$\therefore x = 25 + 15 \sin Bt$
$y = 20 + 15 \cos Bt$
The period is 60 seconds.
So $B = 2\pi/60 = \pi/30$
$\therefore x = 25 + 15 \sin \frac{\pi}{30} t$
$y = 20 + 15 \cos \frac{\pi}{30} t$

b. $dx/dt = \frac{\pi}{2} \cos \frac{\pi}{30} t$
$dy/dt = -\frac{\pi}{2} \sin \frac{\pi}{30} t$
At $t = 5$,
$dx/dt = \frac{\pi}{2} \cos \frac{\pi}{6} = \pi\sqrt{3}/4 = 1.3603...$
$dy/dt = -\frac{\pi}{2} \sin \frac{\pi}{6} = -\pi/4 = -0.7853...$

c. The slope of the circular path is dy/dx.
At $t = 5$,
$\dfrac{dy}{dx} = \dfrac{-\pi/4}{\pi\sqrt{3}/4} = -1/\sqrt{3} = -0.5773...$

d. $\dfrac{x - 25}{15} = \sin \dfrac{\pi}{30} t \Rightarrow \left(\dfrac{x - 25}{15}\right)^2 = \sin^2 \dfrac{\pi}{30} t$
$\dfrac{y - 20}{15} = \cos \dfrac{\pi}{30} t \Rightarrow \left(\dfrac{y - 20}{15}\right)^2 = \cos^2 \dfrac{\pi}{30} t$
Since $\sin^2 \frac{\pi}{30} t + \cos^2 \frac{\pi}{30} = 1$,
$\left(\dfrac{x - 25}{15}\right)^2 + \left(\dfrac{y - 20}{15}\right)^2 = 1$
This is a standard form of the equation of a circle centered at (25, 20) with radius 15, confirming that the path really is a circle.

11. Pendulum Project

The actual solutions will vary depending on the period of the pendulum, as determined by the length of the string. The following solution supposes that the period turns out to be 3.1 seconds.
$x = 30 \cos \dfrac{2\pi}{3.1} t$
$y = 20 \sin \dfrac{2\pi}{3.1} t$
$\dfrac{dy}{dx} = \dfrac{(40\pi/3.1) \cos \frac{2\pi}{3.1} t}{-(60\pi/3.1) \sin \frac{2\pi}{3.1} t} = -\dfrac{2}{3} \cot \dfrac{2\pi}{3.1} t$
At $t = 5$, $x \approx -22.8$, $y \approx -13.0$, and $dy/dx \approx -0.78$.
If the measurements have been accurate, the pendulum will be "right on the money" when $t = 5$.

12. Spring Problem

The graph looks like an ellipse that moves in the x-direction as t increases. Since y starts at a high point and varies between 5 and 1, the ellipse has center at y = 3 and y-radius of 2. Thus an equation for y would be $y = 3 + 2\cos t$.

x starts at 0 and increases. If the ellipse had x-radius of 0.5, an equation for x would be $x = 0.5\sin t$. The graph of this ellipse is

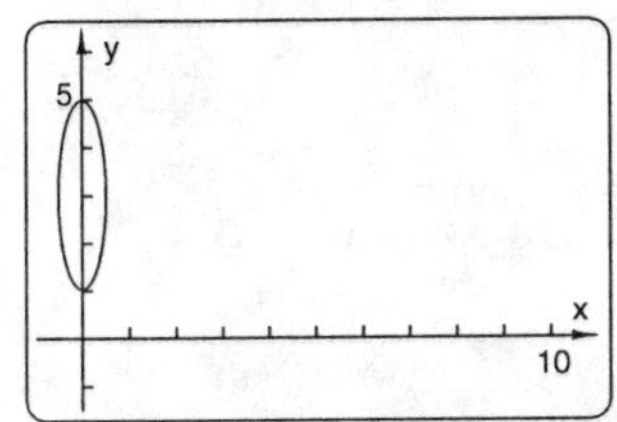

The graph seems to move over one unit to the right each cycle. Thus, if t increases by 2π, x increases by 1. The equations are thus

$x = t/(2\pi) + 0.5\sin t$

$y = 3 + 2\cos t$

The graph below duplicates the one in the text.

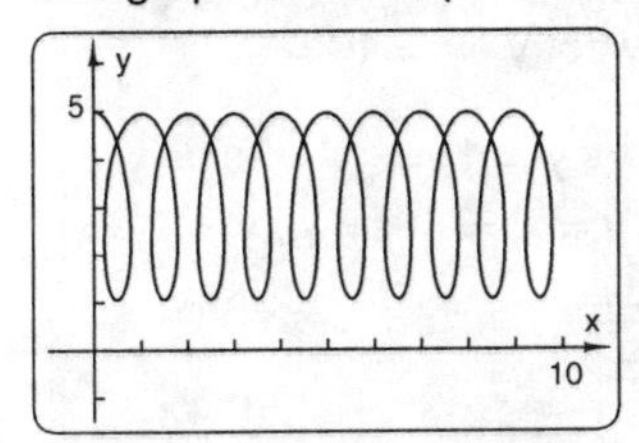

To locate "interesting" features,

$$\frac{dy}{dx} = \frac{dy/dt}{dx/dt} = \frac{-2\sin t}{1/(2\pi) + 0.5\cos t}$$

For horizontal tangents, $dy/dt = 0$ and $dx/dt \neq 0$.

$\therefore 2\sin t = 0 \Leftrightarrow t = 0 + \pi n$ (n an integer)

Thus, x = 0, 0.5, 1, 1.5, ...

For vertical tangents, $dx/dt = 0$ and $dy/dt \neq 0$.

$\therefore 1/(2\pi) + 0.5\cos t = 0 \Leftrightarrow \cos t = -1/\pi$

Solving numerically for t gives

$t = 1.8947... + 2\pi n$ or $4.3884... + 2\pi n$.

For crossing points, x = 0.5, 1.5, 2.5, . . . from symmetry on the graph. If x = 0.5, then

$1/(2\pi)t + 0.5\sin t = 0.5$.

Solving numerically for the value of t closest to 0, t = 0.8278...

$y(0.8278...) = 3 + 2\cos 0.8278... = 4.3529...$

A crossing point is (0.5, 4.3529...) at t = 0.8278... .

13. Lissajous Curves

a. $x = \cos 3t$

$y = \sin t$

Grapher confirms figure in text.

b. Graph. ($x = \cos 4t$, $y = \sin t$)

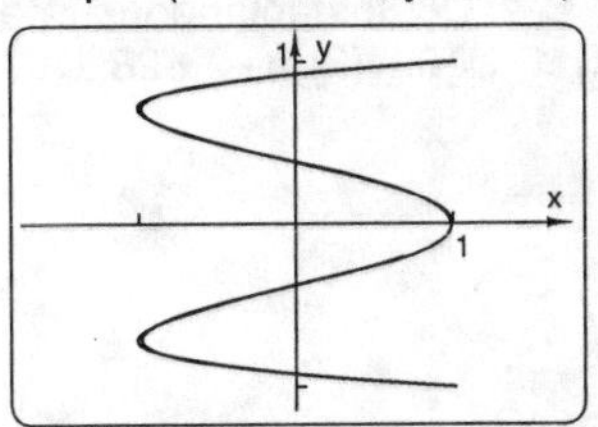

c. If n is an even number, the graph comes to endpoints and retraces its path, making two complete cycles as t goes from 0 to 2π.

If n is an odd number, the graph does not come to endpoints. It makes one complete cycle as t goes from 0 to 2π.

d. i. Graph. ($x = \cos 5t$, $y = \sin t$)

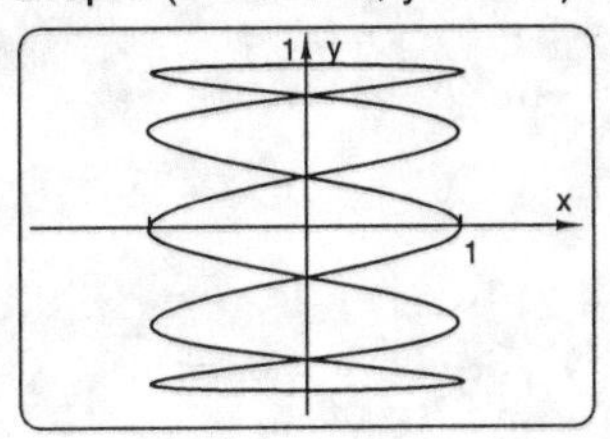

ii. Graph. ($x = \cos 6t$, $y = \sin t$)

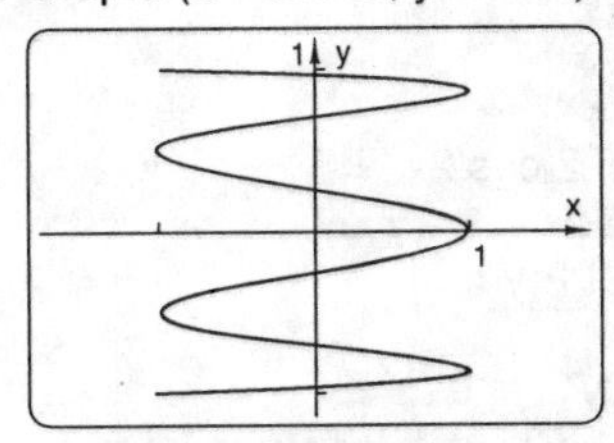

e. See grapher graphs in part d.

f. Graph, n = 1. ($x = \cos t$, $y = \sin t$)

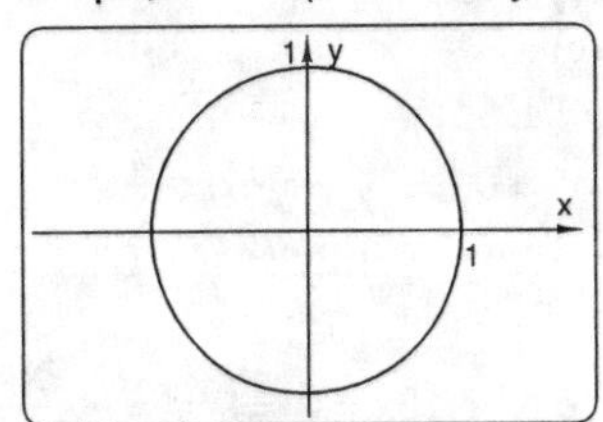

Graph, n = 2. ($x = \cos 2t$, $y = \sin t$)

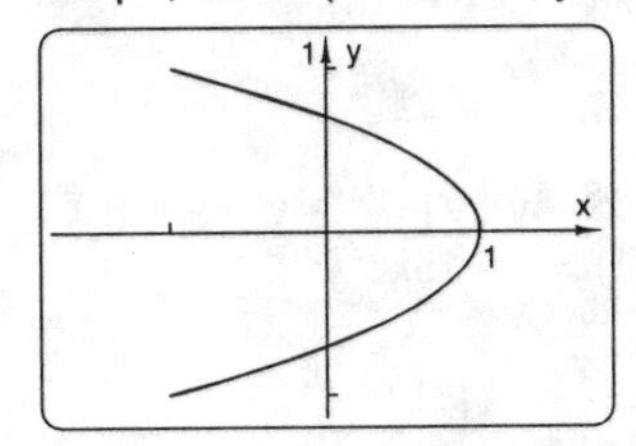

If n = 1, the graph is a circle.

If n = 2, the graph is a parabola.

Q1. $f(\pi) = -1$ Q2. $y' = 2001x^{2000}$
Q3. limit = 5 Q4. $f'(u) = -\csc^2 u$
Q5. . . . product of x and y Q6. $y' = 1/(1 + 9x^2)$
Q7. y could equal x^3 Q8. Instantaneous rate
Q9. Graph. ($y = 2 - x$) Q10. $v(3) = -2.828...$

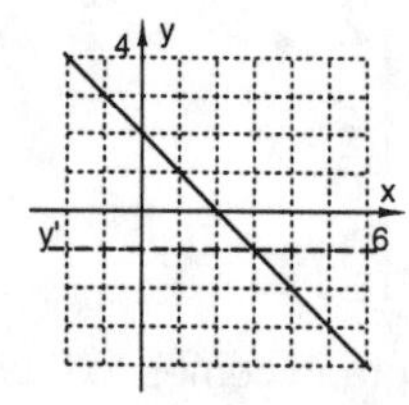

1. $x^3 + 7y^4 = 13 \Rightarrow 3x^2 + 28y^3\, y' = 0 \Rightarrow y' = -\dfrac{3x^2}{28y^3}$

2. $3x^5 - y^4 = 22 \Rightarrow 15x^4 - 4y^3\, y' = 0 \Rightarrow y' = \dfrac{15x^4}{4y^3}$

3. $x^6 y^9 + 3x - y^3 = 10^4 \Rightarrow$
$6x^5y^9 + 9x^6y^8y' + 3 - 3y^2y' = 0 \Rightarrow$
$y'(9x^6y^8 - 3y^2) = -6x^5y^9 - 3 \Rightarrow$
$y' = \dfrac{2x^5y^9 + 1}{y^2 - 3x^6 y^8}$

4. $4x + 8x^2y^6 + y^4 = 21^3 \Rightarrow$
$4 + 16xy^6 + 48x^2y^5y' + 4y^3\, y' = 0 \Rightarrow$
$y'(48x^2y^5 + 4y^3) = -4 - 16xy^6 \Rightarrow$
$y' = \dfrac{-1 - 4xy^6}{12x^2y^5 + y^3}$

5. $x + xy + y = \sin 2x \Rightarrow$
$1 + y + xy' + y' = 2\cos 2x \Rightarrow$
$y'(x + 1) = 2\cos 2x - 1 - y \Rightarrow$
$y' = \dfrac{2\cos 2x - 1 - y}{x + 1}$

6. $\cos(xy) = x - 2y$
$\Rightarrow -\sin(xy)(y + xy') = 1 - 2y'$
$\Rightarrow y'(-x\sin(xy) + 2) = 1 + y\sin(xy)$
$\Rightarrow y' = \dfrac{1 + y\sin(xy)}{2 - x\sin(xy)}$

7. $x^{0.5} - y^{0.5} = 13 \Rightarrow$
$0.5x^{-0.5} - 0.5y^{-0.5}\, y' = 0 \Rightarrow y' = y^{0.5}/x^{0.5}$

8. $x^{1.2} + y^{1.2} = 64 \Rightarrow 1.2x^{0.2} + 1.2y^{0.2}\, y' = 0$
$\Rightarrow y' = -x^{0.2}/y^{0.2}$

9. $4y^2 + 9x^2 = 36 \Rightarrow 8yy' + 18x = 0 \Rightarrow y' = -\dfrac{9x}{4y}$

10. $25y^2 - 16x^2 = 400 \Rightarrow 50yy' - 32x = 0$
$\Rightarrow y' = \dfrac{16x}{25y}$

11. $(x^3y^4)^5 = x - y \Rightarrow$
$5(x^3y^4)^4\,(3x^2y^4 + x^3 \cdot 4y^3\, y') = 1 - y'$
$\Rightarrow y'(20x^{15}\, y^{19} + 1) = 1 - 15x^{14}y^{20}$
$\Rightarrow y' = \dfrac{1 - 15x^{14}y^{20}}{1 + 20x^{15}y^{19}}$

12. $(xy)^6 = x + y \Rightarrow$
$6(xy)^5\,(y + xy') = 1 + y' \Rightarrow$
$y'(6x^6y^5 - 1) = 1 - 6x^5y^6 \Rightarrow$
$y' = -\dfrac{1 - 6x^5y^6}{1 - 6x^6y^5}$

13. $\cos^2 x + \sin^2 y = 1 \Rightarrow$
$2\cos x \cdot (-\sin x) + 2\sin y \cdot \cos y \cdot y' = 0 \Rightarrow$
$y' = \dfrac{\cos x \sin x}{\cos y \sin y}$

14. $\sec^2 y - \tan^2 x = 1 \Rightarrow$
$2\sec y \cdot \sec y \tan y \cdot y' - 2\tan x \cdot \sec^2 x = 0 \Rightarrow$
$y' = \dfrac{\sec^2 x \tan x}{\sec^2 y \tan y}$

15. $\tan(xy) = xy \Rightarrow$
$\sec^2(xy) \cdot (y + xy') = y + xy' \Rightarrow$
$y'(x\sec^2(xy) - x) = y - \sec^2(xy) \cdot y \Rightarrow$
$y' = \dfrac{y(1 - \sec^2(xy))}{x(\sec^2(xy) - 1)} \Rightarrow y' = -\dfrac{y}{x}$

16. $\cos(xy) = xy \Rightarrow$
$-\sin(xy) \cdot (y + xy') = y + xy' \Rightarrow$
$y'(-x - x\sin(xy)) = y + y\sin(xy) \Rightarrow$
$y' = \dfrac{y(1 + \sin(xy))}{x(-1 - \sin(xy))} \Rightarrow y' = -\dfrac{y}{x}$

17. $\sin y = x \Rightarrow \cos y \cdot y' = 1 \Rightarrow y' = \sec y$

18. $\cos y = x \Rightarrow -\sin y \cdot y' = 1 \Rightarrow y' = -\csc y$

19. $\csc y = x \Rightarrow -\csc y \cot y \cdot y' = 1 \Rightarrow$
$y' = -\sin y \tan y$

20. $\cot y = x \Rightarrow -\csc^2 y \cdot y' = 1 \Rightarrow y' = -\sin^2 y$

21. $y = \cos^{-1} x \Rightarrow \cos y = x \Rightarrow -\sin y \cdot y' = 1 \Rightarrow$
$y' = -\dfrac{1}{\sin y} = -\dfrac{1}{\sqrt{1 - x^2}}$

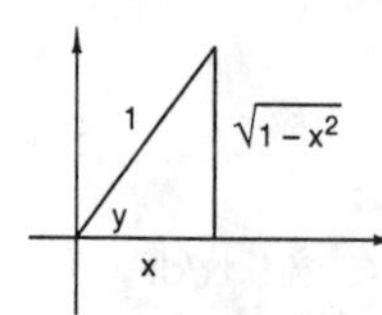

22. $y = \tan^{-1} x \Rightarrow \tan y = x \Rightarrow \sec^2 y \cdot y' = 1 \Rightarrow$
$y' = \dfrac{1}{\sec^2 y} = \dfrac{1}{1 + x^2}$

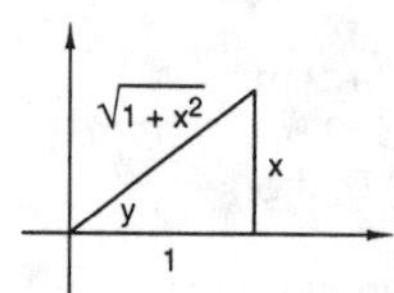

23. $y = x^{11/5} \Rightarrow y^5 = x^{11} \Rightarrow 5y^4 \cdot y' = 11x^{10} \Rightarrow$
$y' = \dfrac{11x^{10}}{5y^4} = \dfrac{11x^{10}}{5(x^{11/5})^4} = \dfrac{11x^{10}}{5x^{44/5}} = \frac{11}{5}\, x^{6/5}$,
which is the answer obtained using the derivative of a power formula, Q.E.D.

24. Derivative of a Rational Power
Prove that if $y = x^n$, where $n = a/b$ and a and b are integers, then $y' = na^{n-1}$.
Proof:
$y = x^n = x^{a/b} \Rightarrow y^b = x^a$.
Since a and b are integers,
$by^{b-1}\, y' = ax^{a-1}$
$y' = \dfrac{ax^{a-1}}{by^{b-1}} = \dfrac{ax^{a-1}}{b(x^{a/b})^{b-1}} = \dfrac{ax^{a-1}}{bx^{a-a/b}} = \dfrac{a}{b}\, x^{a-1-(a-a/b)}$
$= \dfrac{a}{b}\, x^{a/b-1} = nx^{n-1}$, Q.E.D.

25. Circle Problem

a. $x^2 + y^2 = 100$

At (–6, 8), $(-6)^2 + 8^2 = 100$, which shows that (–6, 8) is on the graph, Q.E.D.

b. $x^2 + y^2 = 100 \Rightarrow 2x + 2y \cdot dy/dx = 0 \Rightarrow dy/dx = -x/y$

At (–6, 8), $dy/dx = -(-6)/8 = 0.75$.

A line at (–6, 8) with slope 0.75 is tangent to the graph, showing that the answer is reasonable.

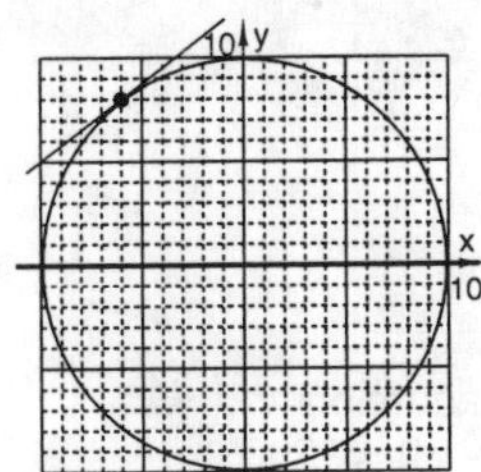

c. $x = 10 \cos t$

$y = 10 \sin t$

$$\frac{dy}{dx} = \frac{10 \cos t}{-10 \sin t} = -\frac{\cos t}{\sin t}$$

At $x = -6$, $t = \cos^{-1}(-0.6)$

$\sin(\cos^{-1}(-0.6)) = 0.8$

$$\therefore \frac{dy}{dx} = -\frac{-0.6}{0.8} = 0.75,$$

which agrees with part b., Q.E.D.

26. Hyperbola Problem

a. $x^2 - y^2 = 36$

At (10, –8), $10^2 - (-8)^2 = 36$, which shows that (10, –8) is on the graph, Q.E.D.

b. $x^2 - y^2 = 36 \Rightarrow 2x - 2y \cdot dy/dx = 0 \Rightarrow dy/dx = x/y$

At (10, –8), $dy/dx = 10/(-8) = -1.25$.

A line at (10, –8) with slope –1.25 is tangent to the graph, showing that the answer is reasonable.

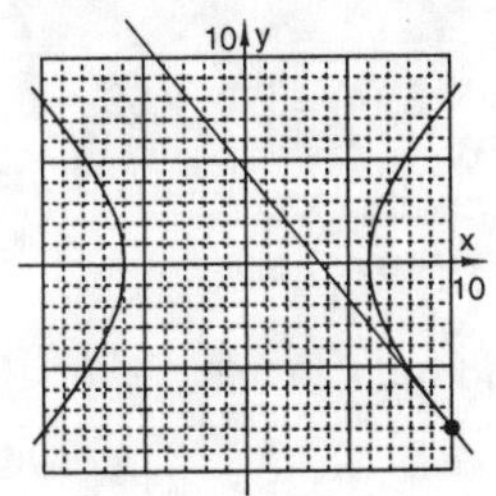

c. $x = 6 \sec t$

$y = 6 \tan t$

$$\frac{dy}{dx} = \frac{6 \sec t \tan t}{6 \sec^2 t} = \frac{\tan t}{\sec t}$$

At $x = 10$, $t = \pm\sec^{-1}(10/6)$.

$\tan(\pm\sec^{-1}(10/6)) = \pm 8/6$.

Choose the negative value, since $y < 0$.

$$\therefore \frac{dy}{dx} = \frac{-10/6}{8/6} = -1.25,$$

which agrees with part b., Q.E.D.

27. Cubic Circle Problem

a. $x^3 + y^3 = 64 \Rightarrow 3x^2 + 3y^2 \cdot dy/dx = 0 \Rightarrow$

$dy/dx = -x^2/y^2$

$x = 0$: $y^3 = 64 \Rightarrow y = 4$.

$\therefore dy/dx = -0/16 = 0$

The tangent is horizontal (see graph below).

$x = 2$: $8 + y^3 = 64 \Rightarrow y^3 = 56 \Rightarrow y = 3.8258...$

$\therefore dy/dx = -2^2/(3.8258...)^2 = -0.2732...$.

The tangent line has a small negative slope, which agrees with the graph.

$x = 4$: $64 + y^3 = 64 \Rightarrow y = 0$.

$\therefore dy/dx = -4^2/0$, which is infinite.

The tangent line is vertical.

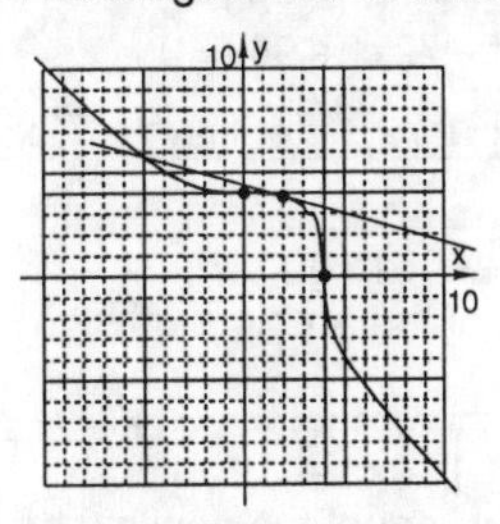

b. $y = x$: $x^3 + x^3 = 64 \Rightarrow x^3 = 32 \Rightarrow x = 3.1748...$

$dy/dx = -x^2/y^2 = -x^2/x^2 = -1$

c. $y = (64 - x^3)^{1/3}$

As x becomes infinite, $(64 - x^3)^{1/3}$ gets closer to $(-x^3)^{1/3}$, which equals $-x$. The graph has a diagonal asymptote at $y = -x$, and $dy/dx \to -1$.

d. By analogy with the equation of a circle, such as $x^2 + y^2 = 64$.

28. Ovals of Cassini Problem

a. First simplify the equation.

$[(x-6)^2 + y^2][(x+6)^2 + y^2] = 1200$

$(x-6)^2(x+6)^2 + (x-6)^2y^2 + (x+6)^2y^2 + y^4 = 1200$

$(x^2 - 36)^2 + (x^2 - 12x + 36 + x^2 + 12x + 36)y^2 + y^4 = 1200$

$x^4 - 72x^2 + 1296 + 2x^2y^2 + 72y^2 + y^4 = 1200$

$x^4 - 72x^2 + 2x^2y^2 + 72y^2 + y^4 = -96$

Differentiate the simplified equation implicitly.

$4x^3 - 144x + 4xy^2 + 4x^2y \cdot dy/dx + 144y \cdot dy/dx + 4y^3 \cdot dy/dx = 0$

$(4x^2y + 144y + 4y^3) \cdot dy/dx = -4x^3 + 144x - 4xy^2$

$$\frac{dy}{dx} = \frac{-x^3 + 36x - xy^2}{x^2y + 36y + y^3}$$

At $x = 8$: $(4 + y^2)(196 + y^2) = 1200$

$784 + 200y^2 + y^4 = 1200$

$y^4 + 200y^2 - 416 = 0$

$$y^2 = \frac{-200 \pm \sqrt{41664}}{2} = 2.058806... \text{ or } -202.0...$$

$y = \pm 1.4348542...$ (No other real solutions.)

At (8, 1.434...), $dy/dx = -1.64211...$.

At (8, –1.434...), $dy/dx = 1.64211...$.

Both answers agree with the moderately steep negative and positive slopes, respectively.

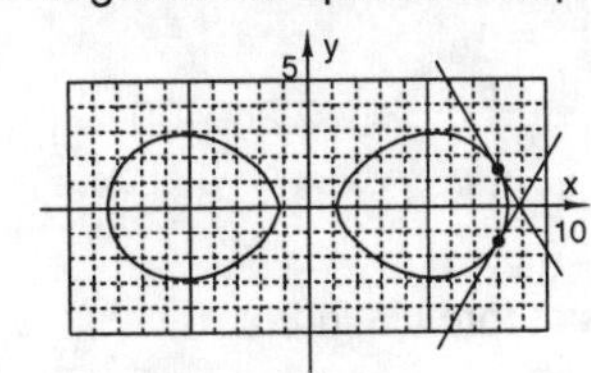

b. At the x-intercepts, $y = 0$.
$\therefore (x-6)^2 (x+6)^2 = 1200$
$(x^2 - 36)^2 = 1200$
$x = \pm\sqrt{36 \pm \sqrt{1200}} = \pm 8.4048...$ or $\pm 1.1657...$
Derivative appears to be <u>infinite</u> at each x-int.

At $x = \sqrt{36 + \sqrt{1200}} = 8.4048...$,
$\frac{dy}{dx} = \frac{-(8.4...)^3 + 36(8.4...) - (8.4...)(0)}{(8.4...)^2 (0) + 36(0) + 0^3}$
$= \frac{896.29...}{0}$, which *is* infinite, as conjectured.

c. From part a,
$x^4 - 72x^2 + 2x^2y^2 + 72y^2 + y^4 = -96 \Rightarrow$
$y^4 + (2x^2 + 72)y^2 + (x^4 - 72x^2 + 96) = 0$

$$y^2 = \frac{-(2x^2 + 72) \pm \sqrt{(2x^2 + 72)^2 - 4(1)(x^4 - 72x^2 + 96)}}{2}$$

$y^2 = -x^2 - 36 \pm \sqrt{144x^2 - 1200}$
Only the positive part of the ambiguous sign $\pm$ gives real solutions for y.

$y = \pm\sqrt{-x^2 - 36 + \sqrt{144x^2 - 1200}}$
Plot the graph letting y_1 equal the positive branch and y_2 equal the negative branch. The graph is as in the text. The two loops may not appear to close, depending on the window you use for x.

d. Repeating the algebra of parts a. and c. with 1400 in place of 1200 gives
$y = \pm\sqrt{-x^2 - 36 + \sqrt{144x^2 - 1400}}$
Plot the graph as in part c. The two ovals in the original graph merge into a single closed figure resembling an (unshelled) peanut.

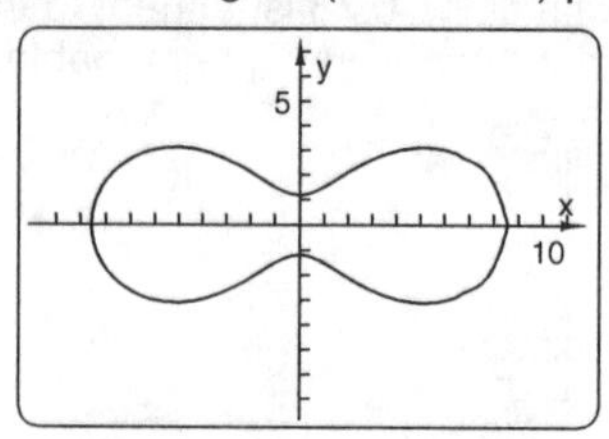

e. The two factors in the equation
$[(x-6)^2 + y^2][(x+6)^2 + y^2] = 1200$
are the squares of the distances from (x, y) to the points (6, 0) and (–6, 0), respectively. The product of the distances is $\sqrt{1200}$, a constant.

<u>Problem Set 4-9, pages 173 to 177</u> <u>Chapter Review and Test</u>

<u>Review Problems</u>

R0. Students should realize that the most important idea in Chapter 4 is algebraic differentiation of more complicated functions. These functions involve products, quotients, and powers with noninteger exponents, as well as functions defined parametrically or implicitly. Through working the real-world problems that have appeared in most sections, the students should realize that the algebraic techniques provide just another way to carry out the applications of derivatives they were doing in the first two chapters.

R1. a. $x = g(t) = t^3 \Rightarrow g'(t) = 3t^2$
$y = h(t) = \cos t \Rightarrow h'(t) = -\sin t$
If $f(t) = g(t) \cdot h(t) = t^3 \cos t$, then, for example,
$f'(1) = 0.7794...$ by numerical differentiation.
$g'(1) \cdot h'(1) = 3(1^2) \cdot (-\sin 1) = -2.5244...$.
$\therefore f'(t) \neq g'(t) \cdot h'(t)$, Q.E.D.

b. If $f(t) = g(t)/h(t) = t^3/\cos t$, then, for example,
$f'(1) = 8.4349...$ by numerical differentiation.
$g'(1)/h'(1) = 3(1^2)/(-\sin 1) = 3.5651....$
$\therefore f'(t) \neq g'(t)/h'(t)$, Q.E.D.

c. $y = \cos t$.
$x = t^3 \Rightarrow t = x^{1/3} \Rightarrow y = \cos(x^{1/3})$
$\frac{dy}{dx} = -\sin(x^{1/3}) \cdot \frac{1}{3} x^{-2/3}$
At $x = 1$, $\frac{dy}{dx} = -\sin 1 \cdot \frac{1}{3} = -0.280490...$
If $x = 1$, then $t = 1^{1/3} = 1$.
$\therefore \frac{dy/dt}{dx/dt} = \frac{-\sin t}{3t^2} = \frac{-\sin 1}{3} = -0.280490...$,
which equals dy/dx, Q.E.D.

R2. a. If $y = uv$, then $y' = u'v + uv'$.
b. See proof of product formula in text.
c. i. $f(x) = x^7 \cos 3x \Rightarrow$
$f'(x) = 7x^6 \cos 3x - 3x^7 \sin 3x$
ii. $g(x) = (\sin x)(\sin 2x) \Rightarrow$
$g'(x) = \cos x \sin 2x + 2 \sin x \cos 2x$
iii. $h(x) = (3x - 7)^5(5x + 2)^3$
$h'(x) = 5(3x - 7)^4(3) \cdot (5x + 2)^3 + (3x - 7)^5(3)(5x + 2)^2(5)$
$= 15(3x - 7)^4 (5x + 2)^2 (5x + 2 + 3x - 7)$
$= 15(3x - 7)^4 (5x + 2)^2 (8x - 5)$
iv. $s(x) = (5^3)(x^8) \Rightarrow s'(x) = 1000x^7$
(Be careful!)

d. $f(x) = (3x + 8)(4x + 7)$
i. $f'(x) = 3(4x + 7) + (3x + 8)(4) = $ <u>$24x + 53$</u>
ii. $f(x) = 12x^2 + 53x + 56$
$f'(x) = $ <u>$24x + 53$</u>, which checks.

R3. a. If $y = u/v$, then $y' = \frac{u'v - uv'}{v^2}$.
b. See proof of quotient formula in text.
c. i. $f(x) = \frac{\sin 10x}{x^5} \Rightarrow$
$f'(x) = \frac{10 \cos 10x \cdot x^5 - \sin 10x \cdot 5x^4}{x^{10}}$
$= \frac{10x \cos 10x - 5 \sin 10x}{x^6}$
ii. $g(x) = \frac{(2x + 3)^9}{(9x - 5)^4} \Rightarrow$
$$g'(x) = \frac{9(2x + 3)^8 \cdot 2(9x - 5)^4 - (2x + 3)^9 \cdot 4(9x - 5)^3 \cdot 9}{(9x - 5)^8}$$
$= \frac{18(2x + 3)^8(5x - 11)}{(9x - 5)^5}$
iii. $h(x) = (100x^3 - 1)^{-5} \Rightarrow$
$h(x) = -5(100x^3 - 1)^{-6} \cdot 300x^2$
$= -1500x^2(100x^3 - 1)^{-6}$

d. $y = 1/x^{10}$
As a quotient:
$y' = \frac{0 \cdot x^{10} - 1 \cdot 10x^9}{x^{20}} = \frac{-10}{x^{11}} = -10x^{-11}$
As a power:
$y = x^{-10}$
$y' = -10x^{-11}$, which checks.

e. $t(x) = \dfrac{\sin x}{\cos x} = \tan x$

$t'(x) = \dfrac{\cos x \cos x - \sin x(-\sin x)}{\cos^2 x}$

$= \dfrac{\cos^2 x + \sin^2 x}{\cos^2 x} = \dfrac{1}{\cos^2 x} = \sec^2 x$

$t'(1) = \sec^2 1 = \underline{3.4255...}$

f. $m(x) = \dfrac{t(x) - t(1)}{x - 1} = \dfrac{\tan x - \tan 1}{x - 1}$

Graph.

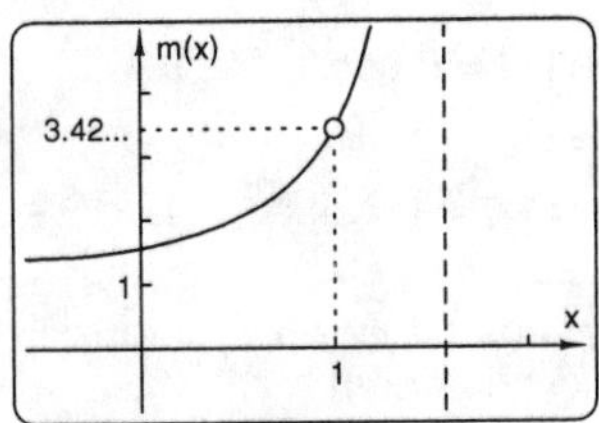

x	m(x)
0.997	3.40959...
0.998	3.41488...
0.999	3.42019...
1	no value
1.001	3.43086...
1.002	3.43622...
1.003	3.44160...

The values get closer to 3.4255... as x approaches 1 from either side, Q.E.D.

R4. a. i. $y = \tan 7x \Rightarrow y' = 7 \sec^2 7x$

ii. $y = \cot(x^4) \Rightarrow y' = -4x^3 \csc^2(x^4)$

iii. $y = 3 \sec x \Rightarrow y' = 3 \sec x \tan x$

iv. $y = \csc x \Rightarrow y' = -\csc x \cot x$

b. See derivation in text for $\tan' x = \sec^2 x$.

c. Graph. The graph is always sloping upward, which is connected to the fact that tan' x equals the square of a function and is thus always positive.

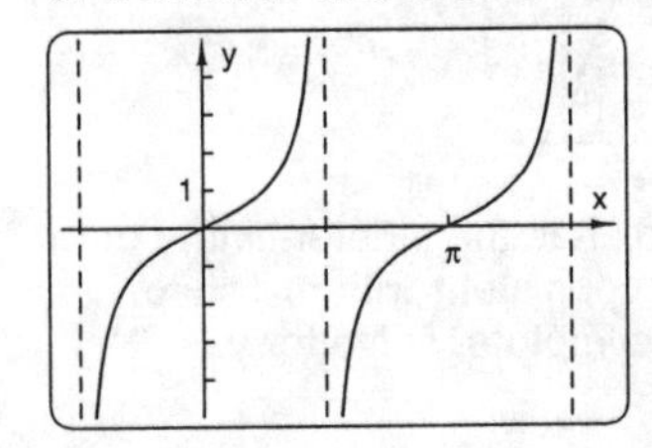

d. $f(t) = 7 \sec t \Rightarrow f'(t) = 7 \sec t \tan t$

$f'(1) = 20.17...$

$f'(1.5) = 1395.44...$

$f'(1.57) = 11038634.0...$

There is an asymptote in the secant graph at $t = \pi/2 = 1.57079...$. As t gets closer to this value, secant changes very rapidly!

R5. a. i. $y = \tan^{-1} 3x \Rightarrow y' = \dfrac{3}{1 + 9x^2}$

ii. $\dfrac{d}{dx}(\sec^{-1} x) = \dfrac{1}{|x|\sqrt{x^2 - 1}}$

iii. $c(x) = (\cos^{-1} x)^2 \Rightarrow c'(x) = \dfrac{-2 \cos^{-1} x}{\sqrt{1 - x^2}}$

b. Graph, $y = \sin^{-1} x$, plotted as

$x = \sin t$

$y = t$

t-window: $[-\pi/2, \pi/2]$

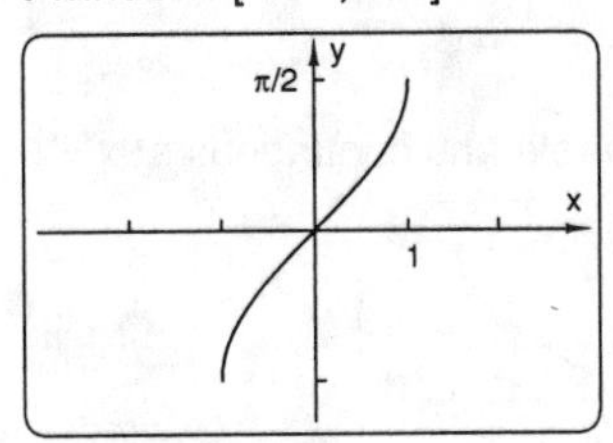

$y'(0) = \dfrac{1}{\sqrt{1 - 0^2}} = 1$, which agrees with the graph.

$y'(1) = \dfrac{1}{\sqrt{1 - 1^2}} = \dfrac{1}{0}$, which is infinite.

The graph becomes vertical as x approaches 1 from the negative side.

y'(2) is undefined because y(2) is not a real number.

R6. a. Differentiability implies continuity.

b. i. Graph (example). ii. Graph (example).

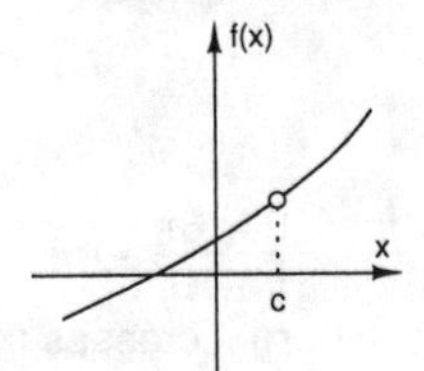

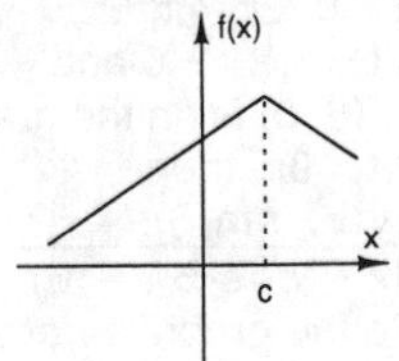

iii. Graph. iv. Graph (example).

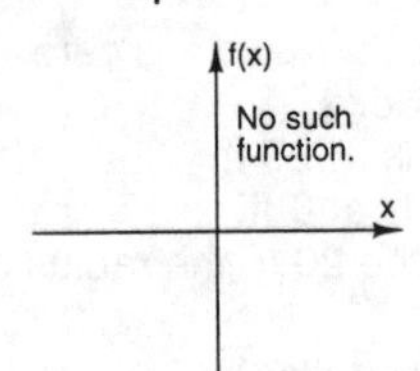

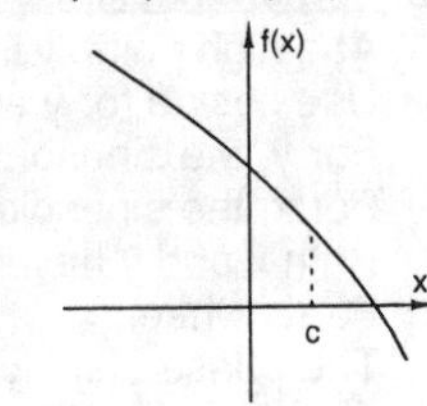

c. i. $f(x) = \begin{cases} x^2 + 1, & \text{if } x < 1 \\ -x^2 + 4x - 1, & \text{if } x \ge 1 \end{cases}$

Graph.

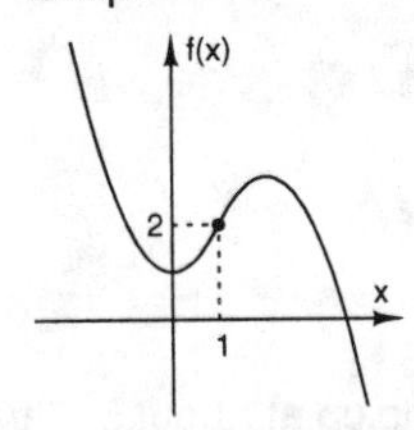

ii. f is continuous at x = 1 because right and left limits both equal 2, which equal f(1).

iii. f is differentiable. Left and right limits of f'(x) are both equal to 2, and f is continuous at x = 2.

d. $g(x) = \begin{cases} \sin^{-1} x, & \text{if } 0 \le x \le 1 \\ x^2 + ax + b, & \text{if } x \le 0 \end{cases}$

$g'(x) = \begin{cases} (1 - x)^{-1/2}, & \text{if } 0 < x < 1 \\ 2x + a, & \text{if } x < 0 \end{cases}$

$\lim_{x \to 0^-} g(x) = 0 + 0a + b = b$

$\lim_{x \to 0^+} g(x) = \sin^{-1} 0 = 0$

$\therefore b = 0.$

$\lim_{x \to 0^-} g'(x) = 0 + a = a$

$\lim_{x \to 0^+} g'(x) = 1^{-1/2} = 1$

$\therefore a = 1.$

Graph, differentiable and continuous at x = 0.

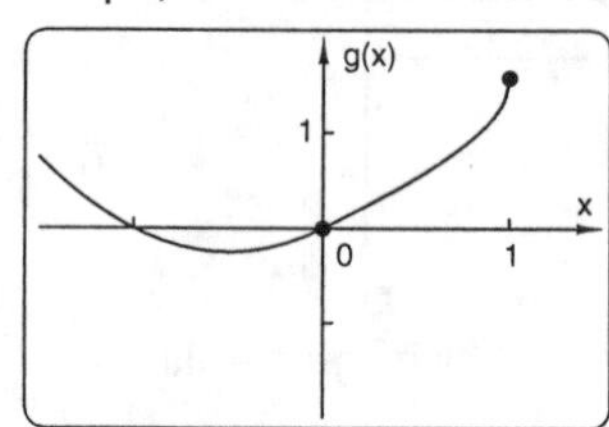

R7. a. $x = (t/\pi) \cos t$

$y = (t/\pi) \sin t$

$$\frac{dy}{dx} = \frac{dy/dt}{dx/dt} = \frac{(1/\pi) \sin t + (t/\pi)(\cos t)}{(1/\pi) \cos t + (t/\pi)(-\sin t)}$$

$$= \frac{\sin t + t \cos t}{\cos t - t \sin t}$$

Where the graph crosses the positive x-axis, $t = 0, 2\pi, 4\pi, 6\pi, \ldots$

If $t = 6\pi$, $x = 6$ and $y = 0$.

$\therefore$ (6, 0) *is* on the graph.

If $t = 6\pi$, then

$$\frac{dy}{dx} = \frac{\sin 6\pi + 6\pi \cos 6\pi}{\cos 6\pi - 6\pi \sin 6\pi} = \frac{0 + 6\pi}{1 - 0} = 6\pi.$$

So the graph is *not* vertical where it crosses the x-axis. It has a slope of $6\pi = 18.84\ldots$.

b. Ferris Wheel Problem

At a high point, y is a maximum and x is zero.
Use cosine for y and sine for x.
For y, the sinusoidal axis is at 25 ft.
For x, the sinusoidal axis is at 0 ft.
Both x and y have amplitude 20 ft, the radius of the Ferris wheel.
The phase displacement is 3 seconds.
The period is 20 seconds, so the coefficient of the arguments of sine and cosine is $2\pi/20 = \pi/10$.

$x = 20 \sin \frac{\pi}{10}(t - 3)$

$y = 25 + 20 \cos \frac{\pi}{10}(t - 3)$

$dx/dt = 2\pi \cos \frac{\pi}{10}(t - 3)$

$dy/dt = -2\pi \sin \frac{\pi}{10}(t - 3)$

When t = 0, $dy/dt = 5.0832\ldots$.
The Ferris wheel is going up at about 5.1 ft/sec.

When t = 0, $dx/dt = 3.6931\ldots$.
The Ferris wheel is going right at about 3.7 ft/sec.

$\frac{dy}{dx} = \frac{dy/dt}{dx/dt}$

dy/dx will be infinite if $dx/dt = 0$ and $dy/dt \ne 0$.

$dx/dt = 0$ if

$2\pi \cos \frac{\pi}{10}(t - 3) = 0$

$\frac{\pi}{10}(t - 3) = \pm\frac{\pi}{2} + 2\pi n$ (where n is an integer)

$t = 3 \pm 5 + 20n$

First positive time is t = <u>8 sec</u>.

R8. a. $y = (12x^{1/3} + 7)^6 \Rightarrow$

$y' = 6(12x^{1/3} + 7)^5 (4x^{-2/3}) = 24x^{-2/3} (12x^{1/3} + 7)^5$

b. $y^3 \sin (xy) = x^{4.5} \Rightarrow$

$3y^2y' \cdot \sin (xy) + y^3 \cdot \cos (xy)[y + xy'] = 4.5x^{3.5}$

$y'[3y^2 \sin (xy) + xy^3 \cos (xy)]$

$= 4.5x^{3/5} - y^4 \cos (xy)$

$$y' = \frac{dy}{dx} = \frac{4.5x^{3.5} - y^4 \cos (xy)}{3y^2 \sin (xy) + xy^3 \cos (xy)}$$

c. Cissoid of Diocles Problem

i. $4y^2 - xy^2 = x^3 \Rightarrow$

$8yy' - y^2 - x \cdot 2yy' = 3x^2$

$y'(8y - 2xy) = 3x^2 + y^2$

$$y' = \frac{dy}{dx} = \frac{3x^2 + y^2}{8y - 2xy}$$

At (2, 2), $dy/dx = 2$. At (2, –2), $dy/dx = -2$.
Lines at these points with these slopes are tangent to the graph (see diagram).

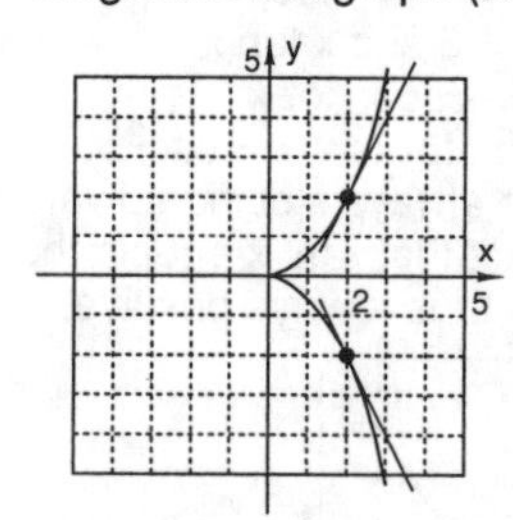

ii. At (0, 0), dy/dx has the indeterminate form 0/0, which is consistent with the cusp.

iii. To find the asymptote, solve for y.

$(4 - x)y^2 = x^3$

$$y^2 = \frac{x^3}{4 - x}$$

As x approaches 4 from the negative side, y becomes infinite. If $x > 4$, y^2 is negative, and thus there are no real values of y.
Asymptote is at x = 4.

Concepts Problems

C1. Historical Problem: Newton's Method

a. Let (x, y) be the coordinates of a point on the tangent line.

$\dfrac{y - y_0}{x - x_0} = m \Rightarrow y = m(x - x_0) + y_0$

b. Substituting $(x_1, 0)$ for (x, y) gives

$0 = m(x_1 - x_0) + y_0 \Rightarrow x_1 = x_0 - \dfrac{y_0}{m}$, Q.E.D.

c. The tangent line intersects the x-axis at $(x_2, 0)$. Repeating the above reasoning with x_2 and x_1 in place of x_1 and x_0 gives

$x_2 = x_1 - \dfrac{y_1}{m}$

Since $y_1 = f(x_1)$ and $m = f'(x_1)$,

$x_2 = x_1 - \dfrac{f(x_1)}{f'(x_1)}$, Q.E.D.

d. Programs will vary according to the kind of grapher used. The following steps are needed:

- Store f(x) in the y= menu.
- Input a starting value of x.
- Find the new x using the numerical derivative.
- Display the new x.
- Save the new x as the old x and repeat.

For $f(x) = x^2 - 9x + 14$, the program should give x = 2, x = 7.

e. For $g(x) = x^3 - 9x^2 + 5x + 10$, first plot the graph to get approximations for the initial values of x.

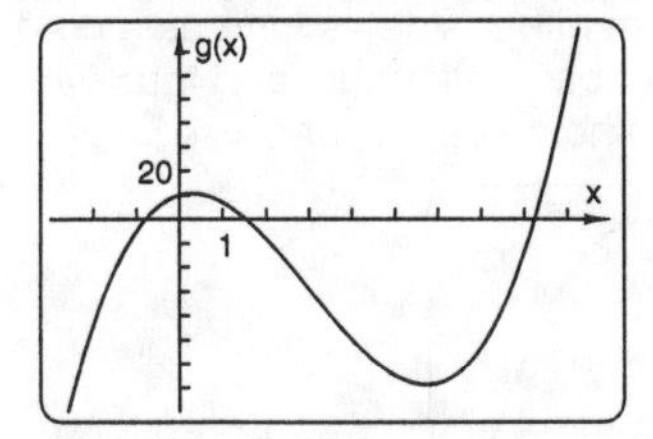

Run the program three times with $x_0 = -1$, 1, and 8. The values of x are

x = −0.78715388...

x = 1.54050386...

x = 8.24665002...

The answers are the same using the built-in SOLVE feature. The same preliminary analysis is needed to find starting values of x.

f. f(x) = sec x − 1.1

Starting with $x_0 = 1$, it takes 7 iterations to get x = 0.429699666... .

Chapter Test

T1. c(x) = cot 3x

$c'(x) = -3 \csc^2 3x$, which is negative for all permissible values of x.

$c'(5) = -3 \csc^2 15 = -3/\sin^2 15 = -7.0943...$

c(t) is decreasing at about 7.1 y-units/x-unit.

T2. f(x) = sec x ⇒ f'(x) = sec x tan x

f'(2) = sec 2 tan 2 = 5.25064633...

Use m(x) for the difference quotient.

$m(x) = \dfrac{1/\cos x - 1/\cos 2}{x - 2}$

x	m(x)
1.997	5.28893631...
1.998	5.27611340...
1.999	5.26335022...
2.000	no value
2.001	5.23800134...
2.002	5.22541482...
2.003	5.21288638...

T3. Graph (example).

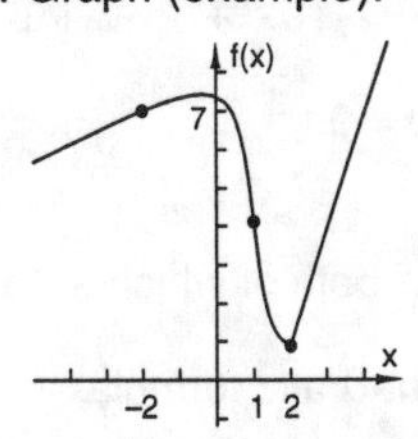

T4. If $y = \dfrac{u}{v}$, where u and v are differentiable functions,

then $y' = \dfrac{u'v - uv'}{v^2}$

T5. If x and y are differentiable functions of t, and $dx/dt \neq 0$, then

$\dfrac{dy}{dx} = \dfrac{dy/dt}{dx/dt}$

T6. f(x) = mx + b

f'(x) = m for all x.

∴ f is differentiable for all x.

∴ f is continuous for all x, Q.E.D.

T7. f(x) = sec 5x ⇒ f'(x) = 5 sec 5x tan 5x

T8. $y = \tan^{7/3} x \Rightarrow y' = \frac{7}{3} \tan^{4/3} x \sec^2 x$

T9. $\dfrac{d}{dx}(3 \csc 11x) = -33 \csc 11x \cot 11x$

T10. $f(x) = (2x - 5)^6(5x - 1)^2$

$f'(x) = 6(2x - 5)^5(2)\cdot(5x - 1)^2 + (2x - 5)^6\cdot 2(5x - 1)\cdot 5$

$= 2(2x - 5)^5(5x - 1)[6(5x - 1) + 5(2x - 5)]$

$= 2(2x - 5)^5(5x - 1)(40x - 31)$

T11. $f(x) = \dfrac{\cot 3x}{\cos^2 3x}$

$f'(x) = \dfrac{-3\csc^2 3x\cdot\cos^2 3x - \cot 3x\cdot 2\cos 3x(-3\sin 3x)}{\cos^4 3x}$

$= \dfrac{-3\csc^2 3x\cdot\cos 3x + 6\cot 3x\cdot\sin 3x}{\cos^3 3x}$

(This answer is sufficiently simplified.)

Simplifying f(x) before differentiating gives

$f(x) = \dfrac{\csc 3x}{\sec 3x}\cdot\sec^2 3x = \csc 3x \sec 3x.$

$f'(x) = -3 \csc 3x \cot 3x \sec 3x + 3 \csc 3x \sec 3x \tan 3x$

[This answer is sufficiently simplified.]

Both answers can be shown by suitable trig to be

$f'(x) = -3 \csc^2 3x + 3 \sec^2 3x$

T12. $5x^3y^7 = y^{1.6} \Rightarrow 15x^2y^7 + 35x^3y^6y' = 1.6y^{0.6}y'$

$y'(35x^3y^6 - 1.6y^{0.6}) = -15x^2y^7$

$y' = \dfrac{dy}{dx} = \dfrac{-15x^2y^7}{35x^3y^6 - 1.6y^{0.6}}$ (May be reduced.)

T13. $x = \sec 2t$

$y = \tan 2t^3$

$$\frac{dy}{dx} = \frac{dy/dt}{dx/dt} = \frac{\sec^2 2t^3 \cdot 6t^2}{\sec 2t \tan 2t \cdot 2} = \frac{3t^2 \sec^2 2t^3}{\sec 2t \tan 2t}$$

T14. $y = 4 \sin^{-1}(5x^3)$

$$y' = 4 \cdot \frac{1}{\sqrt{1 - (5x^3)^2}} \cdot 15x^2 = \frac{60x^2}{\sqrt{1 - 25x^6}}$$

T15. Rotated Ellipse Problem

$9x^2 - 20xy + 25y^2 - 16x + 10y - 50 = 0 \Rightarrow$

$18x - 20y - 20xy' + 50yy' - 16 + 10y' = 0$

$y'(-20x + 50y + 10) = -18x + 20y + 16$

$$y' = \frac{dy}{dx} = \frac{-18x + 20y + 16}{-20x + 50y + 10} = \frac{-9x + 10y + 8}{-10x + 25y + 5}$$

If $x = -2$, then

$36 + 40y + 25y^2 + 32 + 10y - 50 = 0$

$25y^2 + 50y + 18 = 0$

Solving numerically gives

$y = -0.4708...$ or $y = -1.5291...$, both of which agree with the graph.

(Solving algebraically by the quadratic formula,

$y = -1 \pm \sqrt{7/5}$, which agrees with the numerical solutions.)

At (−2, −0.4708...), $dy/dx = 1.60948...$.

At (−2, −1.5291...), $dy/dx = -0.80948...$.

The answers are reasonable, since lines of these slopes are tangent to the graph at the respective points, as shown below.

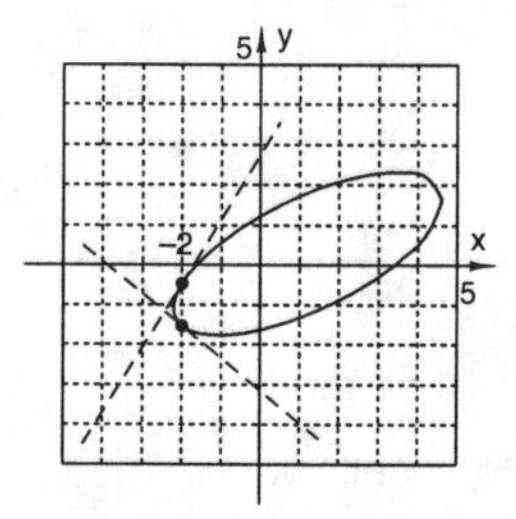

T16. $y = x^{7/3} \Leftrightarrow y^3 = x^7$

$3y^2y' = 7x^6$

$$y' = \frac{7x^6}{3y^2} = \frac{7}{3}\frac{x^6}{(x^{7/3})^2} = \frac{7}{3}x^{6-14/3} = \frac{7}{3}x^{4/3}$$

This answer agrees with $y' = nx^{n-1}$. 4/3 is 7/3 − 1.

T17. $f(x) = \begin{cases} x^3 + 1, \text{ if } x \le 1 \\ a(x-2)^2 + b, \text{ if } x > 1 \end{cases}$

$f'(x) = \begin{cases} 3x^2, \text{ if } x < 1 \\ 2a(x-2), \text{ if } x > 1 \end{cases}$

For equal derivatives on both sides of $x = 1$,

$\lim_{x \to 1^-} f'(x) = 3 \cdot 1^2 = 3$

$\lim_{x \to 1^+} f'(x) = 2a(1 - 2) = -2a$

$\therefore -2a = 3 \Rightarrow a = -1.5$

For continuity at $x = 1$,

$\lim_{x \to 1^-} f(x) = 3 \cdot 1^3 + 1 = 4$

$\lim_{x \to 1^+} f(x) = a(1 - 2)^2 + b = a + b$

$\therefore b - a = 4$

Substituting $a = -1.5$ gives $b = 3.5$.

Graph, showing differentiability at $x = 1$.

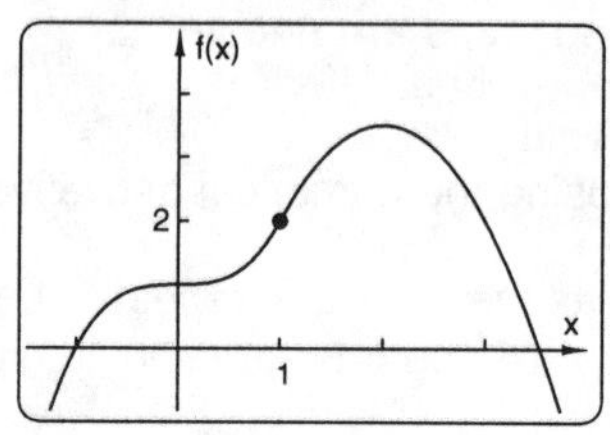

Values of b other than 3.5 will still cause the two branches to have slopes approaching 4 as x approaches 1 from either side as long as $a = -1.5$. However, f will not be continuous, and thus will not be differentiable, as shown below for $b = 4.5$.

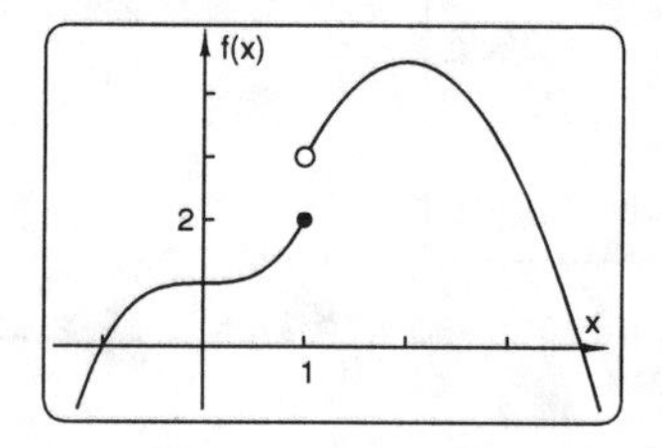

Chapter 5

Exploratory Problem Set 5-1, page 181 — A Definite Integral Problem

Oil Well Problem

1. $c(x) = 20 \cdot 1.0003^x$
   $c(1000) = 20 \cdot 1.0003^{1000} = 26.995... \approx \$27.00/\text{ft}$
   $c(4000) = 20 \cdot 1.0003^{4000} = 66.390... \approx \$66.39/\text{ft}$
2. Using the trapezoidal rule program with n = 6 gives cost $\approx 131580.54... \approx \$131,580$ (rounded to \$10).
3. Average cost $\approx \dfrac{131580.54...}{3000} \approx \$43.86/\text{ft}$
4. Cost $\approx c(1250)\cdot500 + c(1750)\cdot500 + c(2250)\cdot500 + c(2750)\cdot500 + c(3250)\cdot500 + c(3750)\cdot 500$
   $= 131211.44... \approx \$131,210$ (rounded to \$10)
5. Average cost using Problem 4 is
   $\dfrac{131211.44...}{3000} \approx 43.74.$
   Average of c(1000) and c(4000) is
   $0.5(26.995... + 66.390...) = 46.69.$
   The average of c(1000) and c(4000) is significantly higher than the actual average figured either way.
6. $\dfrac{c(1001) - c(999)}{1001 - 999} = 0.00809... \approx 0.0081$ (\$/ft)/ft
   $\dfrac{c(4001) - c(3999)}{4001 - 3999} = 0.01991... \approx 0.020$ (\$/ft)/ft
7. The mathematical word for such a rate is the second derivative. The physical quantity is acceleration.

Problem Set 5-2, pages 182 and 183 — Review of Antiderivatives

Q1. $dy/dx = (-3y)/(2x)$
Q2. $dy/dx = 8.5t^{-2.7}/\sin t$
Q3. $f'(x) = 0$
Q4. $f'(x) = 1/\sqrt{1 - x^2}$
Q5. $y' = \sec x \tan x$
Q6. $y'' = 30x^4$
Q7. $x'(t) = -3 \sin 3t$
Q8. $x''(t) = -9 \cos 3t$
Q9. $\log 15x^2$
Q10. Graph.

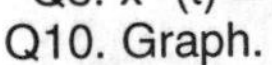

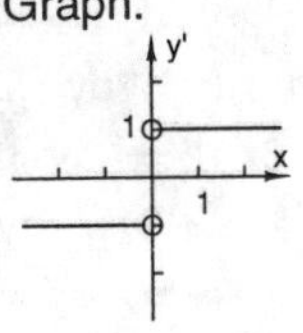

1. $f'(x) = 7x^6 \Rightarrow f(x) = x^7 + C$
2. $f'(x) = 10x^9 \Rightarrow f(x) = x^{10} + C$
3. $f'(x) = x^{-9} \Rightarrow f(x) = -\frac{1}{8}x^{-8} + C$
4. $f'(x) = x^{-1066} \Rightarrow f(x) = -\frac{1}{1065}x^{-1065} + C$
5. $f'(x) = \cos x \Rightarrow f(x) = \sin x + C$
6. $f'(x) = \sin x \Rightarrow f(x) = -\cos x + C$
7. $f'(x) = \csc^2 x \Rightarrow f(x) = -\cot x + C$
8. $f'(x) = \sec x \tan x \Rightarrow f(x) = \sec x + C$
9. $f'(x) = -\csc x \cot x \Rightarrow f(x) = \csc x + C$
10. $f'(x) = \sec^2 x \Rightarrow f(x) = \tan x + C$
11. $f'(x) = \sin 5x \Rightarrow f(x) = -\frac{1}{5}\cos 5x + C$
12. $f'(x) = \cos 4x \Rightarrow f(x) = \frac{1}{4}\sin 4x + C$
13. $f'(x) = \sec^2 8x \Rightarrow f(x) = \frac{1}{8}\tan 8x + C$
14. $f'(x) = \csc 2x \cot 2x \Rightarrow f(x) = -\frac{1}{2}\csc 2x + C$
15. $f'(x) = (4x + 5)^7 \Rightarrow f(x) = \frac{1}{32}(4x + 5)^8 + C$
16. $f'(x) = (8x + 3)^5 \Rightarrow f(x) = \frac{1}{48}(8x + 3)^6 + C$
17. a. Each is an antiderivative of $y' = 5x^4$.
    b. The word is *congruent*.
    For any one value of x, each pair of points on $y = x^5 + 0.3$ and $y_2 = x^5 + 0.7$, for example, are the same *vertical* distance apart, 0.4. However, the graphs are not really parallel, because the *perpendicular* distance from one to another is not constant.
    c. $f'(x) = 3x^2 - 2 \Rightarrow f(x) = x^3 - 2x + C$
    For (1, 0), $0 = 1^3 - 2\cdot1 + C \Rightarrow C = 1$
    $f(x) = x^3 - 2x + 1$ contains (1, 0)
    For (1, 1), $1 = 1^3 - 2\cdot1 + C \Rightarrow C = 2$
    $f(x) = x^3 - 2x + 2$ contains (1, 1)
    For (1, 2), $2 = 1^3 - 2\cdot1 + C \Rightarrow C = 3$
    $f(x) = x^3 - 2x + 3$ contains (1, 2)
    d. Graph.

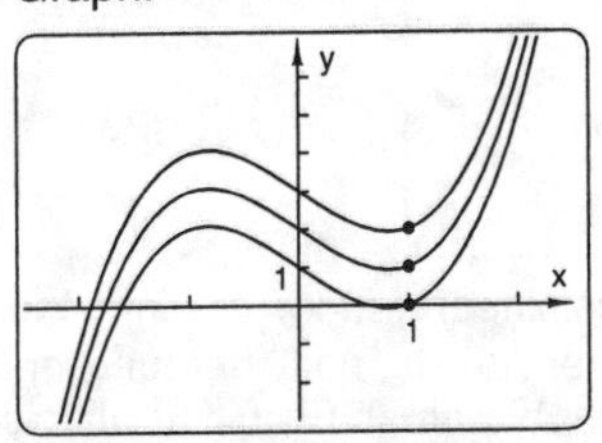

    e. The constant C affects the vertical position of the graph without affecting either its shape or its horizontal position. The antiderivative is a "family" of functions, because there is more than just one function but they look very much alike.

Problem Set 5-3, pages 186 to 189 — Linear Approximations and Differentials

Q1. Graph (example)

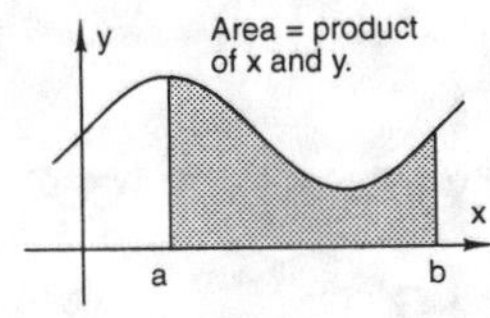

Q2. A derivative is an instantaneous rate of change.
Q3. $f'(x) = -15x^{-6}$
Q4. $y = \sin x + C$
Q5. $y' = 4$ m/sec
Q6. $\sec x \tan x$ (derivative)
Q7. Limit = 1
Q8. Limit = that constant
Q9. Derivative = 0
Q10. Continuous

1. $f(x) = 0.2x^4 \Rightarrow f'(x) = 0.8x^3 \Rightarrow f'(3) = 21.6 \Rightarrow$
   $f(3) = 0.2(3^4) = 16.2$
   $\therefore y - 16.2 = 21.6(x - 3) \Rightarrow y = 21.6x - 48.6$

x	f(x)	y	Error
3.1	18.47042	18.36	0.11042
3.001	16.22161...	16.2216	0.0000108...
2.999	16.17841...	16.1784	0.0000107...

2. $g(x) = \sec x \Rightarrow g'(x) = \sec x \tan x \Rightarrow g'(\pi/3) = 2\sqrt{3}$ $= 3.464...$
$g(\pi/3) = \sec(\pi/3) = 2$
Linear function is $y - 2 = 2\sqrt{3}(x - \pi/3) \Rightarrow$
$y = 2\sqrt{3}(x - \pi/3) + 2$

dx	f(x)	y	Error
0.04	2.15068...	2.13856...	0.01212...
−0.04	1.87184...	1.86143...	0.01041...
0.001	2.003471...	2.003464...	7.01×10^{-6}

3. Local Linearity Problem I
$f(x) = x^2 \Rightarrow f'(x) = 2x \Rightarrow f'(1) = 2$
Tangent line: $y - 1 = 2(x - 1) \Rightarrow$ $y = 2x - 1$
Graph shows zoom by factor of 10.

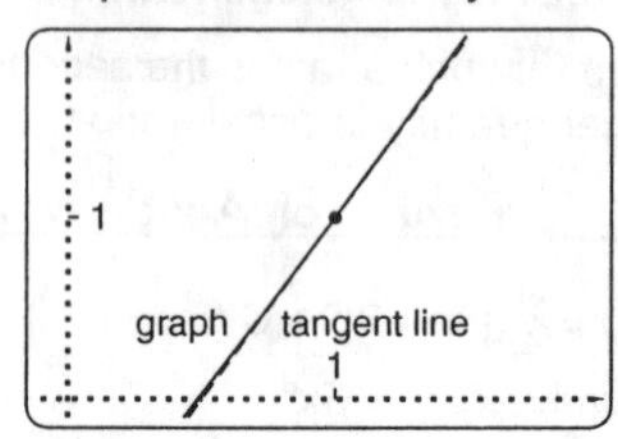

Local linearity describes the property of the function because if you keep x close to 1 (in the "locality" of 1), the curved graph of the function looks like the straight graph of the tangent line.

4. Local Linearity Problem II
$f(x) = x^2 - 0.1(x - 1)^{1/3}$
Graph. Zooming in on (1, 1) shows that the graph goes vertical at x = 1.
This observation is confirmed algebraically.
$f'(x) = 2x - (1/3)(0.1)(x - 1)^{-2/3}$
$f'(1) = 2 - (1/3)(0.1)(0)^{-2/3}$, which is infinite.

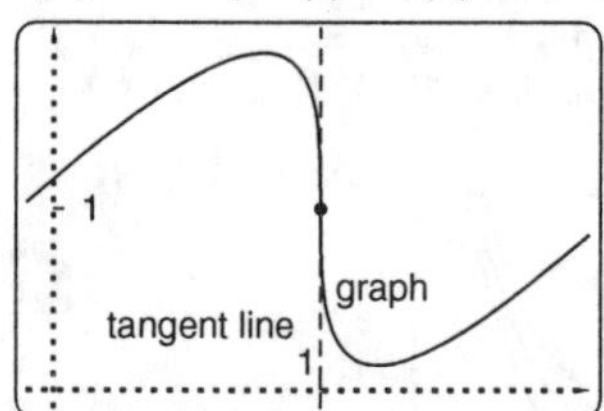

f does not have local linearity at x = 1. Since the slope of the graph becomes infinite, no linear function can approximate the graph there. If f is differentiable at x = c, then f *is* locally linear there. The converse is also true. If f is locally linear at x = c, then f is differentiable there.

5. Steepness of a Hill Problem
a. Let A be the number of radians in θ degrees.
By trigonometry, $\tan A = \dfrac{x}{100} \Rightarrow A = \tan^{-1}\dfrac{x}{100}$
Since 1 radian is $180/\pi$ degrees,
$\theta = \dfrac{180}{\pi}\tan^{-1}\dfrac{x}{100}$, Q.E.D.
b. $d\theta = \dfrac{180}{\pi}\cdot\dfrac{1}{1+(x/100)^2}\cdot\dfrac{1}{100}dx$
$= \dfrac{1.8/\pi}{1+(x/100)^2}dx$
x = 0: $d\theta = 0.5729...\,dx$
x = 10: $d\theta = 0.5672...\,dx$
x = 20: $d\theta = 0.5509...\,dx$
c. At x = 0, θ = 0. For x = 20, dx = 20.
$\therefore\ \theta \approx (0 + 0.5729...)(20) = 11.459...°$
The actual value is $(180/\pi)(\tan^{-1} 0.2) = 11.309....$
The error is 0.1492...°, which is about 1.3%.
d. 0.5729... is approximately 0.5, so multiplying by it is approximately equivalent to dividing by 2.
For a 20% grade, this estimate gives 10°, compared to the actual angle of 11.309...°, an error of about 11.6%.
For a 100% grade, this estimate gives 50°, compared to the actual angle of 45°, an error of about 11.1%.

6. Table of Differentials Problem
$y = x^3 \Rightarrow dy = 3x^2\,dx$
At x = 1, dy = 3 dx. y = 1, so $\Delta y = x^3 - 1$.

x	Δx = dx	Δy	dy	Δy − dy
0.8	−0.2	−0.488	−0.6	0.112
0.9	−0.1	−0.271	−0.3	0.029
0.99	−0.01	−0.029701	−0.03	0.000299
1.01	0.01	0.030301	0.03	0.000301
1.1	0.1	0.331	0.3	0.031
1.2	0.2	0.728	0.6	0.128

When x is close to 1, dy approximates Δy more closely.
(The main point of this problem is for students to see that dy can be estimated quickly, simply by multiplying dx by 3.)

7. $y = 7x^3 \Rightarrow dy = 21x^2\,dx$
8. $y = -4x^{11} \Rightarrow dy = -44x^{10}\,dx$
9. $y = (x^4 + 1)^7 \Rightarrow dy = 28x^3(x^4 + 1)^6\,dx$
10. $y = (5 - 8x)^4 \Rightarrow dy = -32(5 - 8x)^3\,dx$
11. $y = 3x^2 + 5x - 9 \Rightarrow dy = (6x + 5)\,dx$
12. $y = x^2 + x + 9 \Rightarrow dy = (2x + 1)\,dx$
13. $y = -5x^{-1.7} \Rightarrow dy = 8.5x^{-2.7}\,dx$
14. $y = 15x^{1/3} \Rightarrow dy = 5x^{-2/3}\,dx$
15. $y = \sin 3x \Rightarrow dy = 3\cos 3x\,dx$
16. $y = \cos 4x \Rightarrow dy = -4\sin 4x\,dx$
17. $y = \tan^3 x \Rightarrow dy = 3\tan^2 x \sec^2 x\,dx$
18. $y = \sec^3 x \Rightarrow dy = 3\sec^3 x \tan x\,dx$
19. $y = 4x\cos x \Rightarrow dy = (4\cos x - 4x\sin x)\,dx$
20. $y = 3x\sin x \Rightarrow dy = (3\sin x + 3x\cos x)\,dx$
21. $y = x^2/2 - x/4 + 2 \Rightarrow dy = (x - 1/4)\,dx$
22. $y = x^3/3 - x/5 + 6 \Rightarrow dy = (x^2 - 1/5)\,dx$
23. $y = \cos(\sec x) \Rightarrow dy = -\sin(\sec x)\cdot\sec x \tan x\,dx$
24. $y = \sin(\csc x) \Rightarrow dy = -\cos(\csc x)\cdot\csc x \cot x\,dx$
25. $dy = 20x^3\,dx \Rightarrow y = 5x^4 + C$
26. $dy = 36x^4\,dx \Rightarrow y = 7.2x^5 + C$
27. $dy = \sin 4x\,dx \Rightarrow y = -(1/4)\cos 4x + C$
28. $dy = \cos 0.2x\,dx \Rightarrow y = 5\sin 0.2x + C$
29. $dy = (0.5x - 1)^6\,dx \Rightarrow y = (2/7)(0.5x - 1)^7 + C$
30. $dy = (4x + 3)^{-6}\,dx \Rightarrow y = (-1/20)(4x + 3)^{-5} + C$
31. $dy = \sec^2 x\,dx \Rightarrow y = \tan x + C$
32. $dy = \csc x \cot x\,dx \Rightarrow y = -\csc x + C$
33. $dy = 5\,dx \Rightarrow y = 5x + C$
34. $dy = -7\,dx \Rightarrow y = -7x + C$
35. $dy = (6x^2 + 10x - 4)\,dx \Rightarrow y = 2x^3 + 5x^2 - 4x + C$
36. $dy = (10x^2 - 3x + 7)\,dx \Rightarrow$
$y = (10/3)x^3 - (3/2)x^2 + 7x + C$
37. $dy = \sin^5 x \cos x\,dx \Rightarrow y = (1/6)\sin^6 x + C$
38. $dy = \sec^7 x \tan x\,dx = \sec^6 x(\sec x \tan x\,dx) \Rightarrow$
$y = (1/7)\sec^7 x + C$

39. a. $y = (3x + 4)^2(2x - 5)^3 \Rightarrow$
$y' = 2(3x + 4)(3)(2x - 5)^3 + (3x + 4)^2 \cdot 3(2x - 5)^2 \cdot 2$
$= 6(3x + 4)(2x - 5)^2[2x - 5 + 3x + 4]$
$\therefore dy = 6(3x + 4)(2x - 5)^2(5x - 1)\ dx$

b. $dy = 6(7)(-3)^2(4)(-0.04) = -60.48$

c. $x = 1 \Rightarrow y = (7)^2(-3)^3 = -1323$
$x = 0.96 \Rightarrow y = -1383.0218...$
$\therefore \Delta y = -1383.0218... - (-1323) = -60.0218...$

d. -60.48 is close to $-60.0218...$.

40. a. $y = \sin 5x \Rightarrow dy = 5 \cos 5x\ dx$

b. $dy = 5 \cos (5\pi/3) \cdot 0.06 = 0.15$

c. $x = \pi/3 \Rightarrow y = \sin (5\pi/3) = -\sqrt{3}/2 = -0.86602...$
$x = \pi/3 + 0.06 \Rightarrow y = -0.679585565...$
$\therefore \Delta y = -0.679... - (-0.866...) = 0.186439...$

d. 0.15 is (fairly) close to 0.186439....

Problem Set 5-4, pages 193 to 195

Formal Definition of Antiderivative and Indefinite Integral

Q1. Antideriv. $= x^3 + C$
Q2. Indef. int. $= (1/6)x^6 + C$
Q3. $y' = 3x^2$
Q4. $y' = x^5$
Q5. Integral $= \sin x + C$
Q6. $y' = -\sin x$
Q7. hypothesis
Q8. conclusion
Q9. Antider., indef. int.
Q10. Limit = 1

1. $\int 6x^5\ dx = x^6 + C$

2. $\int 5x^4\ dx = x^5 + C$

3. $\int x^{10}\ dx = \frac{1}{11}x^{11} + C$

4. $\int x^{20}\ dx = \frac{1}{21}x^{21} + C$

5. $\int 4x^{-6}\ dx = -\frac{4}{5}x^{-5} + C$

6. $\int 9x^{-7}\ dx = -\frac{3}{2}x^{-6} + C$

7. $\int 102t^{4.1}\ dt = 20\ t^{5.1} + C$

8. $\int 72r^{-1.1}\ dr = -720r^{-0.1} + C$

9. $\int 30p^{-2/5}\ dp = 50p^{3/5} + C$

10. $\int 56v^{-3/7}\ dv = 98v^{4/7} + C$

11. $\int \cos x\ dx = \sin x + C$

12. $\int \sin x\ dx = -\cos x + C$

13. $\int \sin 3m\ dm = -\frac{1}{3} \cos 3m + C$

14. $\int \cos 5u\ du = \frac{1}{5} \sin 5u + C$

15. $\int 4 \cos 7x\ dx = \frac{4}{7} \sin 7x + C$

16. $\int 20 \sin 9x\ dx = -\frac{20}{9} \cos 9x + C$

17. $\int (4v + 9)^2\ dv = \frac{1}{4} \int (4v + 9)^2 (4\ dv) = \frac{1}{12}(4v + 9)^3 + C$

18. $\int (3p + 17)^5\ dp = \frac{1}{3} \int (3p + 17)^5 (3\ dp)$
$= \frac{1}{18}(3p + 17)^6 + C$

19. $\int (8 - 5x)^3\ dx = -\frac{1}{5} \int (8 - 5x)^3 (-5\ dx)$
$= -\frac{1}{20}(8 - 5x)^4 + C$

20. $\int (20 - x)^4\ dx = (-1) \int (20 - x)^4 (-dx) = -\frac{1}{5}(20 - x)^5 + C$

21. $\int (6 + 7b)^{-4}\ dx = \frac{1}{7} \int (6 + 7b)^{-4} (7\ db)$
$= -\frac{1}{21}(6 + 7b)^{-3} + C$

22. $\int (10 + 13t)^{-6}\ dt = \frac{1}{13} \int (10 + 13t)^{-6} (13\ dt)$
$= -\frac{1}{65}(10 + 13t)^{-5} + C$

23. $\int (\sin x)^6 \cos x\ dx = \frac{1}{7} \sin^7 x + C$

24. $\int (\cos x)^8 \sin x\ dx = -\frac{1}{9} \cos^9 x + C$

25. $\int \cos^4 \theta \sin \theta\ d\theta = -\frac{1}{5} \cos^5 \theta + C$

26. $\int \sin^5 \theta \cos \theta\ d\theta = \frac{1}{6} \sin^6 \theta + C$

27. $\int \sin^3 \pi x \cos \pi x\ dx = \frac{1}{\pi} \int \sin^3 \pi x (\cos \pi x \cdot \pi\ dx)$
$= \frac{1}{4\pi} \sin^4 \pi x + C$

28. $\int \cos^8 \pi x \sin \pi x\ dx = -\frac{1}{\pi} \int \cos^8 \pi x (-\sin \pi x \cdot \pi\ dx)$
$= -\frac{1}{9\pi} \cos^9 \pi x + C$

29. $\int (x^2 + 3x - 5)\ dx = \frac{1}{3}x^3 + \frac{3}{2}x^2 - 5x + C$

30. $\int (x^2 - 4x + 1)\ dx = \frac{1}{3}x^3 - 2x^2 + x + C$

31. $\int (r^{-2} + r^2)\ dr = -r^{-1} + \frac{1}{3}r^3 + C$

32. $\int (u^3 - u^{-3})\ du = \frac{1}{4}u^4 + \frac{1}{2}u^{-2} + C$

33. $\int (x^2 + 5)^3\ dx = \int (x^6 + 15x^4 + 75x^2 + 125)\ dx$
$= \frac{1}{7}x^7 + 3x^5 + 25x^3 + 125x + C$

34. $\int (x^3 - 6)^2\ dx = \int (x^6 - 12x^3 + 36)\ dx$
$= \frac{1}{7}x^7 - 3x^4 + 36x + C$

35. $\int \sec^2 x\ dx = \tan x + C$

36. $\int \csc^2 x\ dx = -\cot x + C$

37. $\int \csc 3x \cot 3x\ dx = -\frac{1}{3} \csc 3x + C$

38. $\int \sec 5x \tan 5x\ dx = \frac{1}{5} \sec 5x + C$

39. $\int \tan^7 x \sec^2 x\ dx = \frac{1}{8} \tan^8 x + C$

40. $\int \cot^8 x \csc^2 x\ dx = -\frac{1}{9} \cot^9 x + C$

41. $\int \csc^9 x \cot x\ dx = \int \csc^8 x (\csc x \cot x\ dx)$
$= -\frac{1}{9} \csc^9 x + C$

42. $\int \sec^7 x \tan x\, dx = \int \sec^6 x (\sec x \tan x\, dx)$

$= \frac{1}{7}\sec^7 x + C$

43. Distance from Velocity Problem

$v(t) = 40 + 5\sqrt{t} = 40 + 5t^{1/2}$

$D(t) = \int (40 + 5t^{1/2})\, dt = 40t + \frac{10}{3}t^{3/2} + C$

$D(0) = 0 \Rightarrow 0 = 40 \cdot 0 + \frac{10}{3}0^{3/2} + C \Rightarrow C = 0$

$\therefore D(t) = 40t + \frac{10}{3}t^{3/2}$

$D(10) = 505.4092... \approx 505$ feet

44. Definite Integral Surprise!

a. $f(x) = 0.3x^2 + 1$

$T_{100} = 9.300135$

b. $g(x) = \int (0.3x^2 + 1)\, dx = 0.1x^3 + x + C$

c. $g(4) - g(1) = 6.4 + 4 + C - 0.1 - 1 - C = 9.3$, which is about equal to the definite integral! It is also interesting that the constant C drops out.

45. Integral of a Sum Property

Prove that if f and g are functions that can be integrated, then

$\int (f(x) + g(x))\, dx = \int f(x)\, dx + \int g(x)\, dx$.

Proof:

Let $h(x) = \int f(x)\, dx + \int g(x)\, dx$.

By the derivative of a sum property,

$h'(x) = \frac{d}{dx}\int f(x)\, dx + \frac{d}{dx}\int g(x)\, dx$.

By the definition of indefinite integral applied twice to the right side of the equation,

$h'(x) = f(x) + g(x)$.

By the definition of indefinite integral applied in the other direction,

$h(x) = \int (f(x) + g(x))\, dx$.

By the transitive property, then,

$\int (f(x) + g(x))\, dx = \int f(x)\, dx + \int g(x)\, dx$, Q.E.D.

46. Integral Table Problem

Calvin says $\int x \cos x\, dx = x \sin x + \cos x + C$.

Phoebe checked this by differentiating:

$\frac{d}{dx}(x \sin x + \cos x + C)$

$= 1 \cdot \sin x + x \cdot (\cos x) - \sin x + 0 = x \cos x$.

By the definition of indefinite integral, she knew that Calvin was right.

47. Introduction to Riemann Sums

a.

c	v(t)
1.5	12.25
2.5	16.25
3.5	22.25
Sum:	50.75

Integral ≈ 50.75

b.

c	v(t)
1.25	11.5625
1.75	13.0625
2.25	15.0625
2.75	17.5625
3.25	20.5625
3.75	24.0625
Sum:	101.8750

Integral ≈ (101.8750)(0.5) = 50.9375

c. As shown in Figures 5-4a and 5-4b, the Riemann sum with six increments has smaller regions included above the graph and smaller regions excluded below the graph, so the Riemann sum should be closer to the integral.

d. Conjecture: Exact value is 51.

e. By trapezoidal rule with n = 100, integral ≈ 51.00045, which agrees with the conjecture.

f. The integral is the product of v(t) and t, and thus has the units (ft/min)(min), or feet. So the object went 51 ft.

Average velocity = 51/3 = 17 ft/min.

48. Journal Problem

Answers will vary. Students are on the verge of being able to tell why two different concepts both have the name integral. The reason is that indefinite integrals are used to calculate definite integrals. Problem 44, the Definite Integral Surprise, may have given them a clue to this fact.

Problem Set 5-5, pages 200 to 202 — Riemann Sums and the Definition of Definite Integral

Q1. $y' = \sin x + x \cos x$.

Q2. $\tan x + C$.

Q3. $f'(x) = \sec^2 x$.

Q4. $(1/4)x^4 + C$.

Q5. $z' = -7 \sin 7x$.

Q6. $-\cos u + C$.

Q7. Limit = 8.

Q8. Graph, cusp at (4, 7).

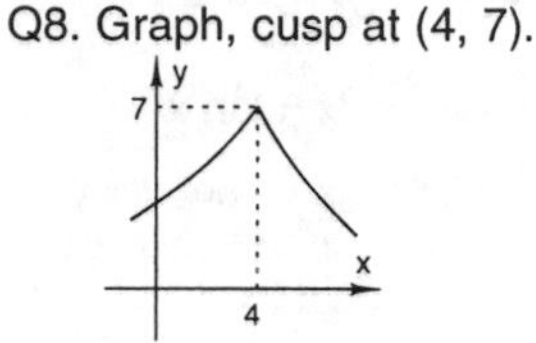

Q9. If a + b = 5, then a = 2 and b = 3.

Q10. No. (False.)

1. $\int_1^4 x^2\, dx$

c	f(c)
1.25	1.5625
1.75	3.0625
2.25	5.0625
2.75	7.5625
3.25	10.5625
3.75	14.0625
Sum =	41.8750

$R_6 = (0.5)(41.875)$
$= 20.9375$

2. $\int_2^6 x^3\, dx$

c	f(c)
2.25	11.390625
2.75	20.796875
3.25	34.328125
3.75	52.734375
4.25	76.765625
4.75	107.171875
5.25	144.703125
5.75	190.109375
Sum =	638.000000

$R_8 = (0.5)(638) = 319$

3. $\int_{-1}^{3} 3^x\,dx$

c	f(c)
−0.75	0.43869...
−0.25	0.75983...
0.25	1.31607...
0.75	2.27950...
1.25	3.94822...
1.75	6.83852...
2.25	11.84466...
2.75	20.51556...
Sum =	47.94108...

$R_8 = (0.5)(47.94...)$
$= \underline{23.97054...}$

4. $\int_{-1}^{2} 2^x\,dx$

c	f(c)
−0.75	0.59460...
−0.25	0.84089...
0.25	1.18920...
0.75	1.68179...
1.25	2.37841...
1.75	3.36358...
Sum =	10.04849...

$R_6 = (0.5)(10.04...)$
$= \underline{5.024249...}$

5. $\int_{1}^{2} \sin x\,dx$

c	f(c)
1.1	0.891207...
1.3	0.963558...
1.5	0.997494...
1.7	0.991664...
1.9	0.946300...
Sum =	4.790225...

$R_5 = (0.2)(4.79...)$
$= \underline{0.958045...}$

6. $\int_{0}^{1} \cos x\,dx$

c	f(c)
0.1	0.995004...
0.3	0.955336...
0.5	0.877582...
0.7	0.764842...
0.9	0.621609...
Sum =	4.214375...

$R_5 = (0.2)(4.21...)$
$= \underline{0.842875...}$

7. $\int_{0.4}^{1.2} \tan x\,dx$
$L_4 = 0.73879...$, $U_4 = 1.16866...$.
$M_4 = 0.92270...$, $T_4 = 0.95373...$.
$\therefore M_4$ and T_4 are between L_4 and U_4, Q.E.D.

8. $\int_{1}^{3} 10/x\,dx$:
$L_4 = 9.5$, $U_4 = 12.8333...$
$M_4 = 10.89754...$, $T_4 = 11.1666...$
$\therefore M_4$ and T_4 are between L_4 and U_4, Q.E.D.

9. Sample Point Problem
a. $h(x) = 3 + 2\sin x$
For an upper sum, take sample points at x equals 1, $\pi/2$, 2, 3, 4, and 6.
b. For a lower sum, take sample points at x equals 0, 1, 3, 4, $3\pi/2$, and 5.
c. $U_6 = 1(h(1) + h(\pi/2) + h(2) + h(3) + h(4) + h(6))$
$= \underline{21.71134...}$
$L_6 = 1(h(0) + h(1) + h(3) + h(4) + h(3\pi/2) + h(5))$
$= \underline{14.53372...}$

10. Program for Riemann Sums Problem
Programs will vary depending on the type of grapher used. See the program in the "Supplementary Programs" section of the Instructor's Materials.

11. Limit of Riemann Sums Problem
a. For $\int_{1}^{4} x^2\,dx$, the program should give the values listed in the text.
b. $L_{100} = 20.77545$, $L_{500} = 20.955018$.
L_n seems to be approaching 21.
c. $U_{100} = 21.22545$, $U_{500} = 21.045018$.
U_n also seems to be approaching 21.
f is integrable on [1, 4] if L_n and U_n have the same limit as n approaches infinity.

d. The trapezoids are circumscribed around the region under the graph and thus contain more area (see left diagram). For rectangles, the "triangular" part of the region that is left out has more area than the "triangular" part that is included, because the "triangles" have equal bases but unequal altitudes (see right diagram).

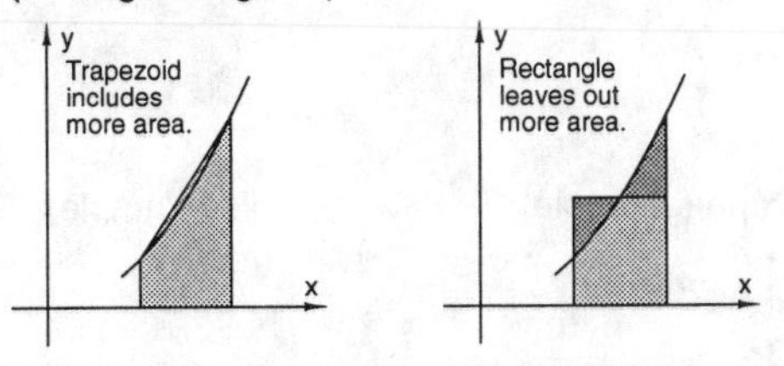

12. Exact Integral of the Square Function by Brute Force Project
a. $\int_{0}^{3} x^2\,dx$
$U_{100} = 9.13545$; $L_{100} = 8.86545$.
Conjecture: Integral equals 9 exactly.
b. The sample points will be at the right of each interval, $1 \cdot 3/n, 2 \cdot 3/n, 3 \cdot 3/n, \ldots, n \cdot 3/n$.
c. $U_n = (3/n)(1 \cdot 3/n)^2 + (3/n)(2 \cdot 3/n)^2 + (3/n)(3 \cdot 3/n)^2 + \ldots + (3/n)(n \cdot 3/n)^2$
d. $U_n = (3/n)^3(1^2 + 2^2 + 3^2 + \ldots + n^2)$
$= (3/n)^3(n/6)(n + 1)(2n + 1)$
$= (4.5/n^2)(n + 1)(2n + 1)$
$U_{100} = (4.4/100^2)(101)(201) = 9.13545$, which is correct.
e. Using the formula, $U_{1000} = 9.013504\ldots$, which *does* seem to be approaching 9.
f. $U_n = 4.5 \cdot \dfrac{n+1}{n} \cdot \dfrac{2n+1}{n}$
$= 4.5(1 + 1/n)(2 + 1/n)$
As n approaches infinity, 1/n approaches zero.
$\therefore U_n$ approaches $4.5(1 + 0)(2 + 0)$, which equals 9, exactly!

13. Exact Integral of the Cube Function Project
$\int_{0}^{2} x^3\,dx$
Find an upper sum using the sample points $1 \cdot 2/n, 2 \cdot 2/n, 3 \cdot 2/n, \ldots, n \cdot 2/n$.
$U_n = (2/n)(1 \cdot 2/n)^3 + (2/n)(2 \cdot 2/n)^3 + (2/n)(3 \cdot 2/n)^3 + \ldots + (2/n)(n \cdot 2/n)^3$
$= (2/n)^4(1^3 + 2^3 + 3^3 + \ldots + n^3) = (2/n)^4[(n/2)(n + 1)]^2$
$= 4/n^2 \cdot (n + 1)^2 = 4(1 + 1/n)^2$
$\lim_{n\to\infty} U_n = 4(1 + 0)^2 = 4$

Q1. $x^2/2 + 2x + C$
Q2. $5t^2 + C$
Q3. $-\cot x + C$
Q4. $-\csc x \cot x$
Q5. $5 \sin^4 x \cos x$
Q6. Graph

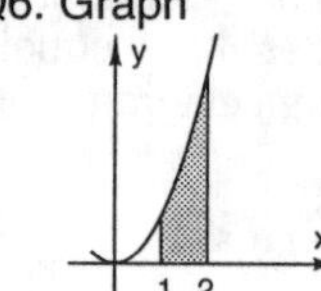

Q7. Graph (example)

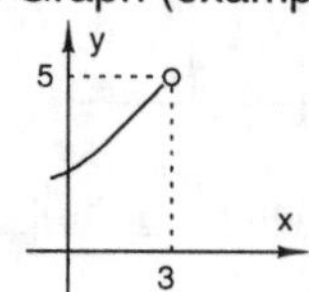

Q8. Graph (example)

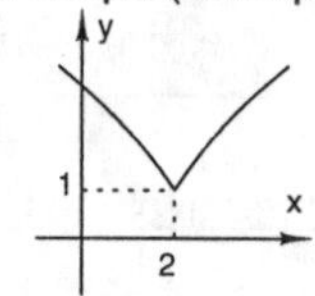

Q9. No limit (infinite)
Q10. $f^{-1}(x) = 0.5x - 3$

1. See statement of mean value theorem in text.
2. See statement of Rolle's theorem in text.
3. Graph, $g(x) = 6/x$; $[1, 4]$

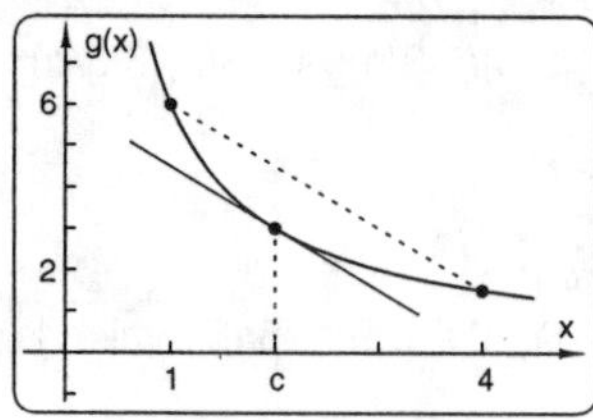

$m = \dfrac{6/4 - 6}{4 - 1} = -3/2$

$g'(x) = -6x^{-2}$

$\therefore -6c^{-2} = -3/2 \Rightarrow c = \underline{2}$

Tangent at x = 2 parallels the secant line.

4. Graph, $f(x) = x^4$; $[-1, 2]$

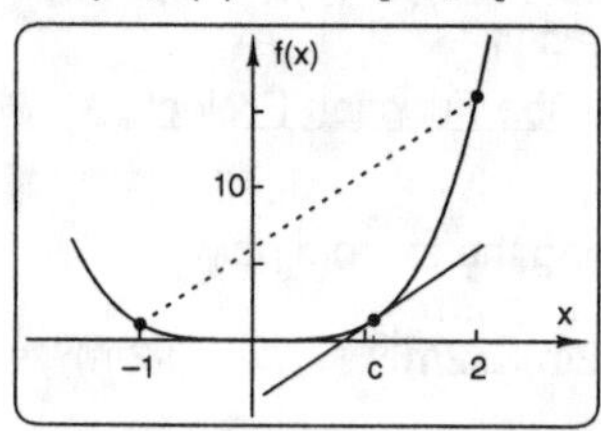

$m = \dfrac{16 - 1}{2 - (-1)} = 5$

$g'(x) = 4x^3$

$\therefore 4c^3 = 5 \Rightarrow c = \sqrt[3]{5/4} = \underline{1.077...}$

Tangent at x = 1.077... parallels the secant line.

5. Graph, $c(x) = 2 + \cos x$; $[0, \frac{\pi}{2}]$

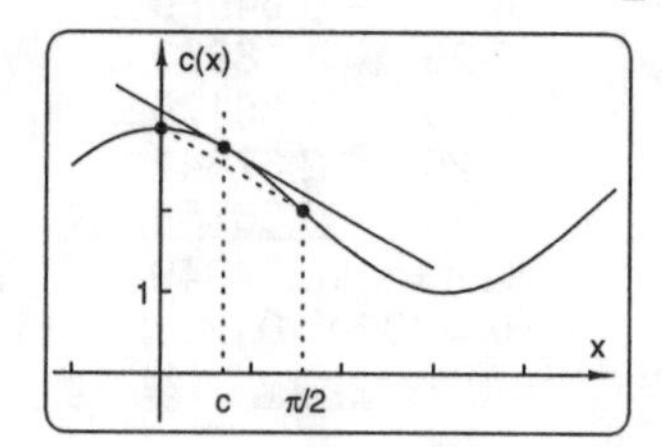

$m = \dfrac{\cos(\pi/2) - \cos 0}{\pi/2 - 0} = -2/\pi = 0.6366...$

$c'(x) = -\sin x$

$\therefore -\sin c = -2/\pi \Rightarrow \underline{c = 0.69010...}$

Tangent at x = 0.690... parallels the secant line.

6. Graph, $h(x) = 5 - \sqrt{x}$; $[1, 9]$

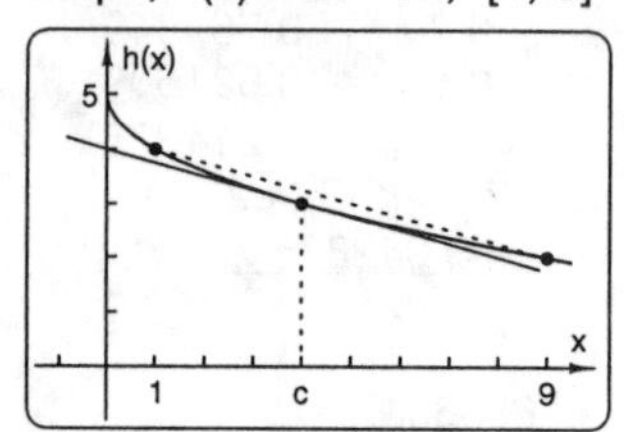

$m = \dfrac{2 - 4}{9 - 1} = -1/4$

$h'(x) = -(1/2)x^{-1/2}$

$\therefore (-1/2)c^{-1/2} = -1/4 \Rightarrow \underline{c = 4}$

Tangent at x = 4 parallels the secant line.

7. Graph, $f(x) = x \cos x$ on $[0, \pi/2]$

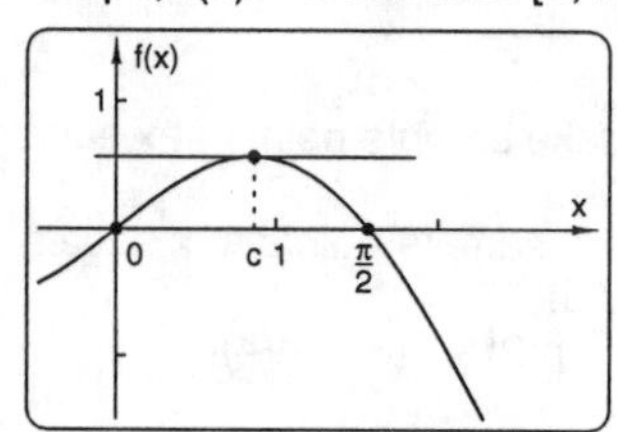

$f'(x) = \cos x - x \sin x$

$\therefore$ f is differentiable for all x.

$x \cos x = 0 \Leftrightarrow x = 0$ or $\cos x = 0$

$\cos x = 0$ at $\pm\pi/2 + 2\pi n$, where n is an integer

$\therefore$ hypotheses are met on $[0, \pi/2]$.

Using SOLVE, $f'(c) = 0$ at $\underline{c = 0.86033...}$.

Horizontal line at x = 0.86033... is tangent.

8. Graph, $f(x) = x^2 \sin x$

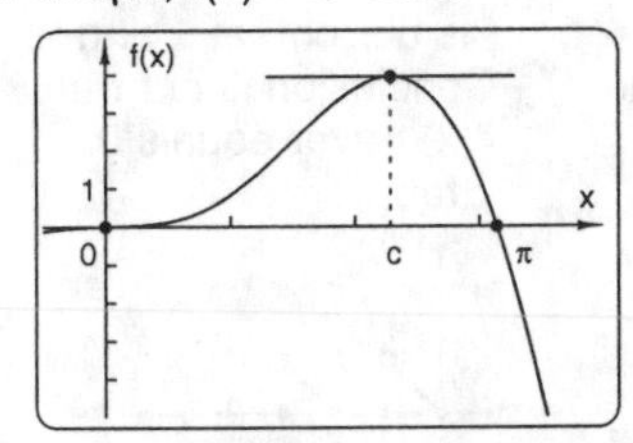

$f'(x) = 2x \sin x + x^2 \cos x$
$\therefore$ f is differentiable for all x.
$x^2 \sin x = 0 \Leftrightarrow x = 0$ or $\sin x = 0$
$\sin x = 0$ at $x = 0 + \pi n$, where n is an integer
Interval: $[0, \pi]$
Using SOLVE, $f'(c) = 0$ at $c = 2.28892...$.
Horizontal line at $x = 2.288...$ is tangent.

9. Graph, $f(x) = (6x - x^2)^{1/2}$

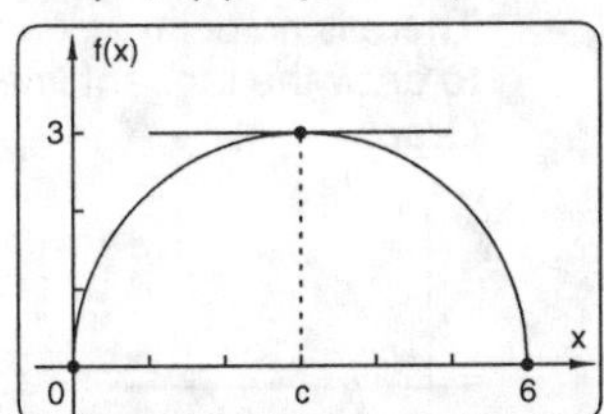

$f'(x) = \frac{1}{2}(6x - x^2)^{-1/2} \cdot (6 - 2x)$
$\therefore$ f is differentiable on (0, 6).
f is continuous at $x = 0$ and $x = 6$.
$(6x - x^2)^{1/2} = 0$
$x^{1/2}(6 - x)^{1/2} = 0 \Rightarrow x = 0$ or 6
Interval: [0, 6]
$(6c - c^2)^{-1/2}(3 - c) = 0 \Rightarrow c = 3$
Horizontal line at $x = 3$ is tangent.

10. Graph, $f(x) = x^{4/3} - 4x^{1/3}$

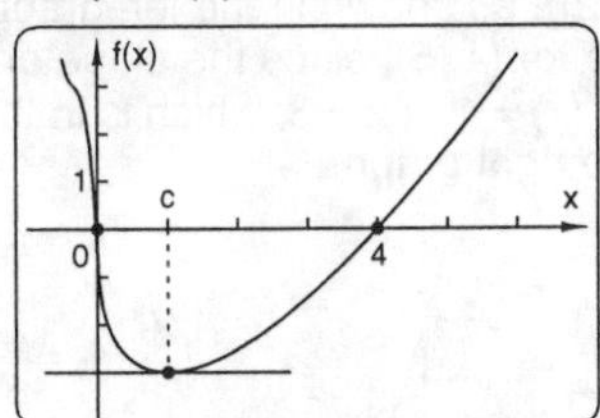

$f'(x) = \frac{4}{3}x^{1/3} - \frac{4}{3}x^{-2/3}$
$\therefore$ f is differentiable for all $x \neq 0$.
f is continuous at $x = 0$.
$f(x) = 0 \Leftrightarrow x^{4/3} - 4x^{1/3} = 0 \Leftrightarrow$
$x^{1/3}(x - 4) = 0 \Leftrightarrow x = 0$ or 4
Interval: [0, 4]
$\frac{4}{3}c^{1/3} - \frac{4}{3}c^{-2/3} = 0$
$\frac{4}{3}c^{-2/3}(c - 1) = 0 \Rightarrow c = 1$
Horizontal line at $x = 1$ is tangent.

11. Compound Interest Problem
a. $d(t) = 1000(1.09^t)$
$d(50) = 1000(1.09^{50}) = 74357.520...$
$=$ $74,357.52 Surprising!
b. Average rate is $\frac{74357.5... - 1000}{50}$
$= 1467.150... \approx$ $1,467.15 per year
c. $d'(0) \approx$ $86.18 per year
$d'(50) \approx$ $6,407.96 per year
The average of these is $3,247.07 per year, which does *not* equal the average in part b.
d. Solving numerically for the numerical derivative equal to 1467.15 gives $t \approx 32.893...$ years
This time is *not* halfway between 0 and 50.

12. Baseball Line Drive Problem (Second Inning)

$$d(t) = \begin{cases} 60.5\left(\frac{0.5 - t}{0.5 + t}\right), & \text{if } t \le 0.5 \\ 150\left(2 - \frac{1}{t}\right), & \text{if } t \ge 0.5 \end{cases}$$

The hypotheses of the mean value theorem do not apply on any interval that contains $t = 0.5$ as an interior point, such as [0, 1] and [0, 2], because d is not differentiable there. The hypotheses do apply on any interval not containing 0.5 and on intervals for which 0.5 is an endpoint, such as [0.5, 2].

The conclusion is true if the instantaneous velocity, $d'(t)$, ever equals the average velocity. The average velocity equals

$m = \frac{d(1) - d(0)}{1} = 89.5$ ft/sec for [0, 1],

$m = \frac{d(2) - d(0)}{2} = 82.25$ ft/sec for [0, 2],

$m = \frac{d(2) - d(0.5)}{1.5} = 150$ ft/sec for [0.5, 2].

Between $t = 0$ and $t = 0.5$, $d'(t)$ is negative.
Above $t = 0.5$, $d'(t) = 150t^{-2}$
For $d'(c) = 89.5$ ft/sec,
$150c^{-2} = 89.5 \Rightarrow c = 1.294...$.
But 1.294... is outside (0, 1), so the conclusion is not true. See the left graph, below.
For $d'(c) = 82.25$ ft/sec,
$150c^{-2} = 82.25 \Rightarrow c = 1.350...$.
Since 1.350... is in (0, 2), the conclusion is true. See the right graph, below.

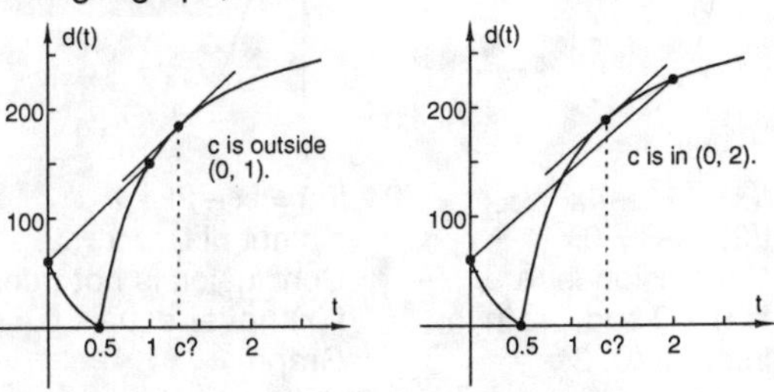

For $d'(c) = 150$, $150c^{-2} = 150 \Rightarrow c = 1$.
Since 1 is in (0.5, 2), the conclusion is true, as is guaranteed by the mean value theorem.

The fact that the conclusion is true when the hypotheses are met illustrates the fact that the hypotheses are sufficient. The fact that the conclusion can be true even if the hypotheses are not met proves that the hypotheses are not necessary.

13. See Figure 5-6d.

14. Graph (example).
No horizontal tangent.

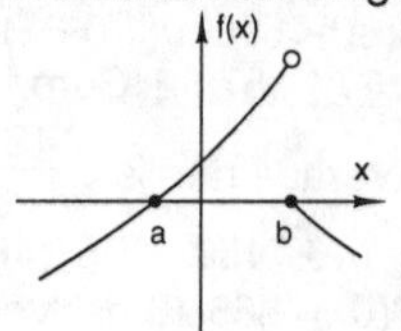

15. Graph (example).

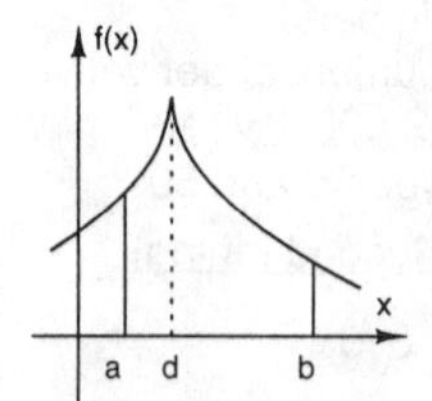

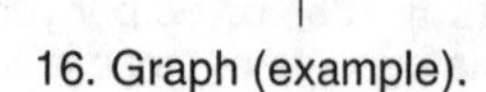
16. Graph (example).

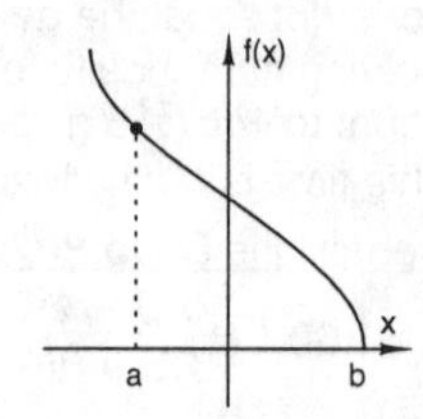

17. See Figure 5-6g.

18. Michel. 1652–1719, in France.

19. $f(x) = x^2 - 4x$
$f(1) = -3 \neq 0$.
Conclusion is not true.
$f'(2) = 0$, but 2 is not in the interval (0, 1).
Graph.

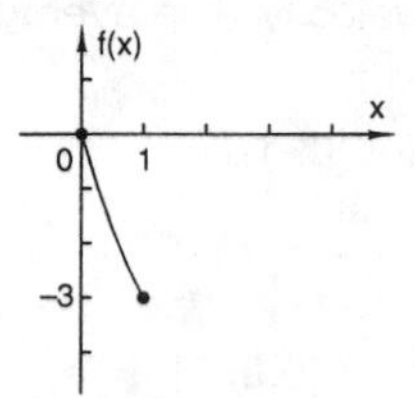

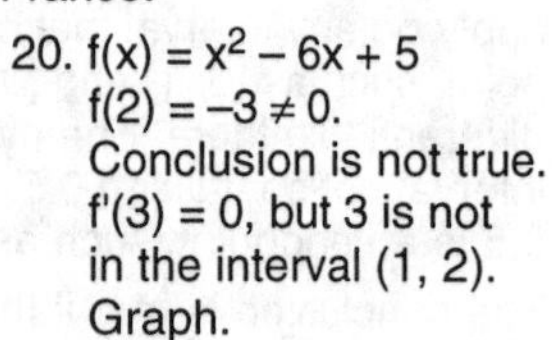
20. $f(x) = x^2 - 6x + 5$
$f(2) = -3 \neq 0$.
Conclusion is not true.
$f'(3) = 0$, but 3 is not in the interval (1, 2).
Graph.

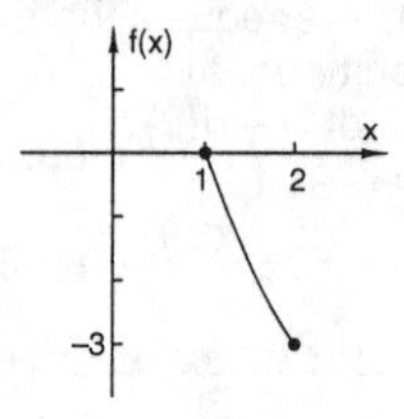

21. $f(x) = x^2 - 4x$
$f(2) = -4 \neq 0$
Conclusion is not true.
$f'(2) = 0$ but 2 is not in the *open* interval (0, 2).
Graph.

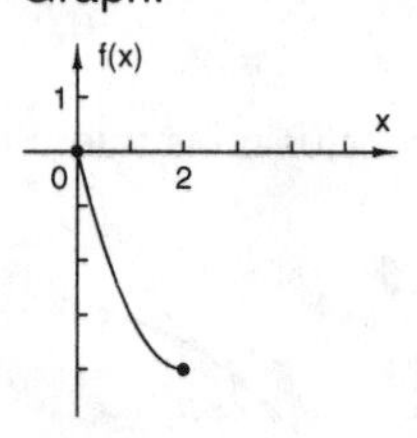

22. $f(x) = x^2 - 6x + 5$
$f(4) = -3 \neq 0$.
Conclusion is true.
$f'(3) = 0$ and 3 is in the interval (1, 4).
Graph.

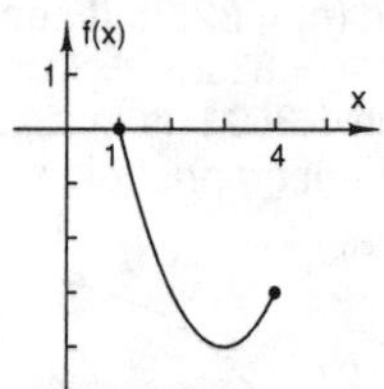

23. $f(x) = x^2 - 4x$
$f(3) = -3 \neq 0$.
Conclusion is true.
$f'(2) = 0$ and 2 is in the interval (0, 3).
Graph.

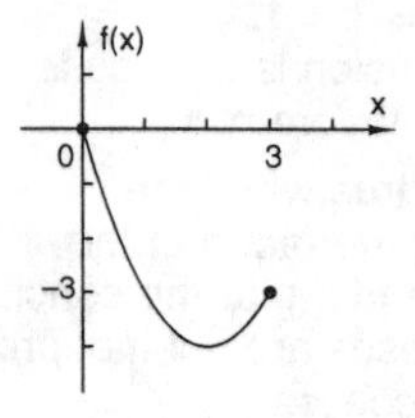

24. $f(x) = |x - 2| - 1$
f is not diff. at x = 2.
Conclusion is not true.
$f'(x)$ never equals 0.
Graph.

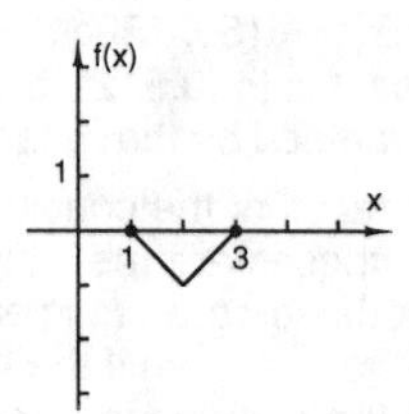

25. $f(x) = 1/x$
$f(0)$ does not exist.
Conclusion is not true.
$f'(x)$ never equals 0.
Graph.

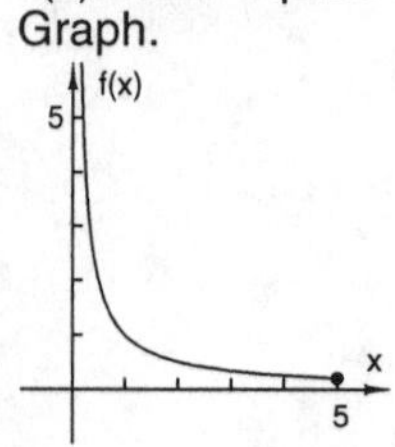

26. $f(x) = x - [x]$
f is discont. at 1 and 2.
Conclusion is not true.
$f'(x)$ never equals 0.
Graph.

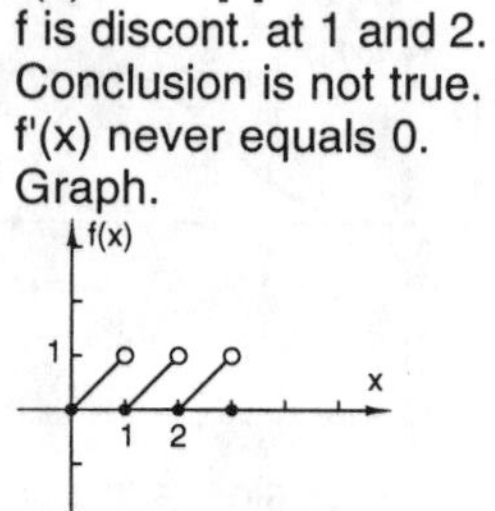

27. $f(x) = 1 - (x - 3)^{2/3}$

f is not diff. at x = 3.
Conclusion is not true.
$f'(x)$ never equals 0.
Graph.

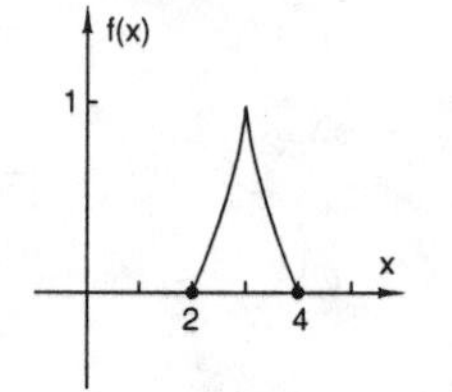

28. $f(x) =$

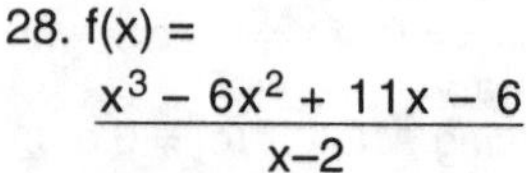

$$\frac{x^3 - 6x^2 + 11x - 6}{x-2}$$

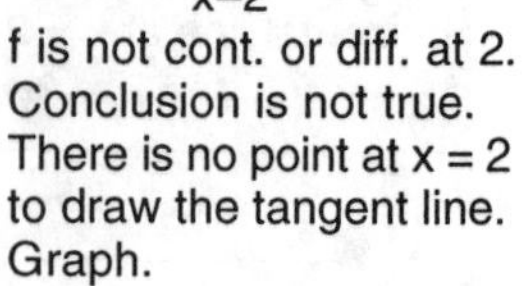
f is not cont. or diff. at 2.
Conclusion is not true.
There is no point at x = 2 to draw the tangent line.
Graph.

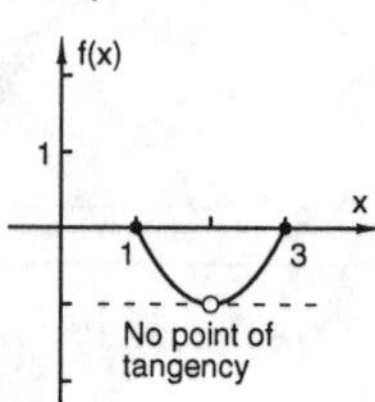

29. $$g(x) = \frac{x^3 - 7x^2 + 13x - 6}{x - 2}$$
$$= \frac{(x - 2)(x^2 - 5x + 3)}{x - 2} = x^2 - 5x + 3,\ x \neq 2.$$

Thus g is discontinuous at x = 2, and the hypotheses of the mean value theorem are not met. The conclusion is *not* true for [1, 3], because the tangent line would have to contain (2, g(2)), as shown in the left graph. The conclusion *is* true for (1, 5), since the slope of the secant line is 1, and $g'(x) = 1$ at x = 3, which is in the interval (1, 5). See the right graph.

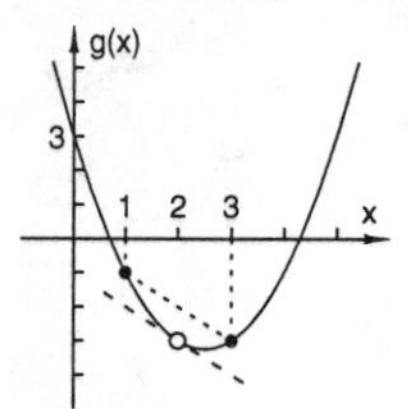

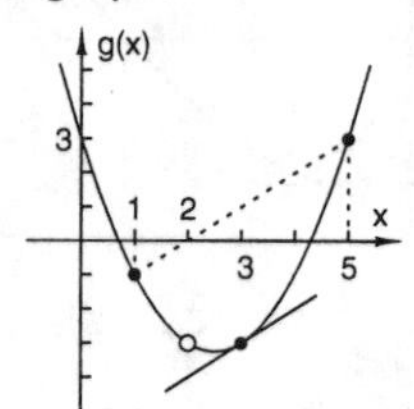

30. $h(x) = x^{2/3} \Rightarrow h'(x) = (2/3)x^{-1/3}$.
$\therefore$ h is differentiable for all $x \neq 0$.
$h'(0)$ would be $0^{-1/3} = 1/(0^{1/3}) = 1/0$, which is infinite.
The hypotheses of the mean value theorem *are* met on the interval [0, 8], since the function need not be differentiable at an endpoint. The hypotheses are *not* met on [–1, 8], since the point x = 0 where h is not differentiable is in the open interval (–1, 8). To see if the conclusion of the mean value theorem is true anywhere, find the slope of the secant line (see graph below).

$$m = \frac{4-1}{8-(-1)} = 1/3$$

The tangent line has slope $h'(c) = 1/3$. Therefore, $(2/3)c^{-1/3} = 1/3 \Rightarrow c^{-1/3} = 1/2 \Rightarrow c^{1/3} = 2 \Rightarrow c = 8$.

So the conclusion of the mvt is *not* true, since 8 is at the *endpoint* of the interval, not in the *open* interval (–1, 8).

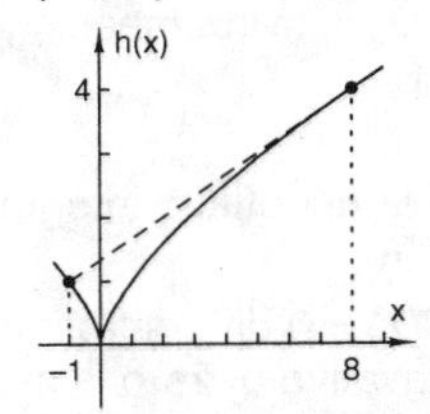

31.a. $f(x) = |x - 3| + 2x$

$$f(x) = \begin{cases} 3x - 3, & \text{if } x \geq 3 \\ x + 3, & \text{if } x < 3 \end{cases}$$

b. Graph.

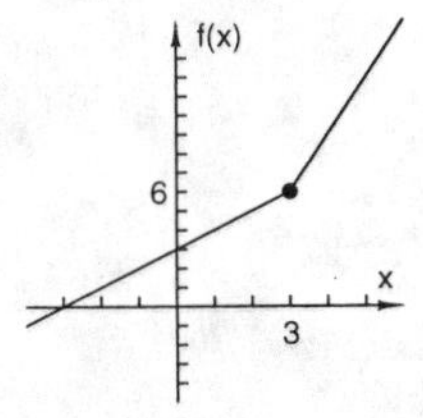

c. f is continuous at x = 3. The right and left limits both equal 6.
d. f is not differentiable at x = 3. The left limit of f'(x) is 1 and the right limit is 3.
e. f is not differentiable at x = 3, which is in (1, 6).
f. The secant line has slope 11/5. The tangent line has slope either 1 or 3, and thus is never 11/5.
g. f *is* integrable on [1, 6]. The integral equals 41.5, the sum of the areas of the two trapezoids shown in the diagram below.

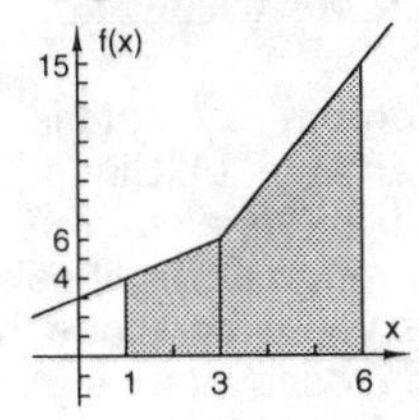

32. New Jersey Turnpike Problem
a. f(t) = no. of miles in t hours.
t = no. of hours driven.
For the mean value theorem to apply on [a, b], f must be differentiable on (a, b) and continuous at t = a and t = b.
b. The 60 mph equals the slope of the *secant* line. Therefore, there must be a *tangent* line at some value t = c in (a, b) with slope equal to 60. This tangent line's slope is the *instantaneous* speed at t = c. Therefore, the speed was exactly 60 at some time between t = a and t = b, Q.E.D..

33. Rolle's Theorem Proof Illustrated by Graph and by Table
a. $f(x) = 25 - (x - 5)^2 + 4\cos(2\pi(x - 5))$
Graph agrees with Figure 5-6ℓ.
b. At x = 5, the cosine is at a high point and the parabola $y = 25 - (x - 5)^2$ is also at a high point.
f(5) = 29
c. $f'(x) = -2(x - 5) - 4\sin(2\pi(x - 5))\cdot 2\pi$
$= -2x + 10 - 8\pi\sin(2\pi(x - 5))$
$f'(5) = 0$
d. Graph, difference quotient $y_2 = m(x)$.

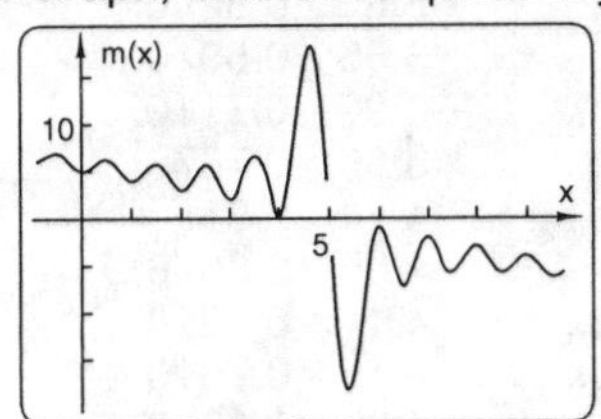

e.

x	m(x)
2.0	3
2.5	5.7
3.0	2
3.5	6.8333...
4.0	1
4.5	16.5
5.0	no value

x	m(x)
5.5	–16.5
6.0	–1
6.5	–6.833...
7.0	–2
7.5	–5.7
8.0	–3

f. As shown in parts d. and e., the difference quotient is positive when x is less than 5 and negative when x is greater than 5. In the proof of Rolle's theorem, the left limit of the difference quotient was shown to be positive or zero and the right limit was shown to be negative or zero.

The unmentioned hypothesis is *differentiability* on the interval (a, b). Function f *is* differentiable on any interval containing x = 5. Since there is a value of f'(5), both the left and right limits of the difference quotient must be equal. This number can only be zero, which establishes the conclusion of the theorem.

The conclusion of Rolle's theorem *can* be true even if the hypotheses aren't met. For instance, f(x) = 2 + cos x has zero derivatives every π units of x, although f(x) is never equal to zero.

34. Mean Value Theorem Proof Illustrated by Graph and by Table

a. See text graph, $f(x) = 1 + x + \cos \pi x$.

b. $m = \dfrac{f(4.5) - f(2)}{2.5} = \dfrac{5.5 - 4}{2.5} = 0.6$

$g(x) - 4 = 0.6(x - 2) \Rightarrow g(x) = 0.6x + 2.8$

See text graph.

c. Graph, $h(x) = f(x) - g(x)$.

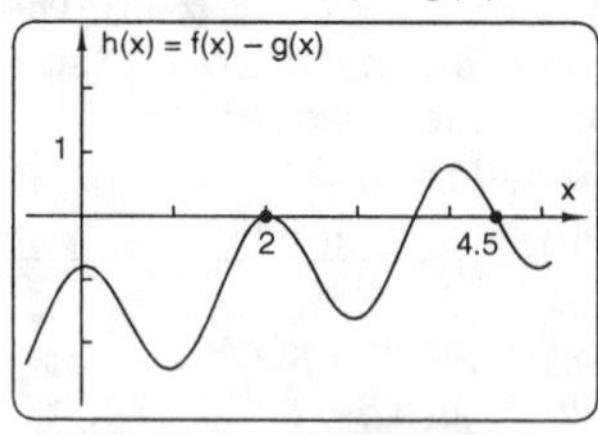

d. $f'(x) = 1 - \pi \sin \pi x$.

Using SOLVE, $f'(c) = 0.6$ at

$c = 2.0406..., 2.9593...,$ and $4.0406...,$

all of which are in (2, 4.5).

e. For c = 2.9593...: For c = 4.0406...:

x	h(x)	x	h(x)
2.75	−1.4071...	3.8	0.5290...
2.8	−1.4890...	3.85	0.6310...
2.85	−1.5510...	3.9	0.7110...
2.9	−1.5910...	3.95	0.7676...
2.95	−1.6076...	4	0.8
3	−1.6	4.05	0.8076...
3.05	−1.5676...	4.1	0.7910...
3.1	−1.5110...	4.15	0.7510...
3.15	−1.4310...	4.2	0.6890...
3.2	−1.3290...	4.25	0.6071...

$h(c) = h(2.9593...) = -1.60811669...$

So h(c) is a lower bound for h(x).

$h(c) = h(4.0406...) = 0.808116698...$

So h(c) is an upper bound for h(x).

f. $h(x) = f(x) - g(x)$

$\therefore h'(x) = f'(x) - g'(x)$

$\therefore h'(c) = f'(c) - g'(c)$

For each of the values of c in part d, $h'(c) = 0$.

$\therefore f'(c) - g'(c) = 0$

$\therefore f'(c) = g'(c)$

$\therefore f'(c) =$ the slope of the secant line, Q.E.D.

g. f meets the hypotheses of the mean value theorem, since f is differentiable for all x.

35. Corollary of the Mean Value Theorem

The hypotheses of the mean value theorem state that f should be differentiable in the *open* interval (a, b) and continuous at x = a and x = b. If f is differentiable in the *closed* interval [a, b], it is automatically continuous at x = a and x = b, because differentiability implies continuity.

36. Converse of a Theorem

a. $h(x) = f(x) - g(x)$

The mean value theorem applies to h, since both f and g are given to be differentiable, and a linear combination of differentiable functions is also differentiable.

b. By the mean value theorem, there is a number c in (a, b) for which

$$h'(c) = \frac{h(b) - h(a)}{b - a}$$

If $f(a) = g(a) + D_1$ and $f(b) = g(b) + D_2$, then $h(a) = D_1$ and $h(b) = D_2$.

$$\therefore h'(c) = \frac{D_2 - D_1}{b - a}$$

c. If $D_1 \neq D_2$, then $h'(c) \neq 0$.

But $h'(x) = f'(x) - g'(x)$ by the derivative of a sum, and thus $h'(x) = 0$ for all x in the domain.

$\therefore h'(c) = 0$, which contradicts $h'(c) \neq 0$.

So the supposition that $D_1 \neq D_2$ is false, meaning that D_1 and D_2 *are* equal, Q.E.D.

37. Antiderivative of Zero

By the definition of antiderivative (indefinite integral), $g(x) = \int 0\,dx$ if and only if $g'(x) = 0$.

Any other function f for which $f'(x) = 0$ differs from g(x) by a constant. Thus the antiderivative of zero is a constant function, Q.E.D.

38. $f(x) = (\cos x + \sin x)^2$ and $g(x) = \sin 2x$. Graph.

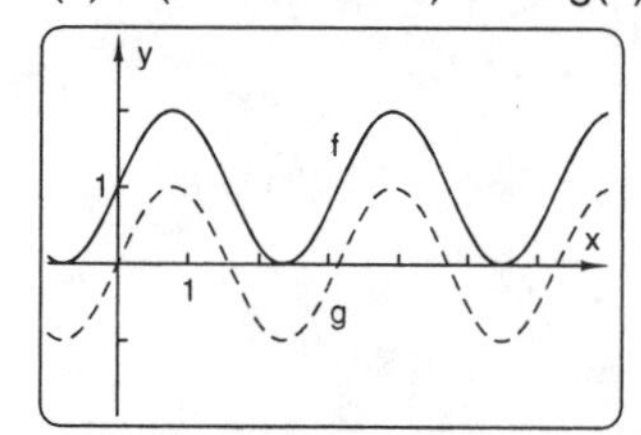

x	f(x)	g(x)
0	1	0
1	1.9092...	0.9092...
2	0.2431...	−0.7568...
3	0.7205...	−0.2794...
4	1.9893...	0.9893...

In each case, $f(x) = g(x) + 1$.

Proof:

$(\cos x + \sin x)^2$

$= \cos^2 x + 2 \cos x \sin x + \sin^2 x$

$= 2 \cos x \sin x + 1$

$= \sin 2x + 1$, Q.E.D.

39. Maximum and Minimum Values of Continuous Functions

The hypotheses of Rolle's theorem say that f is *differentiable* on the open interval (a, b). Since differentiability implies continuity, f is also *continuous* on (a, b). Combining this fact with the hypothesis of continuity at a and at b allows you to conclude that the function is continuous on the *closed* interval [a, b].

40. Intermediate Value Theorem Versus Mean Value Theorem.
The intermediate value theorem applies to continuous functions, whereas the mean value theorem applies to differentiable functions. Both are existence theorems, concluding that there is a value $x = c$ in the open interval (a, b). For the intermediate value theorem, $f(c)$ equals a pre-selected number v between $f(a)$ and $f(b)$. For the mean value theorem, $f'(c)$ equals the slope of the secant line connecting $(a, f(a))$ and $(b, f(b))$.

41. Journal Problem
Answers will vary.

Problem Set 5-7, pages 213 to 215 — Some Very Special Riemann Sums

1. $T_3 = 4.6462643...$.
Since the curve is concave downward, it lies *above* each trapezoid, and thus encloses more area than the trapezoids. So the trapezoidal rule underestimates the actual area. See graph.

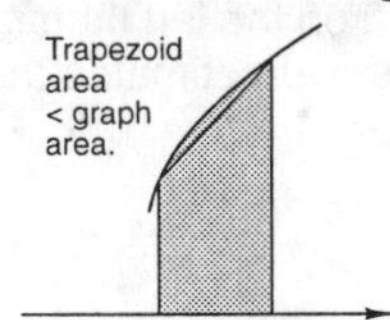

2. $M_3 = 4.6767123...$
M_3 overestimates the area. Draw a tangent line as shown in the diagram below. Since the sample point is at the midpoint, the area of the rectangle equals the area of the trapezoid formed by this tangent line. Also, the two small triangles shown are congruent. Since the graph is concave downward, the rectangle includes more than the actual area on the left side and leaves out less than the actual area on the right side. See graph. See also the analysis in the solution to Problem 11 in Problem Set 5-5.

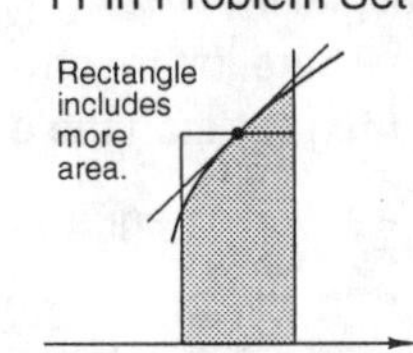

3.

k	x	f(x)
1	1.48584256	1.21895142
2	2.49161026	1.57848353
3	3.49402722	1.86923172
	Sum =	4.66666667

$R_3 = (1)(4.66666667) = 4.66666667$ (Remarkable!)
Answer is between the answer to Problem 1 (which is a *lower* bound) and the answer to Problem 2 (which is an *upper* bound).

4.

k	x	f(x)
1	1.24580513	1.11615641
2	1.74701361	1.32174642
3	2.24768040	1.49922660
4	2.74810345	1.65774047
5	3.24839587	1.80233068
6	3.74861006	1.93613276
	Sum =	9.33333334

$R_6 = (0.5)(9.33333334) = 4.66666667$, which is identical to the answer in Problem 3.

5. $g(x) = (2/3)x^{3/2}$.
$m = \dfrac{g(1.5) - g(1)}{1.5 - 1} = 1.11615640...$
$g'(x) = x^{1/2}$
$\therefore g'(c) = c^{1/2} = 1.1161... \Rightarrow c \approx 1.24580513$
This is the sample point used in Problem 4.

6. g is an indefinite integral of f.

7. Conjecture: Exact area $= 4\frac{2}{3}$

8. $M_{100} = 3.9998$
This sum underestimates the integral, by the same reasoning used in Problem 2. The conclusion is reversed because the graph is concave upward, not downward.

9. $T_{100} = 4.0004$
This sum overestimates the integral, by the same reasoning used in Problem 1. Again, the conclusion is reversed because the graph is concave upward.
Conjecture: Integral = 4, exactly.

10. $g(x) = \int x^3\,dx = \frac{1}{4}x^4 + C$. Let $C = 0$.
$m_1 = \dfrac{g(0.5) - g(0)}{0.5 - 0} = \dfrac{0.0015625 - 0}{0.5} = 0.03125$
$m_2 = \dfrac{g(1) - g(0.5)}{1 - 0.5} = \dfrac{0.25 - 0.015625}{0.5} = 0.46875$
$m_3 = \dfrac{g(1.5) - g(1)}{1.5 - 1} = \dfrac{1.265625 - 0.25}{0.5} = 2.03125$
$m_4 = \dfrac{g(2) - g(1.5)}{2 - 1.5} = \dfrac{4 - 1.265625}{0.5} = 5.46875$

11. $g'(c_1) = c_1^3 = 0.03125 \Rightarrow c_1 = 0.31498026...$
$g'(c_2) = c_2^3 = 0.46875 \Rightarrow c_2 = 0.77680912...$
$g'(c_3) = c_3^3 = 2.03125 \Rightarrow c_3 = 1.26644925...$
$g'(c_4) = c_4^3 = 5.46875 \Rightarrow c_4 = 1.76182468...$
Each value of c is within the respective interval.

12.

k	x	f(x)
1	0.31498026...	0.03125
2	0.77680912...	0.46875
3	1.26644925...	2.03125
4	1.76182468...	5.46875
	Sum =	8.00000

$\therefore R_4 = (0.5)(8) = 4$, which is the conjectured area!

13. Conjecture: Area $= g(2) - g(0)$.
Check: $\frac{1}{4}\cdot 2^4 - \frac{1}{4}\cdot 0^4 = 4 - 0 = 4$, the exact answer.
To find the Riemann sum, R_1,
let $m = \dfrac{g(2) - g(0)}{2 - 0} = \dfrac{4 - 0}{2 - 0} = 2$.
Then $g'(c) = c^3 = 2 \Rightarrow c = \sqrt[3]{2} = 1.25992...$
$f(c) = (1.25992...)^3 = 2$
$\therefore R_1 = (2)(2) = 4$, the exact answer.

Q1. $r'(x) = m(x)$.
Q2. See text definition of derivative.
Q3. Increasing at 6.
Q4. $dy = \sec x \tan x\, dx$.
Q5. $y' = 8x(x^2 + 3)^3$.
Q6. $dz/du = \cos u$.
Q7. $f'(x) = 0$.
Q8. $x = \pi/3$.
Q9. $\cos^2 x + \sin^2 x = 1$.
Q10. See Fig. 5-6b for mean value theorem.

1.a. $I = \int_4^9 10x^{-1.5}\, dx$
$= (-10/0.5)(9^{-0.5}) - (-10/0.5)(4^{-0.5})$
$= -20/3 + 20/2 = \underline{10/3} = \underline{3.33333...}$
The +C and –C add up to zero.

b. Graph, upper sum, n = 5.

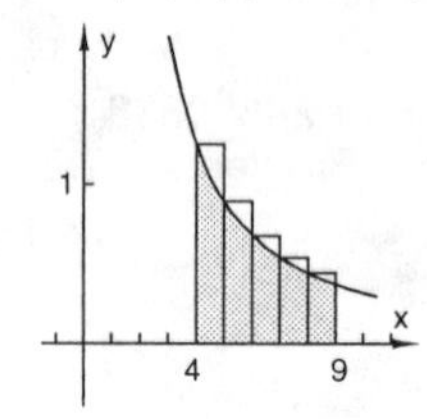

c. Pick sample points at left ends of subintervals for U_5 and at right ends for L_5.

k	x	f(x)
1	4	1.25
2	5	0.89442719...
3	6	0.68041381...
4	7	0.53994924...
5	8	0.44194173...

Sum = 3.80673199...
U_5 = (1)(3.80673199...) = 3.80673199...

k	x	f(x)
1	5	0.89442719...
2	6	0.68041381...
3	7	0.53994924...
4	8	0.44194173...
5	9	0.37037037...

Sum = 2.92710236...
L_5 = (1)(2.92710236...) = 2.92710236...
Average = $(U_5 + L_5)/2$ = 3.36691717... .
Average overestimates the integral, 3.33333... .
This fact is consistent with the fact that the graph is concave *upward*. See the solution to Problem Set 5-7, Problem 1.

d. Use sample points at the midpoints.
M_{10} = 3.32911229...
M_{100} = 3.33329093...
M_{1000} = 3.33333290...
Sums are converging toward 10/3.

2. $I = \int_0^{1.5} \sin x\, dx = -\cos 1.5 - (-\cos 0)$
= 0.92926279...
Using sample points at the midpoints,
M_{10} = 0.93013455...
M_{100} = 0.92927151...
M_{1000} = 0.92926288...
Integral = 0.92926279...
The sums are converging toward the integral.
Graph. The rectangle and the region differ by the two "triangular" regions. Since the sample point is at the midpoint of the subinterval, the "triangles" have equal bases. Since the graph is concave downward, the "triangle" below the horizontal line has a larger altitude, and thus a larger area, than the one above the line. So the rectangle includes more area on the left than it leaves out on the right, and thus overestimates the integral.

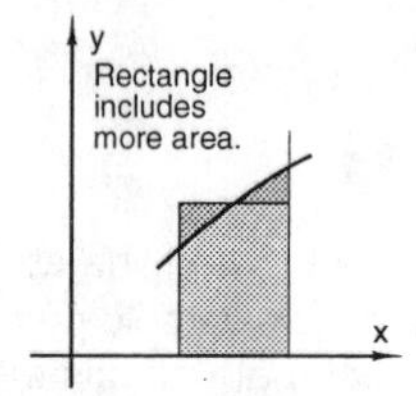

3. See the statement of the fundamental theorem in the text.
4. See the work in the text preceding the proof of the fundamental theorem for a derivation of a Riemann sum that is independent of the number of subintervals.
5. See the text proof of the fundamental theorem.
6. If c is picked as the point in (a, b) where the mean value theorem is true for $g(x) = \int f(x)\, dx$, then the exact integral equals $\dfrac{g(b) - g(a)}{(b - a)} \cdot (b - a)$, which equals $g(b) - g(a)$.
7. Freeway Exit Problem
$v(t) = 100 - 20(t + 1)^{1/2}$
Distance $= \int_0^8 (100 - 20(t + 1)^{1/2})\, dt$
$= 100t - \frac{40}{3}(t + 1)^{3/2} \Big|_0^8$
$= 800 - \frac{40}{3}(9)^{3/2} - 0 + \frac{40}{3}(1)^{3/2}$
$= 453\frac{1}{3}$ feet

8. The Fundamental Theorem Another Way

a. $h(x) = x^{1/2}$

k	x	f(x)
1	4.25	2.0615528...
2	4.75	2.1794494...
3	5.25	2.2912878...
4	5.75	2.3979157...
5	6.25	2.5
6	6.75	2.5980762...
7	7.25	2.6925824...
8	7.75	2.7838821...
9	8.25	2.8722813...
6	8.75	2.9580398...
	Sum =	25.3350679...

$M_{10} = (0.5)(25.3350679...) = 12.66753...$

b. $h(u)\Delta u$ and $h(u + \Delta u)\Delta u$ are terms in a lower and an upper sum, respectively, because $h(x)$ is increasing.
$\therefore h(u)\Delta u < A(u + \Delta u) - A(u) < h(u + \Delta u)\Delta u$

c. $h(u) < \dfrac{A(u + \Delta u) - A(u)}{\Delta u} < h(u + \Delta u)$
But the limits of $h(u)$ and $h(u + \Delta u)$ both equal $h(u)$, since h is continuous and $h(u)$ is independent of Δu. Therefore, by the squeeze theorem,
$\lim_{\Delta u \to 0} \dfrac{A(u + \Delta u) - A(u)}{\Delta u} = h(u).$
But the limit on the left is defined to be dA/du.
$\therefore dA/du = h(u)$, Q.E.D.

d. $dA = h(u)\,du$
$\therefore A(u) = \int h(u)\,du = \int u^{1/2}\,du = (2/3)\,u^{3/2} + C.$
$A(4) = 0 \Rightarrow 0 = (2/3)(4^{3/2}) + C \Rightarrow C = -16/3$
$\therefore A(u) = (2/3)\,u^{3/2} - 16/3.$

e. $A(9) = 12\frac{2}{3}$, which agrees with $M_{10} = 12.667...$.
(Note also that $A(9) < M_{10}$, which is expected because the graph of h is concave downward.)

9. Reimann Sum Sketching Problem

a. Graph (example).

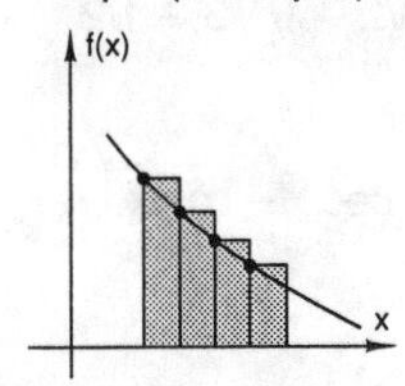

b. Graph (example).

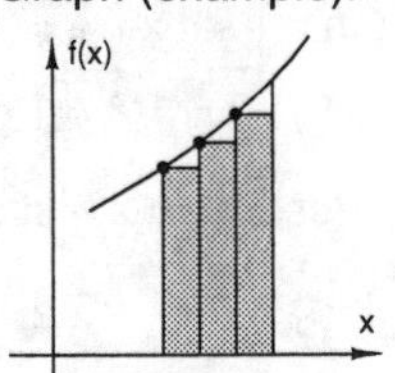

c. Graph (example).

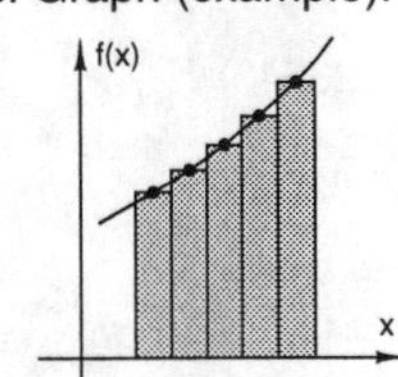

d. Graph (example).

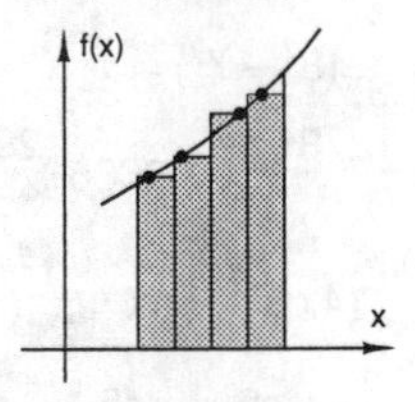

e. Graph (example).

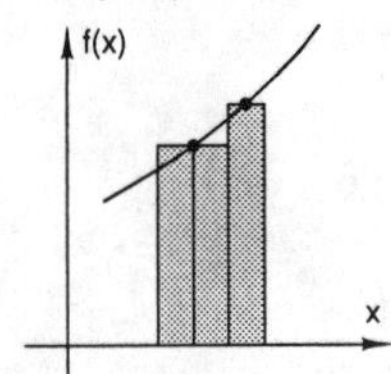

f. Graph (example).

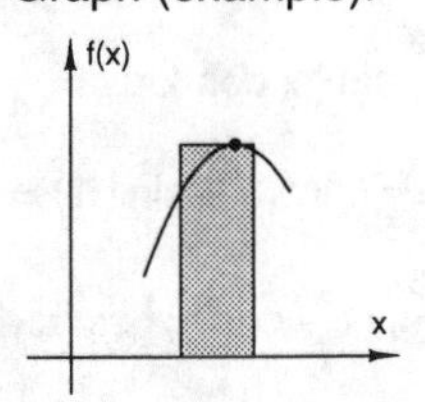

10. Journal Problem
Answers will vary.

Problem Set 5-9, pages 224 and 225 — Definite Integral Properties and Practice

Q1. $\frac{1}{6}x^6 + C.$

Q2. $\frac{1}{18}(3x + 7)^6 + C.$

Q3. $-\frac{1}{3}x^{-3} + C.$

Q4. $\frac{1}{6}\sin^6 x + C.$

Q5. $\frac{1}{5}\sin 5x + C.$

Q6. $x + C.$

Q7. $\tan x + C.$

Q8. $2x \sec x + x^2 \sec x \tan x.$

Q9. definite

Q10. indefinite

1. $\int_1^4 x^2\,dx = \frac{1}{3}x^3 \Big|_1^4 = \frac{1}{3}(64) - \frac{1}{3}(1) = \underline{21}$

2. $\int_2^5 x^3\,dx = \frac{1}{4}x^4 \Big|_2^5 = \frac{1}{4}(625) - \frac{1}{4}(6) = \frac{609}{4} = \underline{152.25}$

3. $\int_{-2}^3 (1 + 3x)^2\,dx = \frac{1}{9}(1 + 3x)^3 \Big|_{-2}^3$
$= \frac{1}{9}(1000) - \frac{1}{9}(-125) = \underline{125}$

4. $\int_{-1}^4 (5x - 2)^2\,dx = \frac{1}{15}(5x - 2)^3 \Big|_{-1}^4$
$= \frac{1}{15}(5832 - (-343)) = \frac{6175}{15} = \frac{1235}{3} = 411\frac{2}{3}$

5. $\int_1^8 60x^{2/3}\,dx = 36x^{5/3} \Big|_1^8 = 36(32 - 1) = \underline{1116}$

6. $\int_1^4 24x^{3/2}\,dx = 9.6x^{5/2} \Big|_1^4 = 9.6(32 - 1) = \underline{297.6}$

7. $\int_2^8 5\,dx = 5x \Big|_2^8 = 40 - 10 = \underline{30}$

8. $\int_{20}^{50} dx = x \Big|_{20}^{50} = 50 - 20 = \underline{30}$

9. $\int_{-2}^0 (x^2 + 3x + 7)\,dx = \frac{1}{3}x^3 + \frac{3}{2}x^2 + 7x \Big|_{-2}^0$
$= 0 - (-\frac{8}{3} + 6 - 14) = \frac{32}{3} = 10\frac{2}{3}$

10. $\int_{-3}^0 (x^2 + 4x + 10)\,dx = \frac{1}{3}x^3 + 2x^2 + 10x \Big|_{-3}^0$
$= 0 - (-9 + 18 - 30) = \underline{21}$

11. $\int_{-1}^1 \sqrt{4x + 5}\,dx = \frac{1}{4}\int_{-1}^1 (4x + 5)^{1/2}\,(4\,dx)$
$= \frac{1}{4}\cdot\frac{2}{3}(4x + 5)^{3/2} \Big|_{-1}^1 = \frac{1}{6}(27 - 1) = \frac{13}{3} = 4\frac{1}{3}$

12. $\int_{-3}^3 \sqrt{2x + 10}\,dx = \frac{1}{2}\int_{-3}^3 (2x + 10)^{1/2}\,(2\,dx)$
$= \frac{1}{2}\cdot\frac{2}{3}(2x + 10)^{3/2} \Big|_{-3}^3 = \frac{1}{3}(64 - 8) = \frac{56}{3} = 18\frac{2}{3}$

13. $\int_0^\pi 4\sin x\,dx = -4\cos x \Big|_0^\pi = -4(-1) + 4(1) = \underline{8}$

14. $\int_{-\pi/2}^{\pi/2} 6\cos x\,dx = 6\sin x \Big|_{-\pi/2}^{\pi/2} = 6(1) - 6(-1) = \underline{12}$
or: Integral of an even function between symmetric limits.
$2\int_0^{\pi/2} 6\cos x\,dx = 12\sin x \Big|_0^{\pi/2} = 12(1) - 0 = \underline{12}$

15. $\int_{\pi/6}^{\pi/3} (\sec^2 x + \cos x)\, dx$
$= \tan x + \sin x \Big|_{\pi/6}^{\pi/3} = \sqrt{3} + \sqrt{3}/2 - 1/\sqrt{3} - 1/2$
$= (7/6)\sqrt{3} - 1/2 = \underline{1.52072...}$

16. $\int_0^{\pi/3} (\sec x \tan x + \sin x)\, dx = \sec x - \cos x \Big|_0^{\pi/3}$
$= 2 - \frac{1}{2} - 1 + 1 = \underline{1.5}$

17. $\int_{1.2}^{1.4} (5x + 1)^6\, dx = \frac{1}{35}(5x + 1)^7 \Big|_{1.2}^{1.4}$
$= \frac{1}{35}(8^7 - 7^7) = \frac{1}{35}(2097152 - 823543)$
$= \frac{1273609}{35} = 36388\frac{29}{35} = 36388.8285...$

18. $\int_{0.4}^{0.7} (4x - 1)^5\, dx = \frac{1}{24}(4x - 1)^6 \Big|_{0.4}^{0.7}$
$= \frac{1}{24}(1.8^6 - 0.6^6) = \underline{1.415232}$ (exactly)

19. $\int_1^2 \sin^3 x \cos x\, dx = \frac{1}{4} \sin^4 x \Big|_1^2$
$= \frac{1}{4}(\sin^4 2 - \sin^4 1) = \underline{0.045566...}$

20. $\int_{-3}^{3} (1 + \cos x)^4 \sin x\, dx = -\frac{1}{5}(1 + \cos x)^5 \Big|_{-3}^{3}$
$= -\frac{1}{5}(1 + \cos 3)^5 + \frac{1}{5}(1 + \cos(-3))^5 = \underline{0}$
or:
Integral equals zero because an odd function is integrated between symmetric limits.

21. $\int_{0.1}^{0.2} \cos 3x\, dx = \frac{1}{3} \sin 3x \Big|_{0.1}^{0.2}$
$= \frac{1}{3}(\sin 0.6 - \sin 0.3) = \underline{0.0897074...}$

22. $\int_0^{0.4} \sin 2x\, dx = -\frac{1}{2} \cos 2x \Big|_0^{0.4}$
$= -\frac{1}{2}(\cos 0.8 - \cos 0) = \underline{0.1516466...}$

23. $\int_{-5}^{5} (x^7 - 6x^3 + 4 \sin x + 2)\, dx = 2\int_0^5 2\, dx$
$= 2(2x) \Big|_0^5 = 20 - 0 = \underline{20}$

24. $\int_{-1}^{1}(\cos x + 10x^3 - \tan x)\, dx = 2\int_0^1 \cos x\, dx$
$= 2 \sin x \Big|_0^1 = 2 \sin 1 - 2 \sin 0 = \underline{1.682941...}$

25. $\int_{-1}^{1} x^{-2}\, dx$ has no value, since $y = x^{-2}$ has a vertical asymptote at $x = 0$, which is within the interval.

26. $\int_{-2}^{2} \sqrt{x}\, dx$ has no value, since the integrand is not a real number for negative values of x.

27. Graph, $f(x) = x^2 - 10x + 16$. Integral = –(area).

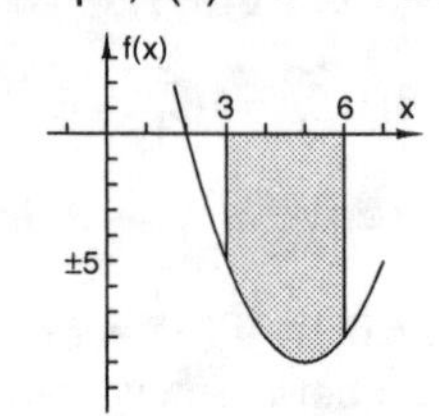

28. Graph, $f(x) = \cos x$. Integral = area.

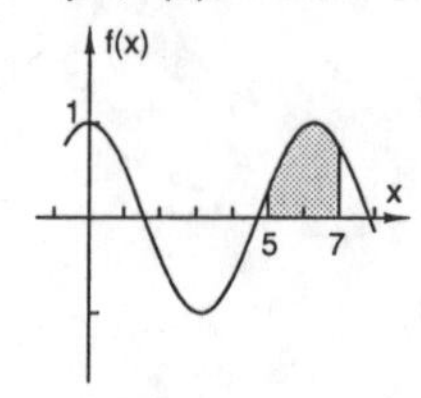

29. Graph, $f(x) = \sin (\pi/6)x$. Integral $\neq$ area.

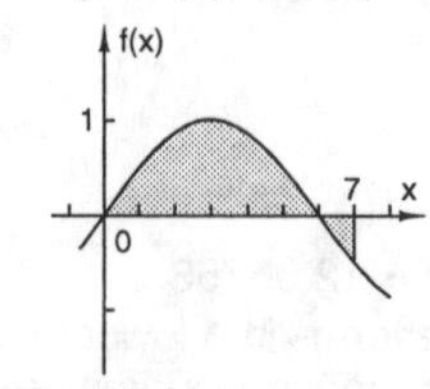

30. Graph, $f(x) = 1/x^2 - 1/4$. Integral $\neq$ area.

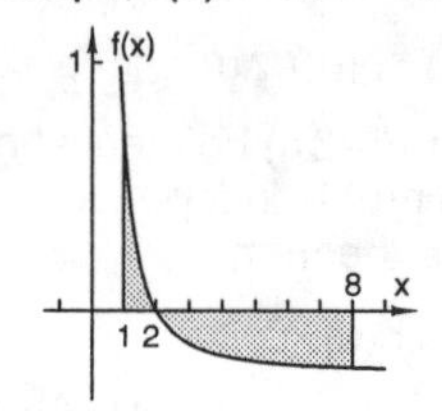

31. $\int_b^a f(x)\, dx = -\int_a^b f(x)\, dx = \underline{-7}$

32. $\int_a^b 4\, f(x)\, dx = 4\int_a^b f(x)\, dx = 4(7) = \underline{28}$

33. $\int_a^c g(x)\, dx = \int_a^b g(x)\, dx + \int_b^c g(x)\, dx = 12 + 13 = \underline{25}$

34. $\int_a^c f(x)\, dx$ cannot be determined.

35. $\int_a^c f(x)\, dx + \int_a^c g(x)\, dx$ cannot be determined.

36. $\int_a^b (f(x) + g(x))dx = \int_a^b f(x)\, dx + \int_a^b g(x)\, dx = 7 + 12$
$= \underline{19}$

37. Statement:
"If $f(x) < g(x)$ for all x in [a, b],
then $\int_a^b f(x)\, dx < \int_a^b g(x)\, dx$."
Converse:
"If $\int_a^b f(x)\, dx < \int_a^b g(x)\, dx$,
then $f(x) < g(x)$ for all x in [a, b]."
The converse can be shown to be false by any counterexample in which the area of the region under the g graph is greater than the area under the f graph, but the g graph touches or crosses the f graph somewhere in [a, b]. One counterexample is $f(x) = 1.5$ and $g(x) = 2 + \cos x$ on $[0, 2\pi]$. Graph.

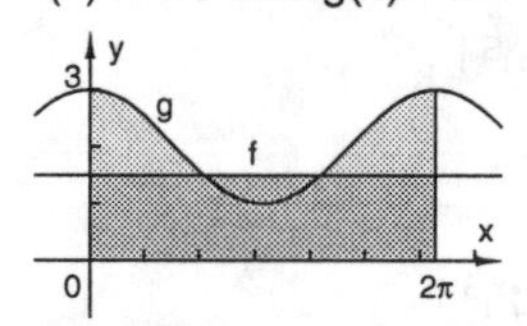

38. Plus C" Problem

$\int_1^4 x^2\, dx = \frac{1}{3}x^3 + C \Big|_1^4 = \frac{1}{3}(4^3) + C - \frac{1}{3}(1^3) - C = 21$
The two Cs will always cancel, so it is not necessary to write them.

Q1. $30x^{2.4} + C$. Q2. $30(4^{2.4} - 1) = 805.72....$

Q3. $y' = -1/\sqrt{1 - x^2}$.

Q4. $f'(x) = 3x^2 \sin x + x^3 \cos x$.

Q5. Graph of $f'(x)$. Q6. Yes, continuous.

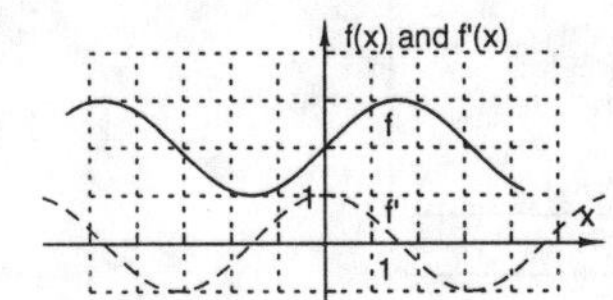

Q7. Increasing at $x = 7$. Q8. $f(a) = f(b) = 0$.

Q9. $v(9) = 450$ ft/sec. Q10. $a(9) = 25$ (ft/sec)/sec.

1. Displacement Problem

a. Graph, $v = 55 + 12t^{0.6}$ from Figure 5-10c, showing a strip and a sample point (t, v).

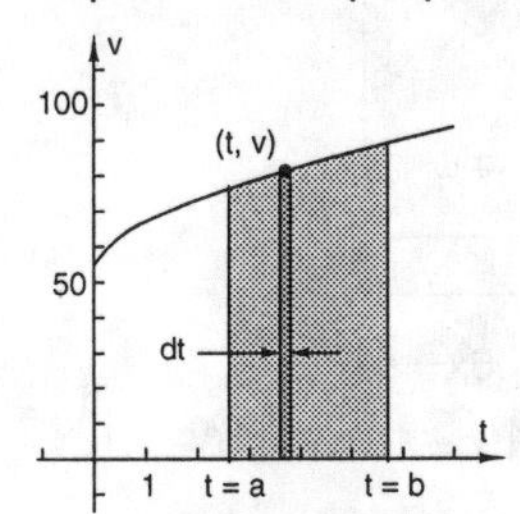

b. $dy = v\,dt = (55 + 12t^{0.6})\,dt$

c. $R = \sum dy = \sum (55 + 12t^{0.6})\,dt$

d. Displacement $= \int_a^b (55 + 12t^{0.6})\,dt$

e. First hour:

Disp. $= \int_0^1 (55 + 12t^{0.6})\,dt = 55t + 7.5t^{1.6} \Big|_0^1$

$= 55 + 7.5 - 0 - 0 =$ $\underline{62.5 \text{ mi}}$

Second hour:

Disp. $= \int_1^2 (55 + 12t^{0.6})\,dt = 55t + 7.5t^{1.6} \Big|_1^2$

$= 110 + 22.735... - 55 - 7.5 \approx 70.2$ mi.

First two hours:

Disp. $= \int_0^2 (55 + 12t^{0.6})\,dt = 55t + 7.5t^{1.6} \Big|_0^2$

$= 110 + 22.735... - 0 - 0 = 132.735...$, which equals the sum of the two integrals above.

f. $v(2) = 55 + 12 \cdot 2^{0.6} = 73.188... \approx$ $\underline{73.2 \text{ mph}}$

g. Let x be the number of hours for 300 miles.

$\therefore \int_0^x (55 + 12t^{0.6})\,dt = 300$

$55t + 7.5t^{1.6} \Big|_0^x = 300$

$55x + 7.5x^{1.6} = 300$

$x \approx 4.13372... \approx 4.134$ hours.

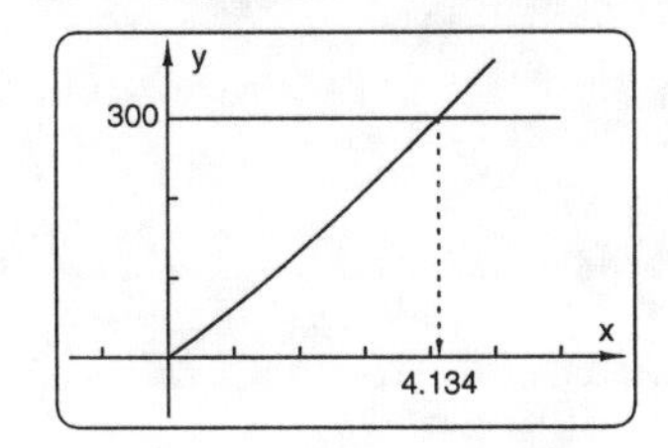

2. Area Problem

a. Graph, $y = 6x - x^2$, showing strip and sample point (x, y).

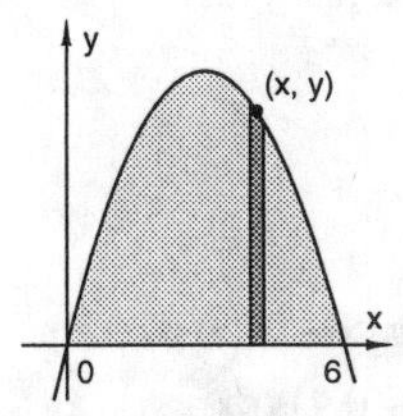

b. $dA = y\,dx = (6x - x^2)\,dx$

c. $R = \sum dA = \sum (6x - x^2)\,dx$

d. $A = \int_0^6 (6x - x^2)\,dx = 3x^2 - \frac{1}{3}x^3 \Big|_0^6$

$= 108 - 72 - 0 + 0 =$ $\underline{36 \text{ square units}}$

The exact area is the limit of the Riemann sums as the number of subintervals becomes infinite. A definite integral is the same thing.

e. The maximum height of the region is $y = 9$ at $x = 3$. So the area of the circumscribed rectangle is $6 \cdot 9 = 54$. The area of the region, 36, is 2/3 of 54.

3. Work Problem

a. Graph, $F = 0.6x$, showing strip and sample point.

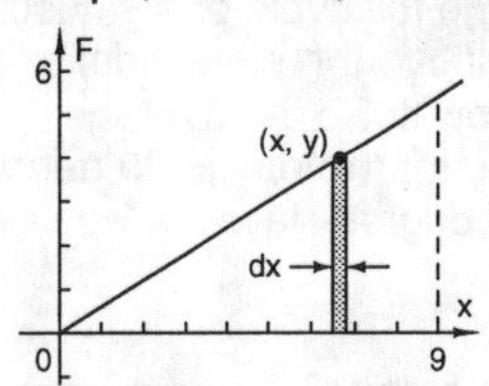

b. $dW = F\,dx = 0.6x\,dx$

c. $W = \int_0^9 0.6x\,dx = 0.3x^2 \Big|_0^9$

$= 24.3 - 0 =$ $\underline{24.3 \text{ inch-pounds}}$

d. $F(4.5) = 2.7$ pounds and $F(9) = 5.4$ pounds. So the force at $x = 9$ *is* twice the force at $x = 4.5$. Work done in stretching from 0 to 4.5 inches is

$W = \int_0^{4.5} 0.6x\,dx = 0.3x^2 \Big|_0^{4.5}$

$= 6.075 - 0 = 6.075$ inch-pounds.

So the work done stretching from 0 to 9 inches is four times the work done stretching from 0 to 4.5 inches, *not* twice the work.

4. <u>Degree-Days Problem</u>
 a. Graph, $T = 20 - 12 \cos 2\pi(x - 0.1)$, showing strip and sample point.

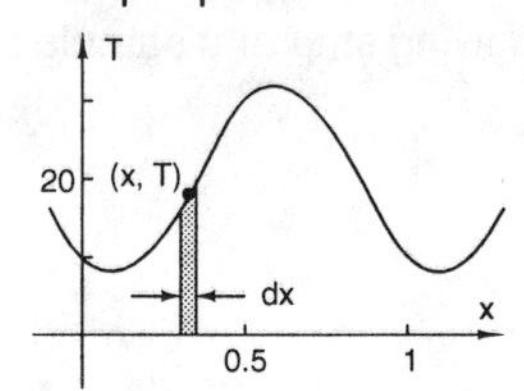

 b. $dD = T\,dx = (20 - 12 \cos 2\pi(x - 0.1))\,dx$
 c. $D = \int_0^{0.5} (20 - 12 \cos 2\pi(x - 0.1))\,dx$
 $= 20x - (6/\pi) \sin 2\pi(x - 0.1) \Big|_0^{0.5}$
 $= 10 - (6/\pi) \sin 0.8\pi - 0 + (6/\pi) \sin (-0.2\pi)$
 $= 7.75482... \approx$ <u>7.75 degree-days</u>
 d. From noon to midnight,
 $D = \int_{0.5}^{1} (20 - 12 \cos 2\pi(x - 0.1))\,dx$
 $= 20x - (6/\pi) \sin 2\pi(x - 0.1) \Big|_{0.5}^{1}$
 $= 20 - (6/\pi) \sin 1.8\pi - 10 + (6/\pi) \sin 0.8\pi$
 $= 12.24517... \approx$ <u>12.25 degree-days</u>
 The total number of degree days is
 $D = 7.75482... + 12.24517... =$ <u>20 degree-days</u>
 Note that this answer can be found more easily by observing that in one full cycle of a sinusoid there is just as much area above the sinusoidal axis, $T = 20$, as there is below it. So the average temperature difference for the day is 20 degrees, making the number of degree-days for 1 day equal to 20.

5. <u>Heat Problem</u>
 a. Graph, $C = -0.016T^3 + 0.678T^2 + 7.45T + 796$, showing strip and sample point (T, C).

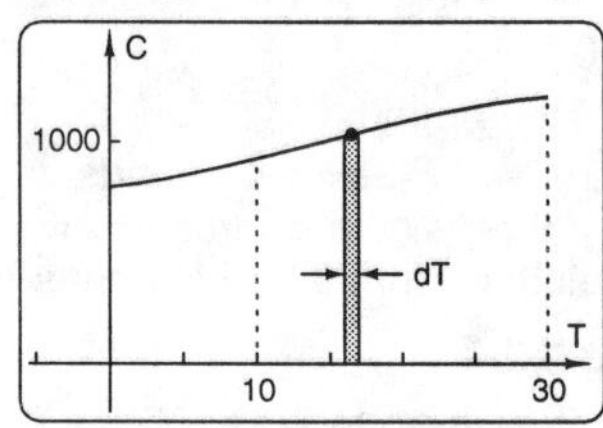

 b. $dH = C\,dT$
 $= (-0.016T^3 + 0.678T^2 + 7.45T + 796)\,dT$
 c. $H = \int_{10}^{30} (-0.016T^3 + 0.678T^2 + 7.45T + 796)\,dT$
 $= -0.004T^4 + 0.226T^3 + 3.725T^2 + 796T \Big|_{10}^{30}$
 $= -3240 + 6102 + 3352.5 + 23880$
 $+ 40 - 226 - 372.5 - 7960$
 $=$ <u>21,576 Btu</u>
 d. $(2000)(21576) =$ <u>43,152,000 Btu</u>
 The property is the integral of a constant times a function. That is,
 $\int_{10}^{30} 2000C\,dT = 2000 \int_{10}^{30} C\,dT$.

 e. The mathematical model does *not* give reasonable answers beyond 3000° (T = 30). As stated in the text, the actual heat capacity rises slowly. The model indicates that it decreases rapidly. See graph.

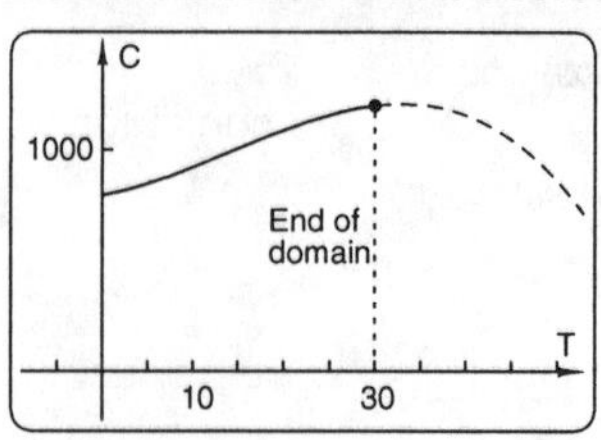

6. <u>Total Cost Problem</u>
 a. Graph, $P = 100 + 0.06x^2$, showing strip and sample point (x, P).

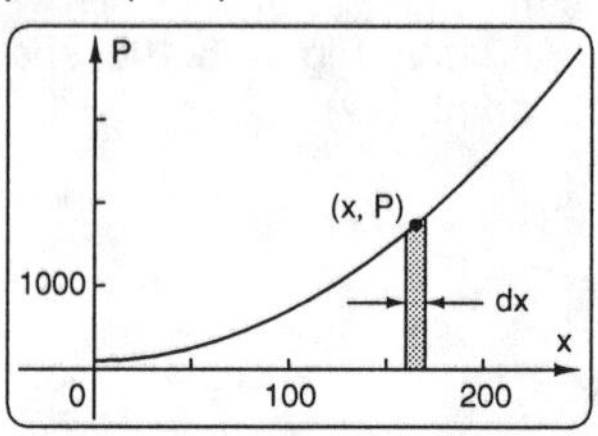

 b. $dC = P\,dx = (100 + 0.06x^2)\,dx$
 $C = \int_0^b (100 + 0.06x^2)\,dx = 100x + 0.02x^3 \Big|_0^b$
 $= 100b + 0.02b^3 - 0 - 0$
 $\therefore C = 100b + 0.02b^3$
 c. $b = 100$: $C = 100(100) + 0.02(100^3) =$ <u>\$30,000</u>
 $b = 200$: $C = 100(200) + 0.02(200^3) =$ <u>\$180,000</u>
 For 100m to 200m the cost should be
 $100{,}000 - 30{,}000 =$ <u>\$150,000</u>.
 As a check,
 $\int_{100}^{200} (100 + 0.06x^2)\,dx = 100x + 0.02x^3 \Big|_{100}^{200}$
 $= 100(200) + 0.02(200^3) - 100(100) - 0.02(100^3)$
 $= 150{,}000$.
 Thus, $\int_0^{200} P\,dx = \int_0^{100} P\,dx + \int_{100}^{200} P\,dx$,
 which shows that the sum of integrals with the same integrand applies.

7. <u>Golf Course Problem</u>
 Using trapezoids, the area is approximately
 $10(0/2 + 38 + 50 + 62 + 60 + 55 + 51 + 30 + 3/2)$
 $= 3475$ ft^2
 The fundamental theorem cannot be used because the function is specified only by data, not by an equation whose antiderivative can be found.

Q1. $\frac{1}{3}x^3 + x + C$ Q2. 24

Q3. $\int \sec^2 x\,dx = \tan x + C$ Q4. $2\sec^2 x \tan x$

Q5. Graph (example) Q6. Graph, strip (see Q5)

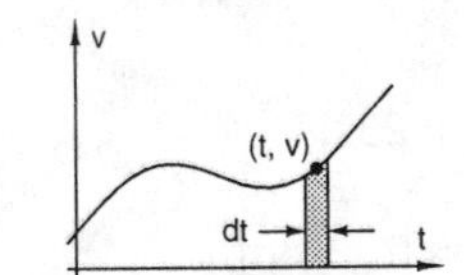

Q7. Graph, point (see Q5) Q8. d(disp) = v dt

Q9. Disp. ≈ R = $\sum v\,dt$ Q10. Disp. = $\int_a^b v\,dt$

1. Velocity Problem
   a. $\int_0^{12}$ (speed) dt ≈ ((2/60)/3)(33 + 4·25 + 2·27 + 4·13 + 2·21 + 4·5 + 9)
   = (1/90)(310) = 3.444... ≈ 3.4 nautical miles
   b. T_6 = (1/30)(33·0.5 + 25 + 27 + 13 + 21 + 5 + 9·0.5)
   = (1/30)(112) = 3.7333... ≈ 3.7 nautical miles
   c. The answer by Simpson's rule should be closer, since the graph is represented by curved segments instead of straight ones.
2. Spleen Mass Problem
   (Data and CAT scans for this problem were provided by Dr. James Stewart of San Antonio.)
   a. $\int_0^8$ A dD ≈ (0.8/3)(6.8 + 4·6.8 + 2·20.1 + 4·25.3 + 2·29.5 + 4·34.6 + 2·38.4 + 4·33.9 + 2·15.8 + 4·6.1 + 2.3)
   = (0.8/3)(643.5) = 171.6 cm^3
   b. The mass will be 171.6 g, which is within the normal range of 150 to 200 g.
3. Tensile Strength Test Problem
   a. Graph, scatterplot of the data.

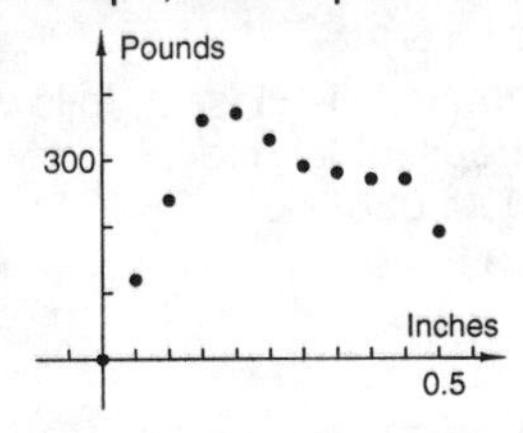

   b. Let F = force, x = displacement, W = work.
   W = $\int_0^{0.5}$ F dx
   ≈ (0.05/3)(0 + 4·120 + 2·240 + 4·360 + 2·370 + 4·330 + 2·290 + 4·280 + 2·270 + 4·270 + 190)
   = (0.05/3)(7970) = 132.8333...
   ≈ 132.8 inch pounds
4. Heat Capacity Problem
   Let C = heat capacity, T = temperature, H = heat.
   H = $\int_{500}^{4500}$ C dT
   Approximate readings from the chart for H_2O

T (°F)	C (Btu/pound mole/°F)	Factor
500	8.44	1
1000	9.25	4
1500	10.08	2
2000	10.84	4
2500	11.47	2
3000	11.97	4
3500	12.35	2
4000	12.68	4
4500	12.93	1

   Multiplying the heat capacity by the Simpson's rule factor and summing gives 268.13.
   ∴ H ≈ (500/3)(268.13) = 44688.333...
   ≈ 44,690 Btu/pound mole
   The answers students get will vary slightly. Assuming students' readings are within ±0.02 of the ones shown, the sum can be off by ±0.48, making the final answer off by as much as ±80 Btu/mole.
5. Sine-Integral Function Problem
   a. Graph, Si x = $\int_0^x \frac{\sin t}{t}\,dt$

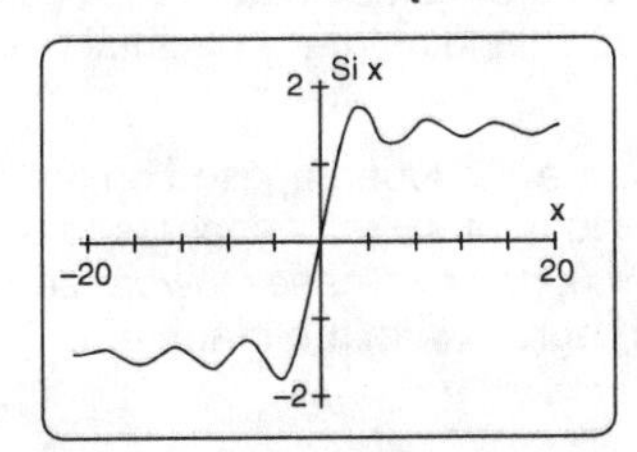

   b. (sin x)/(x) approaches 1 as x approaches 0.
   c. Answers will vary depending on the grapher used. The TI-82 gives Si 0.6 = 0.58812881 using TRACE or 0.588128809608 using TABLE, both of which are correct to as many decimal places as the NBS values.
   d. By TABLE, Si x seems to be oscillating between about 1.53 and 1.61 when x is between 20 and 30. The limit is somewhere between these two numbers, say about 1.57. The actual limit is π/2, which equals 1.570796... .
   e. Graph, f(x) = (sin x)/(x), superimposed on y = Si x. The f graph is positive, and greatest when x is between −π and π, which agrees with the large positive slope of the Si x graph in this region. Each place where the Si x graph has a high or low point, the f(x) graph has a zero, corresponding to the zero slope of the Si x graph.

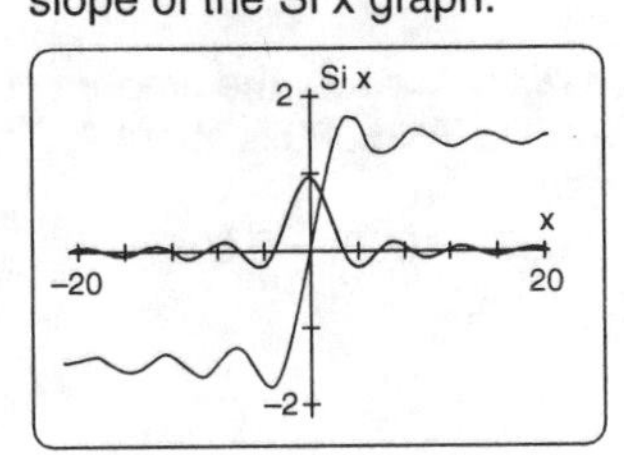

6. Error Function Problem

a. $\text{erf } x = \dfrac{2}{\sqrt{\pi}} \int_0^x e^{-t^2}\, dt$

The integrand e^{-t^2} is an even function integrated between symmetrical limits. Thus, rather than using the entire interval [–x, x], one may find the integral on [0, x] and double the result.

b. Graph, y = erf x.

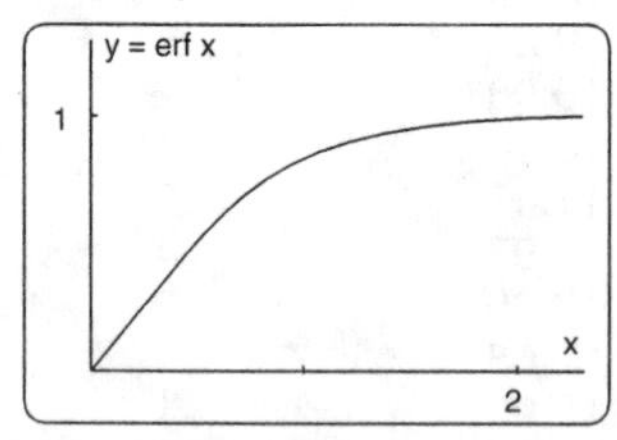

c. By TABLE, values of erf x are

x	erf x
1	0.842700792...
2	0.995322265...
3	0.999977909...
4	0.999999984...

The values approach 1, meaning that the fraction of the data between –x and x is virtually 100% when x is beyond 4.

d. Answers will vary depending on the grapher used. The TI-82 gives erf 0.5 = 0.52049987781... using TABLE, which is correct to as many decimal places as the NBS value.

e. Graph, $f(x) = 2/\sqrt{\pi}\, e^{-x^2}$, superimposed on the graph of y = erf x. The slope of y = erf x appears to equal about 1 when x = 0, and decreases toward zero as x increases, which agrees with the graph of f.

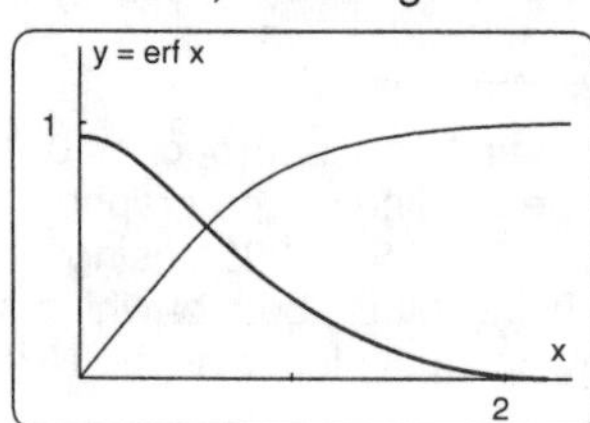

7. $\int_{0.3}^{1.4} \cos x\, dx \approx 0.689929523...$

8. $\int_1^4 (x^2 - 3x + 5)\, dx = 13.5$

9. $\int_0^3 2^x\, dx \approx 10.0988652...$

10. $\int_{0.1}^{1.4} \tan x\, dx \approx 1.76714178...$

11. Answer Check Problem

$\int_{0.3}^{1.4} \cos x\, dx = \sin x \,\Big|_{0.3}^{1.4}$

= sin 1.4 – sin 0.3 = 0.689929523...,

which agrees with Problem 7.

12. Simpson's Rule from Equation Problem

$f(x) = 2^x$

By Simpson's rule with n = 4,

$\int_0^3 2^x\, dx \approx (0.75/3)(2^0 + 4\cdot 2^{0.75} + 2\cdot 2^{1.5} + 4\cdot 2^{2.25} + 2^3)$

= (0.25)(40.4113394...) = 10.1028348...

By trapezoidal rule program with n = 4,

$\int_0^3 2^x\, dx \approx 10.3252863...$

Simpson's rule is high by 0.00396... .

Trapezoidal rule is high by 0.2264... .

Simpson's rule gives a much more accurate approximation to the integral.

13. Program for Simpson's Rule from Data

Programs will vary depending on the type of grapher used. See the program in the "Supplementary Programs" section of the Instructor's Materials.

14. Program for Simpson's Rule from Equation

Programs will vary depending on the type of grapher used. See the program in the "Supplementary Programs" section of the Instructor's Materials.

15. Relative Accuracy Problem

a. $I = \int_0^{\pi} \sin x\, dx$

i. $S_{50} = 2.00000017...$

ii. $T_{50} = 1.99934198...$

iii. INTEGRATE: I = 2

iv. $I = -\cos x \,\Big|_0^{\pi} = -(-1) + 1 = 2$

b. The built-in integrate function is closest, followed by Simpson's rule, then trapezoidal rule.

S_{50} is off by about 0.00000866%.

T_{50} is off by about 0.039%.

Problem Set 5-12, pages 240 to 247 — Chapter Review and Test

Review Problems

R0. Answers will vary.

R1. Heat Capacity Problem

a. Heat needed is (Btu/degree)(degrees), which is a product of independent and dependent variables. Since (Btu/degree) varies, a definite integral must be used.

b. C = –0.4 + 0.3 log T

By trapezoidal rule with n = 100, the amount of heat added from T = 1000 to T = 5000 is about 2527 Btu. (Exact answer: 2527.3016...)

c. Average ≈ 2527/(5000 – 1000) = 0.63175 ≈ 0.632 Btu/degree

R2. a. $f'(x) = 4x^{3/7} \Rightarrow f(x) = 2.8x^{10/7} + C$

b. $f'(x) = 10 \cos 2x \Rightarrow f(x) = 5 \sin 2x + C$

c. $f'(x) = (12x + 5)^{-3} \Rightarrow$

$f(x) = -\dfrac{1}{24}(12x + 5)^{-2} + C$

R3. a. $f(x) = \sin \pi x \Rightarrow f'(x) = \pi \cos \pi x$
$f(1) = \sin \pi = 0$
$f'(1) = \pi \cos \pi = -\pi$
Linear function is $y - 0 = -\pi(x - 1)$
$y = -\pi x + \pi$
At $x = 1.1$, $y = -0.314159...$
$f(1.1) = -0.309016...$
$\text{Error} = -0.005142...$
At $x = 1.001$, $y = -0.003141592...$
$f(1.001) = -0.003141587...$
$\text{Error} = -0.000000005...$

b. i. $y = \csc^5 2x \Rightarrow dy = -10 \csc^5 2x \cot 2x\, dx$
ii. $y = x^5/5 - x^{-3}/3 \Rightarrow dy = (x^4 + x^{-4})\, dx$
iii. $y = (7 - 3x)^4 \Rightarrow dy = -12(7 - 3x)^3\, dx$

c. i. $dy = \sec x \tan x\, dx \Rightarrow y = \sec x + C$
ii. $dy = (3x + 7)^5\, dx \Rightarrow y = \frac{1}{18}(3x + 7)^6 + C$
iii. $dy = 5\, dx \Rightarrow y = 5x + C$

d. i. $y = (2x + 5)^{1/2} \Rightarrow dy = (2x + 5)^{-1/2}\, dx$
ii. $x = 10$ and $dx = 0.3 \Rightarrow dy = 25^{-1/2} \cdot 0.3 = 0.06.$
iii. $\Delta y = (2 \cdot 10.3 + 5)^{1/2} - (2 \cdot 10 + 5)^{1/2}$
$= 0.059644...$
iv. 0.06 is close to 0.059644... .

R4. a. See text definition of *indefinite integral.*

b. i. $\int 12x^{2/3}\, dx = 7.2x^{5/3} + C$
ii. $\int \sin^6 x \cos x\, dx = \frac{1}{7} \sin^7 x + C$
iii. $\int (x^2 - 8x + 3)\, dx = \frac{1}{3}x^3 - 4x^2 + 3x + C$

R5. a. See text definition of *integrability.*

b. See text definition of *definite integral.*

c. $\int_{0.2}^{1.4} \sec x\, dx$
i. $U_6 = 2.845333...$
ii. $L_6 = 1.872703...$
iii. $M_6 = 2.209073...$
iv. $T_6 = 2.359018...$

d. Graphs, U_6 and L_6.

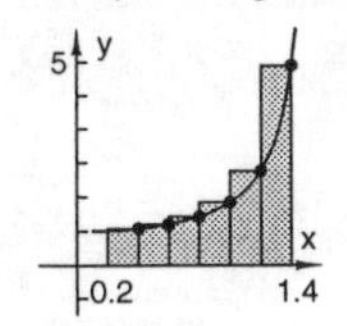

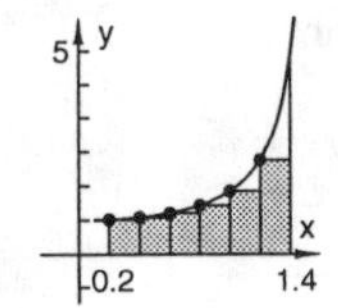

Graphs, M_6 and T_6.

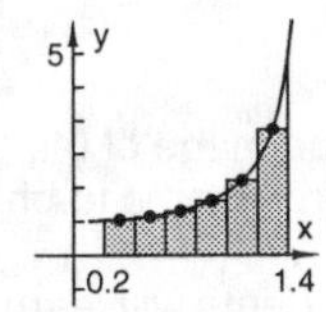

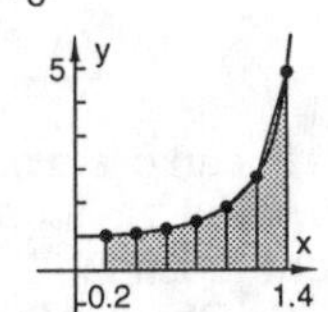

e. $I = \int_0^5 x\, dx$
i. $U_n = (1 \cdot 5/n)(5/n) + (2 \cdot 5/n)(5/n) + (3 \cdot 5/n)(5/n) + \ldots + (n \cdot 5/n)(5/n)$
$= (25/n^2)(1 + 2 + 3 + \ldots + n)$
ii. $U_n = (25/n^2)(0.5n)(n + 1) = (12.5/n)(n + 1)$
$= 12.5(1 + 1/n)$
iii. $\lim_{n \to \infty} U_n = 12.5$ because $1/n \to 0$ as $n \to \infty$.
iv. Integral = area of triangle with base 5 and altitude 5, which is $(1/2)(5)(5) = 12.5$.

R6. a. The hypothesis is the "if" part of a theorem and the conclusion is the "then" part. (Hypo- means "under," and -thesis means "theme.")

b. $d(t) = 20 + 3 \sin \frac{\pi}{4}t$

$\text{Average velocity} = \frac{d(2) - d(0)}{2 - 0} = \underline{1.5 \text{ m/sec}}$

$\text{Instantaneous velocity} = d'(t) = 0.75\pi \cos \frac{\pi}{4}t$

$d'(c) = 0.75\pi \cos \frac{\pi}{4}c = 1.5$

$\frac{\pi}{4}c = \cos^{-1}(2/\pi) = 0.880689...$
$c = 1.12132... \approx \underline{1.12 \text{ sec}}$

c. $g(x) = x^{4/3} - 4x^{1/3} = x^{1/3}(x - 4)$
$g(x) = 0 \Leftrightarrow x = 0$ or $x = 4$. Interval is $\underline{[0, 4]}$.
$g'(x) = (4/3)x^{1/3} - (4/3)x^{-2/3} = (4/3)x^{-2/3}(x - 1)$
$g'(c) = 0 \Leftrightarrow \underline{c = 1}$
At $x = 0$, $g'(0)$ takes the form 1/0, which is infinite. Thus, g is not differentiable at $x = 0$. However, the function need not be differentiable at the endpoints of the interval, just at interior points.

d. See Figure 5-6f, left diagram.

e. See Figure 5-6f, right diagram.

f. g is the linear function containing the points (a, f(a)) and (b, f(b)). h is the function $h(x) = f(x) - g(x)$. Thus $h(a) = h(b) = 0$, satisfying one hypothesis of Rolle's theorem. The other two hypotheses are satisfied because f and g are differentiable and continuous at the appropriate places, and a difference of differentiable and continuous functions also has these properties. The c in (a, b) for which $h'(c) = 0$ turns out to be the c in (a, b) for which $f'(c)$ equals the slope of the secant line, $g'(c)$, which equals $[f(b) - f(a)]/(b - a)$.

g. Graph, $f(x) = 3 + 5 \cos 8\pi x$.
Points are 1/8, 1/4, 3/8, 1/2, 5/8, 3/4, and 7/8.

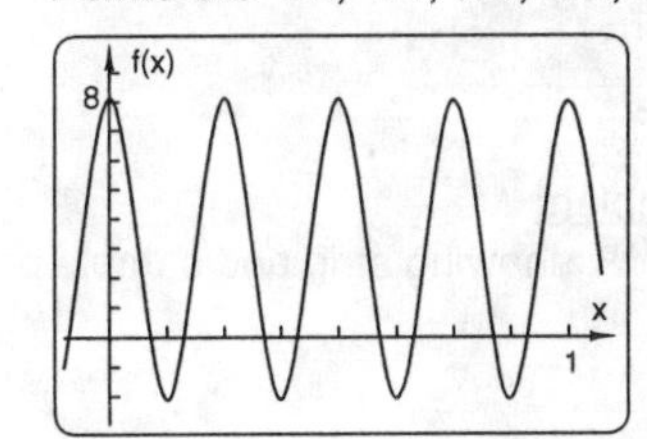

h. If $r'(x) = s'(x)$ for all x in an interval, then $r(x) = s(x) + C$ for some constant C.

R7. $g(x) = \int x^{1.5}\, dx = 0.4x^{2.5} + C$
Without loss of generality, let $C = 0$.
$g'(c_1) = \frac{g(2) - g(1)}{2 - 1} = 1.862741...$
$\therefore c_1^{1.5} = 1.862741... \Rightarrow$
$c_1 = (1.862741...)^{1/1.5} = 1.513915927...$
Similarly, $c_2 = 2.50833898...$
$c_3 = 3.505954424...$
For $\int_1^4 x^{1.5}\, dx$,
$R_3 = (1.513...)^{1.5} + (2.508...)^{1.5} + (3.505...)^{1.5}$
$= 12.4$, which is the exact value of the integral.

R8. a. $\int_{-1}^{3} (10 - x^2)\,dx = 10x - (1/3)x^3 \Big|_{-1}^{3}$
$= 30 - 9 - (-10) + (-1/3) = \underline{92/3} = \underline{30.6666...}$

b. $T_{100} = 30.6656$, which is close to 92/3.

c. $M_{10} = 30.72$
$M_{100} = 30.6672$
$M_{1000} = 30.666672$
These Riemann sums are approaching 92/3.

R9. a. i. $\int_{1}^{5} x^{-2}\,dx = -x^{-1} \Big|_{1}^{5} = -5^{-1} + 1^{-1} = \underline{4/5}$

ii. $\int_{3}^{4} (x^2 + 3)^5 (x\,dx) = (1/2) \int_{3}^{4} (x^2 + 3)^5 (2x\,dx)$
$= (1/12)(x^2 + 3)^6 \Big|_{3}^{4} = (1/12)(19)^6 - (1/12)(12)^6$
$= \underline{3671658.08...}$

iii. $\int_{0}^{\pi} (\sin x - 5)\,dx = -\cos x - 5x \Big|_{0}^{\pi}$
$= -\cos\pi - 5\pi + \cos 0 + 0 = \underline{2 - 5\pi}$

b. Graph, $y = \sin x - 5$.
Integral is negative, since each y-value in the Riemann sum is negative.

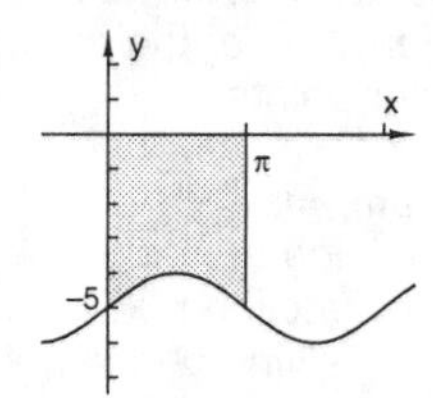

c. $\int_{-10}^{10} (4 \sin x + 6x^7 - 8x^3 + 4)\,dx = 2 \int_{0}^{10} 4\,dx$
$= 8x \Big|_{0}^{10} = \underline{80}$

d. Graph. Total area = sum of two areas.

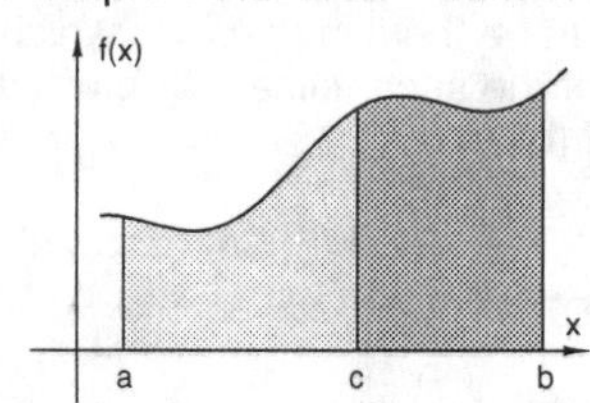

R10. Displacement Problem

a. Graph, $v = 150t^{0.5}$, showing strip and sample point (t, v).

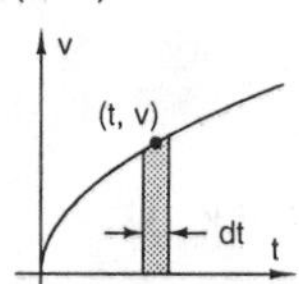

b. $dy = v\,dt = 150t^{0.5}\,dt$

c. $R = \sum 150t^{0.5}\,dt$

d. $\lim_{n\to\infty} R = \int_{0}^{9} 150t^{0.5}\,dt = 100t^{1.5} \Big|_{0}^{9} = \underline{2700 \text{ ft}}$
Mathematical quantity is definite integral.

e. The 2700 in part d is the displacement, 2700 ft.
For [0, 4], $y = \int_{0}^{4} 150t^{0.5}\,dt = 800$
For [4, 9], $y = \int_{4}^{9} 150t^{0.5}\,dt = 2700 - 800 = 1900$
Thus, 2700 = 800 + 1900, Q.E.D.

R11.a. See text graph, Figure 5-11d.
Each parabola requires three points, thus taking two subintervals. Therefore, Simpson's rule uses an even number of increments.

b. See graphs in Figures 5-11a and 5-11b.

c. Displacement = $\int_{3}^{5} v(t)\,dt$
$\approx (0.2/3)(29 + 4{\cdot}41 + 2{\cdot}50 + 4{\cdot}51 + 2{\cdot}44 + 4{\cdot}33 + 2{\cdot}28 + 4{\cdot}20 + 2{\cdot}11 + 4{\cdot}25 + 39)$
$= (0.2/3)(1014) = \underline{67.6 \text{ m}}$

d. $\int_{1}^{10} \log x\,dx \approx 6.0913$
Graph, $y = \log x$. The integral is reasonable because counting squares gives approximately 6.

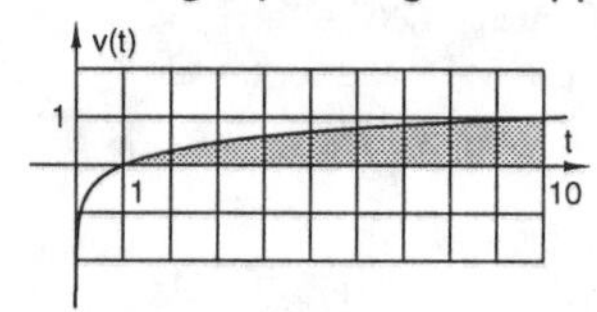

Concepts Problems

C1. Let $f(b) = \int_{0}^{b} 1/(x^2 + 1)\,dx$. Using R_{100},

a. f(0) = 0 (Not asked for, but significant)
$f(1) \approx 0.7854002$
$f(2) \approx 1.1071513$
$f(3) \approx 1.2490480$
$f(4) \approx 1.3258195$
$f(5) \approx 1.3734023$

b. Using R_{1000}, $f(100) \approx 1.560796660...$

c. Graph. The f(b) values for negative values of b are obtained by symmetry.

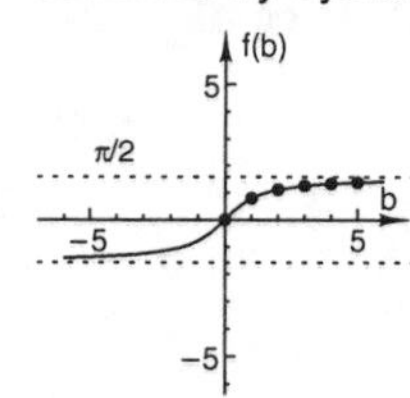

d. Graph. $y = \tan x$

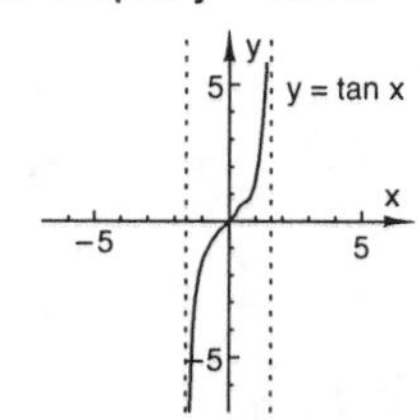

e. The graph of f in part c is a mirror image of the graph of $y = \tan x$ in part d. So function f seems to be the inverse tangent function,
$f(b) = \tan^{-1} b$. (In Chapter 9, students will learn that this is actually true.)

C2. Mean Value Theorem for Quadratic Functions

$f(x) = ax^2 + bx + c$. Graph.

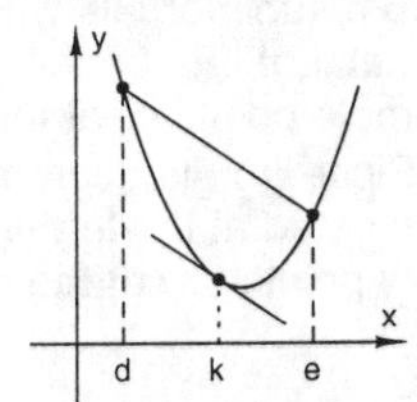

$f(d) = ad^2 + bd + c$

$f(e) = ae^2 + be + c$

$\therefore m = \dfrac{ae^2 + be + c - (ad^2 + bd + c)}{e - d}$

$= \dfrac{a(e^2 - d^2) + b(e - d)}{e - d} = a(e + d) + b$

$f'(x) = 2ax + b \Rightarrow f'(k) = 2ak + b$

$\therefore 2ak + b = a(e + d) + b$

$2ak = a(e + d)$

$k = (1/2)(e + d)$

$\therefore$ k is at the midpoint of [d, e], Q.E.D.

C3. Sum of the Squares Problem

$S(n) = 0^2 + 1^2 + 2^2 + 3^2 + ... + n^2$

a. $S(0) = 0$, $S(1) = 1$, $S(2) = 5$, $S(3) = 14$

b. $S(n) = an^3 + bn^2 + cn + d$

$0 = 0 + 0 + 0 + d$

$1 = a + b + c + d$

$5 = 8a + 4b + 2c + d$

$14 = 27a + 9b + 3c + d$

Solving this system gives

$a = 1/3$, $b = 1/2$, $c = 1/6$, $d = 0$.

$\therefore S(n) = (1/3)n^3 + (1/2)n^2 + (1/6)n$

c. $S(n) = (n/6)(2n^2 + 3n + 1)$

$S(n) = (n/6)(n + 1)(2n + 1)$

This is the form found in mathematical tables.

d. By equation,

$S(4) = (4/6)(5)(9) = 30$

$S(5) = (5/6)(6)(11) = 55$

By addition,

$S(4) = 0 + 1 + 4 + 9 + 16 = 30$, which checks.

$S(5) = 0 + 1 + 4 + 9 + 16 + 25 = 55$, which checks.

e. $S(1000) = (1000/6)(1001)(2001) = 333833500$

f. Prove that $S(n) = (n/6)(n + 1)(2n + 1)$ for *any* positive integer n.

Proof (by induction on n):

Anchor: For $n = 1$, $S(n) = (1/6)(2)(3) = 1$, the correct answer, which anchors the induction.

Induction hypothesis:

Assume that for some integer $n = k > 1$,

$S(k) = (k/6)(k + 1)(2k + 1)$.

Verification for $n = k + 1$:

$S(k+1) = 0^2 + 1^2 + . . . + k^2 + (k + 1)^2$

$= (0^2 + 1^2 + . . . + k^2) + (k + 1)^2$

$= (k/6)(k + 1)(2k + 1) + (k + 1)^2$

$= [(k + 1)/6][k(2k + 1) + 6(k + 1)]$

$= [(k + 1)/6][2k^2 + 7k + 6]$

$= [(k + 1)/6][(k + 2)(2k + 3)]$

$= [(k + 1)/6][(k + 1) + 1][2(k + 1) + 1]$,

which is the formula with $(k + 1)$ in place of k, thus completing the induction.

$\therefore S(n) = (n/6)(n + 1)(2n + 1)$ for *any* positive integer n, Q.E.D.

C4. Sum of the Cubes Problem

$S(n) = 0^3 + 1^3 + 2^3 + 3^3 + . . . + n^3$

$S(0) = 0$

$S(1) = 0 + 1 = 1$

$S(2) = 0 + 1 + 8 = 9$

$S(3) = 0 + 1 + 8 + 27 = 36$

$S(4) = 0 + 1 + 8 + 27 + 64 = 100$

(The answers *are* perfect squares!)

Assume that $S(n) = an^4 + bn^3 + cn^2 + dn + e$.

$0 = 0 + 0 + 0 + 0 + e$

$1 = a + b + c + d + e$

$9 = 16a + 8b + 4c + 2d + e$

$36 = 81a + 27b + 9c + 3d + e$

$100 = 256a + 64b + 16c + 4d + e$

Solving this system gives

$a = 1/4$, $b = 1/2$, $c = 1/4$, $d = 0$, $e = 0$

$\therefore S(n) = (1/4)n^4 + (1/2)n^3 + (1/4)n^2$

$S(n) = (1/4)n^2(n^2 + 2n + 1)$

$S(n) = [(n/2)(n + 1)]^2$,

which agrees with the observation that S(n) is a perfect square.

Prove that $S(n) = [(n/2)(n + 1)]^2$ for *any* positive integer n.

Proof (by induction on n):

Anchor: For $n = 1$, $S(1) = [(1/2)(2)]^2 = 1$, the correct answer, which anchors the induction.

Induction hypothesis:

Assume that for some integer $n = k > 1$,

$S(k) = [(k/2)(k + 1)]^2$.

Verification for $n = k + 1$:

$S(k + 1) = 0^3 + 1^3 + ... + k^3 + (k + 1)^3$

$= (0^3 + 1^3 + ... + k^3) + (k + 1)^3$

$= [(k/2)(k + 1)]^2 + (k + 1)^3$

$= (1/4)(k + 1)^2 [k^2 + 4(k + 1)]$

$= (1/4)(k + 1)^2(k + 2)^2$

$= [(k + 1)/2(k + 2)]^2$,

which is the formula with $(k + 1)$ in place of k, thus completing the induction.

$\therefore S(n) = [(n/2)(n + 1)]^2$ for *any* pos. int. n, Q.E.D.

C5. Radio Wave Integral Problem

a. $\int_0^\pi 4 \sin x \sin 10x\, dx \approx 0$ by numerical integration.

Actual answer depends on the grapher used.

b. $\int_0^\pi 4 \sin x \sin 10x\, dx$

$= \int_0^\pi (-2 \cos 11x + 2 \cos (-9x))\, dx$

$= -\dfrac{2}{11} \sin 11x - \dfrac{2}{9} \sin (-9x) \Big|_0^\pi$

$= -0 - 0 + 0 + 0 = 0$, Q.E.D.

c. There is just as much area below the x-axis as there is above it.

d. $\int_0^\pi 4 \sin x \sin nx\, dx =$

$= \int_0^\pi (-2 \cos (1 + n)x + 2 \cos (1 - n)x)\, dx$

$= \dfrac{-2}{1 + n} \sin (1+n)x + \dfrac{2}{1 - n} \sin (1 - n)x \Big|_0^\pi$

$= \dfrac{-2}{1 + n} \sin (1+n)\pi + \dfrac{2}{1 - n} \sin (1 - n)\pi$

$- \dfrac{-2}{1 + n} \sin 0 - \dfrac{2}{1 - n} \sin 0$

If n is an integer, the first two terms will involve sines of integer multiples of π, and are thus equal to 0. The last two terms are 0 unless $n = \pm 1$. Thus the integral equals 0 for any integer $n > 1$, Q.E.D.

C6. Riemann Sums with Unequal Increments

a. Algebraic solution:

Pick sample points c_k at the right end of each subinterval. Since f(x) is increasing on the interval [1, 9], the high points of f(x) are located at the right ends of the subintervals and the low points are at the left ends.

$\therefore U_n = \sum_{k=1}^{n} f(c_k)\,\Delta x_k$ and $L_n = \sum_{k=1}^{n} f(c_{k-1})\Delta x_k$

Note that $c_0 = 1$ and $c_n = 9$. Subtracting gives

$U_n - L_n = \sum_{k=1}^{n} [f(c_k) - f(c_{k-1})]\Delta x_k$

$= [f(c_1) - f(c_0)]\Delta x_1 + [f(c_2) - f(c_1)]\Delta x_2 + \ldots + [f(c_n) - f(c_{n-1})]\Delta x_n$

$\le [f(c_1) - f(c_0)]\,\|P\| + [f(c_2) - f(c_1)]\,\|P\| + \ldots + [f(c_n) - f(c_{n-1})]\,\|P\|$

$= [f(c_1) - f(c_0) + f(c_2) - f(c_1) + \ldots + f(c_n) - f(c_{n-1})]\,\|P\|$

$= [f(c_n) - f(c_0)]\,\|P\| = \|P\|(1.2^9 - 1.2^1)$

$\therefore U_n - L_n \le \|P\|(1.2^9 - 1.2^1)$, Q.E.D.

Graphical Solution:

The difference $U_n - L_n$ is equal to the area of the spaces between the lower and upper rectangles in Figure 5-12c. Imagine these spaces moved over to the left so that they align at x = 1 (below). The spaces can be circumscribed with a rectangle of base $\|P\|$ and altitude $(1.2^9 - 1.2^1)$. Thus, $U_n - L_n \le \|P\|\,(1.2^9 - 1.2^1)$, Q.E.D.

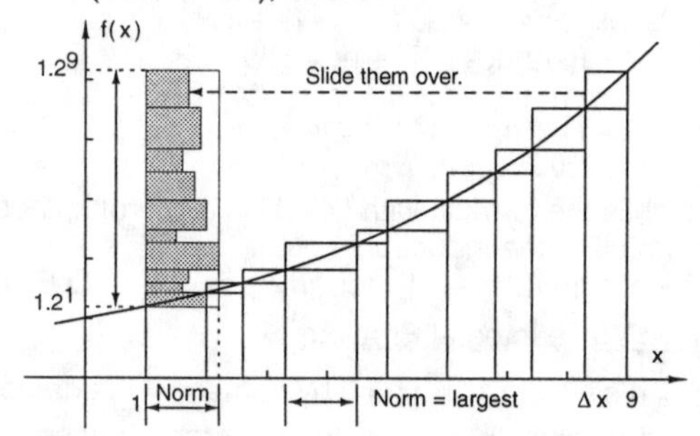

b. From part a., $0 \le U_n - L_n \le \|P\|\,(1.2^9 - 1.2^1)$.

As $\|P\|$ approaches zero, the rightmost member of the inequality goes to zero. By the squeeze theorem,

$\lim_{\|P\|\to 0} (U_n - L_n) = 0$, which implies

$\lim_{\|P\|\to 0} U_n = \lim_{\|P\|\to 0} L_n$

So f is integrable on [1, 9] by the definition of integrability, Q.E.D.

c. Prove that g(x) = 1/x is integrable on [1, 4].

Proof:

Partition the interval [1, 4] into n subintervals whose widths are not necessarily equal. Let $\|P\|$ be the norm of the partition. Pick sample points c_k at the left end of each subinterval. Since g(x) is decreasing on [1, 4], the high points are located at the left ends of the subintervals and the low points are at the right ends (graph).

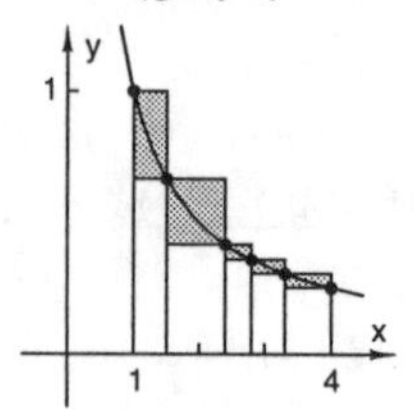

By algebraic or graphical reasoning as in part a, above,

$U_n - L_n \le \|P\|(1 - 1/4)$

As $\|P\|$ approaches zero, $U_n - L_n$ is squeezed to zero.

Thus, U_n and L_n approach the same limit, which implies that g is integrable on [1, 4], Q.E.D.

d. This reasoning cannot be applied directly to h(x) = sin x on the interval [0, 3], because h(x) is both increasing and decreasing on different parts of the interval. Thus, the high points are not always at the same end of the subinterval, and the high point at $\pi/2$ may not be at either end of a subinterval (see graph).

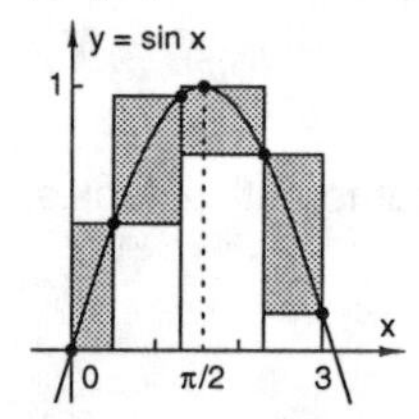

The reasoning could be applied indirectly by first splitting the interval [0, 3] into [0, $\pi/2$] and [$\pi/2$, 3] so that h(x) is increasing on one and decreasing on the other.

Chapter Test

T1. Indefinite integral:

$g(x) = \int f(x)\,dx$ if and only if $g'(x) = f(x)$.

T2. Definite integral:

Let L_n and U_n be lower and upper sums of f(x) on the interval [a, b]. Then

$\int_a^b f(x)\,dx = \lim_{n\to\infty} L_n = \lim_{n\to\infty} U_n$,

provided the two limits are equal.

T3. Fundamental theorem:

If f is an integrable function, and $g(x) = \int f(x)\,dx$, then $\int_a^b f(x)\,dx = g(b) - g(a)$.

T4. $\int_0^2 3^x\,dx$

a. $U_4 = 0.5(3^{0.5} + 3^1 + 3^{1.5} + 3^2) = \underline{9.4641016...}$
$L_4 = 0.5(3^0 + 3^{0.5} + 3^1 + 3^{1.5}) = \underline{5.4641016...}$
Average = $\underline{7.4641016...}$
The average is <u>equal</u> to T_4 by trapezoids.
The average <u>overestimates</u> the integral. Since the graph is concave upward, the trapezoids would be circumscribed around the strips of the region under the graph. Graph.

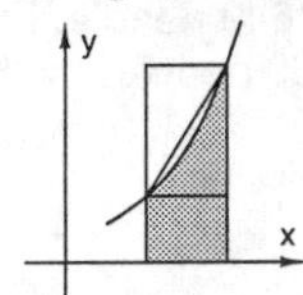

b. $M_4 = 0.5(3^{0.25} + 3^{0.75} + 3^{1.25} + 3^{1.75})$
$= \underline{7.1911621...}$
M_4 <u>underestimates</u> the integral. Graph.

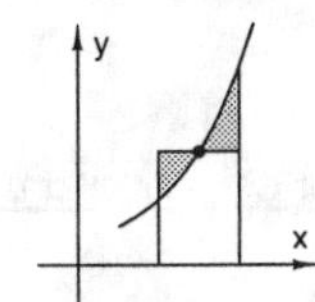

The rectangle and the region differ by the two "triangular" regions. Since the sample point is at the midpoint of the subinterval, the "triangles" have equal bases. Since the graph is concave upward, the "triangle" below the horizontal line has a smaller altitude, and thus a smaller area, than the one above the line. So the rectangle includes less area on the left than it leaves out on the right, and thus underestimates the integral.

c. Simpson's rule: $S_4 = \underline{7.2854688...}$

d. Numerical integration: $\int_0^2 3^x\,dx = \underline{7.28191381...}$
(The exact answer is $8/\ln 3 = 7.28191381...$, which agrees with the numerical answer.)

T5. $\int (3x - 11)^{17}\,dx = \frac{1}{3}\int (3x - 11)^{17}\,(3\,dx)$

$= \frac{1}{54}(3x - 11)^{18} + C$

T6. $\int (\cos 2x)^4 \sin 2x\,dx$

$= -\frac{1}{2}\int (\cos 2x)^4\,(-2 \sin 2x\,dx)$

$= -\frac{1}{10}(\cos 2x)^5 + C$

T7. $\int_{\pi/6}^{\pi/4} \cos 2x\,dx = \frac{1}{2}\sin 2x\,\Big|_{\pi/6}^{\pi/4}$

$= \frac{1}{2}\sin(\pi/2) - \frac{1}{2}\sin(\pi/3)$

$= \frac{1}{2} - \sqrt{3}/4 = \underline{0.06698729...}$

T8. $\int_{-1}^{1} \sec^2 x\,dx = 2\int_0^1 \sec^2 x\,dx = 2\tan x\,\Big|_0^1$
$= 2\tan 1 = \underline{3.1148154...}$

T9. $\int_2^{-2} (12x^3 + 10x^2)\,dx = -2\int_0^2 10x^2\,dx$
$= -\frac{20}{3}x^3\,\Big|_0^2 = -\frac{160}{3} + 0 = -\frac{160}{3} = -53\frac{1}{3}$

T10. $\int_1^8 7x^{-2/3}\,dx = 21x^{1/3}\,\Big|_1^8 = 21(2 - 1) = \underline{21}$

T11. Graph, example, for Rolle's theorem.
Hypotheses: $f(a) = f(b) = 0$.
Differentiable on (a, b).
Continuous at $x = a$ and $x = b$.
Conclusion: There is a c in (a, b) such that $f'(c) = 0$.

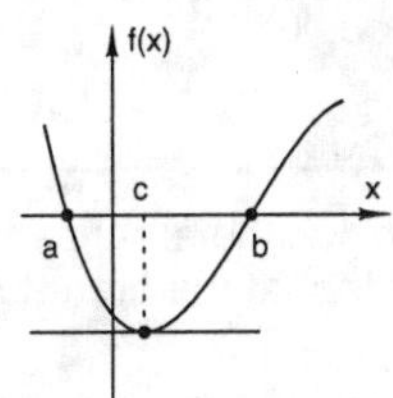

T12.a. $g(x) = \int 0.3x^2\,dx = 0.1x^3 + C = 0.1x^3$

b. Graphs:

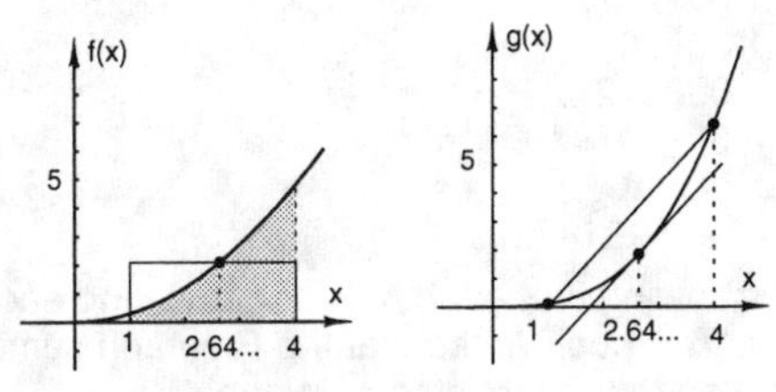

c. $m = \frac{g(4) - g(1)}{4 - 1} = \frac{6.4 - 0.1}{3} = \underline{2.1}$
$g'(x) = f(x) = 0.3x^2$
$\therefore 0.3c^2 = 2.1 \Rightarrow c = \sqrt{7} = \underline{2.6457513...}$
On the right graph, above, the tangent line at $x = 2.64...$ is parallel to the secant line from $x = 1$ to $x = 4$.

d. $f(2.645...) = 0.3(2.645...)^2 = 2.1$ (exactly)
Point is <u>(2.645..., 2.1)</u>.
Area of region under graph equals area of rectangle, as shown in the left graph, above.

Chapter 6

Exploratory Problem Set 6-1, page 251 — Integral of the Reciprocal Function

1. A Population Growth Problem
   The annual rate of population growth, dP/dt, is 5% (0.05) times the current population P.
2. dP/dt is in people/year.
3. $\int_0^{10} 0.05\,dt = 0.05t\,\Big|_0^{10} = 0.5$
   Using the power function method on $\int P^{-1}\,dP$ gives $(1/0)\,P^0$, which involves division by zero.
4. N = 1500: Integral ≈ 0.405465...
   N = 2000: Integral ≈ 0.693147...
5. From the answer to Problem 4 you can tell that the value of N that makes the integral equal 0.5 is somewhere between 1500 and 2000. Setting the numerical integral between t = 1000 and t = N equal to 0.5 and doing a numerical solution for N gives N ≈ 1648.72..., or about 1649 people.
6. Repeating the above calculations for 20 years,
   $\int_0^{20} 0.05\,dt = 0.05t\,\Big|_0^{20} = 1$
   N ≈ 2718.28..., or about 2718 people.
7. The P-versus-t graph is nonlinear. From t = 0 to t = 10 the population increased by 649 people. From t = 10 to t = 20, it increased by 1069 people.

Problem Set 6-2, pages 252 to 253 — Antiderivative of the Reciprocal Function

1. Each value of x uniquely determines the area; as x increases, so does the area. Note that the area does not depend at all on t.
2. g(8) ≈ 2.079441...
   g(7) ≈ 1.945910...
   g(6) ≈ 1.791759...
   g(5) ≈ 1.609437...
   g(4) ≈ 1.386294...
   g(3) ≈ 1.098612...
   g(2) ≈ 0.693147...
   g(1) = 0
   g(0.5) ≈ −0.693147...
3. Graph, showing that each Δt is negative and each value of 1/t is positive, so that the Riemann sums are negative and thus the integral is negative.

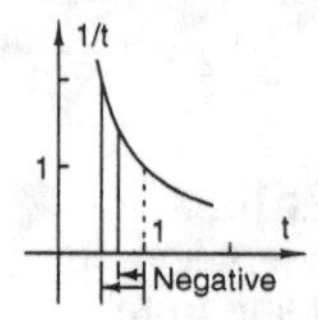

4. Tracing shows that the values are correct.
5. a. g(3) + g(2) = 1.098617... + 0.693142...
   = 1.791759..., which equals g(6).
   b. g(8) − g(2) = 2.079441... − 0.693147...
   = 1.386294..., which equals g(4).
   c. 3·g(2) = 3 · 0.693147... = 2.079441..., which equals g(8).
   d. −g(2) = −0.693147... = g(0.5) = g(1/2).
6. a. g(6) = g(3·2) = g(3) + g(2)
   b. g(4) = g(8/2) = g(8) − g(2)
   c. $g(8) = g(2^3) = 3g(2)$
   d. g(1/2) = −g(2)
7. Graphs, y = g(x) and y = log x.

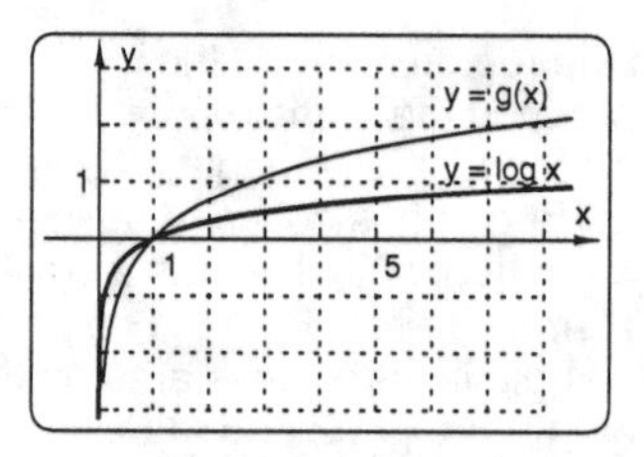

   Both graphs have asymptotes at x = 0, x-intercepts of 1, and slopes tending to zero as x approaches infinity. Both are increasing and concave downward.
8. Graphs, y = g(x) and y = ln x.
   The graphs for g(x) and ln x are identical!

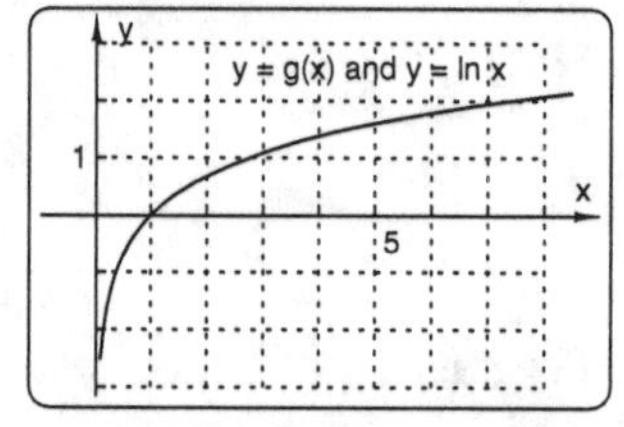

9. $g'(3) \approx \dfrac{g(4) - g(2)}{2} \approx \dfrac{1.38629 - 0.69314}{2}$
   ≈ 0.3466
   By numerical differentiation, (d/dx)(ln x) ≈ 0.33333, which is close to 0.3466.
10. As the definition is stated in the problem, the "if" part explains why $\int (1/x)\,dx = \ln x + C$. If the derivative of ln x + C equals 1/x, then ln x + C equals the integral.
11. Solving numerically for g(b) = 1 gives b ≈ 2.71828... .
12. $\int_{1000}^{N} \frac{1}{P}\,dP = \ln P\,\Big|_{1000}^{N} = \ln N - \ln 1000.$
    ln 1500 − ln 1000 = 0.405465..., which agrees.
    ln 2000 − ln 1000 = 0.693147..., which agrees.

Q1. $\frac{1}{0.7}x^{0.7} + C$ Q2. Integral = 9
Q3. $f'(x) = -2\cos x \sin x$ Q4. continuous
Q5. differentiable Q6. $y' = \frac{1}{\sqrt{1-x^2}}$
Q7. $y' = -\csc(x)\cot(x)$ Q8. Riemann sum
Q9. indefinite integral, or antiderivative Q10. log 12

0. Look-Ahead Problem
Answers will vary.

1. $y = \ln 7x \Rightarrow y' = 1/(7x)\cdot 7 = 1/x$
2. $y = \ln 4x \Rightarrow y' = 1/(4x)\cdot 4 = 1/x$
3. $f(x) = \ln x^5 \Rightarrow f'(x) = 1/(x^5)\cdot 5x^4 = 5/x$
4. $f(x) = \ln x^3 \Rightarrow f'(x) = 1/(x^3)\cdot 3x^2 = 3/x$
5. $h(x) = 6\ln x^{-2} \Rightarrow h'(x) = 6/(x^{-2})\cdot(-2x^{-3}) = -12/x$
6. $g(x) = 13\ln x^{-5} \Rightarrow g'(x) = 13/(x^{-5})\cdot(-5x^{-6}) = -65/x$
7. $r(t) = \ln 3t + \ln 4t + \ln 5t$
   $\Rightarrow r'(t) = 1/(3t)\cdot 3 + 1/(4t)\cdot 4 + 1/(5t)\cdot 5 = 3/t$
8. $v(z) = \ln 6z + \ln 7z + \ln 8z$
   $\Rightarrow v'(z) = 1/(6z)\cdot 6 + 1/(7z)\cdot 7 + 1/(8z)\cdot 8 = 3/z$
9. $y = (\ln 6x)(\ln 4x)$
   $\Rightarrow y' = 1/(6x)\cdot 6\cdot(\ln 4x) + (\ln 6x)(1/(4x)\cdot 4)$
   $= (1/x)(\ln 4x + \ln 6x)$ or $\frac{\ln 24x^2}{x}$
10. $z = (\ln 2x)(\ln 9x)$
   $\Rightarrow z' = 1/(2x)\cdot 2\cdot(\ln 9x) + (\ln 2x)(1/(9x)\cdot 9)$
   $= (1/x)(\ln 9x + \ln 2x)$ or $\frac{\ln 18x^2}{x}$
11. $y = \frac{\ln 11x}{\ln 3x}$
   $\Rightarrow y' = \frac{1/(11x)\cdot 11\cdot(\ln 3x) - (\ln 11x)1/(3x)\cdot 3}{(\ln 3x)^2}$
   $= \frac{\ln 3x - \ln 11x}{x(\ln 3x)^2}$ or $\frac{\ln(3/11)}{x(\ln 3x)^2}$
12. $y = \frac{\ln 9x}{\ln 6x}$
   $\Rightarrow y' = \frac{1/(9x)\cdot 9\cdot(\ln 6x) - (\ln 9x)\cdot 1/(6x)\cdot 6}{(\ln 6x)^2}$
   $= \frac{\ln 6x - \ln 9x}{x(\ln 6x)^2}$ or $\frac{\ln(2/3)}{x(\ln 6x)^2}$
13. $p = (\sin x)(\ln x) \Rightarrow p' = (\cos x)(\ln x) + (\sin x)(1/x)$
14. $m = (\cos x)(\ln x)$
   $\Rightarrow m' = (-\sin x)(\ln x) + (\cos x)(1/x)$
15. $y = \cos(\ln x) \Rightarrow y' = -\sin(\ln x)\cdot(1/x)$
16. $y = \sin(\ln x) \Rightarrow y' = \cos(\ln x)\cdot(1/x)$
17. $y = \ln(\cos x)$, where $\cos x > 0$
   $\Rightarrow y' = (1/\cos x)\cdot(-\sin x) = -\tan x$ (Surprise!)
18. $y = \ln(\sin x)$, where $\sin x > 0$
   $\Rightarrow y' = (1/\sin x)\cdot(\cos x) = \cot x$ (Surprise!!)
19. $T(x) = \tan(\ln x) \Rightarrow T'(x) = \sec^2(\ln x)\cdot(1/x)$
20. $S(x) = \sec(\ln x)$
   $\Rightarrow S'(x) = \sec(\ln x)\cdot\tan(\ln x)\cdot(1/x)$
21. $y = (3x+5)^{-1} \Rightarrow y' = -(3x+5)^{-2}\cdot 3 = -3(3x+5)^{-2}$
22. $y = (x^3-2)^{-1} \Rightarrow y' = -(x^3-2)^{-2}\cdot 3x^2 = -3x^2(x^3-2)^{-2}$
23. $y = x^4\ln 3x$
   $\Rightarrow y' = 4x^3\ln 3x + x^4\cdot 1/(3x)\cdot 3 = 4x^3\ln 3x + x^3$
24. $y = x^7\ln 5x$
   $\Rightarrow y' = 7x^6\ln 5x + x^7\cdot 1/(5x)\cdot 5 = 7x^6\ln 5x + x^6$
25. $y = \ln(1/x) \Rightarrow y' = 1/(1/x)\cdot(-x^{-2}) = -1/x$
26. $y = \ln(1/x^4) \Rightarrow y' = 1/(1/x)^4\cdot(-4x^{-5}) = -4/x$
27. $\int 7/x\,dx = 7\ln|x| + C$
28. $\int 5/x\,dx = 5\ln|x| + C$
29. $\int 1/(3x)\,dx = \frac{1}{3}\ln|x| + C$
30. $\int 1/(8x)\,dx = \frac{1}{8}\ln|x| + C$
31. $\int \frac{x^2}{x^3+5}\,dx = \frac{1}{3}\int\frac{1}{x^3+5}(3x^2\,dx)$
   $= \frac{1}{3}\ln|x^3+5| + C$
32. $\int \frac{x^5}{x^6-4}\,dx = \frac{1}{6}\int\frac{1}{x^6-4}(6x^5\,dx)$
   $= \frac{1}{6}\ln|x^6-4| + C$
33. $\int \frac{x^5}{9-x^6}\,dx = -\frac{1}{6}\int\frac{1}{9-x^6}(-6x^5\,dx)$
   $= -\frac{1}{6}\ln|9-x^6| + C$
34. $\int \frac{x^3}{10-x^4}\,dx = -\frac{1}{4}\int\frac{1}{10-x^4}(-4x^3\,dx)$
   $= -\frac{1}{4}\ln|10-x^4| + C$
35. $\int \frac{\sec x\tan x\,dx}{1+\sec x} = \ln|1+\sec x| + C$
36. $\int \frac{\sec^2 x\,dx}{1+\tan x} = \ln|1+\tan x| + C$
37. $\int \frac{\cos x\,dx}{\sin x} = \ln|\sin x| + C$
38. $\int \frac{\sin x\,dx}{\cos x} = -\int\frac{-\sin x\,dx}{\cos x} = -\ln|\cos x| + C$
39. $\int_{0.5}^{4}(1/w)\,dw = \ln|w|\Big|_{0.5}^{4} = \ln 4 - \ln 0.5$
   $= \underline{\ln 8} = \underline{2.079441...}$
40. $\int_{0.1}^{10}(1/v)\,dv = \ln|v|\Big|_{0.1}^{10} = \ln 10 - \ln 0.1$
   $= \underline{\ln 100} = \underline{4.605170...}$
41. $\int_{-0.1}^{-3}(1/x)\,dx = \ln|x|\Big|_{-0.1}^{-3} = \ln|-3|$
   $- \ln|-0.1|$
42. $\int_{-0.2}^{-4}(1/x)\,dx = \ln|x|\Big|_{-0.2}^{-4} = \ln|-4| - \ln|-0.2|$
   $= \ln 4 - \ln 0.2 = \underline{\ln 20} = \underline{2.995732...}$
43. $\int_4^9 \frac{x^{1/2}\,dx}{1+x^{3/2}} = \frac{2}{3}\int_4^9\frac{1}{1+x^{3/2}}\cdot\frac{3}{2}x^{1/2}\,dx$
   $= \frac{2}{3}\ln|1+x^{3/2}|\Big|_4^9 = \frac{2}{3}(\ln 28 - \ln 9) = \underline{0.756653...}$
44. $\int_1^8 \frac{x^{-1/3}\,dx}{2+x^{2/3}} = \frac{3}{2}\int_1^8\frac{1}{2+x^{2/3}}\cdot\frac{2}{3}x^{-1/3}\,dx$
   $= \frac{3}{2}\ln|2+x^{2/3}|\Big|_1^8 = \frac{3}{2}(\ln 6 - \ln 3) = \underline{1.5\ln 2}$
   $= \underline{1.039720...}$
45. $\int(\ln x)^5\frac{dx}{x} = \frac{1}{6}(\ln x)^6 + C$

46. $\int \frac{\ln x}{x}\, dx = \int (\ln x)^1 \frac{dx}{x} = \frac{1}{2}(\ln x)^2 + C$

47. $f(x) = \int_2^x \cos 3t\, dt \Rightarrow f'(x) = \cos 3x$

48. $f(x) = \int_5^x (t^2 + 10t - 17)dt \Rightarrow f'(x) = x^2 + 10x - 17$

49. $\frac{d}{dx}(\int_2^x \tan^3 t\, dt) = \tan^3 x$

50. $\frac{d}{dx}(\int_{-1}^x 2^t\, dt) = 2^x$

51. $f(x) = \int_1^{x^2} 3^t\, dt \Rightarrow f'(x) = 2x \cdot 3^{x^2}$

52. $g(x) = \int_0^{\cos x} \sqrt{t}\, dt \Rightarrow g'(x) = \sqrt{\cos x} \cdot (-\sin x)$

53. $h(x) = \int_0^{3x-5} \sqrt{1 + t^2}\, dt \Rightarrow h'(x) = 3\sqrt{1 + (3x - 5)^2}$

54. $p(x) = \int_{-1}^{x^3} (t^4 + 1)^7\, dt \Rightarrow p'(x) = (x^{12} + 1)^7 \cdot 3x^2$

55. $\int_1^3 (5/x)\, dx = 5 \ln |x| \Big|_1^3 = 5 \ln 3 - 5 \ln 1 = \underline{5.493061...}$

Midpoint Riemann sum:	M_{100} = 5.492987...
Trapezoidal rule:	T_{100} = 5.493209...
Numerical integration:	5.493061...

56. <u>Look-Ahead Problem Follow-Up</u>
Answers will vary.

57. <u>Population Problem</u>
$\int_{1000}^{N} (1/P)\, dP = \ln |P| \Big|_{1000}^{N} = \ln N - \ln 1000.$
$\int_0^{10} 0.05\, dt = 0.05t \Big|_1^{10} = 0.5$
Solving numerically for N in $\ln N - \ln 1000 = 0.5$,
$N \approx 1648.72... \approx$ <u>1649 people</u>.

58. <u>Tire Pump Work Problem</u>

a. $F + 30 = k/h$
$0 + 30 = k/20 \Rightarrow k = 600$
$\therefore F + 30 = 600/h \Rightarrow \underline{F = 600/h - 30}$

b. Graph.

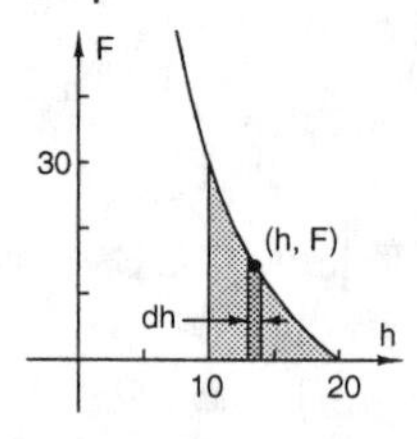

c. Work equals force times displacement. Since the force varies, a definite integral must be used.

d. The work done compressing the air a small amount dh is approximately equal to the force at the sample point (h, F) times dh (see part b).
$dW = F\, dh = (600/h - 30)\, dh$
$\therefore W = \int_{20}^{10} (600/h - 30)\, dh$
$= 600 \ln |h| - 30h \Big|_{20}^{10}$
$= 600 \ln 10 - 300 - 600 \ln 20 + 600$
$= -115.8883... \approx$ <u>−116 inch = pounds</u>
This number is negative because each value of dh is negative and F is positive, making their product negative.

e. Distance is measured in inches, and force is measured in pounds.

59. <u>Radio Dial Derivative Problem</u>

a. $d(f) = a + b \ln f$
$0 = a + b \ln 53$
$10 = a + b \ln 160$
$10 = b \ln 160 - b \ln 53 \Rightarrow$
$b = \frac{10}{\ln 160 - \ln 53} = \underline{9.050741...}$
$a = -9.050741... \ln 53 = \underline{-35.934084...}$

b.

f	d cm	d' (part c)
53	0	0.1707...
60	1.1227...	0.1508...
70	2.5197...	0.1292...
80	3.7265...	0.1131...
100	5.7461...	0.0905...
120	7.3962...	0.0754...
140	8.7914...	0.0646...
160	10.0	0.0565...

The measured distances are close to the calculated distances.

c. $d'(f) = b/f = 9.050.../f$. See table in part b.

d. $d'(f)$ is in cm/10 kHz.

e. $d'(f)$ decreases as f gets larger; this is consistent with the spaces between the numbers getting smaller as f increases.

60. <u>Properties of ln Problem</u>

a. $\ln 2 = 0.693147...$
$\ln 3 = 1.098612...$
$\ln 6 = 1.791759...$, which equals $\ln 2 + \ln 3$.

b. Conjecture: $\ln (ab) = \ln a + \ln b$
Check: $\ln (7 \cdot 11) = \ln 77 = 4.343805...$
$\ln 7 + \ln 11 = 1.945910... + 2.397895...$
$= 4.343805...$ (Checks.)

c. $\ln (10/2) = \ln 5 = 1.609437...$
$\ln 10 = 2.302585...$
$\ln 2 = 0.693147...$
Observation: $\ln (10/2) = \ln 10 - \ln 2$

d. Conjecture: $\ln (a/b) = \ln a - \ln b$
Check: $\ln (21/7) = \ln 3 = 1.098612...$
$\ln 21 = 3.044522...$
$\ln 7 = 1.945910...$
$\ln 21 - \ln 7 = 1.098612...$ (Checks.)

e. $\ln (2^{10}) = \ln 1024 = 6.931471...$
$\ln 2 = 0.6931471...$
Observation: $\ln (2^{10}) = 10 \ln 2$

f. Conjecture: $\ln (a^b) = b \ln a$
Check: $\ln (10^2) = \ln 100 = 4.605170...$
$\ln 10 = 2.302585...$
$2 \ln 10 = 2(2.302585...) = 4.605170...$ (Checks.)

g. $k = \frac{\ln 5}{\log 5} = \frac{1.609437...}{0.698970...} = 2.302585...$
(Check: $\ln 10 = 2.302585...$, which is correct.)

h. Let $x = 57$.
Then $k = \frac{\ln 57}{\log 57} = \frac{4.04351...}{2.302585...} = 2.302585...$,
which does equal $\ln 10$.
k does seem to equal a constant.

61. <u>Journal Problem</u>
Journal entries will vary.

Q1. $y' = 1/(1 + x^2)$
Q2. $(1/24)(4x + 1)^6 + C$
Q3. limit = 1
Q4. limit = 7 (Careful!)
Q5. (1/4)
Q6. 35
Q7. 8
Q8. Graph, integral (y = ln x)

Q9. f is differentiable on (a, b).
Q10. f is continuous at x = a and x = b.

1. ln 6 + ln 4 = 1.79175... + 1.38629... = 3.17805...
   ln 24 = 3.17805... (Checks.)
2. ln 5 + ln 7 = 1.60943... + 1.94591... = 3.55534...
   ln 35 = 3.55534... (Checks.)
3. ln 2001 − ln 667 = 7.60140... − 6.50279...
   = 1.09861...
   ln (2001/667) = ln 3 = 1.09861... (Checks.)
4. ln 1001 − ln 77 = 6.90875... − 4.34380...
   = 2.56494...
   ln (1001/77) = ln 13 = 2.56494... (Checks.)
5. 3 ln 1776 = 3(7.48211...) = 22.44635...
   $\ln(1776^3)$ = ln 5601816576 = 22.44635... (Checks.)
6. 4 ln 1066 = 4(6.97166...) = 27.88667...
   $\ln(1066^4)$ = ln 1291304958736 = 27.88667... (Checks.)
7. See text proof of the uniqueness theorem.
8. Example: ln (2 + 3) = ln 5 = 1.60943...
   ln 2 + ln 3 = 0.69314... + 1.09861... = 1.79175...
   ∴ $\ln(2 + 3) \ne \ln 2 + \ln 3$.
   ∴ ln (a + b) = ln a + ln b is false, Q.E.D.
9. Prove that ln (a/b) = ln a − ln b for all a > 0, b > 0
   Proof:
   Let f(x) = ln (x/b), g(x) = ln x − ln b for x, b > 0
   Then f'(x) = (b/x)(1/b) = 1/x, and
   g'(x) = (1/x) − 0 = 1/x.
   ∴ f'(x) = g'(x) for all x > 0
   f(b) = ln (b/b) = ln 1 = 0
   g(b) = ln b − ln b = 0
   ∴ f(b) = g(b).
   ∴ f(x) = g(x) for all x > 0 by the uniqueness theorem.
   ∴ ln (x/b) = ln x − ln b for all x > 0.
   ∴ ln (a/b) = ln a − ln b for all a > 0 and b > 0, Q.E.D.
10. Prove that $\ln(a^b) = b \ln a$ for all a > 0 and all b.
   Proof:
   Let $f(x) = \ln(x^b)$; g(x) = b ln x for x > 0
   Then $f'(x) = 1/(x^b) \cdot bx^{b-1} = b/x$, and
   g'(x) = b(1/x) = b/x.
   ∴ f'(x) = g'(x) for all x > 0
   $f(1) = \ln(1^b) = \ln 1 = 0$
   g(1) = b ln 1 = b·0 = 0
   ∴ f(1) = g(1).
   ∴ f(x) = g(x) for all x > 0 by uniqueness theorem
   ∴ $\ln(x^b) = b \ln x$ for all x > 0
   ∴ $\ln(a^b) = b \ln a$ for all a > 0, and all b, Q.E.D.
11. Prove that ln (a/b) = ln a − ln b for all a > 0, b > 0.
   Proof:
   $\ln(a/b) = \ln(a \cdot b^{-1}) = \ln a + \ln b^{-1}$
   = ln a + (−1) ln b = ln a − ln b
   ∴ ln (a/b) = ln a − ln b, Q.E.D.
12. See text definition of ln.
13. Base of Natural Logarithms Problem
   a. $y = \log_b x$ and $x = b^y$ are equivalent by the definition of logarithm.
   b. x would equal b^1, which equals b.
   c. When y = 1, x = b ≈ 2.7183.
   d. This number is called e.

Problem Set 6-5, pages 269 to 271 — Derivatives of Exponential Functions—Logarithmic Differentiation

Q1. y' = 3/x
Q2. $(-1/10)(5x)^{-2} + C$.
Q3. $y' = -1/\sqrt{1 - x^2}$
Q4. $(1/7)x^7 + C$
Q5. y' = sec x tan x
Q6. cos x + C
Q7. y' = 0
Q8. 36
Q9. 8
Q10. indeterminate

0. Look -Ahead Problem [to be reinstated]
   Answers will vary.
1. $f(x) = 0.4^{2x} \Rightarrow \ln f(x) = 2x \ln 0.4 \Rightarrow$
   $\frac{1}{f(x)} f'(x) = 2 \ln 0.4 \Rightarrow f'(x) = 0.4^{2x} \cdot 2 \ln 0.4$
2. $f(x) = 10^{-0.2x} \Rightarrow \ln f(x) = -0.2x \ln 10 \Rightarrow$
   $\frac{1}{f(x)} f'(x) = -0.2 \ln 10 \Rightarrow f'(x) = 10^{-0.2x}(-0.2 \ln 10)$
3. $g(x) = 4(7^x) \Rightarrow \ln g(x) = \ln 4 + x \ln 7 \Rightarrow$
   $\frac{1}{g(x)} g'(x) = \ln 7 \Rightarrow g'(x) = 4(7^x) \ln 7$
4. $h(x) = 1000(1.03^x) \Rightarrow \ln h(x) = \ln 1000 + x \ln 1.03$
   $\Rightarrow \frac{1}{h(x)} h'(x) = \ln 1.03 \Rightarrow h'(x) = 1000(1.03^x) \ln 1.03$
5. $c(x) = x^5 \cdot 3^x \Rightarrow \ln c(x) = 5 \ln x + x \ln 3 \Rightarrow$
   $\frac{1}{c(x)} c'(x) = 5/x + \ln 3 \Rightarrow c'(x) = x^5 \cdot 3^x(5/x + \ln 3)$
6. $m(x) = 5^x \cdot x^7 \Rightarrow \ln m(x) = x \ln 5 + 7 \ln x \Rightarrow$
   $\frac{1}{m(x)} m'(x) = \ln 5 + 7/x \Rightarrow m'(x) = 5^x \cdot x^7(\ln 5 + 7/x)$
7. $y = (\cos x)^{0.7x} \Rightarrow \ln y = 0.7x \ln(\cos x)$
   $\Rightarrow (1/y)y' = 0.7 \ln(\cos x) + 0.7x\,(1/\cos x)(-\sin x)$
   $\Rightarrow y' = (\cos x)^{0.7x}\,[0.7 \ln(\cos x) - 0.7x \tan x]$
8. $y = (\tan x)^{4x} \Rightarrow \ln y = 4x \ln(\tan x)$
   $\Rightarrow (1/y)y' = 4 \ln(\tan x) + 4x(1/\tan x)\sec^2 x$
   $\Rightarrow y' = (\tan x)^{4x}\,[4 \ln(\tan x) + 4x \csc x \sec x]$
9. $y = (\csc 5x)^{2x} \Rightarrow \ln y = 2x \ln(\csc 5x) \Rightarrow$
   $\frac{1}{y} y' = 2 \ln(\csc 5x) + 2x \frac{1}{\csc 5x}(-5 \csc 5x \cot 5x)$
   $\Rightarrow y' = (\csc 5x)^{2x}\,[2 \ln(\csc 5x) - 10x \cot 5x]$
10. $y = (\cos 2x)^{3x} \Rightarrow \ln y = 3x \ln(\cos 2x) \Rightarrow$
   $\frac{1}{y} y' = 3 \ln(\cos 2x) + 3x \frac{1}{\cos 2x}(-2 \sin 2x)$
   $\Rightarrow y' = (\cos 2x)^{3x}\,[3 \ln(\cos 2x) - 6x \tan 2x]$
11. $f(t) = t^{\sec t} \Rightarrow \ln f(t) = \sec t \cdot \ln t$
   $\Rightarrow \frac{1}{f(t)} f'(t) = \sec t \tan t \cdot \ln t + \sec t \cdot (1/t)$
   $\Rightarrow f'(t) = t^{\sec t}\,[\sec t \tan t \ln t + (1/t) \sec t]$

12. $r(u) = u^{\ln u} \Rightarrow \ln r(u) = \ln u \cdot \ln u = \ln^2 u \Rightarrow$
$\frac{1}{r(u)} r'(u) = 2 \ln u \cdot \frac{1}{u}$
$\Rightarrow r'(u) = u^{\ln u} \cdot \frac{2}{u} \ln u = 2u^{(\ln u - 1)} \ln u$

13. $v = (x^4 - 1)^x \Rightarrow \ln v = x \ln (x^4 - 1) \Rightarrow$
$\frac{1}{v} v' = \ln (x^4 - 1) + x \cdot \frac{1}{(x^4 - 1)} \cdot 4x^3 \Rightarrow$
$v' = (x^4 - 1)^x \left[\ln (x^4 - 1) + \frac{4x^4}{(x^4 - 1)}\right]$

14. $z = (\sin t)^{\csc t} \Rightarrow \ln z = \csc t \ln \sin t \Rightarrow$
$(1/z)z' = -\csc t \cot t \ln \sin t + \csc t(1/\sin t) \cos t$
$\Rightarrow z' = (\sin t)^{\csc t} (-\csc t \cot t \ln \sin t + \csc t \cot t)$

15. $y = 2^x \ln x \Rightarrow \ln y = x \ln 2 + \ln (\ln x)$
$\Rightarrow (1/y)y' = \ln 2 + 1/(\ln x) \cdot (1/x)$
$\Rightarrow y' = 2^x \ln x[\ln 2 + 1/(x \ln x)]$

16. $y = x(3^{x^2}) \Rightarrow \ln y = \ln x + x^2 \ln 3 \Rightarrow$
$(1/y)y' = 1/x + 2x \ln 3 \Rightarrow y' = x(3^{x^2})(1/x + 2x \ln 3)$

17. $y = 5(3x - 4)^x \Rightarrow \ln y = \ln 5 + x \ln (3x - 4)$
$\Rightarrow (1/y)y' = 0 + \ln (3x - 4) + x \cdot 1/(3x - 4) \cdot 3$
$\Rightarrow y' = 5(3x-4)^x [\ln (3x - 4) + 3x/(3x - 4)]$

18. $y = 8(4x - 5)^x \Rightarrow \ln y = \ln 8 + x \ln (4x - 5)$
$\Rightarrow (1/y)y' = 0 + \ln (4x - 5) + x \cdot 1/(4x - 5) \cdot 4$
$\Rightarrow y' = 8(4x - 5)^x [\ln(4x - 5) + 4x/(4x - 5)]$

19. a. $y = \ln 3x^7 \Rightarrow y' = 1/(3x^7)(21x^6) = 7/x$
b. $y = \ln 3 + 7 \ln x \Rightarrow y' = 0 + 7/x = 7/x$ (Checks.)

20. a. $y = \ln 10x^8 \Rightarrow y' = 1/(10x^8)(80x^7) = 8/x$
b. $y = \ln 10 + 8 \ln x \Rightarrow y' = 0 + 8/x = 8/x$ (Checks.)

21. a. $y = \ln [(3x + 4)(2x - 9)] \Rightarrow$
$y' = \frac{1}{(3x + 4)(2x - 9)} \cdot [3(2x - 9) + (3x + 4) \cdot 2]$
$= \frac{12x - 19}{(3x + 4)(2x - 9)}$
b. $y = \ln (3x + 4) + \ln (2x - 9) \Rightarrow$
$y' = \frac{3}{3x + 4} + \frac{2}{2x - 9}$, which can be transformed to
$\frac{12x - 19}{(3x + 4)(2x - 9)}$. (Checks.)

22. a. $y = \ln [(4x - 7)(x + 10)]$
$y' = \frac{1}{(4x - 7)(x + 10)} \cdot [4(x + 10) + (4x - 7) \cdot 1]$
$= \frac{8x + 33}{(4x - 7)(x + 10)}$
b. $y = \ln (4x - 7) + \ln (x + 10)$
$y' = \frac{4}{4x - 7} + \frac{1}{x + 10}$, which can be transformed to
$\frac{8x + 33}{(4x - 7)(x + 10)}$. (Checks.)

23. a. $y = \ln \frac{5x + 2}{7x - 8}$
$\Rightarrow y' = \frac{7x - 8}{5x + 2} \left(\frac{5(7x - 8) - (5x + 2) \cdot 7}{(7x - 8)^2}\right)$
$= \frac{-54}{(5x + 2)(7x - 8)}$
b. $y = \ln (5x + 2) - \ln (7x - 8)$
$\Rightarrow y' = \frac{5}{5x + 2} - \frac{7}{7x - 8}$, which can be
transformed to $\frac{-54}{(5x + 2)(7x - 8)}$. (Checks.)

24. a. $y = \ln \frac{6x - 5}{3x + 1}$
$\Rightarrow y' = \frac{3x + 1}{6x - 5} \left(\frac{6(3x + 1) - (6x - 5) \cdot 3}{(3x + 1)^2}\right)$
$= \frac{21}{(6x - 5)(3x + 1)}$
b. $y = \ln (6x - 5) - \ln (3x + 1)$
$\Rightarrow y' = \frac{6}{6x - 5} - \frac{3}{3x + 1}$, which can be
transformed to $\frac{21}{(6x - 5)(3x + 1)}$. (Checks.)

25. From Problem 19, $y' = 7/x$
At $x = 2$, $y' = 7/2 = 3.5$.
$\frac{\ln 3(2.001)^7 - \ln 3(2)^7}{0.001} = 3.49912...$, which is close to 3.5.

26. From Problem 20, $y' = 8/x$.
At $x = 2$, $y' = 8/2 = 4$.
$\frac{\ln 10(2.001)^8 - \ln 10(2)^8}{0.001} = 3.9990...$, which is close to 4.

In Problems 27 through 32 it is acceptable to leave the answer in terms of y rather than doing the final substitution.

27. $y = (5x + 11)^7 (7x - 3)^5$
$\Rightarrow \ln y = 7 \ln (5x + 11) + 5 \ln (7x - 3)$
$\Rightarrow (1/y)y' = 35/(5x + 11) + 35/(7x - 3)$
$\Rightarrow y' = y\left(\frac{35}{5x + 11} + \frac{35}{7x - 3}\right)$
$= (5x + 11)^7 (7x - 3)^5 \left(\frac{35}{5x + 11} + \frac{35}{7x - 3}\right)$

28. $y = (4x + 3)^8 (8x - 9)^4$
$\Rightarrow \ln y = 8 \ln (4x + 3) + 4 \ln (8x - 9)$
$\Rightarrow (1/y)y' = 32/(4x + 3) + 32/(8x - 9)$
$\Rightarrow y' = y\left(\frac{32}{4x + 3} + \frac{32}{8x - 9}\right)$
$= (4x + 3)^8 (8x - 9)^4\left(\frac{32}{4x + 3} + \frac{32}{8x - 9}\right)$

29. $y = (3 - 4x)^5 (7 + 5x)^4$
$\Rightarrow \ln y = 5 \ln (3 - 4x) + 4 \ln (7 + 5x)$
$\Rightarrow (1/y)y' = -20/(3 - 4x) + 20/(7 + 5x)$
$\Rightarrow y' = y\left(\frac{-20}{3 - 4x} + \frac{20}{7 + 5x}\right)$
$= (3 - 4x)^5 (7 + 5x)^4\left(\frac{-20}{3 - 4x} + \frac{20}{7 + 5x}\right)$

30. $y = (10 + 3x)^{10} (4 - 5x)^3$
$\Rightarrow \ln y = 10 \ln (10 + 3x) + 3 \ln (4 - 5x)$
$\Rightarrow (1/y)y' = 30/(10 + 3x) - 15/(4 - 5x)$
$\Rightarrow y' = y\left(\frac{30}{10 + 3x} - \frac{15}{4 - 5x}\right)$
$= (10 + 3x)^{10} (4 - 5x)^3\left(\frac{30}{10 + 3x} - \frac{15}{4 - 5x}\right)$

31. $y = \frac{(4x + 1) \csc x}{\sin^5 x}$
$\Rightarrow \ln y = \ln (4x + 1) + \ln \csc x - 5 \ln \sin x$
$\Rightarrow (1/y)y' = 4/(4x + 1) + (1/\csc x) \cdot (-\csc x \cot x) - 5(1/\sin x) \cdot \cos x$
$= 4/(4x + 1) - \cot x - 5 \cot x$
$\Rightarrow y' = y[4/(4x + 1) - 6 \cot x]$
$= \frac{(4x + 1) \csc x}{\sin^5 x} \left(\frac{4}{4x + 1} - 6 \cot x\right)$
Note: Original function is equivalent to
$y = \frac{4x + 1}{\sin^6 x}$.

32. $y = \frac{x^7 \cos x}{5x + 6}$

$\Rightarrow \ln y = 7 \ln x + \ln \cos x - \ln (5x + 6)$

$\Rightarrow (1/y)y' = 7/x + (1/\cos x)(-\sin x) - 5/(5x + 6)$

$\Rightarrow y' = y[7/x - \tan x - 5/(5x + 6)]$

$= \frac{x^7 \cos x}{5x + 6}\left(\frac{7}{x} - \tan x - \frac{5}{5x + 6}\right)$

33. Integral Review Problem

$\int_5^9 \frac{5}{3 - x}\,dx = -\int_5^9 \frac{5}{3 - x}(-dx)$

$= -5 \ln|3 - x|\Big|_5^9 = -5 \ln 6 + 5 \ln 2$

$= \underline{-5 \ln 3} = \underline{-5.493061...}$

34. Look-Ahead Problem Follow-Up

Answers will vary.

35. Continued Exponentiation Problem

a. $f(x) = x^x \Rightarrow \ln f(x) = x \ln x$

$\Rightarrow 1/f(x) \cdot f'(x) = \ln x + x(1/x)$

$\Rightarrow f'(x) = x^x (\ln x + 1)$

b. $g(x) = x^{x^x} \Rightarrow \ln g(x) = x^x \ln x$

$\Rightarrow 1/g(x) \cdot g'(x) = x^x (\ln x + 1) \cdot \ln x + x^x (1/x)$

$\Rightarrow g'(x) = x^{x^x} \cdot x^x [(\ln x)^2 + \ln x + 1/x]$

The derivative of x^x comes from part a.

36. Derivative with Variable Base and Exponent Generalization Problem

a. $f(x) = x^3 \Rightarrow \ln f(x) = 3 \ln x \Rightarrow 1/f(x) \cdot f'(x) = 3/x$

$\Rightarrow f'(x) = 3 f(x)/x = 3x^3/x = 3x^2$, which is nx^{n-1}.

b. $g(x) = 3^x \Rightarrow \ln g(x) = x \ln 3 \Rightarrow 1/g(x) \cdot g'(x) = \ln 3$.

$g'(x) = g(x) \ln 3 = 3^x \ln 3$

Similarity:

$f'(x) = f(x)$ times the derivative of $3 \ln x$.

$g'(x) = g(x)$ times the derivative of $x \ln 3$.

Difference:

For $f'(x)$, the derivative of $3 \ln x$, i.e., $3/x$, can be combined with the expression for $f(x)$.

For $g'(x)$, the derivative of $x \ln 3$, i.e., $\ln 3$, cannot be combined with the expression for $g(x)$.

c. $h(x) = x^x \Rightarrow \ln h(x) = x \ln x$

$\Rightarrow 1/h(x) \cdot h'(x) = \ln x + x \cdot (1/x)$

$\Rightarrow h'(x) = h(x)(\ln x + 1) = x^x \ln x + x^x$.

For comparison purposes, the second term in $h'(x)$ can be written as $x \cdot x^{x-1}$, which has the same form as the derivative of a power. The first term is $h(x)$ times the ln of the base, which has the same form as the derivative of an exponential function such as g.

37. Compound Interest Problem

a. $m(t) = 1000(1.06)^t$

$\ln m(t) = \ln 1000 + t \ln 1.06$

$1/m(t) \cdot m'(t) = 0 + \ln 1.06$

$m'(t) = m(t) \cdot \ln 1.06$

$m'(t) = 1000 (1.06)^t (\ln 1.06)$

$m'(0) = 58.27$ \$/year

$m'(5) = 77.98$ \$/year

$m'(10) = 104.35$ \$/year.

b. $m(0) = \$1000.00$

$m(5) = \$1338.23$

$m(10) = \$1790.85$

The rates are increasing. \$338.23 is earned between 0 and 5 years; \$452.62 is earned between 5 and 10 years, which agrees with the increasing derivatives shown in part a.

c. $\frac{m'(t)}{m(t)} = \frac{1000(1.06)^t (\ln 1.06)}{1000(1.06)^t} = \ln 1.06$.

$\therefore m'(t)/m(t) = \ln 1.06$, a constant.

d. $m(1) = 1060.00$. So you earn \$60.00.

The rate starts out at only \$58.27/year, but has increased enough by year's end to make the total for the year equal to \$60.00.

38. Door-Closer Problem

$d(t) = 200t \cdot 2^{-t} \Rightarrow \ln d(t) = \ln 200t - t \ln 2$

$\frac{1}{d(t)} \cdot d'(t) = 1/t - \ln 2 \Rightarrow d'(t) = (200t \cdot 2^{-t})(1/t - \ln 2)$

$d'(1) = (200 \cdot 2^{-1})(1 - \ln 2) = 30.685...$

$d'(2) = (400 \cdot 2^{-2})(1/2 - \ln 2) = -19.314...$

So the door is opening at about 30.7°/sec at 1 second and closing at about 19.3°/sec at 2 seconds, which agrees with the graph.

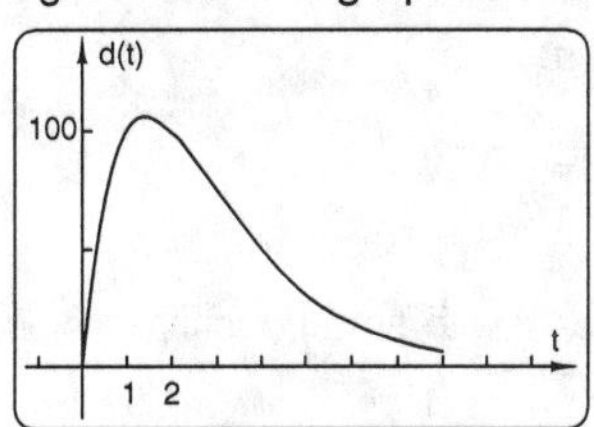

The widest opening occurs when $d'(t) = 0$.

Solving numerically for t in $(200t \cdot 2^{-t})(1/t - \ln 2) = 0$, $t = 1.44269...$.

$d(1.44269...) = 106.147...$

So the widest is about 106° at $t \approx 1.4$ sec.

39. Limit of an Interesting Expression

Using TRACE or TABLE,

n	$(1 + 1/n)^n$
10	2.5937424601...
100	2.7048138294...
1000	2.7169239322...
10000	2.7181459268...
100000	2.7182682371...
1000000	2.7182804693...

The values are increasing toward e, the base of natural logarithms.

[Students may already have seen this limit in Problem 8 of Problem Set 2-5. An effective way to show dynamically the concept of limit is to start the table at n = 1000 and increase by steps of 1000. As you scan down the table, more and more of the first digits remain the same. Only the last digits are changing. Note that round-off will eventually make the calculator give the incorrect answer 1.]

40. Journal Problem

Journal entries will vary.

Q1. $f'(x) = -2 \cos x \sin x$ Q2. $g'(x) = -2x \sin x^2$.
Q3. $h'(x) = -\sin 2^x \cdot (2^x \ln 2)$. Q4. $c'(x) = 0$
Q5. $L'(x) = 1/x$ Q6. $M'(x) = 5/x$
Q7. $N'(x) = 5 \ln^4 x \cdot (1/x)$ Q8. $O'(x) = 1/(1 + x^2)$
Q9. Graph (Function is $y = \ln x$)

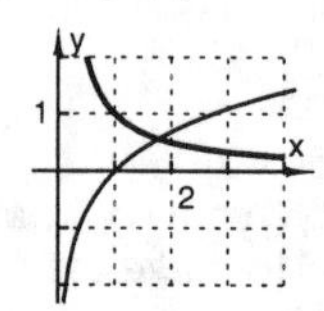

Q10. See statement of uniqueness theorem in 6-4.

1. $f(x) = \log_3 x \Rightarrow f'(x) = 1/(x \ln 3)$
 $f'(5) = 0.182047...$
 Graph, showing tangent with small positive slope

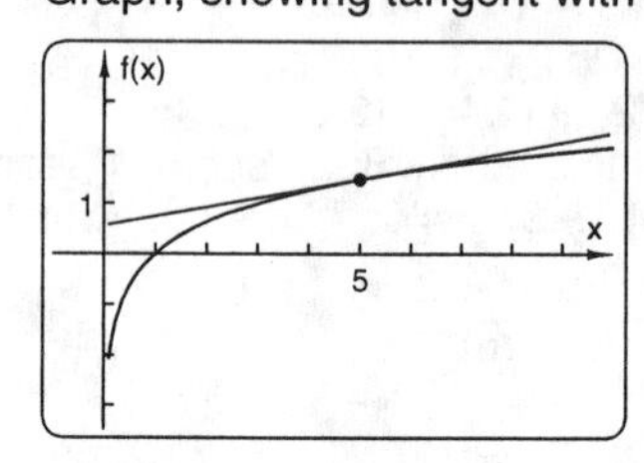

2. $f(x) = \log_7 x \Rightarrow f'(x) = 1/(x \ln 7)$
 $f'(3) = 0.171299...$
 Graph, showing tangent with small positive slope

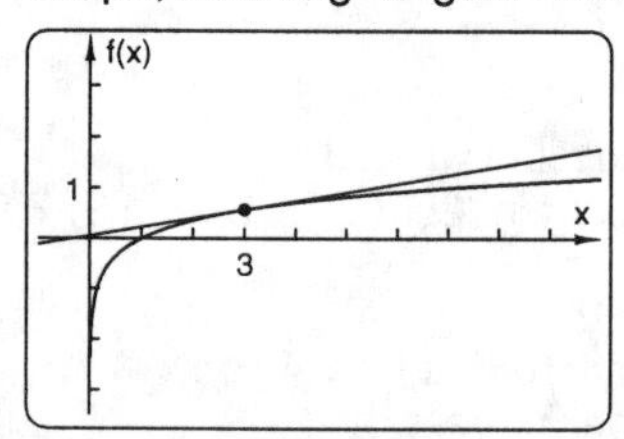

3. $f(x) = \log_{0.6} x \Rightarrow f'(x) = 1/(x \ln 0.6)$
 $f'(9) = -0.217512...$
 Graph, showing tangent with small negative slope

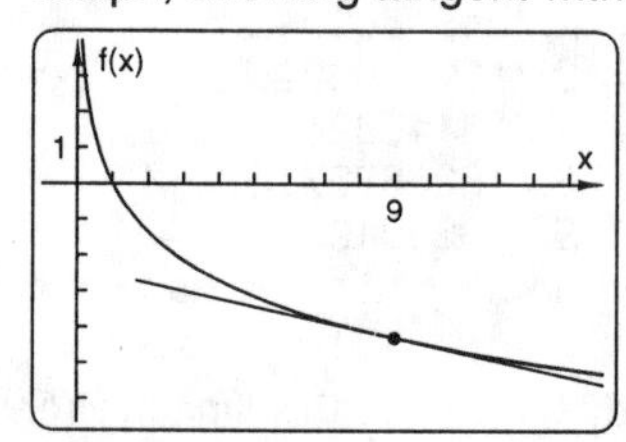

4. $f(x) = \log_{0.8} x \Rightarrow f'(x) = 1/(x \ln 0.8)$
 $f'(4) = -1.120355...$
 Graph, showing tangent with slope ≈ -1

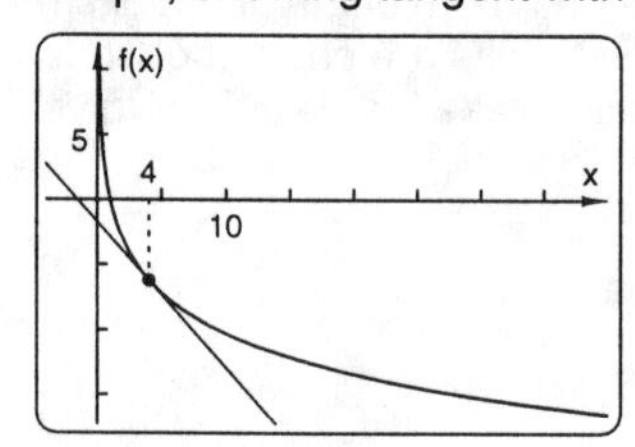

5. $f(x) = 13 \log_e x = 13 \ln x \Rightarrow f'(x) = 13/x$
6. $f(x) = 5 \log_e x = 5 \ln x \Rightarrow f'(x) = 5/x$
7. $g(x) = 8 \log_e (x^5) = 8 \ln (x^5) = 40 \ln x \Rightarrow g'(x) = 40/x$
8. $h(x) = 10 \log_e (x^{0.4}) = 4 \ln x \Rightarrow h'(x) = 4/x$
9. $T(x) = \log_5 (\sin x) \Rightarrow T'(x) = \dfrac{1}{\sin x \cdot \ln 5} \cdot \cos x$
 $T'(x) = (\cot x)/(\ln 5)$
10. $R(x) = \log_4 (\sec x)$
 $\Rightarrow R'(x) = \dfrac{1}{\sec x \cdot \ln 4} \cdot \sec x \tan x$
 $R'(x) = (\tan x)/(\ln 4)$
11. $p(x) = (\log_e x)(\log_5 x) = (\ln x)(\log_5 x)$
 $\Rightarrow p'(x) = (1/x) \cdot (\log_5 x) + (\ln x) \cdot (1/(x \ln 5))$
 $= \dfrac{1 \cdot \ln x}{x \ln 5} + \dfrac{\ln x}{x \ln 5} = (2 \ln x)/(x \ln 5)$
12. $q(x) = (\log_9 x)/(\log_3 x) = \dfrac{\ln x}{\ln 9} \cdot \dfrac{\ln 3}{\ln x} = \dfrac{\ln 3}{2 \ln 3} = \dfrac{1}{2}$
 $\therefore q'(x) = 0$, because $q(x)$ is constant.
13. $y = \log_{10} x \Rightarrow y' = 1/(x \ln 10)$
 $x = 4$: $y' = 1/(4 \ln 10) = 0.108573620...$
 Numerical derivative is 0.1085736... . (Checks.)
14. $y = \log_{0.2} x \Rightarrow y' = 1/(x \ln 0.2)$
 $x = 5$: $y' = 1/(5 \ln 0.2) = -0.12426698...$
 Numerical derivative is $-0.124266...$. (Checks.)
15. $f(x) = \log_{0.9} x = (\ln x)/(\ln 0.9)$
 $f'(x) = 1/(x \ln 0.9)$; $f'(2) = -4.7456...$ Graph

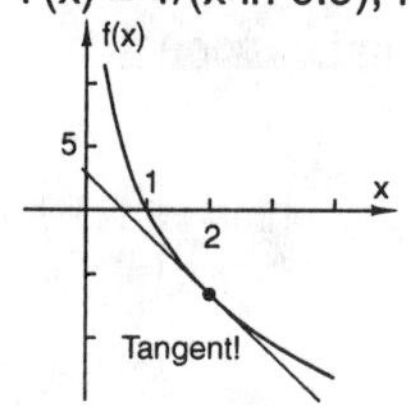

16. $f(x) = \log_{1.4} x = (\ln x)/(\ln 1.4)$
 $f'(x) = 1/(x \ln 1.4)$; $f'(3) = 0.990671...$ Graph

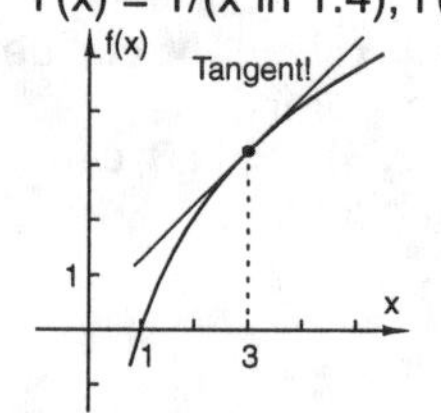

17. Derivative of Logarithm Proof
 See text proof.
18. Equivalence of Natural Logs and Base e Logs
 Prove that $\log_e x = \ln x$ for all values of $x > 0$.
 Proof:
 Let $f(x) = \log_e x$ and $g(x) = \ln x$.
 $f'(x) = (1/x) \log_e e = (1/x) \cdot 1 = 1/x$
 $g'(x) = 1/x$
 $\therefore f'(x) = g'(x)$ for all $x > 0$
 $f(1) = \log_e 1 = 0$; $g(1) = \ln 1 = 0$
 $\therefore f(1) = g(1)$
 $\therefore f(x) = g(x)$ for all $x > 0$
 $\therefore \log_e x = \ln x$ for all $x > 0$, Q.E.D.

19. Lava Flow Problem

a. $y = 7 \cdot (2 - 0.9^x)$
$dy/dx = 7(-0.9^x)(\ln 0.9)$
$dy/dx = 0.737523...(0.9^x)$
$x = 0$: $dy/dx = 0.737...$ mph
$x = 1$: $dy/dx = 0.663...$ mph
$x = 5$: $dy/dx = 0.435...$ mph
$x = 10$: $dy/dx = 0.257...$ mph
Lava is slowing down.

b. $y/7 = 2 - 0.9^x$
$0.9^x = 2 - y/7$
$x \ln 0.9 = \ln(2 - y/7)$
$x = (1/\ln 0.9)[\ln(2 - y/7)]$

c. $\frac{dx}{dy} = (1/\ln 0.9) \cdot \frac{1}{2 - y/7} \cdot (-\frac{1}{7})$
$\frac{dx}{dy} = \frac{9.491221...}{14 - y}$
$y = 10$: $dx/dy = 2.372...$ hours/mile

d. If $x = 10$, then $y = 7(2 - 0.9^{10})$, so
$\frac{dx}{dy} = \frac{9.491221...}{14 - 7(2 - 0.9^{10})} = 3.888651...$

e. 3.88... is the reciprocal of 0.257..., the value of dy/dx when x = 10, not when y = 10.

20. Compound Interest Problem

a. $1000(1.06^t) = M \Rightarrow 1.06^t = M/1000$
$\Rightarrow \log_{1.06} 1.06^t = \log_{1.06}(M/1000)$
$\Rightarrow t = \log_{1.06}(M/1000)$.

b. $dt/dM = \frac{1}{(\ln 1.06)(M/1000)} \cdot \frac{1}{1000} = \frac{1}{M \ln 1.06}$

c. If $M = 1000$, $dt/dM = \frac{1}{1000 \ln 1.06}$
$= 0.01716...$ years/dollar.
At this rate, with \$1000 in the account, it would take 0.017... years, or about 6 days, to earn a dollar of interest.

d. dt/dM gets smaller as M increases; more interest is earned when M is larger, so it takes less time to accumulate \$1000.

21. Proof of the Change-of-Base Property

a. Definition of logarithm (algebraic)
b. Take $\log_b$ of both sides.
c. Log of a power property
d. Divide by $\log_b a$.
e. Substitution

22. The Two Forms of the Definition of e

Let $t = 1/n$ and note $t \to 0$ as $n \to \infty$. So $\lim_{n\to\infty} g(n)$
$= \lim_{t\to 0} g(1/t) = \lim_{t\to 0}(1 + t)^{1/t} = e = \lim_{n\to 0} f(n)$, Q.E.D.

23. Definition of e Journal Problem

A typical journal entry should include the definition of e as the limit of $(1 + 1/x)^x$ as x approaches infinity, a sketch of the graph of $y = (1 + 1/x)^x$ showing asymptotic behavior, a discussion of how TRACE or TABLE gives values that remain the same in the first few decimal places and change only in the last few, and possibly an observation that as x becomes too large the calculator will round off to 1, which is *not* the correct limit.

24. Population Problem Revisited

$\int_{1000}^{N} (1/P)\, dP = \int_0^{10} 0.05\, dt \Rightarrow$
$\ln|N| - \ln 1000 = 0.5 \Rightarrow \ln\left|\frac{N}{1000}\right| = 0.5 \Rightarrow$
$\log_e\left|\frac{N}{1000}\right| = 0.5 \Rightarrow \left|\frac{N}{1000}\right| = e^{0.5}$
$|N| = 1000e^{0.5} = 1648.721... \Rightarrow$
$N \approx 1649$, Q.E.D. (since N is positive)

25. Limit and Function Interchange Journal Problem

A typical journal entry should include the fact that if the outside function is continuous and the inside function has a limit as x approaches c, then $\lim f(g(x)) = f(\lim g(x))$. A simple example is $\lim_{x\to c} f(x) = f(\lim_{x\to c} x) = f(c)$, which is the definition of continuity. The property is used to reverse the log and the limit in finding the derivative of the logarithm function algebraically.

Problem Set 6-7, pages 282 to 284 — The Natural Exponential Function: The Inverse of ln

Q1. $y' = 1/x$
Q2. $y' = 1/x$
Q3. $\ln 1 = 0$
Q4. $\log_3 1 = 0$
Q5. $\ln e^5 = 5$
Q6. $\tan x + C$
Q7. $(\sec x)' = \sec x \tan x$
Q8. $(\sec^{-1} x)' = \frac{1}{|x|\sqrt{x^2 - 1}}$
Q9. Graph (Function is $y = x^2 e^{-0.7x} - 2$.)

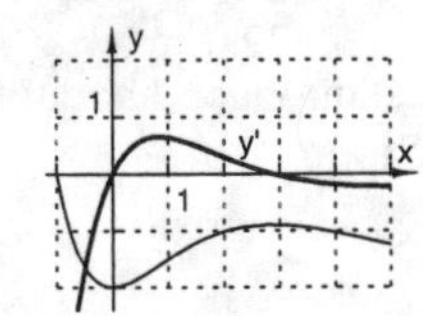

Q10. False (e.g., $f(x) = |x|$ is continuous but not differentiable at $x = 0$)

0. Look-Ahead Problem
Answers will vary.
1. $y = e^{4x} \Rightarrow y' = 4e^{4x}$
2. $y = e^{9x} \Rightarrow y' = 9e^{9x}$
3. $y = 17e^{-5x} \Rightarrow y' = -85e^{-5x}$
4. $y = 667e^{-3x} \Rightarrow y' = -2001e^{-3x}$
5. $f(x) = e^{-x} \Rightarrow f'(x) = -e^{-x}$
6. $f(x) = 3e^{-x} \Rightarrow y' = -3e^{-x}$
7. $h(x) = x^3e^x \Rightarrow h'(x) = 3x^2e^x + x^3e^x = x^2e^x(3 + x)$
8. $g(x) = x^{-6}e^x$
$\Rightarrow g'(x) = -6x^{-7}e^x + x^{-6}e^x = x^{-7}e^x(-6 + x)$
9. $r(t) = e^t \sin t \Rightarrow r'(t) = e^t \sin t + e^t \cos t$
10. $s(t) = e^t \tan t \Rightarrow s'(t) = e^t \tan t + e^t \sec^2 t$
11. $u = 3e^xe^{-x} = 3 \Rightarrow u' = 0$
12. $v = e^{4x}e^{-4x} = 1 \Rightarrow v' = 0$
13. $y = e^{2u} \ln 3u \Rightarrow y' = 2e^{2u} \ln 3u + e^{2u} \cdot (1/u)$
14. $y = e^{-5u} \ln 4u \Rightarrow y' = -5e^{-5u} \ln 4u + e^{-5u} \cdot (1/u)$
15. $y = \frac{\exp x}{\ln x} \Rightarrow y' = \frac{\exp x \ln x - \exp x\,(1/x)}{(\ln x)^2}$
16. $y = \frac{\ln x}{\exp x} \Rightarrow y' = \frac{(1/x)\exp x - \ln x \cdot \exp x}{\exp 2x}$
17. $y = 4e^{\sec x} \Rightarrow y' = 4e^{\sec x} \cdot \sec x \tan x$
18. $y = 7e^{\cos x} \Rightarrow y' = 7e^{\cos x} \cdot (-\sin x)$
19. $f(x) = \csc e^x \Rightarrow f'(x) = -\csc e^x \cot e^x \cdot e^x$
20. $f(x) = \cot e^x \Rightarrow f'(x) = -\csc^2 e^x \cdot e^x$
21. $y = 3 \ln e^{2x} = 3 \cdot 2x = 6x \Rightarrow y' = 6$

22. $y = 4 \ln e^{5x} = 4 \cdot 5x = 20x \Rightarrow y' = 20$

23. $y = (\ln e^{3x})(\ln e^{4x}) = 3x \cdot 4x = 12x^2 \Rightarrow y' = 24x$

24. $y = (\ln e^{-2x})(\ln e^{5x}) = -2x \cdot 5x = -10x^2$
$\Rightarrow y' = -20x$

25. $g(x) = 4e^{\ln 3x} = 4 \cdot 3x = 12x \Rightarrow g'(x) = 12$

26. $h(x) = 6e^{\ln 7x} = 6 \cdot 7x = 42x \Rightarrow h'(x) = 42$

27. $y = 2001(e^{3x})^5 = 2001e^{15x} \Rightarrow y' = 30015e^{15x}$

28. $y = 1001(e^{4x})^7 = 1001e^{28x} \Rightarrow y' = 28028e^{28x}$

29. $y = e^x + e^{-x} \Rightarrow y' = e^x - e^{-x}$

30. $y = e^x - e^{-x} \Rightarrow y' = e^x + e^{-x}$

31. $u = (5 + e^{2t})^7$
$\Rightarrow u' = 7(5 + e^{2t})^6 \cdot 2e^{2t} = 14e^{2t}(5 + e^{2t})^6$

32. $v = (3 + e^{-t})^5$
$\Rightarrow v' = 5(3 + e^{-t})^4 \cdot (-e^{-t}) = -5e^{-t}(3 + e^{-t})$

33. $y = \exp(5x^3) \Rightarrow$
$y' = \exp(5x^3) \cdot 15x^2 = 15x^2 \exp(5x^3)$

34. $y = 8 \exp(x^5) \Rightarrow$
$y' = 8 \exp(x^5) \cdot 5x^4 = 40x^4 \exp(x^5)$

35. $y = (\sin 3)(\ln 5)(e^2) \Rightarrow y' = 0$ (y is a constant.)

36. $y = (\tan 4)(e^6)(\ln 2) \Rightarrow y' = 0$ (y is a constant.)

37. $f(x) = e^{0.4x} \Rightarrow f'(x) = 0.4\, e^{0.4x}$
Algebraically: $f'(2) = 0.4\, e^{0.8} = 0.890216...$
Numerically: $f'(2) \approx 0.890216...$ (Checks.)

38. $f(x) = e^{-2x} \Rightarrow f'(x) = -2e^{-2x}$
Algebraically: $f'(0.6) = -2\, e^{-1.2} = -0.602388...$
Numerically: $f'(0.6) \approx -0.602388...$ (Checks.)

39. $f(x) = 5xe^x \Rightarrow f'(x) = 5e^x + 5xe^x = 5e^x(1 + x)$
$f'(-1) = 5e^{-1}(1 - 1) = 0$
$f(-1) = 5(-1)(e^{-1}) = -1.839...$
Graph: Line at $x = -1$ is tangent to the graph.

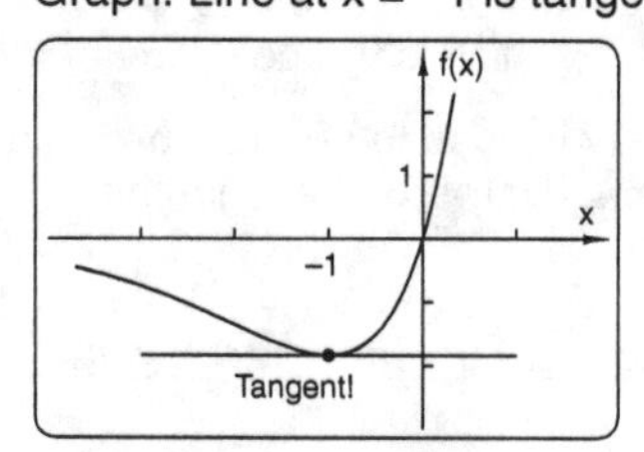

40. $f(x) = 6x^2e^{-x}$
$\Rightarrow f'(x) = 12xe^{-x} + 6x^2e^{-x}(-1) = 6xe^{-x}(2 - x)$
$f'(2) = 6(2)e^{-2}(2 - 2) = 0$
$f(2) = 6(2^2)e^{-2} = 3.2480...$
Graph: Line at $x = 2$ is tangent to the graph.

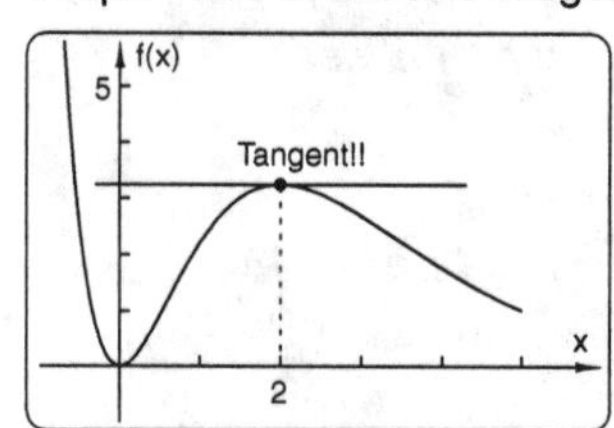

41. $\int e^{5x}\,dx = \frac{1}{5}e^{5x} + C$

42. $\int e^{7x}\,dx = \frac{1}{7}e^{7x} + C$

43. $\int 6 \exp x\,dx = 6 \exp x + C$

44. $\int \exp(0.2x)\,dx = 5 \exp(0.2x) + C$

45. $\int 3e^{-2x}\,dx = -\frac{3}{2}e^{-2x} + C$

46. $\int -4e^{-6x}\,dx = \frac{2}{3}e^{-6x} + C$

47. $\int e^{\sin x} \cos x\,dx = e^{\sin x} + C$

48. $\int e^{\tan x} \sec^2 x\,dx = e^{\tan x} + C$

49. $\int e^{3 \ln x}\,dx = \int x^3\,dx = \frac{1}{4}x^4 + C$

50. $\int 60e^{\ln 5x}\,dx = 60 \int 5x\,dx = 150x^2 + C$

51. $\int (1 + e^{2x})^{50} e^{2x}\,dx = \frac{1}{102}(1 + e^{2x})^{51} + C$

52. $\int (1 - e^{4x})^{100} e^{4x}\,dx = -\frac{1}{404}(1 - e^{4x})^{101} + C$

53. $\int (3 + e^x)^2\,dx = \int (9 + 6e^x + e^{2x})\,dx$
$= 9x + 6e^x + \frac{1}{2}e^{2x} + C$

54. $\int (2 + e^x)^3\,dx = \int (8 + 12e^x + 6e^{2x} + e^{3x})\,dx$
$= 8x + 12e^x + 3e^{2x} + \frac{1}{3}e^{3x} + C$

55. a. $\int_1^2 e^{0.4x}\,dx = 2.5e^{0.4x}\Big|_1^2 = 2.5(e^{0.8} - e^{0.4})$
$= \underline{1.834290...}$
b. Numerically: integral $\approx 1.834290...$ (Checks.)

56. a. $\int_1^3 e^{0.2x}\,dx = 5e^{0.2x}\Big|_1^3 = 5(e^{0.6} - e^{0.2})$
$= \underline{3.003580...}$
b. Numerically: integral $\approx 3.003580...$ (Checks.)

57. a. $\int_0^2 (e^x - e^{-x})\,dx = e^x + e^{-x}\Big|_0^2$
$= e^2 + e^{-2} - 1 - 1 = \underline{5.524391...}$
b. Numerically: integral $\approx 5.524391...$ (Checks.)

58. a. $\int_{-1}^2 (e^x + e^{-x})\,dx = (e^x + e^{-x})\Big|_{-1}^2$
$= e^2 - e^{-2} - e^{-1} + e^1 = \underline{9.604123...}$
b. Numerically: integral $\approx 9.604123...$ (Checks.)

59. <u>Rabbit Population Problem</u>
a. $R(t) = ae^{kt}$
$60{,}000 = ae^{k \cdot 0} \Rightarrow a = 60{,}000$
$2{,}400{,}000 = ae^{k \cdot 2} = 60{,}000\,e^{2k}$
$40 = e^{2k} \Rightarrow 2k = \ln 40 \Rightarrow k = (\ln 40)/2 = 1.844...$
(Store 1.844... without round-off as k.)
$\therefore R(t) = 60{,}000e^{1.844...t}$
b. $R(5) = 60{,}000e^{1.844...(5)} = 607{,}157{,}310.7...$
About 607 million rabbits.
c. $2 = 60{,}000e^{1.844...t} \Rightarrow 1/30{,}000 = e^{1.844...t} \Rightarrow$
$-\ln 30{,}000 = 1.844...t \Rightarrow t = -5.589...$
So the first pair of rabbits was introduced about 5.6 years earlier, or in <u>about 1859</u>.

60. <u>Depreciation Problem</u>

a. $v(t) = 85{,}000e^{-0.05t}$
$v(0) = 85{,}000e^{0} = 85{,}000$
\$85,000 when built.

b. $v(10) = 85{,}000e^{-0.5} = 51555.106...$
$v(11) = 85{,}000e^{-0.55} = 49040.733...$
At 10 years, value is \$51,555.11.
At 11 years, value is \$49,040.73.
So depreciation is 51,555.11 – 49,040.73 = \$2514.38.

c. $v'(t) = -4250\ e^{-0.05t}$
$v'(10) = -4250\ e^{-0.5} = -2577.75...$,
or about \$2578 per year.
This rate is higher than the actual depreciation in part b. because the latter rate is an *average* for the year. The rate at the end will be lower than 2578 to give the average of 2514.

d. $30{,}000 = 85{,}000e^{-0.05t}$
$30/85 = e^{-0.05t}$
$\ln (30/85) = -0.05t$
$t = [\ln (30/85)]/(-0.05) = 20.8290... \approx 21$ years.

61. <u>An Exponential Function Is Not a Power Function!</u>
Counterexample: Let $f(x) = e^x$.
Using the derivative of a power formula, f'(x) would equal xe^{x-1}. Then f'(0) would equal $0 \cdot e^0 = 0$. But the graph of $f(x) = e^x$ crosses the y-axis with a slope of $e^0 = 1$. So the derivative of a power formula produces a wrong answer.

62. <u>Proof of the Function of an Inverse Function Property</u>
Let $y = f^{-1}(x)$, so $x = f(y)$ by definition.
Then $x = f(y) = f(f^{-1}(x))$, substituting $f^{-1}(x)$ for y.
And $f^{-1}(x) = f^{-1}(f(y))$, substituting f(y) for x, Q.E.D.

63. <u>Zero/Zero Problem</u>

a. $f(x) = \dfrac{\ln x + \sin (x-1)}{1 - e^{x-1}}$
$\lim_{x\to 1} (\ln x + \sin (x-1)) = \ln 1 + \sin (1-1) = 0$ and
$\lim_{x\to 1} (1 - e^{x-1}) = 0$ (since ln x, sin (x – 1), and e^{x-1} are continuous at x = 1).
$\therefore$ f(x) takes the indeterminate form 0/0 as $x \to 1$.

b. Graph.

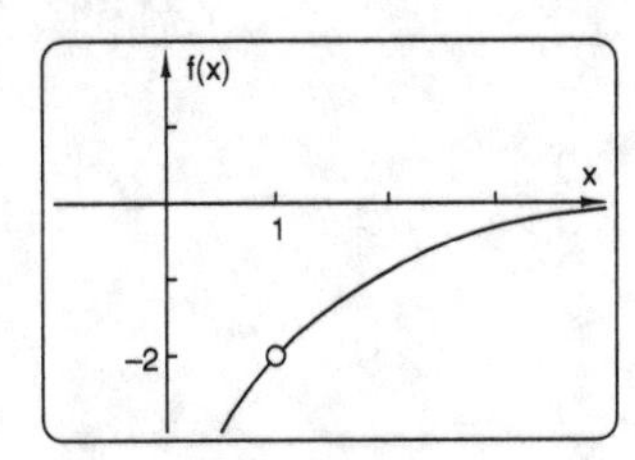

c. f(x) appears to approach –2.

d. $\dfrac{d}{dx}(\ln x + \sin (x-1)) = 1/x + \cos(x-1)$;
At x = 1, $1/1 + \cos(1-1) = 1 + \cos 0 = 2$.
$\dfrac{d}{dx}(1 - e^{x-1}) = -e^{x-1}$; $-e^{1-1} = -e^0 = -1$
Ratio = 2/(–1) = –2, the apparent limit!

64. <u>Journal Problem</u>
Journal entries will vary.

Problem Set 6-8, pages 287 to 290 — Limits of Indeterminate Forms: l'Hospital's Rule

Q1. $e \approx 2.71828$
Q2. $e^{-1} = 1/e \approx 0.3679$
Q3. $\ln e = 1$
Q4. $\ln e^x = x$
Q5. $e^{\ln x} = x$
Q6. b = e
Q7. $\log_b x = (\ln x)/(\ln b)$
Q8. $f'(x) = e^x$
Q9. $\int e^{-x}\,dx = -e^{-x} + C$
Q10. $f'(x) = \sin(\tan x)\sec^2 x$

1. $\lim_{x\to 0} \dfrac{2 \sin 5x}{3x} \to \dfrac{0}{0}$
$= \lim_{x\to 0} \dfrac{10 \cos 5x}{3} = \dfrac{10}{3}$
Graph

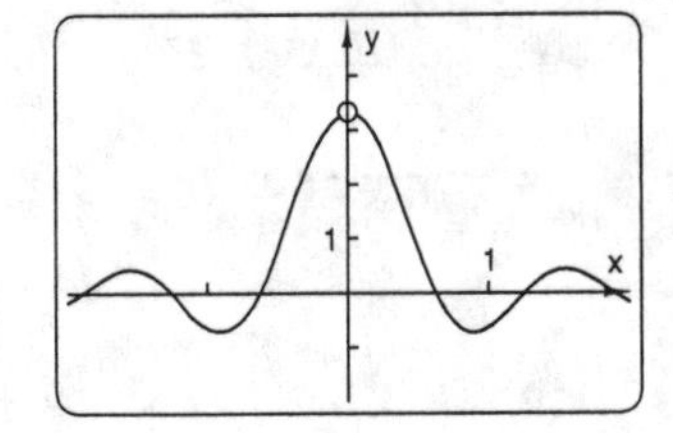

2. $\lim_{x\to 0} \dfrac{4 \tan 3x}{5x} \to \dfrac{0}{0}$
$= \lim_{x\to 0} \dfrac{12 \sec^2 3x}{5} = \dfrac{12}{5}$
Graph

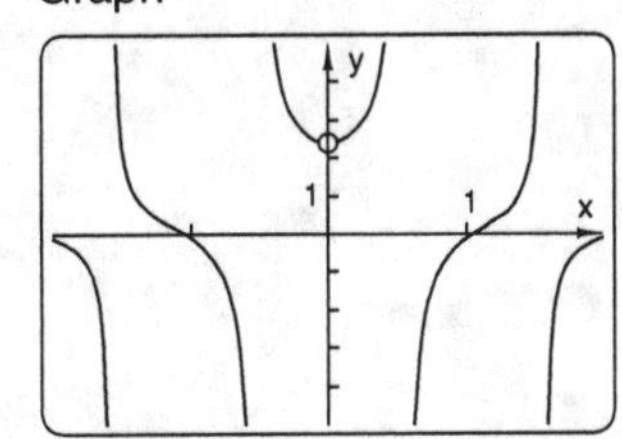

3. $\lim_{x\to 0} \dfrac{\tan x}{x} \to \dfrac{0}{0}$
$= \lim_{x\to 0} \dfrac{\sec^2 x}{1} = 1$

4. $\lim_{x\to 0} \dfrac{\sin x}{x} \to \dfrac{0}{0}$
$= \lim_{x\to 0} \dfrac{\cos x}{1} = 1$, a "well-known" limit.

5. $\lim_{x\to 0} \dfrac{1 - \cos x}{x^2} \to \dfrac{0}{0}$

$= \lim_{x\to 0} \dfrac{\sin x}{2x} \to \dfrac{0}{0}$

$= \lim_{x\to 0} \dfrac{\cos x}{2} = \dfrac{1}{2}$

6. $\lim_{x\to 0} \dfrac{x^2}{\cos 3x - 1} \to \dfrac{0}{0}$

$= \lim_{x\to 0} \dfrac{2x}{-3 \sin 3x} \to \dfrac{0}{0}$

$= \lim_{x\to 0} \dfrac{2}{-9 \cos 3x} = -\dfrac{2}{9}$

7. $\lim_{x\to 0^+} f(\sin x, x^2) \to \dfrac{0}{0}$

$= \lim_{x\to 0^+} \dfrac{\cos x}{2x} = \infty$

8. $\lim_{x\to 0} \dfrac{1 - \cos x}{x + x^2} \to \dfrac{0}{0}$

$= \lim_{x\to 0} \dfrac{\sin x}{1 + 2x} = 0$

9. $\lim_{x\to 0^+} \dfrac{\ln x}{1/x} \to \dfrac{-\infty}{\infty}$

$= \lim_{x\to 0^+} \dfrac{x^{-1}}{-x^{-2}} = \lim_{x\to 0^+} (-x) = 0$

10. $\lim_{x\to 0} \dfrac{e^{3x}}{x^2} = \infty$ (Form is $\dfrac{1}{0}$.)

11. $\lim_{x\to 1} \dfrac{e^x - e}{5 \ln x} \to \dfrac{0}{0}$

$= \lim_{x\to 1} \dfrac{e^x}{5x^{-1}} = \dfrac{e}{5}$

12. $\lim_{x\to 1} \dfrac{\ln x - x + 1}{x^2 - 2x + 1} \to \dfrac{0}{0}$

$= \lim_{x\to 1} \dfrac{x^{-1} - 1}{2x - 2} \to \dfrac{0}{0}$

$= \lim_{x\to 1} \dfrac{-x^{-2}}{2} = -\dfrac{1}{2}$

13. $\lim_{x\to 2} \dfrac{3x + 5}{\cos x} = \dfrac{11}{\cos 2} = -26.43297...$

14. $\lim_{x\to 2} \dfrac{\tan x}{x - 2} = \infty$ (Form is $\dfrac{\tan 2}{0}$.)

15. $\lim_{x\to\infty} \dfrac{e^x}{x^2} \to \dfrac{\infty}{\infty}$

$= \lim_{x\to\infty} f(e^x, 2x) \to \dfrac{\infty}{\infty}$

$= \lim_{x\to\infty} \dfrac{e^x}{2} = \infty$

16. $\lim_{x\to\infty} \dfrac{x^3}{e^x} \to \dfrac{\infty}{\infty}$

$= \lim_{x\to\infty} \dfrac{3x^2}{e^x} \to \dfrac{\infty}{\infty}$

$= \lim_{x\to\infty} \dfrac{6x}{e^x} \to \dfrac{\infty}{\infty}$

$= \lim_{x\to\infty} \dfrac{6}{e^x} = 0$ (Form: $\dfrac{6}{\infty}$.)

17. $\lim_{x\to\infty} \dfrac{3x + 17}{4x - 11} = \lim_{x\to\infty} \dfrac{3}{4} = \dfrac{3}{4}$

18. $\lim_{x\to\infty} \dfrac{2 - 7x}{3 + 5x} = \lim_{x\to\infty} \dfrac{-7}{5} = -\dfrac{7}{5}$

19. $\lim_{x\to\infty} \dfrac{x^3 - 5x^2 + 13x - 21}{4x^3 + 9x^2 - 11x - 17} \to \dfrac{\infty}{\infty}$

$= \lim_{x\to\infty} \dfrac{3x^2 - 10x + 13}{12x^2 + 18x - 11} \to \dfrac{\infty}{\infty}$

$= \lim_{x\to\infty} \dfrac{6x - 10}{24x + 18} \to \dfrac{\infty}{\infty}$

$= \lim_{x\to\infty} \dfrac{6}{24} = \dfrac{1}{4}$

20. $\lim_{x\to\infty} \dfrac{3x^5 + 2}{7x^5 - 8} \to \dfrac{\infty}{\infty}$

$= \lim_{x\to\infty} \dfrac{15x^4}{35x^4} = \lim_{x\to\infty} \dfrac{15}{35} = \dfrac{3}{7}$

21. $L = \lim_{x\to 0^+} x^x \to 0^0$

$\ln L = \lim_{x\to 0^+} (x \ln x) = \lim_{x\to 0^+} \dfrac{\ln x}{x^{-1}} \to \dfrac{-\infty}{\infty}$

$= \lim_{x\to 0^+} \dfrac{x^{-1}}{-x^{-2}} = \lim_{x\to 0^+} (-x) = 0.$

$\therefore L = e^0 = 1$

22. $L = \lim_{x\to 0^+} (\sin x)^{\sin x} \to 0^0$

$\ln L = \lim_{x\to 0^+} \sin x (\ln \sin x) = \lim_{x\to 0^+} \dfrac{\ln \sin x}{\csc x} \to \dfrac{-\infty}{\infty}$

$= \lim_{x\to 0^+} \dfrac{1/(\sin x) \cdot \cos x}{-\csc x \cot x} = \lim_{x\to 0^+} \dfrac{1}{-\csc x}$

$= \lim_{x\to 0^+} (-\sin x) = 0.$

$\therefore L = e^0 = 1$

23. $L = \lim_{x\to \pi/2^-} (\sin x)^{\tan x} \to 0^0$

$\ln L = \lim_{x\to \pi/2^-} \tan x (\ln \sin x) = \lim_{x\to \pi/2^-} \dfrac{\ln \sin x}{\cot x} \to \dfrac{0}{0}$

$= \lim_{x\to \pi/2^-} \dfrac{(1/\sin x) \cdot \cos x}{-\csc^2 x} = \lim_{x\to \pi/2^-} \dfrac{-\cos x \sin^2 x}{\sin x}$

$= \lim_{x\to \pi/2^-} (-\cos x \sin x) = 0$

$\therefore L = e^0 = 1$

24. $L = \lim_{x\to 1^+} x^{1/(x-1)} \to 1^\infty$

$\ln L = \lim_{x\to 1^+} [1/(x - 1) \cdot \ln x] = \lim_{x\to 1^+} \dfrac{\ln x}{x - 1} \to \dfrac{0}{0}$

$= \lim_{x\to 1^+} \dfrac{1/x}{1} = 1$

$\therefore L = e^1 = e$

25. $L = \lim_{x\to\infty} (1 + ax)^{1/x} \to \infty^0$ (Note $a \geq 0$.)

$\ln L = \lim_{x\to\infty} [1/x \cdot \ln (1 + ax)] = \lim_{x\to\infty} \dfrac{\ln (1 + ax)}{x} \to \dfrac{\infty}{\infty}$

$= \lim_{x\to\infty} \dfrac{1/(1 + ax) \cdot a}{1} = \lim_{x\to\infty} \dfrac{a}{1 + ax} = 0$

$\therefore L = e^0 = 1$

26. $L = \lim_{x\to 0} (1 + ax)^{1/x} \to 1^\infty$

$\ln L = \lim_{x\to 0} [1/x \cdot \ln (1 + ax)] = \lim_{x\to 0} \dfrac{\ln (1 + ax)}{x} \to \dfrac{0}{0}$

$= \lim_{x\to 0} \dfrac{1/(1 + ax) \cdot a}{1} = \lim_{x\to 0} \dfrac{a}{1 + ax} = a$

$\therefore L = e^a$

27. $L = \lim_{x\to 0^+} x^{3/(\ln x)} \to 0^0$

$\ln L = \lim_{x\to 0^+} [3/(\ln x) \cdot \ln x] = \lim_{x\to 0^+} 3 = 3$

$\therefore L = e^3 = 20.08553...$

28. $L = \lim_{x\to 0^+} (7x)^{5/(\ln x)} \to 0^0$

$\ln L = \lim_{x\to 0^+} [5/(\ln x)\cdot \ln(7x)] = \lim_{x\to 0^+} \dfrac{5\ln(7x)}{\ln x} \to \dfrac{-\infty}{-\infty}$

$= \dfrac{5\cdot(1/7x)\cdot 7}{1/x} = 5$

$\therefore L = e^5 = 148.4131...$

29. $\lim_{x\to 0} \left(\dfrac{1}{x} - \dfrac{1}{e^x - 1}\right) \to \infty - \infty$

$= \lim_{x\to 0} \dfrac{e^x - 1 - x}{x(e^x - 1)} \to \dfrac{0}{0}$

$= \lim_{x\to 0} \dfrac{e^x - 1}{1(e^x - 1) + x\cdot e^x} \to \dfrac{0}{0}$

$= \lim_{x\to 0} \dfrac{e^x - 1}{e^x - 1 + xe^x} \to \dfrac{0}{0}$

$= \lim_{x\to 0} \dfrac{e^x}{e^x + e^x + xe^x} = \dfrac{1}{2}$

30. $\lim_{x\to 0} \left(\dfrac{1}{x} - \dfrac{1}{\sin x}\right) \to \infty - \infty$

$= \lim_{x\to 0} \dfrac{\sin x - x}{x \sin x} \to \dfrac{0}{0}$

$= \lim_{x\to 0} \dfrac{\cos x - 1}{x\cos x + \sin x} \to \dfrac{0}{0}$

$= \lim_{x\to 0} \dfrac{-\sin x}{-x\sin x + 2\cos x} = 0$

31. Infinity Minus Infinity Problem

$f(x) = \sec^2 \frac{\pi}{2}x - \tan^2 \frac{\pi}{2}x$

Graph. Where secant and tangent are defined, the Pythagorean properties tell us that $f(x) = 1$.

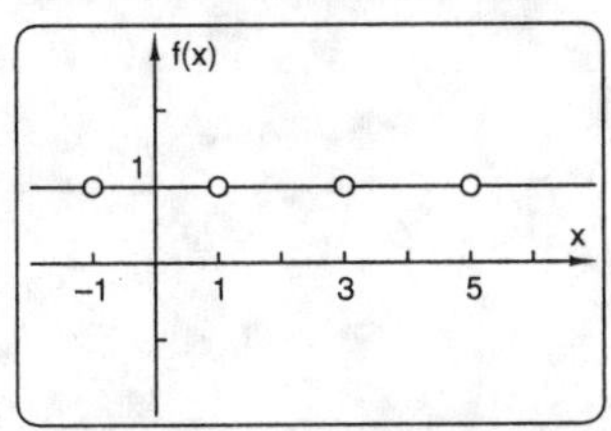

32. L'Hospital's Surprise Problem!

Using l'Hospital's rule leads to:

$\lim_{x\to\pi/2} \dfrac{\sec x}{\tan x} = \lim_{x\to\pi/2} \dfrac{\sec x \tan x}{\sec^2 x}$

$= \lim_{x\to\pi/2} \dfrac{\tan x}{\sec x} = \lim_{x\to\pi/2} \dfrac{\sec^2 x}{\sec x \tan x}$

$= \lim_{x\to\pi/2} \dfrac{\sec x}{\tan x}$, the original expression!

Using $\tan x = (\sec x)/(\csc x)$, the expression reduces to:

$\lim_{x\to\pi/2} \dfrac{\sec x}{(\sec x)/(\csc x)} = \lim_{x\to\pi/2} \csc x = 1.$

33. Zero to the Zero Problem

$L = \lim_{x\to 0^+} x^{k/(\ln x)} \to 0^0$

$\ln L = \lim_{x\to 0^+} [k/(\ln x)\cdot \ln x] = \lim_{x\to 0^+} k = k$

$\therefore L = e^k$

Graph. The graph turns out to be a horizontal line $y = e^k$ defined for $x > 0$.

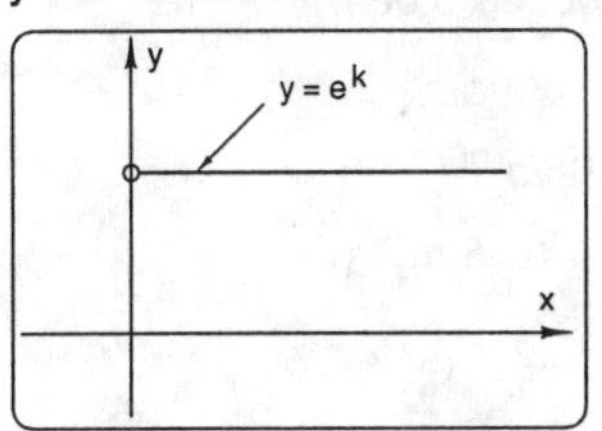

By the definition of a power,

$x^{k/(\ln x)} = (x^k)^{1/\ln x} = (e^{k \ln x})^{1/\ln x} = e^k$

34. L'Hospital's Rule, Geometrically

a. $f(x) = \dfrac{g(x)}{h(x)} = \dfrac{0.3x^2 - 2.7}{0.2x^2 - 2x + 4.2}$

$g(3) = 0.3(9) - 2.7 = 0,$

$h(3) = 0.2(9) - 2(3) + 4.2 = 0$, Q.E.D.

b. $g'(x) = 0.6x \Rightarrow g'(3) = 1.8$

$h'(x) = 0.4x - 2 \Rightarrow h'(3) = -0.8$

Tangent lines at (3, 0) have these equations.

For g: $y_1 = 1.8(x - 3)$

For h: $y_2 = -0.8(x - 3)$

c. $\dfrac{y_1}{y_2} = \dfrac{1.8(x-3)}{-0.8(x-3)} = -2.25$, for $x \neq 3$.

$\dfrac{g'(3)}{h'(3)} = \dfrac{1.8}{-0.8} = -2.25$, which equals y_1/y_2, Q.E.D.

d. Since the ratio $g(x)/h(x)$ approaches the ratio y_1/y_2 as x approaches 3, and since y_1/y_2 equals $g'(3)/h'(3)$ for all $x \neq 3$, the ratio $g(x)/h(x)$ also approaches $g'(3)/h'(3)$ as x approaches 3. This is what l'Hôpital's rule concludes.

If g(3) or h(3) were any number other than 0, the canceling of the (x – 3)s in part c could not be done, and the ratio would almost certainly not equal 1.8/(–0.8).

e. Graph, with removable discontinuity at (3, –2.25)

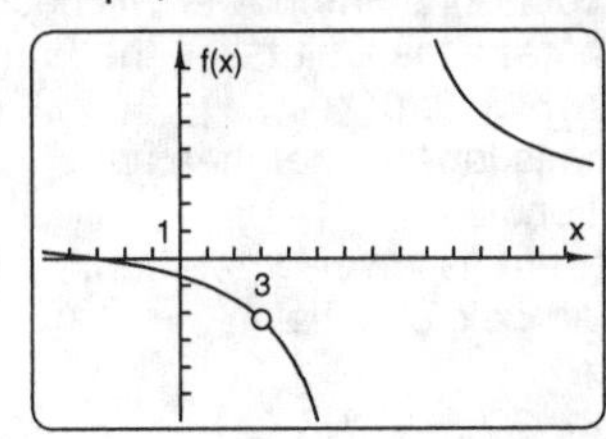

35. Continuous Compounding of Interest Problem

a. For yearly compounding, $m(t) = 1000(1 + 0.06)^t$.
For semiannual compounding,
$m(t) = 1000(1 + 0.06/2)^{2t}$
because there are two compounding periods per year, each of which gets half the interest rate.

b. $m(t) = 1000(1 + 0.06/n)^{nt}$
$\lim_{n\to\infty} m(t) = \lim_{n\to\infty} 1000(1 + 0.06/n)^{nt}$
$= 1000 \lim_{n\to\infty} (1 + 0.06/n)^{nt}$
Let $L = \lim_{n\to\infty} (1 + 0.06/n)^{nt}$
$\ln L = \lim_{n\to\infty} [nt \ln (1 + 0.06/n)]$
$= \lim_{n\to\infty} \dfrac{\ln (1 + 0.06/n)}{1/(nt)} \to \dfrac{0}{0}$
$= \lim_{n\to\infty} \dfrac{1/(1 + 0.06/n)\cdot(-0.06n^{-2})}{-n^{-2}/t}$
$= \lim_{n\to\infty} \dfrac{0.06\ t}{(1 + 0.06/n)} = 0.06t$
$\therefore L = e^{0.06t} \Rightarrow \lim_{n\to\infty} m(t) = 1000\ e^{0.06t}$
When interest is compounded continuously, $m(t) = 1000\ e^{0.06t}$.

c.

t	m(t), Annual	m(t), Cont.	Difference
5	1,338.23	1,349.86	11.63
20	3,207.14	3,320.12	112.98
50	18,420.15	20,085.54	1,665.38

d. For 7% interest, compounded continuously, $m(t) = 1000\ e^{0.07t}$.

36. Order of Magnitude of a Function

a. $f(x) = x^n$, $g(x) = \ln x$, $h(x) = e^x$
$\lim_{x\to\infty} \dfrac{f(x)}{g(x)} = \lim_{x\to\infty} \dfrac{x^n}{\ln x} \to \dfrac{\infty}{\infty}$
$= \lim_{x\to\infty} \dfrac{nx^{n-1}}{1/x} = \lim_{x\to\infty} nx^n = \infty$, if $n > 0$
$\therefore$ a power function is higher-order than the natural log function.
$\lim_{x\to\infty} \dfrac{f(x)}{h(x)} = \lim_{x\to\infty} \dfrac{x^n}{e^x} \to \dfrac{\infty}{\infty}$
$= \lim_{x\to\infty} \dfrac{nx^{n-1}}{e^x} \to \dfrac{\infty}{\infty}$, provided $n-1 > 0$
Eventually, the exponent of the power will become negative, in which case the limit takes the form (constant)/($\infty\cdot\infty$), which is 0.
$\therefore$ a power function is lower-order than an exponential function.
Using "<" to represent "is lower-order than,"
natural log < power < exponential

b. i. $\lim_{x\to\infty} \dfrac{\ln 3x}{x^5} = 0$ ii. $\lim_{x\to\infty} \dfrac{x^{100}}{e^{0.01x}} = 0$

iii. $\lim_{x\to\infty} \dfrac{e^{0.3x}}{100 \ln x} = \infty$

iv. $\lim_{x\to\infty} \dfrac{\sqrt{x}}{x} = \lim_{x\to\infty} \dfrac{1}{\sqrt{x}} = 0$

v. $\lim_{x\to\infty} \dfrac{e^x}{e^{0.2x}} = \lim_{x\to\infty} e^{0.8x} = \infty$

37. Journal Problem

Journal entries will vary. Here is one example of each type of limit.

0/0: $\lim_{x\to 0} \dfrac{\sin 3x}{x} = 3$

∞/∞: $\lim_{x\to\infty} \dfrac{3x^2 + 7}{2x^2 - 8} = 1.5$

$\infty-\infty$: $\lim_{x\to\pi/2} (\tan^2 x - \sec^2 x) = -1$

1^∞: $\lim_{x\to\infty} (1 + 1/x)^x = e$

∞^0: $\lim_{x\to 0} (1 + x)^{1/x} = e$

0^0: $\lim_{x\to 0} x^{3/\ln x} = 3$

Problem Set 6-9, pages 294 to 296 — Derivative and Integral Practice for Transcendental Functions

1. $y = \ln (3x + 4) \Rightarrow y' = 3/(3x + 4)$
2. $y = \ln (3x^5) = \ln 3 + 5 \ln x \Rightarrow y' = 5/x$
3. $y = \ln (e^{3x}) = 3x \Rightarrow y' = 3$
4. $y = \ln (\sin 4x) \Rightarrow y' = \dfrac{4 \cos 4x}{\sin 4x} = 4 \cot 4x$
5. $y = \ln (\cos^5 x) = 5 \ln (\cos x)$
$\Rightarrow y' = \dfrac{-5 \sin x}{\cos x} = -5 \tan x$
6. $y = \ln (e^5) = 5 \Rightarrow y' = 0$ (Derivative of a constant!)
7. $y = \ln (\cos (\tan x))$
$\Rightarrow y' = \dfrac{-\sin (\tan x)}{\cos (\tan x)} \cdot \sec^2 x = -\tan (\tan x) \sec^2 x$
8. $y = \ln \sqrt{x^2 - 2x + 3} = \dfrac{1}{2} \ln (x^2 - 2x + 3)$
$\Rightarrow y' = (1/2) \dfrac{2x - 2}{x^2 - 2x + 3} = \dfrac{x - 1}{x^2 - 2x + 3}$
9. $y = \cos (\ln x) \Rightarrow y' = -(1/x) \sin (\ln x)$
10. $y = \sin x \cdot \ln x \Rightarrow y' = \cos x \cdot \ln x + (1/x) \sin x$
11. $y = e^{7x} \Rightarrow y' = 7e^{7x}$
12. $y = e^{x^3} \Rightarrow y' = 3x^2e^{x^3}$
13. $y = e^{5 \ln x} = e^{\ln x^5} = x^5 \Rightarrow y' = 5x^4$
14. $y = e^{\cos x} \Rightarrow y' = e^{\cos x} \cdot (-\sin x) = -e^{\cos x} \sin x$
15. $y = \cos (e^x) \Rightarrow y' -\sin (e^x) \cdot e^x = -e^x \sin e^x$

16. $y = (\cos^3 x)(e^{3x})$
$\Rightarrow y' = 3\cos^2 x\,(-\sin x)\cdot e^{3x} + \cos^3 x \cdot e^{3x}\cdot 3$
$= -3e^{3x}\cos^2 x \sin x + 3e^{3x}\cos^3 x$
$= 3e^{3x}\cos^2 x\,(-\sin x + \cos x)$ (Factoring optional)

17. $y = \exp(x^5) = e^{x^5} \Rightarrow y' = 5x^4 \exp(x^5) = 5x^4 e^{x^5}$

18. $y = \exp(e^x) = e^{e^x} \Rightarrow y' = e^{e^x}\cdot e^x$

19. $\sin y = e^x \Rightarrow \cos y \cdot y' = e^x$

$\Rightarrow y' = \dfrac{e^x}{\cos y} = \dfrac{e^x}{\sqrt{1 - e^{2x}}}$ (See sketch.)

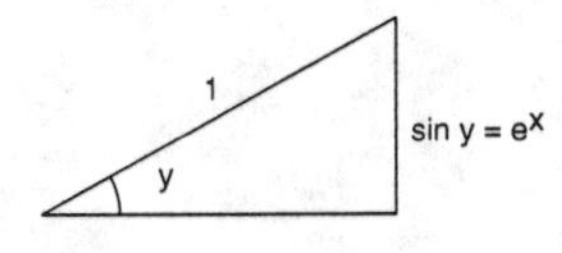

$\cos y = \sqrt{1 - e^{2x}}$

20. $y = e^x \cdot \ln x$
$\Rightarrow y' = e^x \cdot \ln x + e^x \cdot (1/x) = e^x(\ln x + 1/x)$

21. $y = \int_1^x 1/t\,dt \Rightarrow y' = 1/x$

22. $\tan y = e^x \Rightarrow \sec^2 y \cdot y' = e^x$

$\Rightarrow y' = \dfrac{e^x}{\sec^2 y} = \dfrac{e^x}{1 + e^{2x}}$ (See sketch.)

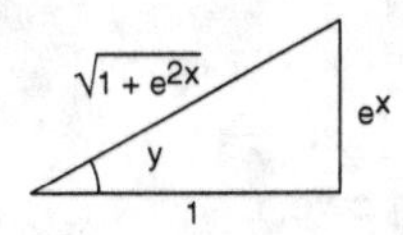

23. $y = \ln(e^{\ln x}) = \ln x \Rightarrow y' = 1/x$

24. $y = 2^x \Rightarrow \ln y = x \ln 2 \Rightarrow (1/y)y' = \ln 2$
$\Rightarrow y' = y \ln 2 = 2^x \ln 2$

25. $y = e^{x \ln 2} = e^{\ln 2^x} = 2^x$
$\Rightarrow y' = 2^x \ln 2$ (See Problem 24.)

26. $y = e^{2 \ln x} = e^{\ln x^2} = x^2 \Rightarrow y' = 2x$

27. $y = x^2 \Rightarrow y' = 2x$

28. $y = e^{x \ln x}$ (which equals x^x)
$y' = e^{x \ln x}(\ln x + x(1/x)) = x^x(\ln x + 1)$.

29. $y = x^x = (e^{\ln x})^x = e^{x \ln x}$
$\Rightarrow y' = x^x(\ln x + 1)$ (See Problem 28.)

30. $y = x \ln x - x \Rightarrow y' = \ln x + x \cdot (1/x) - 1 = \ln x$
(Note: This answer reveals that the *integral* of $\ln x$ is $x \ln x - x$.)

31. $y = e^x(x - 1) \Rightarrow y' = e^x(x - 1) + e^x \cdot 1 = xe^x$

32. $y = \frac{1}{2}(e^x + e^{-x}) \Rightarrow y' = \frac{1}{2}(e^x - e^{-x})$

33. $y = \frac{1}{2}(e^x - e^{-x}) \Rightarrow y' = \frac{1}{2}(e^x + e^{-x})$
(Problems 32 and 33 are the hyperbolic cosine and sine functions, respectively. See Chapter 8.)

34. $y = \dfrac{e^x}{1 + e^x}$

$\Rightarrow y' = \dfrac{e^x \cdot (1 + e^x) - e^x \cdot (e^x)}{(1 + e^x)^2} = \dfrac{e^x}{(1 + e^x)^2}$

35. $y = 5^x \Rightarrow \ln y = x \ln 5 \Rightarrow (1/y)y' = \ln 5$
$\Rightarrow y' = y \ln 5 = 5^x \ln 5$

36. $y = \log_5 x = \dfrac{\ln x}{\ln 5} \Rightarrow y' = \dfrac{1/x}{\ln 5} = \dfrac{1}{x \ln 5}$

37. $y = x^{-7}\log_2 x = x^{-7}\cdot\dfrac{\ln x}{\ln 2} \Rightarrow$

$y' = \dfrac{1}{\ln 2}(-7x^{-8}\cdot \ln x + x^{-7}\cdot \dfrac{1}{x}) = \dfrac{x^{-8}}{\ln 2}(-7\ln x + 1)$

38. $y = 2^{-x}\cos x$
$\Rightarrow y' = 2^{-x}(-\ln 2)\cdot \cos x + 2^{-x}(-\sin x)$
$= -2^{-x}(\ln 2 \cdot \cos x + \sin x)$ (Optional factoring)

39. $y = e^{-2x}\ln 5x$
$\Rightarrow y' = -2e^{-2x}\cdot \ln 5x + e^{-2x}\cdot(1/x)$
$= e^{-2x}(-2\ln 5x + 1/x)$.

40. $y = \dfrac{7^x}{\ln 7} \Rightarrow y' = \dfrac{1}{\ln 7}\cdot 7^x \ln 7 = 7^x$

41. $y = \dfrac{\log_3 x}{\log_3 e} = \log_e x = \ln x \Rightarrow y' = \dfrac{1}{x}$

42. $y = \dfrac{\log_{10} x}{\log_{10} e} = \log_e x = \ln x \Rightarrow y' = \dfrac{1}{x}$

43. $y = (\log_8 x)(\ln 8) = \dfrac{\ln x}{\ln 8}\cdot \ln 8 = \ln x \Rightarrow y' = \dfrac{1}{x}$

44. $y = (\log_4 x)^{10}$

$\Rightarrow y' = 10(\log_4 x)^9 \cdot \dfrac{1}{x \ln 4} = \dfrac{10(\log_4 x)^9}{x \ln 4}$

45. $y = \log_5 x^7 = 7\log_5 x = \dfrac{7\ln x}{\ln 5} \Rightarrow y' = \dfrac{7}{x \ln 5}$

46. $y = \tan e^x \Rightarrow y' = \sec^2 e^x \cdot e^x = e^x \sec^2 e^x$

47. $y = e^{\sin x} \Rightarrow y' = e^{\sin x}\cos x$

48. $y = \ln \csc x$
$\Rightarrow y' = (1/\csc x)\cdot(-\csc x \cot x) = -\cot x$

49. $y = 3^5 \Rightarrow y' = 0$. (Derivative of a constant!)

50. $y = \ln(\cos^2 x + \sin^2 x) = \ln 1 = 0 \Rightarrow y' = 0$

51. $y = \sin x \Rightarrow y' = \cos x$

52. $y = \sin^{-1} x \Rightarrow y' = \dfrac{1}{\sqrt{1 - x^2}}$

53. $y = \csc x \Rightarrow y' = -\csc x \cot x$

54. $y = \tan^{-1} x \Rightarrow y' = \dfrac{1}{1 + x^2}$

55. $y = \tan x \Rightarrow y' = \sec^2 x$

56. $y = \cot x \Rightarrow y' = -\csc^2 x$

57. $\int e^{4x}\,dx = \frac{1}{4}e^{4x} + C$

58. $\int e^4\,dx = e^4 x + C$

59. $\int x^3 e^{x^4}\,dx = \frac{1}{4}\int e^{x^4}(4x^3\,dx) = \frac{1}{4}e^{x^4} + C$

60. $\int \cos x \cdot e^{\sin x}\,dx = \int e^{\sin x}(\cos x\,dx) = e^{\sin x} + C$

61. $\int \dfrac{(\ln x)^5}{x}\,dx = \int (\ln x)^5 \dfrac{1}{x}\,dx = \dfrac{1}{6}(\ln x)^6 + C$

62. $\int 5^x\,dx = \int e^{x \ln 5}\,dx = (1/\ln 5)\int e^{x \ln 5}\ln 5\,dx$
$= \dfrac{1}{\ln 5}e^{x \ln 5} + C = \dfrac{5^x}{\ln 5} + C$

63. $\int e^{x \ln 5}\,dx = \int 5^x\,dx = \dfrac{5^x}{\ln 5} + C$ (Same as Prob. 62)

64. $\int \frac{1}{2}(e^x + e^{-x})\,dx = \frac{1}{2}(e^x - e^{-x}) + C$

65. $\int_1^x \frac{1}{t}\,dt = \ln x$ (By definition!)

66. $\int e^{-x}\,dx = -e^{-x} + C$

67. $\int 2^x\,dx = \frac{2^x}{\ln 2} + C$

68. $\int (x^{-0.2} + 3^x)\,dx = 1.25x^{0.8} + \frac{3^x}{\ln 3} + C$

69. $\int (3/x)\,dx = 3\ln|x| + C$

70. $\int_1^2 4^x\,dx = \frac{4^x}{\ln 4}\Big|_1^2 = \frac{12}{\ln 4} = 8.656170...$

71. $\int (\ln x)^9 \frac{1}{x}\,dx = \frac{1}{10}(\ln x)^{10} + C$

72. $\int \cos x\,dx = \sin x + C$

73. $\int e^{\ln x}\,dx = \int x\,dx = \frac{1}{2}x^2 + C$

74. $\int \ln(e^{3x})\,dx = \int 3x \ln e\,dx = \int 3x\,dx = \frac{3}{2}x^2 + C$

75. $\int 0\,dx = C$ (Integral of zero is a constant.)

76. $\int \cos x \sec x\,dx = \int 1\,dx = x + C$

77. $\int \sec 2x\,dx = \frac{1}{2}\int \sec 2x\,(2\,dx)$

$= \frac{1}{2}\ln|\sec 2x + \tan 2x| + C$

78. $\int \tan 3x\,dx = \frac{1}{3}\int \tan 3x\,(3\,dx) = \frac{1}{3}\ln|\sec 3x| + C$

79. $\int \cot 4x\,dx = \frac{1}{4}\int \cot 4x\,(4\,dx) = \frac{1}{4}\ln|\sin 4x| + C$

80. $\int \csc 5x\,dx = \frac{1}{5}\int \csc 5x\,(5\,dx)$

$= -\frac{1}{5}\ln|\csc 5x + \cot 5x| + C$

81. $\lim_{x\to 0} \frac{1 - \cos x}{x} \to \frac{0}{0}$

$= \lim_{x\to 0} \frac{\sin x}{1} = 0$

82. $\lim_{x\to 0} \frac{x}{1 - \cos x} \to \frac{0}{0}$

$= \lim_{x\to 0} \frac{1}{\sin x} = \infty$ (Reciprocal of Problem 81)

83. $\lim_{x\to \pi/2} \frac{x}{1 - \cos x} = \frac{\pi/2}{1 - \cos(\pi/2)} = \frac{\pi}{2}$

84. $\lim_{x\to \pi} \frac{x}{1 + \cos x} = \infty$. (Form: $\frac{\pi}{0}$)

85. $\lim_{x\to 0} \frac{5x - \sin 5x}{x^3} \to \frac{0}{0}$

$= \lim_{x\to 0} \frac{5 - 5\cos 5x}{3x^2} \to \frac{0}{0}$

$= \lim_{x\to 0} \frac{25\sin 5x}{6x} \to \frac{0}{0}$

$= \lim_{x\to 0} \frac{125\cos 5x}{6} = \frac{125}{6} = 20.8333...$

86. $\lim_{x\to\infty} (1 + 0.03/x)^x \to 1^\infty$

Let $L = \lim_{x\to\infty} (1 + 0.03/x)^x$.

$\ln L = \ln \lim_{x\to\infty} (1 + 0.03/x)^x = \lim_{x\to\infty} \ln(1 + 0.03/x)^x$

$= \lim_{x\to\infty} [x \ln(1 + 0.03/x)]$

$= \lim_{x\to\infty} \frac{\ln(1 + 0.03x^{-1})}{x^{-1}} \to \frac{0}{0}$

$= \lim_{x\to\infty} \frac{1/(1 + 0.03/x)\cdot(-0.03x^{-2})}{-x^{-2}} = 0.03$

$\therefore L = e^{0.03} = 1.03045...$

87. $\lim_{x\to\infty} (1 + 0.03x)^{1/x} \to \infty^0$

Let $L = \lim_{x\to\infty} (1 + 0.03x)^{1/x}$.

$\ln L = \lim_{x\to\infty} [(1/x)\ln(1 + 0.03x)] \to 0\cdot\infty$

$= \lim_{x\to\infty} \frac{\ln(1 + 0.03x)}{x} \to \frac{\infty}{\infty}$

$= \lim_{x\to\infty} \frac{1/(1 + 0.03x)\cdot 0.03}{1} = 0$

$\therefore L = e^0 = 1$

88. $\lim_{x\to\infty} \frac{2^x}{x^2} \to \frac{\infty}{\infty}$

$= \lim_{x\to\infty} \frac{2^x \ln 2}{2x} \to \frac{\infty}{\infty}$

$= \lim_{x\to\infty} \frac{2^x (\ln 2)^2}{2} = \infty$

or: $\lim_{x\to\infty} \frac{2^x}{x^2} = \infty$ by (exponential)/(power).

89. $\lim_{x\to 2} (0.5x)^{3/(2-x)} \to 1^\infty$

Let $L = \ln(0.5x)^{3/(2-x)}$.

$\ln L = \lim_{x\to 2} \left(\frac{3}{2 - x}\cdot \ln 0.5x\right) \to \infty\cdot 0$

$= \lim_{x\to 2} \frac{3\ln 0.5x}{2 - x} \to \frac{0}{0}$

$= \lim_{x\to 2} \frac{3/(0.5x)\cdot 0.5}{-1} = -\frac{3}{2}$

$\therefore L = e^{-3/2} = 0.22313...$

90. $\lim_{x\to 0} \left(\frac{1}{e^{3x} - 1} - \frac{1}{3x}\right) \Rightarrow \infty - \infty$

$= \lim_{x\to 0} \frac{3x - (e^{3x} - 1)}{3x(e^{3x} - 1)} \to \frac{0}{0}$

$= \lim_{x\to 0} \frac{3 - 3e^{3x}}{3(e^{3x} - 1) + 3x\cdot 3e^{3x}} \to \frac{0}{0}$

$= \lim_{x\to 0} \frac{-9e^{3x}}{9e^{3x} + 9e^{3x} + 27xe^{3x}} = -\frac{1}{2}$

Review Problems

R0. Journal entries will vary.

R1.a. $dM/dt = 0.06M \Rightarrow M^{-1}\,dM = 0.06\,dt$

$\therefore \int_{100}^{x} M^{-1}\,dM = \int_{0}^{5} 0.06\,dt$, Q.E.D.

$\int_0^5 0.06\,dt = 0.06t\,\Big|_0^5 = 0.3$

b. Solving numerically for x in

$\int_{100}^{x} M^{-1}\,dM = 0.3$

gives $x \approx 134.9858\ldots$.

c. There will be \$134.99 in the account, so the interest will be \$34.99.

R2.a. Integrating x^{-1} by the power rule results in division by zero: $\dfrac{x^{-1+1}}{-1+1} + C$.

b. $L(2) = 0.693\ldots$, which equals ln 2.
$L(3) = 1.098\ldots$, which equals ln 3.
$L(4) = 1.386\ldots$, which equals ln 4.
$L(8) = 2.079\ldots$, which equals ln 8.
$L(12) = 2.484\ldots$, which equals ln 12.

c. $L(3{\cdot}4) = 2.484\ldots = 1.098\ldots + 1.386\ldots = L(3) + L(4)$
$L(12/3) = 1.386\ldots = 2.484\ldots - 1.098\ldots = L(12) - L(3)$
$L(2^3) = L(8) = 2.079\ldots = 3 \cdot 0.693\ldots = 3\,L(2)$

R3.a. i. $y = (\ln 5x)^3 \Rightarrow y' = (3/x)(\ln 5x)^2$

ii. $f(x) = \ln x^9 = 9 \ln x \Rightarrow f'(x) = 9/x$

iii. $y = \csc(\ln x)$
$\Rightarrow y' = -\csc(\ln x)\cot(\ln x)\cdot(1/x)$

iv. $g(x) = \int_1^{x^2} \csc t\,dt \Rightarrow g'(x) = 2x \csc x^2$

b. i. $\int \dfrac{\sec x \tan x}{\sec x}\,dx = \int \dfrac{1}{\sec x}\sec x \tan x\,dx$
$= \ln|\sec x| + C$

ii. $\int_{-2}^{-3} \dfrac{10}{x}\,dx = 10 \ln|x|\Big|_{-2}^{-3} = 10 \ln|-3| - 10 \ln|-2|$
$= 10(\ln 3 - \ln 2) = 4.054651\ldots$

iii. $\int x^2(x^3-4)^{-1}\,dx = \dfrac{1}{3}\int (x^3-4)^{-1}(3x^2\,dx)$
$= \dfrac{1}{3}\ln|x^3 - 4| + C$

c. <u>Memory Retention Problem</u>

i. $y(100) \approx 70$ names; 70% remembered
$y(1) = 1$ name; 100% remembered

ii. $y' = \dfrac{101}{100 + x}$
$y'(100) = 101/(200) = 0.505$ names/person
$y'(1) = 101/101 = 1$ name/person

iii. Paula has probably not forgotten any names as long as $x - y < 0.5$. After meeting 11 people she remembers about $10.53\ldots \approx 11$ names, but after meeting 12 people she remembers about $11.44\ldots \approx 11$ names.

R4. a. See text definition of ln.
b. See text definition of logarithm.
c. See text statement of the uniqueness theorem.
d. See text statement of ln of a power.
e. See text for ln of a quotient property, and see the solution for Problems 9 and 11, Problem Set 6-4, for proof of the quotient property.

R5.a. i. $y = 100^x \Rightarrow y' = 100^x \cdot \ln 100$

ii. $f(x) = 3.7 \cdot 10^{0.2x}$
$\Rightarrow f'(x) = 3.7 \cdot (10^{0.2x})(\ln 10)(0.2)$
$= (0.74 \ln 10)(10^{0.2x})$

iii. $r(t) = t^{\tan t} \Rightarrow \ln r(t) = \tan t \cdot \ln t$
$\Rightarrow (1/r(t)) \cdot r'(t) = \sec^2 t \cdot \ln t + \tan t \cdot (1/t)$
$\Rightarrow r'(t) = t^{\tan t}[\sec^2 t \ln t + (\tan t)/(t)]$

b. $y = (5x-7)^3(3x+1)^5$
$\Rightarrow \ln y = 3\ln(5x-7) + 5\ln(3x+1)$
$\Rightarrow \dfrac{1}{y}y' = \left(\dfrac{15}{5x-7} + \dfrac{15}{3x+1}\right)$
$\Rightarrow y' = (5x-7)^3(3x+1)^5\left(\dfrac{15}{5x-7} + \dfrac{15}{3x+1}\right)$

c. <u>Vitamin C Problem</u>

i. From Figure 6-10b, the maximum concentration is about 150 ppm at about 2 hours.
(These values can be found more precisely by setting the numerical or algebraic derivative equal to zero, solving to get $t = -1/\ln 0.6 = 1.9576\ldots$. Then $C(1.9576\ldots) = -200/(e \ln 0.6) = 144.0332\ldots$.)

ii. $C(t) = 200t \cdot 0.6^t$
$C'(t) = 200t \cdot 0.6^t \ln 0.6 + 200 \cdot 0.6^t$
$C'(1) = 200 \cdot 0.6^1(\ln 0.6 + 1) = 58.70\ldots$
$C'(5) = 200 \cdot 0.6^5(5 \ln 0.6 + 1) = -24.16\ldots < 0$
C(t) is increasing at about 58.7 ppm/hr when t = 1, and decreasing at about 24.2 ppm/hr when t = 5. The concentration is increasing if C'(t) is positive and decreasing if it is negative.

iii. Solving $50 = 200t \cdot 0.6t$ numerically for t gives $t \approx 0.2899\ldots$ and $t \approx 6.3245\ldots$.
So $C(t) > 50$ for $6.3245\ldots - 0.2899\ldots = 6.03\ldots$, or about 6 hours.

iv. Graph, $C_1(t) = 200t \cdot 0.3^t$

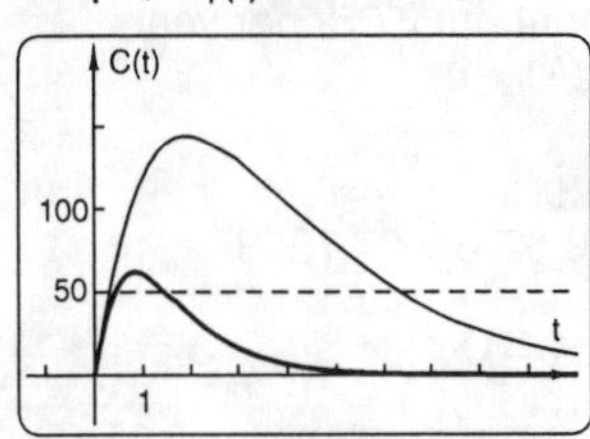

From the graph, the maximum is about 60 ppm around t = 1. (Exactly, $t = -1/\ln 0.3 = 0.8305\ldots$, for which $C(0.8305\ldots) = -200/(e \ln 0.3) = 61.11092\ldots \approx 61.1$ ppm.)
Repeating the computations of part iii, above, gives $C(t) > 50$ for $0.409\ldots < t < 1.473\ldots$, or for about 1.06 hours.
In conclusion, the concentration peaks *sooner* at a *lower* concentration, and stays above 50 ppm for a much *shorter* time.

R6.a. $e = \lim_{n\to 0}(1+n)^{1/n} = \lim_{n\to\infty}(1 + 1/n)^n$

b. $\log_e x = \ln x$

c. $\log_b x = \dfrac{\ln x}{\ln b}$

d. i. $y = \log_4 x = \dfrac{\ln x}{\ln 4} \Rightarrow y' = \dfrac{1}{x \ln 4}$

ii. $f(x) = \log_2(\cos x) = \dfrac{\ln(\cos x)}{\ln 2}$
$\Rightarrow f'(x) = \dfrac{1}{(\cos x)(\ln 2)} \cdot (-\sin x) = -\dfrac{\tan x}{\ln 2}$

iii. $y = \log_5 9^x = x \log_5 9 \Rightarrow y' = \log_5 9$

e. Journal entries will vary.

R7. a. i. $y = e^x$ ii. $y = \exp(-x)$ iii. $y = \ln x$

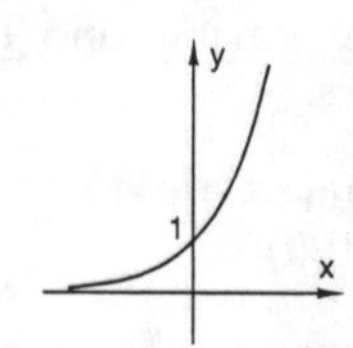

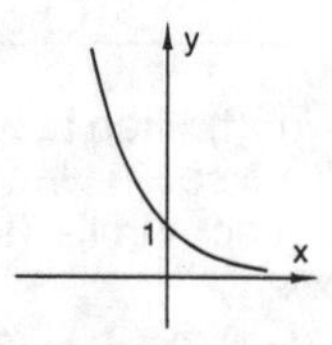

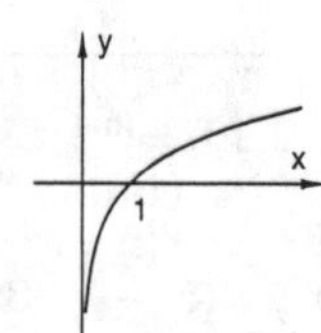

b. i. $f(x) = x^{1.4}\exp(5x)$

$\Rightarrow f'(x) = 1.4x^{0.4}\exp(5x) + x^{1.4}5\exp(5x)$

$= x^{0.4}\exp(5x)\cdot(1.4 + 5x)$ (Optional factoring)

ii. $g(x) = \sin e^{-2x} \Rightarrow g'(x) = -2e^{-2x}\cos e^{-2x}$

iii. $y = e^{\ln x} = x \Rightarrow y' = 1$

c. i. $\int 10e^{-2x}\,dx = -5e^{-2x} + C$

ii. $\int e^{\cos x}\sin x\,dx = -e^{\cos x} + C$

iii. $\int_{-2}^{2}\exp(-0.1x)\,dx = -10\exp(-0.1x)\Big|_{-2}^{2}$

$= -10\exp(-0.2) + 10\exp(0.2) = 4.0267200...$

d. The number e is used as the base in calculus because the algebraic formulas for the derivatives are simpler.

Exponentials: $d(e^x)/dx = e^x$; $d(a^x) = a^x\cdot\ln a$

Logs: $d(\ln x)/dx = 1/x$; $d(\log_b x)/dx = (1/x)/\ln b$

e. Radioactive Decay Problem

i. $p(t) = 100e^{-0.025t}$

$p(5) = 100e^{-0.125} = 88.2496...$

About 88% remains.

ii. $p'(t) = -2.5e^{-0.025t}$

$p'(0) = -2.5e^{0} = -2.5$

Decreasing at about 2.5% per year

$p'(5) = -2.5e^{-0.125} = -2.2064...$

Decreasing at about 2.2% per year

iii. $50 = 100e^{-0.025t}$

$0.5 = e^{-0.025t}$

$\ln 0.5 = -0.025t$

$t = (\ln 0.5)/(-0.025) = 27.7258...$

About 28 years

iv. $0.001 = 100e^{-0.25t}$

$0.00001 = e^{-0.025t}$

$\ln 0.00001 = -0.025t$

$t = (\ln 0.00001)/(-0.025) = 460.5170...$

About 461 years

f. Chemotherapy Problem

i. The exposure is the product of C(t) and t, where C(t) varies. Thus, a definite integral must be used.

ii. $E(x) = \int_0^x 150e^{-0.16t}\,dt = 937.5(-e^{-0.16x} + 1)$

$E(5) = 937.5(-e^{-0.8} + 1)$

$= 516.25...$ ppm·days

$E(10) = 937.5(-e^{-1.6} + 1)$

$=748.22...$ ppm·days

As x grows very large, E(x) seems to approach 937.5.

iii. $E'(x) = 150e^{-0.16x} = C(x)$

$E'(5) = 67.39...$ ppm (or ppm·days per day)

$E'(10) = 30.28...$ ppm

R8.a. $\lim_{x\to\infty}\dfrac{2x^2-3}{7-5x^2} \to \dfrac{\infty}{-\infty}$

$= \lim_{x\to\infty}\dfrac{4x}{-10x} = -\dfrac{2}{5}$

b. $\lim_{x\to 0}\dfrac{x^2-\cos x+1}{e^x-x-1} \to \dfrac{0}{0}$

$= \lim_{x\to 0}\dfrac{2x+\sin x}{e^x-1} \to \dfrac{0}{0}$

$= \lim_{x\to 0}\dfrac{2+\cos x}{e^x} = \dfrac{2+1}{1} = 3$

c. $\lim_{x\to\infty} x^3e^{-x} \to \infty\cdot 0$

$= \lim_{x\to\infty}\dfrac{x^3}{e^x} \to \dfrac{\infty}{\infty}$

$= \lim_{x\to\infty}\dfrac{3x^2}{e^x} \to \dfrac{\infty}{\infty}$

$= \lim_{x\to\infty}\dfrac{6x}{e^x} \to \dfrac{\infty}{\infty}$

$= \lim_{x\to\infty}\dfrac{6}{e^x} = 0$ (Form: $6/\infty$)

d. $L = \lim_{x\to 1} x^{\tan(\pi x/2)} \to 1^{\infty}$

$\ln L = \lim_{x\to 1}[\tan(\pi x/2)\cdot\ln x]$

$= \lim_{x\to 1}\dfrac{\ln x}{\cot(\pi x/2)} \to \dfrac{0}{0}$

$= \lim_{x\to 1}\dfrac{1/x}{-(\pi/2)\csc^2\pi x/2} = \dfrac{1}{-\pi/2} = \dfrac{-2}{\pi}$

$\therefore L = e^{-2/\pi} = 0.529077...$

e. $\lim_{x\to 2} 3x^4 = 48$ (Don't be fooled!)

f. $\lim_{x\to\pi/2}(\tan^2 x - \sec^2 x) = \lim_{x\to\pi/2}(-1) = -1$

g. Examples of indeterminate forms:

$0/0$, ∞/∞, $0\cdot\infty$, 0^0, 1^∞, ∞^0, $\infty - \infty$

R9.a. i. $y = \ln(\sin^4 7x) = 4\ln\sin 7x$

$\Rightarrow y' = 4(1/\sin 7x)\cdot\cos 7x\cdot 7 = 28\cot 7x$

ii. $y = x^{-3}e^{2x}$

$\Rightarrow y' = -3x^{-4}\cdot e^{2x} + x^{-3}\cdot 2e^{2x}$

$= x^{-4}e^{2x}(2x-3)$

iii. $y = \cos(2^x) \Rightarrow y' = -\sin(2^x)\cdot 2^x\ln 2$

iv. $y = \log_3 x^4 = \dfrac{4\ln x}{\ln 3} \Rightarrow y' = \dfrac{4}{x\ln 3}$

b. i. $\int e^{-1.7x}\,dx = (-1/1.7)\,e^{-1.7x} + C$

ii. $\int 2^{\sec x}\sec x\tan x\,dx$

$= \int e^{\ln 2\sec x}\sec x\tan x\,dx$

$= (1/\ln 2)\int e^{\ln 2\sec x}(\ln 2\cdot\sec x\tan x\,dx)$

$= (1/\ln 2)\,e^{\sec x\ln 2} + C = (1/\ln 2)\,2^{\sec x} + C$

iii. $\int(5+\sin x)^{-1}\cos x\,dx = \ln(5+\sin x) + C$ (No absolute value is needed this time.)

iv. $\int_1^5 \dfrac{1}{z}\,dz = \ln 5$ (by definition!)

c. i. $\lim_{x\to 0} \frac{\tan 3x}{x^2} \to \frac{0}{0}$

$= \lim_{x\to 0} \frac{3\sec^2 3x}{2x} \to \frac{3}{0}$

$= \infty$

ii. $L = \lim_{x\to\infty} (1 - 3/x)^x \to 1^\infty$

$\ln L = \lim_{x\to\infty} [x \ln (1 - 3/x)]$

$= \lim_{x\to\infty} \frac{\ln (1 - 3x^{-1})}{x^{-1}} \to \frac{0}{0}$

$= \lim_{x\to\infty} \frac{1/(1 - 3x^{-1})\cdot 3x^{-2}}{-x^{-2}}$

$= \lim_{x\to 0} \frac{-3}{1 - 3x^{-1}} = -3$

$\therefore L = e^{-3} = 0.049787...$

Concepts Problems

C1. Derivation of the Memory Equation

The first condition is reasonable because you remember one person after you've met one person.

The second condition is reasonable because you remember *all* the people you have met at first, a rate of 1 person per person.

The third condition is reasonable because you would expect to remember only a fraction of the first 100 people you have met, say only 80 as in this case.

$y = a + b \ln (x + c)$

$y' = b/(x + c)$

Substituting the three initial conditions gives the following system of equations in a, b, and c:

$1 = a + b \ln (1+ c)$

$1 = \frac{b}{1 + c}$

$80 = a + b \ln (100 + c)$

Combining the first and last gives

$79 = b \ln (100 + c) - b \ln (1 + c)$

$79 = b \ln \frac{100 + c}{1 + c}$

From the second equation, $b = 1 + c$.

Solve $79 = (1 + c) \ln \frac{100 + c}{1 + c}$ numerically.

$c \approx 180.3758...$

$b \approx 181.3758...$

$a = 1 - b \ln (1 + c) = 1 - b \ln b$

$a \approx -942.258...$

C2. Integral of ln Problem

One might first assume that $\int \ln x\,dx$ is a multiple of ln x. But the decimal places for the integral do not match those for ln x. However, multiplying ln x by x gives the following table of values:

x	ln x	$\int \ln x\,dx$	x ln x
0.5	−0.6931...	−0.8465...	−0.3465...
1.0	0	−1	0
2.0	0.6931...	−0.6137...	1.3862...
3.0	1.0986...	0.2958...	3.2958...
4.0	1.3862...	1.5451...	5.5451...
5.0	1.6094...	3.0471...	8.0471...
6.0	1.7917...	4.7505...	10.7505...
10.0	2.3025...	13.0258...	23.0258...

For $x \ge 3$, x ln x has the same decimal part as the integral. But x ln x is too high by the value of x.

Conjecture: $\int \ln x\,dx = x \ln x - x + C$.

Upon subtracting x from x ln x, you get the correct answer for x = 0.5, 1, and 2 also.

(In Chapter 9 you will learn integration by parts. At that time, you will learn an algebraic method for verifying that this conjecture is correct.)

From Problem 30 of Problem Set 6-9, you recall that the derivative of $x \ln x - x$ equals ln x, which implies that $\int \ln x\,dx = x \ln x - x + C$.

C3. Continued Exponentiation Function Problem

The following solution is based on an unpublished paper written by the author's students Allan Kost and Humphrey Price during the 1971–72 school year. Here is an excerpt from their paper:

"Here we come across a problem. When the contoid [that is, x] is not an integer, what does one do? How can one 'take x and an exponent 1/2 times' or '3/2 times' or '$\sqrt{2}$ times'?" What is cont (x) when $x < 0$? Clearly our present definition of cont (x) is inadequate, so we will invent a new one.

Definition of cont (x):

Let $x = n + \Delta$, where n is an integer and $0 \le \Delta < 1$... .

Therefore, cont $x = (x)^{(x_1)^{(x_2)^{\cdots (x_{n+1})^{\Delta}}}}$"

It is left to the students to show that this definition of cont x really has the desired properties. Copies of the paper can be obtained by writing to the author:

Paul A. Foerster
7 Sissinghurst
San Antonio, TX 78209

C4. Every Number Is the ln of Some Positive Number

a. Suppose there is a number $M > 0$ such that $\ln x \le M$ for all $x > 0$.
Let $x = e^{M+1}$.
Then $\ln x = \ln e^{M+1} = (M+1) \ln e = M+1 > M$.
This contradicts $\ln x \le M$ for all $x > 0$.
Thus the supposition is false, and there can be no such number M that is an upper bound for ln x, Q.E.D.

b. If M were a lower bound for ln x, then −M would be an upper bound for ln (1/x), but part a shows no such number can exist.

c. $\ln' x = 1/x$, which shows that ln is differentiable for all $x > 0$. Thus, ln is continuous for all $x > 0$ because differentiability implies continuity.

d. Since ln is continuous for all $x > 0$, the intermediate value theorem applies. Thus, if k is between ln a and ln b, there is a number c between a and b such that ln c = k. Graph

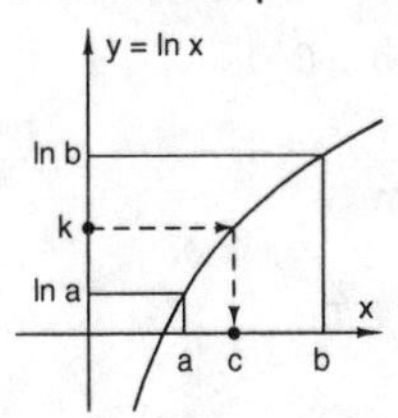

e. Part a shows k cannot be an upper bound for ln, so there must be some $b > 0$ such that $\ln b > k$. Similarly, part b shows k is not a lower bound, so some $a > 0$ exists for which $\ln a < k$. By part d there is some number c between a and b such that $\ln c = k$, Q.E.D.

f. The domain of ln is the positive reals, and the range is all reals; the domain of the inverse to ln (i.e., exp) is the range of ln (i.e., all reals), and the range of the inverse is the domain of ln (i.e., positive reals).

C5. Derivative of an Integral with Both Variable Upper and Lower Limits

a. $g(x) = \int_{x^2}^{4} \sin t\, dt = -\int_{4}^{x^2} \sin t\, dt$

$\Rightarrow g'(x) = -2x \sin x^2$

b. $g(x) = \int_{x^2}^{\tan x} \sin t\, dt = \int_{x^2}^{4} \sin t\, dt + \int_{4}^{\tan x} \sin t\, dt$

$\Rightarrow g'(x) = -2x \sin x^2 + \sin(\tan x) \sec^2 x$

c. $g(x) = \int_{u(x)}^{v(x)} f(t)\, dt$

$\Rightarrow g'(x) = f(v(x))\cdot v'(x) - f(u(x))\cdot u'(x)$

C6. log cabin

(or log cabin + C, which equals "houseboat")

Chapter Test

T1. $\ln x = \int_1^x \frac{1}{t}\, dt$

T2. $\ln 1.8 = \int_1^{1.8} \frac{1}{t}\, dt$

$M_4 = 0.5866447...$

Actual value is ln 1.8 = 0.587786... . (Close!)

T3. $g(x) = \int_2^x \sin t\, dt \Rightarrow g'(x) = \sin x$

Fundamental theorem of calculus, derivative of the integral form

T4. Let $h(x) = f(x) - g(x)$.

Then $h(a) = f(a) - g(a) = 0$, and

$h(b) = f(b) - g(b) \neq 0$.

$\therefore \frac{h(b) - h(a)}{b - a} \neq 0$

By the mean value theorem, there is a number c between a and b such that

$h'(c) = \frac{h(b) - h(a)}{b - a}$.

$\therefore h'(c) \neq 0$

But $h'(x) = f'(x) - g'(x)$, which equals 0 for all values of x.

$\therefore h'(c) = 0$

This result thus contradicts the mean value theorem, Q.E.D.

T5. Prove that $\ln x = \log_e x$ for all $x > 0$.

Proof:

Let $f(x) = \ln x$, and $g(x) = \log_e x$.

$f'(x) = 1/x$, and

$g'(x) = (1/x) \cdot \log_e e = (1/x) \cdot 1 = 1/x$

$\therefore f'(x) = g'(x)$ for all $x > 0$

$f(1) = \ln 1 = 0$, and $g(1) = \log_e 1 = 0$

$\therefore f(1) = g(1)$

$\therefore$ by the uniqueness theorem,

$f(x) = g(x)$ for all $x > 0$

$\therefore \ln x = \log_e x$ for all $x > 0$, Q.E.D.

T6. $f(x) = \ln (x^3 e^x)$

a. $f'(x) = \frac{1}{x^3 e^x} \cdot (3x^2 e^x + x^3 e^x) = \underline{3/x + 1}$

b. $f(x) = 3 \ln x + x \ln e = 3 \ln x + x$

$\Rightarrow f'(x) = \underline{3/x + 1}$ (Checks.)

T7. $y = e^{2x} \ln x^3 = 3e^{2x} \ln x$

$\Rightarrow y' = 6e^{2x}\cdot \ln x + 3e^{2x}\cdot(1/x) = 3e^{2x}(2 \ln x + 1/x)$

T8. $v = \ln (\cos 10x)$

$\Rightarrow v' = 1/(\cos 10x) \cdot (-10 \sin 10x) = -10 \tan 10x$

T9. $f(x) = (\log_2 4x)^7 = [(\ln 4x)/(\ln 2)]^7$

$\Rightarrow f'(x) = 7[(\ln 4x)/(\ln 2)]^6 \cdot [(1/4x) \cdot 4 \cdot (1/\ln 2)]$

$= \frac{7(\log_2 4x)^6}{x \ln 2}$

T10. $t(x) = \ln (\cos^2 x + \sin^2 x) = \ln 1 = 0 \Rightarrow t'(x) = 0$

T11. $p(x) = \int_1^{\ln x} e^t \sin t\, dt \Rightarrow p'(x) = e^{\ln x} \sin \ln x \cdot 1/x$

$= \sin \ln x$

T12. $\int e^{5x}\, dx = \frac{1}{5}e^{5x} + C$

T13. $\int (\ln x)^6 (dx/x) = \frac{1}{7} (\ln x)^7 + C$

T14. $\int \sec 5x\, dx = \frac{1}{5} \ln |\sec 5x + \tan 5x| + C$

T15. $\int_0^2 5^x\, dx = \frac{1}{\ln 5} 5^x \Big|_0^2 = \frac{1}{\ln 5}(25 - 1) = 14.9120...$

T16. $\lim_{x\to\infty} \frac{5 - 3x}{\ln 4x} \to \frac{-\infty}{\infty}$

$= \lim_{x\to\infty} \frac{-3}{(1/4x) \cdot 4} = \lim_{x\to\infty} (-3x) = -\infty$

T17. $L = \lim_{x\to\pi/2^-} (\tan x)^{\cot x} \to \infty^0$

$\ln L = \lim_{x\to\pi/2^-} [\cot x \cdot \ln (\tan x)] \to 0\cdot\infty$

$= \lim_{x\to\pi/2^-} \frac{\ln (\tan x)}{\tan x} \to \frac{\infty}{\infty}$

$= \lim_{x\to\pi/2^-} \frac{(1/\tan x)\cdot\sec^2 x}{\sec^2 x} = \lim_{x\to\pi/2^-} \cot x = 0$

$\therefore L = e^0 = 1$

T18.a. $F(x) = 60e^{0.1x} \Rightarrow F'(x) = 6e^{0.1x}$ so

$F'(5) = 6e^{0.5} = 9.8923...$ lbs/ft

$F'(10) = 6e = 16.3096...$ lbs/ft

b. Work equals force times displacement. But the force varies at different displacements. Thus, a definite integral has to be used.

c. Graph, showing strip of width dx and sample point (x, F).

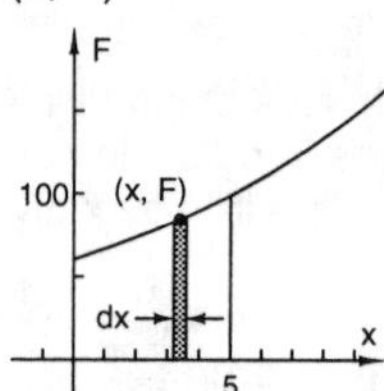

$dW = F\, dx = 60\, e^{0.1x}\, dx$

$W = \int_0^5 60\, e^{0.1x}\, dx$

$= 600e^{0.1x}\Big|_0^5 = 600(e^{0.5} - 1)$

$W \approx 389.23$ ft-lbs

1. $f(x) = 2^x$

   $f'(3) \approx \dfrac{2^{3.1} - 2^{2.9}}{0.2} = \underline{5.549618...}$

2. There are about 10.0 squares, each 20 units.

   $\therefore \int_{10}^{50} g(x)\,dx \approx 200$

   (Function is $g(x) = 2 + 0.1x + \sin \frac{2\pi}{15} x$, so exact answer is 200.)

3. $L = \lim_{x\to c} f(x)$ if and only if
   for any $\varepsilon > 0$ there is a $\delta > 0$ such that
   if x is within δ units of c but not equal to c,
   f(x) is within ε units of L.

4. Graph (example)

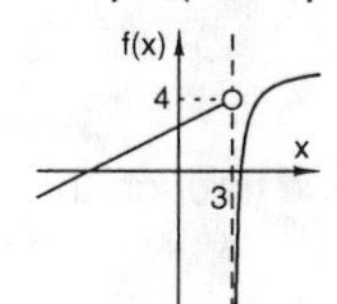

5. $f'(x) = \lim_{h\to 0} \dfrac{f(x+h) - f(x)}{h}$ or $f'(c) = \lim_{x\to c} \dfrac{f(x) - f(c)}{x - c}$

6. $f(x) = x^3$

   $f'(x) = \lim_{h\to 0} \dfrac{(x + h)^3 - x^3}{h}$

   $= \lim_{h\to 0} \dfrac{x^3 + 3x^2h + 3xh^2 + h^3 - x^3}{h}$

   $= \lim_{h\to 0} (3x^2 + 3xh + h^2) = 3x^2$, Q.E.D.

7. $f(x) = x^3 \Rightarrow f'(x) = 3x^2$

   $f'(5) = 3\cdot 5^2 = \underline{75}$

   $f'(5) \approx \dfrac{5.01^3 - 4.99^3}{0.02} = \underline{75.0001}$

   $f'(5) \approx \dfrac{5.001^3 - 4.999^3}{0.002} = \underline{75.000001}$

   The symmetric differences are getting closer to 75 as Δx gets closer to zero, Q.E.D.

8. $f(x) = \sqrt{3x - 5} = (3x - 5)^{1/2}$

   $f'(x) = \frac{1}{2}(3x - 5)^{-1/2} \cdot 3 = 1.5(3x - 5)^{-1/2}$

   $f'(7) = 1.5(21 - 5)^{-1/2} = 1.5/4 = \underline{0.375} = \underline{3/8}$

9. Graph. Line with slope of 3/8 is tangent to the graph at x = 7.

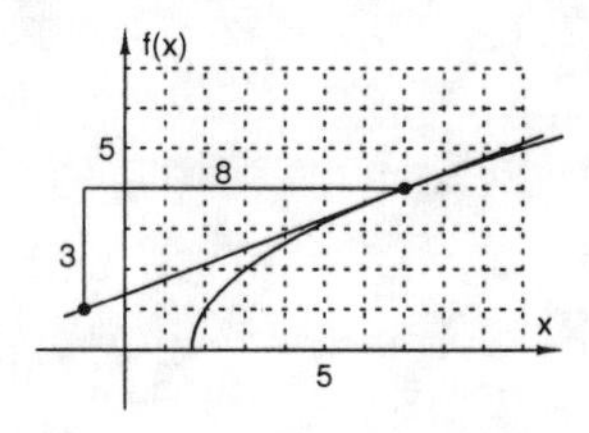

10. Optional graph showing upper sum.

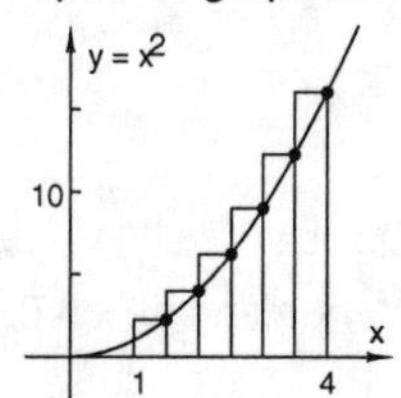

   $\int_1^4 x^2\,dx$

   $U_6 = 0.5(1.5^2 + 2^2 + 2.5^2 + 3^2 + 3.5^2 + 4^2) = \underline{24.875}$

11. $M_{10} = 20.9775$

    $M_{100} = 20.999775$

    Sums seem to be approaching 21.

12. a. $\int \cos^5 x \sin x\,dx = -\frac{1}{6}\cos^6 x + C$

    b. $\int (1/x)\,dx = \ln |x| + C$

    c. $\int \tan x\,dx = \ln |\sec x| + C = -\ln |\cos x| + C$

    d. $\int \sec x\,dx = \ln |\sec x + \tan x| + C$

    e. $\int (3x - 5)^{1/2}\,dx = \frac{1}{3}\int (3x - 5)^{1/2}(3\,dx)$

    $= \frac{1}{3}\cdot\frac{2}{3}(3x - 5)^{3/2} + C = \frac{2}{9}(3x - 5)^{3/2} + C$

13. $\int_1^4 x^2\,dx = \frac{1}{3}x^3 \Big|_1^4 = \frac{64}{3} - \frac{1}{3} = 21$,

    which agrees with the conjecture in Problem 10.

14. Graph, example, showing tangent line parallel to secant line at x = c

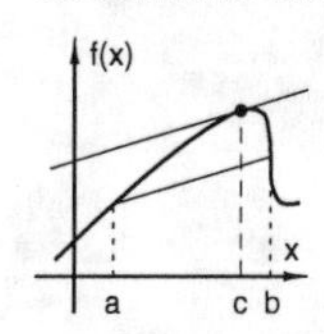

    Statement:

    If f is differentiable on (a, b) and continuous at x = a and x = b, then there is a number x = c in (a, b) such that $f'(x) = \dfrac{f(b) - f(a)}{b - a}$.

15. $y = x^{9/7}$

    Either:

    $y^7 = x^9$

    $7y^6 y' = 9x^8$

    $y' = \dfrac{9x^8}{7y^6} = \dfrac{9x^8}{7(x^{9/7})^6} = \frac{9}{7}x^{8-54/7} = \frac{9}{7}x^{2/7} = \frac{9}{7}x^{9/7-1}$

    as from the derivative of a power formula, or:

    $\ln y = \frac{9}{7}\ln x \Rightarrow (1/y)y' = \frac{9}{7}(1/x) \Rightarrow$

    $y' = \frac{9}{7}(1/x)\cdot y = \frac{9}{7}(1/x)\cdot x^{9/7} = \frac{9}{7}x^{2/7} = \frac{9}{7}x^{9/7-1}$,

    as from the derivative of a power formula.

16. If x^{-1} were the derivative of a power, then the power would have to be x^0. But $x^0 = 1$, so its derivative equals 0, not x^{-1}. Thus, x^{-1} is not the derivative of a power, Q.E.D.

17. $f(x) = \int_1^{\tan x} \cos 3t\, dt \Rightarrow$
$f'(x) = \cos(3 \tan x) \cdot \sec^2 x$

18. $f(x) = \int_1^x (1/t)\, dt \Rightarrow f'(x) = 1/x$, Q.E.D.

19. Prove $\ln x^a = a \ln x$ for any constant a and all $x > 0$.
Proof:
Let $f(x) = \ln x^a$ and $g(x) = a \ln x$.
Then $f'(x) = \frac{1}{x^a} \cdot ax^{a-1} = a \cdot \frac{1}{x} = \frac{a}{x}$ and
$g'(x) = a \cdot \frac{1}{x} = \frac{a}{x}$.
$\therefore f'(x) = g'(x)$ for all $x > 0$
$f(1) = \ln(1^a) = \ln 1 = 0$ and
$g(1) = a \ln 1 = 0$
$\therefore f(1) = g(1)$
$\therefore f(x) = g(x)$ for all $x > 0$, and thus
$\ln x^a = a \ln x$ for all $x \geq 0$, Q.E.D.

20. $x = 5 \cos t$
$y = 3 \sin t$
$\therefore \frac{dy}{dx} = \frac{3 \cos t}{-5 \sin t}$

21. At $t = 2$, $(x, y) = (5 \cos 2, 3 \sin 2)$
$= (-2.08..., 2.72...)$
At $t = 2$, $\frac{dy}{dx} = \frac{3 \cos 2}{-5 \sin 2} = \underline{0.2745...}$
Graph, showing that a line of slope 0.27... at point (–2.08..., 2.72...) is tangent to the curve.

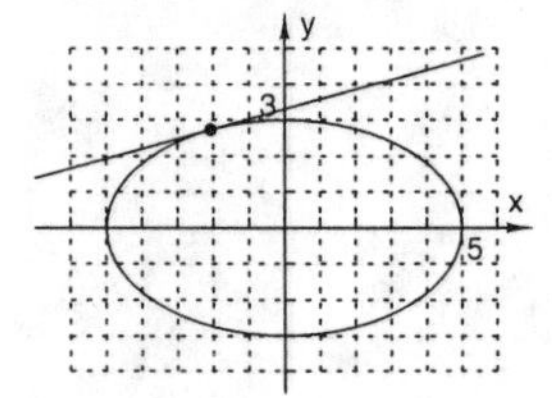

22. $y = \tan^{-1} t$
$v = \frac{dy}{dt} = \frac{1}{1 + t^2} = (1 + t^2)^{-1}$
$a = \frac{dv}{dt} = -1(1 + t^2)^{-2} \cdot 2t = -\frac{2t}{(1 + t^2)^2}$

23. $\lim_{x \to 0} \frac{e^{3x} - 1}{\sin 5x} \to \frac{0}{0}$
$= \lim_{x \to 0} \frac{3e^{3x}}{5 \cos 5x} = \frac{3}{5}$

24. $L = \lim_{n \to 0} (1 + n)^{1/n} \to 1^\infty$
$\ln L = \lim_{n \to 0} (\frac{1}{n} \ln(1 + n)) \to \infty \cdot 0$
$= \lim_{n \to 0} \frac{\ln(1 + n)}{n} \to \frac{0}{0}$
$= \lim_{n \to 0} \frac{1/(1 + n)}{1} = 1$
$\therefore L = e^1 = e$, Q.E.D.

25. $\int_2^5 f(x)\, dx \approx (1/3)(0.5)(100 + 4 \cdot 150 + 2 \cdot 170 + 4 \cdot 185 + 2 \cdot 190 + 4 \cdot 220 + 300)$
$= (1/3)(0.5)(3340) = 556\frac{2}{3}$

26. Area of cross-section $= \pi y^2$
Since the end of the radius is on a line through the origin with slope r/h, $y = (r/h)x$.
$\therefore \text{Area} = \pi[(r/h)x]^2 = \frac{\pi r^2}{h^2} x^2$
Graph, showing Area as a function of x, with strip of width dx and sample point (x, y) on the graph within the strip.

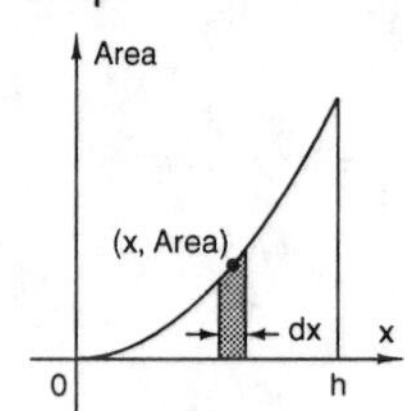

$dV = (\text{Area})\, dx$
$\therefore V = \int_0^h (\text{Area})\, dx = \int_0^h \frac{\pi r^2}{h^2} x^2\, dx$
$= \frac{\pi r^2}{h^2} \cdot \frac{1}{3} x^3 \Big|_0^h = \frac{1}{3} \pi \frac{r^2}{h^2} (h^3 - 0^3) = \frac{1}{3} \pi r^2 h$, Q.E.D.

27. Responses about writing in calculus will vary. Many will find that writing has helped them learn the subject and clarify their understanding. A few will feel that writing has been an unnecessary burden.

Chapter 7

Problem Set 7-1, page 309 — Direct Proportion Property of Exponential Functions

1. $D(t) = 500 \cdot (1.06^t)$
   where D(t) is in dollars and t is in years.
   Use the TABLE feature.

t	D(t)
0	500
10	895.4238482...
20	1603.567736...

2. $D'(t) = 500 \cdot (\ln 1.06) \cdot (1.06^t)$ dollars/year

t	D'(t)
0	29.13445406...
10	52.17536994...
20	93.43814108...

   The rate of change dollars/year is increasing as the amount in the account is increasing.

3. $R(t) = \dfrac{D'(t)}{D(t)} = \dfrac{500 \cdot (\ln 1.06) \cdot (1.06^t)}{500 \cdot (1.06^t)} = \ln 1.06$

t	R(t)
0	0.0582689081...
10	0.0582689081...
20	0.0582689081...

4. The percent interest rate stays the same: approx. 5.83%
5. $f(x) = a \cdot b^x$
   $\Rightarrow f'(x) = a \cdot (\ln b) \cdot b^x = (\ln b)(a \cdot b^x) = (\ln b) \cdot f(x)$
   So f'(x) is directly proportional to f(x).
6. Read Section 7-2.

Problem Set 7-2, pages 312 to 316 — Exponential Growth and Decay

Q1. $y = e^x$

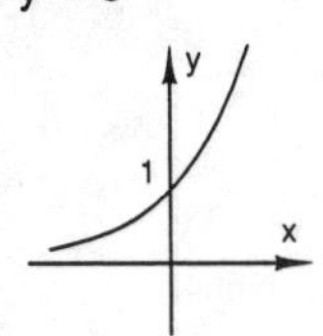

Q2. $y = e^{-x}$

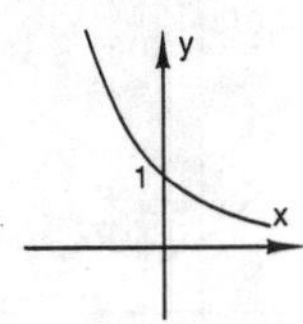

Q3. $y = \ln x$

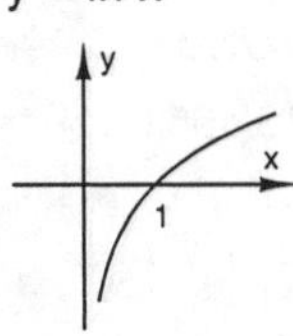

Q4. $y = x^2$

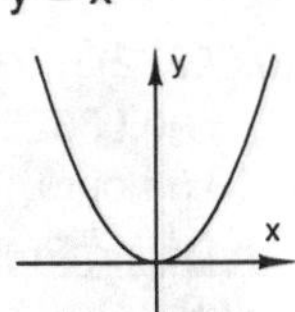

Q5. $y = x^3$

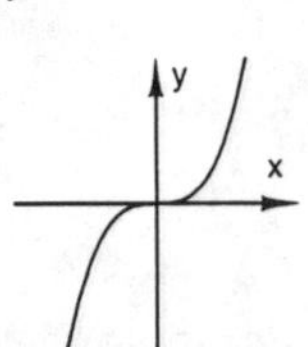

Q6. $y = \dfrac{1}{x}$

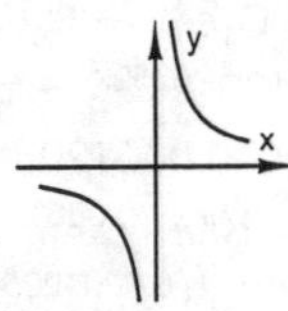

Q7. $y = x$

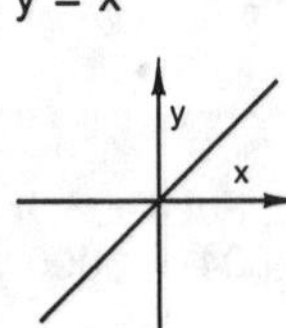

Q8. $y = 3$

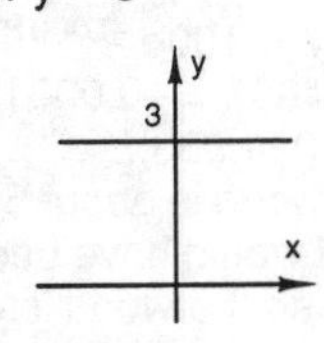

Q9. $x = 4$

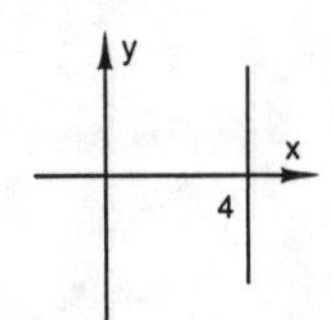

Q10. $y = 3 - x$

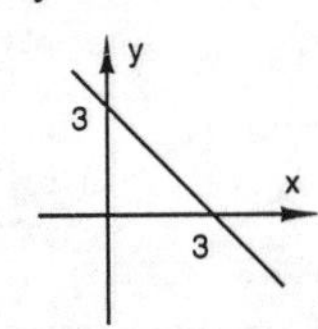

1. Bacteria Problem
   a. B = no. of millions of bacteria; t = no. of hours.
   $dB/dt = kB \Rightarrow \int dB/B = \int k\,dt \Rightarrow \ln |B| = kt + C$
   $|B| = e^{kt+C} = e^{kt} \cdot e^C \Rightarrow B = C_1e^{kt}$

   b. $5 = C_1e^{k \cdot 0} \Rightarrow C_1 = 5$
   $7 = 5e^{3k} \Rightarrow \ln(7/5) = 3k$
   $\Rightarrow k = (\frac{1}{3}) \cdot \ln(\frac{7}{5}) = 0.112157...$
   $\therefore B = 5e^{(1/3)(\ln(7/5))t} = 5(\frac{7}{5})^{t/3} = 5e^{0.112157...t}$

   c. Graph

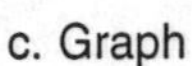

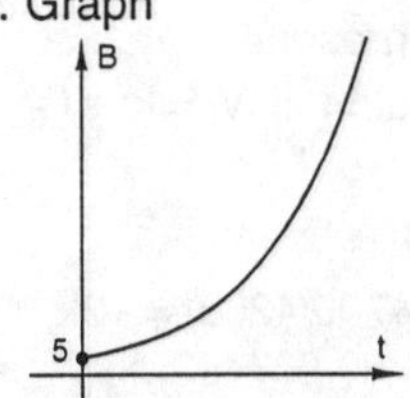

   d. $B = 5(7/5)^{24/3} = 73.78945...$
   About 74 million

   e. $1000 = 5(7/5)^{t/3} \Rightarrow \ln(1000/5) = t/3 \cdot \ln(7/5)$
   $t = \dfrac{3 \ln 200}{\ln(7/5)} = 47.24001...$
   About 47 hours after start

2. Nitrogen 17 Problem
   a. N = no. of units of radiation from N_{17}
   t = no. of seconds
   $dN/dt = kN \Rightarrow \int dN/N = \int k\,dt \Rightarrow \ln |N| = kt + C$
   $|N| = e^{kt+C} \Rightarrow N = C_1e^{kt}$

   b. $3 \times 10^{17} = C_1e^{k \cdot 0} \Rightarrow C_1 = 3 \times 10^{17}$
   $5.6 \times 10^{13} = 3 \times 10^{17}e^{60k}$
   $\Rightarrow \ln(1.866... \times 10^{-4}) = 60k \Rightarrow k = -0.143103...$
   $\therefore N = 3 \times 10^{17}e^{-0.143103...t}$

   c. Graph

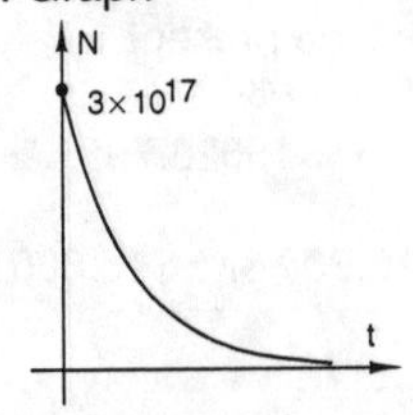

   d. $t = 5(60) = 300$ sec
   $N = 3 \times 10^{17}e^{(-0.143103...)(300)} = 0.067991...$
   Will not be safe, since 0.067... > 0.007

3. Chemical Reaction Problem

a. F = no. of mg; t = no. of minutes

$dF/dt = kF \Rightarrow \int dF/F = \int k\,dt \Rightarrow \ln|F| = kt + C$

$|F| = e^{kt+C} \Rightarrow F = C_1e^{kt}$

$50 = C_1e^{k \cdot 0} \Rightarrow C_1 = 50$

$30 = 50e^{20k} \Rightarrow \ln(30/50) = 20k$

$\Rightarrow k = (1/20) \cdot \ln(0.6) = -0.025541...$

$\therefore F = 50e^{\ln(0.6)t/20} = 50(0.6)^{t/20} = 50e^{-0.025541...t}$

b. Graph

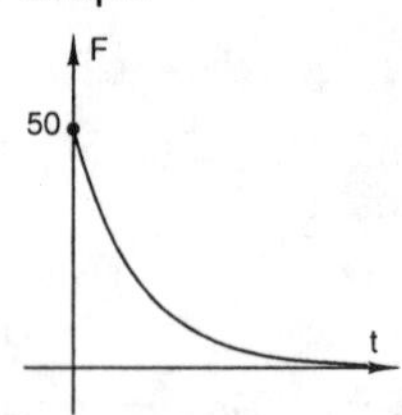

c. $F = 50(0.6)^{(60/20)} = 10.8$ mg (exactly).

d. $0.007 = 50(0.6)^{t/20} \Rightarrow \ln(0.007/50) = \ln(0.6)\,t/20$

$\Rightarrow t = 347.4323...$

About 5 hr 47 min

4. Car Trade-in Problem

a. V = no. of dollars trade-in value;
t = no. of months from the present

$dV/dt = kV \Rightarrow \int dV/V = \int k\,dt \Rightarrow \ln|V| = kt + C$

$|V| = e^{kt+C} \Rightarrow V = C_1e^{kt}$

b. $4200 = C_1e^{k \cdot 0} \Rightarrow C_1 = 4200$

$4700 = 4200e^{(k)(-3)} \Rightarrow \ln(4700/4200) = -3k$

$k = (-1/3)\ln(4700/4200) = -0.037492...$

$\therefore V = 4200e^{-0.037492...t}$

c. Graph

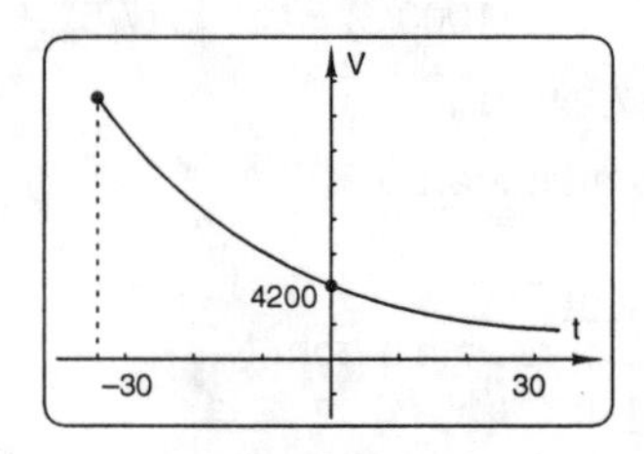

d. At 1 year after V = 4700, t = 9 months.

$V = 4200e^{(-0.037492...)(9)} = 2997.116...$

About \$3000

e. $1200 = 4200e^{-0.037492...t}$

$\Rightarrow \ln(1200/4200) = -0.037492...t$

$\Rightarrow t = (-1/0.037492...) \cdot \ln(1200/4200)$

$= 33.4135...$

About 33 or 34 months from the present

f. 31 months before V = 4700, t = –34.

$\therefore V = 4200e^{(-0.037492...)(-34)} = 15026.795...$

About \$15,000

g. The difference between \$16,000 and \$15,000 is the dealer's profit.

5. Biological Half-Life Problem

a. $dC/dt = kC$

b. $\int dC/C = \int k\,dt \Rightarrow \ln|C| = kt + D$

$\Rightarrow |C| = e^{kt+D} \Rightarrow C = D_1e^{kt}$

$0.00372 = D_1e^{k \cdot 0} \Rightarrow D_1 = 0.00372$

$0.00219 = 0.00372e^{8k}$

$\Rightarrow \ln(0.00219/0.00372) = 8k$

$\Rightarrow k = (1/8) \cdot \ln(219/372) = -0.0662277...$

$\therefore C = 0.00372e^{-0.0662277...t}$

c. Either: $C = 0.015$

$\Rightarrow 0.015 = 0.00372e^{-0.0662277...t}$

$\ln 4.0322... = -0.0662277...\,t$

$t = -21.05...$, which is before the poison was inhaled,

or: $t = -20 \Rightarrow C = 0.00372e^{-0.0662277...(-20)}$

$C = 0.0139...$, which is less than 0.015

$\therefore$ concentration never was that high.

d. Graph

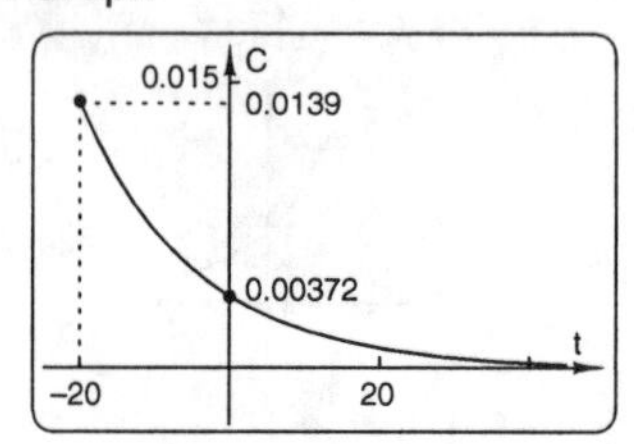

e. $(1/2)(0.00372) = 0.00372e^{-0.0662277...t}$

$\ln(1/2) = -0.0662277...\,t \Rightarrow t = 10.4661...$

About 10.5 hours

6. Carbon 14 Dating Problem

a. $dP/dt = kP$

b. $\int dP/P = \int k\,dt \Rightarrow \ln|P| = kt + C$

$\Rightarrow |P| = e^{kt+C} \Rightarrow P = C_1e^{kt}$

$100 = C_1e^{k \cdot 0} \Rightarrow C_1 = 100$

$50 = 100e^{5750k} \Rightarrow \ln 0.5 = 5750k$

$\Rightarrow k = -0.0001205473...$

$\therefore P = 100e^{-0.0001205473...t}$

c. $P = 100e^{(-0.0001205473...)(4000)} = 61.74301...$

About 61.7%

d. $48.37 = 100e^{-0.0001205473...t}$

$\ln 0.4837 = -0.0001205473...\,t$

$t = 6024.939...$

The wood is about 6025 years old. For 1996, the flood would have been 1996 – (–4004) = 6000 years ago, so the wood is old enough.

e. Graph

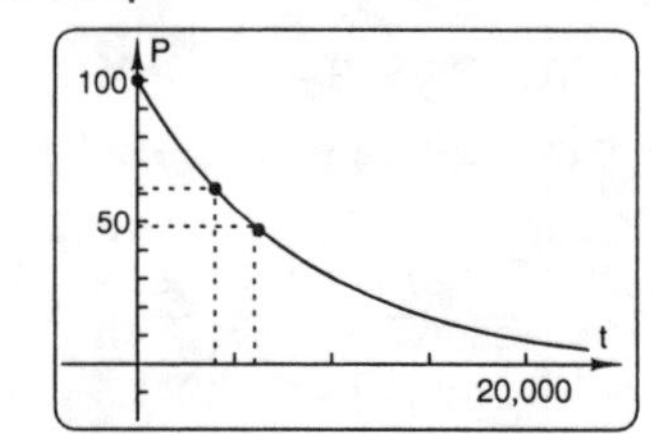

f. See the article. Because of slight variations in the production rate of carbon 14, some older rings have higher C_{14} concentrations than younger rings. Thus, there may be more than one age corresponding to a particular concentration. Renfrew proposes that these errors are large enough to cast doubt on the common assumption that civilization in Europe started in the east and moved west.

7. Compound Interest Problem I

$dM/dt = kM \Rightarrow M = Ce^{kt}$ by the techniques in Problems 1 through 6, where C is the initial investment.

$\therefore$ M varies exponentially with t.

Let i = interest rate as a decimal.

$dM/dt = Ck \cdot e^{kt}$

At t = 0, dM/dt = Ci

$\therefore Ci = Ck \cdot e^0 \Rightarrow i = k$

Examples:
$1000 at 7% for 5 years: $1419.07
$1000 at 7% for 10 years: $2013.75
$1000 at 14% for 5 years: $2013.75
$1000 at 14% for 10 years: $4055.20
Leaving the money twice as long has the *same* effect as doubling the interest rate. Doubling the amount invested doubles the money at any particular time.

8. Compound Interest Problem II

Assume an investment of $1000 at 7% per year.
For 5 years, as in Problem 7, above:
Annually: $M = 1000(1.07)^5 = \$1402.55$
Quarterly: $M = 1000(1.0175)^{20} = \$1414.78$
Daily: $M = 1000(1.0001917808...)^{1825} = \$1419.02$
Continuously (Prob. 7): $1419.07
Note that compounding continuously is only 5 cents better than daily compounding for a $1000 investment in five years!

$M = M_0(1 + k/n)^{nt}$

Let $L = \lim_{n\to\infty} (1 + k/n)^{nt} \to 1^\infty$

$\ln L = \lim_{n\to\infty} [nt \cdot \ln (1 + k/n)] \to \infty \cdot 0$

$= \lim_{n\to\infty} \dfrac{t \cdot \ln(1 + k/n)}{n^{-1}} \to \dfrac{\infty}{\infty}$

$= \lim_{n\to\infty} \dfrac{t \cdot \dfrac{1}{1 + k/n} \cdot (-kn^{-2})}{-n^{-2}}$

$= \lim_{n\to\infty} \dfrac{kt}{1 + k/n} = kt$

$\therefore L = e^{kt}$

$\therefore \lim_{n\to\infty} M = M_0e^{kt}$,

which is the continuous compounding equation

9. Generalization Problem

$dy/dx = ky \Rightarrow \int dy/y = \int k\,dx \Rightarrow \ln |y| = kx + C_1$

$|y| = e^{kx+C_1} \Rightarrow y = Ce^{kx}$, Q.E.D.

Problem Set 7-3, pages 320 to 325 — Other Differential Equations for Real-World Applications

Q1. Ce^{kx}
Q2. $(kx^2)/2 + C$
Q3. $kx + C$
Q4. $-\cos x + C$
Q5. $1/\sqrt{1 - x^2}$
Q6. $5 \cos x$
Q7. $\tan x$
Q8. Graph [Chg.: y(1) = 0)] $(y' = 0.24(x - 5)^2 - 1)$

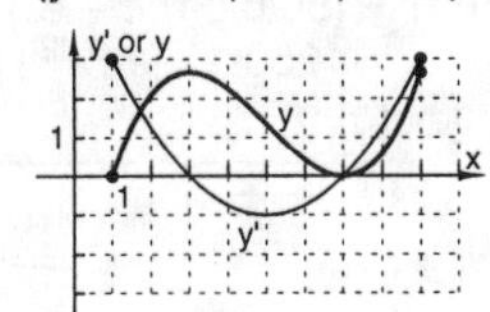

Q9. $\lim_{\Delta x\to 0} L_n = \lim_{\Delta x\to 0} U_n$.
Q10. 16

1. Sweepstakes Problem I

a. dM/dt = 100 − S

b. $S = kM \Rightarrow dM/dt = 100 - kM$

c. $\int \dfrac{dM}{100 - kM} = \int dt \Rightarrow -\dfrac{1}{k}\int \dfrac{-k\,dM}{100 - kM} = \int dt \Rightarrow$

$-\dfrac{1}{k} \ln |100 - kM| = t + C \Rightarrow |100 - kM| = e^{-kt}e^{-kC} \Rightarrow$

$100 - km = C_1e^{-kt} \Rightarrow kM = 100 - C_1e^{-kt} \Rightarrow$

$M = \dfrac{1}{k}(100 - C_1e^{-kt})$.

Substitute M = 0 when t = 0.

$0 = \dfrac{1}{k}(100 - C_1e^0) \Rightarrow C_1 = 100$

$\therefore M = \dfrac{100}{k}(1 - e^{-kt})$

d. $k = 0.02 \Rightarrow M = 5000(1 - e^{-0.02t})$

e. Graph

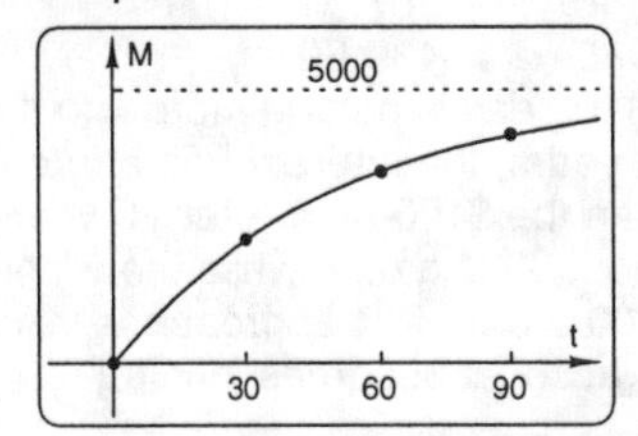

f. t = 30: $2255.94 ($3000 in, $744.06 spent)
t = 60: $3494.03 ($6000 in, $2505.97 spent)
t = 90: $4173.51 ($9000 in, $4826.49 spent)

g. t = 365: (366 could be used.)
$M = 5000(1 - e^{-7.30}) = 4996.622...$
≈ $4996.62 in the account
$dM/dt = 100 - 0.02(4996.622...) = 0.06755...$
Increasing at about $0.07 per day

h. $\lim_{t\to\infty} M = \lim_{t\to\infty} 5000(1 - e^{-0.02t}) = 5000(1 - 0)$
= 5000

2. Sweepstakes Problem II

$dM/dt = 100 + kM$ (k = daily interest rate)

$\int \frac{dM}{100 + kM} = \int dt \Rightarrow \frac{1}{k}\int \frac{k\,dM}{100 + kM} = \int dt \Rightarrow$

$\frac{1}{k} \ln |100 + kM| = t + C \Rightarrow |100 + kM| = e^{kt}e^{kC} \Rightarrow$

$100 + km = C_1e^{kt} \Rightarrow kM = -100 + C_1e^{kt} \Rightarrow$

$M = \frac{1}{k}(C_1e^{kt} - 100)$.

Substitute M = 0 when t = 0

$0 = \frac{1}{k}(C_1e^0 - 100) \Rightarrow C_1 = 100$

$\therefore M = \frac{100}{k}(e^{kt} - 1)$

Let k = 0.0002 (0.02% per day).

$\therefore M = (500000)(e^{0.0002t} - 1)$

Graph: Almost straight. The \$100/day deposits far exceed the interest for the first few years.

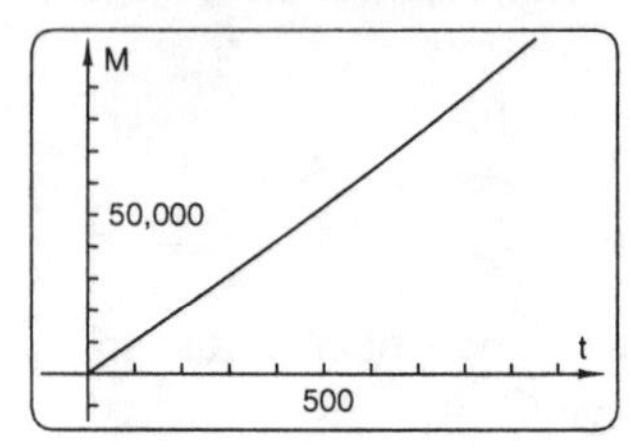

Make a table of M and dm/dt for various numbers of years. Neglect leap years.

Years	M	dM/dt
0	0	100.00
1	37,865	107.57
10	537,540	207.51
20	1,652,980	430.60

After 1 year, the \$100/day is putting more into the account. After 10 years, the interest has started putting in more than the \$100/day. After 20 years, the interest puts in about \$331 a day, while the winnings still put in only \$100 a day. As t approaches infinity, the amount in the account becomes infinite!

3. Electrical Circuit Problem

a. $E = RI + L(dI/dt)$

b. $L\,dI/dt = E - RI$

$\int \frac{L\,dI}{E - RI} = \int dt \Rightarrow -\frac{L}{R}\int \frac{-R dI}{E - RI} = \int dt \Rightarrow$

$-\frac{L}{R} \ln |E - RI| = t + C \Rightarrow |E - RI| = e^{-(R/L)t}e^{-(R/L)C}$

$\Rightarrow E - RI = C_1e^{-(R/L)t} \Rightarrow I = \frac{1}{R}(E - C_1e^{-(R/L)t})$

Substitute I = 0 when t = 0.

$0 = \frac{1}{R}(E - C_1e^0) \Rightarrow C_1 = E$

$\therefore I = \frac{E}{R}(1 - e^{-(R/L)t})$

c. $I = \frac{110}{10}(1 - e^{-(10/20)t})$

$I = 11(1 - e^{-0.5t})$

Graph

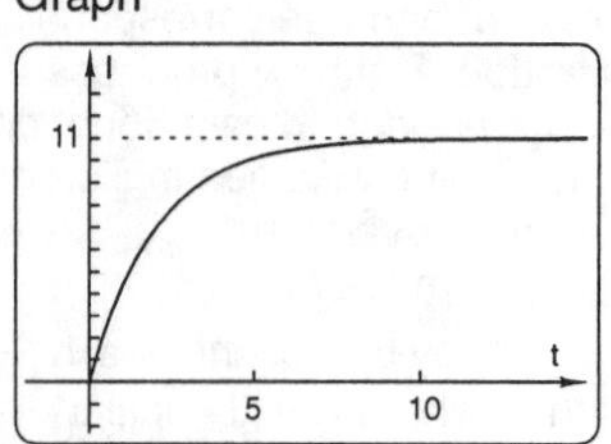

d. i. $I = 11(1 - e^{-0.5}) = 4.3281... \approx 4.33$ amps

ii. $I = 11(1 - e^{-5}) = 10.9258... \approx 10.93$ amps

iii. $\lim_{t\to\infty} I = \lim_{t\to\infty} 11(1 - e^{-0.5t}) = 11(1 - 0) = 11$ amps

e. $I = 0.95(11) = 10.45$

$10.45 = 11(1 - e^{-0.5t})$

$0.95 = 1 - e^{-0.5t}$

$e^{-0.5t} = 0.05$

$-0.5t = \ln 0.05$

$t = -2 \ln 0.05 = 5.9914...$

About 6 seconds

4. Newton's Law of Cooling Problem

a. $R = C(dT/dt) + hT$

b. $C\,dT/dt = R - hT$

$\int C\,dT/(R - hT) = \int dt \Rightarrow -\frac{C}{h}\int \frac{-h dT}{R - hT} = \int dt \Rightarrow$

$-\frac{C}{h} \ln |R - hT| = t + D \Rightarrow |R - hT| = e^{-(h/C)t}e^{-(h/C)D} \Rightarrow R$

$- hT = D_1e^{-(h/C)t} \Rightarrow T = (1/h)(R - D_1e^{-(h/C)t})$.

Substitute T = 0 when t = 0.

$0 = \frac{1}{h}(R - D_1e^0) \Rightarrow D_1 = R$.

$\therefore T = \frac{R}{h}(1 - e^{-(h/C)t})$

c. $T = (50/0.04)(1 - e^{-(0.04/2)t})$

$T = 1250(1 - e^{-0.02t})$

d. Graph

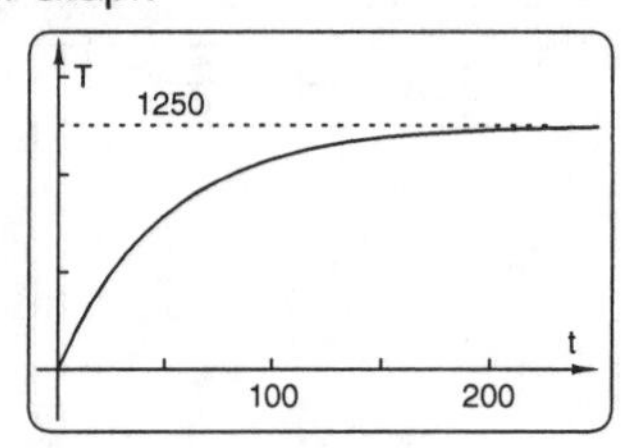

e. Use TRACE or TABLE.

t = 10:	T = 226.586...	≈ 227°
t = 20:	T = 412.099...	≈ 412°
t = 50:	T = 790.150...	≈ 790°
t = 100:	T = 1080.830...	≈ 1081°
t = 200:	T = 1227.105...	≈ 1227°

f. $\lim_{t\to\infty} T = \lim_{t\to\infty} 1250(1 - e^{-0.02t}) = 1250(1 - 0) = 1250°$

g. $T = 0.99(1250) = 1237.5$

$1237.5 = 1250(1 - e^{-0.02t})$

$0.99 = 1 - e^{-0.02t}$

$e^{-0.02t} = 0.01$

$-0.02t = \ln 0.01$

$t = -50 \ln 0.01 = 230.258...$

About 230 seconds

5. Hot Tub Problem

a. $\frac{dV}{dt} = kV^{1/2}$

b. $\int V^{-1/2}\,dV = k\int dt \Rightarrow$

$\Rightarrow 2V^{1/2} = kt + C \Rightarrow V = (\frac{kt + C}{2})^2$

V varies quadratically with t.

c. Initial conditions t = 0; V = 196; dV/dt = –28:

$196^{1/2} = \frac{k \cdot 0 + C}{2} \Rightarrow C = 28$

and: $-28 = k \cdot 196^{1/2} \Rightarrow k = -2$

$\therefore V = (\frac{-2t + 28}{2})^2 \Rightarrow V = (t - 14)^2$

d. False. Since dV/dt = 2t – 28, the water flows out at 28 only when t = 0. For instance, at t = 5, dV/dt = –18, which means water flows out at only 18 ft^3/sec. So it takes longer than 7 minutes to empty the tub.

e. $0 = (t - 14)^2 \Rightarrow$ the tub is empty at t = 14 minutes.

f. Graph

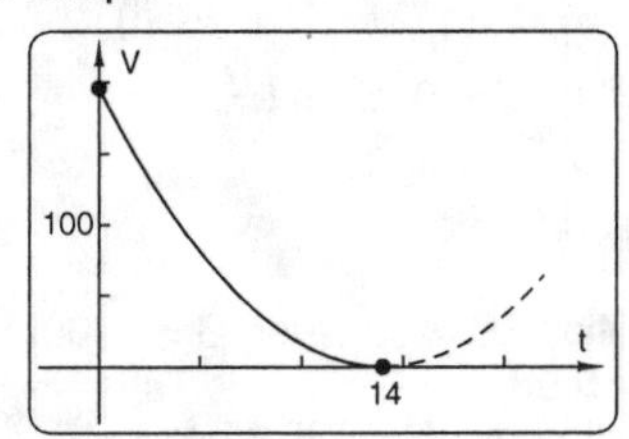

g. See Problem Set 7–7, #C4.

6. Burette (Water Leakage) Experiment

The following data were gathered in the author's class in December 1994. Times t are in seconds and volumes are in ml. Note that a burette reads the amount of fluid *delivered*, so you must subtract the reading (rdg.) from 50 to find the volume (vol.) remaining. Use food coloring in the water to make the liquid level easier to read. Read from the *bottom* of the meniscus (the curved surface of the liquid).

Sec.	Rdg.	Vol.	Sec.	Rdg.	Vol.
0	0	50	150	27.4	22.6
10	2.4	47.6	160	28.6	21.4
20	4.4	45.6	170	30.0	20.0
30	6.4	43.6	180	31.3	18.7
40	8.5	41.5	190	32.6	17.4
50	10.5	39.5	200	33.8	16.2
60	12.4	37.6	210	35.1	14.9
70	14.3	35.7	220	36.4	13.6
80	16.1	33.9	230	37.4	12.6
90	17.8	32.2	240	38.5	11.5
100	19.9	30.1	250	39.5	10.5
110	21.2	28.8	260	40.6	9.4
120	22.8	27.2	...		
130	24.5	25.6	320	46.1	3.9
140	25.6	24.4	360	49.3	0.7

Using quadratic regression with these data,
$V = 0.000202955...t^2 - 0.20964...t + 49.54$

The data and the equation can be plotted on the grapher, as shown.

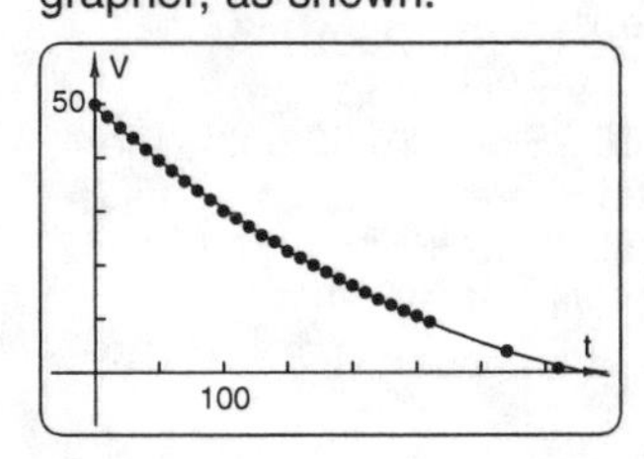

The volume *does* seem to vary quadratically with time. Since there is still fluid in the burette when V is 0, the graph crosses the t-axis, unlike those in Problem 5 and Example 1. The position of the vertex can be used to predict the position of the stopcock and the time when the fluid would all be gone if the burette were of uniform diameter all the way down to the stopcock. For the data above, the vertex is at

$t = -\frac{-0.20964...}{(2)(0.000202955...)} \approx 516$ seconds.

$V \approx -4.6$ ml

So the stopcock should be found at a point corresponding to 4 or 5 ml below the bottom mark.

7. Differential Equation Generalization Problem

a. n = 1, k = 1, C = –3:

$\therefore dy/dx = y \Rightarrow \int dy/y = \int dx \Rightarrow \ln|y| = x - 3$

$\Rightarrow |y| = e^{x-3} = e^x e^{-3} \Rightarrow y = \pm\, 0.04978...e^x$

Graph, two branches

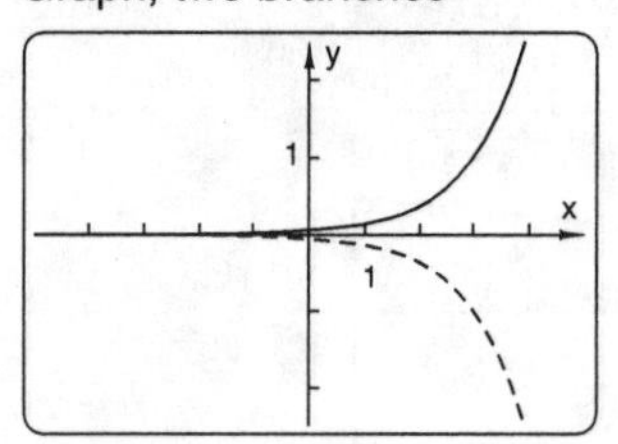

b. n = 0.5, k = 1, C = –3:

$\therefore dy/dx = y^{0.5} \Rightarrow \int y^{-0.5}\,dy = \int dx$

$\Rightarrow 2y^{0.5} = x - 3 \Rightarrow y = \frac{1}{4}(x - 3)^2$

Note: $x \geq 3$ because the symbol $y^{0.5}$ stands for a positive number.

Graph, $x \geq 3$

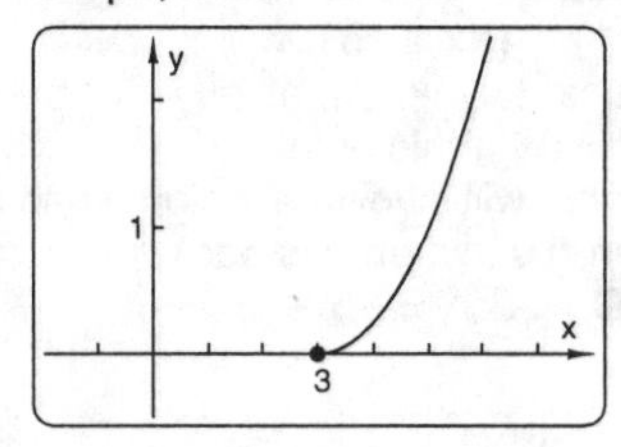

c. $n = -1 \Rightarrow dy/dx = ky^{-1} \Rightarrow \int y\, dy = k \int dx$

$\Rightarrow \frac{1}{2}y^2 = kx + C \Rightarrow y = \pm\sqrt{2kx + 2C}$

$k = 1, C = -3 \Rightarrow y = \pm\sqrt{2x - 6}$

Graph, two branches

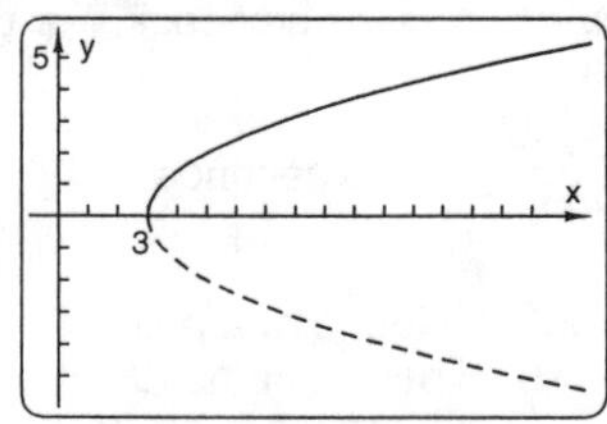

$n = -2 \Rightarrow dy/dx = ky^{-2} \Rightarrow \int y^2\, dy = k \int dx$

$\Rightarrow \frac{1}{3}y^3 = kx + C \Rightarrow y = \sqrt[3]{3kx + 3C}$

$k = 1, C = -3 \Rightarrow y = \sqrt[3]{3x - 9}$

Graph

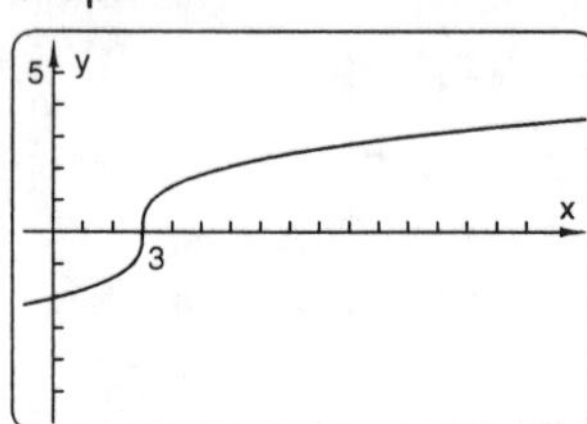

d. For $n > 1$, $\frac{dy}{dx} = ky^n \Rightarrow \int y^{-n}\, dy = k\int dx$

$\Rightarrow -\frac{y^{-(n-1)}}{n - 1} = kx + C$ since $n > 1$,

so $y = \frac{-1}{\sqrt[n-1]{(n - 1) \cdot (kx + C)}}$,

which has a vertical asymptote at $x = -C/k$ because the denominator = 0 for this point.

Note that the radical will involve a ± sign when the root index is even (i.e., when n is odd).

For $n = 2, k = 1, C = -3$: $y = -(x - 3)^{-1}$

Graph

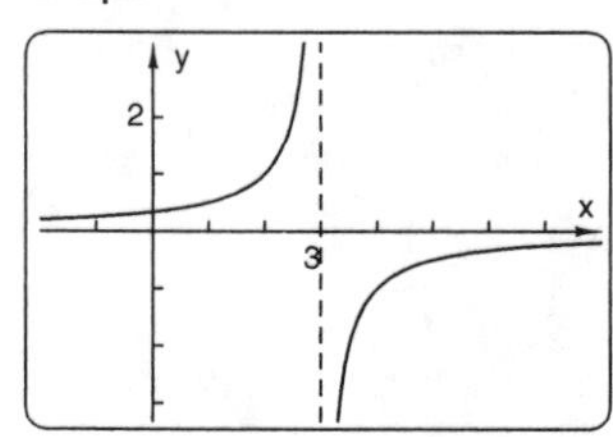

For $n = 3, k = 1, C = -3$: $y = \frac{-1}{\pm\sqrt{2x - 6}}$

Graph, showing the two branches

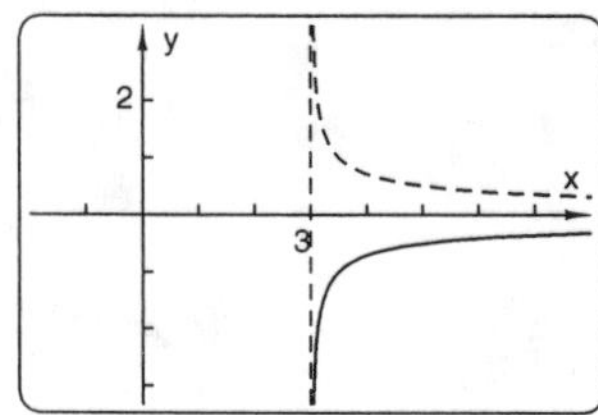

e. For $n = 0$, $\frac{dy}{dx} = ky^0 = k$, so $y = kx + C$, a linear function. For $k = 1, C = -3, y = x - 3$.

Graph

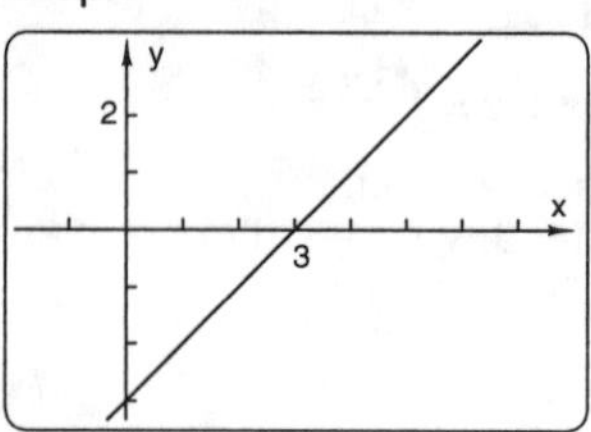

8. <u>Advertising Project</u>

$kB + c \cdot dB/dt = M$, where k and c are constants.

$c \cdot dB/dt = M - kB$

$c\int \frac{dB}{M - kB} = \int dt \Rightarrow -\frac{c}{k}\int \frac{-k\, dB}{M - kB} = \int dt \Rightarrow$

$-\frac{c}{k} \ln |M - kB| = t + C \Rightarrow |M - kB| = e^{-(k/c)t}e^{-(k/c)C} \Rightarrow$

$M - kB = C_1 e^{-(k/c)t} \Rightarrow B = \frac{1}{k}(M - C_1e^{-(k/c)t})$

Use the initial condition B = 0 when t = 0.

$0 = (1/k)(M - C_1e^0) \Rightarrow C_1 = M$.

$\therefore B = \frac{M}{k}(1 - e^{-(k/c)t})$

Use the initial condition kB = 80 when B = 1000.

$80 = k(1000) \Rightarrow k = 0.08$

Use the initial condition dB/dt = 500 when t = 0.

From $c \cdot dB/dt = M - kB$,

$500c = M - 0 \Rightarrow c = 0.002M$

∴ Particular equation is:

$B = (M/0.08)(1 - e^{-(0.08/0.002M)t})$

$B = 12.5M(1 - e^{-(40/M)t})$.

Assume various values of M:

$M = 1000$: $B = 12500(1 - e^{-0.04t})$

$M = 5000$: $B = 62500(1 - e^{-0.008t})$

$M = 10000$: $B = 125000(1 - e^{-0.004t})$

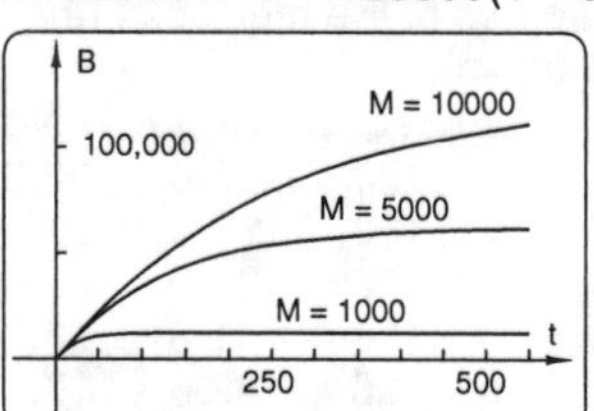

As shown on the graph, the sales start out increasing at the same rate (500 bottles/day). As t increases, the number of bottles/day increases, approaching a steady state equal to 12.5M.

To find break-even time, first find the total number of bottles sold as a function of time. Since B is in bottles per day, the total sales in x days, T(x), is

$T(x) = \int_0^x B\, dt$.

Use, for example, M = \$10,000/day.

$T(x) = \int_0^x 125{,}000(1 - e^{-0.004t})\, dt$

$= (125{,}000(t + (1/0.004)e^{-0.004t})\Big|_0^x$

$= 125{,}000(x + 250e^{-0.004x} - 0 - 250)$

$= 125{,}000(x - 250(1 - e^{-0.004x}))$

For selling prices of \$0.25 and \$0.50/bottle the numbers of dollars, total, are

$D_{25}(x) = 31250(x - 250(1 - e^{-0.004x}))$

$D_{50}(x) = 62500(x - 250(1 - e^{-0.004x}))$.

The total amount spent on advertising is Mx, or $A(x) = 10000x$.

The three graphs can be plotted by grapher. For \$0.25/bottle, the break-even time is 207 days. For \$0.50/bottle, the break-even time is 90 days (less than half!).

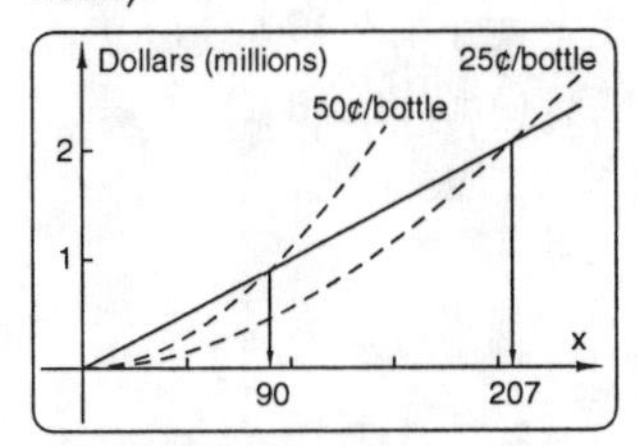

9. Water Heater Project

d.e. is $dT/dt = k(1200 - L)$, and $L = h(T - 70)$, where h is a proportionality constant.

$\therefore dT/dt = k(1200 + 70h - hT)$

$\int dT/(1200 + 70h - hT) = \int k\,dt$

$(-1/h) \ln |1200 + 70h - hT| = kt + C$

$\ln |1200 + 70h - hT| = -kht - hC$

$|1200 + 70h - hT| = e^{-kht} \cdot e^{-hC}$

$1200 + 70h - hT = C_1e^{-kht} \Rightarrow$

$hT = 1200 + 70h - C_1e^{-kht}$

$T = 1200/h + 70 - (C_1/h) \cdot e^{-kht}$.

Use $T = 70$ when $t = 0$.

$70 = 1200/h + 70 - C_1/h \cdot e^{-kh0}$

$\Rightarrow C_1 = 1200$

$\therefore T = 1200/h + 70 - 1200/h \cdot e^{-kht}$

$T = 70 + (1200/h)(1 - e^{-kht})$

Substitute $t = 0$, $L = 0$, and $dT/dt = 3$ into the original differential equation.

$3 = k(1200 - 0) \Rightarrow k = 0.0025$

$\therefore T = 70 + (1200/h)(1 - e^{-0.0025ht})$

Using $T = 96$ when $t = 10$,

$26 = (1200/h)(1 - e^{-0.025h})$.

Solving numerically gives $h \approx 11.7347...$.

$\therefore$ Equation is $T \approx 70 + 102.26...(1 - e^{-0.02933...t})$.

Time data for various temperatures can be found by grapher, or by substituting for T and solving for t.

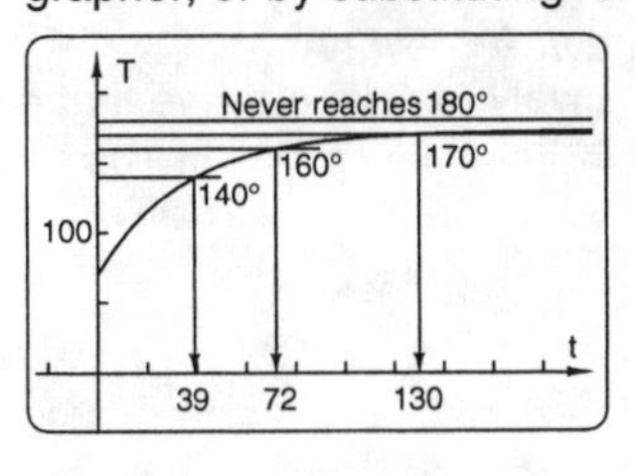

T	t
140°	39 min.
155°	61 min.
160°	72 min.
170°	130 min.
180°	Never!

The limit of T as t increases is $70 + 102.26...(1 + 0)$, which equals 172.26...°. Thus, the temperature never reaches 180°.

When the heater turns off, the differential equation becomes

$\frac{dT}{dt} = -kh(T - 70) \Rightarrow$

$T = 70 + C_2e^{-kht}$

Using $T = 160$ at time $t = 0$ when the heater turns off, $T = 70 + 90e^{-0.02933...t}$.

To find the time taken to drop to 155°, substitute:

$155 = 70 + 90e^{-0.02933...t}$.

Solving numerically or algebraically gives $t = 1.9...$. Thus it takes only 2 minutes for the temperature to drop 5°! By contrast, from the above table, it takes 11 minutes ($t = 61$ to $t = 72$ in the table above) to warm back up from 155° to 160°.

The design of the heater is inadequate because it takes much longer to warm up by a certain amount than it does to cool back down again. Near 172° a slight increase in the thermostat setting for the heater makes a great increase in the time taken to reach that setting. For instance, it takes an hour (72 minutes to 130 minutes) to warm the 10 degrees from 160° to 170°. These inadequacies could be corrected most easily by adding more insulation. The resulting decrease in h would make the heater cool more slowly, heat up faster, and reach the 180 degrees it currently cannot reach. Decreasing h would also reduce the power consumption.

10. Vapor Pressure Project

a. $dP/dT = kP/T^2$

$\int dP/P = k \int dT/T^2 \Rightarrow \ln |P| = -kT^{-1} + C$

$\Rightarrow |P| = e^{-k/T + C} \Rightarrow P = C_1e^{-k/T}$

b. $0.054 = C_1e^{-k/293}$

$3.95 = C_1e^{-k/343}$

$(3.95/0.054) = e^{(-k/343 + k/293)}$

$\ln (3.95/0.054) = -k/343 + k/293$

$k = [\ln (3.95/0.054)]/(-1/343 + 1/293)$

$= 8627.812641...$

From $\ln |P| = -kT^{-1} + C$,

$C = \ln 0.054 + 8627.812641.../293$.

$C = 26.52768829... \Rightarrow C_1 = e^{26.52768829...}$

$\therefore P = e^{26.52768829...} e^{-8627.812641../T}$

$P = e^{(26.52768829... - 8627.812641../T)}$

c.

Temp	T	P	Actual*
10	283	0.0190...	0.021
20	293	0.054	0.054
30	303	0.142...	0.133
40	313	0.354...	0.320
50	323	0.832...	0.815
60	333	1.85...	1.83
70	343	3.95	3.95
80	353	8.05...	7.4 (melting pt.)
90	363	15.7...	12.6
100	373	29.8...	18.5
110	383	54.6...	27.3
200	473	3972. ...	496.5

*Source: *Lange's Handbook of Chemistry*, 1952, p. 1476.

The function models the data well up to the melting point, but not above it. The differences between the predicted and actual answers are most likely due to the fact that naphthalene changes from solid to liquid at 80°C; the constants for solid and liquid naphthalene differ.

Use initial conditions for T = 90, 110 as in part b to get a better equation for the liquid:
$12.6 = C_1e^{-k/363}$
$496.5 = C_1e^{-k/473}$
$k = [\ln (496.5/12.6)]/(-1/473 + 1/363)$
$= 5734.569702...$
$C = \ln 12.6 + 5734.569702.../363$
$=18.33140949...$
$\Rightarrow C_1 = e^{18.33140949...}$
$\therefore P = e^{(18.33140949... - 5734.569702.../T)}$
With the new equation,

Temp	T	P	Actual*
10	283	0.144...	0.021
20	293	0.289...	0.054
30	303	0.551...	0.133
40	313	1.01...	0.320
50	323	1.78...	0.815
60	333	3.03...	1.83
70	343	5.01...	3.95
80	353	8.05...	7.4 (melting pt.)
90	363	12.6	12.6
100	373	19.2...	18.5
110	383	28.7...	27.3
200	473	496.5	496.5

So the new equation models the data above the melting point, but not below it.

d. Using the equation for liquid naphthalene:
$760 = e^{(18.33140949... - 5734.569702.../T)}$
$\ln 760 = 18.33140949... - 5734.569702..../T$
$$T = \frac{5734.569702...}{18.33140949... - \ln 760} = 490.214...$$
About 490 K, or 217°C (Actual: 218°C)

e. (Individual answers)

Problem Set 7-4, pages 329 to 333 — Graphical Solution of Differential Equations by Using Slope Fields

Q1. $y' = 5x^4$
Q2. $y' = 5^x \ln 5$
Q3. $(1/8)x^8 + C$
Q4. $7^x/\ln 7 + C$
Q5. $y' = -y/x$ or $y' = -3x^{-2}$
Q6. 87.5 (trapezoid area)
Q7. Graph, $y = x^2$
Q8. Graph, $y = 2^x$

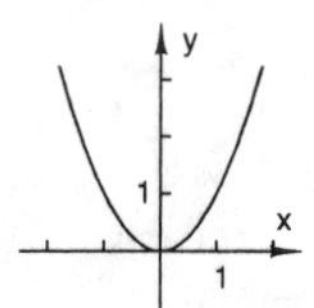

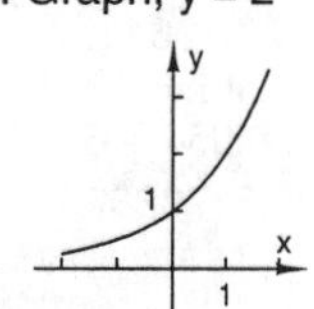

Q9. $g(5) - g(1)$
Q10. Slope = −1/6 (−1/y')

1. a. $dy/dx = x/(2y)$
At (3, 5), $dy/dx = 3/10 = 0.3$
At (−5, 1), $dy/dx = -5/2 = -2.5$
On the graph, the line at (3, 5) slopes upward with a slope less than 1. At (−5, 1) the line slopes downward with a slope much steeper than −1.

b. Graph. The figure looks like one branch of a hyperbola opening in the y-direction. (The lower branch shown on the graph is also part of the solution, but students would not be expected to find this graphically.)

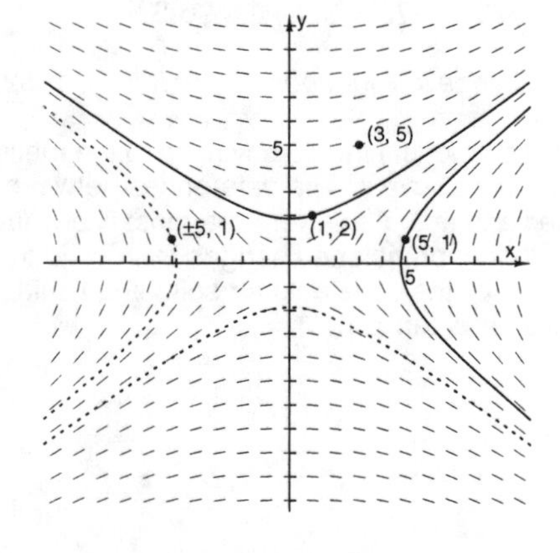

c. Graph, above. The figure looks like the right-hand branch of a hyperbola opening in the x-direction. (The left-hand branch is also part of the solution, but students would not be expected to find this graphically.)

d. $\frac{dy}{dx} = \frac{x}{2y} \Rightarrow \int 2y\,dy = \int x\,dx \Rightarrow y^2 = \frac{1}{2}x^2 + C$
$x = 5, y = 1 \Rightarrow C = 1 - 12.5 = -11.5.$
By algebra, $x^2 - 2y^2 = 23$
This is the particular equation of a hyperbola opening in the x-direction, which confirms the observations in part c.

2. Graph of slope field. $dy/dx = -x/(2y)$
(To get the graph relatively rapidly, observe that each slope is the *opposite* of the one in Problem 1.)

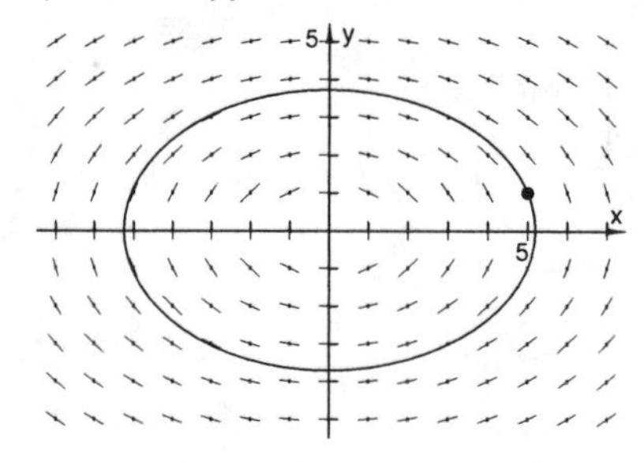

$\frac{dy}{dx} = -\frac{x}{2y} \Rightarrow \int 2y\,dy = -\int x\,dx \Rightarrow y^2 = -\frac{1}{2}x^2 + C$
$x = 5, y = 1 \Rightarrow C = 1 + 12.5 = -13.5$
Multiply both sides by 2 to get: $x^2 + 2y^2 = 27.$
Graph is an ellipse with x-radius $\sqrt{27} \approx 5.2$ and y-radius $\sqrt{13.5} \approx 3.7$. As shown on the graph above, the ellipse follows the pattern of the slope field.

3. a. Graph

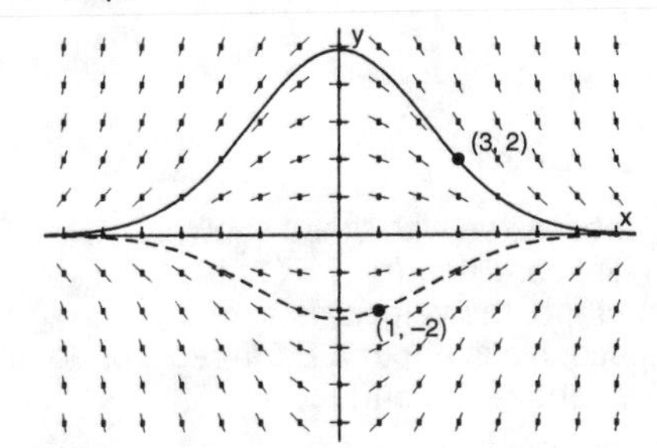

b. $\frac{dy}{dx} = -0.2xy$

Evidence: At (1, 1) the slope was given to be −0.2, which is true for this differential equation. As x or y increases from this point, the slope gets steeper in the negative direction, which is also true for this differential equation. In quadrants I and III the slopes are all negative, and in quadrants II and IV they are all positive.

(Note: The algebraic solution is $y = Ce^{-0.1x^2}$)

4. <u>Dependence on Initial Conditions Problem</u>

a. $\frac{dy}{dx} = 0.1x + 0.2y$. Graph, initial condition (0, 2).

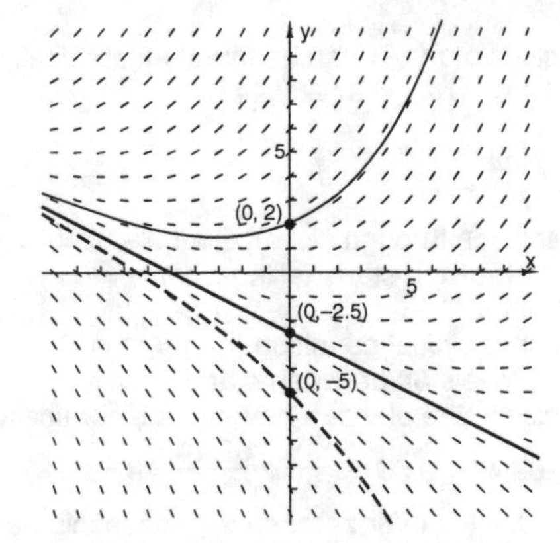

b. Graph, initial condition (x, y) = (0, −5)

The graph goes toward −∞ in the y-direction instead of to +∞.

c. Graph. If a ruler is aligned with the slope lines, the ones that form a straight line are the ones crossing the y-axis at −2.5 with slope −1/2.

(In courses on differential equations, students will learn that the given equation is a first-order linear equation that can be solved using an integrating factor. The general solution is $y = Ce^{0.2x} - 0.5x - 2.5$. For C = 0, the curve is a line $y = -0.5x - 2.5$, which intersects the y-axis at (0,−2.5).)

5. Graph (d.e. is $dy/dx = (x/5) \sin(\pi y/8) + y/10$.)

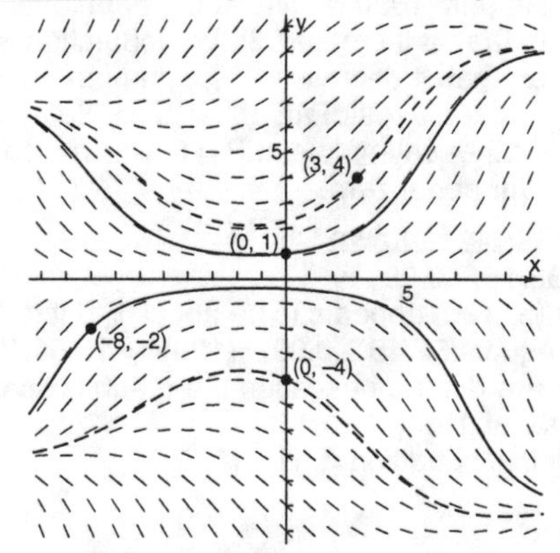

6. Graph (d.e. is $dy/dx = \sin(\pi xy/30)$.)

The change from (0, 8) to (0, 10) puts an extra cycle in the graph on each side of the y-axis.

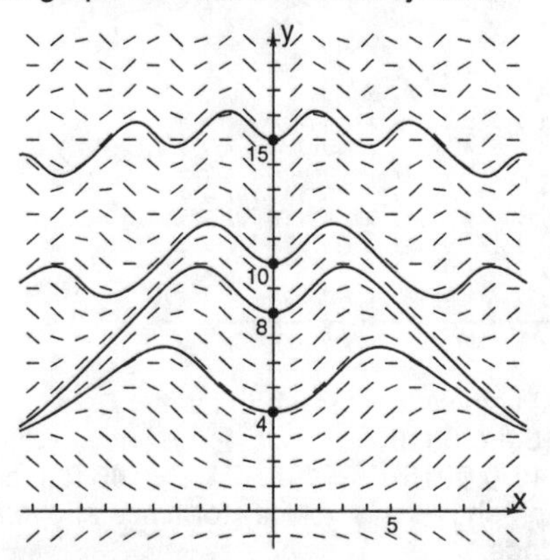

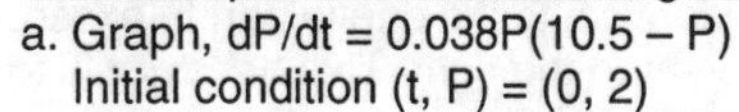

7. <u>Rabbit Population Overcrowding Problem</u>

a. Graph, $dP/dt = 0.038P(10.5 - P)$

Initial condition (t, P) = (0, 2)

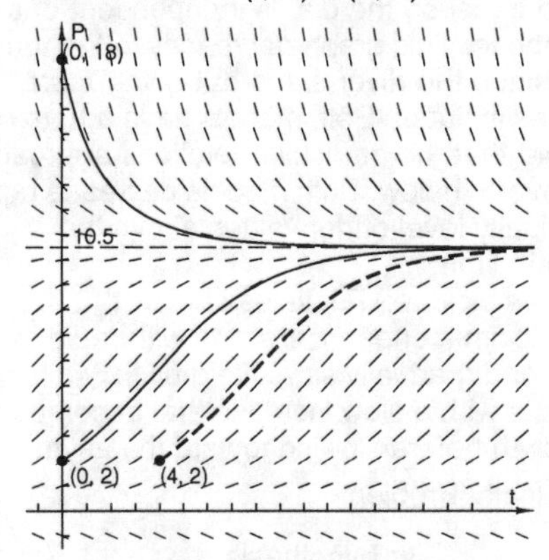

b. Graph, above. Initial condition (4, 2)

The graph is identical to that in part a shifted over 4 months. This behavior is to be expected because dP/dt depends only on P, not on t, and both initial conditions have the same value of P.

c. Graph, above. Initial condition (0, 18)

The population is *decreasing* to the same asymptote, P = 10.5, as in parts a and b.

d. The asymptote at $P = 10.5$ indicates that the island can sustain only 1050 rabbits. If the population is lower than that, it increases. If the population is higher than that, it decreases. The number 10.5 is a value of P that makes dP/dt equal zero. Note that there is another asymptote at $P = 0$, which also makes dP/dt equal zero.

8. Terminal Velocity Problem

a. $dv/dt = 32.16 - 0.0015v^2$

Slope at (5, 120) appears to be about 1, but dv/dt actually equals $32.16 - 0.0015(120)^2 = 10.56$. The answers are different because the graph is scaled by a factor of 10.

b. Graph. Initial condition (t, v) = (0, 0)

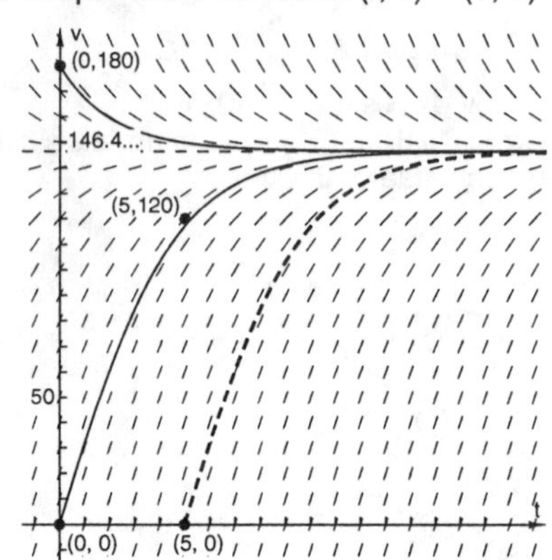

c. Terminal velocity occurs when dv/dt = 0.

$0 = 32.16 - 0.0015v^2$

$v = (32.16/0.0015)^{1/2} = 146.424... \approx 146$ ft/sec

The graph shows this velocity for times above about 15 seconds.

d. Graph, above. Initial condition (t, v) = (5, 0)

The graph is identical to the one in part b, except shifted 5 seconds to the right. This behavior is to be expected because the d.e. is independent of t.

e. Graph, above. This graph *decreases* to the terminal velocity since the diver starts out going *faster*.

f. Similarities include: Both models have a horizontal asymptote that the particular solutions approach from above or below. Both models decrease rapidly and gradually level off for values above the asymptotic limit.

Differences include: For values below the asymptotic limit, one model starts with rapid increase and gradually slows its growth, while the other starts with a slow increase that becomes more rapid growth before slowing toward the asymptote.

9. Escape Velocity Problem

a. $ma = \dfrac{mg}{r^2}$	By hypothesis
$\dfrac{dv}{dt} = \dfrac{g}{r^2}$	Divide by m; $a = \dfrac{dv}{dt}$
$\dfrac{dv}{dr} \cdot \dfrac{dr}{dt} = \dfrac{g}{r^2}$	Chain rule
$\dfrac{dv}{dr} \cdot v = \dfrac{g}{r^2}$	$v = \dfrac{dr}{dt}$ (r = distance)
$\dfrac{dv}{dr} = \dfrac{g}{r^2 v}$	Divide by v

b. $\dfrac{dv}{dr}(5,2) = -1.2488$

$\dfrac{dv}{dr}(1,10) = -6.244$

$\dfrac{dv}{dr}(10,4) = -0.1561$

These slopes agree with those shown.

c. Graph. Initial condition (r, v) = (1, 10)

From the graph, the velocity is zero at $r \approx 5$.

So the spaceship is about 4 Earth radii, or about 25,000 km, above the surface.

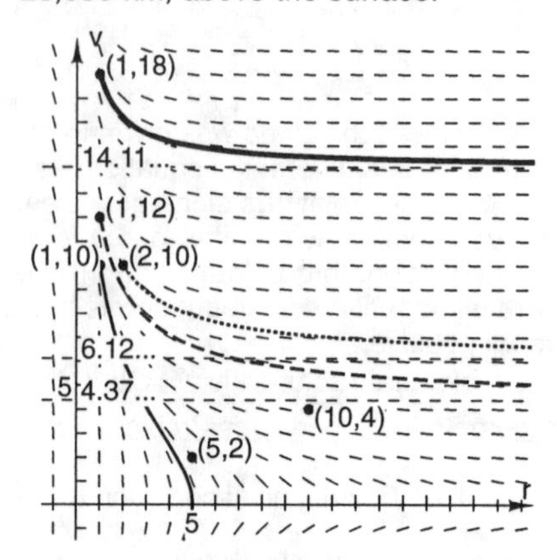

The precise value of r can be found algebraically.

$\dfrac{dv}{dr} = \dfrac{-62.44}{r^2 v} \Rightarrow \int v\,dv = \int \dfrac{-62.44}{r^2}\,dr$

$\Rightarrow \dfrac{v^2}{2} = \dfrac{62.44}{r} + C$

For the solution through (1,10), $C = 50 - 62.44 = -12.44$, so the ship starts falling when $v = 0$ at $r = 62.44/12.44 \approx 5$.

d. Graph, above. Initial condition (r, v) = (1, 12)

The graph levels off between 4 and 5 km/s.

The precise value of v can be found algebraically.

$C = 72 - 62.44 = 9.56 \Rightarrow \dfrac{v^2}{2} = \dfrac{62.44}{r} + 9.56$

Since $r > 0$, v is never zero, so the spaceship never stops and falls back.

As r approaches infinity, $v^2/2$ approaches 9.56, and thus v approaches $\sqrt{(2)(9.56)} = 4.37...$ km/s.

e. Graph, above. Initial condition (r, v) = (1, 18)

The graph levels off at $v \approx 14$ km/sec. Here the spaceship loses about 4 km/s of velocity, whereas it loses 7 or 8 km/s when starting at 12 km/s. Both cases lose the same amount of kinetic energy, which is proportional to v^2 (the change in v^2 is the same in both cases).

The precise value of v can be found algebraically as in part d. For the solution through (1,18), $C = 162 - 62.44 = 99.56$.

As $r \to \infty$, $v \to \sqrt{(2)(99.56)} = 14.11...$ km/s.

f. Graph, above. Initial condition (r, v) = (2, 10)

The graph levels off at about 6 km/sec, so the spaceship does escape.

Alternatively, note that the solution through (2,10) lies above the solution through (1,12).

The precise value of v can be found algebraically as in parts d and e. For the solution through (2,10), $C = 50 - 31.22 = 18.78$.

As $r \to \infty$, $v \to \sqrt{(2)(18.78)} = 6.12...$ km/s.

10. Slope Fields on the Grapher

See supplementary grapher programs.

Q1. ky

Q2. $y = Ce^{3x}$

Q3. 4.8

Q4. 100

Q5. $-\ln|1 - v| + C$

Q6. $\sec x \tan x$

Q7. $f'(x) = (3x + 5)^4$

Q8. Graph

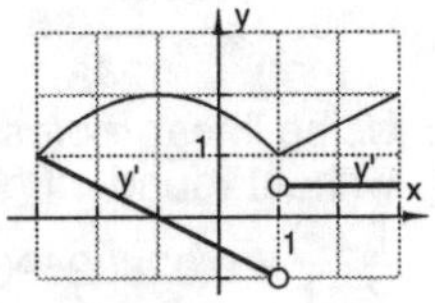

Q9. $3x^2y^5 + 5x^3y^4y' = 1 + y'$.

Q10. continuous

1. How Euler's Method Works

a. $\dfrac{dy}{dx} = -\dfrac{x}{2y}$

At (0, 3), $\dfrac{dy}{dx} = 0$

At $x = 0.5$, $y \approx 3$

b. At (0.5, 3), $\dfrac{dy}{dx} = -0.0833\ldots$.

$dy = (-0.0833\ldots)(0.5) = -0.04166\ldots$

At $x = 1$, $y \approx 3 - 0.04166\ldots = 2.9583\ldots$.

c.

x	y	slope	dy
1	2.9583...	−0.1690...	−0.0845...
1.5	2.8738...	−0.2609...	−0.1304...
2	2.7433...	−0.3645...	−0.1822...
2.5	2.5610...	−0.4880...	−0.2440...
3	2.3170...	−0.5463...	−0.3236...
3.5	1.9933...	−0.8779...	−0.4385...
4	1.5543...	−1.2866...	−0.6433...
4.5	0.9110...	−2.4696...	−1.2348...
5	−0.3237...	7.7213...	3.8606...
5.5	3.5368...	−0.7775...	−0.3887...
6	3.1481...	−0.9529...	−0.4764...
6.5	2.6716...	−1.2164...	−0.6082...
7	2.0634...	−1.6962...	−0.8481...

d. Graph.

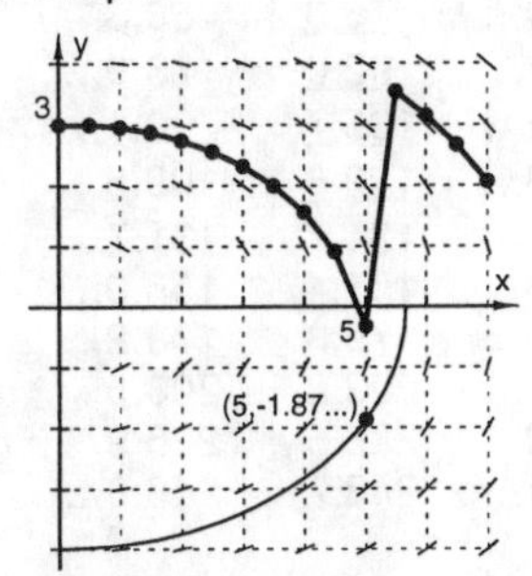

The values of y follow the slope field through $x = 4.5$. At $x = 5$, y becomes negative. As a result, dy/dx is positive and the curve jumps up in the positive direction. Thus, for $x > 5$ the y-values by Euler's method are clearly wrong. Note that the values follow another curve that has initial condition (5.5, 3.5368...).

2. Numerical Program for Euler's Method

See supplementary grapher programs.

3. Accuracy of Euler's Method

a. $\dfrac{dy}{dx} = -\dfrac{x}{2y} \Rightarrow \int 2y\,dy = -\int x\,dx \Rightarrow y^2 = -\dfrac{1}{2}x^2 + C$

Initial condition $(x, y) = (0, -4) \Rightarrow 16 = C$

$y^2 = -\dfrac{1}{2}x^2 + 16 \Rightarrow y = -\sqrt{16 - 0.5x^2}$

The negative root is picked because y is negative when $x = 0$.

For $x = 5$, $y = -\sqrt{3.5} = -1.8708\ldots$.

The point (5, −1.87...) is on the graph (see Problem 1, part d.)

b. $\Delta x = 0.5$

x	y
0	−4
1	−3.9687...
2	−3.8097...
3	−3.5085...
4	−3.0292...
5	−2.2823...
6	−0.9420...
7	−1.8486...

c. Graph, $\Delta x = 0.5$

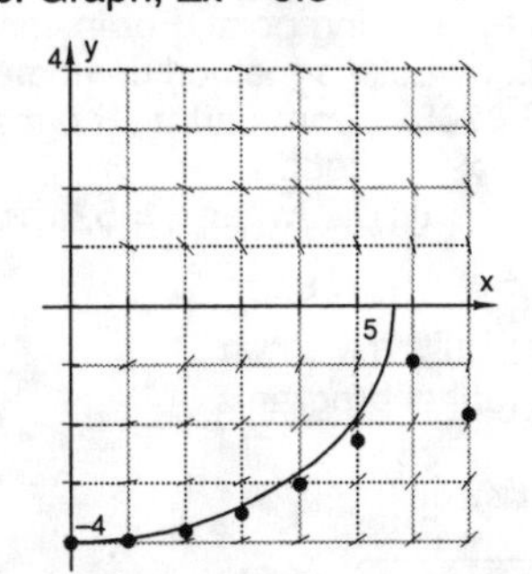

Euler's method gives a good approximation close to the starting point, but gets progressively worse farther away from the starting point. The answers are meaningless beyond the x-intercept, where the slope is infinite.

d. $\Delta x = 0.1$

x	y
0	−4
1	−3.9434...
2	−3.7555...
3	−3.4155...
4	−2.8715...
5	−1.9696...
6	0.7600...
7	2.1652...

Graph, $\Delta x = 0.1$

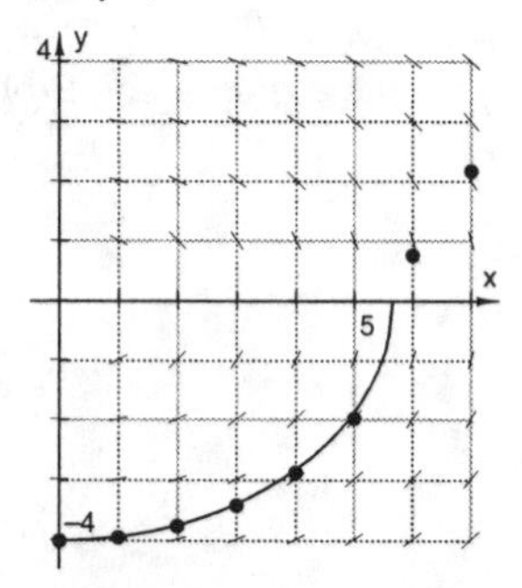

The approximation is better if Δx is smaller. The values still diverge slightly from the actual values as x gets farther from the starting point. For instance, if $x = 5$, $y \approx -1.9696...$ by Euler's method compared to the exact value, −1.8708..., from part a. The method still fails beyond the x-intercept.

e. Using $\Delta x = 0.01$, $y \approx -1.8812...$ when $x = 5$, which is quite close to $-\sqrt{3.5} = -1.8708...$.

4. Graphical Program for Euler's Method
See supplementary grapher programs.

5. a–b. Graph, $\dfrac{dy}{dx} = -0.2xy$

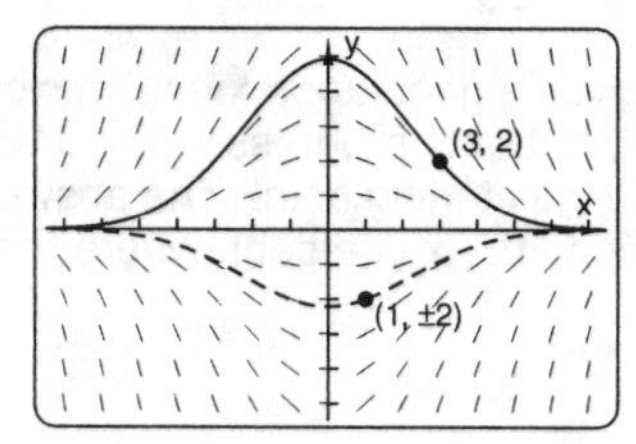

6.a–b. Graph, $\dfrac{dy}{dx} = -0.1x + 0.2y$

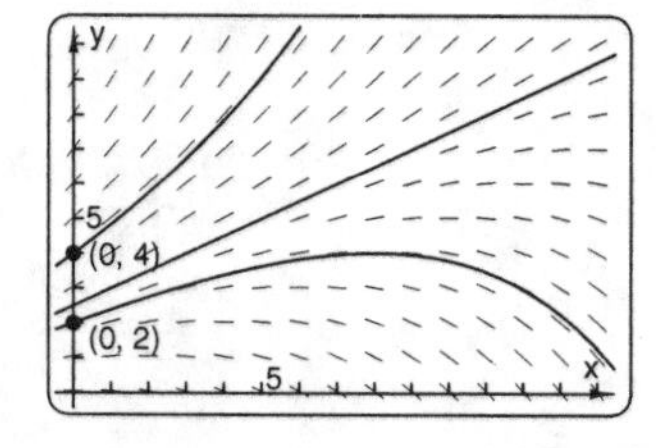

c. When the graph is observed, the slope lines seem to follow a straight path using (0, 2.5) as an initial condition. Euler's method confirms this.
(In differential equations, students will learn how to solve such first-order linears by multiplying both sides by the integrating factor $e^{-0.2x}$. The general solution is
$y = Ce^{0.2x} - 0.5x - 2.5$.
For C, = 0 the particular solution is $y = 0.5x + 2.5$.)

7. U.S. Population Project

a–b.

Year	P	$\Delta P/\Delta t$	$(\Delta P/\Delta t)/P$
1940	131.7		
1950	151.4	2.38	0.01571...
1960	179.3	2.59	0.01444...
1970	203.2	2.36	0.01161...
1980	226.5	2.275	0.01004...
1990	248.7		

c. Using linear regression on the values of $(\Delta P/\Delta t)/P$ without round-off gives

$$\frac{1}{P}\frac{\Delta P}{\Delta t} \approx 0.02802596... - 0.0000792747...P$$

The correlation coefficient is $r = -0.98535...$.
For the other types of regression:
$r = -0.978...$ for logarithmic
$r = -0.981...$ for exponential
$r = -0.981...$ for power
Thus, a linear function fits best because r is closest to −1.

d. $\dfrac{1}{P}\dfrac{dP}{dt} \approx 0.02802596... - 0.0000792747...P$

$\Rightarrow \dfrac{dP}{dt} = P(0.02802596... - 0.0000792747...P)$

e. Graph

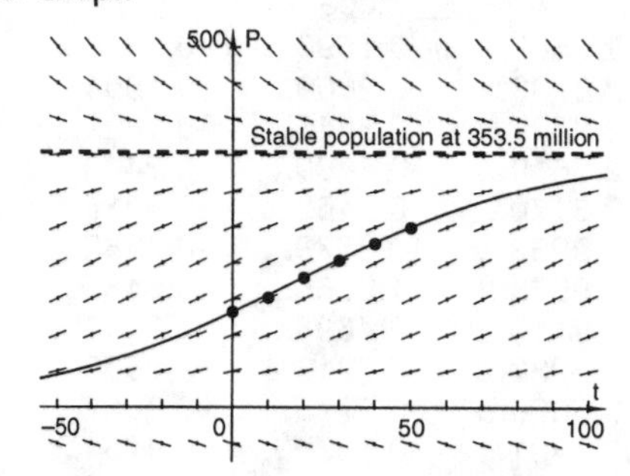

f.

Year	t	Euler	Actual*	Euler **
1890	−50	44.6...	62.9	46.1...
1900	−40	56.9...	76.0	58.3...
1910	−30	71.7...	92.0	73.9...
1920	−20	89.2...	105.7	90.1...
1930	−10	109.3...	122.8	109.8...
1940	0	131.7	131.7	131.7
1950	10	155.4...	151.4	155.0...
1960	20	180.1...	179.3	179.2...
1970	30	204.7...	203.2	203.5...
1980	40	228.2...	226.5	226.9...
1990	50	249.4...	248.7	248.8...
2000	60	269.3...		
2010	70	286.1...		
2020	80	300.2...		
2030	90	311.8...		
2040	100	321.1...		

*Data from The World Book Encyclopedia
**Note that although linear regression gives the "best" fit for $(\Delta P/\Delta t)/P$ versus P, actually plotting the graph shows that the data point for 1960 is considerably out of line.

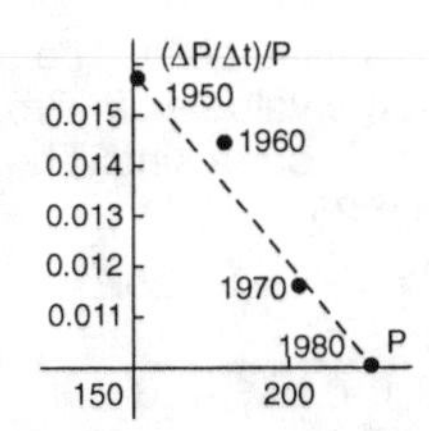

Using the two endpoints, 1950 and 1980, gives $(\Delta P/\Delta t)/P = 0.002716... - 0.00007558...P$.
Using this equation gives populations much closer to the actual ones for the given years, as shown in the rightmost column above. This is, of course, no guarantee that the later model fits any better in the future than the former one.

g. The population growth rate is zero if $dP/dt = 0$.
Let $P(0.02802596... - 0.0000792747...P) = 0$.
$P = 0$ or
$P = (0.02802596...)/(0.0000792747...) = 353.5...$
Predicted ultimate population $\approx$ 353.5 million
d.e.: $P = 353.5...$ makes $dP/dt = 0$.
Graph: $P = 353.5...$ is a horizontal asymptote.

h. Graph, part f. Data do follow the solution.

i. Example answer: "The predicted populations agree fairly well with the data for the six given years. The fit is exact for 1940 since this point was used as an initial condition. For the other five years, the predicted populations are a bit higher than the actual population."

j. Actual data are underlined in the table in part f.

k. The predicted population for 2000 from part f is 269.3... million. Using 469.3 million as an initial condition in 2000 gives the following predictions:

Year	t	Euler
2000	60	469.3
2010	70	433.9...
2020	80	410.6...
2030	90	394.8...
2040	100	383.7...

The logistic model predicts that the population will *drop*, approaching the ultimate value of 353.5 million from *above.* This behavior shows up in the slope field of part c, since the slopes are *negative* for populations above 353.5.

8. a. $\frac{1}{y(10-y)} = \frac{A}{y} + \frac{B}{10-y} = \frac{A(10-y) + By}{y(10-y)}$
The numerator of the first fraction must equal that of the last fraction for all values of y. That is,
$1 = 10A - Ay + By$.
The constant and linear coefficients on the left must equal the corresponding ones on the right.
Thus, $1 = 10A$ and $0 = -Ay + By$.
So $A = B = 0.1$.

b. $\int \frac{1}{y(10-y)}\,dy = \int \left(\frac{0.1}{y} + \frac{0.1}{10-y}\right) dy$
$= 0.1\int \left(\frac{1}{y} - \frac{1}{y-10}\right) dy$, which equals $3\int dx$.
$\therefore 0.1(\ln|y| - \ln|y-10|) = 3x + C$
$\ln\left|\frac{y}{y-10}\right| = -\ln\left|\frac{y-10}{y}\right| = 30x + 10C$
$\left|\frac{y-10}{y}\right| = \left|1 - \frac{10}{y}\right| = e^{-(30x+10C)}$
$\frac{10}{y} = 1 \pm e^{-10C}e^{-30x}$
$y = \frac{10}{1+ke^{-30x}}$ where $k = \pm e^{-10C}$, Q.E.D.

c. $\frac{dP}{dt} = P(0.02802... - 0.00007927...P)$
$= 0.00007927...P(353.5... - P)$
$\int \frac{1}{P(353.5... - P)}\,dP = 0.00007927...\int dt$
$= \frac{1}{353.5...}\int \left(\frac{1}{P} - \frac{1}{P - 353.5...}\right) dP$
$= 0.00007927...\int dt$
$\ln|P| - \ln|P - 353.5...|$
$= 353.5...(0.00007927...t + C)$
$\ln\left|\frac{P}{P-353.5...}\right| = -\ln\left|\frac{P-353.5...}{P}\right|$
$= 0.02802...t + 353.5...C$
$\left|\frac{P-353.5...}{P}\right| = e^{-(0.02802...t + 353.5...C)}$
$\frac{353.5...}{P} = 1 + ke^{0.02802...t}$
$P = \frac{353.5...}{1+ke^{-0.02802...t}}$.
For the initial condition $t = 0$, $P = 131.7$,
$k = \frac{353.5...}{131.7} - 1 = 1.684...$.

d.

Year	t	Algebraic	Euler	Actual
1940	0	131.7	131.7	131.7
1950	10	155.5...	155.4...	151.4
1960	20	180.2...	180.1...	179.3
1970	30	204.7...	204.7...	203.2
1980	40	228.2...	228.2...	226.5
1990	50	249.8...	249.9...	248.7

The two methods of evaluating the mathematical model agree almost perfectly. However, the fact that they agree with each other is no guarantee that they will fit the real world as closely as they match each other.

9. Journal Problem
Journal entries will vary.

Problem Set 7-6, pages 339 to 340 — Predator-Prey Population Problems

Q1. definition of definite integral
Q2. fundamental theorem of calculus
Q3. definition of indefinite integral
Q4. the intermediate value theorem
Q5. Rolle's theorem
Q6. the mean value theorem
Q7. the chain rule
Q8. general
Q9. particular
Q10. initial

1. $\frac{dR}{dt} = k_1R \Rightarrow \frac{dR}{R} = k_1dt \Rightarrow \ln|R| = k_1t + C$
$\Rightarrow |R| = e^Ce^{k_1t} \Rightarrow R = C_1e^{k_1t}$
R is increasing since $k_1 > 0$.

2. $\frac{dF}{dt} = -k_2F \Rightarrow \frac{dF}{F} = -k_2dt \Rightarrow \ln|F| = -k_2t + C$
$\Rightarrow |F| = e^Ce^{-k_2t} \Rightarrow F = C_2e^{-k_2t}$
F is decreasing since $-k_2 < 0$.

3. $\frac{dR}{dt} = k_1R - k_3RF$
$\frac{dF}{dt} = -k_2F + k_4RF$

4. $\frac{dF}{dR} = \frac{dF/dt}{dR/dt} = \frac{-k_2F + k_4RF}{k_1R - k_3RF}$
The dt cancels out.

5. R = 70, F = 15

$$\Rightarrow \frac{dF}{dR} = \frac{-15 + 0.025\cdot 1050}{70 - 0.04\cdot 1050} = \frac{11.25}{28} = 0.4017...$$

6. Graph. The slope at (70, 15) is about 0.4.

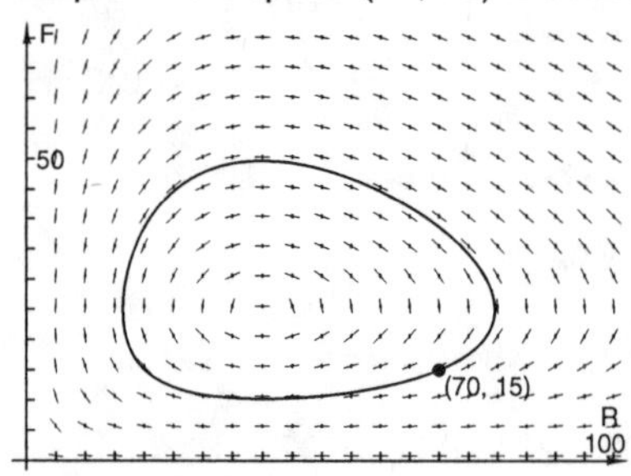

At R = 70, F = 15, $\frac{dR}{dt} = 28$ and $\frac{dF}{dt} = 11.25$, which are both positive. So both populations are increasing and the graph starts up and to the right.

7. The populations vary periodically and the graph is cyclical. The foxes reach their maximum 1/4 cycle after the rabbits.

8. Neither population changes when dR/dt = dF/dt = 0.

dR/dt = 0 ⇔ F = 0 or R = 1/0.025 = 40 (4000 rabbits)

dF/dt = 0 ⇔ R = 0 or F = 1/0.04 = 25 foxes

9. Assume that dF/dt still equals –F + 0.025RF.

$$\frac{dF}{dR} = \frac{dF/dt}{dR/dt} = \frac{-F + 0.025RF}{R - 0.04RF - 0.01R^2}$$

R = 70 and F = 15 ⇒ $\frac{dF}{dR} = \frac{11.25}{-21} = -0.5357...$

10. Graph. The slope at (70, 15) is now *negative*.

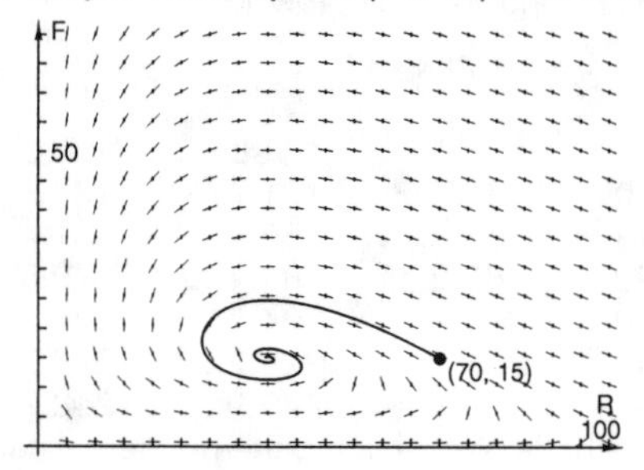

11. The populations now spiral to a fixed point. The rabbit population stabilizes at the same value as in Problem 8, R = 40 (4000 rabbits), which is surprising. The stable fox population decreases from 25 to 15.

12. Assume that dF/dt still equals = –F + 0.025RF.

$$\frac{dF}{dR} = \frac{dF/dt}{dR/dt} = \frac{-F + 0.025RF}{R - 0.04RF - 0.01R^2 - 10}$$

R = 70 and F = 15 ⇒ $\frac{dF}{dR} = \frac{11.25}{-31} = -0.3629...$

13. Graph. The slope at (70, 15) is about –0.4.

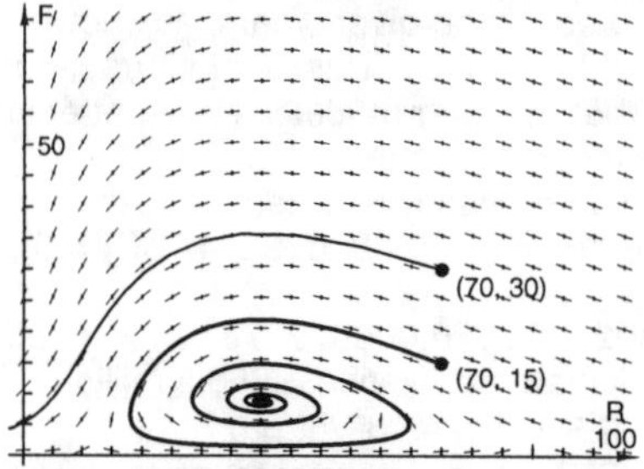

14. The fox and rabbit populations spiral toward a fixed point. Again, the rabbits stabilize at R = 40 (4000). But the stable fox population is reduced to 8 or 9. Along the way, the model shows that the foxes are reduced to about 1, thus becoming in danger of extinction!

15. Graph in Problem 13, starting at (70, 30). With this many foxes and hunters chasing rabbits, the rabbits become extinct. At this point the foxes have been reduced to just 5. After the rabbits become extinct, the foxes decrease exponentially with time, eventually becoming extinct themselves.

Problem Set 7-7, pages 341 to 346 — Chapter Review and Test

Review Problems

R0. Journal entries will vary.

R1. Punctured Tire Problem

$P(t) = 35(0.98^t)$

$P'(t) = 35(0.98^t) \ln 0.98$

t	P(t)	P'(t)	P'(t)/P(t)
0	35	–0.7070...	–0.2020...
10	28.597...	–0.5777...	–0.2020...
20	23.366...	–0.4720...	–0.2020...

$$\frac{P'(t)}{P(t)} = \frac{35(0.98^t)\ln 0.98}{35(0.98^t)} = \ln 0.98 = -0.2020...,$$

which is a constant, Q.E.D.

R2. Ramjet Problem

a. V = speed in mph, t = time in seconds.

$$\frac{dV}{dt} = kV$$

b. $\int \frac{dV}{V} = k\int dt$

$\ln|V| = kt + C \Rightarrow |V| = e^{kt+C} = e^C \cdot e^{kt} \Rightarrow$

$V = C_1e^{kt}$

Mathematically, C_1 can be positive or negative, so the absolute value sign is not needed for V. In the real world V is positive, which also makes the absolute value sign unnecessary.

c. $400 = Ce^{k\cdot 0} \Rightarrow C = 400.$

$500 = 400e^{k\cdot 40} \Rightarrow k = \frac{\ln 1.25}{40} = 0.005578...$

$V = 400e^{0.005578...t}$

d. $750 = 400e^{0.005578...t}$

$\Rightarrow t = \frac{\ln 1.875}{0.005578...} = 112.68... \approx$ <u>113 seconds</u>

R3. a. $\int y^{-1/2}\,dy = 6\int dx \Rightarrow y = (3x + C)^2$

b. $y = (3x - 4)^2$

c. Graph

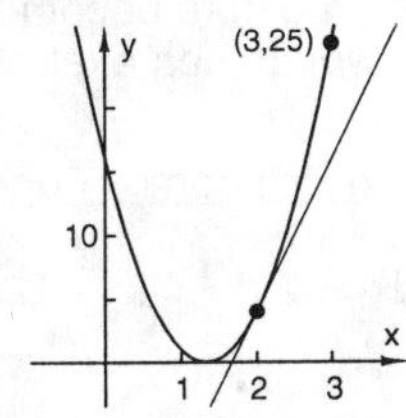

d. At $x = 2$, $y' = 12$ and $y = 4$.
A line through (2, 4) with slope 12 is tangent to the graph, showing that 12 is reasonable.

e. Memory Retention Problem

i. $dN/dt = 100 - kN$

$\int \frac{dN}{100 - kN} = \int dt$

$-(1/k)\ln|100 - kN| = t + C$

Using (0, 0) gives $-(1/k)\ln 100 = C$.

Substituting this value for C gives

$-(1/k)\ln|100 - kN| = t - (1/k)\ln 100$.

$\ln|100 - kN| - \ln 100 = -kt$

$\ln|1 - (k/100)N| = -kt$

$1 - (k/100)N = e^{-kt}$

$N = (100/k)(1 - e^{-kt})$

Using (7, 600) and solving numerically gives $k \approx 0.045236$.

$\therefore N = 2210.6...(1 - e^{-0.045236t})$

ii. $t = 30$: About 1642 names

iii. $\lim_{t\to\infty} N = 2210.6...(1 - 0) = 2210.6...$

Brain saturates at about 2211 names.

iv. Let $dN/dt = 30$.

$30 = 100 - kN \Rightarrow N = \frac{70}{k} = 1547.4...$ names

Substituting this for N gives

$1547.4... = 2210.6...(1 - e^{-0.045236t})$.

$e^{-0.045236t} = 1 - \frac{1547.4...}{2210.6...} = 0.3$ (exactly)

$t = \frac{\ln 0.3}{-0.04523...} = 26.6... \approx$ 27 days

or:

$30 = N(t) - N(t - 1)$

$= 2210.6...(-e^{-0.045236t} + e^{-0.045236(t-1)})$

$= 2210.6...e^{-0.045236t(t-1)}(-e^{-0.045236} + 1)$

$\Rightarrow t \approx 27$ days

R4. a. $\frac{dy}{dx} = -\frac{20}{xy} + 0.05y$

At (2,5), $dy/dx = -1.75$.

At (10, 16), $dy/dx = 0.675$.

The slopes at (2, 5) and (10, 16) agree with these numbers as shown on the graph in part b.

b. Graph, initial conditions (1,8) and (1, 12)

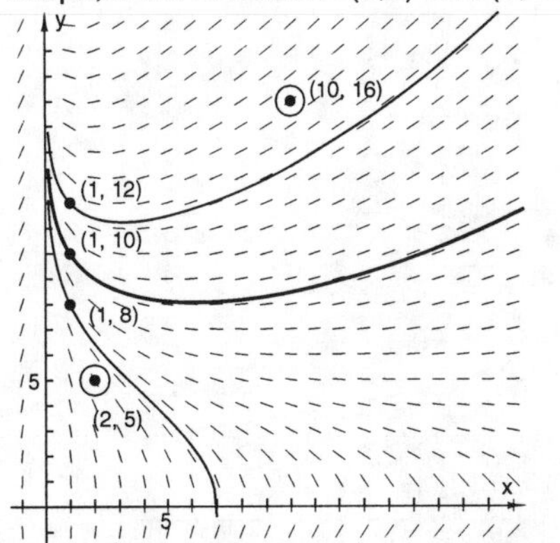

The solution containing (1,8) crosses the x-axis near $x = 7$, converges asymptotically to the y-axis as x approaches zero, and is symmetric across the x-axis. The solution containing (1,12) goes to infinity as x goes to infinity.

c. Graph, initial condition (1, 10)

The solution containing (1,10) behaves more like the one containing (1,12), although a slight discrepancy in plotting may make it seem to go the other way.

R5. a. $\frac{dy}{dx} = -\frac{20}{xy} + 0.05y$

Table, initial condition (1, 9), $\Delta x = 1$

x	y (Δx = 1)	y (Δx = 0.1)
1	9	9
2	7.227...	7.707...
3	6.205...	6.949...
4	5.441...	6.413...
5	4.794...	5.999...
6	4.200...	5.662...
7	3.616...	5.377...
8	3.007...	5.130...
9	2.326...	4.910...
10	1.488...	4.712...
11	0.2185...	4.529...
12	−8.091...	4.359...
13		4.199...
14		4.045...
15		3.896...
16		3.750...
17		3.604...
18		3.457...
19		3.306...
20		3.150...
21		2.986...
22		2.811...
23		2.621...
24		2.410...
...		...
28.9		0.1344...
29		−0.3796...

Graph, $\Delta x = 1$, crosses x-axis at about $x = 11$.

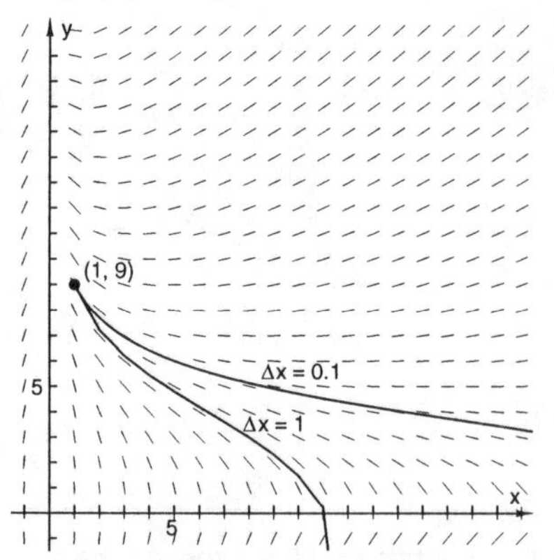

For $\Delta x = 1$, the graph crosses the x-axis at about $x = 11$, and for $\Delta x = 0.1$, the graph crosses the x-axis at about $x = 28.9$.

b. Table in part a, $\Delta x = 0.1$
Graph in part a shows different pattern.

c. The accuracy far away from the initial condition is very sensitive to the size of the increment. For instance, in part a the first step took the graph so far down that it crosses the x-axis before running off the edge of the grid. The greater accuracy with $\Delta x = 0.1$ shows that the graph actually does not cross the x-axis before $x = 20$.

d. Continuing the computations in part c, the graph crosses the x-axis close to $x = 28.9$. See the table in part a.

R6. Predator-Prey Problem

a. $\dfrac{dy}{dx} = \dfrac{-0.5(x-6)}{(y-7)}$
$dy = 0$ when $x = 6$ and $dx = 0$ when $y = 7$. So the stable point is (6, 7), corresponding to the present population of 600 Xaltos natives and 7000 yaks. (Note that the general solution to the diff. eq. is $(x-6)^2 + 2(y-7)^2 = C$, and the specific solution for the given initial condition is $(x-6)^2 + 2(y-7)^2 = 0$, whose graph is a single point.)

b. Graph, initial condition (9, 7)

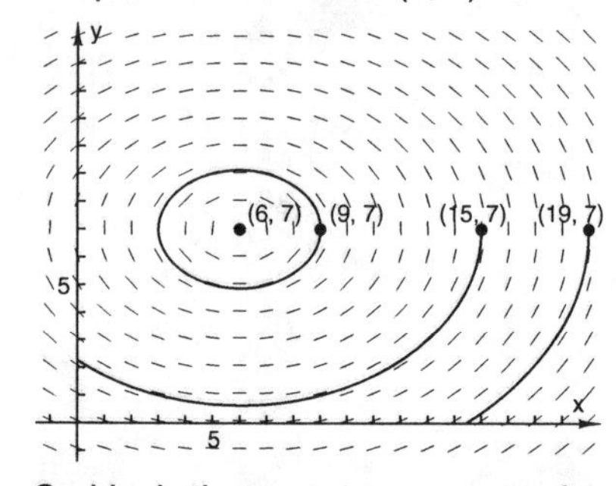

Suddenly there are too many predators for the number of prey, so the yak population declines. Since y is decreasing from (9, 7), the graph follows a clockwise path.

c. Graph, initial condition (19, 7), in part b
The graph crosses the x-axis at $x \approx 14.4$, indicating that the yaks are hunted to extinction. (The Xaltos would then starve or become vegetarian!)

d. Graph, initial condition (15, 7), in part b
The graph never crosses the x-axis, but crosses the y-axis at $y \approx 2.3$, indicating that the yak population becomes so sparse that the predators become extinct. (The yak population would then explode!)

Concepts Problems

C1. Differential Equations Leading to Polynomial Functions

a. $\dfrac{dy}{dx} = k \cdot y^{1/2} \Rightarrow y^{-1/2}\,dy = k\,dx \Rightarrow 2y^{1/2} = kx + C$ so
$y = (0.5(kx + C))^2$.

b. The differential equation would have to become $y^{1/3}$ after it is integrated. So the original equation would have to contain $y^{-2/3}$ after the variables have been separated.
Conjecture: $\dfrac{dy}{dx} = ky^{2/3}$

c. Confirmation:
$\dfrac{dy}{dx} = ky^{2/3} \Rightarrow y^{-2/3}\,dy = k\,dx \Rightarrow 3y^{1/3} = kx + C \Rightarrow$
$y = [(1/3)(kx + C)]^3$, a cubic function, Q.E.D.

d. For $n \neq 0$, $\dfrac{dy}{dx} = k \cdot y^{(n-1)/n} \Rightarrow y^{-(n-1)/n}\,dy = k\,dx \Rightarrow$
$ny^{1/n} = kx + C \Rightarrow y = [(1/n)(kx + C)]^n$.
For example: $\dfrac{dy}{dx} = y^{7/8} \Rightarrow y^{-7/8}\,dy = dx$
$\Rightarrow 8y^{1/8} = x + C \Rightarrow y = [(1/8)(x + C)]^8$

C2. Film Festival Problem

a.

Ticket Price	People
2.00	460
2.50	360
3.00	320
4.00	260
4.50	140
5.50	120
6.00	80

b. Graph

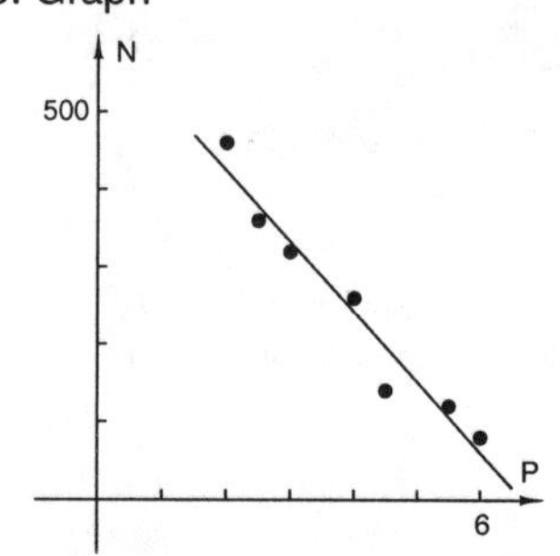

Function behaves (more or less) linearly.
Let N = no. of tickets and P = no. of \$/ticket.
By linear regression,
$N \approx -90.83P + 605.4$,
with correlation coefficient $r = -0.9747...$

c. Let M = total number of dollars.
$M \approx P \cdot N = P(-90.83P + 605.4)$
$M \approx -90.83P^2 + 605.4P$

d. Maximize M: $M' \approx -181.66P + 605.4$

$M' = 0 \Leftrightarrow P \approx \frac{605.4}{181.66} = 3.332...$

Maximum M at $P \approx 3.332...$ because M' changes from positive to negative there (or because the graph of M is a parabola opening downward).

Charge \$3.30 or \$3.35.

e. Charging more than the optimum price reduces attendance enough to reduce the total amount made. Charging less than the optimum price increases attendance, but not enough to make up for the lower price per ticket.

Because M has a local maximum at this price.

C3. Gompertz Growth Curve Problem

a. $g(t) = 10e^{-0.8e^{-0.5t}}$

Graph does look like Figure 7-7d.

$\lim_{t\to\infty} 10e^{-0.8e^{-0.5t}} = 10e^{-0.8 \lim_{t\to\infty} e^{-0.5t}}$

$= 10e^{-0.8 \cdot 0} = 10$

Limit is 10, indicating max. possible population.

b. a = 421.3692..., c = 0.7303036..., and k = 0.01589546..., either by twice taking logarithms as suggested, or by this method:

Taking ln once $\Rightarrow \ln a - ce^{-kt} = \ln P$, so

$\ln a - ce^{10k} = \ln 179$

$\ln a - c = \ln 203$

$\ln a - ce^{-10k} = \ln 226;$

then substituting $\ln a = c + \ln 203$ gives

$c(1 - e^{10k}) = \ln 179 - \ln 203$

$c(1 - e^{-10k}) = \ln 226 - \ln 203;$

Substituting $c(1 - e^{-10k}) = c(e^{10k} - 1)e^{-10k}$

$= -e^{-10k}(\ln 179 - \ln 203)$ into the first equation yields

$$e^{-10k} = -\frac{\ln 226 - \ln 203}{\ln 179 - \ln 203} = \frac{\ln 226 - \ln 203}{\ln 203 - \ln 179}$$

$$\text{so } k = -\frac{1}{10}\ln\left(\frac{\ln 226 - \ln 203}{\ln 203 - \ln 179}\right) = 0.01589... .$$

Then find c using $c(1 - e^{-10k}) = \ln 226 - \ln 203$ and find a with $203 = ae^{-c}$.

Graph

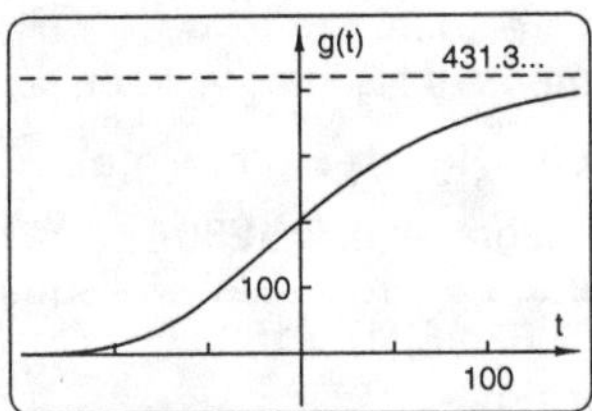

Note that this model predicts an ultimate population $\lim_{t\to\infty} P(t) \approx 421$ million people.

c. Now a = 551.1655..., c = 0.9988291..., k = 0.01186428..., and the ultimate population is $\lim_{t\to\infty} P(t) \approx 551$ million people.

Thus, the Gompertz model is quite sensitive to a small change in initial conditions. The predicted ultimate population increased by 130 million with only a 1 million change in one data point!

C4. Hot Tub Problem, Continued

$\frac{dV}{dt} = -2V^{1/2} + F$, where F is a constant.

$\int \frac{dV}{F - 2V^{1/2}} = \int dt$

The integral on the right is not the integral of the reciprocal function because the numerator cannot be made the differential of the denominator. A slope field gives information about the solutions. The graph below is for F = 20 ft^3/min flowing in. (The dotted line shows the solution with F = 0, the original condition.) Starting with 196 ft^3 in the tub, the volume levels off near 100 ft^3. Starting below 100 ft^3, the volume would increase toward 100.

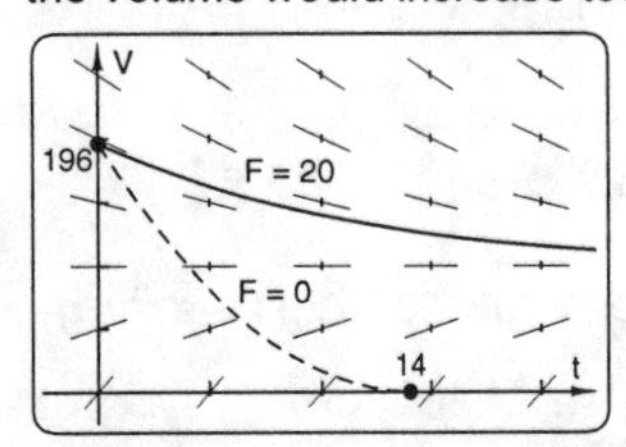

If the inflow rate is too high, the tub will overflow. The graph below is for F = 40 ft^3/min. In this case, the stable volume is above the initial 196 ft^3.

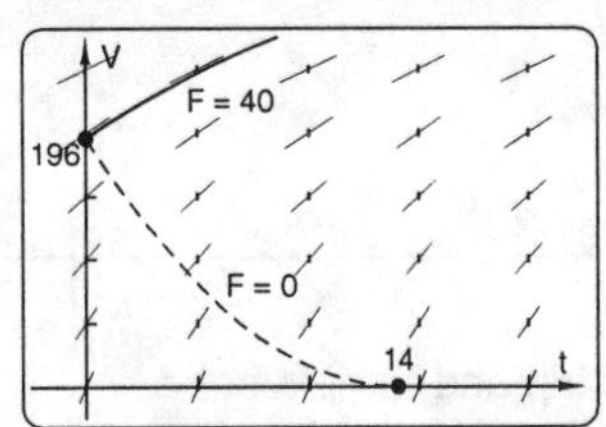

It is possible to antidifferentiate the left side, above, by the algebraic substitution method of Problem Set 9–11, Problems 101–106. The general solution is

$$t + C = -\frac{F}{2}\ln(F - 2V^{1/2}) - V^{1/2},$$

and the particular solution for V = 196 at t = 0 is

$$t - 14 = -\frac{F}{2}\ln\left|\frac{F - 28}{F - 2V^{1/2}}\right| - V^{1/2}.$$

Unfortunately, it is difficult or impossible to solve for V. The volume will asymptotically approach $F^2/4$, overflowing the tub if $F^2/4 >$ tub capacity.

Chapter Test

T1. Phoebe's Space Leak Problem

a. $\frac{dP}{dt} = kP \Rightarrow P = Ce^{kt}$

$P = 3000$ at $t = 0 \Rightarrow P = 3000e^{kt}$

b. $P = 2300$ at $t = 5 \Rightarrow k = \frac{1}{5}\ln\frac{2300}{3000} = -0.05314...$ P(25)

$= 794.6...$

Phoebe will not quite make it because the pressure has dropped just below 800 psi by time t = 25.

or:

$800 = 3000e^{-0.05314...t}$

$t = \frac{1}{-0.05314...}\ln\frac{800}{3000} = 24.87...$

Phoebe will not quite make it because the pressure has dropped to 800 just before t = 25.

T2. Swimming Pool Chlorination Problem

a. Let y = no. of grams of chlorine dissolved.
Let t = no. of hours since chlorinator was started.
$\frac{dy}{dt} = 30 - ky$
$\int \frac{dy}{30 - ky} = \int dt$
$-\frac{1}{k} \ln |30 - ky| = t + C$
$\ln |30 - ky| = -kt + C_1$
$30 - ky = C_2 e^{-kt}$
$y = 0$ when $t = 0 \Rightarrow C_2 = 30$
$\therefore ky = 30(1 - e^{-kt})$
$y = \frac{30}{k}(1 - e^{-kt})$
The rate of escape ky = 13 when y = 100
So k = 0.13.
$\therefore y = \frac{30}{0.13}(1 - e^{-0.13t}) = 230.7...(1 - e^{-0.13t})$

b. $200 = 230.7...(1 - e^{-0.13t})$
$e^{-0.13t} = 1 - \frac{200}{230.7...} = 0.1333...$
$t = \frac{\ln 0.1333...}{-0.13} = 15.499... \approx 15.5$ hours

T3. a. Graph, $\frac{dy}{dx} = -0.36\frac{x}{y}$, initial condition (0, 4)

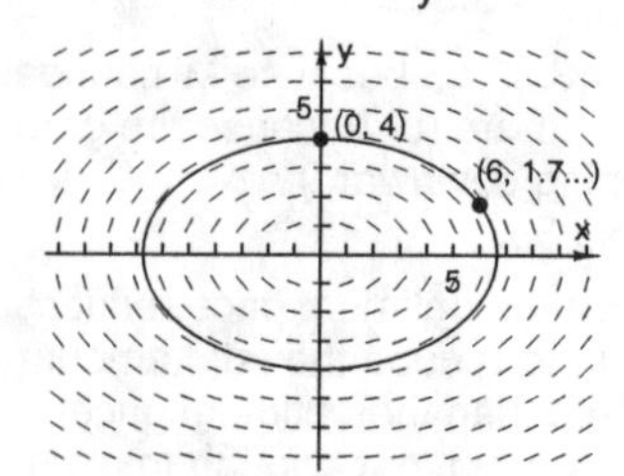

b. For $\Delta x = 0.1$, $y = 1.838591$ at $x = 6$.

c. $\int y\, dy = -0.36 \int x\, dx$
$\frac{1}{2}y^2 = -0.18x^2 + C$
$0.36x^2 + y^2 = C_1$ (the equation of an ellipse)
$y = \pm\sqrt{C_1 - 0.36x^2}$
For the initial condition (0, 4),
$0 + 16 = C_1 \Rightarrow 0.36x^2 + y^2 = 16.$
$y = \pm\sqrt{16 - 0.36x^2}$

d. For x = 6, $y = \pm\sqrt{16 - 0.36 \cdot 36} = \pm\sqrt{3.04} =$ $\pm 1.74355...$.
The 1.838... by Euler's method is within 0.095 of the positive solution. The error is about 5%.

T4. Answers will vary.

Problem Set 7-8, pages 347 to 349

Rocket Problems

1. Graph, showing strip and sample point.
v(t) dt represents the distance traveled in time dt.

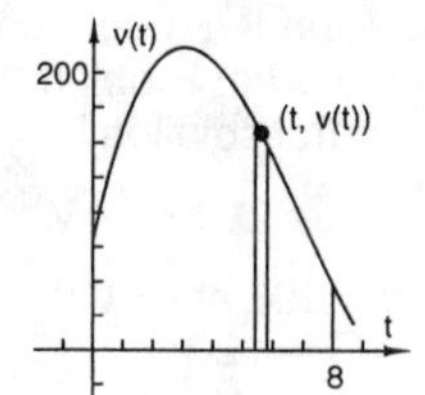

2. Definite integral

3. $\int_0^8 (t^3 - 21t^2 + 100t + 80)\, dt$
$= \frac{1}{4}t^4 - 7t^3 + 50t^2 + 80t \Big|_0^8$
= 1280 mi

4. $M_{100} = 1280.0384$
$M_{1000} = 1280.000384$
The Riemann sums seem to be approaching 1280 as n increases. Thus, the 1280 that was found by purely algebraic methods seems to give the correct value of the limit of the Riemann sum.

5. Graph, showing the upper sum U_8.

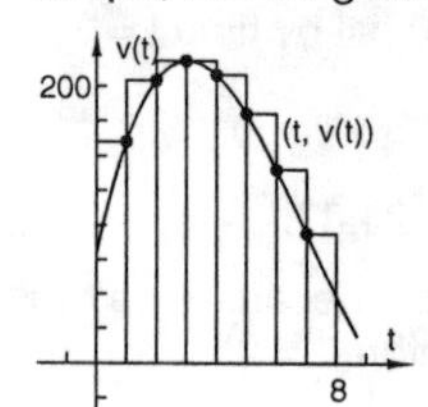

Cumulative Review: Chapters 1–7

6. Any Riemann sum is bounded by the corresponding lower and upper sums. That is,
$L_n \le R_n \le U_n$.
By the definition of integrability, the limits of L_n and U_n are equal to each other, and to the definite integral. By the squeeze theorem, then, the limit of R_n is also equal to the definite integral.

7. Definition: $\int_a^b f(x)\, dx = \lim_{\Delta x \to 0} L_n = \lim_{\Delta x \to 0} U_n$ provided that the two limits are equal.
Fundamental theorem: If f is integrable on [a, b] and $g(x) = \int f(x)\, dx$, then $\int_a^b f(x)\, dx = g(b) - g(a)$.

8. Numerically, the integral equals 1280.
By counting, there are approximately 52 squares.
Thus, the integral ≈ 52(25)(1) = 1300.

9. $v'(4) \approx \frac{v(4.1) - v(3.9)}{0.2} = -19.9$ (mi/min)/min
$v'(4) \approx \frac{v(4.01) - v(3.99)}{0.02} = -19.9999$ (mi/min)/min

10. $f'(c) = \lim_{x \to c} \frac{f(x) - f(c)}{x - c}$ or
$f'(x) = \lim_{\Delta x \to 0} \frac{f(x + \Delta x) - f(x)}{\Delta x}$

11. $v'(t) = 3t^2 - 42t + 100 \Rightarrow v'(4) = -20$

12. Slowing down. $v'(4) < 0 \Rightarrow$ velocity is decreasing.

13. Graph, showing line of slope –20 through (4, 208). The line is tangent to the graph.

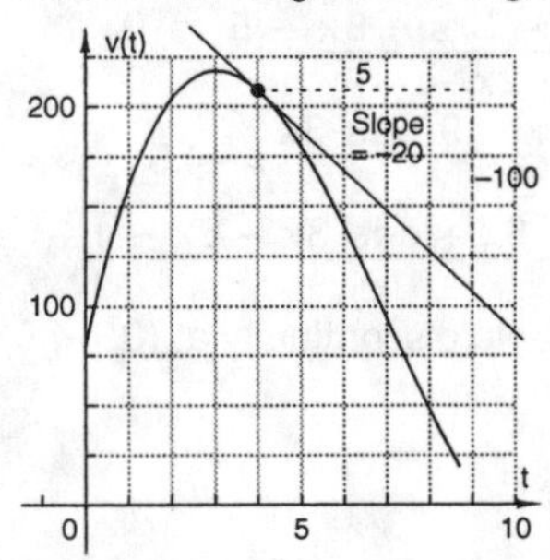

14. Acceleration.

15. At a maximum of v(t), v'(t) will equal zero.

$3t^2 - 42t + 100 = 0 \Leftrightarrow t = \dfrac{42 \pm \sqrt{42^2 - 4 \cdot 3 \cdot 100}}{6}$

t = 10.958... or 3.041...

So the maximum is *not* at exactly t = 3.

16. $v''(t) = 6t - 42$

Compound Interest Problems

17. $\dfrac{dm}{dt} = km$

18. $\int \dfrac{dm}{m} = k \int dt \Rightarrow \ln |m| = kt + C \Rightarrow$

$|m| = e^{kt + C} \Rightarrow m = C_1 e^{kt}$

19. Exponentially

20. General

21. $10{,}000 = C_1 e^0 \Rightarrow C_1 = 10{,}000$

$10{,}900 = 10{,}000e^{k \cdot 1}$

$\Rightarrow k = \ln 1.09,\ m = 10{,}000e^{\ln(1.09)t} = 10{,}000(1.09)^t$

22. False. The rate of increase changes as the amount in the account increases. At t = 10,

$m = 10{,}000(1.09)^{10} \approx 23{,}673.64$.

The amount of money would grow by $13,673.64, not just $9,000.

Discrete Data Problems

23. By Simpson's rule, $\int_{30}^{42} y\,dx$

$\approx \frac{2}{3}(74 + 4 \cdot 77 + 2 \cdot 83 + 4 \cdot 88 + 2 \cdot 90 + 4 \cdot 91 + 89)$

$= 1022$

24. By symmetric difference quotient, at x = 36

$y' \approx \dfrac{90 - 83}{2(2)} = 1.75$

Mean Value Theorem Problems

25. If f is differentiable on (a, b), and continuous at x = a and x = b, and if f(a) = f(b) = 0, then there is a number x = c in (a, b) such that f'(c) = 0.

26. Graph, example

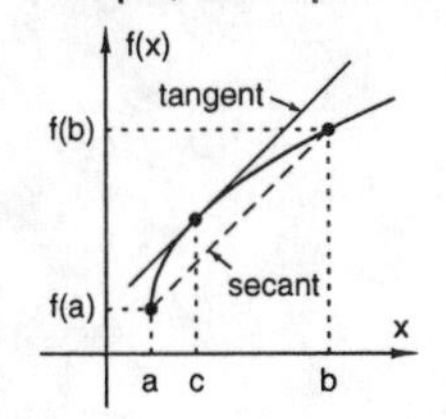

Graphing Problems

27. Graph. Equation is

$$f(x) = \begin{cases} x^3/6 - 1.5x^2 + 2.5x + 11/6, & \text{if } x \le 7 \\ 10 - x, & \text{if } x > 7 \end{cases}$$

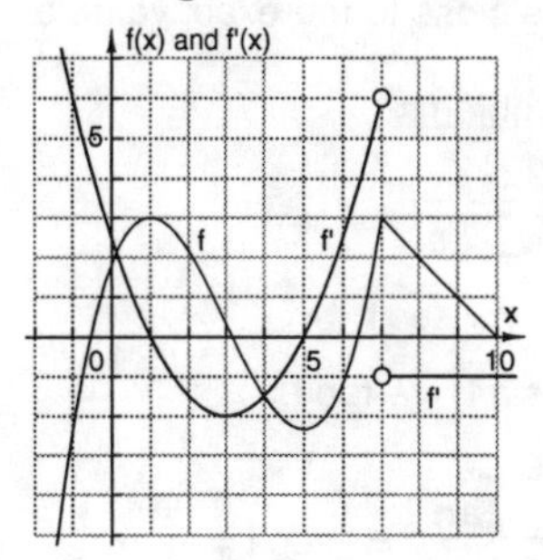

28. Graph, $f(x) = 2^x - \dfrac{|x - 1|}{x - 1}$

Step discontinuity at x = 1

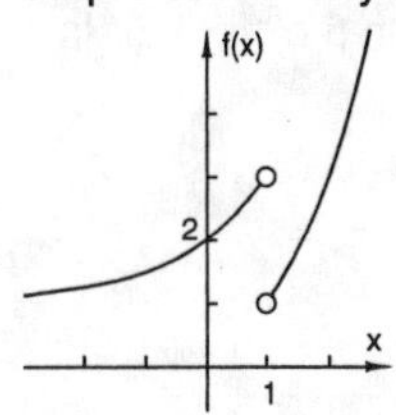

29. $g(x) = x^{1/3}(x - 1)$

$g'(x) = x^{1/3} + \frac{1}{3}x^{-2/3}(x - 1) = \frac{1}{3}x^{-2/3}(4x - 1)$

g'(0) is undefined because $0^{-2/3}$ takes on the form $1/0^{2/3}$ or 1/0.

Graph

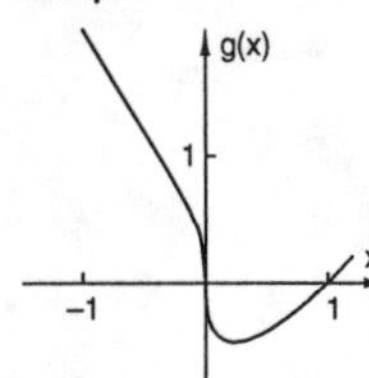

Differential Equation Problems

30. Graph, $\dfrac{dy}{dx} = 0.25\dfrac{x}{y}$

Initial conditions: (0, 3) and (10, 4)

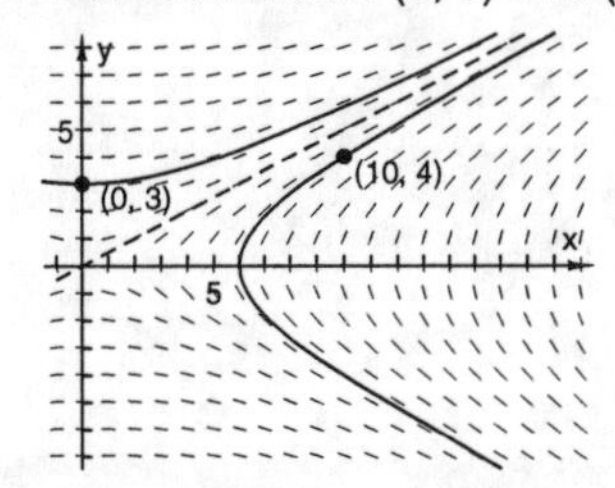

31. Graph, Problem 30. Any initial condition such as (2, 1) for which y = 0.5x gives the asymptote.

32. $\int y\,dy = 0.25 \int x\,dx \Rightarrow 0.5y^2 = 0.125x^2 + C_1 \Rightarrow$

$x^2 - 4y^2 = C$

Initial condition: (10, 4)

$100 - 64 = C \Rightarrow C = 36$

$\therefore x^2 - 4y^2 = 36 \Rightarrow y = \pm 0.5\sqrt{x^2 - 36}$

33. $x = 10.5$: $y = 0.5\sqrt{10.5^2 - 36} = 4.30842...$

34. At (10, 4), $\frac{dy}{dx} = 0.25\frac{10}{4} = 0.625$.
Using $\Delta x = 0.5$, $y(10.5) \approx 4 + (0.625)(0.5)$ $= 4.3125$, which is close to the exact value of 4.30842... .

Algebraic Techniques Problems

35. $\frac{d}{dx}(\sin^{-1} x^3) = \frac{3x^2}{\sqrt{1 - x^6}}$

36. $x = \ln(\cos t)$ and $y = \sec t$
$dx/dt = \frac{1}{\cos t} \cdot (-\sin t) = -\tan t$
$dy/dt = \sec t \tan t$
$\frac{dy}{dx} = \frac{dy/dt}{dx/dt} = \frac{\sec t \tan t}{-\tan t} = -\sec t = -y$

37. $\int \frac{dx}{4 - 3x} = -\frac{1}{3} \ln|4 - 3x| + C$

38. $h(x) = 5^x = e^{x \cdot \ln 5} \Rightarrow h'(x) = \ln 5\, e^{5 \cdot \ln 5} = 5^x \ln 5$

39. $\lim_{x\to 0} \frac{\sin 5x + \cos 3x - 5x - 1}{x^2} \to \frac{0}{0}$
$= \lim_{x\to 0} \frac{5\cos 5x - 3\sin 3x - 5}{2x} \to \frac{0}{0}$
$= \lim_{x\to 0} \frac{-25\sin 5x - 9\cos 3x}{2} = -4.5$

40. Graph, $y = \frac{\sin 5x + \cos 3x - 5x - 1}{x^2}$,
showing a removable discontinuity at (0, –4.5)

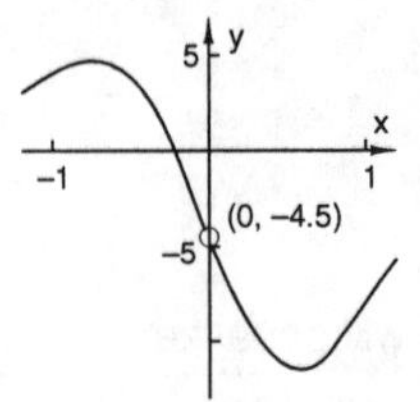

Journal Problems

41. Journal entries will vary.

42. Journal entries will vary.

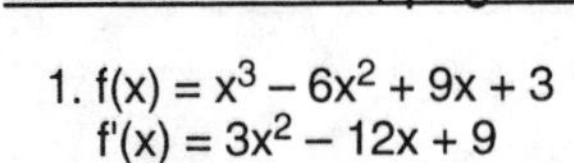

Chapter 8

Problem Set 8-1, page 353 — Cubic Functions and Their Derivatives

1. $f(x) = x^3 - 6x^2 + 9x + 3$
   $f'(x) = 3x^2 - 12x + 9$
   Graph

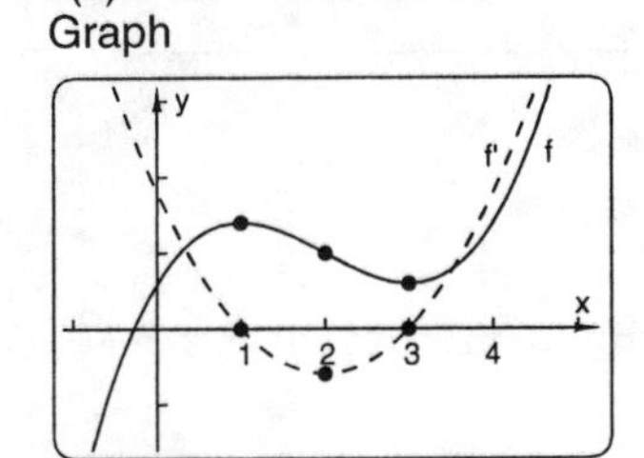

$g(x) = x^3 - 6x^2 + 15x - 9$
$g'(x) = 3x^2 - 12x + 15$
Graph

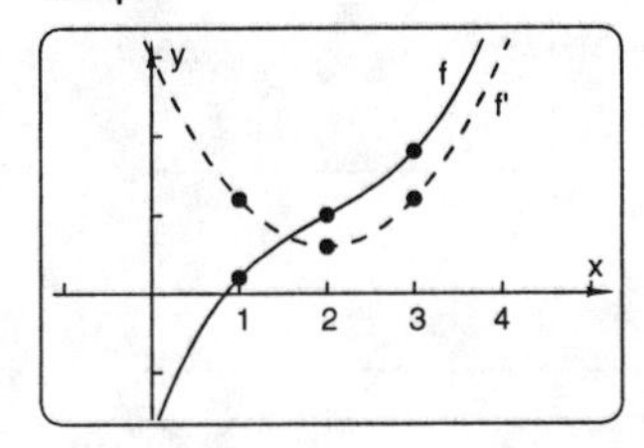

$h(x) = x^3 - 6x^2 + 12x - 3$
$h'(x) = 3x^2 - 12x + 12$
Graph

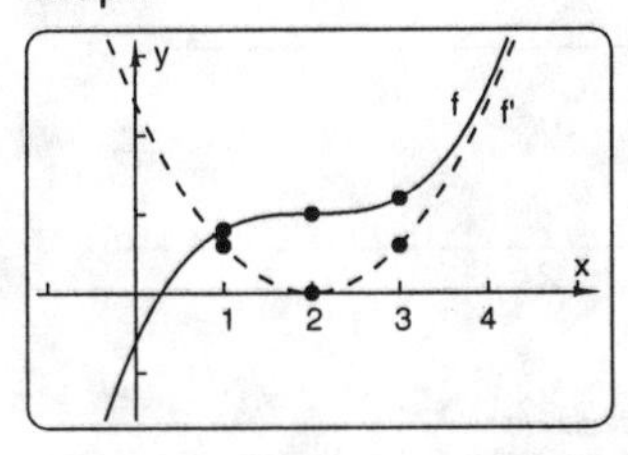

Positive derivative ⇒ increasing function
Negative derivative ⇒ decreasing function
Zero derivative ⇒ function could be at a high point or a low point, but not always.

2. The functions have vertex points at values of x where their derivatives change sign. If the derivative is never zero, as for function g, the function graph has no vertex points. If the derivative is zero, but does not change sign, as for function h, the function graph just levels off, then continues in the same direction, with no vertex.

3. $g''(x) = (d/dx)(3x^2 - 12x + 15) = 6x - 12$
   $h''(x) = (d/dx)(3x^2 - 12x + 12) = 6x - 12$
   All the second derivatives are the same!

4. The curves are concave upward where the second derivative is positive, and concave downward where the second derivative is negative.

5. Inflection points occur where the first derivative graph reaches a minimum.
   Inflection points occur where the second derivative graph crosses the x-axis.

Problem Set 8-2, pages 362 to 369 — Critical Points and Points of Inflection

Q1. $y = x^2$

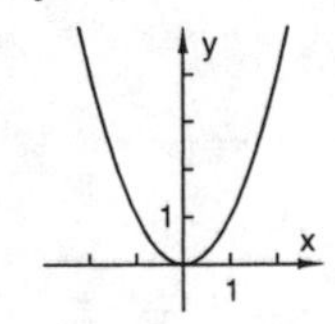

Q2. $y = x^3$

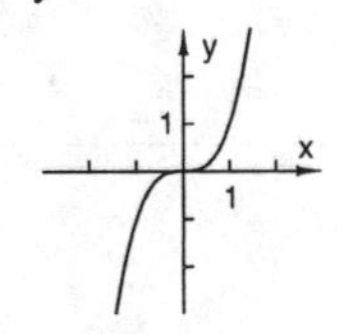

Q3. $y = \cos x$

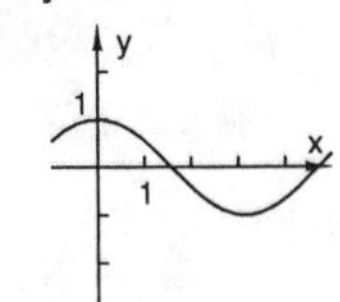

Q4. $y = \sin^{-1} x$

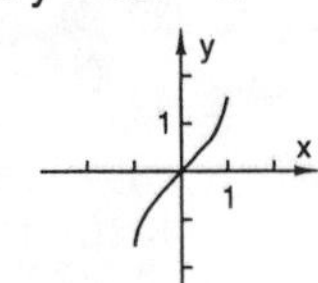

Q5. $y = e^{-x}$

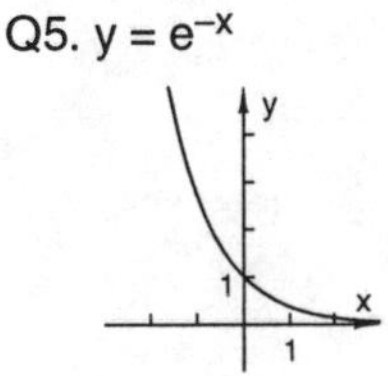

Q6. $y = \ln x$

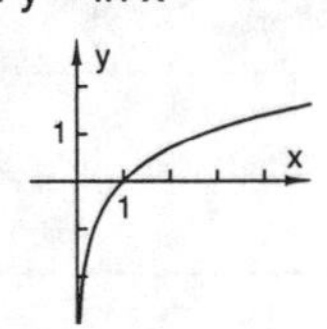

Q7. $y = \tan x$

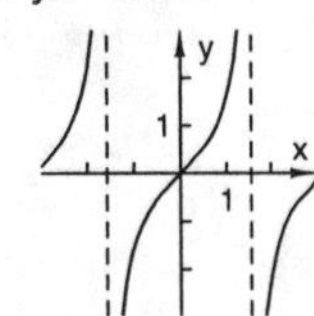

Q8. $y = x$

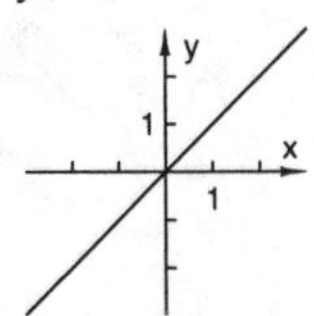

Q9. $y = 1/x$

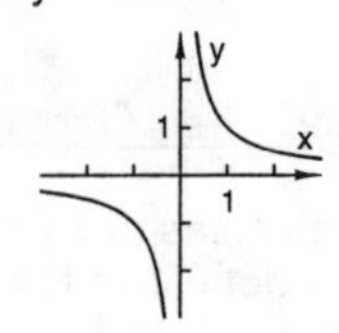

Q10. $x = 2$

1.

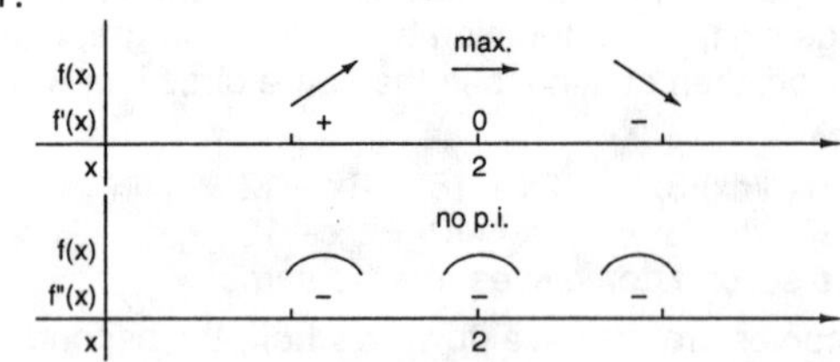

2.

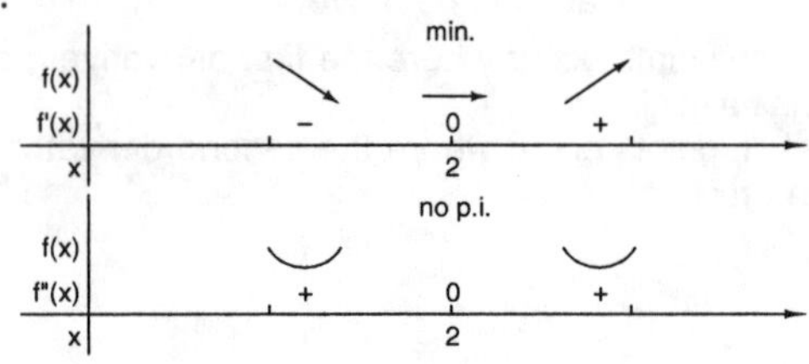

3.

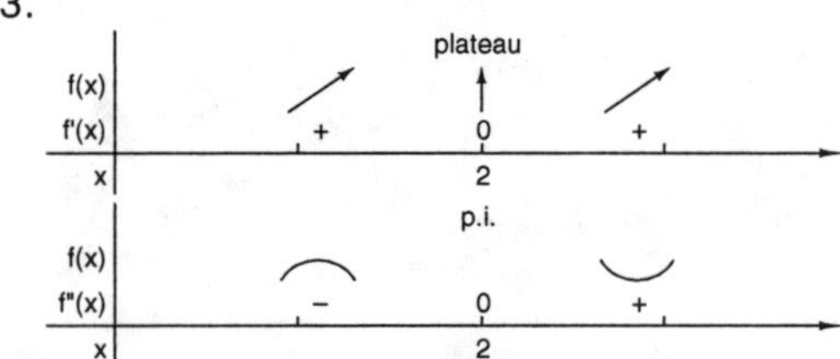

4.

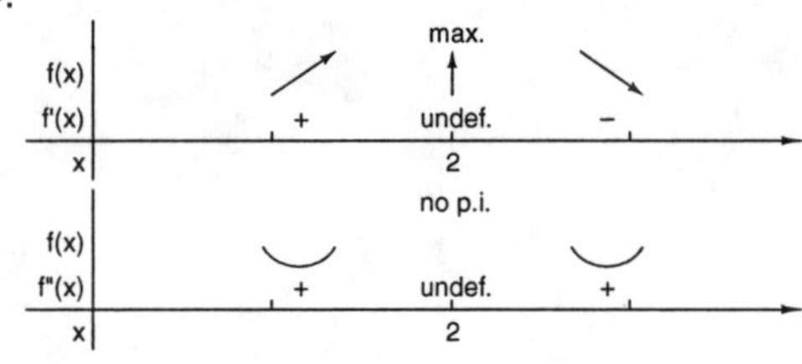

5.

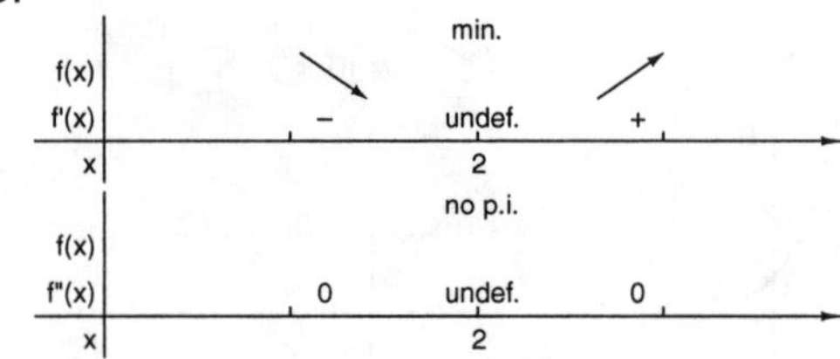

6.

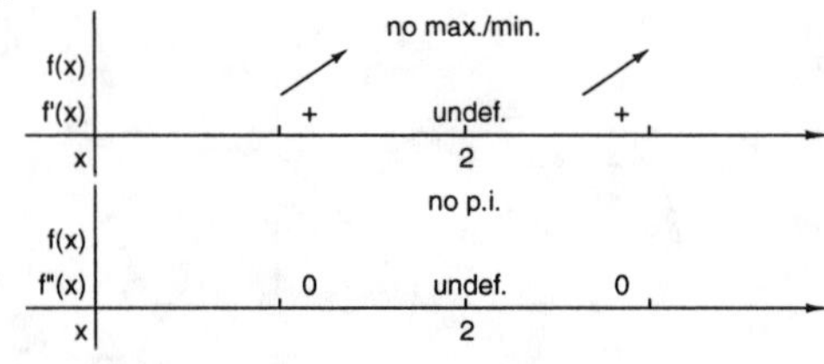

7.

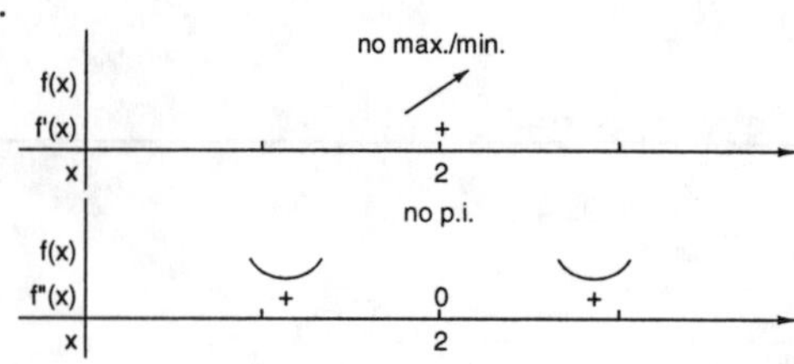

8.

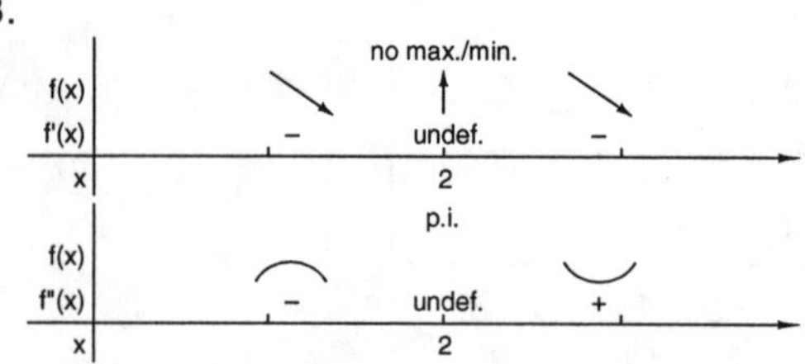

9.

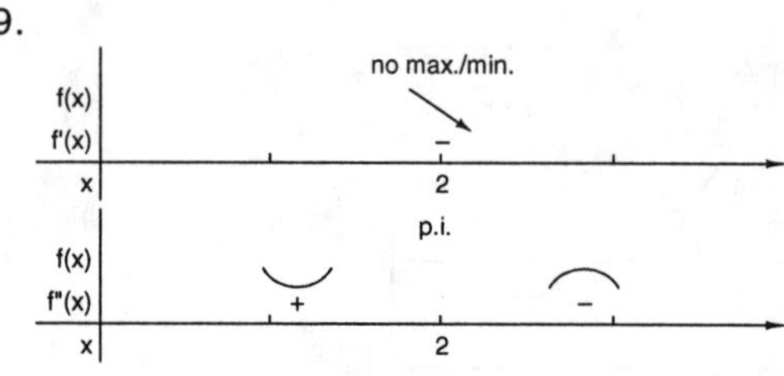

10.

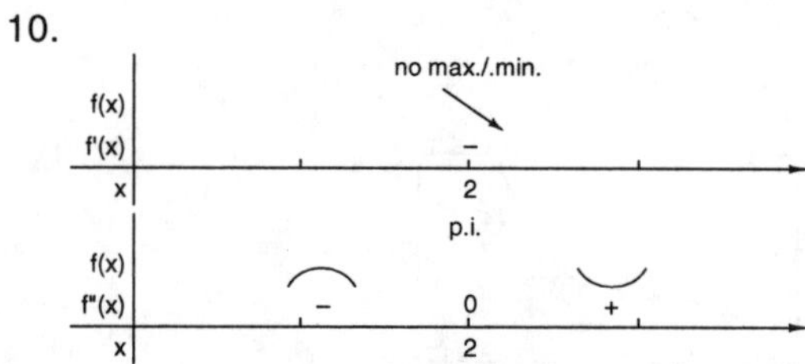

11.

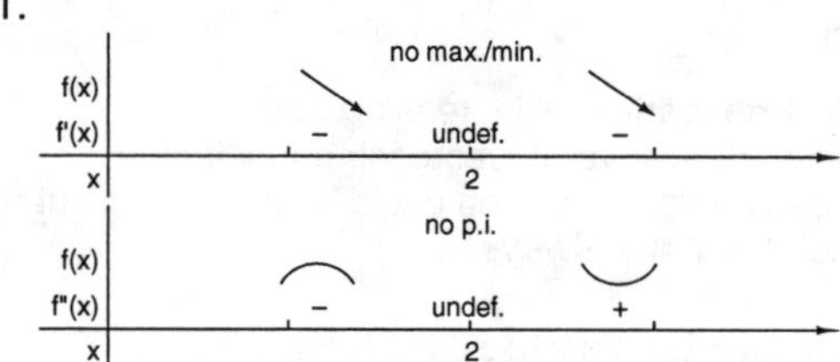

12.

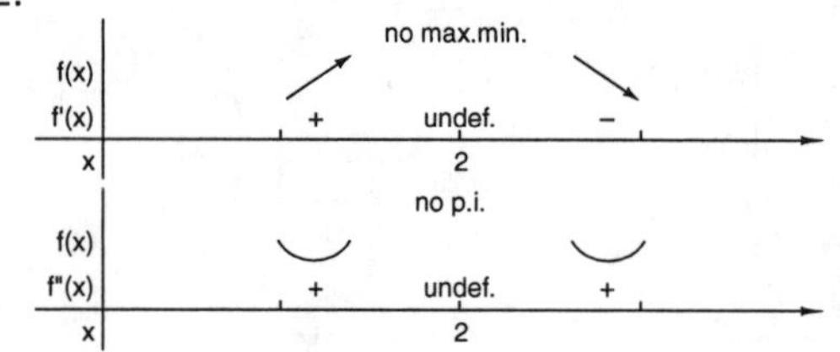

13. Number lines and sample graph

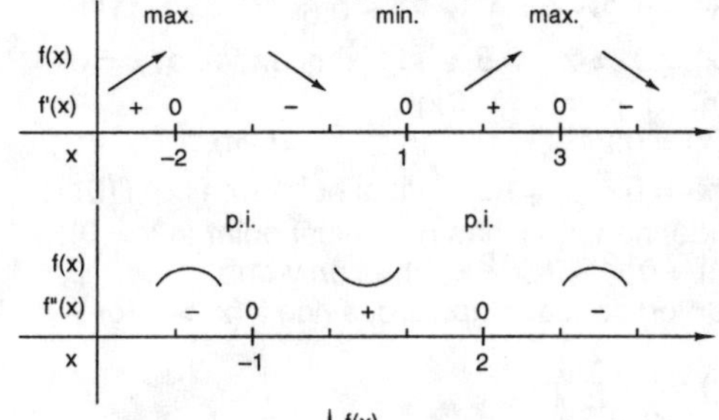

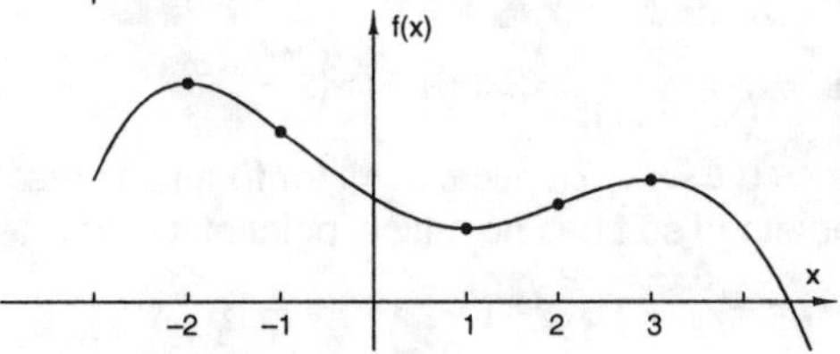

14. Number lines and sample graph

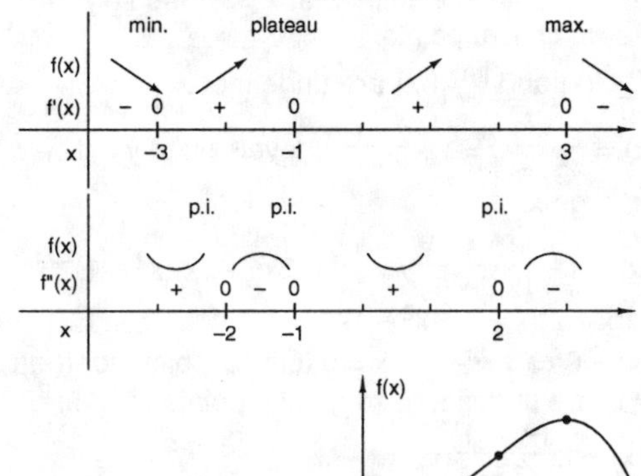

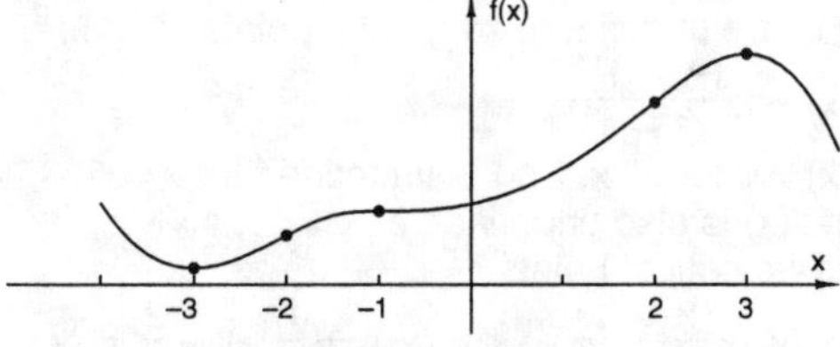

15. Number lines and sample graph

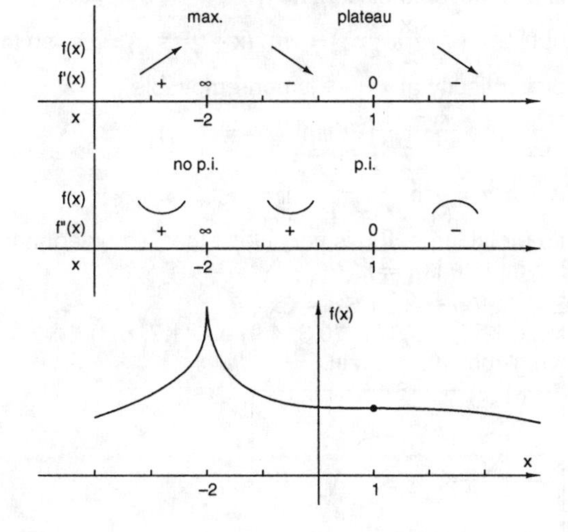

16. Number lines and sample graph

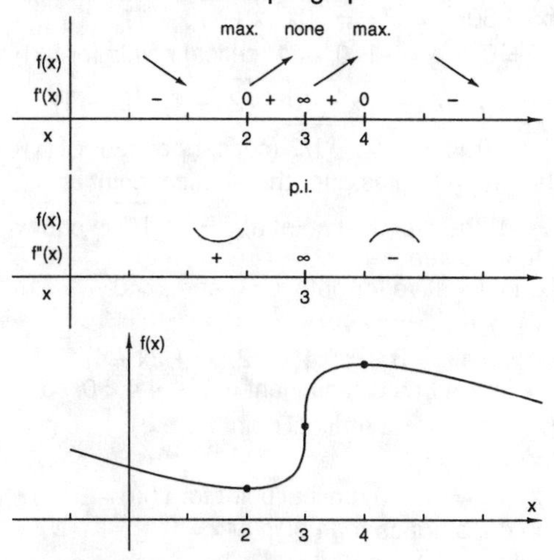

17. Number lines and sample graph

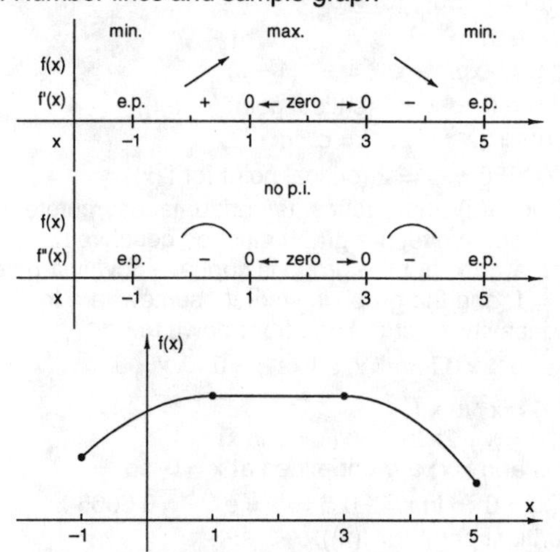

18. Number lines and sample graph

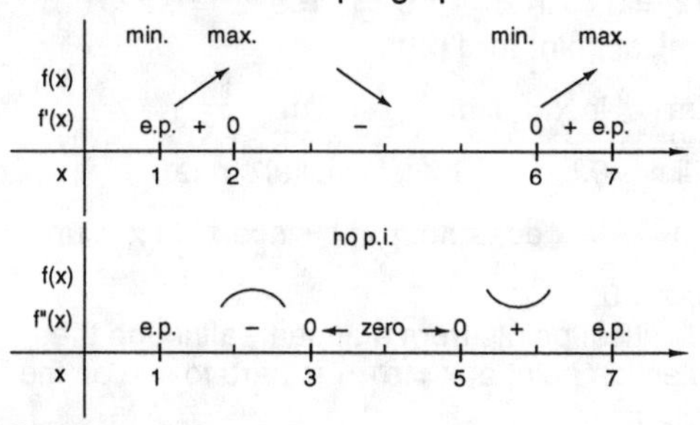

Graph:

19. a. $f(x) = 6x^5 - 10x^3$
$f'(x) = 30x^4 - 30x^2 = 30x^2(x+1)(x-1)$
$f'(x) = 0 \Leftrightarrow x = -1, 0, \text{ or } 1$ (critical points for f(x))
$f''(x) = 120x^3 - 60x = 60x(\sqrt{2}x + 1)(\sqrt{2}x - 1)$
$f''(x) = 0 \Leftrightarrow x = 0, \pm\sqrt{1/2}$ (critical points for f'(x))
b. The graph begins after the f-critical point at $x = -1$; the f'-critical point at $x = -\sqrt{1/2}$ is shown, but is hard to see.
c. f'(x) is negative for both $x < 0$ and $x > 0$.

20. a. $f(x) = 0.1x^4 - 3.2x + 7$
$f'(x) = 0.4x^3 - 3.2 = 0.4(x-2)(x^2 + 2x + 4)$
$x^2 + 2x + 4$ has discriminant $= 2^2 - 4 \cdot 4 < 0$, so
$f'(x) = 0 \Leftrightarrow x = 2$ (critical point for f(x)).
$f''(x) = 1.2x^2$
$f''(x) = 0 \Leftrightarrow x = 0$ (critical point for f'(x))
b. f''(x) does not change sign at $x = 0$ ($f''(x) \ge 0\ \forall x$).
c. $f''(c) = 0$, but $f'(c) \ne 0$

21. a. $f(x) = xe^{-x}$
$f'(x) = -xe^{-x} + e^{-x} = e^{-x}(1 - x)$
$f'(x) = 0 \Leftrightarrow x = 1$ (critical point for f(x))
$f''(x) = xe^{-x} - 2e^{-x} = e^{-x}(x - 2)$
$f''(x) = 0 \Leftrightarrow x = 2$ (critical point for f'(x))
b. Since f(x) approaches its horizontal asymptote (y = 0) from above, the graph must be concave upward for large x; but the graph is concave downward near x = 1, and the graph is smooth; somewhere the concavity must change from down to up.
c. No. $e^{-x} \ne 0$ for all x, so $xe^{-x} = 0 \Leftrightarrow x = 0$.

22. a. $f(x) = x^2 \ln x$
$f'(x) = x + 2x \ln x = x(1 + 2 \ln x)$
f(x) and f'(x) are undefined at x = 0, so
$f'(x) = 0 \Leftrightarrow \ln x = -0.5 \Leftrightarrow x = e^{-0.5} = 0.6065 \ldots$
(critical point for f(x)).
$f''(x) = 3 + 2 \ln x$
$f''(x) = 0 \Leftrightarrow \ln x = -1.5 \Leftrightarrow x = e^{-1.5} = 0.2231 \ldots$
(critical point for f'(x))
b. $\lim_{x\to 0^+} x^2 \ln x = \lim_{x\to 0^+} \frac{\ln x}{x^{-2}} = \lim_{x\to 0^+} \frac{1/x}{-2x^{-3}}$
$= \lim_{x\to 0^+} -0.5x^2 = 0$ by L'Hospital's rule.
$\lim_{x\to 0^-} x^2 \ln x$ does not exist, since $x^2 \ln x$ is undefined for $x < 0$.
c. All critical points from a appear, although the inflection point at $x = e^{-1.5}$ is hard to see on the graph.

23. a. $f(x) = x^{5/3} + 5x^{2/3}$
$f'(x) = \frac{5}{3}x^{2/3} + \frac{10}{3}x^{-1/3} = \frac{5}{3}x^{-1/3}(x + 2)$
$f'(x) = 0 \Leftrightarrow x = -2$, and f'(x) is undefined at x = 0 (critical points for f(x)).
$f''(x) = \frac{10}{9}x^{-1/3} - \frac{10}{9}x^{-4/3} = \frac{10}{9}x^{-4/3}(x - 1)$
$f''(x) = 0 \Leftrightarrow x = 1$ (critical point for f'(x); f'(0) is undefined, so f' has no critical point at x = 0).
b. The y-axis (x = 0) is a tangent line because the slope approaches infinity from both sides.
c. No inflection point at x = 0, because concavity is down for both sides, but there is an inflection point at x = 1.

24. a. $f(x) = x^{1.2} - 3x^{0.2}$
$f'(x) = 1.2x^{0.2} - 0.6x^{-0.8} = 0.6x^{-0.8}(2x - 1)$
$f'(x) = 0 \Leftrightarrow x = 0.5$, and f'(x) is undef. at x = 0 (critical points for f(x)).
$f''(x) = 0.24x^{-0.8} + 0.48x^{-1.8} = 0.24x^{-1.8}(x + 2)$
$f''(x) = 0 \Leftrightarrow x = -2$ (critical point for f'(x); f'(0) is undefined, so f' has no critical point at x = 0).
b. $f(0) = 0^{1.2} - 3 \cdot 0^{0.2} = 0$ has only one value.
c. Curved concave upward, since $f''(x) > 0$ for $x < -2$

25. a. $f(x) = \frac{x^2}{x^2 - 1}$
$f'(x) = \frac{2x}{(x^2 - 1)^2} = 2x(x + 1)^{-2}(x - 1)^{-2}$
$f'(x) = 0 \Leftrightarrow x = 0$ (critical point for f(x); f(±1) are undefined so f has no critical point at x = ±1).
$f''(x) = -\frac{6x^2 + 2}{(x^2 - 1)^3} = (6x^2 + 2)(x + 1)^{-3}(x - 1)^{-3}$
$f''(x) \ne 0$ for all x, f''(x) is undefined for x = ±1, but f'(x) is also undefined at x = ±1, so f'(x) has *no* critical points.
b. $\lim_{x\to -1} f(x)$ and $\lim_{x\to 1} f(x)$ are undefined.
c. $f(x) = \frac{x^2}{x^2 - 1} = 1 + \frac{1}{x^2 - 1}$ levels off to y = 1 for large x.

26. a. $f'(x) = 1 - \frac{(x - 1)^2}{(x^2 - 1)^2} = (x^4 - 3x^2 + 2x)(x^2 - 1)^{-2}$
$= x(x + 2)(x - 1)^2(x^2 - 1)^{-2}$
$f'(x) = 0 \Leftrightarrow x = -2$ or $x = 0$ (critical points for f(x); f(±1) are undefined, so no crit. points at ±1).
$f''(x) = 2\frac{(x - 1)^3}{(x^2 - 1)^3}$
$f''(x) \ne 0$ for all x, f''(x) is undefined for x = ±1, but f'(x) is also undefined at x = ±1, so f'(x) has *no* critical points.
b. $\lim_{x\to 1} (x + \frac{(x - 1)}{(x^2 - 1)}) = \lim_{x\to 1} (x + \frac{1}{x + 1}) = \frac{3}{2}$, so (1,1.5) is a removable discontinuity;
but $\lim_{x\to -1} (x + \frac{x - 1}{x^2 - 1}) = \lim_{x\to -1} (x + \frac{1}{x + 1}) = \pm\infty$, so the discontinuity at x = −1 is nonremovable.
c. $\lim_{|x|\to\infty} (x + \frac{x - 1}{x^2 - 1}) = \lim_{|x|\to\infty} (x + \frac{1}{x + 1})$
$= \lim_{|x|\to\infty} x + \lim_{|x|\to\infty} \frac{1}{x + 1} = \lim_{|x|\to\infty} x$,
so for |x| large, f(x) is very close to x. The diagonal asymptote is y = x.

27. a. Graph, $f(x) = -x^3 + 5x^2 - 6x + 7$
Max. (2.5, 7.6) Min. (0.8, 4.9) p.i. (1.7, 6.3)
No global max. or min.

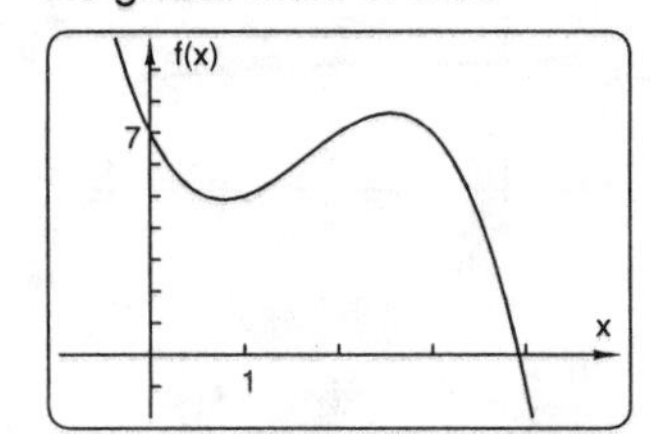

b. $f'(x) = -3x^2 + 10x - 6$

$f'(x) = 0 \Leftrightarrow x = \frac{1}{3}(5 \pm \sqrt{7}) = 2.548 \ldots$ or $0.784 \ldots$

$f''(x) = -6x + 10$; $f''(x) = 0 \Leftrightarrow x = \frac{5}{3} = 1.666 \ldots$

c. Critical and inflection points occur only where f, f', or f'' is undefined (no such points exist) or is zero (all such points are found above).

28. a. Graph, $f(x) = x^3 - 7x^2 + 9x + 10$
Max. (0.8, 13.2) Min. (3.9, –2.1) p.i. (2.3, 5.8)
No global max. or min.

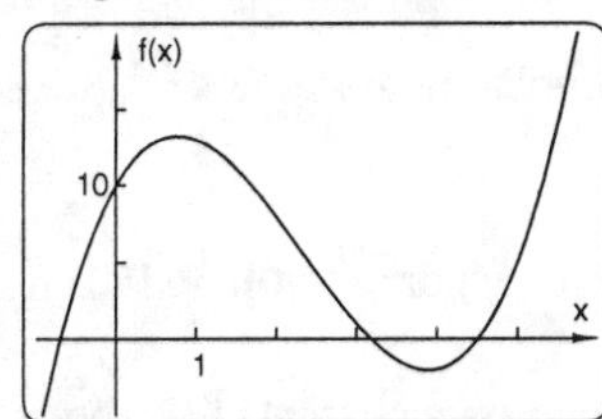

b. $f'(x) = 3x^2 - 14x + 9$

$f'(x) = 0$ at $x = \frac{1}{3}(7 \pm \sqrt{22}) = 3.896 \ldots$ or $0.769 \ldots$

$f''(x) = 6x - 14$; $f''(x) = 0$ at $x = \frac{7}{3} = 2.333 \ldots$

c. Critical and inflection points occur only where f, f', or f'' is undefined (no such points exist) or is zero (all such points are found above).

29. a. Graph, $f(x) = 0.1x^3 + 1.5x^2 + 7.6x - 3$
No local max. or min. (Plateau at (–5, –16)?)
p.i. (–5, –16)
No global max. or min.

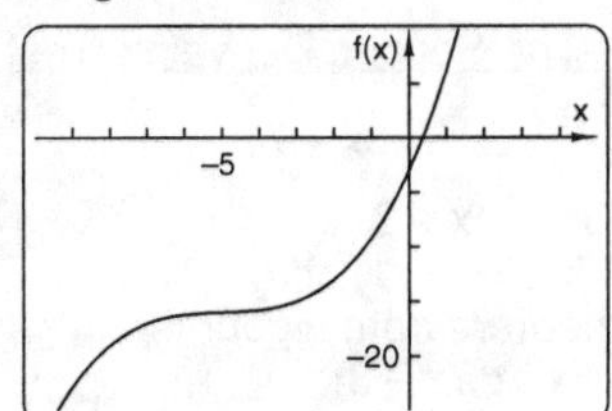

b. $f'(x) = 0.3x^2 + 3x + 7.6$; $f'(x) \neq 0$ for all x, confirming that there are no local max. or min., and refuting the apparent plateau at x = –5.
$f''(x) = 0.6x + 3$; $f''(x) = 0 \Leftrightarrow x = -5$

c. Critical and inflection points occur only where f, f', or f'' is undefined (no such points exist) or is zero (all such points are found above).

30. a. Graph, $f(x) = -x^3 + 9x^2 - 28x + 20$
No local max. or min. (Plateau at (3, –10)?)
p.i. at (3, –10)
No global max. or min.

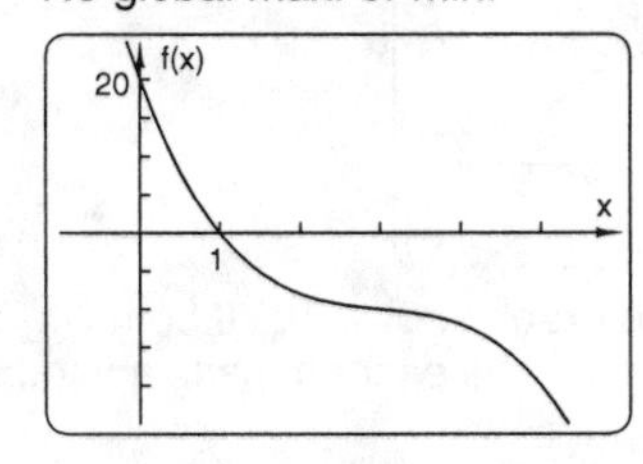

b. $f'(x) = -3x^2 + 18x - 28$; $f'(x) \neq 0$ for all x, confirming that there are no local max. or min., and refuting the apparent plateau at x = 3.
$f''(x) = -6x + 18$; $f''(x) = 0 \Leftrightarrow x = 3$

c. Critical and inflection points only occur where f, f', or f'' are undefined (no such points exist) or are zero (all such points are found above).

31. a. Graph, $f(x) = 3x^4 + 8x^3 - 6x^2 - 24x + 37$, $x \in [-3, 2]$
Max. (–3, 82), (–1, 50), (2, 77)
Min. (–2, 45), (1, 18)
p.i. (–1.5, 45.7), (0.2, 32.0)

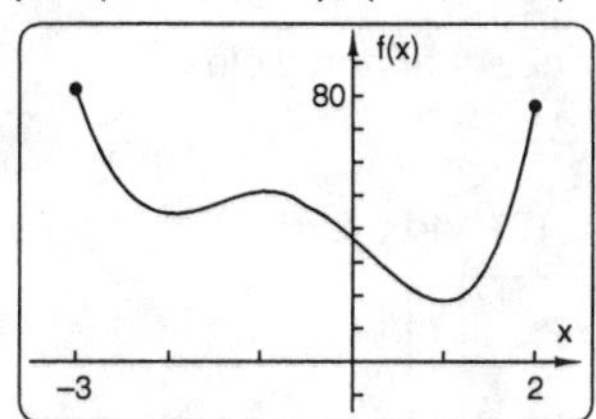

b. $f'(x) = 12x^3 + 24x^2 - 12x - 24$
$= 12(x + 2)(x - 1)(x + 1)$
$f'(x) = 0 \Leftrightarrow x = -2, -1, 1$
$f'(x)$ is undefined $\Leftrightarrow x = -3, 2$.
$f''(x) = 36x^2 + 48x - 12 = 12(3x^2 + 4x - 1)$;
$f''(x) = 0 \Leftrightarrow x = -\frac{1}{3}(2 \pm \sqrt{7}) = 0.21 \ldots$ or $-1.54 \ldots$
$f''(x)$ is undefined $\Leftrightarrow x = -3, 2$.

c. Critical and inflection points occur only where f, f', or f'' is undefined (only at endpoints) or is zero (all such points are found above).

32. a. Graph, $f(x) = (x - 1)^5 + 4$, $x \in [-1, 3]$
Max. (3, 36)
Min. (–1, –28)
Plateau and p.i. (1, 4)

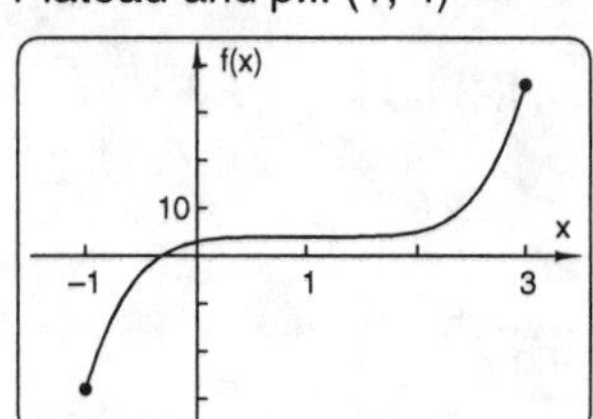

b. $f'(x) = 5(x - 1)^4$
$f'(x) = 0 \Leftrightarrow x = 1$; $f'(x)$ is undefined $\Leftrightarrow x = -1, 3$.
$f''(x) = 20(x - 1)^3$;
$f''(x) = 0 \Leftrightarrow x = 1$; $f''(x)$ is undefined $\Leftrightarrow x = -1, 3$.

c. Critical and inflection points occur only where f, f', or f'' is undefined (only at endpoints) or is zero (all such points are found above).

33. Point of Inflection of a Cubic Function
$f(x) = ax^3 + bx^2 + cx + d$; $f'(x) = 3ax^2 + 2bx + c$; $f''(x) = 6ax + 2b \Rightarrow f''(x) = 0$ at $x = -b/(3a)$
Since the equation for $f''(x)$ is a line with nonzero slope, $f''(x)$ changes sign at $x = -b/(3a)$, so there is a point of inflection at $x = -b/(3a)$.

34. Max. and Min. Points of a Cubic Function
f(x) may not have a local max. or min. (if f'(x) is never zero); if this is not the case, then the max. and min. occur where $f'(x) = 3ax^2 + 2bx + c = 0$, at

$$x = \frac{-2b \pm \sqrt{4b^2 - 4 \cdot 3a \cdot c}}{6a} = \frac{-b}{3a} \pm \frac{\sqrt{b^2 - 3ac}}{3a},$$

and the max. and min. occur at $\sqrt{b^2 - 3ac}/(3a)$ units on either side of the inflection point $-b/(3a)$ (see Problem 33).

35. Equation from Critical Points

$f(x) = ax^3 + bx^2 + cx + d$

$f'(x) = 3ax^2 + 2bx + c$; $f''(x) = 6ax + 2b$

p.i. at (2, 3) $\Rightarrow f''(3) = 0 \Rightarrow 18a + 2b = 0$

max. at (5, 10) $\Rightarrow f'(5) = 0 \Rightarrow 75a + 10b + c = 0$

(3, 2) and (5, 10) are on the graph $\Rightarrow$

$27a + 9b + 3c + d = 2$

$125a + 25b + 5c + d = 10$

Solving this system of equations yields

$f(x) = -\frac{1}{2}x^3 + \frac{9}{2}x^2 - \frac{15}{2}x - \frac{5}{2}$.

Graph, with max. (5, 10) and p.i. (3, 2)

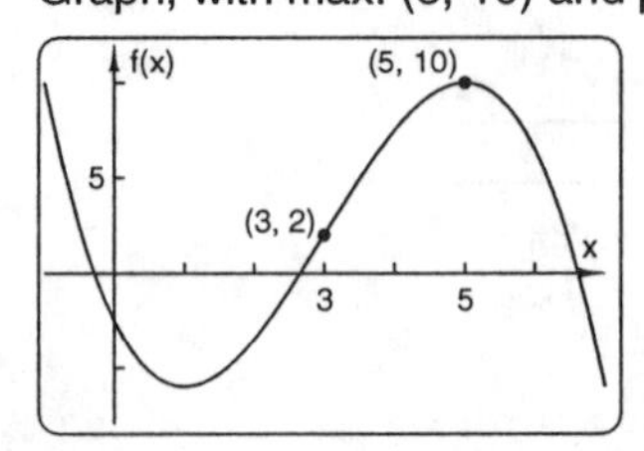

36. Can You Generate This Figure?

$f(3) = 1 \Rightarrow c + \sqrt{3-3} = 1 \Rightarrow c = 1$

For differentiability at x = 2,

$\frac{-b}{(x-1)^2} = \frac{-1}{2\sqrt{3-x}}$ at $x = 2 \Rightarrow b = \frac{1}{2}$

For continuity at x = 2, $f(2) = 1 + \sqrt{3-2} = 2$, so

$a + \frac{b}{2-1} = 2 \Rightarrow a + b = 2$.

Using b = 1/2, $a = \frac{3}{2}$.

For continuity at x = 4, $f(4) = 1 + \sqrt{4-3} = 2$, so

$4m + d = 2$.

From the graph, m = −1, so d = 6.

Equations are:

[1,2]: $f(x) = \frac{3}{2} + \frac{1}{2(x-1)}$

[2,3]: $f(x) = 1 + \sqrt{3-x}$

[3,4]: $f(x) = 1 + \sqrt{x-3}$

[4,5]: $f(x) = mx + 2 - 4m$.

Graph does duplicate Figure 8-2w.

37. Concavity Concept Problem

a. $f(x) = x^3 \Rightarrow f'(x) = 3x^2$

$f'(-0.8) = 1.92$

$f'(-0.5) = 0.75$

$f'(0.5) = 0.75$

$f'(0.8) = 1.92$

b. The slope seems to be decreasing from −0.8 to −0.5; $f''(x) = 6x < 0$ on $-0.8 \le x \le -0.5$, which confirms that the slope decreases.

The slope seems to be increasing from 0.5 to 0.8; $f''(x) = 6x > 0$ on $0.5 \le x \le 0.8$, which confirms that the slope increases.

c. The curve lies above the tangent line.

38. Naïve Graphing Problem

Ima could notice that y' = 0 at x = 0 (or y' = 3 at x = ±1), so the graph could not possibly be a straight line with slope = 1.

39. Connections Between a Zero First Derivative and the Graph

a. The graph may have a minimum or plateau there.

b. Example: $f(x) = -(x-1)^2 + 4 = -x^2 + 2x + 3$

c. Example: $f(x) = (x-1)^2 + 2 = x^2 - 2x + 3$

d. Example: $f(x) = (x-1)^3 + 3 = x^3 - 3x^2 + 3x + 2$

e. Example: $f(x) = 2$ for $1 \le x \le 4$

40. Infinite Curvature Problem

$f(x) = 10(x-1)^{4/3} + 2$

$f(1) = 2$, so $f(1)$ is defined.

$f'(x) = \frac{40}{3}(x-1)^{1/3}$

$f'(1) = 0$, so f is differentiable at x = 1.

$f''(x) = \frac{40}{9}(x-1)^{-2/3}$

$f''(1)$ has the form $\frac{40}{9}(0^{-2/3})$ or $\frac{40}{9}(1/0)$, so $f''(1)$ is infinite.

Graph. There seems to be a cusp at (1, 2), but zooming in on this point reveals that the tangent is actually horizontal there.

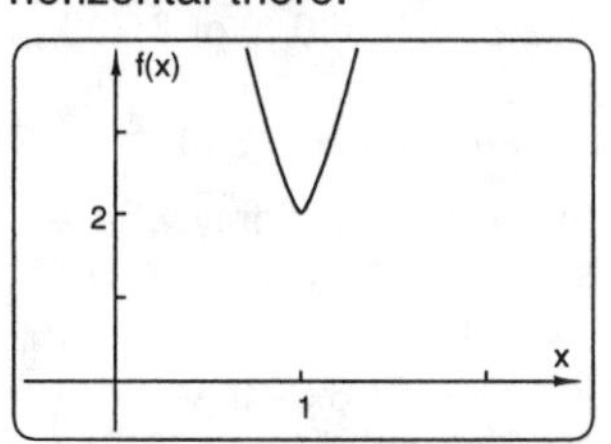

See Problem 16 in Problem Set 10-7 for calculation of curvature.

41. Historical Problem—The Second Derivative Test

a. $f(x) = \frac{1}{5}x^5 - x^4 + \frac{2}{3}x^3 + 2x^2 - 3x + 7$

$f'(x) = x^4 - 4x^3 + 2x^2 + 4x - 3$

By TABLE, $f'(x) = 0$ if x = −1, 1, or 3.

Using the factor theorem from algebra,

$f'(x) = (x+1)(x^3 - 5x^2 + 7x - 3)$

$= (x+1)(x-1)(x^2 - 4x + 3)$

$= (x+1)(x-1)^2(x-3)$.

b. $f''(x) = 4x^3 - 12x^2 + 4x + 4$

$f'(x) = 0$ at x = −1, 1, 3;

$f''(-1) = -16$; $f''(1) = 0$; $f''(3) = 16$

c. x = −1: concave down, local maximum

x = 1: not concave, can't tell max./min.

x = 3: concave up, local minimum

Graph, confirming these results

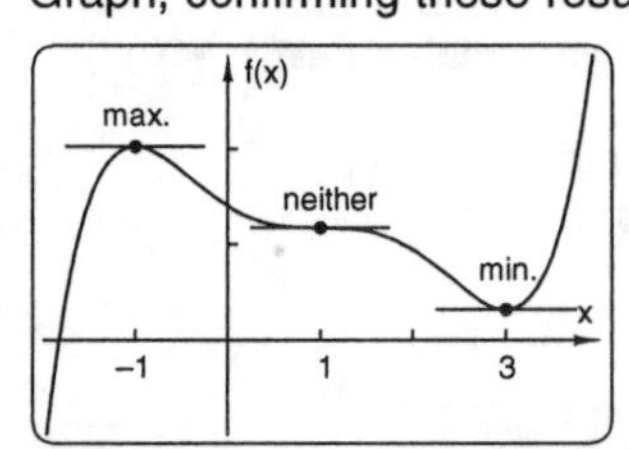

d. Graphs. The third graph shows that if both f'(x) and f''(c) are 0, there could be either a max., a min., or a plateau.

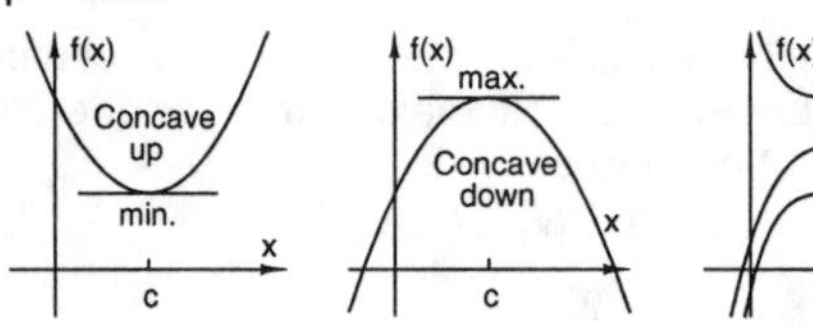

42. Exponential and Polynomial Look-Alike Problem
$f(x) = e^{0.06x}$, $f'(x) = 0.06e^{0.06x}$, $f''(x) = 0.0036e^{0.06x}$
$g(x) = 1 + 0.06x + 0.0018x^2 + 0.000036x^3$
$g'(x) = 0.06 + 0.0036x + 0.000108x^2$
$g''(x) = 0.0036 + 0.000216x$
$f(0) = 1$ and $g(0) = 1$
$f'(0) = 0.06$ and $g'(0) = 0.06$
$f''(0) = 0.0036$ and $g''(0) = 0.0036$
(In fact, $f'''(0) = g'''(0)$.)
But $f(10) = e^{0.6} = 1.822 \ldots \neq g(10) = 1.816$;
$f'(10) = 0.109 \ldots \neq g'(10) = 0.1068$
Since $f(x) > 0$ for all x, f has no x-intercept.
But $g(0) = 1$ and $g(-100) = -23$.
By the intermediate value theorem, $g(x) = 0$ somewhere between $x = -100$ and $x = 0$ meaning that g *does* have an x-intercept.

43. A Pathological Function

a. $f(x) = \begin{cases} (x-1)^3 \sin \dfrac{1}{x-1} + 2, \text{ if } x \neq 1 \\ 2, \ldots \text{if } x = 1 \end{cases}$

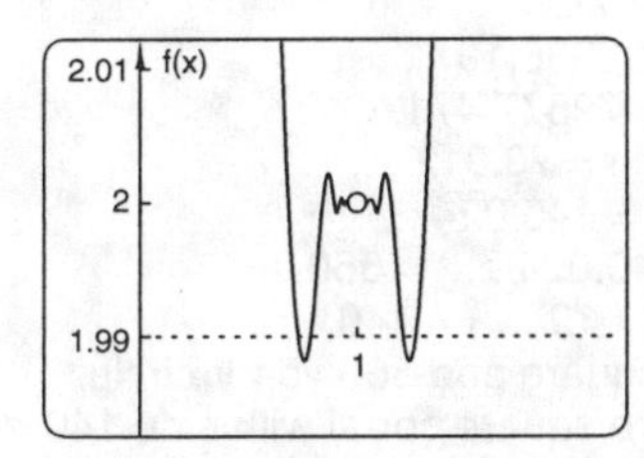

b. $\lim_{x\to1} f(x) = \lim_{x\to1} (x-1)^3 \cdot \sin \dfrac{1}{x-1} + 2 = 2 = f(1)$
(The limit of the first term is 0 because $(x-1)^3$ approaches 0 and the sine factor is bounded.)
$\therefore$ f is continuous at $x = 1$.

c. $f'(1) = \lim_{x\to1} \dfrac{f(x) - f(1)}{x-1}$
$= \lim_{x\to1} \dfrac{(x-1)^3 \sin(1/(x-1)) + 2 - 2}{x-1}$
$= \lim_{x\to1} (x-1)^2 \sin \dfrac{1}{x-1} = 0$
$(x-1)^2 \to 0$ and the sine factor is bounded.
$\therefore f'(1) = 0$

d. Graph, zoomed by a factor of 10 both ways.
The graph does appear to be locally linear at $x = 2$. Although the sine factor makes an infinite number of cycles in any neighborhood of $x = 1$, the $(x-1)^3$ factor approaches zero so rapidly that the graph is "flattened out." The name *pathological* is used to describe the fact that the graph makes an infinite number of cycles in a bounded neighborhood of $x = 1$.

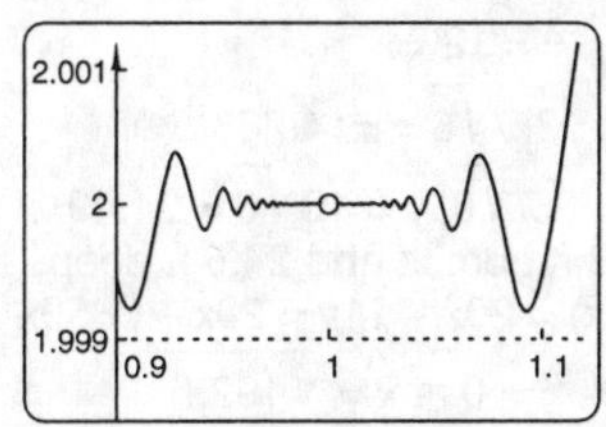

e. The graph could make an infinite number of cycles in the neighborhood of c. Thus, there will always be points both higher and lower than f(c) for values of x in that neighborhood, and f(c) is thus neither a max. nor a min.

44. Journal Problem
Journal entries will vary.

Problem Set 8-3, pages 372 to 380 — Maxima and Minima in Plane and Solid Figures

Q1. $y' = -3(3x+5)^{-2}$
Q2. $\ln|x+6| + C$
Q3. $-\frac{2}{3}x^{-5/3}$
Q4. $3x^{1/3} + C$
Q5. $-x^{-1} + C$
Q6. $x + C$
Q7. $-1/\sqrt{1-x^2}$
Q8. $\ln|\sin x| + C$
Q9. Graph, $y = x^{1/3}$

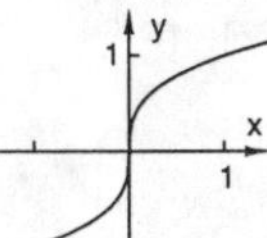

Q10. Graph, y"

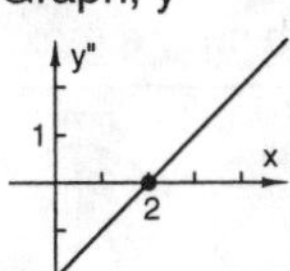

1. Divided Stock Pen Problem
Let x = total width of pen; y = length of pen.
Domains: $0 \le x \le 300$, $0 \le y \le 200$
Maximize $A(x) = xy$.
$2x + 3y = 600 \Rightarrow y = 200 - \frac{2}{3}x$
$\therefore A(x) = 200x - \frac{2}{3}x^2$
Graph shows max at $x \approx 150$.

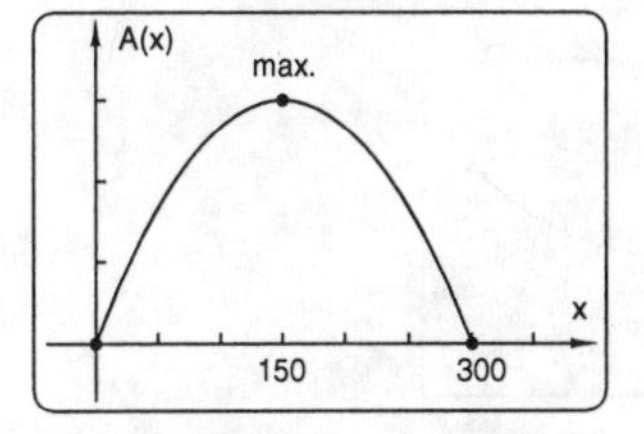

Algebraically, $A'(x) = 200 - \frac{4}{3}x$.
$A'(x) = 0 \Leftrightarrow x = 150$, confirming the graph.
$x = 150 \Rightarrow y = 200 - \frac{2}{3}150 = 100$
Make the total width 150 ft and length 100 ft.
(Note: The maximum area was not asked for.)

2. Motel Problem

a. Let x = width of a room across the front.
Let y = depth of a room from front to back.
Domains: $x \ge 0$, $y \ge 0$
Minimize $P(x) = 12x + 7y$.
$xy = 350 \Rightarrow y = 350x^{-1}$
$\therefore P(x) = 12x + 2450x^{-1}$
Graph shows minimum at $x \approx 14$.

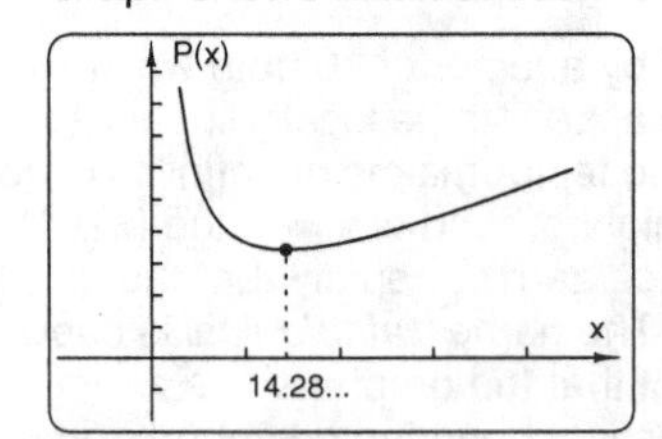

Algebraically, $P'(x) = 12 - 2450x^{-2}$.
$P'(x) = 0 \Leftrightarrow 2450x^{-2} = 12 \Leftrightarrow$
$x = \pm\sqrt{2450/12} = \pm 35/\sqrt{6} = \pm 14.288 \ldots$
Minimum is at $x = 35/\sqrt{6}$, $y = 10\sqrt{6} = 24.49 \ldots$.
Make rooms 14.3 ft across and 24.5 ft deep.

b. For 10 rooms, $P(x) = 20x + 11y = 20x + 3850x^{-1}$
$P'(x) = 20 - 3850x^{-2} = 0$ at $x = \sqrt{192.5}$
Min. at $x = \sqrt{192.5} = 13.87 \ldots$,
$y = 350/\sqrt{192.5} = 25.22 \ldots$
Make rooms 13.9 ft across and 25.2 ft deep.
For 3 rooms, $P(x) = 6x + 4y = 6x + 1400x^{-1}$
$P'(x) = 6 - 1400x^{-2} = 0$ at $x = \sqrt{1400/6} = 10\sqrt{7/3}$
Min. at $x = 10\sqrt{7/3} = 15.27 \ldots$,
$y = 5\sqrt{21} = 22.91 \ldots$
Make rooms 15.3 ft across and 22.9 ft deep.

3. Two-Field Problem

a. Let x = width of rectangle, 2x = length of rectangle, y = width of square.
$A_{rect} = 2x^2$, $A_{sq} = y^2$
For minimal rectangle, $2x^2 \ge 800 \Rightarrow x \ge 20$.
For minimal square, $y^2 \ge 100 \Rightarrow y \ge 10$.
Perimeter $P = 6x + 4y = 600 \Rightarrow y = 150 - 1.5x$
$\therefore 150 - 1.5x \ge 10 \Rightarrow x \le 140/1.5 = 93.33 \ldots$
Domain: $20 \le x \le 93.333 \ldots$

b. Total area $A(x) = 2x^2 + y^2 = 2x^2 + (150 - 1.5x)^2$
$A(x) = 22500 - 450x + 4.25x^2$
Graph

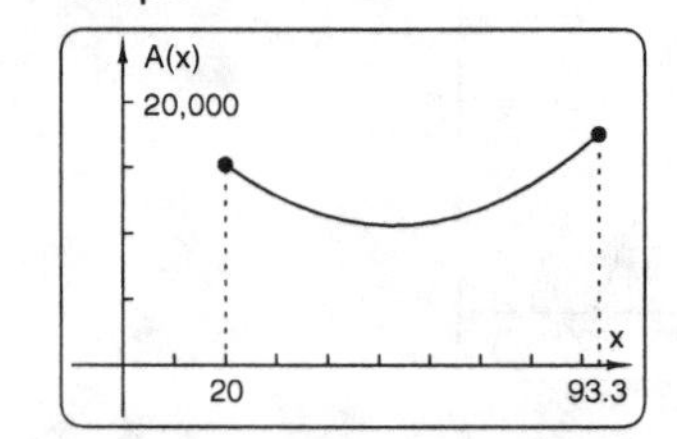

c. Graph shows max. at endpoint $x = 93.3 \ldots$.
$A'(x) = -450 + 8.5x$
$A'(x) = 0 \Leftrightarrow x = 450/8.5 = 52.941 \ldots$
Since $A(52.9 \ldots)$ is a *minimum,* the max. occurs at an endpoint.
$A(20) = 15200$, $A(93.33 \ldots) = 17522.222 \ldots$
Greatest area $\approx 17{,}522$ ft^2

4. Two-Corral Problem

a. Let r = radius of circle, s = width of square
Diameter $\ge 50 \Rightarrow r \ge 25$
Circumference $\le 1000 \Rightarrow 2\pi r \le 1000 \Rightarrow r \le 500/\pi$
Domain of r: $25 \le r \le 500/\pi = 159.154 \ldots$
Minimize $A(r) = \pi r^2 + s^2$
Perimeter $2\pi r + 4s = 1000 \Rightarrow s = 250 - \pi r/2$
$\therefore A(r) = \pi r^2 + (250 - \pi r/2)^2$
Graph shows minimum area at $x \approx 70$.

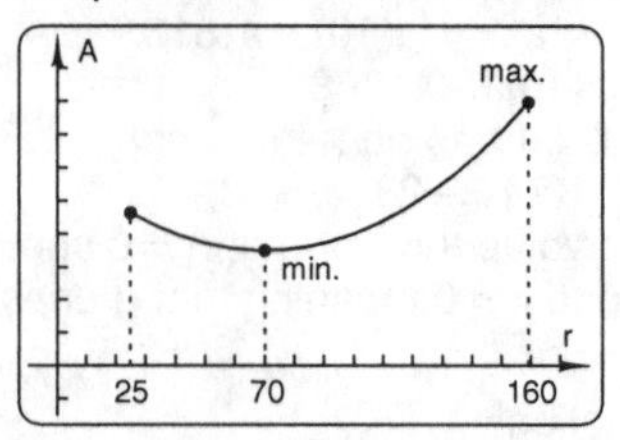

$A'(r) = 2\pi r + 2(250 - \pi r/2)(\pi/2)$
$A'(r) = 0 \Leftrightarrow 2\pi r + 2(250 - \pi r/2)(\pi/2) \Rightarrow$
$r = 500/(4 + \pi) = 70.012 \ldots$
$A(25) = 46370.667 \ldots$
$A(70.012 \ldots) = 35006.197 \ldots$;
$A(159.154 \ldots) = 79577.471 \ldots$
Minimum area at $r = 70.012 \ldots$,
$s = 1000/(4 + \pi) = 140.024 \ldots$.
For square, $4(140.024 \ldots) \approx 560$.
For circle, $2\pi(70.012 \ldots) \approx 440$.
Use 440 yd for square and 560 yd for circle.
(You could build a square corral with side 140 *around* the circular fence of radius 70 to enclose a total area of only 19607, but Big Bill might not like your solution!)

b. Graph of A vs. r shows that the maximum area occurs at the largest possible circle.
Big Bill should use all 1000 yards for the circular fence and not build a corral.

5. Open Box I

a. Let x = length of square base, z = height of box
Domain of x: $0 \le x \le \sqrt{120} = 10.954 \ldots$
Maximize $V(x) = x^2z$.
Area $= x^2 + 4xz = 120 \Rightarrow z = 30/x - x/4$
$\therefore V(x) = 30x - x^3/4$
Graph shows max. at $x \approx 6.3$.

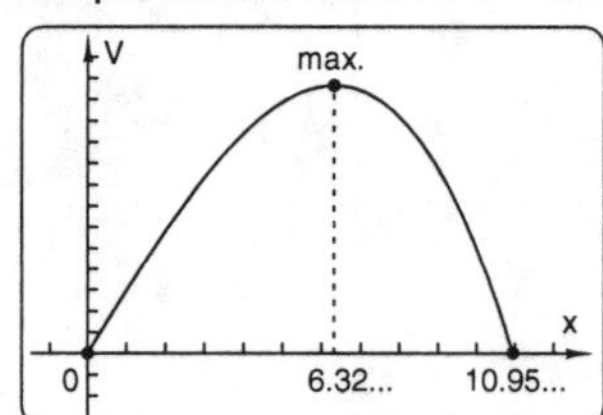

$V'(x) = 30 - 3x^2/4 = 0$ at $x = \pm\sqrt{40}$
$x = -\sqrt{40}$ is out of the domain.
Critical points at $x = 0$, $x = \sqrt{40}$, $x = \sqrt{120}$
$V(0) = 0$, $V(\sqrt{120}) = 0$
$V(\sqrt{40}) = 20\sqrt{40} = 126.49 \ldots$
Max. at $x = \sqrt{40} = 6.324 \ldots$, $z = \sqrt{40}/2 = 3.162 \ldots$
Make the box 6.32 cm square by 3.16 cm deep.

b. Conjecture: An open box with square base and fixed surface area A will have maximal volume when the base length is twice the height, which occurs when $x = \sqrt{A/3}$ (see Problem 8b).

6. Open Box II (Project)
   a. Domain of x is $0 \le x \le 6$
   b. $V(0) = 0$ cm²
      $V(1) = 180$ cm²
      $V(2) = 256$ cm² largest volume for x, an integer
      $V(3) = 252$ cm²
      $V(4) = 192$ cm²
      $V(5) = 100$ cm²
      $V(6) = 0$ cm²
   c. $V(x) = (20 - 2x)(12 - 2x)x = 240x - 64x^2 + 4x^3$
      Graph shows max. at $x \approx 2.4$.

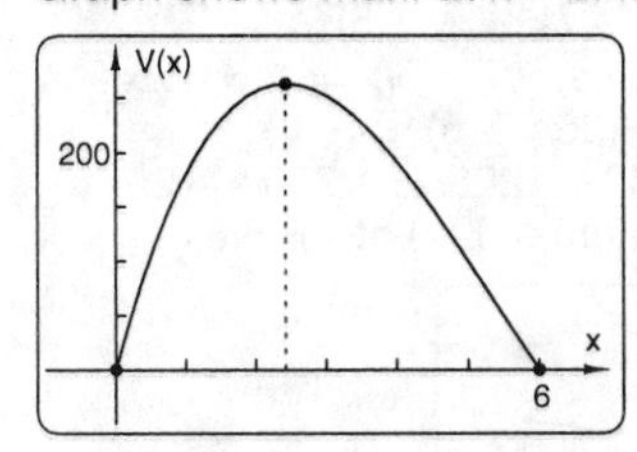

$V'(x) = 240 - 128x + 12x^2 = 0$ at
$x = \left(128 \pm \sqrt{4864}\right)/24 = 2.427 \ldots$ or $8.239 \ldots$
$x = 8.239 \ldots$ is out of the domain.
$V(2.427 \ldots)$ = is a max. because it is positive and $V(0) = V(6) = 0$.
$V(2.427 \ldots) = 262.68 \ldots$
Maximum volume ≈ 262.7 cm² at x ≈ 2.43 cm.

7. Open Box III Problem
   Let x = length, y = depth, C(x) = total cost
   Domains: $x > 0$, $y > 0$
   Area of bottom = 5x

   Total area of sides is $(10 + 2x)y$
   Minimize $C(x) = 10(5x) + 5(10 + 2x)y$.
   Volume = 72 ⇒ $5xy = 72 \Rightarrow y = 72/(5x) = 14.4x^{-1}$
   $\therefore C(x) = 50x + 5(10 + 2x)(14.4x^{-1})$
   $C(x) = 50x + 720x^{-1} + 144$
   Graph shows minimum at $x \approx 3.8$.

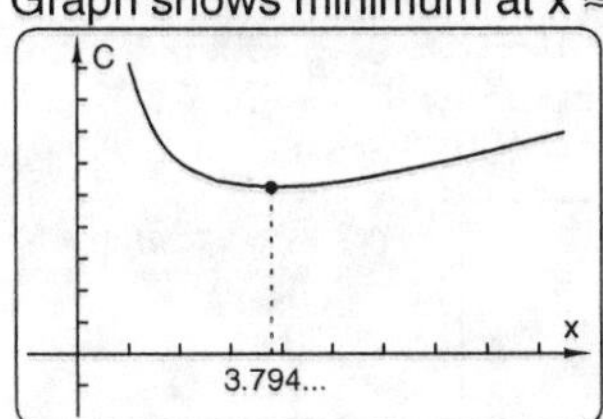

$C'(x) = 50 - 720x^{-2} = 0 \Leftrightarrow x = \pm\sqrt{72/5} = \pm 3.7947 \ldots$
$x = -3.7947 \ldots$ is out of the domain.
Minimum at $x = 3.7947$ since $C'(x)$ changes from neg. to pos. there.

$C(3.7947 \ldots) = 120\sqrt{10} + 144 \approx 523.47$
Minimum cost is \$523.47.

8. Open Box IV (Project)
   a. Maximize $V = xyz$.
      Fixed area $A = xy + 2xz + 2yz$
      $\Rightarrow y = (A - 2xz)/(x + 2z)$
      $\therefore V = \dfrac{Axz - 2x^2z^2}{x + 2z}$
      $\dfrac{dV}{dx} = \dfrac{-2z^2x^2 - 8z^3x + 2Az^2}{(x + 2z)^2}$
      $\dfrac{dV}{dx} = 0$ at $x = -2z + \sqrt{4z^2 + A}$

      $y = \dfrac{A - 2z(-2z + \sqrt{4z^2 + A})}{-2z + \sqrt{4z^2 + A} + 2z} =$
      $-2z + \sqrt{4z^2 + A}$
      Therefore, x = y for maximum volume, Q.E.D.
   b. Let x = y. Maximize $V = xyz = x^2z$.
      Fixed area $A = xy + 2xz + 2yz = x^2 + 4xz$
      $\Rightarrow z = A/(4x) - x/4$
      $\therefore V = (A/4)x - x^3/4$
      $\dfrac{dV}{dx} = (A/4) - 3x^2/4 = 0$ at $x = \pm\sqrt{A/3}$

      dV/dx goes from pos. to neg. at $x = \sqrt{A/3} \Rightarrow$
      max. at $x = \sqrt{A/3}$.
      $z = A/(4\sqrt{A/3}) - \sqrt{A/3}/4 = \dfrac{1}{2}\sqrt{A/3} = \dfrac{1}{2}x$
   c. For the maximal box in part b, the depth is half the length of the base. Thus, the box is short and fat. This makes sense since the problem is equivalent to maximizing the volume of two open boxes with the second box placed upside-down on the first. The resulting single closed box will have maximal volume when it is a cube, which will happen if each open box is half a cube.

9. Shortest-Distance Problem
   For $y = e^x$, minimize $D(x) = \sqrt{x^2 + y^2} = \sqrt{x^2 + e^{2x}}$.
   Graph shows minimum at $x \approx -0.43$.

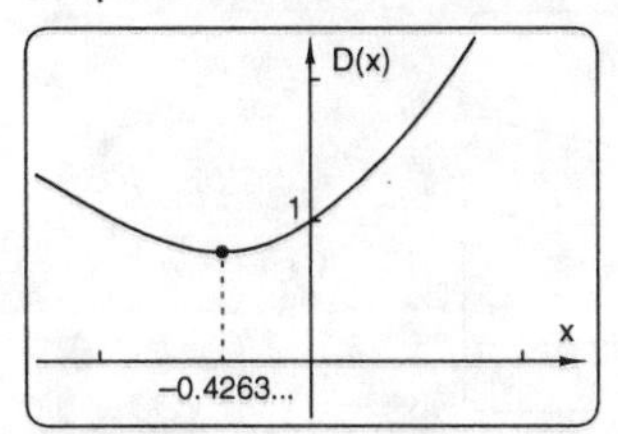

$D'(x) = \dfrac{1}{2}(x^2 + e^{2x})^{-1/2}(2x + 2e^{2x})$

$D'(x) = 0 \Leftrightarrow 2x + 2e^{2x} = 0 \Leftrightarrow x = -e^{2x}$
Since x appears both algebraically and exponentially, there is no analytic solution.
Solving numerically gives $x \approx -0.4263$
By graphing D(x), D(−0.4263) is a minimum.
Closest point to the origin is
$(x, y) \approx (-0.4263, 0.6529)$.

10. Track and Field Problem
Minimize $A(r) = \pi r^2 + 2rx$, $r \geq 20$.
$2\pi r + 2x = 400 \Rightarrow x = 200 - \pi r$
$x \geq 100 \Rightarrow r \leq 100/\pi$
$\therefore$ Domain is $20 \leq r \leq 100/\pi$.
$A(r) = \pi r^2 + 2r(200 - \pi r) = 400r - \pi r^2$
Graph shows minimum at endpoint x = 20.

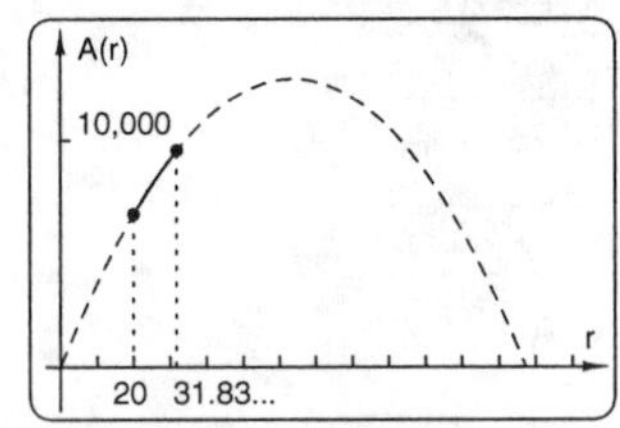

$A' = 400 - 2\pi r$
$A' = 0 \Leftrightarrow r = 200/\pi = 63.6$ ... (Out of domain.)
$A' > 0$ for all r in the domain.
$\therefore$ min. occurs at left end of domain, r = 20.
$x = 200 - 20\pi = 137.168$ ...
Make radius 20m and straights 137.17 m.

11. Ladder Problem

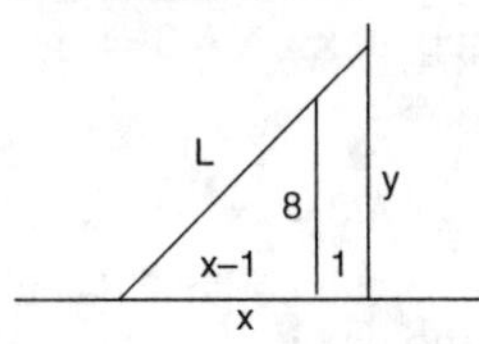

$L(x) = \sqrt{x^2 + y^2}$
Domains: $x \geq 1$, $y \geq 8$
Minimize $L^2(x) = x^2 + y^2$.
Using similar triangles, $\dfrac{y}{x} = \dfrac{8}{x - 1} \Rightarrow y = \dfrac{8x}{x - 1}$.
$\therefore L^2(x) = x^2 + \dfrac{64x^2}{(x - 1)^2}$
Graph shows minimum of L(x) at $x \approx 5$.

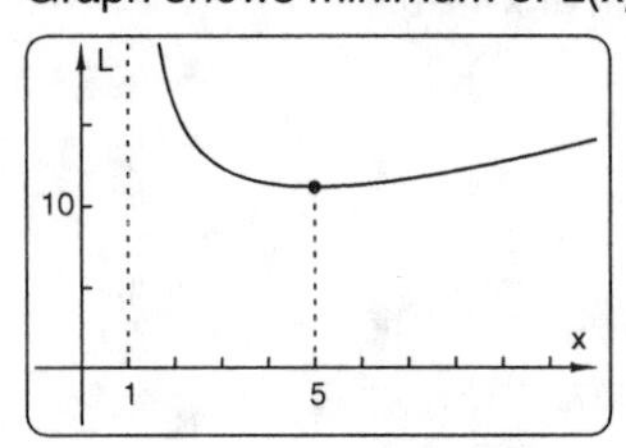

$(L^2)'(x) = 2x - \dfrac{128x}{(x - 1)^3}$
$(L^2)'(x) = 0 \Leftrightarrow 2x = \dfrac{128x}{(x - 1)^3} \Leftrightarrow$
x = 0 (out of domain) or $(x - 1)^3 = 64 \Leftrightarrow x = 5$
By graph, L(x) is a minimum at x = 5.
Shortest ladder has length $L(5) = 5\sqrt{5} \approx 11.18$ ft.

12. Ladder in the Hall Problem
Let x and y be the segments shown.

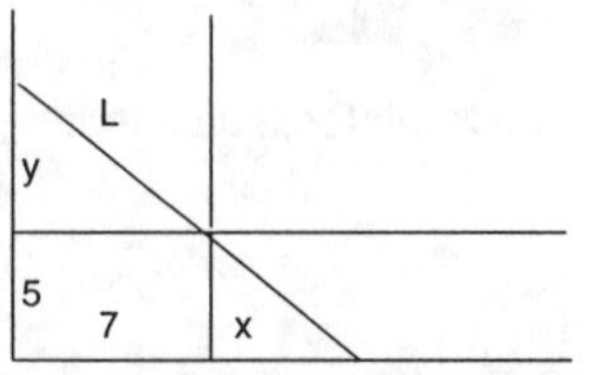

$L(x) = \sqrt{(x + 7)^2 + (y + 5)^2}$
Maximize $L^2(x) = (x + 7)^2 + (y + 5)^2$
Using similar triangles, $y/7 = 5/x \Rightarrow y = 35/x$.
$\therefore L^2(x) = (x + 7)^2 + (35/x + 5)^2$
$L^2(x) = x^2 + 14x + 49 + 1225/x^2 + 350/x + 25$
Graph shows minimum of L(x) at $x \approx 5.6$.

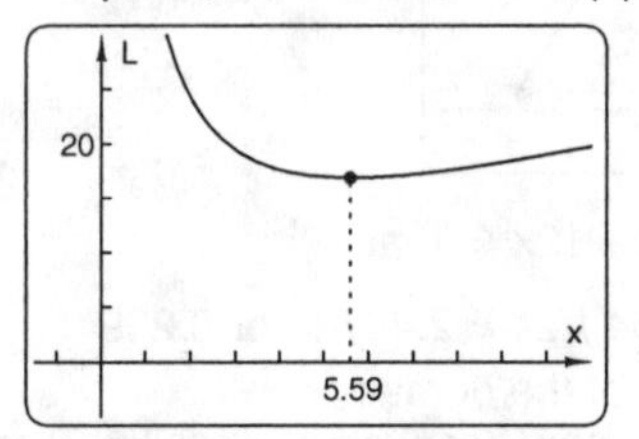

$(L^2(x))' = 2x + 14 - 350x^{-2} - 2450x^{-3}$
By numerical solution, $(L^2)' = 0$ at $x \approx 5.5934$ ... .
(Exact answer is $x = \sqrt[3]{175}$.)
But a minimum distance L in the hall implies that the *maximal* ladder that will go through the hall is at x = 5.5934 ... .
$L^2(5.5934 ...) = 285.3222$ ...
$L(5.5934 ...) = 16.8914$ ...
No ladder longer than 16.8 ft (rounded down) can pass through the hall.

13. Rotated Rectangle Problem
Let r = radius; h = height.
$V = \pi r^2 h$
$2r + 2h = 1200 \Rightarrow h = 600 - r$
$\therefore V = \pi r^2(600 - r) = \pi(600r^2 - r^3)$
Graph shows max. at $r \approx 400$.

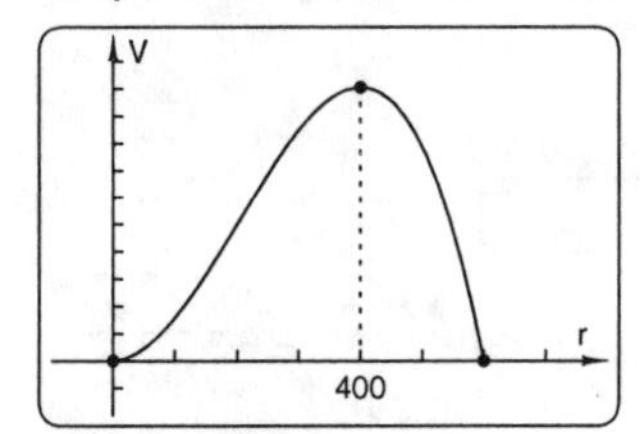

$V' = \pi(1200r - 3r^2)$
$V' = 0 \Leftrightarrow r = 0$ or $r = 400$.
From graph, max. is at r = 400.
h = 600 – 400 = 200
Max. volume with rectangle 400 mm wide (radius), 200 mm high

14. Rotated Rectangle Generalization Problem
Rotating a square does *not* give the maximal volume. The solution to Problem 13 gives a counterexample. Repeating the calculations with perimeter P instead of 1200 gives r = (1/3)P and h = (1/6)P, showing that the proportions for maximal volume are with radius *twice* the altitude.

15. Tin Can Problem

a. Let r = radius; h = height.
$V = \pi r^2 h = \pi(3.65^2)(10.6) = 141.2185\pi$
$= 443.65 \ldots \text{ cm}^3$

b. $A = 2\pi rh + 2\pi r^2$
$V = \pi r^2 h = 141.2185\pi \Rightarrow h = 141.2185/r^2$
$\therefore A = 2\pi r(141.2185/r^2) + 2\pi r^2$
$A = 2\pi(141.2185r^{-1} + r^2)$

c. Graph shows min. at $x \approx 4.1$.

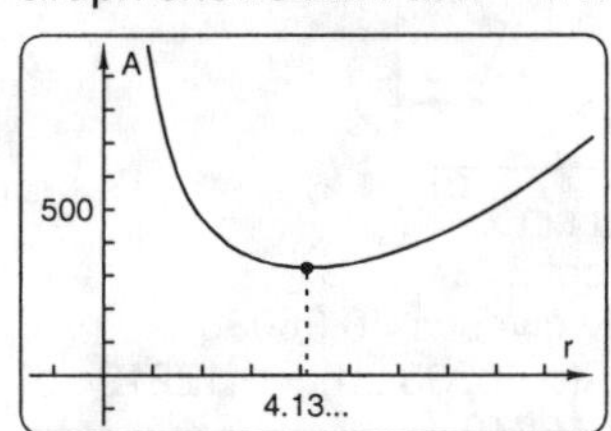

$A' = 2\pi(-141.2185r^{-2} + 2r)$
$A' = 2\pi/r^2(-141.2185 + 2r^3)$
$A' = 0 \Leftrightarrow r^3 = 70.60925 \Rightarrow$
$r = \sqrt[3]{70.60925} = 4.1332 \ldots$
Min. at r = 4.1 ... since A' goes from neg. to pos.
$h = 141.2815/(\sqrt[3]{70.60925})^2 = 2\sqrt[3]{70.60925}$
$= 8.266 \ldots$
Radius ≈ 4.1 cm, altitude ≈ 8.3 cm
Since altitude = 2 × radius, altitude = diameter.
So minimal can is neither tall and skinny nor short and fat.

d. Normally proportioned can is taller and thinner than minimal can. For normal can,
$A = 2\pi(3.65)(10.6) + 2\pi(3.65)^2 = 326.804 \ldots$.
For minimal can,
$A = 2\pi(4.13 \ldots)(8.26 \ldots) + 2\pi(4.13 \ldots)^2 = 322.014 \ldots$.
Difference is $4.78 \ldots \text{ cm}^2$.
Percent: (4.789 ...)(100)/326.80 ... = 1.465 ...
≈ 1.5% of metal in normal can

e. Saving $= (0.06)(20 \times 10^6)(0.01465 \ldots)(365)$
$= 6.419 \ldots \times 10^6$, or about \$6.4 million!

16. Tin Can Generalization Project

a. $C(r) = 2\pi r^2 k + 2\pi rh = 2\pi r^2 k + 282.437\pi r^{-1}$
$C'(r) = 4\pi rk - 282.437\pi r^{-2}$
$= 4\pi r^{-2}(kr^3 - 70.60925)$
$C'(r) = 0$ at $r = \sqrt[3]{70.60925/k}$
$C''(r) = 4\pi k + 564.874\pi r^{-3} > 0$ for all $r > 0$, so this is a local min.
If the normal can is the cheapest to make, then 3.65
$= \sqrt[3]{70.60925/k} \Rightarrow$
$k = 70.60925(3.65)^{-3} = 1.4520 \ldots$.
This is reasonable because metal for the ends is cut into circles, so some must be wasted.

b. Now it takes $(2r)^2$ cm^2 of metal to make each end of the can, so the function to minimize is:
$C(r) = 8r^2 k + 2\pi rh = 8r^2 k + 282.437\pi r^{-1}$.
$C'(r) = 16rk - 282.437\pi r^{-2}$
$C'(r) = 0$ at $r = \sqrt[3]{\dfrac{282.437\pi}{16k}}$
$C''(r) = 16k + 564.874\pi r^{-3} > 0$ for all $r > 0$, so this is a local min.
If the normal can is the cheapest to make, then 3.65
$= \sqrt[3]{\dfrac{282.437\pi}{16k}} \Rightarrow k = \dfrac{282.437\pi}{16(3.65)^3} = 1.1404 \ldots$.

c. If the metal for the ends can be cut without waste, then it takes $\pi(r + 0.6)^2$ to make each end and $(2\pi r + 0.5)h$ to make the sides, so minimize:
$C(r) = 2\pi(r + 0.6)^2 + (2\pi r + 0.5)h$
$= 2\pi(r + 0.6)^2 + 141.2185(2\pi r + 0.5)r^{-2}$
$C'(r) = 4\pi(r + 0.6) - 282.437\pi r^{-2} - 141.2185r^{-3}$
$C'(r) = 0$ at $r \approx 3.9966$ by graphing calculator
$C''(r) = 4\pi + 564.874\pi r^{-3} + 423.6555r^{-4} > 0$
for all $r > 0$, so this is a minimum point.
Minimal can has $r \approx 3.9966 \ldots$, $h \approx 8.8411 \ldots$ cm.
But if the metal for the ends is cut from squares, then it takes $4(r + 0.6)^2$ to make each end and $(2\pi r + 0.5)h$ to make the sides, so minimize:
$C(r) = 8(r + 0.6)^2 + (2\pi r + 0.5)h$
$= 8(r + 0.6)^2 + 141.2185(2\pi r + 0.5)r^{-2}$
$C'(r) = 16(r + 0.6) - 282.437\pi r^{-2} - 141.2185r^{-3}$
$C'(r) = 0$ at $r \approx 3.6776 \ldots$ by graphing calculator
$C''(r) = 16 + 564.874\pi r^{-3} + 423.6555r^{-4} > 0$
for all $r > 0$, so this is a minimum point.
Minimal can has $r \approx 3.6776 \ldots$, $h \approx 10.4411 \ldots$.
This is close to the normal can!

17. Cup Problem

a. Volume of cup = $\pi(2.5)^2 \cdot 7 = 43.75\pi$

Let r = radius of cup; h = altitude of cup

Minimize $A(r) = \pi r^2 + 2\pi rh$.

$\pi r^2 h = 43.75\pi \Rightarrow h = 43.75r^{-2}$

$\therefore A(r) = \pi r^2 + 87.5\pi r^{-1}$

Graph shows minimum at $r \approx 3.5$ cm.

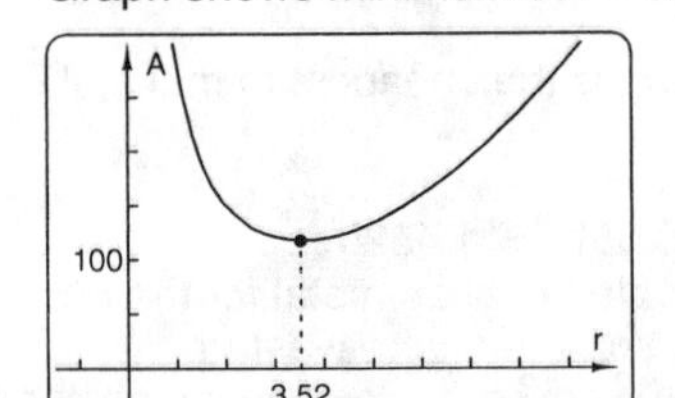

$A'(r) = 2\pi r - 87.5\pi r^{-2} = 2\pi r^{-2}(r^3 - 43.75)$

$A'(r) = 0$ at $r = \sqrt[3]{43.75} = 3.5236 \ldots$.

There is a minimum at x = 3.5236 ... because A(r) goes from decreasing to increasing. (See graph.)

$h = 43.75(43.75)^{-2/3} = \sqrt[3]{43.75} = r$

Minimal cup has $r \approx 3.52$ cm, $h \approx 3.52$ cm.

b. Ratio is d:h = 2r:h = 2:1.

c. Current cup design uses $\pi(2.5)^2 + 5\pi 7 = 41.25\pi$ $= 129.59 \ldots \text{ cm}^2 = 0.012959 \ldots \text{ m}^2$ per cup, which costs (300,000,000)(0.012959 ...)(2.00) $\approx$ \$7,775,441.82 per year.

Minimal cup design uses $3\pi(43.75)^{2/3}$ $= 117.01 \ldots \text{ cm}^2 = 0.011701 \ldots \text{ m}^2$ per cup, which costs (300,000,000)(0.011701 ...)(2.00) $\approx$ \$7,021,141.88 per year.

Switching to minimal cup design would save 754,299.93 $\approx$ \$754,000 per year in paper costs (about 10% of the current annual paper bill), but would likely result in loss of sales, since a cup of that shape is hard to drink from.

d. Let r = radius of cup; h = altitude of cup.

$\pi r^2 h = V \Rightarrow h = (V/\pi)r^{-2}$

Minimize $A(r) = \pi r^2 + 2\pi rh = \pi r^2 + 2Vr^{-1}$.

$A'(r) = 2\pi r - 2Vr^{-2} = 0$ at $r = \sqrt[3]{V/\pi}$

$A''(r) = 2\pi + 4Vr^{-3} > 0$ for all $r > 0$, so this is a min.

Minimal cup has $r = \sqrt[3]{V/\pi}$,

$h = (V/\pi)(V/\pi)^{-2/3} = \sqrt[3]{V/\pi} = r$.

18. Duct Problem

a. $A = yz = (30 + 0.2x)(40 - 0.2x)$

$A(x) = 1200 + 2x - 0.04x^2$

Left rectangle: $A(0) = 1200$ in.^{2};

Right rectangle: $A(100) = 1000$ in.^{2}

b. $A(80) = 1104$ in.^{2}

c. Graph shows maximum at $x \approx 25$.

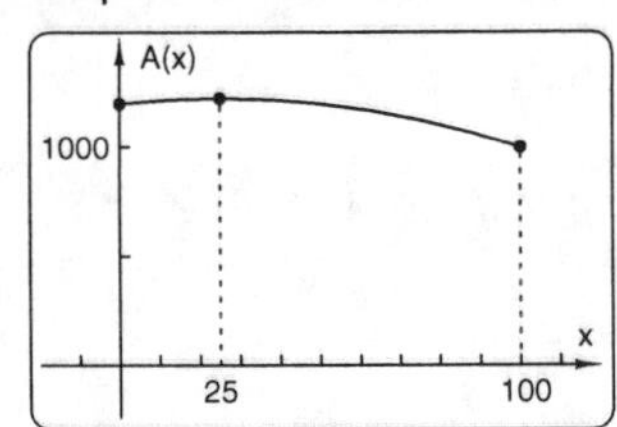

$A'(x) = 2 - 0.08x = 0$ at $x = 25$

Critical points at x = 0, 25, 100

$A(25) = 1225$ in.^{2};

$A(0) = 1200$ in.^{2}; $A(100) = 1000$ in.^{2} (from (a))

Max. area at x = 25 in, min. area for x = 100 in.

19. Rectangle in Sinusoid Problem

Maximize $A(x) = 2xy = 2x \cos x$.

Use $0 \le x \le \pi/2$ for the domain of x.

Graph shows maximum at $x \approx 0.86$.

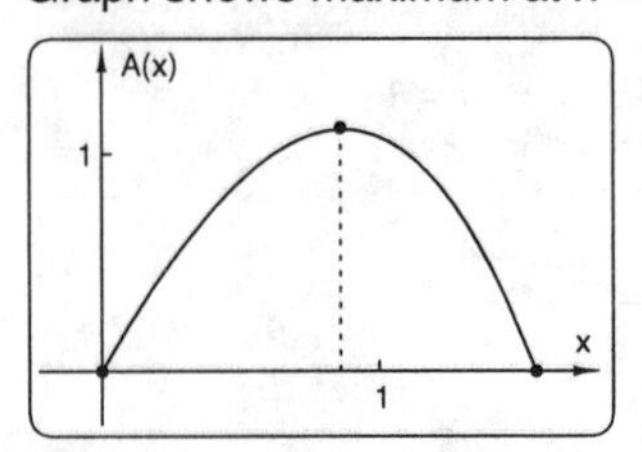

$A'(x) = 2 \cos x - 2x \sin x$

$A'(x) = 0$ when $x = \cot x$

Solving numerically gives $x \approx 0.86033 \ldots$.

$A(0) = A(\pi/2) = 0$; $A(0.86033 \ldots) = 1.12219 \ldots$

Maximum area = 1.12219 ...

20. Building Problem

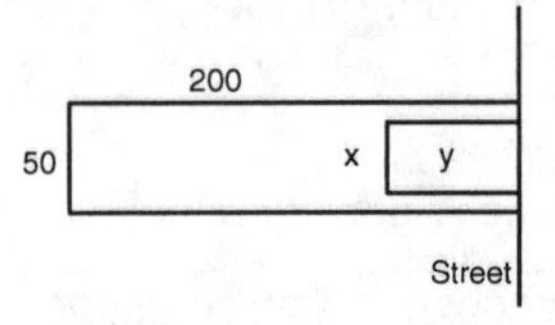

Let x = width of store, y = length of store.

Minimize $C(x) = 100x + 80(x + 2y)$.

$xy = 4000 \Rightarrow y = 4000x^{-1}$

$C(x) = 180x + 640{,}000x^{-1}$

$y \le 200 \Rightarrow x \ge 20$, so domain of x is $20 \le x \le 50$.

Graph shows minimum at x endpoint x = 50.

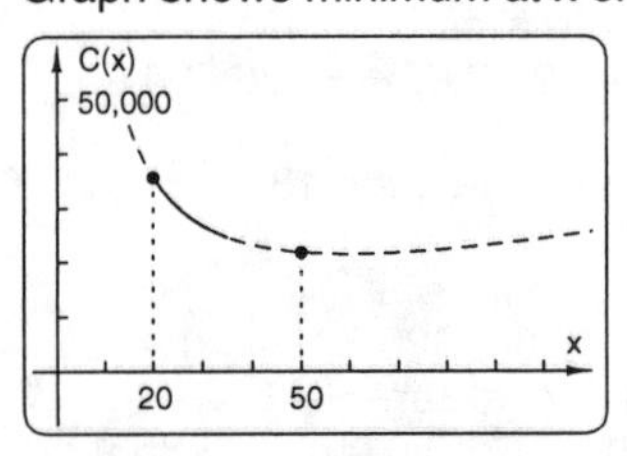

$C'(x) = 180 - 640{,}000x^{-2} = 0$

at $x = \dfrac{80\sqrt{5}}{3} = 59.628 \ldots$, outside the domain.

C(20) = \$35,600.00; C(50) = \$21,800.00

Minimum cost is at x = 50, y = 4000/50 = 80.

Bill should build the store 50 ft x 80 ft.

21. Triangle Under Cotangent Problem

a. $A = 0.5xy = 0.5x \cot x$

$$\lim_{x\to 0} A = \lim_{x\to 0} \frac{x}{2 \tan x} \to \frac{0}{0}$$

$$= \lim_{x\to 0} \frac{1}{2 \sec^2 x}$$

$$= \frac{1}{2}.$$

b. Domain of x is $0 < x \le \pi/2$.
Graph shows that the area approaches a maximum as x approaches the endpoint x = 0 from the positive side.

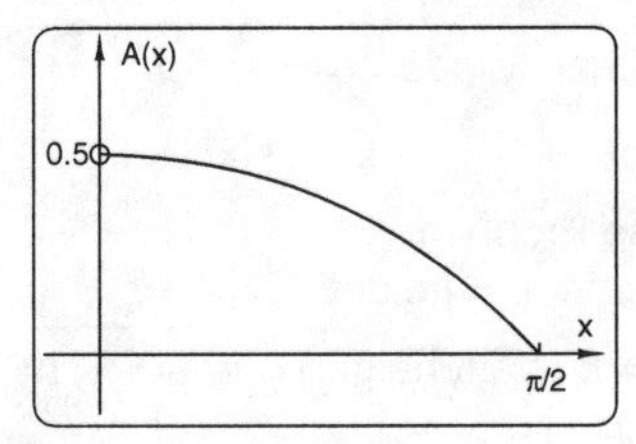

$A'(x) = \frac{1}{2}(\cot x - x \csc^2 x)$
$A'(x) = 0$ when $x = \cos x \sin x$ or
$2x = 2 \sin x \cos x = \sin 2x$,
which happens at x = 0.
$A(\pi/2) = 0$, so the "maximum" occurs at x = 0.
But x = 0 is not in the domain; A(x) can get arbitrarily close to 1/2, but never achieve it.

22. Triangle Under Exponential Curve Problem

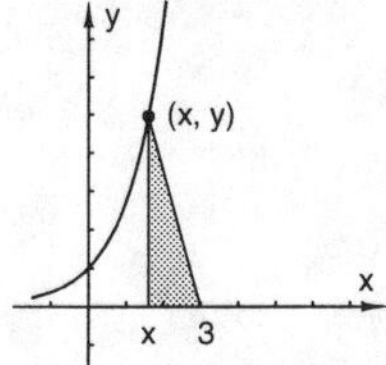

Domain of x is $0 \le x \le 3$.
Maximize $A = 0.5(3-x)(y) = 0.5(3 - x)e^x$
$= 1.5e^x - 0.5xe^x$.
Graph shows max. at $x \approx 2$.

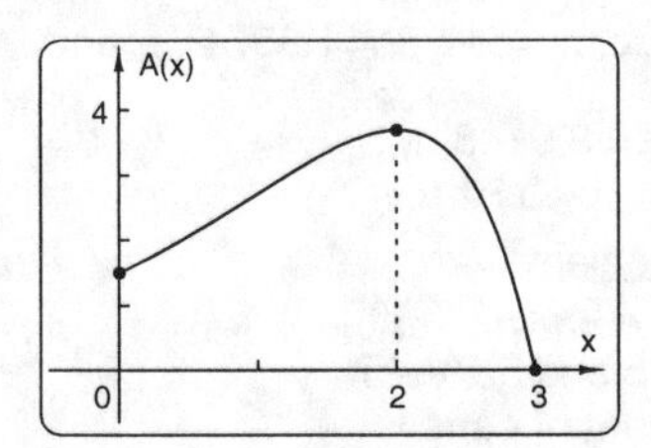

$A'(x) = 1.5e^x - 0.5e^x - 0.5xe^x = 0.5e^x(2 - x)$
$A'(x) = 0$ at x = 2, confirming the graph.
$A'(x) > 0$ for $x < 2$, and $A'(x) < 0$ for $x > 2$, confirming maximum point at x = 2.
Maximum area $A(2) = e^2/2 = 3.69452 \ldots$.

23. Rectangle in Parabola Problem

a. Maximize $A(x) = 2xy = 2x(9 - x^2) = 18x - 2x^3$
Domain: $0 \le x \le 3$
Graph shows max. at $x \approx 1.7$.

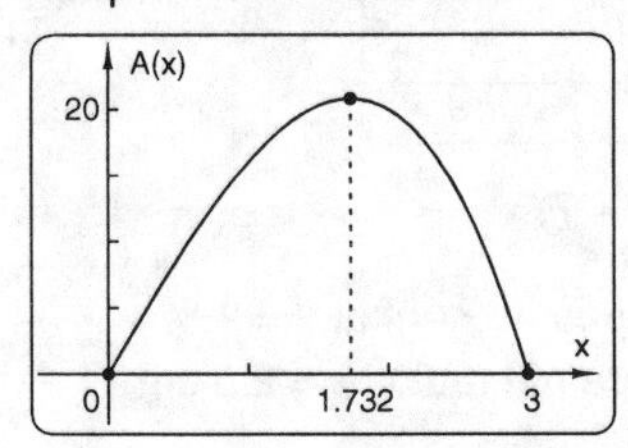

$A'(x) = 18 - 6x^2 = 0$ at $x = \pm\sqrt{3} = \pm 1.732 \ldots$
-1.732 is out of the domain.
$A(0) = A(3) = 0$; $A(\sqrt{3}) = 12\sqrt{3} = 20.7846 \ldots$
Max. rect. has width = $2\sqrt{3}$, length = 9 − 3 = 6.

b. Maximize $P(x) = 4x + 2y = 4x + 18 - 2x^2$.
Graph shows max. at $x \approx 1$.

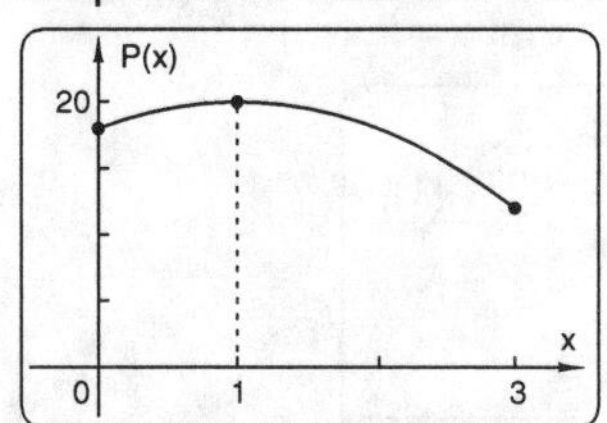

$P'(x) = 4 - 4x = 0$ at x = 1
P(0) = 18; P(1) = 20; P(3) = 12
Max. rectangle has width = 2, length = 9 − 1 = 8.

c. No. The maximum-area rectangle is $2\sqrt{3}$ by 6. The maximum-perimeter rectangle is 2 by 8.

24. Cylinder in Paraboloid Problem

a. Maximize $V(x) = \pi x^2 y = \pi x^2(9 - x^2) = 9\pi x^2 - \pi x^4$.
Domain: $0 \le x \le 3$
Graph shows max. at $x \approx 2.1$.

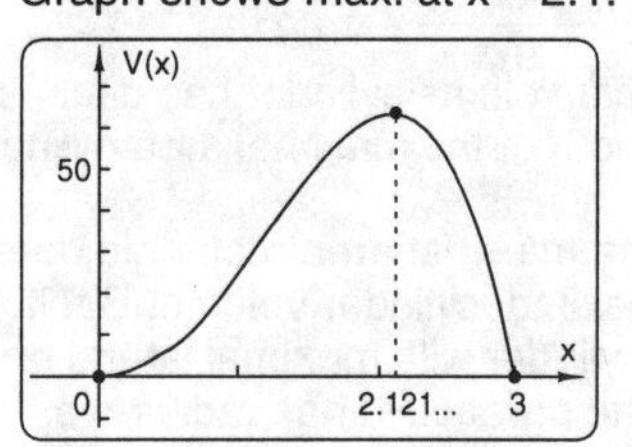

$V'(x) = 18\pi x - 4\pi x^3 = 0$ at $x = 0, \pm\sqrt{4.5}$
$-\sqrt{4.5}$ is out of the domain.
$V(0) = V(3) = 0$, $V(\sqrt{4.5}) = 20.25\pi = 63.6172 \ldots$
Max. is at $x = \sqrt{4.5}$, y = 9 − 4.5 = 4.5.
Max. cylinder has radius = $\sqrt{4.5} = 2.12132 \ldots$ and altitude = 4.5.

b. Maximize $L(x) = 2\pi xy = 2\pi x(9 - x^2)$
$= 18\pi x - 2\pi x^3$
Graph shows max. at $x \approx 1.7$.

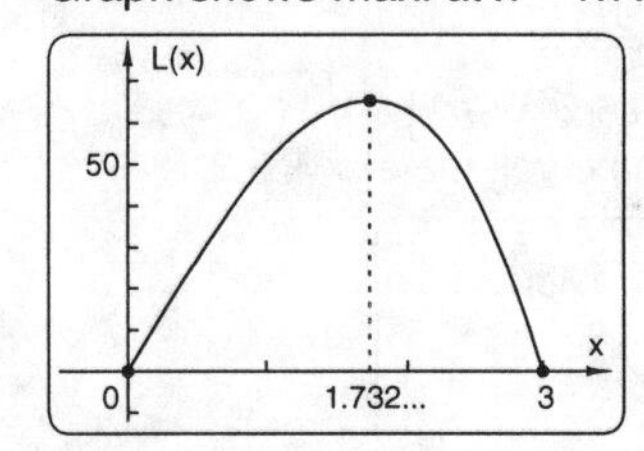

$L'(x) = 18\pi - 6\pi x^2 = 0$ at $x = \pm\sqrt{3}$
$-\sqrt{3}$ is out of the domain.
$L(0) = L(3) = 0$; $L(\sqrt{3}) = 12\pi\sqrt{3} = 65.2967 \ldots$
Max. is at $x = \sqrt{3}$, y = 9 − 3 = 6.
Max. cylinder has radius = $\sqrt{3} = 1.7320 \ldots$, and altitude = 6.

c. Maximize $A(x) = 2\pi x^2 + 2\pi xy$
$= 2\pi x^2 + 2\pi x(9 - x^2) = 2\pi x^2 + 18\pi x - 2\pi x^3$.
Graph shows max. at $x \approx 2.1$.

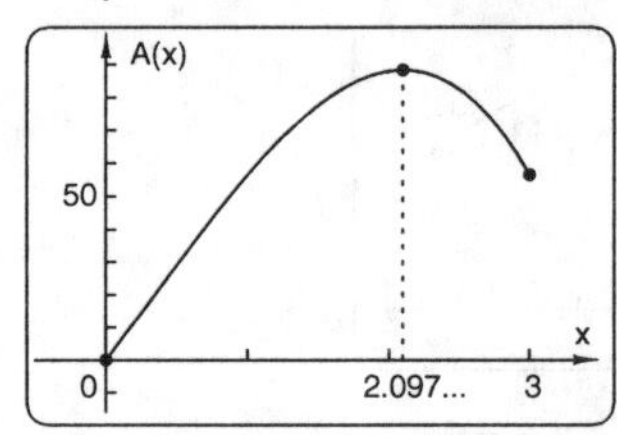

$A'(x) = 18\pi + 4\pi x - 6\pi x^2$

$A'(x) = 0$ at $x = \dfrac{1 \pm 2\sqrt{7}}{3} = 2.0971 \ldots$ or $-1.430 \ldots$

$-1.430 \ldots$ is out of the domain.

$A(0) = 0$; $A(2.0971 \ldots) = 88.2727 \ldots$;

$A(3) = 18\pi = 56.5486 \ldots$

Max. cylinder has radius $= \dfrac{1 + 2\sqrt{7}}{3} = 2.0971 \ldots$,

and altitude $= \dfrac{52 - 4\sqrt{7}}{9} = 4.6018 \ldots$.

d. No. The maximal-volume cylinder has dimensions different from both of the maximal area cylinders in parts b and c

e. No. Rotating the maximal-area rectangle does not produce the maximal-cylinder volume. But it produces the cylinder with maximal lateral area.

f. If $y = a^2 - x^2$, the paraboloid has radius $= a$.
$V = \pi x^2(a^2 - x^2) = \pi(a^2x^2 - x^4)$
$V' = \pi(2a^2x - 4x^3)$

$V' = 0 \Leftrightarrow x = 0$ or $x = \pm a/\sqrt{2}$.

V is max. at $x = a/\sqrt{2}$.
For the cylinder of maximum volume,

(cyl. radius):(paraboloid radius) $= 1/\sqrt{2}$, a const.
Note: This ratio is also constant for the cylinder of maximum lateral area, but is *not* constant for the cylinder of maximum total area.

25. Cylinder in Sphere Problem

a. $x^2 + y^2 = 100$, $0 \le x \le 10$

Maximize $V(x) = \pi x^2 \cdot y = 2\pi x^2\sqrt{100 - x^2}$.

b. Graph shows max. volume at $x \approx 8.2$.

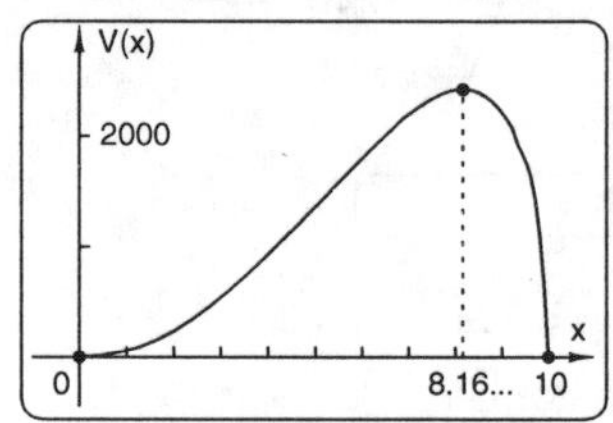

$$V'(x) = \frac{-2\pi x^3}{\sqrt{100 - x^2}} + 4\pi x\sqrt{100 - x^2}$$
$$= \frac{-6\pi x^3 + 400\pi x}{\sqrt{100 - x^2}}$$

$V'(x) = 0$ at $x = 0$, $\sqrt{\dfrac{200}{3}} = \dfrac{10\sqrt{6}}{3} = 8.1649 \ldots$

$V(0) = V(10) = 0$;

$V\left(\dfrac{10\sqrt{6}}{3}\right) = \dfrac{4000\pi\sqrt{3}}{9} = 2418.399 \ldots$

Maximal cylinder has radius $= 8.1649 \ldots$, altitude $=$

$\dfrac{20\sqrt{3}}{3} = 11.5470 \ldots$, and volume $= 2418.39 \ldots$.

c. Altitude $=$ Radius $\cdot \sqrt{2}$

Volume of sphere $V_s = \dfrac{4}{3}\pi 1000 = \dfrac{4000\pi}{3}$

Volume of maximal cylinder $V_c = \dfrac{4000\pi\sqrt{3}}{9}$

$\therefore V_c = V_s/\sqrt{3}$

26. Conical Nose Cone Problem

Let r = radius of cone, h = height.

Lateral area $A(r) = \pi r$(slant height) $= \pi r\sqrt{r^2 + h^2}$

$V = \dfrac{1}{3}\pi r^2 h = 5\pi \Rightarrow h = 15r^{-2}$

$\therefore A(r) = \pi r\sqrt{r^2 + 225r^{-4}}$

$h \ge 2r \Rightarrow 2r \le 15r^{-2}$

Domain of r is $0 < r \le \sqrt[3]{7.5} = 1.9574 \ldots$.

Graph shows min. of $A(r)$ at endpoint $r = 1.957 \ldots$.

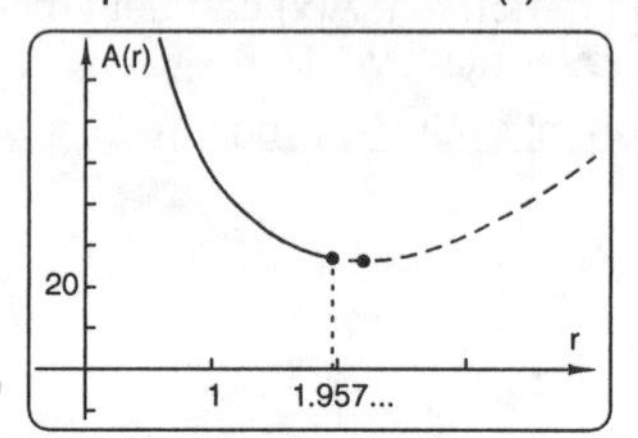

Minimize $A^2(r) = \pi^2(r^4 + 225r^{-2})$.

$(A^2(r))' = \pi^2(4r^3 - 450r^{-3}) = 0$ at $r = \sqrt[6]{112.5} = 2.1971 \ldots$, which is out of the domain.

$A(1.9574 \ldots) = 26.915 \ldots$, $\lim\limits_{r \to 0^+} A(r) = \infty$.

Minimal cone has radius $= \sqrt[3]{7.5} = 1.9574 \ldots$, and

height $= 2r = 2\sqrt[3]{7.5} = 3.9148 \ldots$.

Make $r \approx 1.96$ ft and $h \approx 3.91$ ft.

27. Cylinder in Cone Problem

a. Lateral area $L(x) = 2\pi xy$

Domains: $0 \le x \le 5$ and $0 \le y \le 7$

Equation of element of cone is

$y = -\dfrac{7}{5}x + 7 \Rightarrow y = -1.4x + 7$.

$\therefore L(x) = 2\pi x(-1.4x + 7) = 2\pi(-1.4x^2 + 7x)$

Graph shows maximum of $L(x)$ at $x \approx 2.5$.

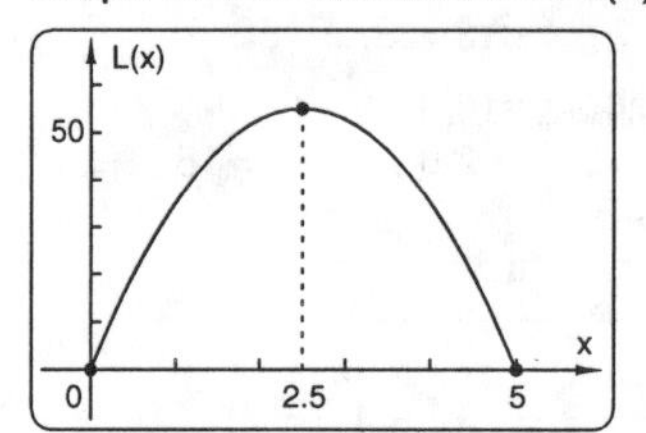

$L'(x) = 2\pi(-2.8x + 7)$

$L'(x) = 0$ at $x = 2.5$.

$L'(x)$ goes from pos. to neg. at $x = 2.5$.

$\therefore$ Max. lateral area at radius $x = 2.5$ cm

b. Total area $A(x) = 2\pi xy + 2\pi x^2$
$= 2\pi x(-1.4x + 7) + 2\pi x^2$
$A(x) = 2\pi(7x - 0.4x^2)$
Graph shows max. at endpoint $x = 5$.

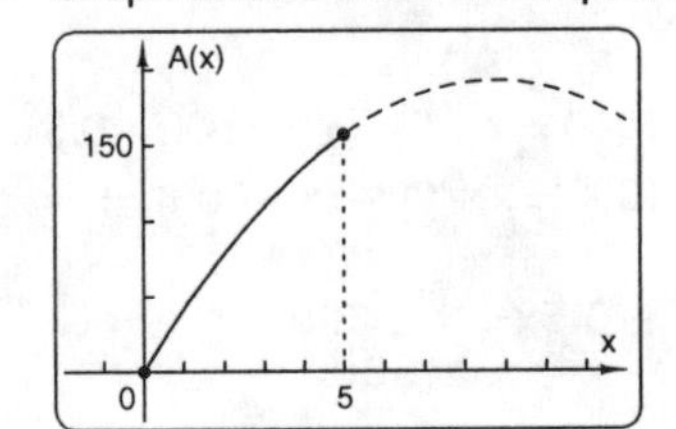

$A'(x) = 2\pi(7 - 0.8x) = 0$ at $x = 8.75$, out of domain.
$\therefore$ Max. is at an endpoint $x = 5$.
$A(0) = 0$; $A(5) = 2\pi(5^2) = 50\pi = 157.07$ ...
Max. area is with the degenerate cylinder consisting only of the top and bottom, radius 5 and altitude 0.

28. General Cylinder in Cone Problem

a. Let r = radius; h = altitude of cone (constants).
Let (x, y) be a sample point on cone element.
Domain of x is $0 \le x \le r$
$L(x) = 2\pi xy$.
Equation of element of cone is $y = (-h/r)x + h$.
$\therefore L(x) = 2\pi x((-h/r)x + h) = 2\pi h(-x^2/r + x)$
$L'(x) = 2\pi h(-2x/r + 1)$
$L'(x) = 0$ at $x = r/2$
$L'(x)$ goes from pos. to neg. at $x = r/2$.
$\therefore$ Max. lateral area at radius $x = r/2$

b. $A(x) = 2\pi xy + 2\pi x^2 = 2\pi x(h - (h/r)x) + 2\pi x^2$
$A(x) = 2\pi((1 - h/r)x^2 + hx)$
$A'(x) = 2\pi(2(1 - h/r)x + h) = 0$ at $x = \dfrac{-h}{2(1 - h/r)}$
$A'(x) = 0$ at $x = \dfrac{-h}{2 - 2h/r} = \dfrac{rh}{2(h - r)}$
If $h \le 2r$ then $A'(x) \ne 0$ for all $x \le r$, so in this case the critical points are the endpoints, $x = 0, r$;
$A(0) = 0$; $A(r) = 2\pi r^2$
If $h \ge 2r$, then $0 \le \dfrac{rh}{2(h - r)} \le r$ so this is a critical point; $A\left(\dfrac{rh}{2(h - r)}\right) = \dfrac{\pi rh^2}{2(h - r)}$
$A'(x)$ goes from pos. to neg. at $x = \dfrac{rh}{2(h - r)}$.
Max. area at $x = \dfrac{rh}{2(h - r)}$ if $h \ge 2r$; $x = r$ otherwise.

c. From part b, the maximal cylinder degenerates to two circular bases if the radius of the cone is at least half the altitude.

29. Elliptical Nose Cone Problem

Maximize $V = \pi y^2 x$.
Ellipse equation is $(x/9)^2 + (y/4)^2 = 1$, from which $y^2 = (16/81)(81 - x^2)$.
$\therefore V = (16\pi/81)(81x - x^3)$
Domain: $0 \le x \le 9$
Graph shows max. V at $x \approx 5.2$.

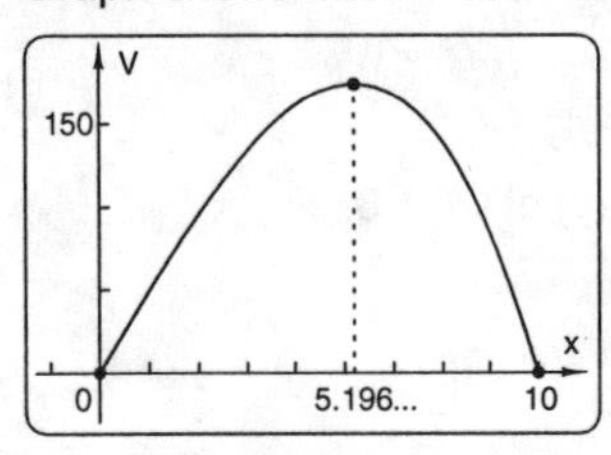

$V' = (16\pi/81)(81 - 3x^2) = (16\pi/27)(27 - x^2)$
$V' = 0$ at $x = \pm\sqrt{27} = \pm 5.196$ ...
-5.196 ... is out of domain.
$V(0) = v(9) = 0$; $V(\sqrt{27}) = 32\pi\sqrt{3} = 174.1$ ...
At $x = 5.196$ ..., $y = \sqrt{32/3} = 3.265$ ... .
$y^2 = (16/81)(81 - 27) = 32/3 \Rightarrow y = 3.2659$ ... .
$\therefore$ Max. volume ≈ 174.1 cm^3 at radius ≈ 3.27m and altitude ≈ 5.20m

30. Submarine Pressure Hull (Project)

Maximize $C(y) = \pi y^2 x$, the area of the cylinder.
Parabola has equation of form $x = ay^2 + 16$.
$0 = a \cdot 16 + 16 \Rightarrow a = -1 \Rightarrow x = 16 - y^2$
$V(y) = \pi y^2(16 - y^2) = \pi(16y^2 - y^4)$
Domain: $0 \le y \le 4$.
Graph shows max. V(y) at $y \approx 2.8$.

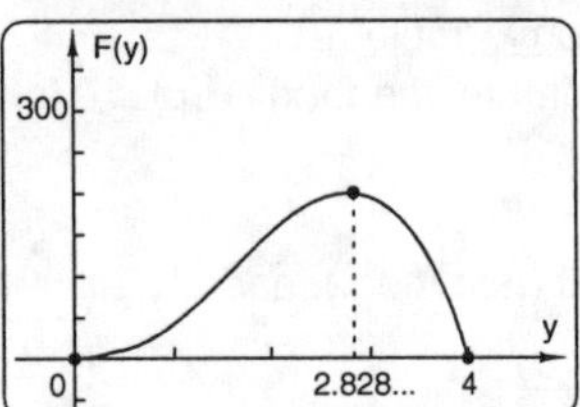

$C'(y) = 32\pi y - 4\pi y^3 = 0$ at $y = 0, \pm\sqrt{8}$
$y = -\sqrt{8}$ is out of the domain.
$C(0) = C(4) = 0$, $C(\sqrt{8}) = 64\pi = 201.0619$ ...
Max. of C(y) is at $y = \sqrt{8}$.
At $y = \sqrt{8}$, $x = 8$.
Max. cylinder has radius $= \sqrt{8} \approx 2.83$ m, altitude = 8m, and volume $= 64\pi \approx 201.1$ m^3.

Maximize F(y), the volume of the frustum.
Note that $V_f = (1/3)\pi h(R^2 + r^2 + Rr)$, where V_f = volume of frustum, h = altitude of frustum, R = larger radius, and r = smaller radius.

$\therefore F(y) = \frac{1}{3}\pi x(16 + y^2 + 4y)$

$= \frac{1}{3}\pi(16 - y^2)(y^2 + 4y + 16)$

$F(y) = \frac{1}{3}\pi(256 + 64y - 4y^3 - y^4)$

Graph shows max. F(y) at y ≈ 1.8.

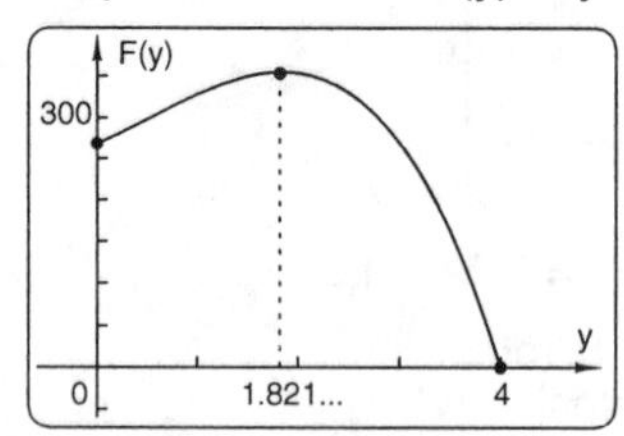

$F'(y) = \frac{1}{3}\pi(64 - 12y^2 - 4y^3)$

$F'(y) = 0 \Leftrightarrow 64 - 12y^2 - 4y^3 = 0$

Solving numerically for y close to 1.8 gives y ≈ 1.8216 ... .
Substituting y = 1.8216 ... gives $x = 16 - y^2 \approx 12.6816$ ... .

$F(1.8216\ldots) = \frac{1}{3}\pi x(16 + y^2 + 4y) \approx 353.318\ldots$.

Maximal frustum has radii = 4m and ≈ 1.82m, altitude ≈ 12.68m, and volume ≈ 353.3m^3.
The maximal frustum contains ≈ 152.3m^3 more than the maximal cylinder, about 75.7% more.

31. Local Maximum Property Problem

a. If f(c) is a local maximum, then f(x) – f(c) ≤ 0 for x in a neighborhood of c.
For x to the left of c, x – c < 0.
Thus $\frac{f(x) - f(c)}{x - c} \geq 0$ (neg./neg.), and
$f'(c) = \lim_{x\to 0^-} \frac{f(x) - f(c)}{x - c} \geq 0$.
For x to the right of c, x – c > 0.
Thus $\frac{f(x) - f(c)}{x - c} \leq 0$ (neg./pos.) and
$f'(c) = \lim_{x\to 0^+} \frac{f(x) - f(c)}{x - c} \leq 0$.
Therefore, 0 ≤ f'(c) ≤ 0.
Since f'(c) exists, f'(c) = 0 by the squeeze theorem, Q.E.D.

b. If f is not differentiable at x = c, then f'(c) does not exist, and thus cannot equal 0. Without this hypothesis, the reasoning in 31a shows only that f'(x) changes sign at x = c. There could be a cusp, a removable discontinuity, or a step discontinuity at x = c.

c. The converse would say that if f'(c) = 0, then f(c) is a local maximum. This statement is false because f(c) could be a local minimum or a plateau point.

32. Corral with Short Wall Project

a. Let x = length of corral (parallel to wall).
Let y = width of corral (perpendicular to wall).
A = xy

If x ≤ 600, then 1000 = x + 2y ⇔ y = 500 – 0.5x.
If x ≥ 600, then 1000 = x + 2y + (x – 600) ⇔ y = 800 – x.

$\therefore A = \begin{cases} 500x - 0.5x^2, & x \leq 600 \\ 800x - x^2, & x \geq 600 \end{cases}$

Graph shows max. A at x ≈ 500.

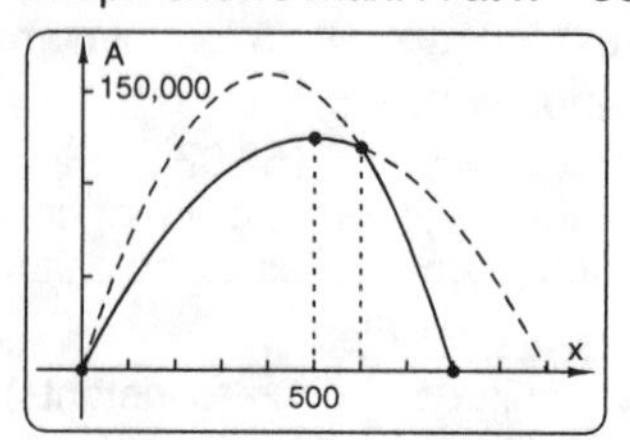

$A' = \begin{cases} 500 - x, & x < 600 \\ 800 - 2x, & x > 600 \end{cases}$

For x < 600, A' = 0 ⇔ x = 500.
For x > 600, A' = 0 ⇔ x = 400 (out of domain).
Max. at x = 500, since graph is parabola opening downward.
Or: Check the critical points.
$A = 500(500) - 0.5(500)^2 = 125{,}000$
Max. area is 125,000 ft^2.

b. If x ≤ 400, then 1000 = x + 2y ⇔ y = 500 – 0.5x.
If x ≥ 400, then 1000 = x + 2y + (x – 400) ⇔ y = 700 – x.

$\therefore A = \begin{cases} 500x - 0.5x^2, & x \leq 400 \\ 700x - x^2, & x \geq 400 \end{cases}$

Graph shows max. A at the cusp, x = 400.

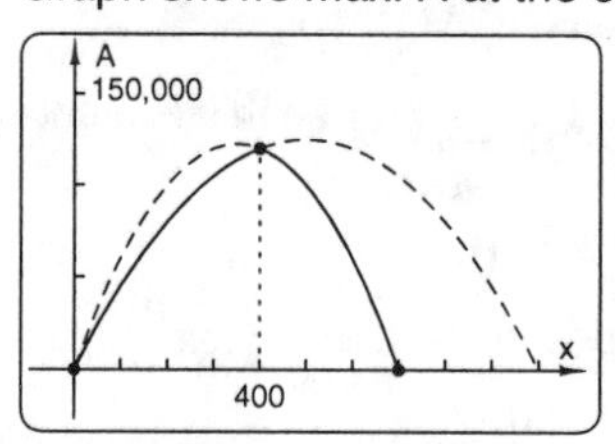

$A' = \begin{cases} 500 - x, & x < 400 \\ 700 - 2x, & x > 400 \end{cases}$

For x < 400, A' = 0 ⇔ x = 500 (out of domain).
For x > 400, A' = 0 ⇔ x = 350 (out of domain).
Max. area is at the cusp, x = 400.
$A = 700(400) - 400^2 = 120{,}000$
Max. area is 120,000 ft^2.

c. If $x \le 200$, then $1000 = x + 2y \Leftrightarrow y = 500 - 0.5x$

If $x \ge 200$, then $1000 = x + 2y + (x - 200) \Leftrightarrow$
$y = 600 - x$.

$\therefore\ A = \begin{cases} 500x - 0.5x^2, & x \le 200 \\ 600x - x^2, & x \ge 200 \end{cases}$

Graph shows max. A at $x \approx 300$.

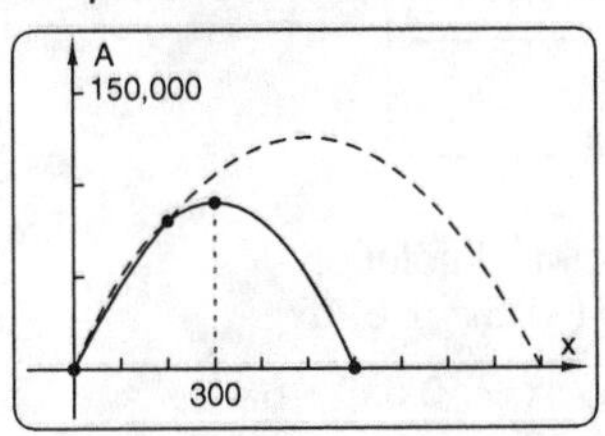

$A' = \begin{cases} 500 - x, & x < 200 \\ 600 - 2x, & x > 200 \end{cases}$

For $x < 200$, $A' = 0 \Leftrightarrow x = 500$ (out of domain).

For $x > 200$, $A' = 0 \Leftrightarrow x = 300$.

Max. area is at $x = 300$ since graph is a parabola opening downward.

Or: Check critical points.

$A = 600(300) - 300^2 = 90{,}000$

Max. area is 90,000 ft^2.

33. Journal Problem

Journal entries will vary.

Problem Set 8-4, pages 383 to 385 — Area of a Plane Region

Q1. $-x^{-1} + C$ Q2. $\ln|u| + C$

Q3. $\dfrac{u^{n+1}}{n+1} + C$ (for $n \ne -1$) Q4. $(\ln x)^8/8 + C$

Q5. $x \ln 3 + C$ Q6. $4^x/\ln 4 + C$

Q7. $\sec x + C$ Q8. Graph, $y' = \begin{cases} 1 & x > 2 \\ -1 & x < 2 \end{cases}$

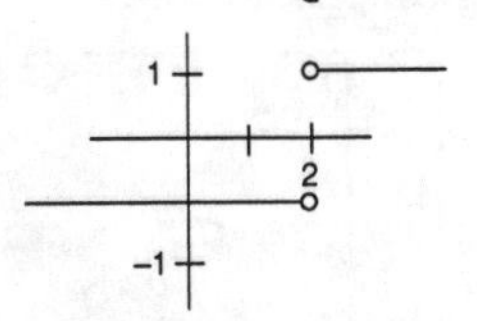

Q9. $A = 2x(4 - x^2)$ Q10. $A_{max} = 32/(3\sqrt{3})$

Plan of attack for area problems:

- Do geometry to get dA in terms of sample point (x, y).
- Do algebra to get dA in terms of one variable.
- Do calculus to add up the dA's and take the limit (i.e., integrate).

1. Graph, $y = -x^2 + 6x - 5$, intersecting the x-axis at $x = 1$ and $x = 5$.

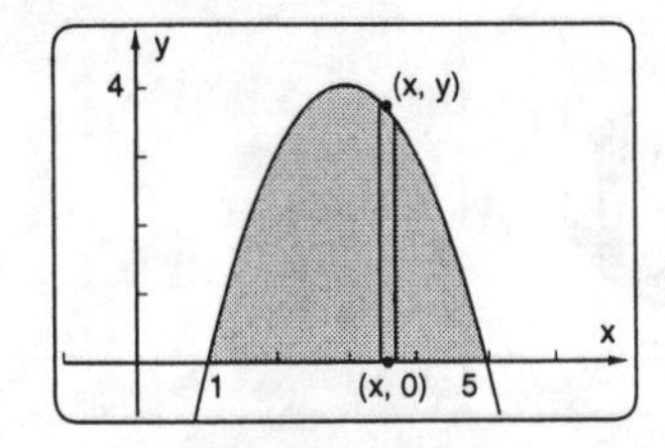

$y = -x^2 + 6x - 5 = -(x - 1)(x - 5) = 0 \Leftrightarrow x = 1, 5$, which confirms the graphical solution.

$dA = (y - 0)\,dx = (-x^2 + 6x - 5)\,dx$

$A = \int_1^5 (-x^2 + 6x - 5)\,dx = -\frac{1}{3}x^3 + 3x^2 - 5x \Big|_1^5$

$= -\frac{125}{3} + 75 - 25 + \frac{1}{3} - 3 + 5 = 10\frac{2}{3}$

2. Graph, $y = x^2 - x - 6$, intersecting the x-axis at $x = -2$ and $x = 3$.

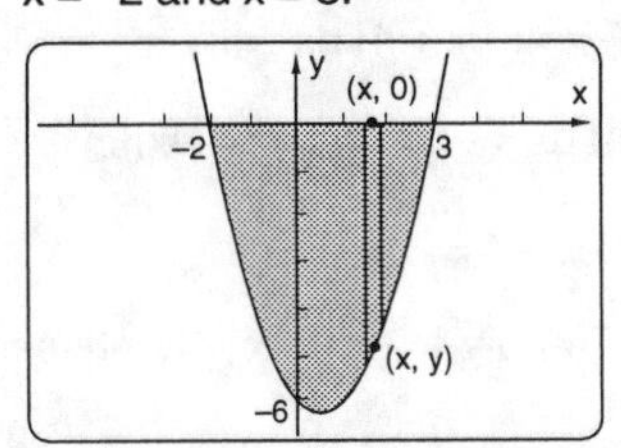

$y = x^2 - x - 6 = (x + 2)(x - 3) = 0 \Leftrightarrow x = -2, 3$, which confirms the graphical solution.

$dA = (0 - y)\,dx = (-x^2 + x + 6)\,dx$

$A = \int_{-2}^3 (-x^2 + x + 6)\,dx = -\frac{1}{3}x^3 + \frac{1}{2}x^2 + 6x \Big|_{-2}^3$

$= -9 + \frac{9}{2} + 18 - \frac{8}{3} - 2 + 12 = 20\frac{5}{6}$

3. Graph, $x = (y - 1)(y - 4)$, intersecting the y-axis at $y = 1$ and $y = 4$.

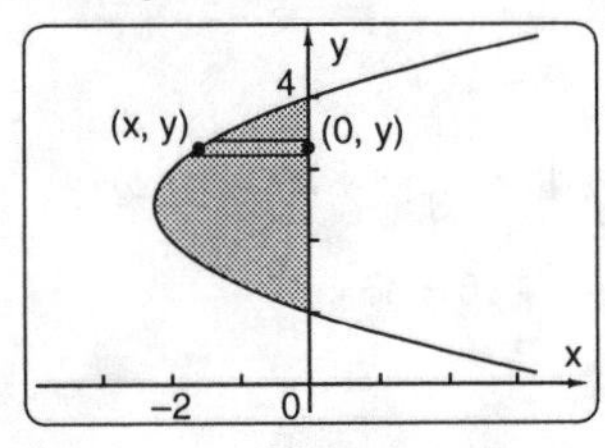

$x = (y - 1)(y - 4) = y^2 - 5y + 4 = 0 \Leftrightarrow y = 1, 4$, which confirms the graphical solution.

$dA = (0 - x)\,dy = (-y^2 + 5y - 4)\,dy$

$A = \int_1^4 (-y^2 + 5y - 4)\,dy = -\frac{1}{3}y^3 + \frac{5}{2}y^2 - 4y \Big|_1^4$

$= -\frac{64}{3} + 40 - 16 + \frac{1}{3} - \frac{5}{2} + 4 = 4\frac{1}{2}$

4. Graph, $x = 5 + 4y - y^2$, intersecting the y-axis at $y = -1$ and $y = 5$

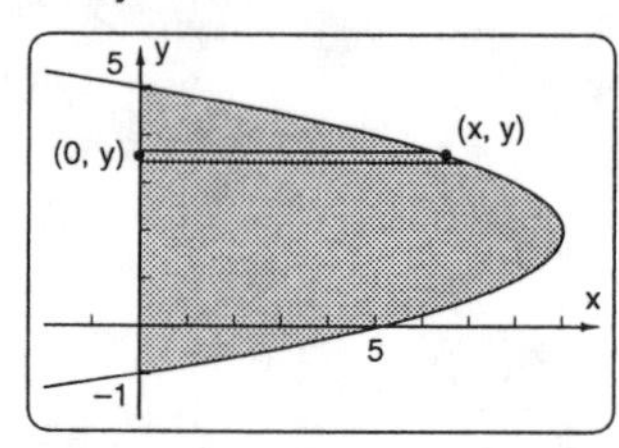

$x = 5 + 4y - y^2 = (1 + y)(5 - y) = 0 \Leftrightarrow y = -1, 5$, which confirms the graphical solution.
$dA = (x - 0)\, dy = (5 + 4y - y^2)\, dy$

$\text{Area} = \int_{-1}^{5} (5 + 4y - y^2)\, dy = 5y + 2y^2 - \frac{1}{3}y^3 \Big|_{-1}^{5}$

$= 25 + 50 - \frac{125}{3} + 5 - 2 - \frac{1}{3} = 36$

5. Graphs, $y_1 = x^2 - 2x - 2$ and $y_2 = x + 2$, intersecting at $x = -1$ and $x = 4$

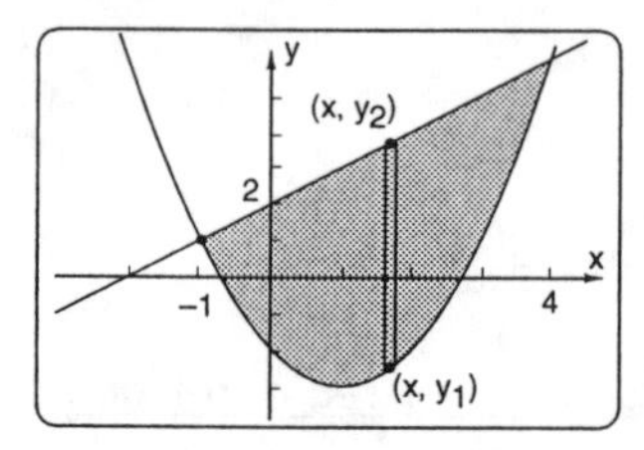

$x^2 - 2x - 2 = x + 2 \Leftrightarrow x^2 - 3x - 4 = 0 \Leftrightarrow x = -1, 4$, which confirms the graphical solution.
$dA = (y_2 - y_1)\, dx = (-x^2 + 3x + 4)\, dx$

$A = \int_{-1}^{4} (-x^2 + 3x + 4)\, dx = -\frac{1}{3}x^3 + \frac{3}{2}x^2 + 4x \Big|_{-1}^{4}$

$= -\frac{64}{3} + 24 + 16 - \frac{1}{3} - \frac{3}{2} + 4 = 20\frac{5}{6}$

6. Graphs, $y_1 = -2x + 7$ and $y_2 = x^2 - 4x - 1$, intersecting at $x = -2$ and $x = 4$

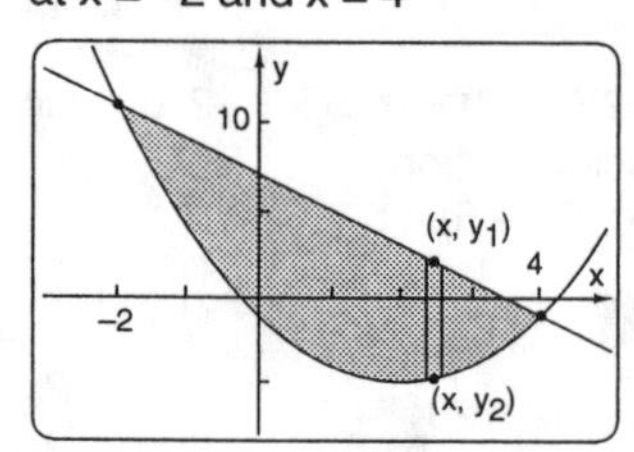

$-2x + 7 = x^2 - 4x - 1 \Leftrightarrow x^2 - 2x - 8 = 0$
$\Leftrightarrow (x + 2)(x - 4) = 0 \Leftrightarrow x = -2, 4$, which confirms the graphical solution.
$dA = (y_1 - y_2)\, dx = (-x^2 + 2x + 8)\, dx$

$A = \int_{-2}^{4} (-x^2 + 2x + 8)\, dx = -\frac{1}{3}x^3 + x^2 + 8x \Big|_{-2}^{4}$

$= -\frac{64}{3} + 16 + 32 - \frac{8}{3} - 4 + 16 = 36$

7. Graphs, $y_1 = 0.5x^2 + 2x$ and $y_2 = -x^2 + 2x + 6$, intersecting at $x = -2$ and $x = 2$.

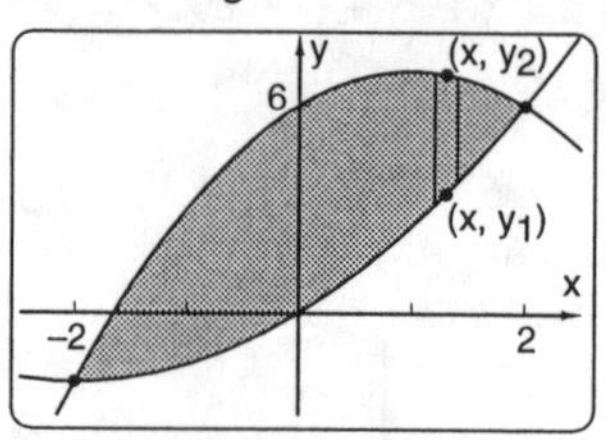

$0.5x^2 + 2x = -x^2 + 2x + 6 \Leftrightarrow 1.5x^2 = 6 \Leftrightarrow x = -2, 2$, confirming the graphical solution.
$dA = (y_2 - y_1)\, dx = (-1.5x^2 + 6)\, dx$

$A = \int_{-2}^{2} (-1.5x^2 + 6)\, dx = -0.5x^3 + 6x \Big|_{-2}^{2}$
$= -4 + 12 - 4 + 12 = 16$

8. Graphs, $y_1 = 0.2x^2 + 3$ and $y_2 = x^2 - 4x + 3$, intersecting at $x = 0$ and $x = 5$

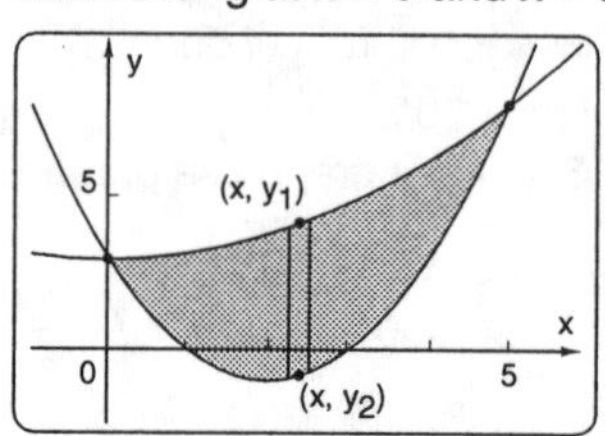

$0.2x^2 + 3 = x^2 - 4x + 3 \Leftrightarrow 0.8x^2 = 4x \Leftrightarrow x = 0, 5$, which confirms the graphical solution.
$dA = (y_1 - y_2)\, dx = (-0.8x^2 + 4x)\, dx$

$A = \int_{0}^{5} (-0.8x^2 + 4x)\, dx = -\frac{4}{15}x^3 + 2x^2 \Big|_{0}^{5}$

$= -\frac{500}{15} + 50 + 0 - 0 = 16\frac{2}{3}$

9. Graphs, $y_1 = 2e^{0.2x}$ and $y_2 = \cos x$, $x = 0$ and $x = 5$

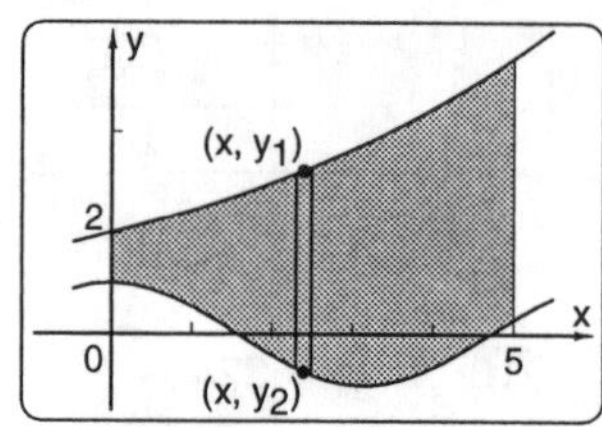

$dA = (y_1 - y_2)\, dx = (2e^{0.2x} - \cos x)\, dx$

$A = \int_{0}^{5} (2e^{0.2x} - \cos x)\, dx = 10e^{0.2x} - \sin x \Big|_{0}^{5}$
$= 10e - \sin 5 - 10 + 0 = 18.1417\ldots$

10. Graphs, $y_1 = \sec^2 x$ and $y_2 = e^{2x}$, intersecting at $x = 0$ in Quadrant I and ending at $x = 1$

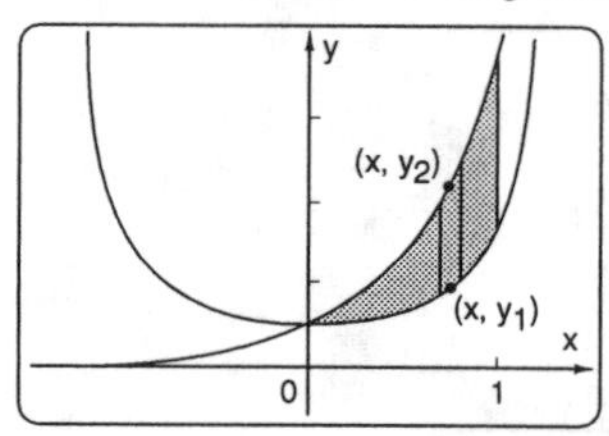

$dA = (y_2 - y_1)\, dx = (e^{2x} - \sec^2 x)\, dx$

$A = \int_{0}^{1} (e^{2x} - \sec^2 x)\, dx = 0.5e^{2x} - \tan x \Big|_{0}^{1}$
$= 0.5e^2 - \tan 1 - 0.5 + 0 = 1.6371\ldots$

11. Graphs, $y = x_1 + 3$ and $x_2 = -y^2 + 6y - 7$, intersecting at $y = 1$ and $y = 4$

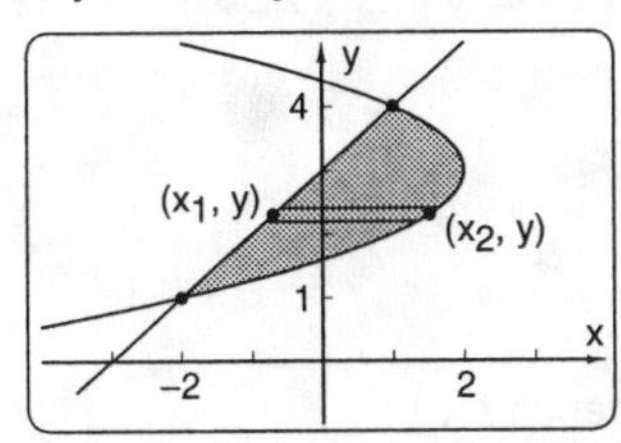

Write $y = x + 3$ as $x = y - 3$.
$y - 3 = -y^2 + 6y - 7 \Leftrightarrow y^2 - 5y + 4 = 0$
$\Leftrightarrow (y - 1)(y - 4) = 0 \Leftrightarrow y = 1, 4$, which confirms the graphical solution.
$dA = (x_2 - x_1)\, dy = (-y^2 + 5y - 4)\, dy$
$A = \int_1^4 (-y^2 + 5y - 4)\, dy = -\frac{1}{3}y^3 + \frac{5}{2}y^2 - 4y \Big|_1^4$
$= -\frac{64}{3} + 40 - 16 + \frac{1}{3} - \frac{5}{2} + 4 = 4\frac{1}{2}$

12. Graphs, $y = -2x_1 + 11$, $x_2 = 0.25y^2 - 0.5y - 0.75$, intersecting at $y = -5$ and $y = 5$.

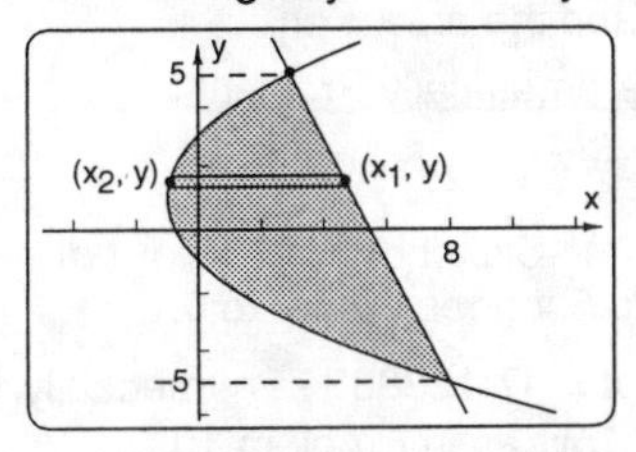

Write $y = -2x_1 + 11$ as $x_1 = 5.5 - 0.5y$.
$5.5 - 0.5y = 0.25y^2 - 0.5y - 0.75$
$\Leftrightarrow 0.25y^2 = 6.25 \Leftrightarrow y = -5, 5$, which confirms the graphical solution.
$dA = (x_1 - x_2)\, dy = (-0.25y^2 + 6.25)\, dy$
$A = \int_{-5}^{5} (-0.25y^2 + 6.25)\, dy = -\frac{1}{12}y^3 + \frac{25}{4}y \Big|_{-5}^{5}$
$= -\frac{125}{12} + \frac{125}{4} - \frac{125}{12} + \frac{125}{4} = 41\frac{2}{3}$

13. Graphs, $y_1 = x^3 - 4x$ and $y_2 = 3x^2 - 4x - 4$, intersecting at $x = -1$ and $x = 2$

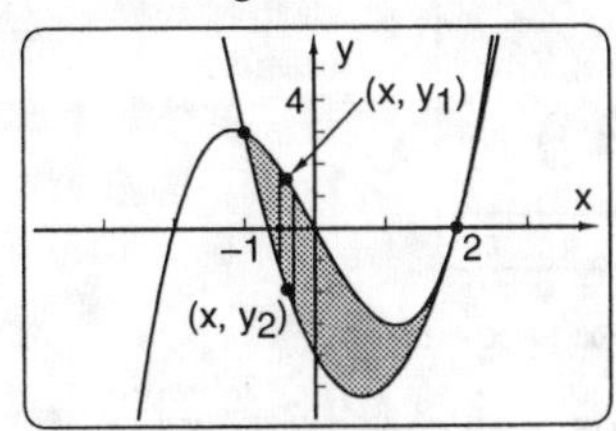

$x^3 - 4x = 3x^2 - 4x - 4$
$\Leftrightarrow x^3 - 3x^2 + 4 = (x + 1)(x - 2)^2 = 0 \Leftrightarrow x = -1, 2$,
which confirms the graphical solution.
$dA = (y_1 - y_2)\, dx = (x^3 - 3x^2 + 4)\, dx$
$A = \int_{-1}^{2} (x^3 - 3x^2 + 4)\, dx = \frac{1}{4}x^4 - x^3 + 4x \Big|_{-1}^{2}$
$= 4 - 8 + 8 - \frac{1}{4} - 1 + 4 = 6\frac{3}{4}$

14. Graphs, $y_1 = x^{2/3}$ and $y_2 = (x + 1)^{1/2} + 1$, intersecting at $x = -1$ and $x = 8$

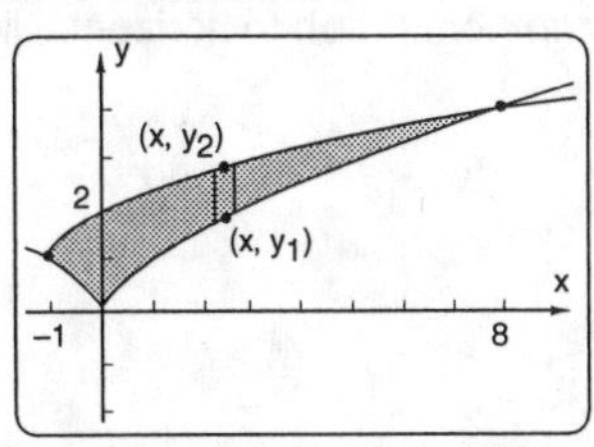

$x^{2/3} = (x + 1)^{1/2} + 1 \Leftrightarrow x = -1, 8$ numerically, which confirms the graphical solution.
Or $x^{2/3} - 1 = (x + 1)^{1/2} \Leftarrow (x^{2/3} - 1)^2 = x + 1$
Write $t = x^{1/3}$ so $(t^2 - 1)^2 = t^3 + 1$.
$\Leftrightarrow t^4 - t^3 - 2t^2 = t^2(t + 1)(t - 2) = 0 \Leftrightarrow t = 0, -1, 2$
$\Leftrightarrow x = t^3 = 0, -1, 8$.
But $x = 0$ is extraneous from the irreversible step of squaring both sides. So $x = -1, 8$.
$dA = (y_2 - y_1)\, dx = ((x + 1)^{1/2} + 1 - x^{2/3})\, dx$
$A = \int_{-1}^{8} ((x + 1)^{1/2} + 1 - x^{2/3})\, dx$
$= \frac{2}{3}(x + 1)^{3/2} + x - \frac{3}{5}x^{5/3} \Big|_{-1}^{8}$
$= 18 + 8 - \frac{96}{5} - 0 + 1 - \frac{3}{5} = 7\frac{1}{5}$

15. Wanda: You can always tell the right way because the altitude of the strip should be <u>positive</u>. This will happen if you take (larger value) − (smaller value). In this case, if you slice vertically it's <u>line minus curve</u> (see graph).

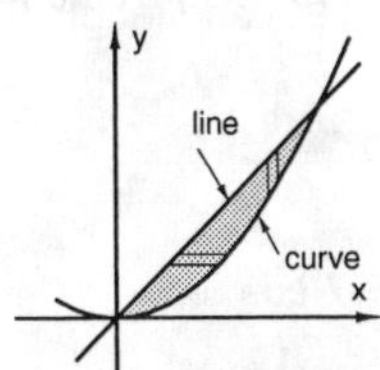

For curve minus line, you'd get the opposite of the right answer. Note that if you slice horizontally it would be curve minus line.

16.a. Peter: Horizontal slicing would be awkward because for some values of y the length of the strip would be given by line − curve, but in others it would be boundary − curve, and yet elsewhere it would be curve − curve. If you use vertical slices, the length of the strip will always be line − curve. (See graphs below.)

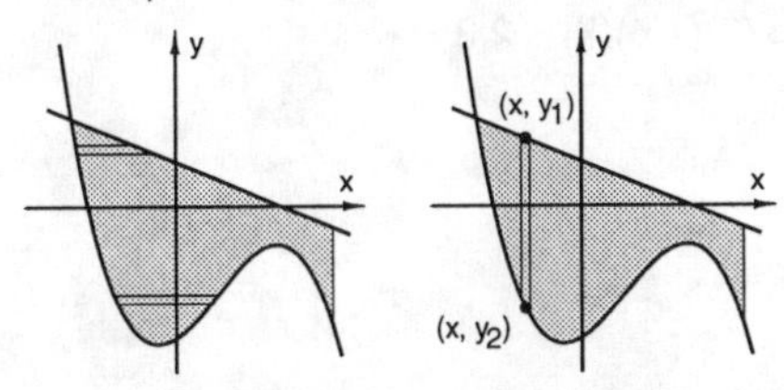

b. Peter: In the right-hand graph above, $y_1 - y_2$ will be positive. Since y_2 is negative, you will get (pos.) − (neg.), which is equivalent to (pos.) + (pos.). Thus, the altitude for the strip is positive.

17. Parabolic Region Problem

Graph, showing Figure 8-4g with parabolic region from $x = -h$ to $x = h$ and strip from graph to horizontal line at $y = ah^2$.

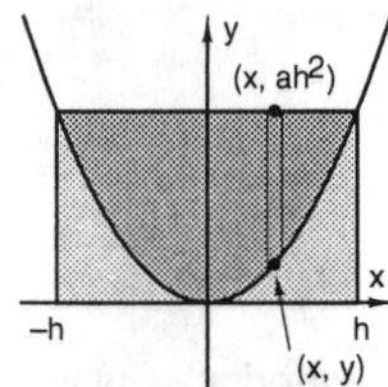

$dA = (ah^2 - y)\,dx = (ah^2 - ax^2)\,dx$

$A = \int_{-h}^{h} (ah^2 - ax^2)\,dx = 2(ah^2x - \frac{1}{3}ax^3)\Big|_0^h$

$= 2a(h^3 - \frac{1}{3}h^3) = \frac{4}{3}ah^3$

Area of rectangle $= 2h(ah^2) = 2ah^3$

$\therefore \dfrac{\text{area of region}}{\text{area of rectangle}} = \dfrac{(4/3)ah^3}{2ah^3} = \dfrac{2}{3}$, Q.E.D.

Graph, $y = 67 - 0.6x^2$ and line $y = 7$, with circumscribed rectangle

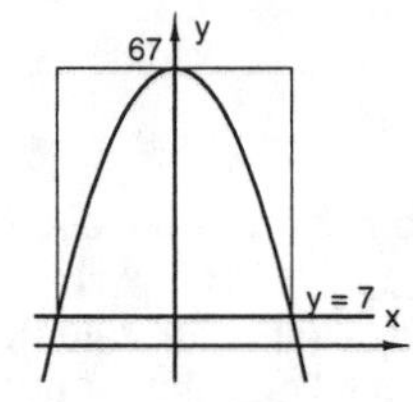

$7 = 67 - 0.6x^2 \Leftrightarrow 0.6x^2 = 60 \Leftrightarrow x = \pm 10$

Rectangle has width $10 - (-10) = 20$, and length $67 - 7 = 60$.

Area of region $= \frac{2}{3}(20)(60) = 800$

18. Sinusoidal Region Problem

Graphs, left: $y = \sin x$, right: $y = 7\cos 5x$

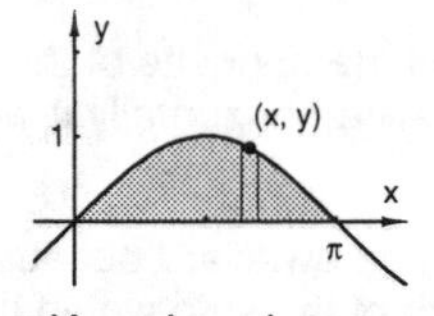

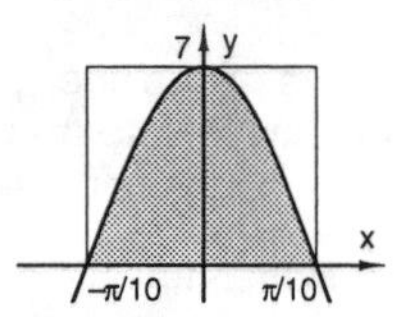

$dA = \sin x\,dx$

$A = \int_0^{\pi} \sin x\,dx = -\cos x\Big|_0^{\pi} = -(-1) + 1 = 2$, which is a rational number.

For $y = 7\cos 5x$, width is 1/5 as much and altitude is 7 times as much.

$\therefore$ Area $= (2)(1/5)(7) = 2.8$

19. Ellipse Area Problem

Graph, $9x^2 + 25y^2 = 225 \Leftrightarrow y = \pm\frac{1}{5}\sqrt{225 - 9x^2}$

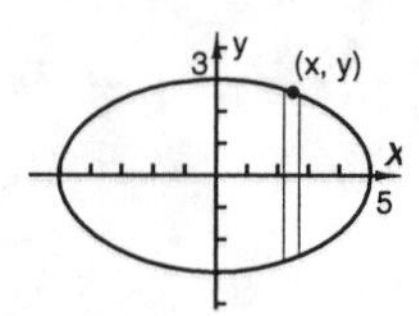

Using the positive branch for y,

$dA = 2y\,dx = \frac{2}{5}\sqrt{225 - 9x^2}\,dx$

$A = \int_{-5}^{5} \frac{2}{5}\sqrt{225 - 9x^2}\,dx.$

Using the grapher's numerical integration,
$A \approx 47.123889 \ldots$.

Conjecture: Area is a multiple of π.

Divide by π: $47.123889 \ldots / \pi \approx 15$.

The 15 is the product of the semimajor and semiminor axes, 5 and 3, respectively.

Conjecture: $A = \pi ab$, where a = semimajor axis and b = semiminor axis.

This is consistent with the area of a circle with radius r, in which $a = b = r$ and the area $= \pi r^2$.

20. Area of a Region Parametrically Problem

$x = 5\cos t$

$y = 3\sin t$

$dA = 2y\,dx = 2(3\sin t)(-5\sin t\,dt) = -30\sin^2 t\,dt$

As x goes from –5 to 5, t goes from π to 0.

$\therefore A = -\int_{\pi}^{0} 30\sin^2 t\,dt = 47.123889 \ldots$ numerically.

This answer equals 15π, as in Problem 19.

21. Golf Course Problem

Counting squares shows that the area of the course is approximately 37.1 yd². Differences in counting fractional squares could account for variations of about half a square yard.

22. Area Check Problem

Graphs, $y_1 = x^2$ and $y_2 = x + 6$, intersecting at $x = -2$ and $x = 3$.

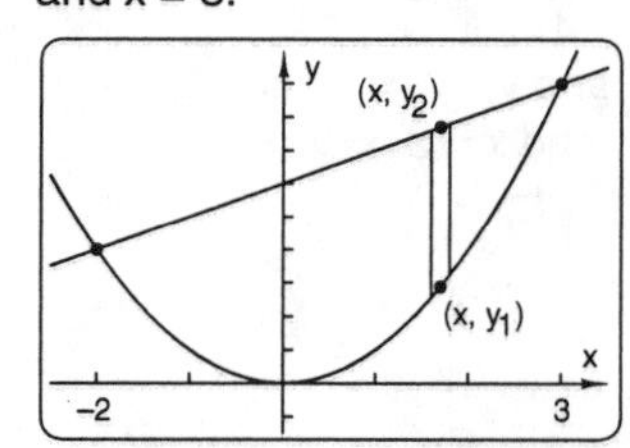

$dA = (y_2 - y_1)\,dx = (-x^2 + x + 6)\,dx$

$A = \int_{-2}^{3} (-x^2 + x + 6)\,dx = -\frac{1}{3}x^3 + \frac{1}{2}x^2 + 6x\Big|_{-2}^{3}$

$= -9 + \frac{9}{2} + 18 + (-\frac{8}{3}) - 2 - (-12) = 20\frac{5}{6} = 20.8333 \ldots$

$R_{10} = 20.9375$

$R_{100} = 20.834375$

$R_{1000} = 20.83334375$

The Riemann sums seem to be approaching the exact answer.

23. Curve Sketching Review Problem

Graph, $t(x) = x + \sin x$

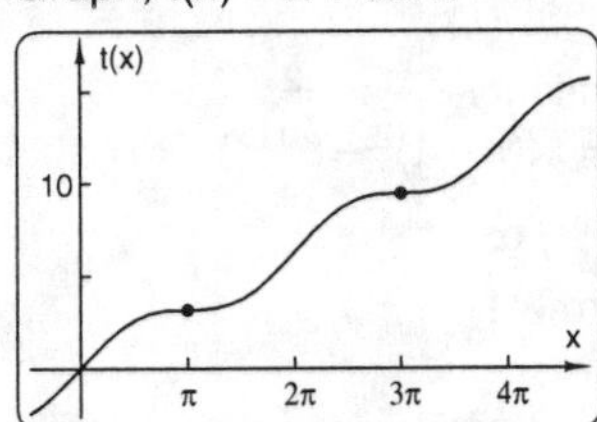

$t'(x) = 1 + \cos x$

$t'(x) = 0 \Leftrightarrow \cos x = -1 \Leftrightarrow$

$x = \pi + 2\pi n = ..., \pi, 3\pi, 5\pi, ...$

$t'(x)$ is never negative, so $t'(x)$ does not change signs. These points are plateau points.

24. Maximum-Minimum Review Problem

Graph, $9x^2 + 25y^2 = 225$, as in Figure 8-4i, and sample point (x, y) in Quadrant I

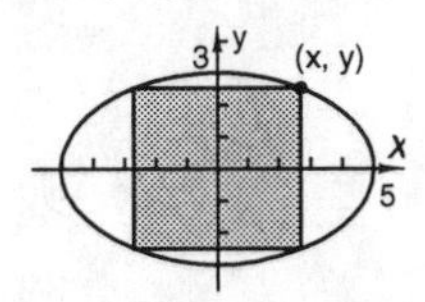

$A(x) = (2x)(2y) = 4xy$

$y = \frac{1}{5}\sqrt{225 - 9x^2}$; domain of x is $0 \le x \le 5$.

$\therefore A(x) = 4x \cdot \frac{1}{5}\sqrt{225 - 9x^2}$

Maximize $A^2(x) = \frac{16}{25}(225x^2 - 9x^4)$.

$A^{2\prime}(x) = 16(18x - \frac{36}{25}x^3) = 0 \Leftrightarrow x = 0, \pm 2.5\sqrt{2}$

$A(0) = A(5) = 0$; $A(2.5\sqrt{2}) = 30$

Maximal rectangle has area = 30.

Problem Set 8-5, pages 389 to 395 — Volume of a Solid by Plane Slicing

Q1. $\frac{1}{3}x^3 + \frac{1}{2}x^2 + x + C$

Q2. $\frac{4}{7}x^{7/4} + C$

Q3. $y' = \frac{2}{3}x^{-1/3}$

Q4. $-\frac{1}{3}e^{-3x} + C$

Q5. $-\csc x + C$

Q6. x^{-1}

Q7. See Sec. 5-5

Q8. mean value

Q9. E.g., $y = |x - 4| + 1$

Q10. $y = 2^{-x}$

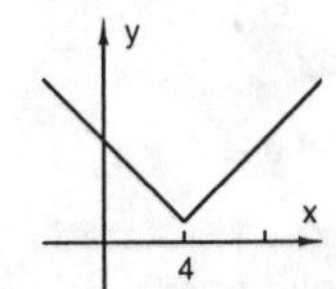

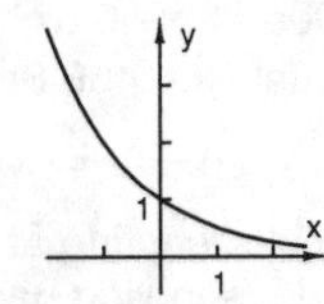

Plan of attack for volume problems:

- Do geometry to get dV in terms of sample point (x, y).
- Do algebra to get dV in terms of one variable.
- Do calculus to add up the dVs and take the limit (i.e., integrate).

1. Paraboloid Problem
   a. $dV = \pi x^2\, dy$
      $y = 9 - x^2 \Rightarrow x^2 = 9 - y$
      $\therefore dV = \pi(9 - y)\, dy$
      $...V = \int_0^9 \pi(9 - y)\, dy = \pi(9y - 0.5y^2) \Big|_0^9$
      $= \pi(81 - 40.5) - \pi(0 - 0) = 40.5\pi = 127.2345 ...$
   b. Numerically, $V \approx 127.2345$ ..., which checks.
   c. Inside cone of radius = 3 and altitude = 9 has volume $\frac{\pi r^2 h}{3} = 27\pi = 84.823 ... < V$, and outside cylinder has volume $81\pi = 254.4690 ... > V$.

2. Cone Problem
   a. $dV = \pi x^2\, dy$
      $y = 10 - 2x \Leftrightarrow x = 5 - 0.5y$
      $\therefore dV = \pi(5 - 0.5y)^2\, dy$
      $V = \int_0^{10} \pi(5 - 0.5y)^2\, dy = -\frac{2}{3}\pi(5 - 0.5y)^3 \Big|_0^{10}$
      $= -\frac{2}{3}\pi(0) + \frac{2}{3}\pi(125) = \frac{250\pi}{3} = 261.7993 ...$
   b. Volume of a cone is $V = \frac{1}{3}\pi r^2 h$.
      Here r = 5 and h = 10, so
      $V = \frac{1}{3}\pi(5^2)(10) = \frac{250\pi}{3}$, as in part a.
   c. The volume of the cylinder is given by $\pi r^2 h$, so volume of cone =(1/3)(volume of cylinder).

3. Graph, $y = 4x - x^2$, rotated about the x-axis.

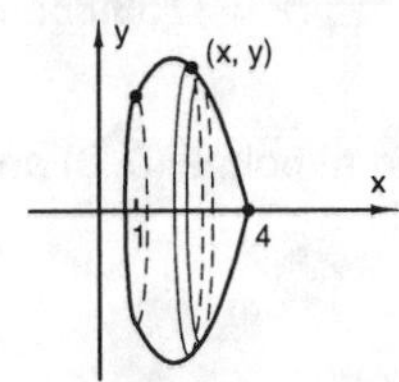

$dV = \pi y^2\, dx = \pi(4x - x^2)^2\, dx$

$V = \int_1^4 \pi(4x - x^2)^2\, dx = \pi \int_1^4 (16x^2 - 8x^3 + x^4)\, dx$

$= \pi\left(\frac{16}{3}x^3 - 2x^4 + \frac{1}{5}x^5\right) \Big|_1^4 = 30.6\pi = 96.132 ...$

4. Graph, $y = x^{1.5}$ rotated about the x-axis

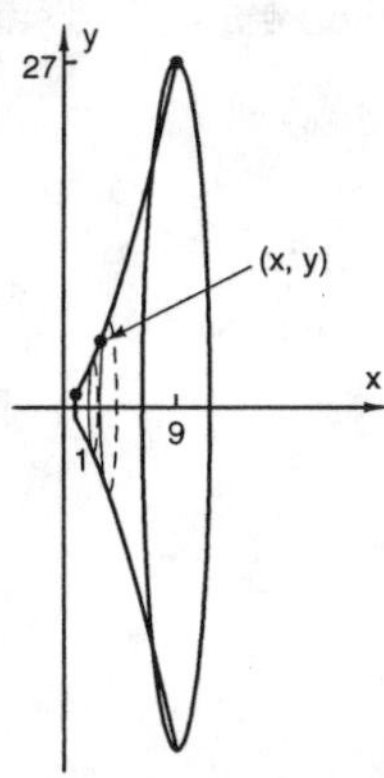

$dV = \pi y^2\, dx = \pi x^3\, dx$

$V = \int_1^9 \pi x^3\, dx = \pi \cdot \frac{1}{4}x^4 \Big|_1^9 = 1640\pi = 5152.211\ldots$

5. Graph, $y = \ln x \Rightarrow x = e^y$, rotated about y-axis

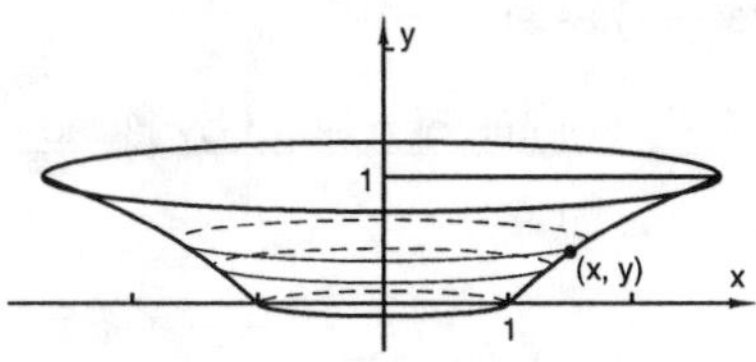

$dV = \pi x^2\, dy = \pi e^{2y}\, dy$

$V = \int_0^1 \pi e^{2y}\, dy = \frac{\pi}{2}e^{2y} \Big|_0^1 = \frac{\pi}{2}(e^2 - 1) = 10.0359\ldots$

6. Graph, $y = x^{3/4} \Rightarrow x = y^{4/3}$, rotated about y-axis

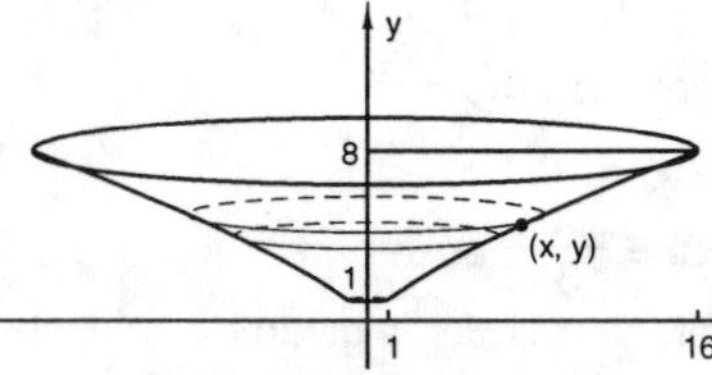

$dV = \pi x^2\, dy = \pi y^{8/3}\, dy$

$V = \int_1^8 \pi y^{8/3}\, dy = \pi \cdot \frac{3}{11}y^{11/3} \Big|_1^8 = \frac{6141}{11}\pi = 1753.865\ldots$

7. <u>Washer Slices Problem</u>
$y = x_1^4$ and $y = 8x_2$, intersecting at points (0, 0) and (2, 16), rotated about the y-axis
Area of cross section is $\pi x_1^2 - \pi x_2^2$

$x_1 = y^{1/4}$ and $x_2 = \frac{1}{8}y$

$\therefore dV = \pi(x_1^2 - x_2^2)\, dy = \pi(y^{1/2} - \frac{1}{64}y^2)\, dy$

$V = \int_0^{16} \pi(y^{1/2} - \frac{1}{64}y^2)\, dy = \pi(\frac{2}{3}y^{3/2} - \frac{1}{192}y^3) \Big|_0^{16}$

$= \frac{64}{3}\pi = 67.0206\ldots$

Circumscribed cylinder minus the cone (both of radius = 2, height = 16) has volume = $\pi r^2 h - \pi r^2 h/3 = 128\pi/3 = 134.0412\ldots > V$.
Numerical integration gives $V \approx 67.0206\ldots$, which agrees with the exact answer.

8. <u>Exponential Horn Problem</u>
$y_1 = e^{0.4x}$ and $y_2 = x + 1$, from $x = 0$ to $x = 3$, rotated about the x-axis.
Area of cross section is $\pi y_2^2 - \pi y_1^2$.
$dV = \pi(y_2^2 - y_1^2)\, dx = \pi((x + 1)^2 - e^{0.8x})\, dx$

$V = \int_0^3 \pi((x + 1)^2 - e^{0.8x})\, dx$

$= \pi(\frac{1}{3}(x + 1)^3 - 1.25e^{0.8x}) \Big|_0^3$

$= \pi(\frac{64}{3} - 1.25e^{2.4} - \frac{1}{3} + 1.25)$

$= \pi(22.25 - 1.25e^{2.4}) = 26.6125\ldots$

Numerical integration gives $V \approx 26.6125\ldots$, which agrees with the exact answer.

9. Graphs, $y_1 = x^{1/3}$ and $y_2 = 10e^{-0.1x}$, from $x = 0$ to 8, rotated about the x-axis, back half of solid only

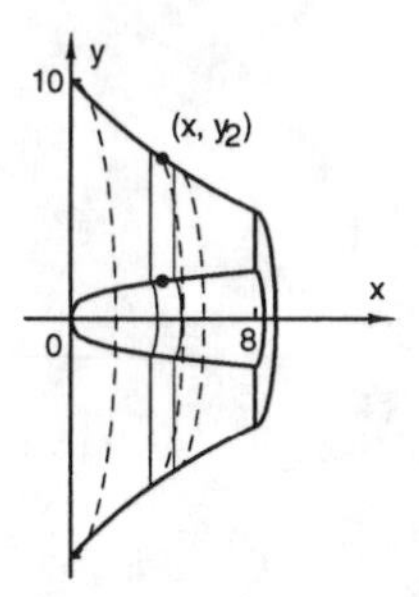

$dV = \pi(y_2^2 - y_1^2)\, dx = \pi(100e^{-0.2x} - x^{2/3})\, dx$

$V = \int_0^8 \pi(100e^{-0.2x} - x^{2/3})\, dx$

$= \pi(-500e^{-0.2x} - 0.6x^{5/3}) \Big|_0^8$

$= \pi(-500e^{-1.6} + 480.8) = 1193.3394\ldots$

10. Graphs, $y = 4 - x_1 \Rightarrow x_1 = 4 - y$, and $y = 4 - x_2^2 \Rightarrow x_2 = \sqrt{4 - y}$, intersecting at $x = 0$ and $x = 1$, rotated about the y-axis, showing back half of solid only

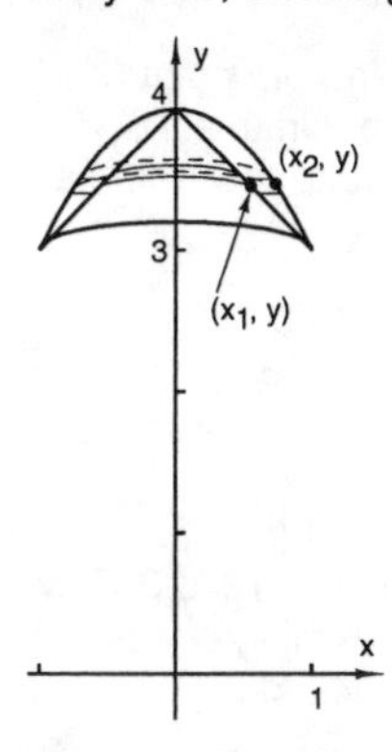

$dV = \pi(x_2^2 - x_1^2)\, dy = \pi((4 - y) - (4 - y)^2)\, dy$

$= \pi(-y^2 + 7y - 12)\, dy$

$V = \int_3^4 \pi(-y^2 + 7y - 12)\, dy = \pi(-\frac{1}{3}y^3 + \frac{7}{2}y^2 - 12y) \Big|_3^4$

$= \pi(-\frac{64}{3} + 56 - 48 + 9 - \frac{63}{2} + 36) = \frac{1}{6}\pi = 0.523598\ldots$

11. Paraboloid Volume Formula Problem

Graph, parabola $y = ax^2 \Rightarrow x = (y/a)^{1/2}$ from point (0, 0) to (r, h), rotated about the y-axis

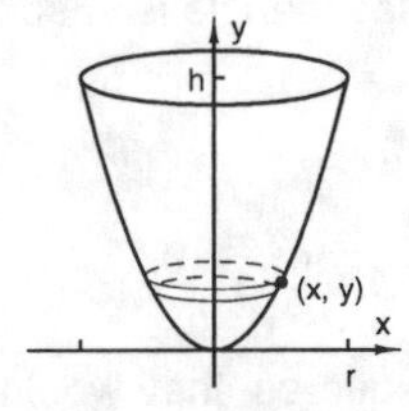

$dV = \pi x^2\, dy = \pi(y/a)\, dy = (\pi/a)y\, dy$

$V = \int_0^h (\pi/a)y\, dy = (\pi/a)\cdot\frac{1}{2}y^2 \Big|_0^h = \frac{1}{2}(\pi/a)(h)^2 - 0$

Because $y = ax^2$, $h = ar^2$.

$\therefore V = \frac{1}{2}(\pi/a)(ar^2)^2 = \frac{1}{2}\pi ar^4$

Volume of circumscribed cylinder is

$V_c = \pi r^2 h = \pi r^2\,(ar^2) = \pi ar^4$.

Thus, the volume of the paraboloid is half the volume of the circumscribed cylinder, Q.E.D.

12. Riemann Sum Limit Problem

a. Graph, $y = 0.3x^{1.5}$, from x = 0 to x = 4, rotated about the x-axis

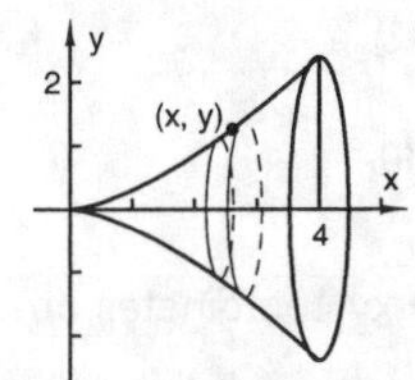

$dV = \pi y^2\, dx = \pi(0.3x^{1.5})^2\, dx = \pi(0.09x^3)\, dx$

$V.09x^3) = \int_0^4 \pi(0\, dx = 0.0225\pi x^4 \Big|_0^4$

$= 5.76\pi = 18.09557\ldots$

b. $R_{10} = 5.7312\pi$

$R_{100} = 5.75971\ldots\,\pi$

$R_{1000} = 5.7599971\ldots\,\pi$

Values are getting closer to $V = 5.76\pi$.

13. Different Axis Problem No. I

$y = 4 - x^2 \Rightarrow x = (4 - y)^{1/2}\, dy$

Inner radius is 3 – x; outer radius is 3.

$dV = \pi(3^2 - (3 - x)^2)\, dy = \pi(9 - (3 - (4 - y)^{1/2})^2)\, dy$

$= \pi(6(4 - y)^{1/2} - 4 + y)\, dy$

$V = \int_0^4 \pi(6(4 - y)^{1/2} - 4 + y)\, dy$

$= \pi(-4(4 - y)^{3/2} - 4y + 0.5y^2) \Big|_0^4$

$= \pi(0 - 16 + 8 + 32 + 0 - 0) = 24\pi = 75.3982\ldots$

14. Different Axis Problem No. II

Graph, $y = 4 - x^2$, from x = 0 to x = 4, rotated about the line y = –5, showing back half of the solid only

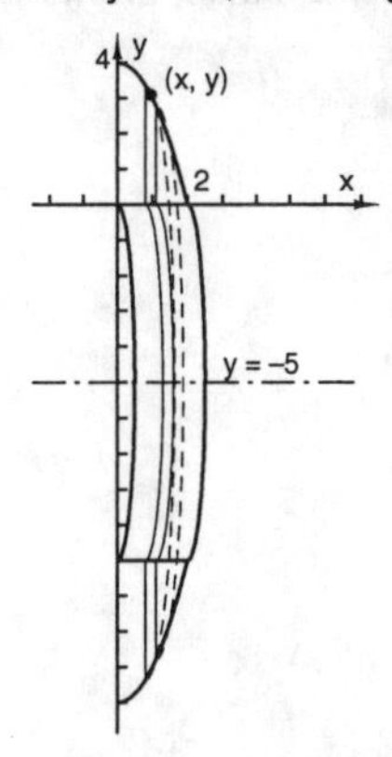

$dV = \pi((y + 5)^2 - 5^2)\, dx$

$= \pi((9 - x^2)^2 - 5^2)\, dx = \pi(56 - 18x^2 + x^4)\, dx$

$V = \int_0^2 \pi(56 - 18x^2 + x^4)\, dx$

$= \pi(56x - 6x^3 + 0.2x^5) \Big|_0^2$

$= \pi(112 - 48 + 6.4 - 0 + 0 - 0)$

$= 70.4\pi = 221.168\ldots$

15. New Integral Problem No. I

a. Graph, y = sin x, from x = 0 to x = 1.2, rotated about the x-axis

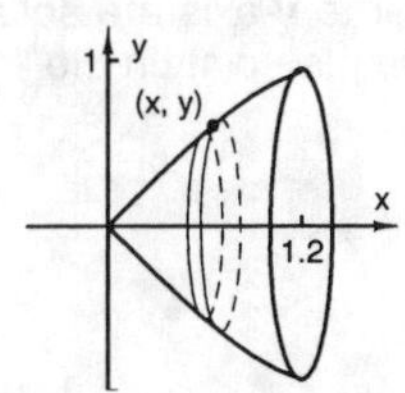

$dV = \pi y^2\, dx = \pi \sin^2 x\, dx$

$V = \int_0^{1.2} \pi \sin^2 x\, dx$.

b. $V \approx 1.354448\ldots$ numerically

c. Using $\cos 2x = \cos^2 x - \sin^2 x = 1 - 2\sin^2 x$

$\Rightarrow \sin^2 x = \frac{1}{2}(1 - \cos 2x)$, write

$V = \frac{\pi}{2}\int_0^{1.2} (1 - \cos 2x)\, dx = \frac{\pi}{2}(x - \frac{1}{2}\sin 2x) \Big|_0^{1.2}$

$= 0.6\pi - \frac{\pi}{4}\sin 2.4 = 1.354448\ldots$, which agrees with the numerical answer.

16. New Integral Problem No. II

a. Graph, $y = \tan x$, from $x = 0$ to $x = \tan^{-1} 1 = 0.785398 \ldots$, rotated about the x-axis, showing back half of solid only

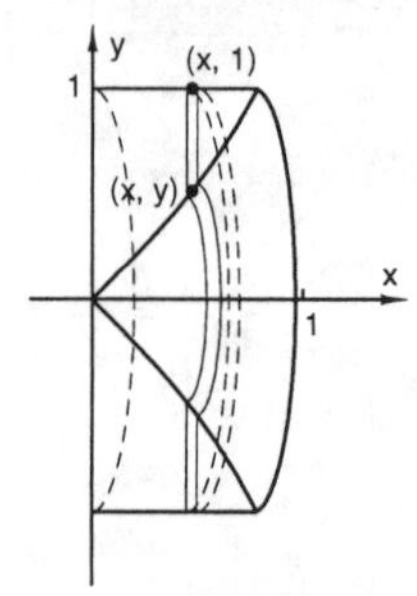

$dV = \pi(1^2 - y^2)\,dx = \pi(1 - \tan^2 x)\,dx$

$V = \int_0^{0.78\ldots} \pi(1 - \tan^2 x)\,dx$

b. By numerical integration, $V \approx 1.7932095 \ldots$

c. Use $\tan^2 x = \sec^2 x - 1$.

$V = \int_0^{0.78\ldots} \pi(2 - \sec^2 x)\,dx$

$= \pi(2x - \tan x)\Big|_0^{0.78\ldots}$

$= \pi(2\tan^{-1} 1 - \tan(\tan^{-1} 1) - 0 + 0)$

$= \pi(2\tan^{-1} 1 - 1) = 1.7320954 \ldots$, which agrees with the numerical solution.

17. Pyramid Problem

Cross sections perpendicular to y-axis are squares of edge 2x, where (x, y) is a sample point on the line in the xy-plane.

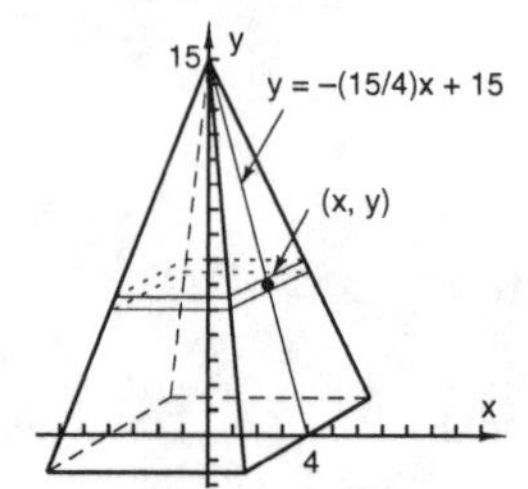

Equation of line is $y = -\frac{15}{4}x + 15 \Leftrightarrow x = 4 - \frac{4}{15}y$

$dV = (2x)^2\,dy = 4(4 - \frac{4}{15}y)^2\,dy = 64(1 - \frac{1}{15}y)^2\,dy$

$\int_0^{15} 64(1 - \frac{1}{15}y)^2\,dy = -320(1 - \frac{1}{15}y)^3 \Big|_0^{15} = 320 \text{ cm}^2.$

The circumscribed box has volume $l \cdot w \cdot h = 8 \cdot 8 \cdot 15 = 960 = 3V$, so the pyramid is 1/3 the volume of the circumscribed rectangular solid, Q.E.D.

18. Horn Problem

Center line: $y = 0.2x^2$

Upper bound: $y = 0.16x^2 + 1$

Radius of circular cross section is $1 - 0.04x^2$.

The tip of the "horn" is where $0.2x^2 = 0.16x^2 + 1$ with $x \ge 0$, which is at $x = 5$.

$dV = \pi(1 - 0.04x^2)^2\,dx$

$= \pi(1 - 0.08x^2 + 0.0016x^4)\,dx$

$V = \int_0^5 \pi(1 - 0.08x^2 + 0.0016x^4)\,dx$

$= \pi(x - \frac{0.08}{3}x^3 + \frac{0.0016}{5}x^5)\Big|_0^5 = \pi(5 - \frac{10}{3} + 1 - 0 + 0 - 0)$

$= \frac{8}{3}\pi = 8.3775 \ldots \approx 8.4 \text{ cm}^3$

19. Triangular Cross-Section Problem

a. $y = x^{0.6}$

Pick sample point (x, y) on the curve within the slice. One leg of the isosceles triangle is y, so the other leg is also equal to y.

$dV = \frac{1}{2}y^2\,dx = \frac{1}{2}x^{1.2}\,dx$

$V = \int_0^4 \frac{1}{2}x^{1.2}\,dx = \frac{1}{4.4}x^{2.2}\Big|_0^4 = \frac{1}{4.4}\cdot 4^{2.2} - 0$

$= 4.79821 \ldots$.

b. If the cross sections were squares, they would have twice the area of the triangles, so dV would be twice as much and $V = \frac{1}{2.2}\cdot 4^{2.2} = 9.5964 \ldots$.

20. Wedge Problem

a. Line has equation $y = \frac{1}{2}x$, $0 \le x \le 6$.

b. The log has radius = 6, so the circle is $x^2 + z^2 = 36$, or $z = \sqrt{36 - x^2} = (36 - x^2)^{1/2}$.

c. $dV = y \cdot 2z \cdot dx = \frac{1}{2}x \cdot 2(36 - x^2)^{1/2} \cdot dx$

$= (36 - x^2)^{1/2}(x\,dx)$

$V = \int_0^6 (36 - x^2)^{1/2}(x\,dx)$

$= -\frac{1}{2}\int_0^6 (36 - x^2)^{1/2}(-2x\,dx)$

$= -\frac{1}{2}\cdot\frac{2}{3}(36 - x^2)^{3/2}\Big|_0^6 = 72 \text{ in.}^3$

21. Generalized Wedge Problem

The points (0,0) and (r, h) in xy-coordinates are on the line running up the top surface, so the line is $y = \frac{h}{r}x$.

The circle forming the boundary for the bottom surface has radius = r and center (0,0) in xz-coordinates, so the circle is $x^2 + z^2 = r^2$, or $z = \sqrt{r^2 - x^2}$. The slab at $x = x_0$ is rectangular of height y = \F(hx_0,r), width 2z = $2\sqrt{r^2 - x_0^2}$, and thickness dx, so

$dV = \frac{2hx}{r}\sqrt{r^2 - x^2}\,dx$, and

$V = \frac{2h}{r}\int_0^r x\sqrt{r^2 - x^2}\,dx = -\frac{h}{r}\int_0^r (r^2 - x^2)^{1/2}(-2x\,dx)$

$= -\frac{2}{3}\cdot\frac{h}{r}(r^2 - x^2)^{3/2}\Big|_0^r = -\frac{2}{3}\cdot\frac{h}{r}(0^{3/2} - r^3)$

$= \frac{2}{3}r^2h.$

22. Cone Volume Formula Proof Problem

A cone of radius r and altitude h can be generated by rotating about the x-axis the line

$y = \frac{r}{h}x$ from $x = 0$ to h.

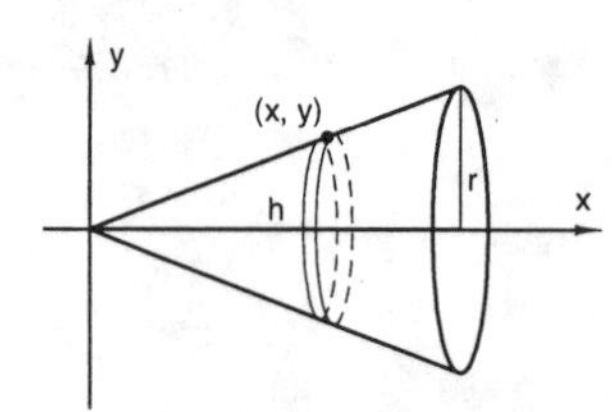

$dV = \pi y^2\,dx = \pi\frac{r^2}{h^2}x^2\,dx$

$V = \frac{\pi r^2}{h^2}\int_0^h x^2\,dx = \frac{\pi r^2}{h^2}\cdot\frac{1}{3}x^3\Big|_0^h = \frac{1}{3}\pi r^2 h$, Q.E.D.

23. Sphere Problem

a. Equation of circle in xy-plane is $x^2 + y^2 = 100$.

$dV = \pi x^2\,dy = \pi(100 - y^2)\,dy$

$V = \int_{-10}^{10} \pi(100 - y^2)\,dy = \pi(100y - \frac{1}{3}y^3)\Big|_{-10}^{10}$

$= \pi(1000 - \frac{1}{3}(1000) + 1000 - \frac{1}{3}(1000))$

$= \frac{4}{3}\pi(1000)$ cm^3

b. Formula: $V = \frac{4}{3}\pi r^3 = \frac{4}{3}\pi 10^3 = \frac{4}{3}\pi(1000)$ cm^3, which agrees with the answer by calculus.

24. General Volume of a Sphere Problem

Sphere can be generated by rotating about the y-axis the circle $x^2 + y^2 = r^2$.

Slicing perpendicular to the y-axis as in Problem 23 gives $dV = \pi x^2\,dy = \pi(r^2 - y^2)\,dy$.

$V = \int_{-r}^{r} \pi(r^2 - y^2)\,dy = \pi(r^2y - \frac{1}{3}y^3)\Big|_{-r}^{r}$

$= \pi(r^3 - \frac{1}{3}r^3) - \pi(-r^3 + \frac{1}{3}r^3) = \frac{4}{3}\pi r^3$, Q.E.D.

25. Volume of an Ellipsoid Problem

Graph from text showing slice perpendicular to x-axis with sample points (x, y) and (x, z)

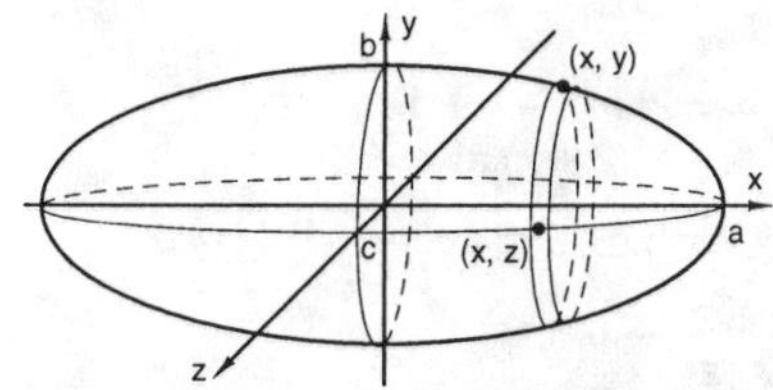

Equation of ellipsoid is $(\frac{x}{a})^2 + (\frac{y}{b})^2 + (\frac{z}{c})^2 = 1$.

For a fixed value of x, the x-term will be constant. Subtracting this term from both sides of the equation gives an equation of the form

$(\frac{y}{b})^2 + (\frac{z}{c})^2 = k^2$

where $k^2 = 1 - (x/a)^2$. Dividing both sides by k^2 gives

$(\frac{y}{kb})^2 + (\frac{z}{kc})^2 = 1$.

Thus, the y- and z-radii are kb and kc, which have the original ratio b/c. Therefore, each elliptical cross-section is similar to the ellipse at the yz-plane, Q.E.D.

$dV = \pi yz\,dx$

Because $z = (c/b)y$, $dV = \pi(c/b)y^2\,dx$.

The ellipse in the xy-plane (z = 0) has equation

$(\frac{x}{a})^2 + (\frac{y}{b})^2 = 1$,

from which $y^2 = (b/a)^2(a^2 - x^2)$.

$\therefore\ dV = \pi(c/b)(b/a)^2(a^2 - x^2)\,dx$

$V = \int_{-a}^{a} \pi(c/b)(b/a)^2(a^2 - x^2)\,dx$

$= \pi(c/b)(b/a)^2(a^2x - \frac{1}{3}x^3)\Big|_{-a}^{a}$

$= \pi(c/b)(b/a)^2 \cdot \frac{4}{3}a^3 = \frac{4}{3}\pi abc$

Note that the volume formula for a sphere is a special case of the volume formula for an ellipsoid in which a = b = c = r, the radius of the sphere.

26. Highway Cut Problem

Diagram:

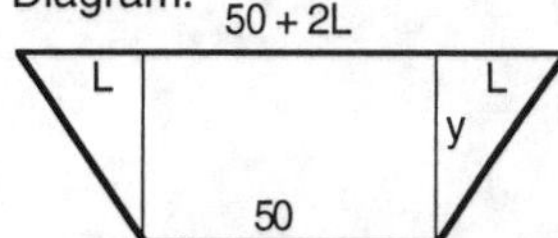

Note that the top of each isosceles trapezoidal cross section has length 50 + 2L yards, where

$\frac{y}{L} = \tan(52°) \Rightarrow L = y\cot(52°) = y\cot\frac{52\pi}{180}$. So each slab is $dV = \frac{1}{2}(50 + 2L + 50)y\,dx$;

$dV = 50y + y^2\cot\frac{52\pi}{180}\,dx$, and

$V = \int_0^{600} (50y + y^2\cot\frac{52\pi}{180})\,dx$

$V \approx S_{20} = 1{,}647{,}388.8 \ldots \approx 1{,}647{,}389$ yd^3

Cost $\approx 12 \cdot 1{,}647{,}388.8 \ldots \approx \$19{,}768{,}666$

27. Submarine Problem

a. Graph, $y = 2x^{0.5} - 0.02x^{1.5}$

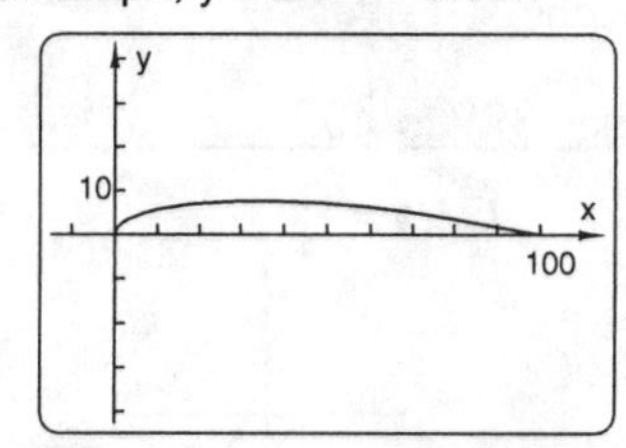

b. Solve $2x^{0.5} - 0.02x^{1.5} = 0.02x^{0.5}(100 - x) = 0$

$\Leftrightarrow x = 0$ or 100m. The sub will be 100m long, or about as long as a football field.

c. Maximize $D(x) = 2(2x^{0.5} - 0.02x^{1.5})$.

$D'(x) = 2(x^{-0.5} - 0.03x^{0.5}) = 2x^{-0.5}(1 - 0.03x)$

$D'(x) = 0 \Leftrightarrow x = \frac{1}{0.03} = 33\frac{1}{3}$ m

$D(0) = D(100) = 0,\ D(100/3) = \frac{80}{9}\sqrt{3} = 15.3960 \ldots$

$\therefore$ D(100/3) is a maximum, which is confirmed by the graph in part a.

Maximum diameter is about 15.40 m, at about 33.3 m from the bow.

d. $\frac{\text{Length}}{\text{Beam}} = \frac{100}{80\sqrt{3}/9} = \frac{15\sqrt{3}}{4} = 6.4951 \ldots < 7$, so the sub will be fairly slow.

e. The shape of the sub is obtained by rotating about the x-axis the curve $y = 2x^{0.5} - 0.02x^{1.5}$, $0 \le x \le 100$, as shown.

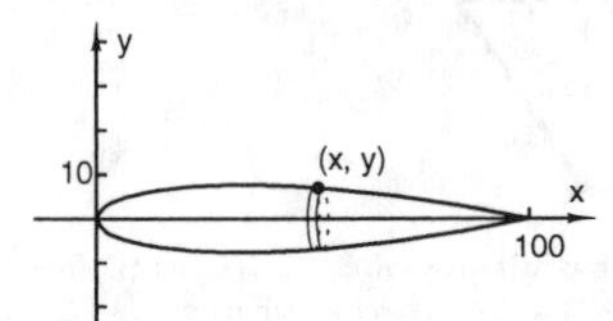

$dV = \pi y^2\, dx = \pi(4x - 0.08x^2 + 0.0004x^3)\, dx$

$V = \int_0^{100} \pi(4x - 0.08x^2 + 0.0004x^3)\, dx$

$= \pi(2x^2 - \frac{0.08}{3}x^3 + 0.0001x^4)\, \Big|_0^{100}$

$= \pi(20000 - \frac{80000}{3} + 10000) = \frac{10000}{3}\pi$

$= 10{,}471.97\ldots \approx 10{,}472\ \text{m}^3$

f. When the Black November is submerged, it will displace $10{,}000\pi/3\ \text{m}^3$ of seawater, weighing

$\frac{10000}{3}\pi \cdot 1{,}042 = 10{,}911{,}798.48\ldots$ kg

$\approx 10{,}912$ metric tons.

28. Preview Problem

Graph. The figure is a cylindrical shell, similar to a tin can with its top and bottom cut off.

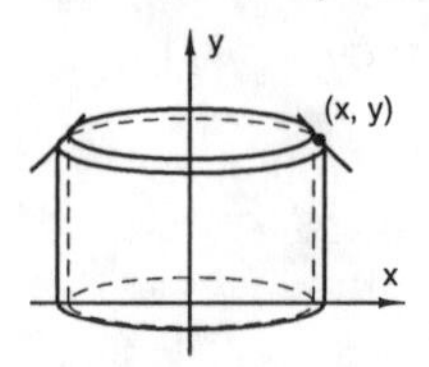

To figure out what dV equals, imagine the shell cut vertically and rolled out into a flat slab. The length of the slab will be approximately the circumference of the shell measured at the sample point (x, y). The width of the slab will be approximately the height of the shell, y, at the sample point. The thickness of the slab will equal dx. Thus,

$dV = 2\pi x \cdot y \cdot dx$.

See Section 8-6 for details.

Problem Set 8-6, pages 399 to 402 — Volume of a Solid of Revolution by Cylindrical Shells

Q1. $y = x^2$

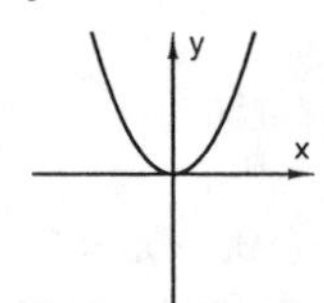

Q2. $y = -x^2$

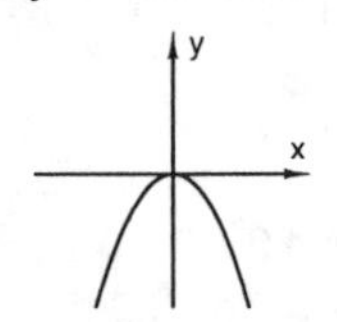

Q3. $y = x^{-2}$

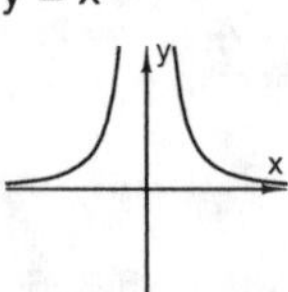

Q4. $y = 2^x$

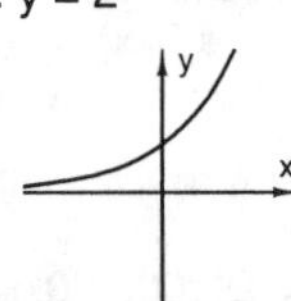

Q5. $y = 2^{-x}$

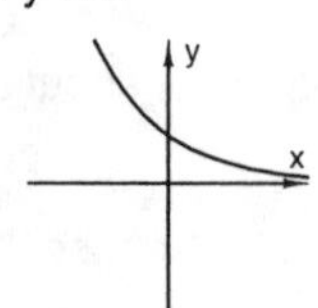

Q6. $y = 2x$

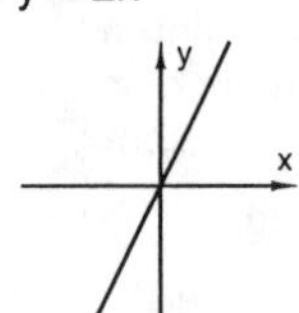

Q7. $y = \ln x$

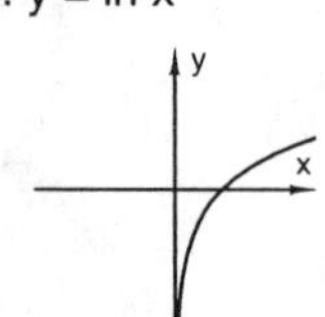

Q8. E.g., $y = |x - 2| + 1$

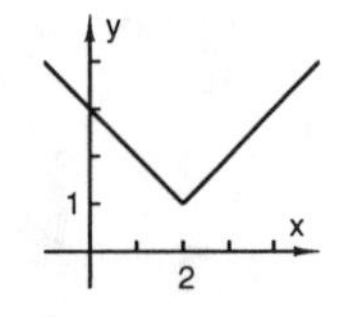

Q9. 1

Q10. $\int \sec^2 x\, dx = \tan x + C$

1. a. $y = 4 - x^2$

$dV = 2\pi xy \cdot dx = 2\pi(4x - x^3)\, dx$

b. $0 = 4 - x^2 = (2 - x)(2 + x)$ at $x = \pm 2$.

$V = \int_0^2 2\pi(4x - x^3)\, dx = \pi(4x^2 - \frac{1}{2}x^4)\, \Big|_0^2$

$= 8\pi = 25.1327\ldots$

c. $y = 4 - x^2 \Rightarrow x^2 = 4 - y$

Upper bound of solid is at $y = 4$.

$dV = \pi x^2\, dy = \pi(4 - y)\, dy$

$V = \int_0^4 \pi(4 - y)\, dy = \pi(4y - 0.5y^2)\, \Big|_0^4$

$= 8\pi = 25.1327\ldots$, which is the same answer as by cylindrical shells in part b.

2. a. Altitude of cylinder $= 8 - x$

b. $y = x^{2/3} \Rightarrow x = y^{3/2}$

$dV = 2\pi(8 - x)y\, dy = 2\pi(8 - y^{3/2})y\, dy$

$= 2\pi(8y - y^{5/2})\, dy$

c. At $x = 8$, $y = 8^{2/3} = 4$.

$V = \int_0^4 2\pi(8y - y^{5/2})\, dy = 2\pi(4y^2 - \frac{2}{7}y^{7/2})\, \Big|_0^4$

$= \frac{384}{7}\pi = 172.3387\ldots$.

d. $dV = \pi y^2\, dx = \pi x^{4/3}\, dx$

$V = \int_0^8 \pi x^{4/3}\, dx = \frac{3}{7}\pi x^{7/3}\, \Big|_0^8$

$= \frac{384}{7}\pi = 172.3387\ldots$, which is the same as the volume by cylindrical shells in part c.

3. Graph, $y = -x^2 + 4x + 3$, from $x = 1$ to $x = 4$, sliced parallel to the y-axis, with sample point (x, y), rotated about the y-axis, showing back half of solid only

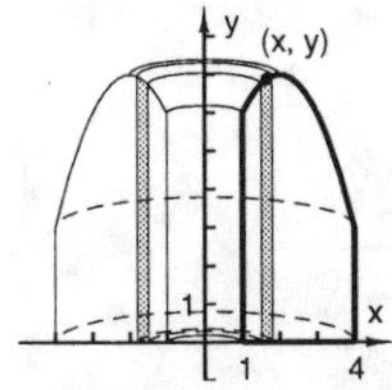

$dV = 2\pi xy \cdot dx = 2\pi(-x^3 + 4x^2 + 3x)\,dx$
$V = \int_1^4 2\pi(-x^3 + 4x^2 + 3x)\,dx$
$\approx 268.6061 \ldots$ (exactly 85.5π)
Circumscribed hollow cylinder of radii 1 and 4 and altitude 7 has volume $\pi(4^2 - 1^2) \cdot 7 = 329.8 \ldots$, which is a reasonable upper bound for the calculated volume.

4. Graph, $y = x^2 - 8x + 17$, from $x = 2$ to $x = 5$, sliced parallel to the y-axis, with sample point (x, y), rotated about the y-axis, showing back half of solid only

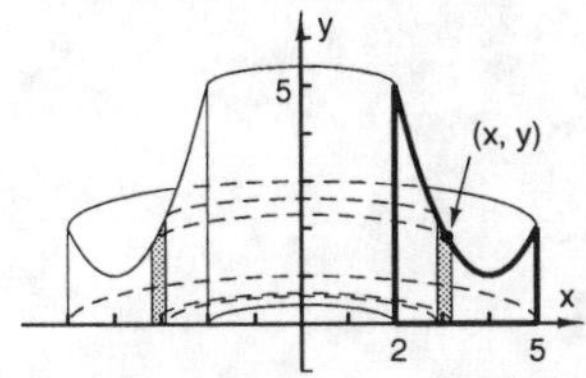

$dV = 2\pi xy \cdot dx = 2\pi(x^3 - 8x^2 + 17x)\,dx$
$V = \int_2^5 2\pi(x^3 - 8x^2 + 17x)\,dx$
$\approx 117.8097 \ldots$ (exactly 37.5π)
Circumscribed hollow cylinder of radii 2 and 5 and altitude 5 has volume $\pi(5^2 - 2^2) \cdot 5 = 329.8 \ldots$, which is a reasonable upper bound for the calculated volume. Assuming that the part of the solid above $y = 2$ could be fit into the "trough," the volume is approximately $\pi(5^2 - 2^2) \cdot 2 = 131.9 \ldots$, which is close to the calculated volume.

5. Graph, $x = -y^2 + 6y - 5$, intersecting y-axis at $y = 1$ and $y = 5$, rotated about the x-axis, showing back half of solid only

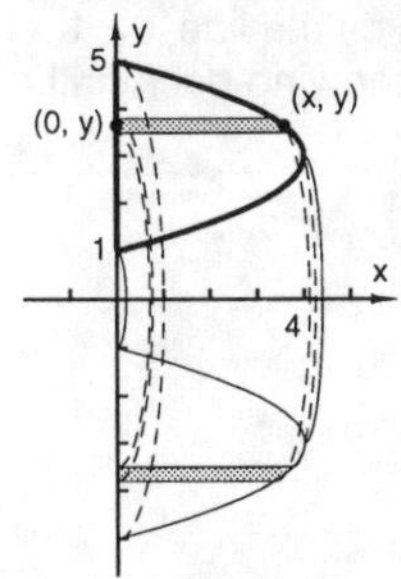

$dV = 2\pi y(x - 0) \cdot dy = 2\pi(-y^3 + 6y^2 - 5y)\,dy$
$V = \int_1^5 2\pi(-y^3 + 6y^2 - 5y)\,dy$
$\approx 201.0619 \ldots$ (exactly 64π)
Circumscribed hollow cylinder of radii 1 and 5 and altitude 4 has volume $\pi(5^2 - 1^2) \cdot 4 = 301.5 \ldots$, which is a reasonable upper bound for calculated volume.

6. Graph, $x = y^2 - 10y + 24$, intersecting y-axis at $y = 4$ and 6, rotated about the x-axis, showing back half of solid only

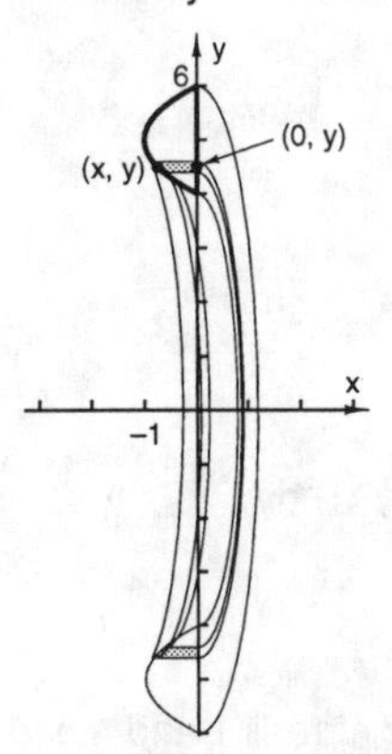

$dV = 2\pi y(0 - x) \cdot dy = 2\pi(-y^3 + 10y^2 - 24y)\,dy$
$V = \int_4^6 2\pi(-y^3 + 10y^2 - 24y)\,dy$
$\approx 41.8879 \ldots$ (exactly $\frac{40}{3}\pi$)
Circumscribed hollow cylinder of radii 4 and 6 and altitude 1 has volume $\pi(6^2 - 4^2) \cdot 1 = 62.83 \ldots$, which is a reasonable upper bound for calculated volume.

7. $y = x^3$, intersecting the line $y = 8$ at $x = 2$, and line $x = 1$, as in text figure. Rotate about the y-axis. Slice parallel to the y-axis. Pick sample points ... (x, y) on the graph and (x, 8) on the line $y = 8$.
$dV = 2\pi x(8 - y) \cdot dx = 2\pi(8x - x^4)\,dx$
$V = \int_1^2 2\pi(8x - x^4)\,dx$
$\approx 36.4424 \ldots$ (exactly 11.6π). Circumscribed hollow cylinder of radii 2 and 1 and altitude 7 has volume $\pi(2^2 - 1^2) \cdot 7 = 65.9 \ldots$, which is a reasonable upper bound for the calculated volume.

8. Graph, $y = 1/x$, intersecting line $y = 4$ at $x = 0.25$ and line $x = 3$, rotated about the y-axis, showing back half of solid only.

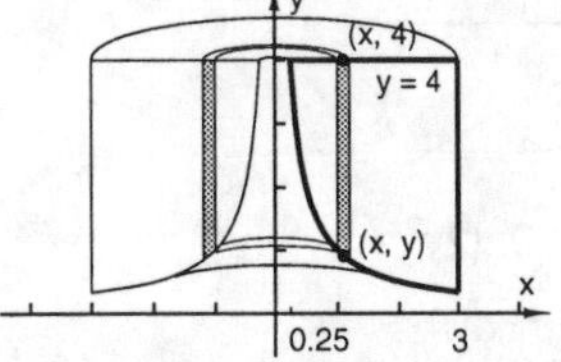

$dV = 2\pi x \cdot (4 - y) \cdot dx = 2\pi(4x - 1)\,dx$
$V = \int_{0.25}^3 2\pi(4x - 1)\,dx$
$\approx 95.0331 \ldots$ (exactly 30.25π)
Circumscribed hollow cylinder of radii 0.25 and 4 and altitude 3.7 has volume $\pi(3^2 - 0.25^2)(3.7) = 103.8 \ldots$, which is a reasonable upper bound for the calculated volume.

9. $y = 1/x^2$, intersecting the line $x = 5$ at $y = 0.04$, and the line $y = 4$, as in the text figure. Rotate about the x-axis. Slice parallel to the x-axis. Pick sample points (x, y) on the graph and (5, y) on the line $x = 5$.
$dV = 2\pi y(5 - x) \cdot dy = 2\pi(5y - y^{1/2})\,dy$
$V = \int_{0.04}^4 2\pi(5y - y^{1/2})\,dy$
$\approx 217.8254 \ldots$ (exactly 69.336π)
Circumscribed cylinder of radius 4 and altitude 5 has volume $\pi \cdot 4^2 \cdot (5 - 0.5) = 226.1 \ldots$, which is a reasonable upper bound for calculated volume.

10. Graph, $y = x^{2/3}$, intersecting the line $y = 1$ and intersecting the line $x = 8$ at $y = 4$, rotated about the x-axis, showing back half of solid only

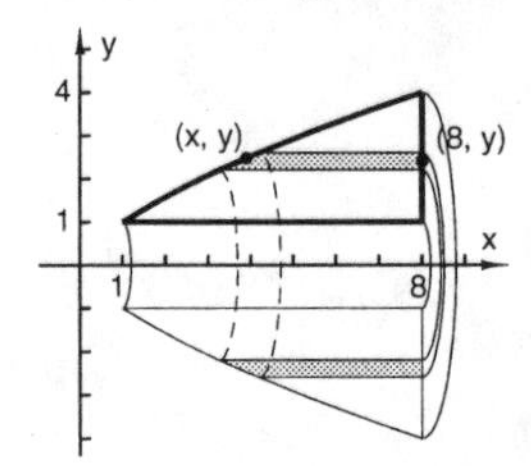

$dV = 2\pi y(8 - x)\cdot dy = 2\pi(8y - y^{5/2})\, dy$

$V = \int_1^4 2\pi(8y - y^{5/2})\, dy$

$\approx 149.0012 \ldots$ (exactly $47\frac{3}{7}\pi$)

Circumscribed hollow cylinder of radii 1 and 4 and altitude 7 has volume $\pi(4^2 - 1^2)\cdot 7 = 329.8 \ldots$, which is a reasonable upper bound for calculated volume.

11. Graphs $y_1 = x^2 - 6x + 7$ and $y_2 = x + 1$, intersecting at (1, 2) and (6, 7), as in the text figure. Rotate about the y-axis. Slice parallel to y-axis. Pick sample points (x, y_1) and (x, y_2).

$dV = 2\pi x\cdot(y_2 - y_1)\cdot dx = 2\pi(-x^3 + 7x^2 - 6x)\, dx$

$V = \int_1^6 2\pi(-x^3 + 7x^2 - 6x)\, dx$

$\approx 458.1489 \ldots$ (exactly $145\frac{5}{6}\pi$)

Circumscribed hollow cylinder of radii 1 and 6 and altitude 7 has volume $\pi(6^2 - 1^2)\cdot 7 = 769.6 \ldots$, which is a reasonable upper bound for calculated volume.

12. Graphs $y = x_1^{1/3} \Rightarrow x_1 = y^3$ and $y = 0.5x_2 - 2 \Rightarrow x_2 = 2y + 4$, intersecting at (8, 2) in Quadrant I and bounded by the x-axis, rotated about the x-axis, showing back half of solid only

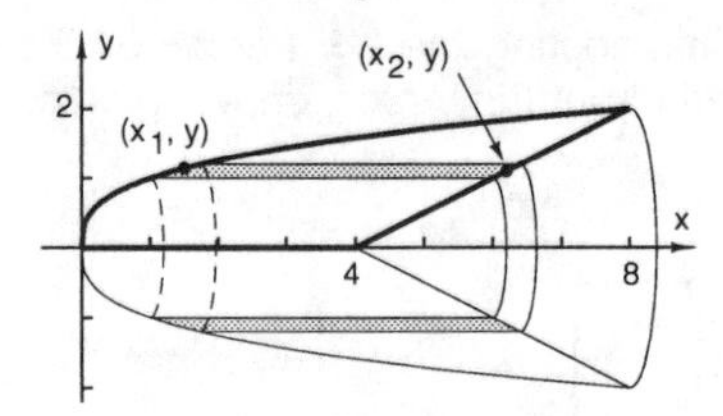

$dV = 2\pi y(x_2 - x_1)dy = 2\pi(2y^2 + 4y - y^4)\, dy$

$V = \int_0^2 2\pi(2y^2 + 4y - y^4)\, dy$

$\approx 43.5634 \ldots$ (exactly $13\frac{13}{15}\pi$)

Circumscribed cylinder of radius 2 and altitude 8 has volume $\pi\cdot 2^2\cdot 8 = 100.5 \ldots$, which is a reasonable upper bound for the calculated volume.

13. Graph, $y = x^{3/2}$, from $x = 1$ to $x = 4$, as in the text figure. Rotate about the line $x = 5$. Slice parallel to the y-axis. Pick sample point (x, y).

$dV = 2\pi(5 - x)y\cdot dx = 2\pi(5x^{3/2} - x^{5/2})\, dx$

$V = \int_1^4 2\pi(5x^{3/2} - x^{5/2})\, dx$

$\approx 161.5676 \ldots$ (exactly $51\frac{3}{7}\pi$)

Circumscribed hollow cylinder of radii 1 and 4 and altitude 8 has volume $\pi(4^2 - 1^2)\cdot 8 = 376.9 \ldots$, which is a reasonable upper bound for calculated volume.

14. Graph, $y = x^{-2}$ from $x = 1$ to $x = 2$, rotated about the line $x = 3$, showing back half of solid only

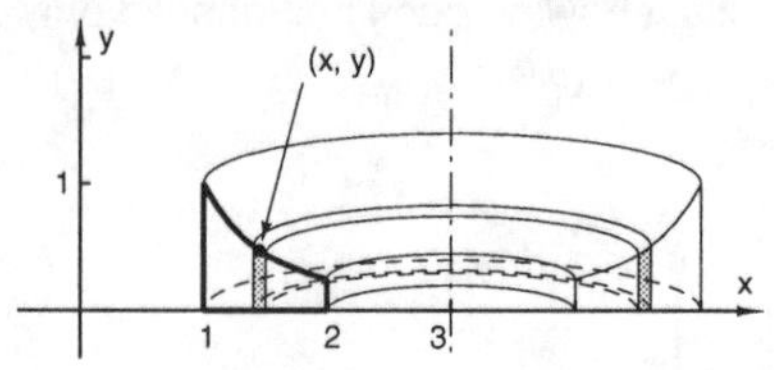

$dV = 2\pi(3 - x)y\cdot dx = 2\pi(3x^{-2} - x^{-1})\, dx$

$V = \int_1^2 2\pi(3x^{-2} - x^{-1})\, dx$

$\approx 5.0696 \ldots$ (exactly $\pi(3 - 2\ln 2)$)

Circumscribed hollow cylinder of radii 1 and 2 and altitude 1 has volume $\pi(2^2 - 1^2)\cdot 1 = 9.4 \ldots$, which is a reasonable upper bound for calculated volume.

15. Graphs, $y_1 = x^4$ and $y_2 = 5x + 6$, intersecting at $x = -1$ and $x = 2$, rotated about the line $x = 4$, showing back half of solid only

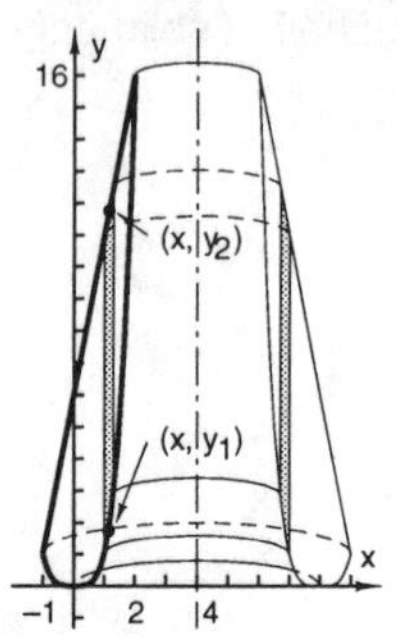

$dV = 2\pi(4 - x)(y_2 - y_1)\cdot dx$

$= 2\pi(4 - x)(5x + 6 - x^4)\, dx$

$V = \int_{-1}^2 2\pi(4 - x)(5x + 6 - x^4)\, dx$

$\approx 390.1858 \ldots$ (exactly 124.2π)

Circumscribed hollow cylinder of radii 2 and 5 and altitude 16 has volume $\pi(5^2 - 2^2)\cdot 16 = 1055.5 \ldots$, which is a reasonable upper bound for the calculated volume.

16. Graphs, $y_1 = \sqrt{x} = x^{1/2}$ and $y_2 = 6 - x$, intersecting at $x = 4$ in Quadrant I and bounded by the line $x = 1$, rotated about the line $x = -1$, showing back half of solid only

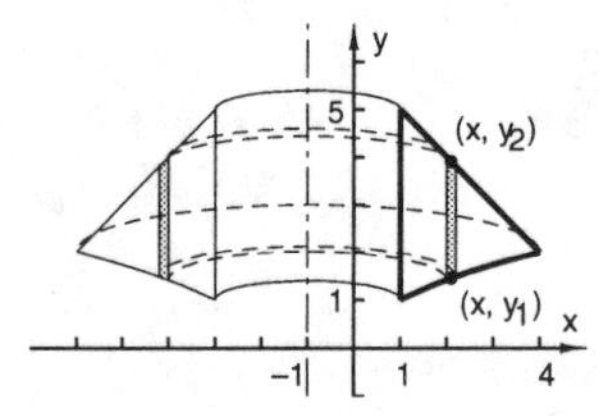

$dV = 2\pi(x + 1)(y_2 - y_1)\cdot dx$

$= 2\pi(x + 1)(6 - x - x^{1/2})\, dx$

$V = \int_1^4 2\pi(x + 1)(6 - x - x^{1/2})\, dx$

$\approx 109.5368 \ldots$ (exactly $34\frac{13}{15}\pi$)

Circumscribed hollow cylinder of radii 2 and 5 and altitude 4 has volume $\pi(5^2 - 2^2)\cdot 4 = 263.8 \ldots$, which is a reasonable upper bound for the calculated volume.

17. $y_1 = -x^2 + 4x + 1$ and $y_2 = 1.4^x$, intersecting at $x = 0$ and $x = 3.3740$ ... (store as b), as in the text figure. Rotate about the line $x = -2$. Slice parallel to the y-axis. Pick sample points (x, y_1) and (x, y_2).
$dV = 2\pi(x + 2)\cdot(y_1 - y_2)\cdot dx$
$= 2\pi(x + 2)(-x^2 + 4x + 1 - 1.4^x)\ dx$
$V = \int_0^b 2\pi(x + 2)(-x^2 + 4x + 1 - 1.4^x)\ dx$
≈ 163.8592 ...
Circumscribed hollow cylinder with radii 2 and 5.4 and altitude 4 has volume $\pi(5.4^2 - 2^2)\cdot 4 = 316.1$ ..., a reasonable upper bound for calculated volume.

18. Graphs, as in Problem 17, but rotated about the line $y = -1$, showing back half of solid only. Slicing perpendicular to the x-axis is appropriate because slicing parallel to it would give strips of length (curve) – (curve) at some values of y and (curve) – (other curve) at other values of y.

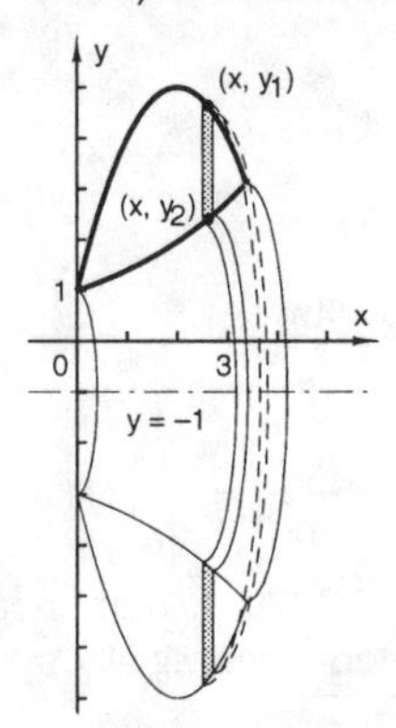

$dV = \pi[(y_1 + 1)^2 - (y_2 + 1)^2]\ dx$
$= \pi[(-x^2 + 4x + 2)^2 - (1.4^x + 1)^2]\ dx$
Limits of integration are 0 to b, where $b = 3.3740$ ..., as in Problem 17.
$V = \int_0^b \pi[(-x^2 + 4x + 2)^2 - (1.4^x + 1)^2]\ dx$
≈ 181.0655 ...
Circumscribed hollow cylinder of radii 2 and 6 and altitude 3.4 has volume $\pi(6^2 - 2^2)\cdot 3.4 = 341.8$ ..., a reasonable upper bound for the calculated volume.

19. Slice perpendicular to the y-axis. Pick sample points (x, y) on the graph of $y = x^3$ and (1, y) on the line $x = 1$.
$y = x^3 \Rightarrow x = y^{1/3}$; $y^{1/3} = 1$ at $y = 1$
$dV = \pi(x^2 - 1^2)\ dy = \pi(y^{2/3} - 1)\ dy$
$V = \int_1^8 \pi(y^{2/3} - 1)\ dy$
≈ 36.4424 ... (exactly 11.6π), which agrees with the answer to Problem 7.

20. See diagram for Problem 8. Slice perpendicular to the y-axis. Pick sample points (x, y) on the graph of $y = 1/x$ and (3, y) on the line $x = 3$.
$dV = \pi(3^2 - x^2)\ dy = \pi(9 - y^{-2})\ dy$
$V = \int_{1/3}^4 \pi(9 - y^{-2})\ dy \approx 95.0331$ ... (exactly 30.25π), which agrees with the answer to Problem 8.

21. Limit of Riemann Sum Problem
Graph, $y = x^{1/3}$, from $x = 0$ to $x = 8$, rotated about the x-axis, showing back half of solid only

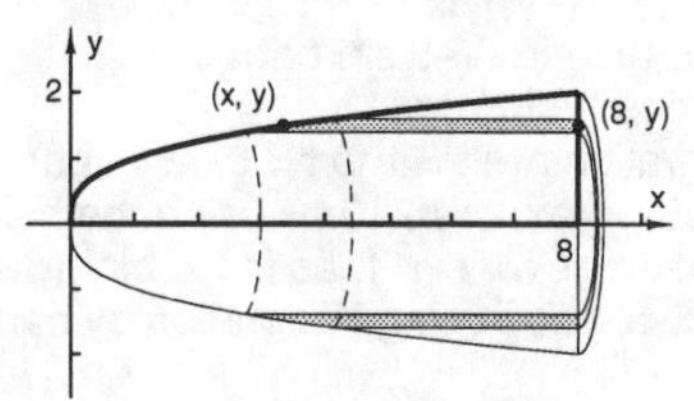

$y = x^{1/3} \Rightarrow x = y^3$
$dV = 2\pi y(8 - x)\cdot dy = 2\pi(8y - y^4)\ dy$
$V = \int_0^2 2\pi(8y - y^4)\ dy = 2\pi(4y^2 - \frac{1}{5}y^5)\Big|_0^2$
$= 2\pi(16 - 6.4) = 19.2\pi = 60.3185789$ ...
$R_8 = 19.3662109 \ldots \pi \ldots = 60.8407460$ ...
$R_{100} = 19.2010666 \ldots \pi = 60.3219299$ ...
$R_{1000} = 19.2000106 \ldots \pi = 60.3186124$ ...
R_n is approaching 19.2π as n increases.

22. Unknown Integral Problem
a. $y = \sin x$ from $x = 0$ to $x = 2$, rotated about the y-axis, as in the text figure. Slice parallel to the y-axis. Pick sample point (x, y) on the graph.
$dV = 2\pi xy\cdot dx = 2\pi x \sin x\ dx$
$V = \int_0^2 2\pi x \sin x\ dx \approx 10.9427$ ... numerically.
(exactly $2\pi(\sin 2 - 2\cos 2)$, integrating by parts).
b. The integrand, $x \sin x$, is a product of two functions, for which the antiderivative cannot be found using techniques known so far.

23. Parametric Curve Problem
a. $x = 5\cos t$, $dx = -5\sin t\ dt$
$y = 3\sin t$, $dy = 3\cos t\ dt$
Slice parallel to the x-axis, then rotate about the x-axis. Pick sample points (–x, y) at the left end of the strip and (x, y) at the right end.
$dV = 2\pi y(x - (-x))\cdot dy = 4\pi xy\ dy$
$= 4\pi(5\cos t)(3\sin t)(3\cos t\ dt)$
$= 180\pi \cos^2 t \sin t\ dt$
Limits of integration are $y = 0$ to $y = 3$.
At $y = 0$, $t = 0$. At $y = 3$, $t = \pi/2$.
$V = \int_0^{\pi/2} 180\pi \cos^2 t \sin t\ dt = -60\pi \cos^3 t\Big|_0^{\pi/2}$
$= -60\pi(0 - 1) = 60\pi = 188.4955$ ... .
b. Slice the region in Quadrant I perpendicular to the x-axis, then rotate about the x-axis. Pick sample point (x, y) on graph.
$dV = \pi y^2\ dx = \pi(3\sin t)^2(-5\sin t\ dt)$
$= -45\pi \sin^3 t\ dt$
Limits of integration are from $x = -5$ to $x = 5$.
At $x = -5$, $t = \pi$. At $x = 5$, $t = 0$.
$V = \int_\pi^0 -45\pi \sin^3 t\ dt$
≈ 188.4955 ... (exactly 60π), which agrees with the volume found in part a.
The integral can be found algebraically using the Pythagorean properties from trigonometry.
$\sin^3 t = (1 - \cos^2 t)\sin t = \sin t - \cos^2 t \sin t$
$V = \int_\pi^0 -45\pi \sin t\ dt - \int_\pi^0 45\pi \cos^2 t\ (-\sin t\ dt)$
$= 45\pi \cos t - 15\pi \cos^3 t\Big|_\pi^0$
$= 45\pi - 15\pi - (-45\pi) + (-15\pi) = 60\pi$

c. Slice the region parallel to the line $x = 7$ and rotate about that line. Pick sample points (x, y) and $(x, -y)$ on the upper and lower branches.
$dV = 2\pi(7 - x)(y - (-y))\cdot dx$
$= 4\pi(7 - 5\cos t)(3\sin t)(-5\sin t\, dt)$
$= -60\pi(7 - 5\cos t)(\sin^2 t)\, dt$
Limits of integration are $t = \pi$ to $t = 0$, as in part b.
$V \approx 2072.6169\ldots$ (exactly $210\pi^2$, using the half-argument properties for $\sin^2 t$, as in Problem 15 of Problem Set 8-5, or by using integration by parts as in Chapter 9).

24. Journal Problem
Journal entries will vary.

Problem Set 8-7, pages 406 to 409 — Length of a Plane Curve—Arc Length

Q1. $y = x^2$

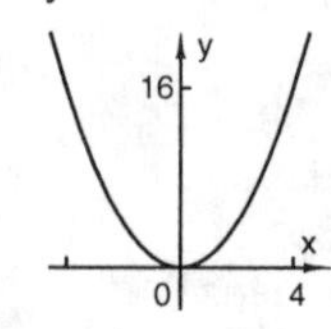

Q2. $y = x^2;\ 1 \le x \le 4$

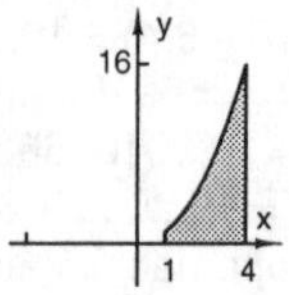

Q3. $A = \int_1^4 x^2\, dx$

Q4. $A = \frac{1}{3}x^3 \Big|_1^4$

Q5. $A = 21$

Q6. Graph

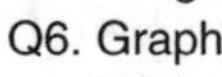

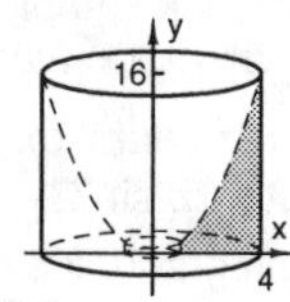

Q7. $V = \int_1^4 2\pi x^3\, dx$

Q8. $V = \frac{\pi}{2}x^4 \Big|_1^4$

Q9. $V = 127.5\pi$

Q10. mean value

1. a. Graph, $y = e^x$, from $x = 0$ to $x = 2$

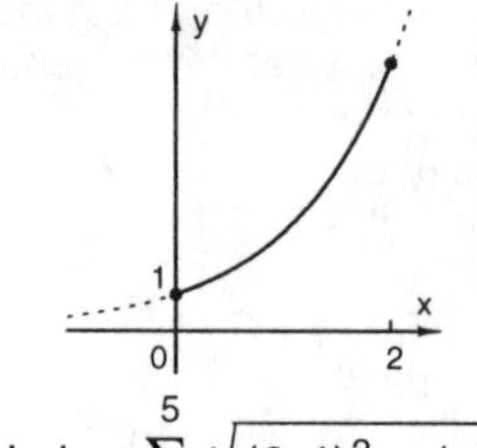

b. $L \approx \sum_{n=1}^{5} \sqrt{(0.4)^2 + (e^{0.4n} - e^{0.4(n-1)})^2}$
$= 6.7848\ldots$

c. $dy = e^x\, dx$
$dL = \sqrt{dx^2 + dy^2} = \sqrt{1 + e^{2x}}\, dx$
$L = \int_0^2 \sqrt{1 + e^{2x}}\, dx \approx 6.7886\ldots$ numerically
(The integral can be evaluated algebraically by substituting $u = \sqrt{1 + e^{2x}} \Rightarrow du = (u^2 - 1)/u\, dx$, so
$\int \sqrt{1 + e^{2x}}\, dx$
$= \sqrt{1 + e^{2x}} + \ln|\sqrt{1 + e^{2x}} - 1| - x + C.$)

2. a. Graph, $y = 2^x$, from $x = 0$ to $x = 3$

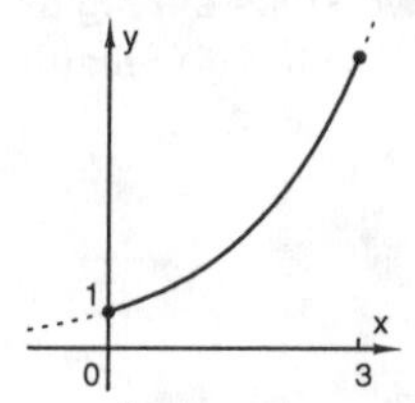

b. $L \approx \sum_{n=1}^{5} \sqrt{(0.6)^2 + (2^{0.6n} - 2^{0.6(n-1)})^2}$
$= 7.7853\ldots$.

c. $dy = (2^x \ln 2)\, dx$
$dL = \sqrt{dx^2 + dy^2} = \sqrt{1 + (2^x \ln 2)^2}\, dx$
$L = \int_0^3 \sqrt{1 + (2^x \ln 2)^2}\, dx \approx 7.7920\ldots$ numerically
(The integral can be evaluated algebraically by substituting $u = \sqrt{1 + (2^x \ln 2)^2}$
$\Rightarrow du = \ln 2\, (u^2 - 1)/u\, dx$,
so $\int \sqrt{1 + (2^x \ln 2)^2}\, dx$
$= \frac{1}{\ln 2}\sqrt{1 + (2^x \ln 2)^2}$
$+ \frac{1}{\ln 2}\ln|\sqrt{1 + (2^x \ln 2)^2} - 1| - x + C.$)

3. a. Graph, $y = \tan x$, from $x = 0$ to $x = 1.5$

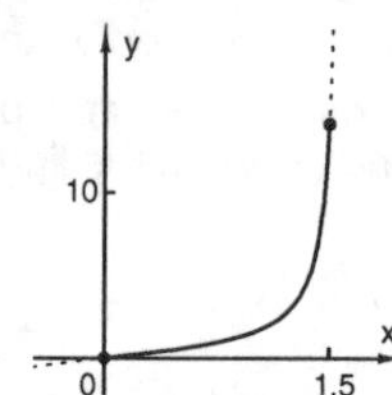

b. $L \approx \sum_{n=1}^{5} \sqrt{(0.3)^2 + (\tan 0.3n - \tan 0.3(n-1))^2}$
$= 14.4394\ldots$

c. $dy = \sec^2 x\, dx$
$dL = \sqrt{dx^2 + dy^2} = \sqrt{1 + \sec^4 x}\, dx$
$L = \int_0^{1.5} \sqrt{1 + \sec^4 x}\, dx \approx 14.4488\ldots$ numerically

4\. a. Graph, $y = \sec x$, from $x = 0$ to $x = 1.5$

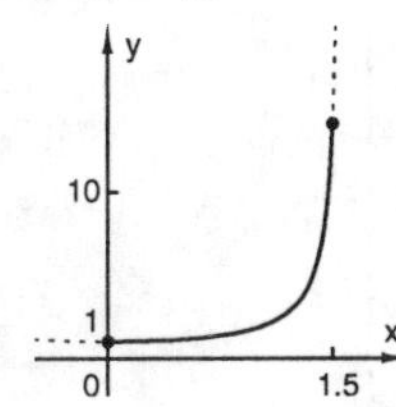

b. $L \approx \sum_{n=1}^{5} \sqrt{(0.3)^2 + (\sec 0.3n - \sec 0.3(n-1))^2}$

$= 13.7141 \ldots$

c. $dy = \sec x \tan x \, dx$

$dL = \sqrt{dx^2 + dy^2} = \sqrt{1 + \tan^2 x \sec^2 x} \, dx$

$L = \int_0^{1.5} \sqrt{1 + \tan^2 x \sec^2 x} \, dx$

$\approx 13.7304 \ldots$ numerically

5\. a. Graph, $y = x^2 - 5x + 3$, x in $[1, 6]$

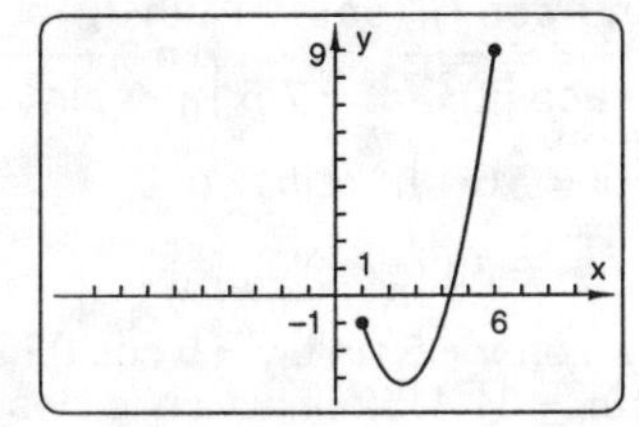

b. $dy = (2x - 5) \, dx$

$dL = \sqrt{dx^2 + dy^2} = \sqrt{1 + (2x - 5)^2} \, dx$

$L = \int_1^6 \sqrt{1 + (2x - 5)^2} \, dx \approx 15.8617 \ldots$

c. Low point is $(2.5, -3.25)$. Chords from $(1, -1)$ to $(2.5, -3.25)$ and from $(2.5, -3.25)$ to $(6, 9)$ have length $\sqrt{7.3125} + \sqrt{162.3125} = 15.4 \ldots$, which is a reasonable lower bound for L.

6\. a. Graph, $y = 4x - x^2$, x in $[0, 4]$

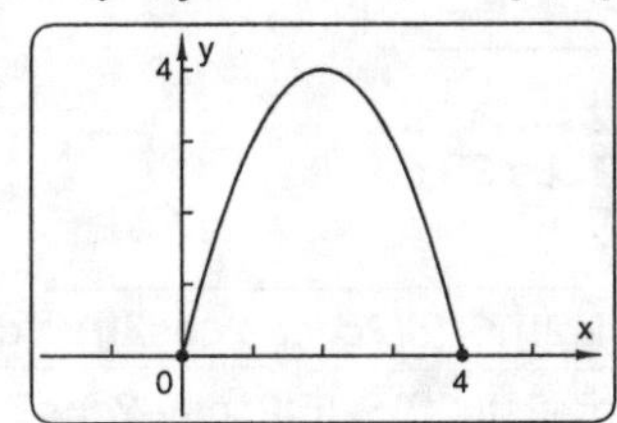

b. $dy = (4 - 2x) \, dx$

$dL = \sqrt{dx^2 + dy^2} = \sqrt{1 + (4 - 2x)^2} \, dx$

$L = \int_0^4 \sqrt{1 + (4 - 2x)^2} \, dx \approx 9.2935 \ldots$

c. Chords from $(0, 0)$ to $(2, 4)$ and from $(2, 4)$ to $(4, 0)$ have length $2\sqrt{20} = 8.9442 \ldots$, which is a reasonable lower bound for L.

7\. a. Graph, $y = 16 - x^4$, x in $[-1, 2]$

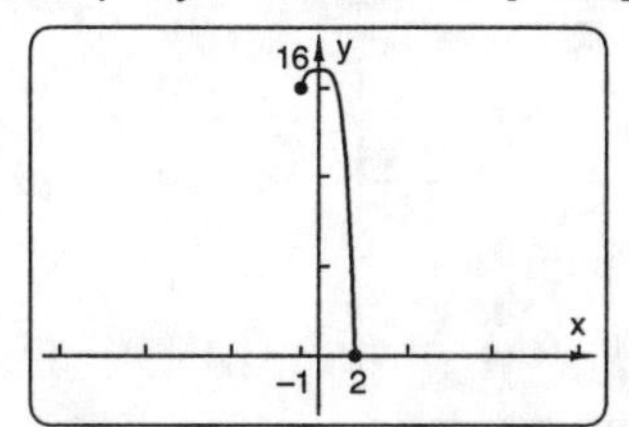

b. $dy = -4x^3 \, dx$

$dL = \sqrt{dx^2 + dy^2} = \sqrt{1 + 16x^6} \, dx$

$L = \int_{-1}^{2} \sqrt{1 + 16x^6} \, dx \approx 18.2470 \ldots$

c. Chords from $(-1, 15)$ to $(0, 16)$ and $(0, 16)$ to $(2, 0)$ have length $\sqrt{2} + \sqrt{260} = 17.5 \ldots$, which is a reasonable lower bound for L.

8\. a. Graph, $x^3 - 9x^2 + 5x + 50$, x in $[-1, 9]$

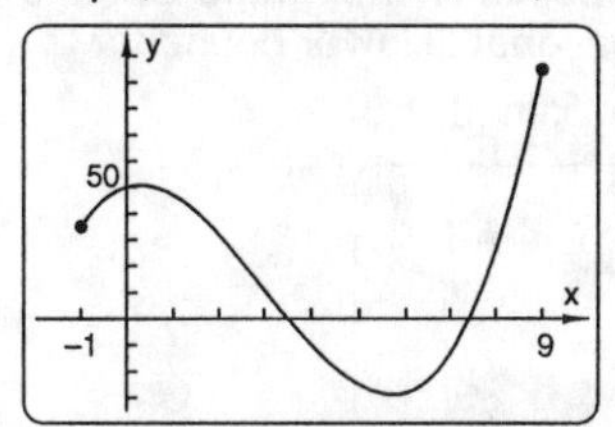

b. $dy = (3x^2 - 18x + 5) \, dx$

$dL = \sqrt{dx^2 + dy^2}$

$= \sqrt{1 + (3x^2 - 18x + 5)^2} \, dx$

$L = \int_{-1}^{9} \sqrt{1 + (3x^2 - 18x + 5)^2} \, dx$

$\approx 219.4873 \ldots$

c. Using five chords with $\Delta x = 2$, $L \approx 204.4605 \ldots$, which is a reasonable lower bound for L.

9\. a. Graph, $y = (\ln x)^2$, x in $[0.1, e]$

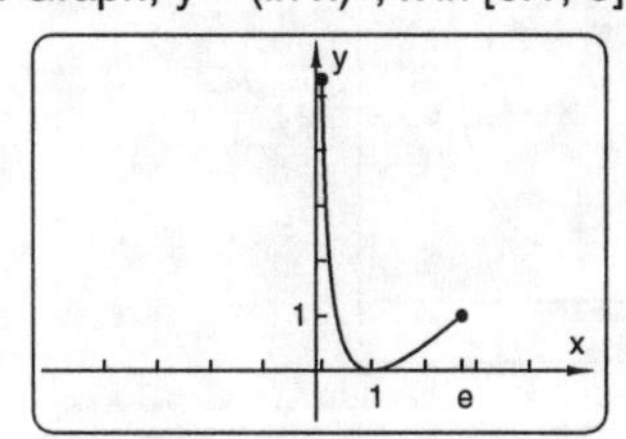

b. $dy = 2 \ln x \cdot x^{-1} \, dx = 2x^{-1} \ln x \, dx$

$dL = \sqrt{dx^2 + dy^2} = \sqrt{1 + (2x^{-1} \ln x)^2} \, dx$

$L = \int_{0.1}^{e} \sqrt{1 + (2x^{-1} \ln x)^2} \, dx \approx 7.6043 \ldots$

c. Chords from $x = 0.1$ to $x = 1$, and $x = 1$ to $x = e$, together have length $7.3658 \ldots$, which is a reasonable lower bound for L.

10. a. Graph, $y = x \sin x$, x in $[0, 4\pi]$

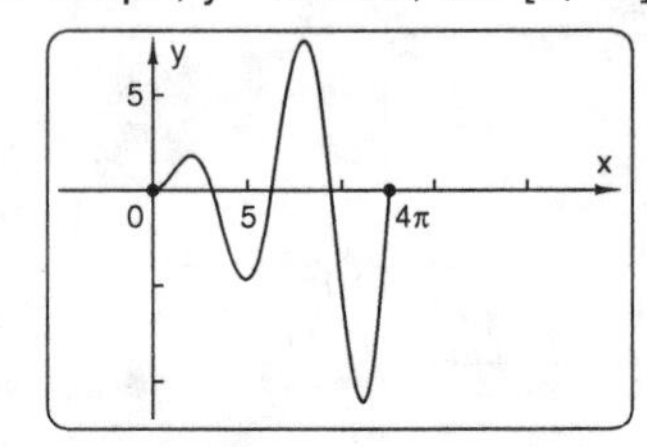

b. $dy = (\sin x + x \cos x)\,dx$

$dL = \sqrt{dx^2 + dy^2}$

$= \sqrt{1 + (\sin x + x \cos x)^2}\,dx$

$L = \int_0^{4\pi} \sqrt{1 + (\sin x + x \cos x)^2}\,dx$

$\approx 54.1699 \ldots$

c. Eight chords of $\Delta x = \pi/2$ extend from middle to high to middle to low points on the graph. Lengths sum 52.6109 ..., a reasonable lower bound for L.

11. a. Graph, $y = \tan x$, x in $[0, 1.5]$.

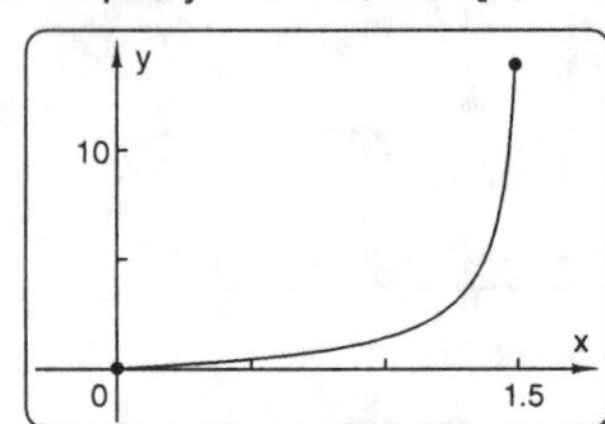

b. $dy = \sec^2 x\,dx$

$dL = \sqrt{dx^2 + dy^2} = \sqrt{1 + \sec^4 x}\,dx$

$L = \int_0^{1.5} \sqrt{1 + \sec^4 x}\,dx \approx 14.4488 \ldots$

c. Distance between the endpoints is 14.1809 ..., which is a reasonable lower bound for L.

12. a. Graph, $y = \sec x$, x in $[0, 1.5]$.

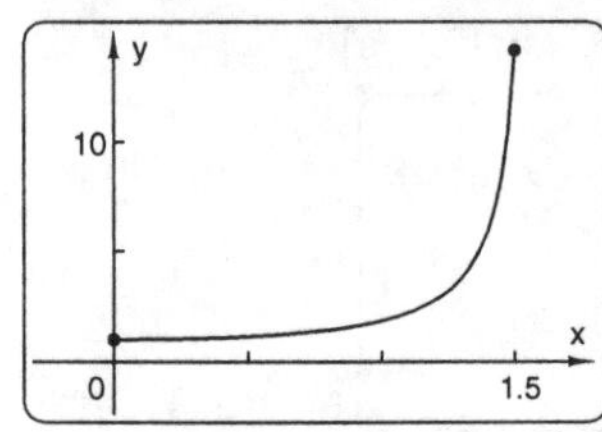

b. $dy = \sec x \tan x\,dx$

$dL = \sqrt{1 + (\sec x \tan x)^2}\,dx$

$L = \int_0^{1.5} \sqrt{1 + (\sec x \tan x)^2}\,dx \approx 13.7304 \ldots$

c. Distance between the endpoints is 13.2221 ..., which is a reasonable lower bound for L.

13. a. Graph, $x = 5\cos^3 t$, $y = 5\sin^3 t$, t in $[0, 2\pi]$

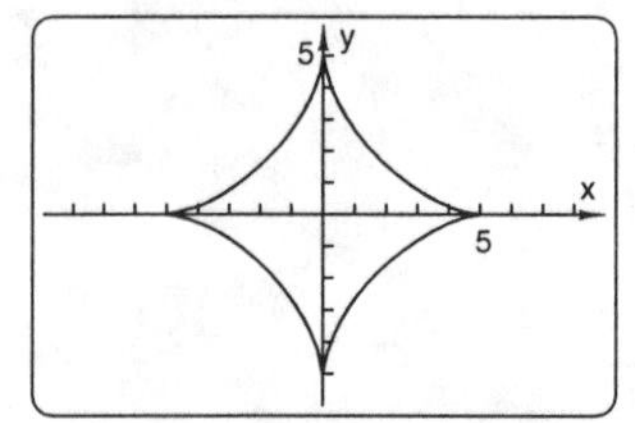

b. $dx = -15\cos^2 t \sin t\,dt$, $dy = 15\sin^2 t \cos t\,dt$

$dL = \sqrt{dx^2 + dy^2}$

$= \sqrt{(-15\cos^2 t \sin t)^2 + (15\sin^2 t \cos t)^2}\,dt$

$L = \int_0^{2\pi} \sqrt{(-15\cos^2 t \sin t)^2 + (15\sin^2 t \cos t)^2}\,dt$

$\approx 30.$

To see why the answer is so simple, transform the radicand and use the fundamental theorem.

$L = \int_0^{2\pi} \sqrt{225(\sin t \cos t)^2(\cos^2 t + \sin^2 t)}\,dt$

$= 7.5\int_0^{2\pi} \sqrt{(2\sin t \cos t)^2}\,dt = 7.5\int_0^{2\pi} \sqrt{\sin^2 2t}\,dt$

$= 7.5\int_0^{2\pi} |\sin 2t|\,dt = 7.5 \cdot 4\int_0^{\pi/2} \sin 2t\,dt$

$= 30(\frac{1}{2})(-\cos 2t)\Big|_0^{\pi/2} = 30$ (exactly!).

c. Circle of radius 5 (i.e., $x = 5\sin t$, $y = 5\cos t$) has circumference $10\pi = 31.4152 \ldots$, which is close to the calculated value of L.

14. a. Graph, $x = 5(2\cos t - \cos 2t)$,
$y = 5(2\sin t - \sin 2t)$, t in $[0, 2\pi]$.

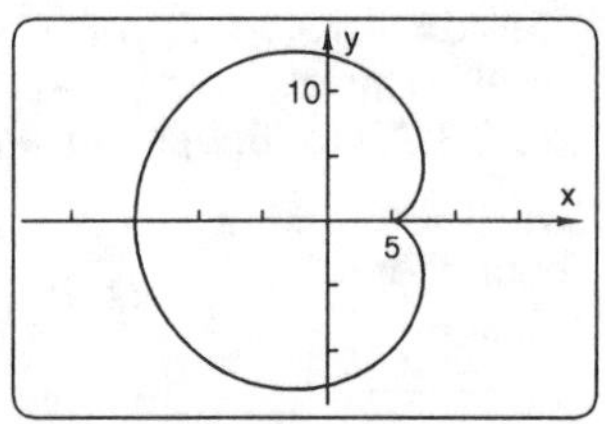

b. $dx = 5(-2\sin t + 2\sin 2t)\,dt$
$dy = 5(2\cos t - 2\cos 2t)\,dt$

$dL = \sqrt{dx^2 + dy^2}$

$= \sqrt{(5(-2\sin t + 2\sin 2t))^2 + (5(2\cos t - 2\cos 2t))^2)}\,dt$

$L = \int_0^{2\pi} \sqrt{(5(-2\sin t + 2\sin 2t))^2 + (5(2\cos t - 2\cos 2t))^2}\,dt$

≈ 80

To see why the answer is so simple, transform the radicand algebraically and use the fundamental theorem.

$L = 10\int_0^{2\pi} \sqrt{2 - 2\sin t \sin 2t - 2\cos t \cos 2t}\,dt$

$= 10\sqrt{2}\int_0^{2\pi} \sqrt{1 - \cos t}\,dt$ (using $\cos(A - B)$)

$= 10\sqrt{2}\int_0^{2\pi} \frac{\sqrt{1 - \cos^2 t}}{\sqrt{1 + \cos t}}\,dt$

$= 10\sqrt{2}\int_0^{2\pi} \frac{|\sin t|}{\sqrt{1 + \cos t}}\,dt$

$= 20\sqrt{2}\int_0^{\pi} (1 + \cos t)^{-1/2}(\sin t\,dt)$

$= -40\sqrt{2}(1 + \cos t)^{1/2}\Big|_0^{\pi}$

$= -40\sqrt{2}(1 - 1)^{1/2} + 40\sqrt{2}(1 + 1)^{1/2} = 80$

c. Max./min. values of y are $\pm 7.5\sqrt{3}$. Circle of radius $7.5\sqrt{3}$ has circumference $15\pi\sqrt{3} = 81.6209 \ldots$.

15. a. Graph, $x = 5\cos t - \cos 5t$, $y = 5\sin t - \sin 5t$, t in $[0, 2\pi]$

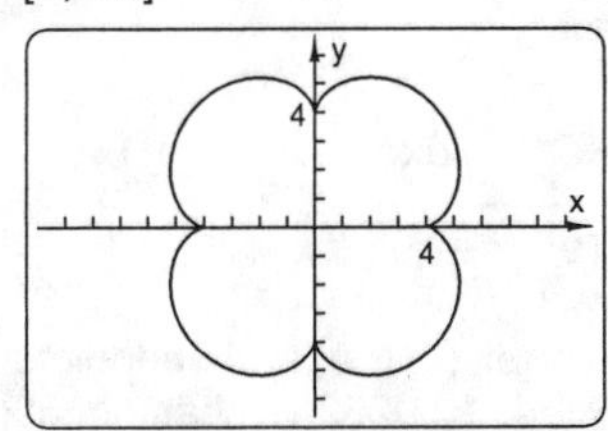

b. $dx = (-5\sin t + 5\sin 5t)\,dt$

$dy = (5\cos t - 5\cos 5t)\,dt$

$dL = \sqrt{dx^2 + dy^2}$

$= \sqrt{(-5\sin t + 5\sin 5t)^2 + (5\cos t - 5\cos 5t)^2}\,dt$

$L = \int_0^{2\pi} \sqrt{(-5\sin t + 5\sin 5t)^2 + (5\cos t - 5\cos 5t)^2}\,dt$

$\approx 40.$

To see why the answer is so simple, transform the radicand and use the fundamental theorem.

$L = 5\int_0^{2\pi} \sqrt{2 - 2\sin t \sin 5t - 2\cos t \cos 5t}\,\,dt$

$... = 5\sqrt{2}\int_0^{2\pi} \sqrt{1 - \cos 4t}\,dt$ (using cos A − B)

$... = 5\sqrt{2}\int_0^{2\pi} \frac{\sqrt{1 - \cos^2 4t}}{\sqrt{1 + \cos 4t}}\,dt$

$... = 5\sqrt{2}\int_0^{2\pi} \frac{|\sin 4t|}{\sqrt{1 + \cos 4t}}\,dt$

$... = 40\sqrt{2}\int_0^{\pi/4} (1 + \cos 4t)^{-1/2}(\sin 4t\,dt)$

$... = -20\sqrt{2}\,(1 + \cos 4t)^{1/2}\Big|_0^{\pi/4}$

$= -0 + 20\sqrt{2}\cdot\sqrt{2} = 40$

c. Max./min. values of x, y are $\pm 3\sqrt{3}$. Circle of radius $3\sqrt{3}$ has circumference 32.6483 ..., which is close.

16. a. Graph, $x = \cos t + t\sin t$, $y = \sin t - t\cos t$, t in $[0, 4\pi]$

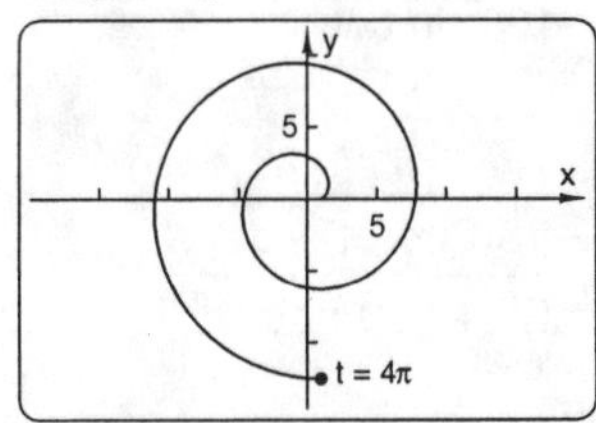

b. $dx = (-\sin t + \sin t + t\cos t)\,dt = t\cos t\,dt$

$dy = (\cos t - \cos t + t\sin t)\,dt = t\sin t\,dt$

$dL = \sqrt{dx^2 + dy^2} = \sqrt{(t\cos t)^2 + (t\sin t)^2}\,dt$

$= |t|\,dt = t\,dt$ (since $t \ge 0$)

$L = \int_0^{4\pi} t\,dt = 0.5t^2\Big|_0^{4\pi} = 8\pi^2 = 78.9568 \ldots$.

c. Circle of radius $4\pi = 12.5663$ ... would have circumference $= 8\pi^2$.

17. a. Graph, $y = 4x^{3/2}$, x in [0, 4]

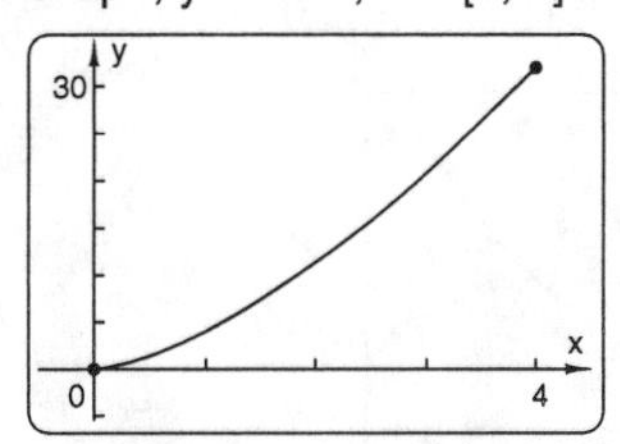

b. $dy = 6x^{1/2}\,dx$

$dL = \sqrt{dx^2 + dy^2} = \sqrt{1 + 36x}\,\,dx$

$L = \int_0^4 \sqrt{1 + 36x}\,dx = \frac{1}{36}\int_0^4 (1 + 36x)^{1/2}(36\,dx)$

$= \frac{1}{54}(1 + 36x)^{3/2}\Big|_0^4 = \frac{1}{54}(145^{3/2} - 1) = 32.3153 \ldots$

c. The chord connecting the endpoints has length 32.2490 ..., which is a reasonable lower bound for L.

18. a. Graph, $y = \frac{x^3}{12} + \frac{1}{x}$, x in [1, 2].

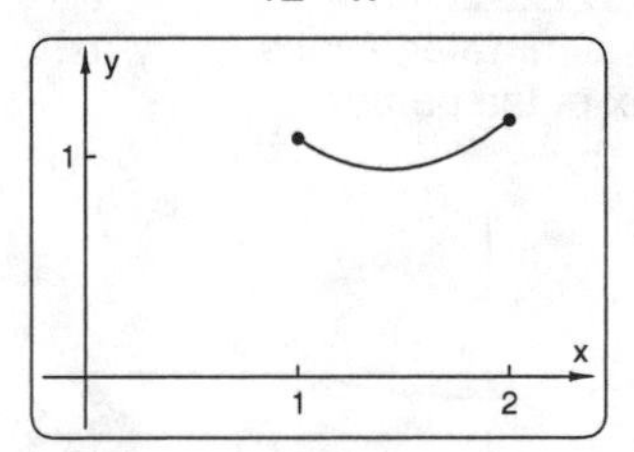

b. $dy = (x^2/4 - x^{-2})\,dx$

$dL = \sqrt{dx^2 + dy^2} = \sqrt{1 + (x^2/4 - x^{-2})^2}\,dx$

$= \sqrt{1 + x^4/16 - 1/2 + x^{-4}}\,dx$

$... = \sqrt{(x^2/4 + x^{-2})^2}\,dx = |x^2/4 + x^{-2}|\,dx$

$L = \int_1^2 (x^2/4 + x^{-2})\,dx$ (because integrand > 0)

$= x^3/12 - x^{-1}\Big|_1^2 = 1\frac{1}{12} = 1.0833 \ldots$

c. Distance between endpoints is $\sqrt{1.006944 \ldots} =$ 1.00346 ..., which is a reasonable lower bound for.

19. a. Graph, $y = 3x^{2/3} + 5$, x in [1, 8]

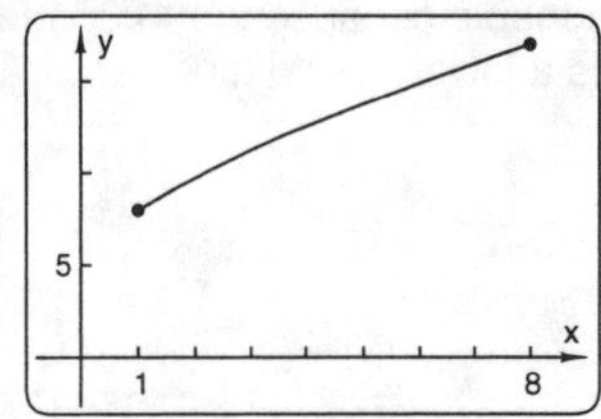

b. $dy = 2x^{-1/3}\,dx$

$dL = \sqrt{dx^2 + dy^2} = \sqrt{1 + 4x^{-2/3}}\,dx$

$L = \int_1^8 \sqrt{1 + 4x^{-2/3}}\,dx = \int_1^8 (x^{2/3} + 4)^{1/2}(x^{-1/3}\,dx)$

$= \frac{3}{2}\int_1^8 (x^{2/3} + 4)^{1/2}(\frac{2}{3}x^{-1/3}\,dx)$

$= \frac{3}{2}\cdot\frac{2}{3}(x^{2/3} + 4)^{3/2}\Big|_1^8 = 8\sqrt{8} - 5\sqrt{5} = 11.4470 \ldots$.

c. Distance between endpoints is $\sqrt{130} = 11.4017 \ldots$, which is a reasonable lower bound for.

20. a. Graph, $y = \frac{1}{3}(x^2 + 2)^{3/2}$, x in [0, 3]

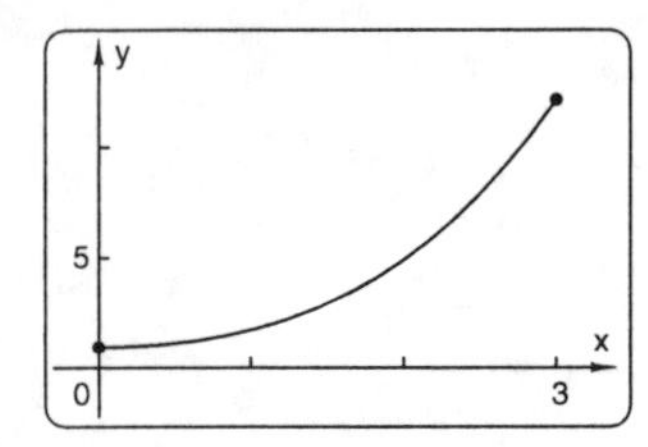

b. $dy = \frac{1}{2}(x^2 + 2)^{1/2} 2x\,dx = x(x^2 + 2)^{1/2}\,dx$

$dL = \sqrt{dx^2 + dy^2} = \sqrt{1 + x^2(x^2 + 2)}\,dx$

$= \sqrt{1 + x^4 + 2x^2}\,dx = (1 + x^2)\,dx$

$L = \int_0^3 (1 + x^2)\,dx = x + \frac{1}{3}x^3 \Big|_0^3 = 12$

c. Distance between endpoints is 11.6123 ..., which is a reasonable lower bound for L.

21. Golden Gate Bridge Problem

Construct an x-axis at water level and a y-axis through the vertex of the parabola.

Graph

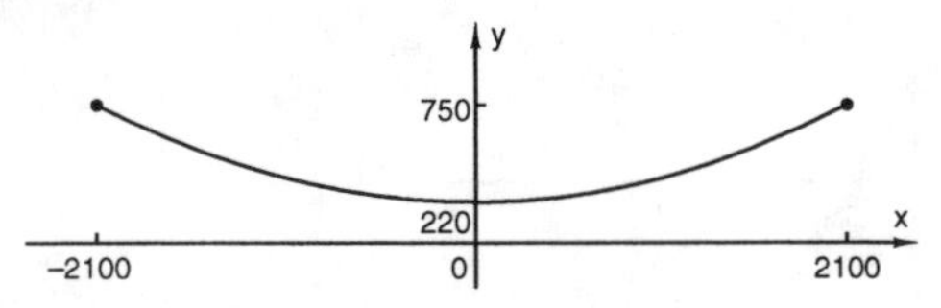

General equation is $y - 220 = ax^2$.

Substitute (2100, 750) for (x, y).

$750 - 220 = a \cdot 2{,}100^2 \Rightarrow a = \frac{53}{441000}$

Equation of parabola is $y = \frac{53}{441000}x^2 + 220$.

$dy = \frac{106}{441000}x\,dx$

$dL = \sqrt{dx^2 + dy^2} = \sqrt{1 + (106/441{,}000)^2 x^2}\,dx$

$L = \int_{-2100}^{2100} \sqrt{1 + (106/441{,}000)^2 x^2}\,dx$

≈ 4372.0861 ... numerically ≈ 4372 feet.

The answer is reasonable because the 4200 feet between supports is a lower bound for L.

22. Chain Problem

$y = 0.2(e^x + e^{-x})$, $dy = 0.2(e^x - e^{-x})\,dx$

$dL = \sqrt{dx^2 + dy^2}$

$= \sqrt{1 + 0.04(e^x - e^{-x})^2}\,dx$

$L = \int_{-4}^{4} \sqrt{1 + 0.04(e^x - e^{-x})^2}\,dx$

$\approx 24.1722 \ldots \approx 24.2$ ft

The parabola with vertex (0, 0.4) and endpoints $(\pm 4, 0.2(e^4 + e^{-4}) = (\pm 4, 10.9232 \ldots)$ has equation $y = ax^2 + 0.4$. Substituting (4, 10.9232...) gives $10.9232 \ldots = 16a + 0.4 \Rightarrow a = 0.6577 \ldots$.

$y = 0.6577 \ldots x^2 + 0.4 \Rightarrow dy = 1.3154 \ldots x\,dx$

$dL = \sqrt{dx^2 + dy^2} = \sqrt{1 + 1.7303 \ldots x^2}\,dx$

$L = \int_{-4}^{4} \sqrt{1 + 1.7303 \ldots x^2}\,dx$

$\approx 23.2193 \ldots \approx 23.2$ ft, which is about a foot shorter than the catenary, as shown by graph

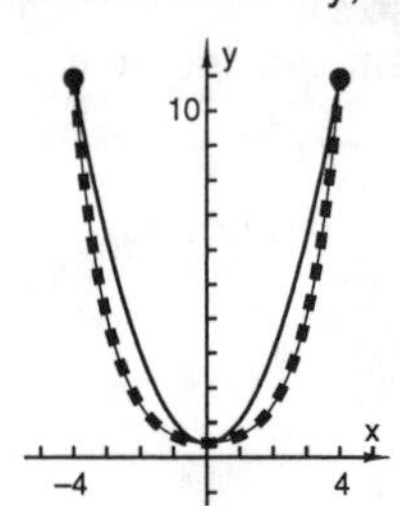

23. Stadium Problem

Outer ellipse:

$x = 120\cos t$, $dx = -120\sin t\,dt$

$y = 100\sin t$, $dy = 100\cos t\,dt$

$dL = \sqrt{dx^2 + dy^2}$

$= \sqrt{(-120\sin t)^2 + (100\cos t)^2}\,dt$

$L = \int_0^{2\pi} \sqrt{(-120\sin t)^2 + (100\cos t)^2}\,dt$

$\approx 692.5791 \ldots \approx 692.6$ m

Inner ellipse:

$x = 100\cos t$, $dx = -100\sin t\,dt$

$y = 50\sin t$, $dy = 50\cos t\,dt$

$dL = \sqrt{dx^2 + dy^2}$

$= \sqrt{(-100\sin t)^2 + (50\cos t)^2}\,dt$

$L = \int_0^{2\pi} \sqrt{(-100\sin t)^2 + (50\cos t)^2}\,dt$

$\approx 484.4224 \ldots \approx 484.4$ m

24. Parabola Surprise Problem!

Graph, $x = 8\cos 2t$, $y = 5\sin t$, t in $[0, 2\pi]$

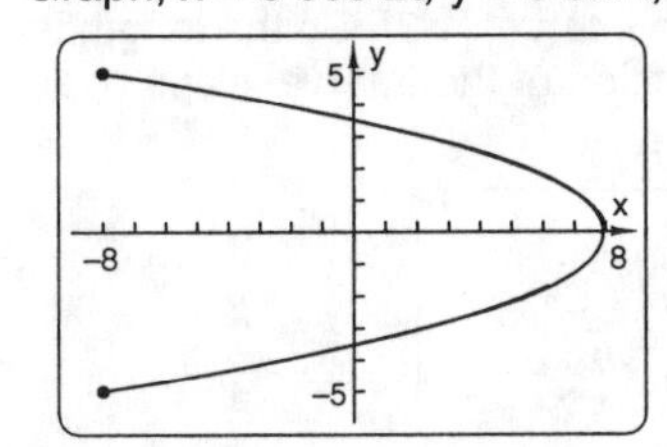

$dx = -16\sin 2t$, $dy = 5\cos t$

$dL = \sqrt{dx^2 + dy^2}$

$= \sqrt{(-16\sin 2t)^2 + (5\cos t)^2}\, dt$

Curve appears to have length

$L = \int_0^{2\pi} \sqrt{(-16\sin 2t)^2 + (5\cos t)^2}\, dt$

$= 68.7694\ldots$.

Length should be less than the lengths of three circumscribing segments, $16 + 16 + 10 = 42$.

The discrepancy is explained by the fact that the parabola is traced *twice* as t goes from 0 to 2π. Actual length $\approx (0.5)(68.7694\ldots) = 34.384\ldots$, for which 42 is a reasonable upper bound.

25. Implicit Relation Problem No. I

$9x^2 = 4y^3 \Leftrightarrow x = \pm\frac{2}{3}y^{3/2}$. Graph, $(0, 0)$ to $(2\sqrt{3}, 3)$.

Negative branch is out of the domain.

$dx = y^{1/2}\, dy$

$dL = \sqrt{dx^2 + dy^2} = (y + 1)^{1/2}\, dy$

$L = \int_0^3 (y + 1)^{1/2}\, dy = \frac{2}{3}(y + 1)^{3/2} \Big|_0^3$

$= 4\frac{2}{3} = 4.6666\ldots$

26. Implicit Relation Problem No. II

$x^2 = y^3 \Leftrightarrow x = \pm y^{1.5}$. Graph, $(-1, 1)$ to $(8, 4)$

$2x\, dx = 3y^2\, dy \Rightarrow 4x^2\, dx^2 = 9y^4\, dy^2$

$\Rightarrow 4y^3\, dx^2 = 9y^4\, dy^2 \Rightarrow dx^2 = \frac{9}{4}y\, dy^2$.

Note that $dy < 0$ between $(-1,1)$ and $(0,0)$:

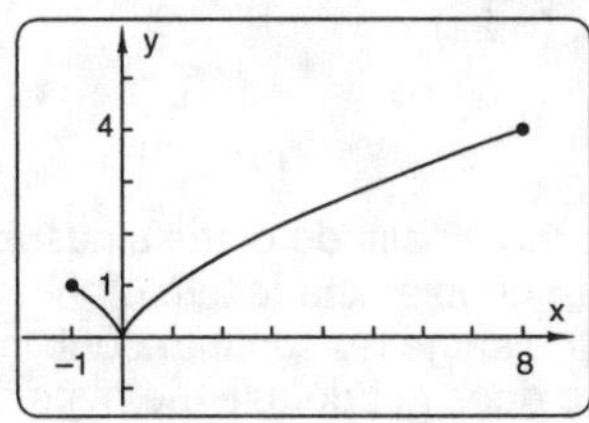

For x in $[-1, 0]$, $x = -y^{1.5}$, $dx = -1.5y^{0.5}\, dy$,

$dL = -\sqrt{dx^2 + dy^2} = -\sqrt{2.25y + 1}\, dy$.

For x in $[0, 8]$, $x = y^{1.5}$, $dx = 1.5y^{0.5}\, dy$,

$dL = \sqrt{dx^2 + dy^2} = \sqrt{2.25y + 1}\, dy$.

$L = \int_1^0 -\sqrt{2.25y + 1}\, dy + \int_0^4 \sqrt{2.25y + 1}\, dy$

$= -\frac{8}{27}(2.25y + 1)^{3/2} \Big|_1^0 + \frac{8}{27}(2.25y + 1)^{3/2} \Big|_0^4$

$= \frac{8}{27}(-1 + 3.25^{3/2} + 10^{3/2} - 1) = 10.5131\ldots$

27. Spiral Problem

$x = \frac{t}{\pi}\cos t$, $dx = \frac{1}{\pi}(\cos t - t\sin t)\, dt$

$y = \frac{t}{\pi}\sin t$, $dy = \frac{1}{\pi}(\sin t + t\cos t)\, dt$

$dL = \sqrt{dx^2 + dy^2}$

$= \frac{1}{\pi}\sqrt{(\cos t - t\sin t)^2 + (\sin t + t\cos t)^2}\, dt$

$= \frac{1}{\pi}\sqrt{1 + t^2}\, dt$

The curve crosses the x-axis exactly when $\sin t = 0$, when t is a multiple of π. There are seven crossings after the beginning, so t should run between 0 and 7π.

To check this, note that the curve ends at $(-7, 0)$, so solve $(t/\pi)\cos t = -7$ with $t = n\pi \Rightarrow$ $(n\pi/\pi)\cos n\pi = -7 \Rightarrow n\cos n\pi = -7$ $\Rightarrow n = 7 \Rightarrow 0 \le t \le 7\pi$.

$L = \frac{1}{\pi}\int_0^{7\pi} \sqrt{1 + t^2}\, dt \approx 77.6508\ldots$

The integral can be evaluated algebraically by trigonometry substitution as in Section 9-6, giving

$\int \sqrt{1 + t^2}\, dt = \frac{1}{2}[t\sqrt{t^2 + 1} + \ln(t + \sqrt{1 + t^2})] + C$.

28. Length of a Circle Problem

$x = r\cos t$, $dx = -r\sin t\, dt$

$y = r\sin t$, $dy = r\cos t\, dt$

$dL = \sqrt{dx^2 + dy^2} = \sqrt{r^2\sin^2 t + r^2\cos^2 t}\, dt$

$= r\, dt$ (for $r \ge 0$)

The range $0 \le t \le 2\pi$ generates the entire circle.

Circumference $= \int_0^{2\pi} r\, dt = rt \Big|_0^{2\pi} = 2\pi r$, Q.E.D.

29. Sinusoid Length Investigation Problem

$y = A \sin x$, $dy = A \cos x\, dx$

$dL = \sqrt{dx^2 + dy^2} = \sqrt{1 + A^2 \cos^2 x}\, dx$

Pick a convenient interval for x such as $[0, 2\pi]$.

$L = \int_0^{2\pi} \sqrt{1 + A^2 \cos^2 x}\, dx$

A	L
0	6.283185 ... (= 2π)
1	7.640395 ...
2	10.540734 ...
3	13.974417 ...

Doubling A doubles the amplitude of the sinusoid. However, it less than doubles the length of the sinusoid, for much the same reason that doubling one leg of a right triangle does not double the hypotenuse. In the limit as A approaches infinity, doubling A approaches doubling the length.

30. Ellipse Length Investigation Problem

$x = \cos t$, $dx = -\sin t\, dt$

$y = A \sin t$, $dy = A \cos t\, dt$

$dL = \sqrt{dx^2 + dy^2} = \sqrt{\sin^2 t + A^2 \cos^2 t}\, dt$

The entire ellipse is generated as t increases from 0 to 2π.

$L = \int_0^{2\pi} \sqrt{\sin^2 t + A^2 \cos^2 t}\, dt$

A	L
0	4 (a double line segment)
1	6.283185 ... (= 2π)
2	9.688448 ...
3	13.364893 ...

Doubling A doubles one axis of the ellipse without changing the other axis. That is why the length does *not* double when A doubles. The reasoning is similar to that in Problem 29.

31. Fatal Error Problem

The function $y = (x - 2)^{-1}$ has a vertical asymptote at x = 2, which is in the interval [1,3]. So the length is infinite. Mae's partition of the interval skips over the discontinuity. Graph

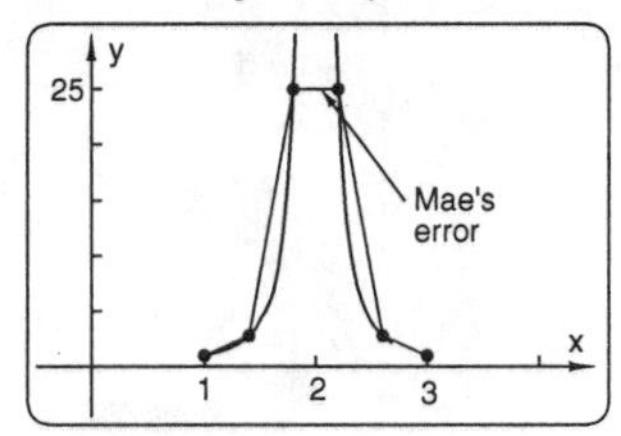

32. Mistake Problem

The sample points are all of the form $(n/2, \sin n\pi)$, which all lie on the x-axis and therefore fail to measure the wiggly bits. Graph.

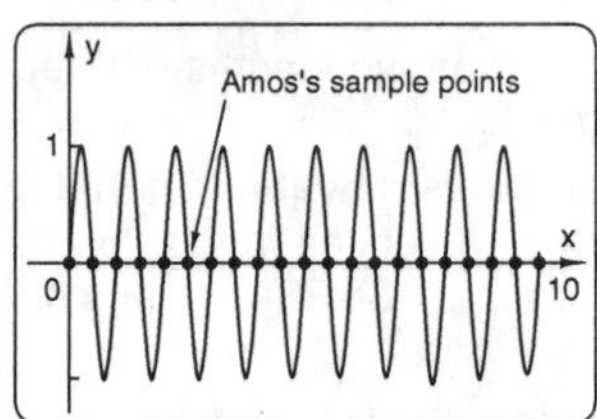

The length of the curve is 40 times the length of the part from x = 0 to x = 0.25 (by symmetry), so Amos could use five subintervals of [0, 0.25] to estimate the length of half of one arch, then multiply his answer by 40 to find the total length.

33. Program for Arc Length by Brute Force

See the Supplementary Programs section of the Instructor's Guide.

Problem Set 8-8, pages 413 to 416 — Area of a Surface of Revolution

Q1. $\sqrt{1 + 9x^4}\, dx$

Q2. $\sqrt{1 + \sec^2 x}\, dx$

Q3. $\frac{1}{6}\sin^6 x + C$

Q4. 156

Q5. $xe^x + e^x$

Q6. max. y = 7 (at x = 1)

Q7. integrable

Q8. $f'(x) = \lim_{\Delta x \to 0} \frac{f(x+\Delta x) - f(x)}{\Delta x}$ or $f'(c) = \lim_{x \to c} \frac{f(x) - f(c)}{x - c}$

Q9. Instantaneous rate

Q10. $\frac{1}{2}\ln|\sec 2x + \tan 2x| + C$

1. Paraboloid Problem

a. Graph, $y = 0.5x^2$, from x = 0 to x = 3, about y-axis

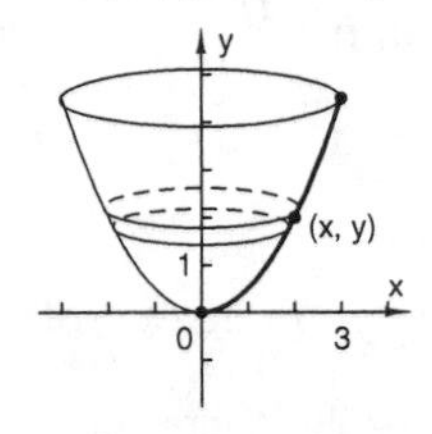

$dy = x\, dx$

$dL = \sqrt{dx^2 + dy^2} = \sqrt{1 + x^2}\, dx$

$dS = 2\pi x \cdot dL = 2\pi x\sqrt{1 + x^2}\, dx$

$S = \int_0^3 2\pi x\sqrt{1 + x^2}\, dx \approx 64.1361 \ldots$

b. The inscribed cone of height 4.5 and radius 3 has lateral surface area $= \pi r L = \pi \cdot 3 \cdot \sqrt{3^2 + 4.5^2} =$ 50.9722 ..., which is a reasonable lower bound for S.

c. $S = \int_0^3 \pi(1 + x^2)^{1/2}\, (2x\, dx)$

$= \frac{2}{3}\pi(1 + x^2)^{3/2} \Big|_0^3 = \frac{2}{3}\pi(10\sqrt{10} - 1) = 64.1361 \ldots,$

agreeing with the answer found numerically.

2. Rotated Sinusoid Problem

a. Graph, $y = \sin x$, from x = 0 to $x = \pi$, about x-axis

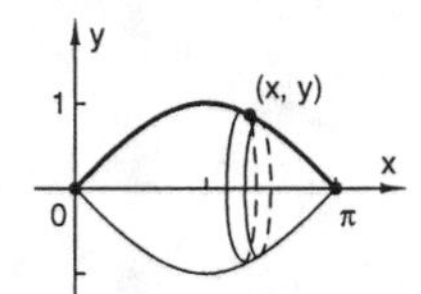

b. $dy = \cos x\, dx$

$dL = \sqrt{dx^2 + dy^2} = \sqrt{1 + \cos^2 x}\, dx$

$dS = 2\pi y \cdot dL = 2\pi \sin x \sqrt{1 + \cos^2 x}\, dx$

$S = \int_0^{\pi} 2\pi \sin x \sqrt{1 + \cos^2 x}\, dx \approx 14.4235 \ldots .$

c. The circumscribed cylinder of length π and radius 1 has lateral area $= 2\pi^2 = 19.7392 \ldots$, which is a reasonable upper bound for S.

3. Ln-Curved Surface, Problem I
Graph, $y = \ln x$, from $x = 1$ to $x = 3$, about x-axis

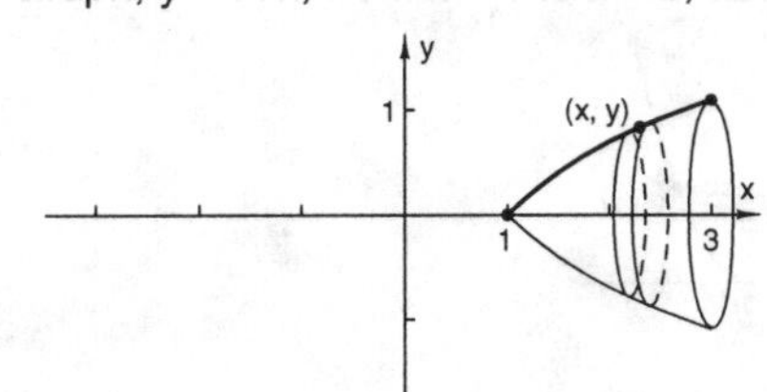

$dy = x^{-1}\,dx$

$dL = \sqrt{dx^2 + dy^2} = \sqrt{1 + x^{-2}}\,dx$

$dS = 2\pi y \cdot dL = 2\pi \ln x \sqrt{1 + x^{-2}}\,dx$

$S = \int_1^3 2\pi \ln x \sqrt{1 + x^{-2}}\,dx \approx 9.0242\ldots$

4. Ln-Curved Surface, Problem II
Graph, $y = \ln x$, from $x = 1$ to $x = 3$, rotated about the y-axis, showing back half of surface only.

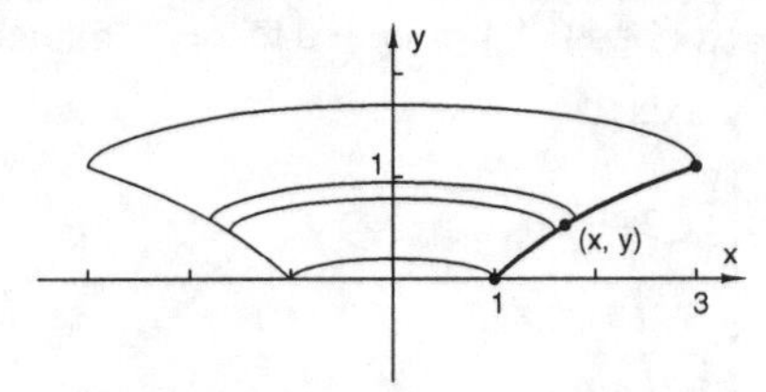

$dL = \sqrt{1 + x^{-2}}\,dx$, from Problem 3.

$dS = 2\pi x \cdot dL = 2\pi x \sqrt{1 + x^{-2}}\,dx$

$S = \int_1^3 2\pi x \sqrt{1 + x^{-2}}\,dx \approx 28.3047\ldots$

5. Reciprocal Curved Surface Problem I
Graph, $y = 1/x = x^{-1}$, from $x = 0.5$ to $x = 2$, rotated about the y-axis

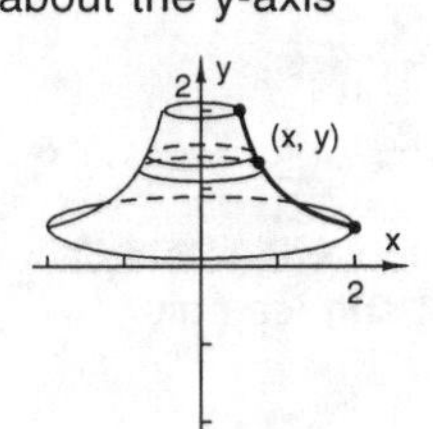

$dy = -x^{-2}\,dx$

$dL = \sqrt{dx^2 + dy^2} = \sqrt{1 + x^{-4}}\,dx$

$dS = 2\pi x \cdot dL = 2\pi x \sqrt{1 + x^{-4}}\,dx$

$S = \int_{0.5}^2 2\pi x \sqrt{1 + x^{-4}}\,dx \approx 15.5181\ldots$

6. Reciprocal Curved Surface Problem II
Graph, $y = 1/x = x^{-1}$, from $x = 0.5$ to $x = 2$, rotated about the x-axis

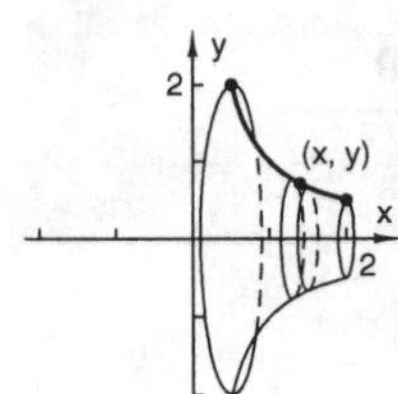

$dL = \sqrt{1 + x^{-4}}\,dx$ from Problem 5.

$dS = 2\pi y \cdot dL = 2\pi x^{-1} \sqrt{1 + x^{-4}}\,dx$

$S = \int_{0.5}^2 2\pi x^{-1} \sqrt{1 + x^{-4}}\,dx \approx 15.5181\ldots$

(Note surfaces 5 and 6 are identical.)

7. Cubic Paraboloid Problem I
Graph, $y = x^3$, from $x = 0$ to $x = 2$, rotated about the y-axis

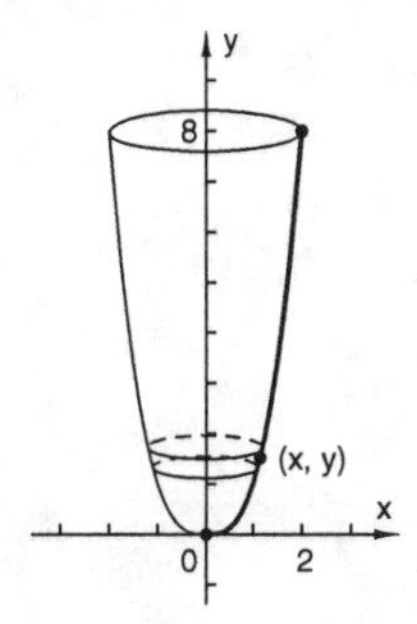

$dy = 3x^2\,dx$

$dL = \sqrt{dx^2 + dy^2} = \sqrt{1 + 9x^4}\,dx$

$dS = 2\pi x \cdot dL = 2\pi x\sqrt{1 + 9x^4}\,dx$

$S = \int_0^2 2\pi x\sqrt{1 + 9x^4}\,dx \approx 77.3245\ldots$

8. Cubic Paraboloid Problem II
Graph, $y = -x^3 + 5x^2 - 8x + 6$, from $x = 0$ to $x = 3$, rotated about the y-axis

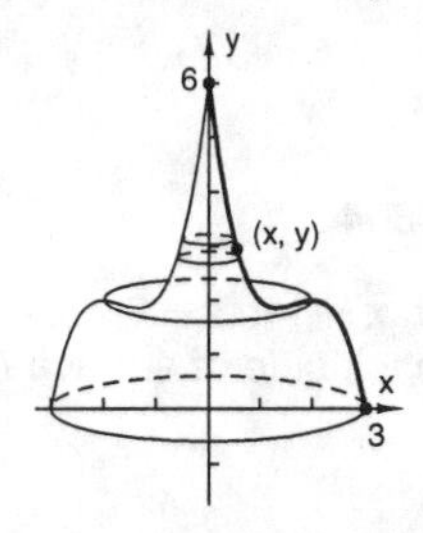

$dy = (-3x^2 + 10x - 8)\,dx$

$dL = \sqrt{dx^2 + dy^2}$

$= \sqrt{1 + (-3x^2 + 10x - 8)^2}\,dx$

$dS = 2\pi x \cdot dL$

$= 2\pi x \sqrt{1 + (-3x^2 + 10x - 8)^2}\,dx$

Graph intersects x-axis where $y = 0$.

$-x^3 + 5x^2 - 8x + 6 = -(x - 3)(x^2 - 2x + 2) = 0$

at $x = 3$.

$S = \int_0^3 2\pi x \sqrt{1 + (-3x^2 + 10x - 8)^2}\,dx$

$\approx 58.7946\ldots$.

9. Graph, $y = \sqrt{x} = x^{1/2}$, from $x = 0$ to $x = 1$, rotated about the x-axis.

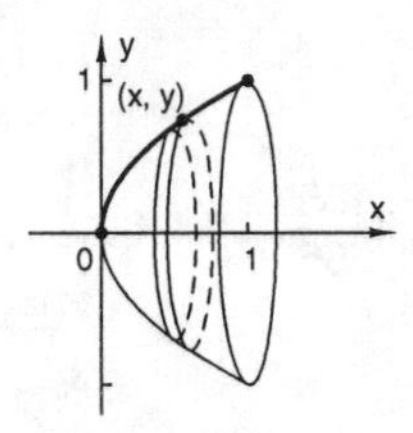

$dy = 0.5x^{-1/2}\,dx$

$dL = \sqrt{dx^2 + dy^2} = \sqrt{1 + 0.25x^{-1}}\,dx$

$dS = 2\pi y \cdot dL = 2\pi x^{1/2} \sqrt{1 + 0.25x^{-1}}\,dx$

$= 2\pi \sqrt{x + 0.25}\,dx = 2\pi(x + 0.25)^{1/2}\,dx$

$S = \int_0^1 2\pi(x + 0.25)^{1/2}\,dx = \frac{4\pi}{3}(x + 0.25)^{3/2}\Big|_0^1$

$= \frac{4\pi}{3}(1.25^{3/2} - 0.125) = 5.3304\ldots$

10. $y = x^3$, from $x = 1$ to $x = 2$, rotated about the x-axis, showing back half of surface only

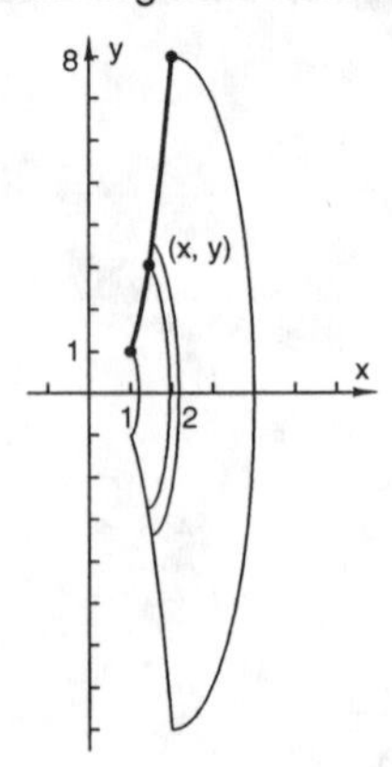

$dy = 3x^2\,dx$

$dL = \sqrt{dx^2 + dy^2} = \sqrt{1 + 9x^4}\,dx$

$dS = 2\pi y \cdot dL = 2\pi x^3(1 + 9x^4)^{1/2}\,dx$

$S = \int_1^2 2\pi x^3(1 + 9x^4)^{1/2}\,dx$

$= \frac{\pi}{18}\int_1^2 (1 + 9x^4)^{1/2}(36x\,dx)$

$= \frac{\pi}{18}\cdot\frac{2}{3}(1 + 9x^4)^{3/2}\Big|_1^2$

$= \frac{\pi}{27}(145^{3/2} - 10^{3/2}) = 199.4804\ldots$

11. Graph, $y = x^4/8 + x^{-2}/4$, from $x = 1$ to $x = 2$, rotated about the x-axis, showing back side of surface only

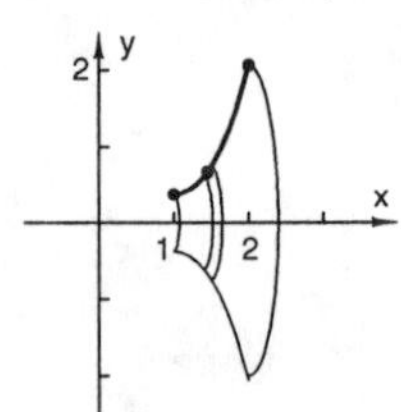

$dy = (x^3/2 - x^{-3}/2)\,dx = 0.5(x^3 - x^{-3})\,dx$

$dL = \sqrt{dx^2 + dy^2} = \sqrt{1 + 0.25(x^3 - x^{-3})^2}\,dx$

$= \sqrt{1 + 0.25x^6 - 0.5 + 0.25x^{-6}}\,dx$

$= \sqrt{0.25(x^3 + x^{-3})^2}\,dx = 0.5(x^3 + x^{-3})\,dx$

$dS = 2\pi y \cdot dL = 2\pi(x^4/8 + x^{-2}/4)[0.5(x^3 + x^{-3})]\,dx$

$= \frac{\pi}{8}(x^7 + 3x + 2x^{-5})\,dx$

$S = \frac{\pi}{8}\int_1^2 (x^7 + 3x + 2x^{-5})\,dx$

$= \frac{\pi}{8}(\frac{1}{8}x^8 + \frac{3}{2}x^2 - \frac{1}{2}x^{-4})\Big|_1^2$

$= \frac{\pi}{8}(32 + 6 - \frac{1}{32} - \frac{1}{8} - \frac{3}{2} + \frac{1}{2}) = 4\frac{155}{256}\pi = 14.4685\ldots$

12. Graph, $y = x^2$, from $x = 0$ to $x = 2$, about the y-axis.

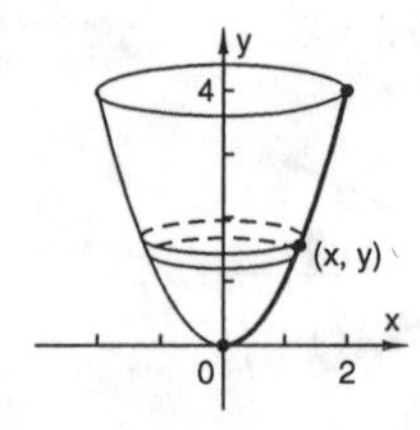

$dy = 2x\,dx$

$dL = \sqrt{dx^2 + dy^2} = \sqrt{1 + 4x^2}\,dx$

$dS = 2\pi x \cdot dL = 2\pi x\sqrt{1 + 4x^2}\,dx$

$S = 2\pi\int_0^2 x\sqrt{1 + 4x^2}\,dx$

$= \frac{\pi}{4}\int_0^2 (1 + 4x^2)^{1/2}(8x\,dx) = \frac{\pi}{6}(1 + 4x^2)^{3/2}\Big|_0^2$

$= \frac{\pi}{6}(17^{3/2} - 1) = 36.1769\ldots$

13. Graph, $y = \frac{1}{3}(x^2 + 2)^{3/2}$, from $x = 0$ to $x = 3$, rotated about the y-axis

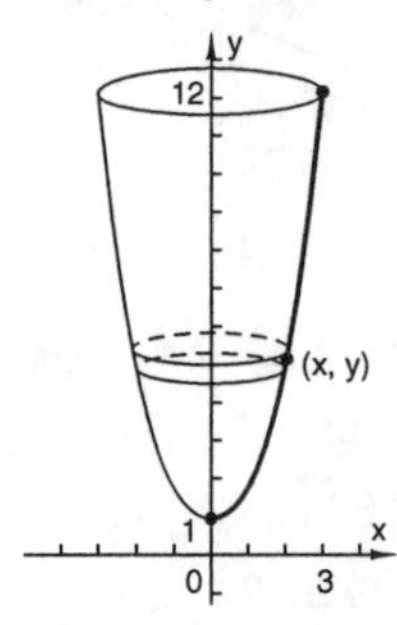

$dL = (1 + x^2)\,dx$ (from 8-7 Problem 20)

$dS = 2\pi x \cdot dL = 2\pi(x + x^3)\,dx$

$S = \int_0^3 2\pi(x + x^3)\,dx = \pi(x^2 + \frac{1}{2}x^4)\Big|_0^3$

$= 49.5\pi = 155.5088\ldots$

14. Graph, $y = 2x^{1/3}$, from $x = 1$ to $x = 8$, rotated about the y-axis, showing back half of surface only

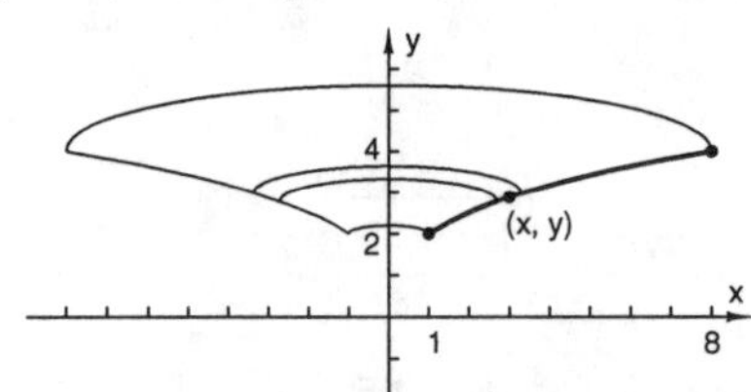

$dy = \frac{2}{3}x^{-2/3}\,dx$

$dL = \sqrt{dx^2 + dy^2} = \sqrt{1 + \frac{4}{9}x^{-4/3}}\,dx$

$dS = 2\pi x \cdot dL = 2\pi x\sqrt{1 + \frac{4}{9}x^{-4/3}}\,dx$

$S = 2\pi\int_1^8 x\sqrt{1 + \frac{4}{9}x^{-4/3}}\,dx$

$= 2\pi\int_1^8 x^{1/3}(x^{4/3} + \frac{4}{9})^{1/2}\,dx$

$= \frac{3}{2}\pi\int_1^8 (x^{4/3} + \frac{4}{9})^{1/2}\cdot\frac{4}{3}x^{1/3}\,dx$

$= \pi(x^{4/3} + \frac{4}{9})^{3/2}\Big|_1^8$

$= \frac{\pi}{27}(148^{3/2} - 13^{3/2}) = 204.0435\ldots$

15. Graph, $y = \frac{1}{3}x^3 + \frac{1}{4}x^{-1}$, from x = 1 to x = 3, rotated about the line y = –1, showing back half of surface only.

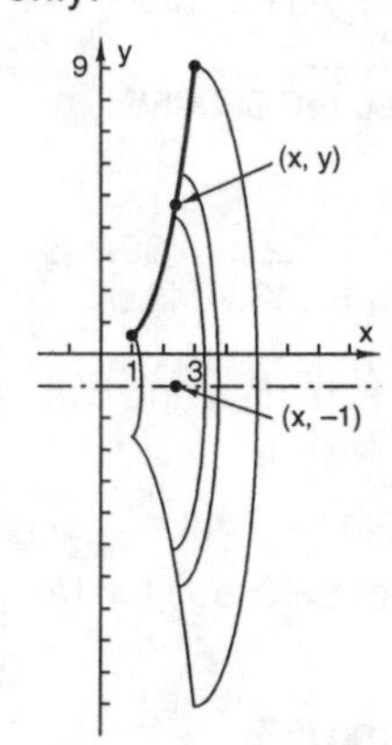

$dx = (x^2 - \frac{1}{4}x^{-2})\,dx$

$dL = \sqrt{dx^2 + dy^2} = \sqrt{1 + (x^2 - \frac{1}{4}x^{-2})^2}\,dx$

$= \sqrt{1 + x^4 - \frac{1}{2} + \frac{1}{16}x^{-4}}\,dx$

$= \sqrt{(x^2 + \frac{1}{4}x^{-2})^2}\,dx = (x^2 + \frac{1}{4}x^{-2})\,dx$

$dS = 2\pi(y + 1)\cdot dL$

$= 2\pi(\frac{1}{3}x^3 + \frac{1}{4}x^{-1} + 1)(x^2 + \frac{1}{4}x^{-2})\,dx$

$= 2\pi(\frac{1}{3}x^5 + x^2 + \frac{1}{3}x + \frac{1}{4}x^{-2} + \frac{1}{16}x^{-3})\,dx$

$S = 2\pi\int_1^3 (\frac{1}{3}x^5 + x^2 + \frac{1}{3}x + \frac{1}{4}x^{-2} + \frac{1}{16}x^{-3})\,dx$

$= 2\pi(\frac{1}{18}x^6 + \frac{1}{3}x^3 + \frac{1}{6}x^2 - \frac{1}{4}x^{-1} - \frac{1}{32}x^{-2})\,\Big|_1^3$

$= 101\frac{5}{18}\pi = 318.1735\ ...$

16. Graph, $y = \frac{1}{3}x^3 + \frac{1}{4}x^{-1}$, x = 1 to x = 3, about line x = 4

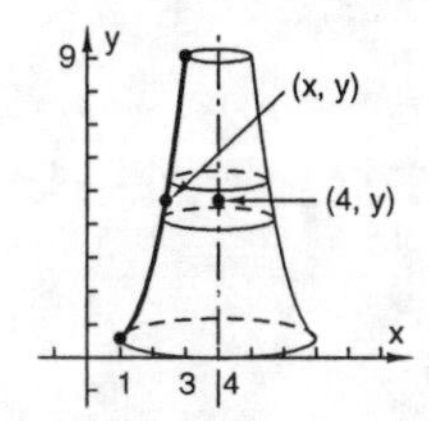

$dL = (x^2 + \frac{1}{4}x^{-2})\,dx$ from Problem 15, above

$dS = 2\pi(4 - x)\cdot dL = 2\pi(4 - x)(x^2 + \frac{1}{4}x^{-2})\,dx$

$= 2\pi(4x^2 - x^3 + x^{-2} - \frac{1}{4}x^{-1})\,dx$

$S = 2\pi\int_1^3 (4x^2 - x^3 + x^{-2} - \frac{1}{4}x^{-1})\,dx$

$= 2\pi(\frac{4}{3}x^3 - \frac{1}{4}x^4 - x^{-1} - \frac{1}{4}\ln|x|)\,\Big|_1^3$

$= 2\pi(15\frac{1}{3} - \frac{1}{4}\ln 3) = 94.6164\ ...$

17. Sphere Zone Problem

a. $x^2 + y^2 = 25 \Rightarrow y = \sqrt{25 - x^2}$

$dy = -x(25 - x^2)^{-1/2}\,dx$

$dL = \sqrt{dx^2 + dy^2} = \sqrt{1 + x^2(25 - x^2)^{-1}}\,dx$

$dS = 2\pi y\cdot dL$

$= 2\pi\sqrt{25 - x^2}\sqrt{1 + x^2(25 - x^2)^{-1}}\,dx$

$= 2\pi\sqrt{25 - x^2 + x^2}\,dx = 10\pi\,dx$

b. i. $S_{0,1} = \int_0^1 10\pi\,dx = 10\pi x\,\Big|_0^1 = 10\pi$

ii. $S_{1,2} = \int_1^2 10\pi\,dx = 10\pi x\,\Big|_1^2 = 10\pi$

iii. $S_{2,3} = \int_2^3 10\pi\,dx = 10\pi x\,\Big|_2^3 = 10\pi$

iv. $S_{3,4} = \int_3^4 10\pi\,dx = 10\pi x\,\Big|_3^4 = 10\pi$

v. $S_{4,5} = \int_4^5 10\pi\,dx = 10\pi x\,\Big|_4^5 = 10\pi$

c. The two features exactly balance each other. The area of a zone of a sphere is a function of the altitude of the zone only, and is independent of where the zone is located on the sphere.

18. Sphere Total Area Formula Problem

Suppose that the sphere is centered at the origin, as in Problem 17. The equation of a great circle in the xy-plane is $x^2 + y^2 = r^2$, from which

$y = \sqrt{r^2 - x^2} = (r^2 - x^2)^{1/2}$.

$dy = -x\,(r^2 - x^2)^{-1/2}\,dx$

$dL = \sqrt{dx^2 + dy^2} = \sqrt{1 + x^2(r^2 - x^2)^{-1}}\,dx$

$dS = 2\pi y\cdot dL$

$= 2\pi(r^2 - x^2)^{1/2}\sqrt{1 + x^2(r^2 - x^2)^{-1}}\,dx$

$= 2\pi\sqrt{r^2 - x^2 + x^2}\,dx = 2\pi r\,dx$ (if r > 0)

$S = \int_{-r}^{r} 2\pi r\,dx = 2\pi rx\,\Big|_{-r}^{r} = 4\pi r^2$, Q.E.D.

19. Spherical Volume and Surface Problem

Pick a sample point in the spherical shell at radius r from the center. Surface area at the sample point is $4\pi r^2$. Volume of shell is approximately (surface area)(thickness).

$dV = 4\pi r^2\cdot dr$

$V = \int_0^R 4\pi r^2\,dr = \frac{4}{3}\pi r^3\,\Big|_0^R = \frac{4}{3}\pi R^3$, Q.E.D.

20. Sphere Rate of Change of Volume Problem

$V = \frac{4}{3}\pi r^3 \Rightarrow \frac{dV}{dr} = 4\pi r^2 = S$, Q.E.D.

Or: $V = \int S\,dr \Rightarrow \frac{dV}{dr} = S$ by the definition of indefinite integral.

21. Paraboloid Surface Area Problem

$y = ax^2$, $dy = 2ax\,dx$

$dL = \sqrt{dx^2 + dy^2} = (1 + 4a^2x^2)^{1/2}\,dx$

$dS = 2\pi x\cdot dL = 2\pi x(1 + 4a^2x^2)^{1/2}\,dx$

$S = 2\pi\int_0^r x(1 + 4a^2x^2)^{1/2}\,dx$

$= \frac{\pi}{4a^2}\int_0^r (1 + 4a^2x^2)^{1/2}\,(8a^2x\,dx)$

$= \frac{\pi}{6a^2}(1 + 4a^2x^2)^{3/2}\,\Big|_0^r = \frac{\pi}{6a^2}[(1 + 4a^2r^2)^{3/2} - 1]$

22. Zone of a Paraboloid Problem

Let h be the altitude of the paraboloid from the vertex to the center of the base. Since h is the value of y when $x = r$, $h = ar^2$. Substituting into the formula for S from Problem 21, above, gives

$S = \frac{\pi}{6a^2}[(1 + 4ah)^{3/2} - 1]$.

Let a = 1 and evaluate S for various h. Find the zone areas by subtracting. Use TABLE feature.

h	S	Zone
0	$\frac{\pi}{6}(0)$	N.A.
1	$\frac{\pi}{6}(10.1803 \ldots)$	$\frac{\pi}{6}(10.1803 \ldots)$
2	$\frac{\pi}{6}(26)$	$\frac{\pi}{6}(15.8196 \ldots)$
3	$\frac{\pi}{6}(45.8721 \ldots)$	$\frac{\pi}{6}(19.8721 \ldots)$
4	$\frac{\pi}{6}(69.0927 \ldots)$	$\frac{\pi}{6}(23.2206 \ldots)$
5	$\frac{\pi}{6}(95.2340 \ldots)$	$\frac{\pi}{6}(26.1412 \ldots)$
6	$\frac{\pi}{6}(124)$	$\frac{\pi}{6}(28.7659 \ldots)$

The property is *not* true for paraboloids. The areas of zones of equal altitude are greater if the zone is farther away from the vertex.

23. Ellipsoid Problem

$x = 5 \cos t$, $dx = -5 \sin t\, dt$

$y = 3 \sin t$, $dy = 3 \cos t\, dt$

Graph, rotating about the x-axis

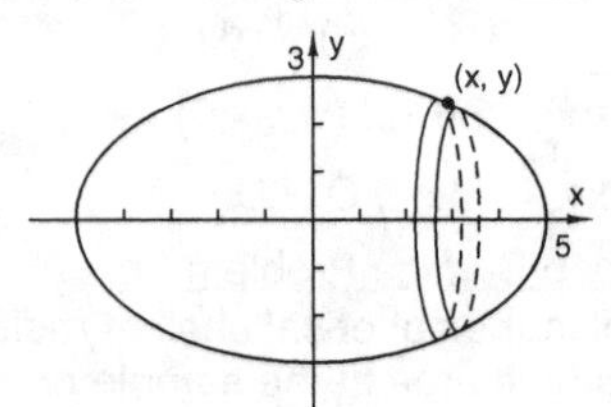

$dL = \sqrt{dx^2 + dy^2}$

$= \sqrt{(-5 \sin t)^2 + (3 \cos t)^2}\, dt$

$dS = 2\pi y \cdot dL$

$= 2\pi(3 \sin t)\sqrt{(-5 \sin t)^2 + (3 \cos t)^2}\, dt$

$S = \int_0^{\pi} 6\pi \sin t \sqrt{(-5 \sin t)^2 + (3 \cos t)^2}\, dt$

$\approx 165.7930 \ldots$.

From $(x/5)^2 + (y/3)^2 = 1$, $y = \pm 0.6\sqrt{25 - x^2}$.

Using the upper branch of the graph,

$dy = -0.6x(25 - x^2)^{-1/2}\, dx$.

$dL = \sqrt{dx^2 + dy^2}$

$= \sqrt{1 + 0.36x^2(25 - x^2)^{-1}}\, dx$

At $x = \pm 5$, dL involves division by zero, which is awkward, and makes the Cartesian equation inappropriate for finding the arc length of an ellipse. For the surface area, however, the offending denominator cancels out, giving

$dS = 0.24\pi\sqrt{25^2 - 16x^2}\, dx$,

which is defined at $x = \pm 5$.

24. Cooling Tower Problem

a. $x = 35 \sec t$, $dx = 35 \sec t \tan t\, dt$

$y = 100 + 80 \tan t$, $dy = 80 \sec^2 t\, dt$

$y = 0 \Leftrightarrow 100 + 80 \tan t = 0 \Rightarrow \tan t = -5/4$

$t = \tan^{-1}(-5/4) = -0.896055 \ldots$

Radius at base is $x = 35 \sec(-0.896055 \ldots)$

$= 56.0273 \ldots \approx 56.0$ ft.

b. At top, $t = 0.5$.

Radius: $x = 35 \sec 0.5 = 39.8822 \ldots \approx 39.9$ ft

Height: $y = 100 + 80 \tan 0.5 = 143.7041 \ldots$

≈ 143.7 ft

c. From the information given in parts a and b, it can be assumed that $-\pi/2 < t < \pi/2$.

...Minimize x: $\frac{dx}{dt} = 35 \sec t \tan t = 0$ at $t = 0$

(or, since cos t has a max at t = 0, $\sec t = 1/\cos t$ has a minimum there).

Minimum radius = 35 ft

Height = $y = 100 + \tan 0 = 100$ ft

d. $dL = \sqrt{dx^2 + dy^2}$

$= \sqrt{35^2 \sec^2 t \cdot \tan^2 t + 80^2 \sec^4 t}\, dt$

$dS = 2\pi x \cdot dL$

$= 2\pi(35 \sec t)\sqrt{35^2 \sec^2 t \cdot \tan^2 t + 80^2 \sec^4 t}\, dt$

$S = \int_{-0.89\ldots}^{0.5} dS \approx 37{,}756.5934 \ldots \approx 37{,}757$ ft^2

e. Volume $\approx S \cdot \frac{4}{12} = 12{,}585.5311 \ldots$ ft^3

$= 466.1307 \ldots \approx 466.1$ yd^3

25. Lateral Area of a Cone Problem

From the figure in the text, a circle of radius L has area πL^2 and circumference $2\pi L$. The circumference of the cone's base is $2\pi R$, which is equal to the arc length of the sector of the circle of radius L. Thus, the sector is $(2\pi R)/(2\pi L) = R/L$ of the circle, and has surface area $S = \pi L^2(R/L) = \pi RL$, Q.E.D.

26. Lateral Area of a Frustum Problem

$S = \pi RL - \pi rl$

The objective is to get the lateral area in terms of the slant height of the frustum, $L - l$.

$S = \pi R(L - \frac{r}{R} l)$

$= \pi R(L - \frac{l}{L} l)$

$= \frac{\pi R}{L}(L^2 - l^2)$

$= \frac{\pi R}{L}(L + l)(L - l)$

$= \pi(R + R \cdot \frac{l}{L})(L - l)$

$= \pi(R + R \cdot \frac{r}{R})(L - l)$

$= \pi(R + r)(L - l)$

$= 2\pi(\frac{R + r}{2})(L - l)$, Q.E.D.

Q1. $15x^2 - 14x + 4$ Q2. $12(4x - 9)^2$
Q3. $3 \sin^2 x \cos x$ Q4. $3 \sec 3x \tan 3x$
Q5. $-e^{-x}$ Q6. $-1/x^2$
Q7. $\ln|x| + C$ Q8. $\frac{1}{2}x^2 + C$
Q9. $3x + C$ Q10. $x + C$

1. a. $r = 10 \sin\theta \Rightarrow dA = 50 \sin^2\theta\, d\theta$
   $A = \int_0^{2\pi} 50 \sin^2\theta\, d\theta \approx 157.0796...$ (exactly 50π).
   b. The area of the circle is $\pi \cdot 5^2 = 25\pi$.
   The calculated area is twice this because the circle is traced out twice as θ increases from 0 to 2π. Although r is negative for $\pi < \theta < 2\pi$, dA is positive because r is squared.
2. a. $r = 10 \sin\theta \Rightarrow dr = 10 \cos\theta\, d\theta$
   $dL = \sqrt{dr^2 + (r\, d\theta)^2}$
   $= \sqrt{100 \cos^2\theta + 100 \sin^2\theta}\; d\theta = 10\, d\theta$
   $L = \int_0^{2\pi} 10\, d\theta = 10\theta \Big|_0^{2\pi} = 20\pi$.
   The circumference is $2\pi \cdot 5 = 10\pi$. The calculated length is twice this value because the circle is traced out twice as θ increases from 0 to 2π. The calculus of this section always gives the *dynamic* answer as the distance traveled by a point on the curve as θ increases from one value to another. This path length does not necessarily equal the length of the curve.
3. a. $r = 4 + 3 \sin\theta$
   Calculator graph confirms that the text figure is traced out once as θ increases from 0 to 2π.
   b. $dA = \frac{1}{2}(4 + 3 \sin\theta)^2\, d\theta$
   $A = \int_0^{2\pi} dA \approx 64.4026...$ (exactly 20.5π)
   c. $dr = 3 \cos\theta\, d\theta$
   $dL = \sqrt{dr^2 + (r\, d\theta)^2}$
   $= \sqrt{(3 \cos\theta)^2 + (4 + 3 \sin\theta)^2}\; d\theta$
   $L = \int_0^{2\pi} dL \approx 28.8141...$
4. a. $r = 5 - 3 \cos\theta$
   Calculator graph confirms that the text figure is traced out once as θ increases from 0 to 2π.
   b. $dA = \frac{1}{2}(5 - 3 \cos\theta)^2\, d\theta$
   $A = \int_0^{2\pi} dA \approx 92.6769...$ (exactly 29.5π)
   c. $dr = 3 \sin\theta\, d\theta$
   $dL = \sqrt{dr^2 + (r\, d\theta)^2}$
   $= \sqrt{(3 \sin\theta)^2 + (5 - 3 \cos\theta)^2}\; d\theta$
   $L = \int_0^{2\pi} dL \approx 34.3136...$
5. a. $r = 7 + 3 \cos 2\theta$
   Calculator graph confirms that the text figure is traced out once as θ increases from 0 to 2π.
   b. $dA = \frac{1}{2}(7 + 3 \cos 2\theta)^2\, d\theta$
   $A = \int_0^{2\pi} dA \approx 168.0752...$ (exactly 53.5π)
   c. $dr = -6 \sin 2\theta\, d\theta$
   $dL = \sqrt{dr^2 + (r\, d\theta)^2}$
   $= \sqrt{(-6 \sin 2\theta)^2 + (7 + 3\cos 2\theta)^2}\; d\theta$
   $L = \int_0^{2\pi} dL \approx 51.4511...$.
6. a. $r = 8 \cos 2\theta$
   Calculator graph confirms that the text figure is traced out once as θ increases from 0 to 2π.
   b. $dA = \frac{1}{2}(8 \cos 2\theta)^2\, d\theta$
   $A = \int_0^{2\pi} dA \approx 100.5309...$ (exactly 32π).
   c. $dr = -16 \sin\theta\, d\theta$
   $dL = \sqrt{dr^2 + (r\, d\theta)^2}$
   $= \sqrt{(-16 \sin 2\theta)^2 + (8 \cos 2\theta)^2}\; d\theta$
   $L = \int_0^{2\pi} dL \approx 77.5075...$
7. a. $5 = 5 + 5 \cos\theta$
   Calculator graph confirms that the text figure is traced out once as θ increases from 0 to 2π.
   b. $dA = \frac{1}{2}(5 + 5 \cos\theta)^2\, d\theta$
   $A = \int_0^{2\pi} dA \approx 117.8097...$ (exactly 37.5π)
   c. $dr = -5 \sin\theta\, d\theta$
   $dL = \sqrt{dr^2 + (r\, d\theta)^2}$
   $= \sqrt{(-5 \sin\theta)^2 + (5 + 5 \cos\theta)^2}\; d\theta$
   $L = \int_0^{2\pi} dL = 40$ (exactly)
8. a. $r = \dfrac{10}{3 - 2 \cos\theta}$
   Calculator graph confirms that the text figure is traced out once as θ increases from 0 to 2π.
   b. $dA = \frac{1}{2}\left(\dfrac{10}{3 - 2 \cos\theta}\right)^2$
   $A = \int_0^{2\pi} dA \approx 84.2977...$ (exactly $12\sqrt{5}\,\pi$)
   c. $dr = \dfrac{-20 \sin\theta}{(3 - 2 \cos\theta)^2}\, d\theta$
   $dL = \sqrt{dr^2 + (r\, d\theta)^2}$
   $= \sqrt{\left(\dfrac{-20\sin\theta}{(3-2\cos\theta)^2}\right)^2 + \left(\dfrac{10}{3-2\cos\theta}\right)^2}\; d\theta$
   $L = \int_0^{2\pi} dL \approx 33.0744...$
9. a. Graph, $r = \sin 3\theta$, making one complete cycle as θ increases from 0 to π

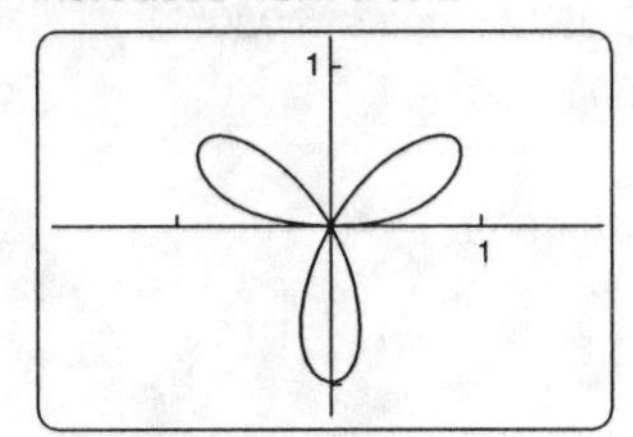

   b. $dA = \frac{1}{2}(\sin 3\theta)^2\, d\theta$
   $A = \int_0^{\pi} dA \approx 0.7853...$ (exactly 0.25π)

c. $dr = 3\cos 3\theta \, d\theta$

$dL = \sqrt{dr^2 + (r\,d\theta)^2}$

$= \sqrt{(3\cos 3\theta)^2 + (\sin 3\theta)^2}\, d\theta$

$L = \int_0^{\pi} dL \approx 6.6824 \ldots$

10. a. Graph, $r = 4\sec\theta - 4\cos\theta$, between lines $\theta = -1$ and $\theta = 1$

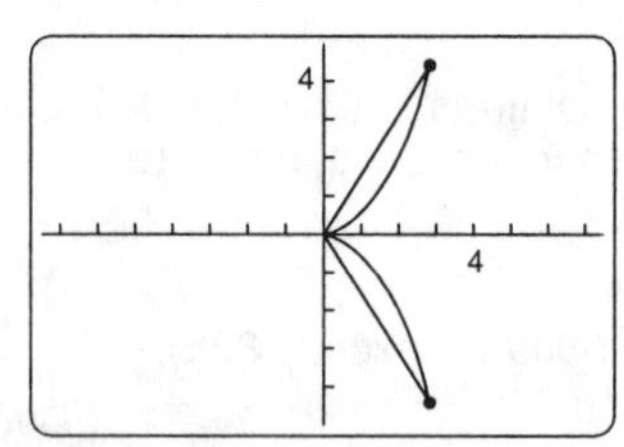

b. $dA = \frac{1}{2}(4\sec\theta - 4\cos\theta)^2\, d\theta$

$A = \int_{-1}^{1} dA \approx 4.5557 \ldots$

(exactly $16\tan 1 - 24 + 4\sin 2$)

c. $dr = 4(\sec\theta\tan\theta + \sin\theta)\, d\theta$

$dL = \sqrt{dr^2 + (r\,d\theta)^2}$

$= 4\sqrt{(\sec\theta\tan\theta + \sin\theta)^2 + (\sec\theta - \cos\theta)^2}\, d\theta$

$L = \int_{-1}^{1} dL \approx 10.9534 \ldots$

11. $r = \sqrt{49\cos 2\theta}$

$r = 0 \Leftrightarrow 2\theta = \cos^{-1} 0 = \pm\pi/2 + 2\pi n$ (n an integer)

$\theta = \pm\pi/4 + \pi n$

The right-hand loop corresponds to nonnegative values of the integrand, $-\pi/4 \le \theta \le \pi/4$.

$dA = \frac{1}{2}(49\cos\theta)\, d\theta$

$A = \int_{-\pi/4}^{\pi/4} \frac{1}{2}(49\cos\theta)\, d\theta = 24.5\sin\theta \Big|_{-\pi/4}^{\pi/4}$

$= 24.5\sqrt{2} = 34.6482 \ldots$

Area of both loops is $49\sqrt{2} = 69.2964 \ldots$.

12. Graph, $r = \csc\theta + 4$, showing closed loop from $\theta \approx 3.4$ to $\theta \approx 6$.

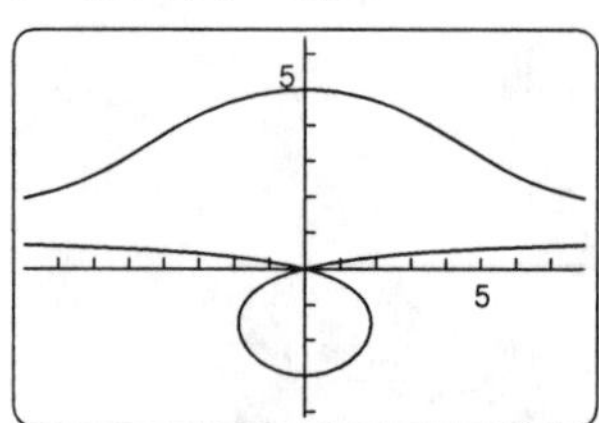

Graph passes through the pole where $r = 0$.

$\csc\theta + 4 = 0 \Leftrightarrow \theta = \csc^{-1}(-4) = \sin^{-1}(-0.25)$

$= -0.2526 \ldots + 2\pi n$ or $(\pi - (-0.2526 \ldots)) + 2\pi n$

Desired range is $3.3942 \ldots \le \theta \le 6.0305 \ldots$.

$dA = \frac{1}{2}(\csc\theta + 4)^2\, d\theta$

$A = \int_{3.3942\ldots}^{6.0305\ldots} dA \approx 8.4553 \ldots$

13. $r_1 = 4 + 4\cos\theta$ and $r_2 = 10\cos\theta$

Graphs intersect where

$4 + 4\cos\theta = 10\cos\theta$

$\theta = \cos^{-1}(2/3) = \pm 0.8410 \ldots + 2\pi n$.

(The graphs also touch at the pole, but not for the same value of θ. For the cardioid, $\theta = \pi + 2\pi n$. For the circle, $\theta = \pi/2 + 2\pi n$.)

Region outside the cardioid and inside the circle is generated as θ goes from $-0.841 \ldots$ to $0.841 \ldots$.

$dA = \frac{1}{2}(r_2^2 - r_1^2)\, d\theta$

$= \frac{1}{2}[(10\cos\theta)^2 - (4 + 4\cos\theta)^2]\, d\theta$

$A = \int_{-0.841\ldots}^{0.841\ldots} dA \approx 18.8863 \ldots$

(exactly $26\cos^{-1}(2/3) - (4/3)\sqrt{5}$)

14. Graphs, $r_1 = 5$ and $r_2 = 5 - 5\cos\theta$, intersection at $\theta = -\pi/2$ and $\pi/2$

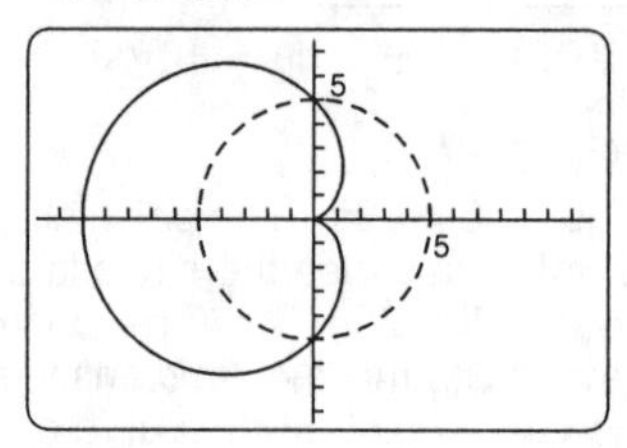

$dA = \frac{1}{2}(r_1^2 - r_2^2)\, d\theta$

$= \frac{1}{2}[5^2 - (5 - 5\cos\theta)^2]\, d\theta$

Integrate from $-\pi/2$ to $\pi/2$, since in Quadrants II and III the cardioid lies outside the circle.

$A = \int_{-\pi/2}^{\pi/2} dA \approx 30.3650 \ldots$ (exactly $50 - 6.25\pi$)

15. a. $r = 0.5\theta$

The graph starts at $\theta = 0$ and makes three revolutions, so θ increases from 0 to 6π.

$dr = 0.5\, d\theta$

$dL = \sqrt{dr^2 + (r\,d\theta)^2} = \sqrt{0.5^2 + (0.5\theta)^2}\, d\theta$

$L = \int_0^{6\pi} dL \approx 89.8589 \ldots$

b. $dA = \frac{1}{2}(0.5\theta)^2\, d\theta = \frac{1}{8}\theta^2\, d\theta$

Area swept out for third revolution in Quadrant I is

$A_3 = \int_{4\pi}^{4.5\pi} \frac{1}{8}\theta^2\, d\theta = \frac{1}{24}\theta^3\Big|_{4\pi}^{4.5\pi} = \frac{217}{192}\pi^3$.

Area swept out for second revolution in Quadrant I is

$A_2 = \int_{2\pi}^{2.5\pi} \frac{1}{8}\theta^2\, d\theta = \frac{1}{24}\theta^3\Big|_{2\pi}^{2.5\pi} = \frac{61}{192}\pi^3$.

Area of region between second and third revolution in Quadrant I is $A_3 - A_2 = \frac{13}{16}\pi^3 = 25.1925 \ldots$.

16. Graph, $r = 4 + 6\cos\theta$, showing loop from $\theta \approx 2.3$ to $\theta \approx 4.0$

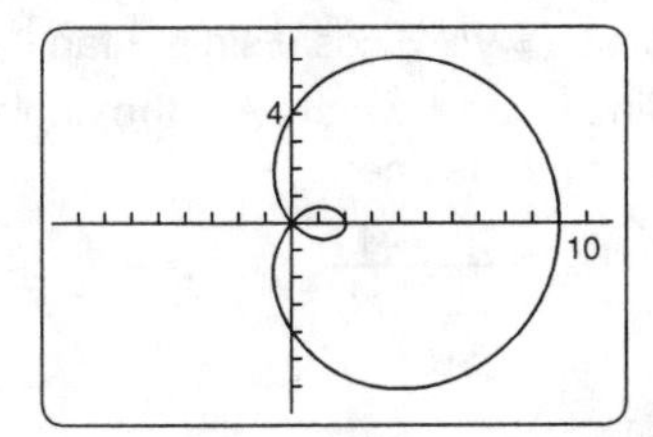

$r = 4 + 6\cos\theta = 0 \Leftrightarrow \cos\theta = -2/3$

$\theta = \cos^{-1}(-2/3) = \pm 2{,}3005 \ldots + 2\pi n$

$dA = \frac{1}{2}(4 + 6\cos\theta)^2\, d\theta$

The outer loop is swept out as θ increases from $-2.3005 \ldots$ to 2.3005.

$A_1 = \int_{-2.3005\ldots}^{2.3005\ldots} dA \approx 105.0506 \ldots$

The inner loop is generated as θ increases from $2.3005 \ldots$ to $3.9826 \ldots$

$A_2 = \int_{2.3005\ldots}^{3.926\ldots} dA \approx 1.7635 \ldots$

Area of the region between the loops is

$A_1 - A_2 \approx 103.2871 \ldots$

17. Column Scroll Problem

a. Graph, $r = 5\theta^{-1/2}$, from $\theta = 0$ to $\theta = 6\pi$

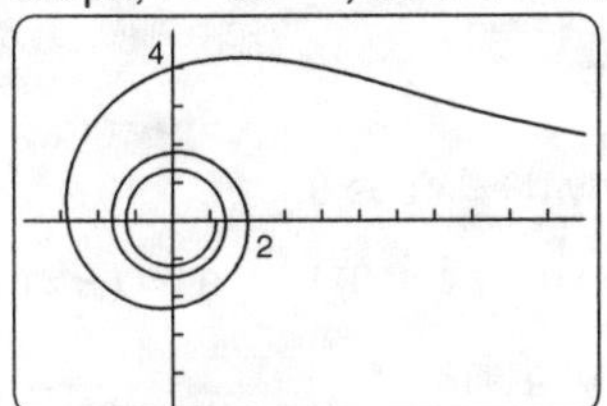

$dr = -2.5\theta^{-1.5}\, d\theta$

$dL = \sqrt{dr^2 + (r\, d\theta)^2} = \sqrt{6.25\theta^{-3} + 25\theta^{-1}}\, d\theta$

$\int_{\pi/2}^{6\pi} dL \approx 31.0872 \ldots$

b. Graph, showing sectors of central angles 1, 2, and 3 radians

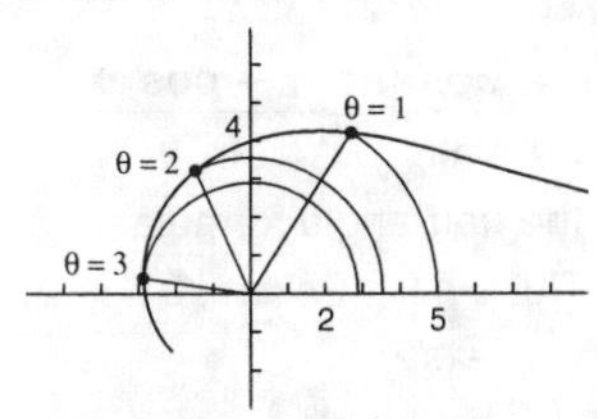

Area of sector is $A(\theta) = \frac{1}{2}r^2\theta$.

$A(1) = \frac{1}{2}(5)^2(1) = 12.5$

$A(2) = \frac{1}{2}(3.5355 \ldots)^2(2) = 12.5$

$A(3) = \frac{1}{2}(2.8867 \ldots)^2(3) = 12.5$

In general, $A(\theta) = \frac{1}{2}(5\theta^{-1/2})^2(\theta) = 12.5$, which is independent of the value of θ.

18. Line Problem

Graph, $r = \sec\theta$, showing segment from $\theta = 0$ to 1.5

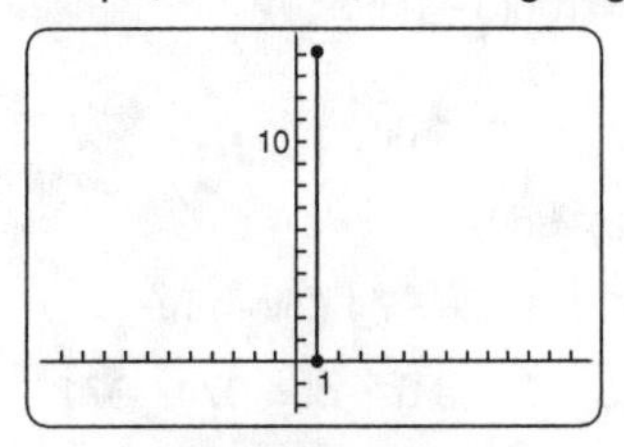

The point with polar coordinates (r, θ) has xy-coordinates $x = r\cos\theta$, $y = r\sin\theta$. The graph given by $r = \sec\theta$ can be written

$x = r\cos\theta = \sec\theta\cos\theta = 1$

$y = r\sin\theta = \sec\theta\sin\theta = \tan\theta$ (i.e. $-\infty < y < \infty$). Thus this graph is the line $x = 1$.

By calculus, the segment from $\theta = 0$ to $\theta = 1.5$ has length as follows:

$dr = \sec\theta\tan\theta\, d\theta$

$dL = \sqrt{dr^2 + (r\, d\theta)^2}$

$= \sqrt{(\sec\theta\tan\theta)^2 + \sec^2\theta}\, d\theta$

$= \sec\theta\sqrt{\tan^2\theta + 1}\, d\theta = \sec^2\theta\, d\theta$

$L = \int_0^{1.5} \sec^2\theta\, d\theta = \tan\theta \Big|_0^{1.5}$

$= \tan 1.5 - 0 = 14.1014 \ldots$

As shown above, $y = \tan\theta$.

At $\theta = 1.5$, $y = \tan 1.5$, confirming the calculus.

19. LP Record Project

A typical record has grooves of inner radius 6.6 cm and outer radius 14.6 cm, and takes about 24 minutes to play. There are thus (33.333 ...)(24) or about 800 grooves in a space of (14.6 – 6.6) or 8.0 cm. Thus, the grooves decrease in radius by about 8.0/800 = 0.01 cm per revolution. A simple equation of the spiral is

$r = \frac{0.01}{2\pi}\theta = \frac{0.005}{\pi}\theta$,

which assumes that the grooves start at the center and have a pitch of 0.01 cm. The innermost actual groove is at $\theta = 6.6\pi/0.005 = 1320\pi$, and the outermost groove is at $\theta = 14.6\pi/0.005 = 2920\pi$.

$dr = -(0.005/\pi)\, d\theta$

$dL = \sqrt{dr^2 + (r\, d\theta)^2}$

$= \sqrt{(0.005/\pi)^2 + (0.005/\pi)\theta^2}\, d\theta$

$= \frac{0.005}{\pi}\sqrt{1 + \theta^2}\, d\theta$

$L = \int_{1320\pi}^{2920\pi} dL \approx 53{,}281.4120 \ldots$ cm

$= 16{,}960.0002 \ldots \pi$ cm

Rough check: Average radius = 10.6 cm.

L should equal approximately the sum of 800 circles of radius 10.6 cm.

$L \approx 800(2\pi \cdot 10.6) = 16{,}960\pi$ cm, which is very close to the calculated $16{,}960.0002 \ldots \pi$ cm.

(The integral can be evaluated algebraically by the tangent trigonometry substitution from Ch. 9. The result, $16{,}960.00021 \ldots \pi$, is remarkably close both to the numerical answer and to the sum of the lengths of the 800 circles of average radius 10.6 cm.)

20. Kepler's Law Project

a. $r = \dfrac{100}{3 - 2\cos\theta} = 100(3 - 2\cos\theta)^{-1}$

$dA = \frac{1}{2}(100(3 - 2\cos\theta)^{-1})^2\,d\theta$

$= 5000(3 - 2\cos\theta)^{-2}\,d\theta$

$A = \int_0^{0.2} dA \approx 974.3071 \ldots \approx 974$ (kilo-mi)^2

b. Solving $\int_{0.8}^{\theta} 5000(3 - 2\cos t)^{-2}\,dt = 974.3071 \ldots$ gives $\theta \approx 1.88976 \ldots$.

c. $P = ka^{1.5}$

$(27.3)(24) = k(240)^{1.5}$

$k = 0.17622 \ldots$

d. The major axis of the spaceship's orbit is 120 thousand miles, so $a = 60$.

$P = k \cdot 60^{1.5} = 81.9$ hours (precise answer)

e. The total area of the ellipse is

$A = \int_0^{2\pi} 5000(3 - 2\cos\theta)^{-2}\,d\theta$

$= 8429.7776 \ldots$ (kilo-mi)^2.

Fraction of area from $\theta = 0$ to $\theta = 0.2$ is $(974.3071 \ldots)/(8429.7776 \ldots) = 0.1155 \ldots$

This fraction is the same as the fraction of the period. Thus, the time is $0.1155 \ldots(81.9)$ $= 9.4659 \ldots$ hours to go from $\theta = 0$ to $\theta = 0.2$, and the same for θ to go from 0.8 to 1.88976 ... .

f. $dr = -100(3 - 2\cos\theta)^{-2} \cdot (2\sin\theta)\,d\theta$

$= -200\sin\theta\,(3 - 2\cos\theta)^{-2}\,d\theta$

$dL = \sqrt{dr^2 + (r\,d\theta)^2}$

$= [(-200\sin\theta\,(3 - 2\cos\theta)^{-2})^2 + (100(3 - 2\cos\theta)^{-1})^2]^{1/2}\,d\theta$

From $\theta = 0$ to $\theta = 0.2$,

$L = \int_0^{0.2} dL \approx 20.2228 \ldots \approx 20.2$ kilo-mi.

From $\theta = 0.8$ to $\theta = 1.88976 \ldots$,

$L = \int_{0.8}^{1.88 \ldots} dL \approx 56.7896 \ldots \approx 56.8$ kilo-mi.

g. Average speed from $\theta = 0$ to $\theta = 0.2$ is

$\dfrac{20.2228 \ldots}{9.4659 \ldots} = 2.1363 \ldots$, or about 2136 mph.

Average speed from $\theta = 0.8$ to $\theta = 1.88976 \ldots$ is

$\dfrac{56.7896 \ldots}{9.4659 \ldots} = 5.9993 \ldots$, or about 5999 mph.

h. When the spaceship is farthest from Earth, its radial velocity (toward the Earth) is zero. As it proceeds in its orbit, it can be thought of as falling toward the Earth, thus picking up speed. The reverse is true on the other side of the Earth, where it is moving away and is thus being slowed by gravity.

21. The Derivative dy/dx for Polar Coordinates Problem

a. Count 5 spaces to the right and about 7.5 spaces down from the given point. Slope ≈ -1.5.

b. $r = \theta$

$x = \theta\cos\theta \Rightarrow dx = d\theta \cdot \cos\theta - \theta\sin\theta\,d\theta$

$y = \theta\sin\theta \Rightarrow dy = d\theta \cdot \sin\theta + \theta\cos\theta\,d\theta$

$\dfrac{dy}{dx} = \dfrac{dy/d\theta}{dx/d\theta} = \dfrac{\sin\theta + \theta\cos\theta}{\cos\theta - \theta\sin\theta}$

At $\theta = 7$, $dy/dx = -1.54338 \ldots$, thus confirming the answer found graphically.

22. The Angle Between the Radius and the Tangent Line (Project)

a. $x = r\cos\theta$, $y = r\sin\theta \Rightarrow y/x = \cos\theta/\sin\theta = \tan\theta$

b. The slope of any line is $\tan\phi$, where ϕ is the angle between the x-axis and the line:

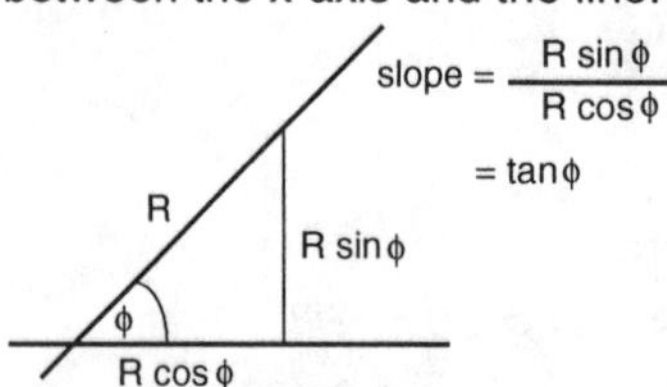

In particular, since the tangent line has slope $\dfrac{dy}{dx} = \dfrac{dy/d\theta}{dx/d\theta}$ (by the chain rule), $\tan\phi = \dfrac{dy/d\theta}{dx/d\theta}$.

c. $\tan\psi = \tan(\phi - \theta)$

$= \dfrac{\tan\phi - \tan\theta}{1 + \tan\phi\tan\theta}$

$= \dfrac{\dfrac{dy/d\theta}{dx/d\theta} - \dfrac{y}{x}}{1 + \dfrac{y}{x} \cdot \dfrac{dy/d\theta}{dx/d\theta}} \cdot \left(\dfrac{x\,dx/d\theta}{x\,dx/d\theta}\right)$

$= \dfrac{x\dfrac{dy}{d\theta} - y\dfrac{dx}{d\theta}}{x\dfrac{dx}{d\theta} + y\dfrac{dy}{d\theta}}$

d. $dx/d\theta = -r\sin\theta$; $dy/d\theta = r\cos\theta$

$x\dfrac{dy}{d\theta} - y\dfrac{dx}{d\theta} = r\cos\theta \cdot (r\cos\theta) - r\sin\theta \cdot (-r\sin\theta)$

$= r^2\cos^2\theta + r^2\sin^2\theta = r^2$

e. $r^2 = x^2 + y^2 \Rightarrow 2r\dfrac{dr}{d\theta} = 2x\dfrac{dx}{d\theta} + 2y\dfrac{dy}{d\theta}$

$\Rightarrow r\dfrac{dr}{d\theta} = x\dfrac{dx}{d\theta} + y\dfrac{dy}{d\theta}$.

Substitute these expressions in parts d and e into the top and bottom of the expression in part c to show the property.

f. $\tan\psi = \dfrac{r}{dr/d\theta} = \dfrac{a - a\cos\theta}{a\sin\theta} = \dfrac{1 - \cos\theta}{\sin\theta}$

$= \tan\theta/2$, using the half-angle formula.

Then $\psi = \theta/2 + n\pi$. But $0 \le \theta \le 2\pi$, and $0 \le \psi \le \pi$, which implies $n = 0$. $\psi = \theta/2$.

g. $\tan\psi = \dfrac{r}{dr/d\theta} \Rightarrow \dfrac{dr}{d\theta} = \text{const} \cdot r$

$\Rightarrow r = Ce^{k\theta}$, $\therefore k = \cot\psi$

Review Problems

R0. Journal entries will vary.

R1.a. Graphs,

$f(x) = x^3 - 9x^2 + 30x - 10$
$g(x) = x^3 - 9x^2 + 27x - 10$
$h(x) = x^3 - 9x^2 + 24x - 10$

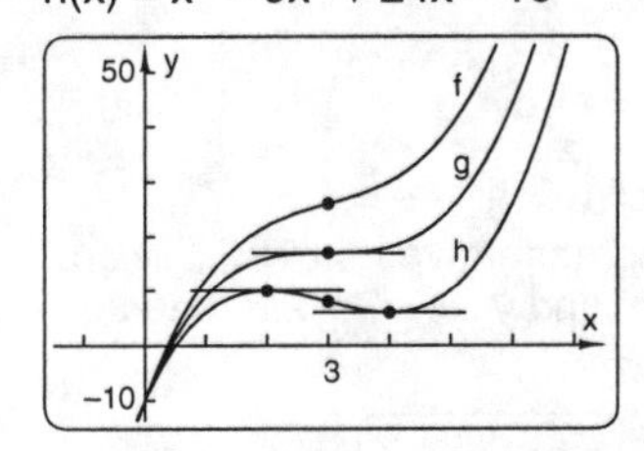

b. $f'(x) = 3x^2 - 18x + 30$; $f''(x) = 6x - 18$
$g'(x) = 3x^2 - 18x + 27$; $g''(x) = 6x - 18$
$h'(x) = 3x^2 - 18x + 24$; $h''(x) = 6x - 18$

c. $h'(x) = 3(x - 2)(x - 4) = 0$ at $x = 2$ and 4
$h''(2) = -6 < 0$, so h has a local max at $x = 2$.
$h''(4) = 6 > 0$, so h has a local min at $x = 4$.

d. $g'(x) = 3(x - 3)^2 = 0$ only at $x = 3$
$g'(x) > 0$ on both sides of $x = 3$, so this is neither a max. nor a min. point.

e. From the graphs, each point of inflection appears at $x = 3$. Since each second derivative equals $6x - 18$, each one equals zero when $x = 3$.

R2.a. Number-line graphs

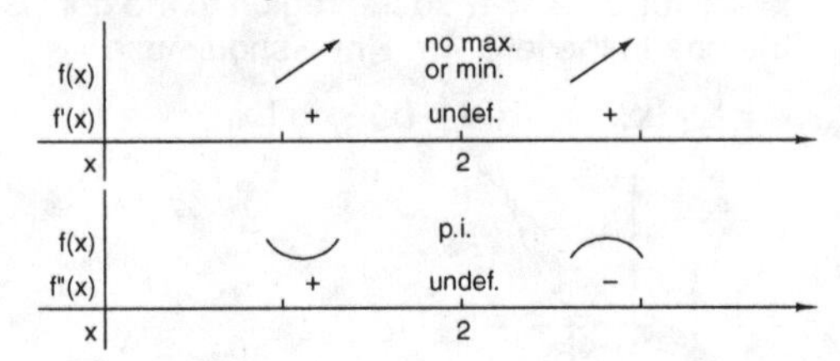

b. Graph, example

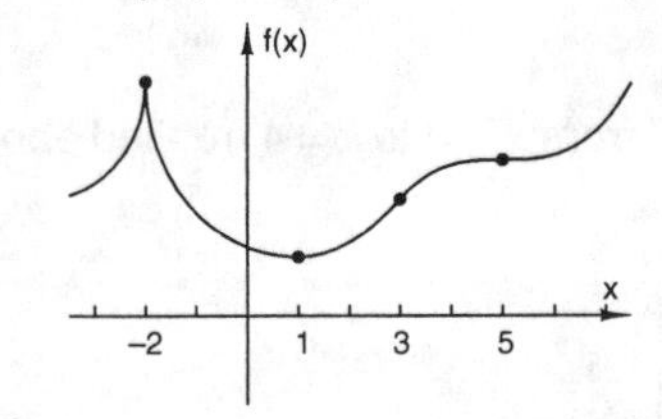

c. $f(x) = x^{2/3} - x$

i. $f'(x) = \frac{2}{3}x^{-1/3} - 1$, $f''(x) = \frac{-2}{9}x^{-4/3}$

ii. Zooming in shows that there is a local minimum cusp at (0, 0) and a local maximum with zero derivative at $x \approx 0.3$. Graph

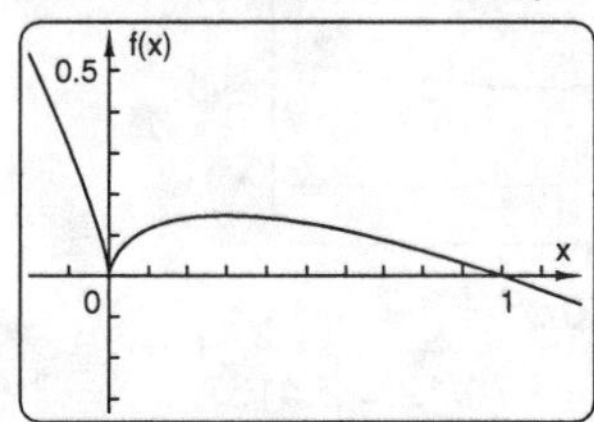

Algebraically,
$f'(x) = 0$ at $x = (2/3)^3 = 8/27$, and
$f'(x)$ is undefined at $x = 0$, thus locating precisely the min. and max. found by graph.
Since there are no other critical values of x, there are no other max. or min. points.

iii. $f''(x)$ is undefined at $x = 0$, and $f''(x) < 0$ everywhere else; f'' never changes sign, so there are no inflection points.

iv. $f(0) = 0$, $f(8/27) = 4/27$, $f(5) = -2.0759 \ldots$.
Global max. at (8/27,4/27)
Global min. at (5,−2.0759...)

d. Graph, $f(x) = x^2 e^{-x}$, local min. at $x = 0$, local max at $x \approx 2$, and points of inflection at $x \approx 3.4$ and at $x \approx 0.6$.

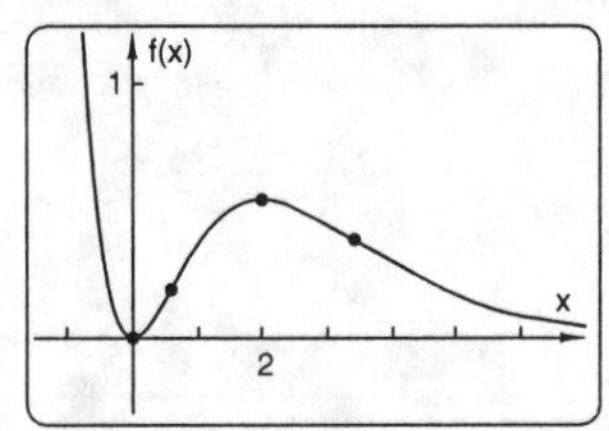

$f'(x) = 2xe^{-x} - x^2e^{-x} = x(2 - x)e^{-x}$
$f''(x) = 2e^{-x} - 4xe^{-x} + x^2e^{-x} = (2 - 4x + x^2)e^{-x}$
$f'(x) = 0$ at $x = 0, 2$
Min. at (0, 0). max. at (2, 0.5413 ...).
$f''(x) = 0$ at $x = 2 + \sqrt{2} = 3.4142 \ldots$, and at $x = 2 - \sqrt{2} = 0.5857 \ldots$
$f''(x)$ changes sign at each of these x-values, which implies points of inflection at (0.5857 ..., 0.1910 ...), (3.4142 ..., 0.3835 ...).

R3. a. Storage Battery Problem

Let x = width of a cell; y = length of the cell.

$xy = 10 \Rightarrow y = 10x^{-1}$; $0 < x$

Minimize $L(x) = 12x + 7y = 12x + 70x^{-1}$.

Graph, showing minimum L(x) at $x \approx 2.4$.

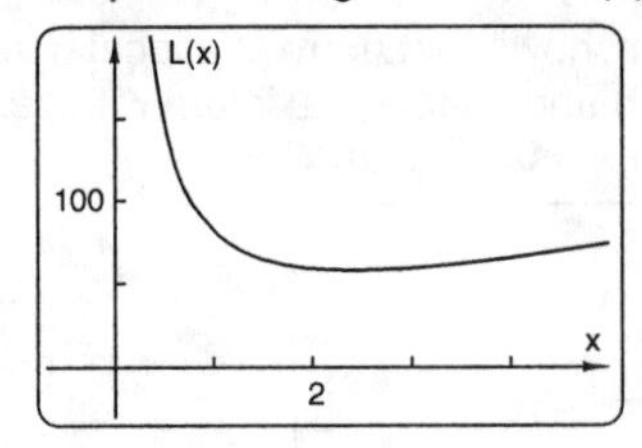

$L'(x) = 12 - 70x^{-2}$

$L'(x) = 0$ at $x = \sqrt{70/12} = 2.4152...$

At $x = \sqrt{70/12}$, $y = 10\sqrt{12/70} = 4.1403 ...$

Overall length of battery is 6(2.4152...)

= 14.4913 ... .

Optimal battery is about 14.5" by 4.1", which is longer and narrower than the typical battery, 9" by 6.7". Thus, minimal wall length does *not* seem to be a major consideration in battery design.

b. Cylinder In Cubic Paraboloid Problem

Graph, $y = 8 - x^3$, from x = 0 to x = 2, with rectangle touching sample point (x, y) on the graph, rotated about the y-axis, generating cubic paraboloid and inscribed cylinder.

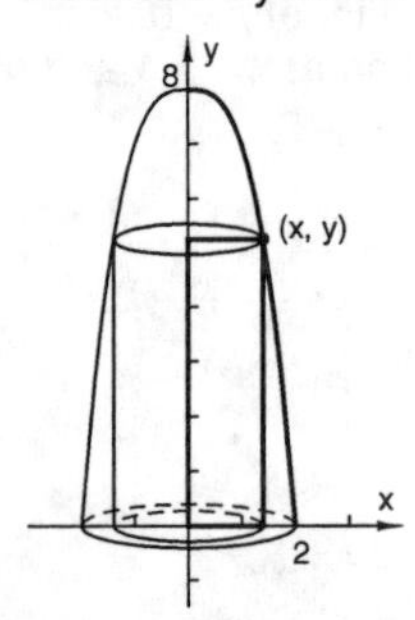

Domain of x is $0 \le x \le 2$.

Maximize $V(x) = \pi r^2 h = \pi x^2 y = 8\pi x^2 - \pi x^5$

Graph, showing V(x) with max at $x \approx 1.5$

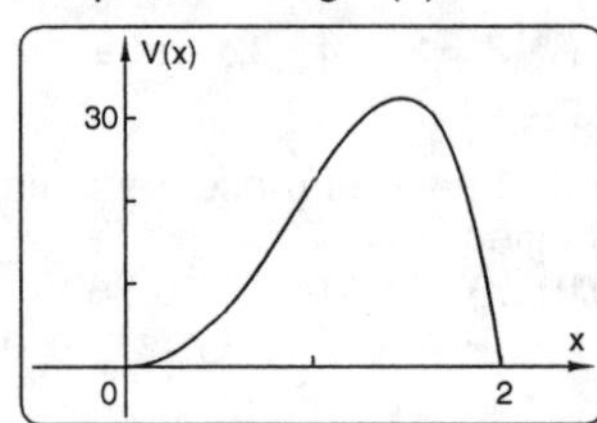

$V'(x) = 16\pi x - 5\pi x^4 = \pi x(16 - 5x^3)$

$V'(x) = 0$ at $x = 0$, and $x = \sqrt[3]{16/5} = 1.4736 ...$

Max. rectangle has $x = \sqrt[3]{16/5} = 1.4736 ...$,

$y = 8 - 16/5 = 4.8$.

R4. a. Graph, $y = \ln x$, between y = 1 and y = 2

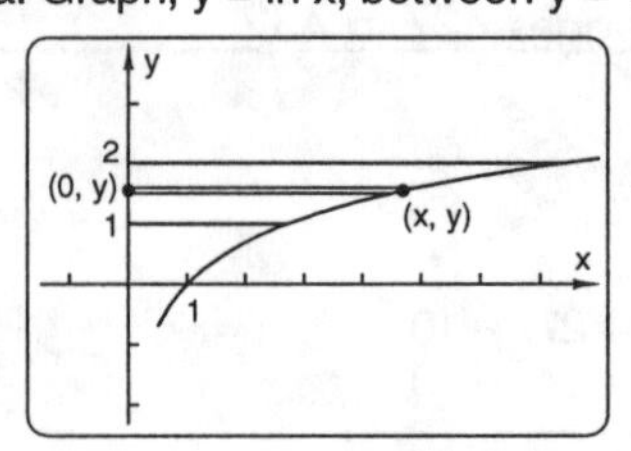

$dA = (x - 0)\, dy = e^y\, dy$

$A = \int_1^2 e^y\, dy = e^y \Big|_1^2 = e^2 - e = 4.6707 ...$

Numerical integration gives 4.6707 ... also.

b. Graph, $y_1 = x^{1/3}$ and $y_2 = x/3 - 2/3$, intersecting at x = −1 and x = 8

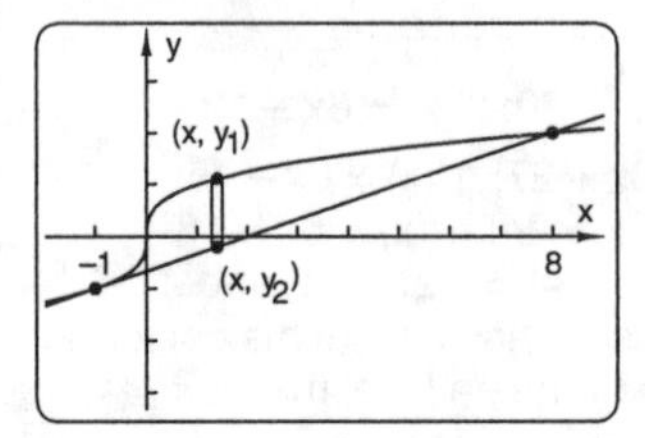

$dA = (y_1 - y_2)\, dx = (x^{1/3} - \frac{1}{3}x + \frac{2}{3})\, dx$

$A = \int_{-1}^{8} dA = \frac{3}{4}x^{4/3} - \frac{1}{6}x^2 + \frac{2}{3}x \Big|_{-1}^{8} = 6.75$

c. Mystery Problem

The graphs cross at x = 0; for $-1 < x < 0$, $x^3 > x$, but $x^3 < x$ for $0 < x < 1$, so the region to the right cancels the one to the left! Mr. Rhee should use

$A = \int_{-1}^{0} (x^3 - x)\, dx + \int_0^1 (x - x^3)\, dx$.

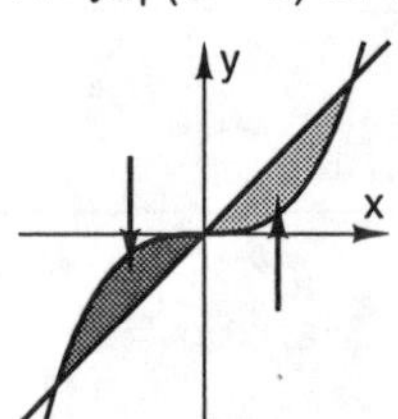

R5.a. Graph, $y = e^{0.2x}$ from x = 0 to x = 4, rotated about the x-axis

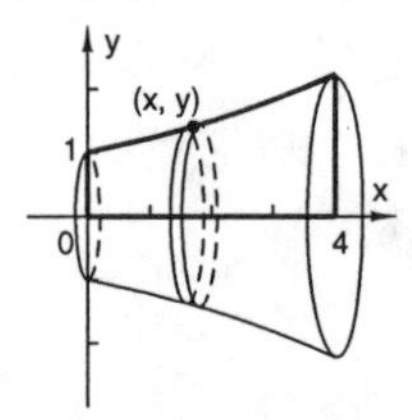

$dV = \pi y^2\, dx = \pi e^{0.4x}\, dx$

$V = \int_0^4 \pi e^{0.4x}\, dx = 2.5\pi e^{0.4x} \Big|_0^4$

$= 2.5\pi(e^{1.6} - 1) = 31.0470 ...$

b. Graph, $y = x_1^{0.25}$, $y = x_2$, intersecting at (0, 0) and (1, 1) in Q.I, rotated about the y-axis, showing back half of solid only

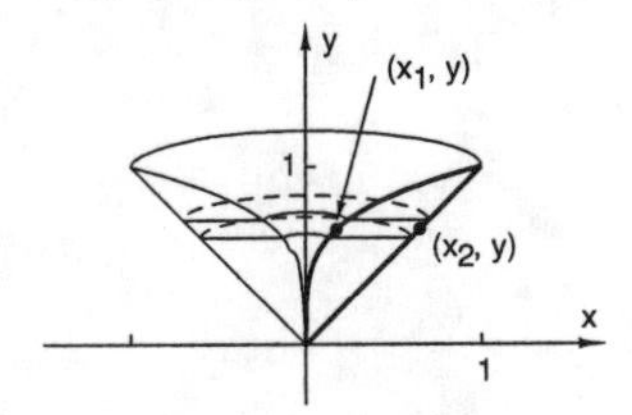

$y = x_1^{0.25} \Rightarrow x_1 = y^4$

$y = x^2 \Rightarrow x_2 = y$

$dV = \pi(x_2^2 - x_1^2)\, dy = \pi(y^2 - y^8)\, dy$

$V = \int_0^1 \pi(y^2 - y^8)\, dy = \pi(\frac{1}{3}y^3 - \frac{1}{9}y^9)\, \Big|_0^1$

$= \frac{2}{9}\pi = 0.6981 \ldots .$

c. Oblique Cone Problem

$y = x_1 + 2 \Rightarrow x_1 = y - 2$

$y = 3x_2 - 6 \Rightarrow x_2 = \frac{1}{3}y + 2$

Graphs intersect at y = 6.

Diameter of circular cross section is $(x_2 - x_1)$.

$dV = \pi[0.5(x_2 - x_1)]^2\, dy$

$= \frac{\pi}{4}[(\frac{1}{3}y + 2) - (y - 2)]^2\, dy = \frac{\pi}{4}[4 - \frac{2}{3}y]^2\, dy$

$V = \int_0^6 dV \approx 25.1327 \ldots$ (exactly 8π)

The right circular cone of altitude 6 and radius 2 also has volume $\frac{1}{3}\pi \cdot 2^2 \cdot 6 = 8\pi$.

R6.a. Graph, $y = x_1^{1/3}$ and $y = x_2^2$, intersecting at (0, 0) and (1, 1), rotated about the x-axis, sliced parallel to the x-axis, showing back half of solid only

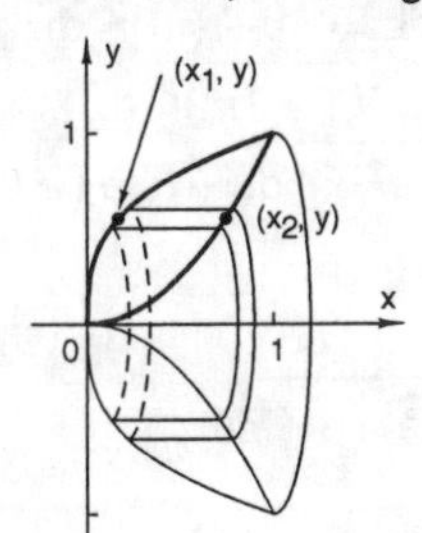

$x_1 = y^3$, $x_2 = y^{1/2}$

$dV = 2\pi y(x_2 - x_1) \cdot dy = 2\pi y(y^{1/2} - y^3)\, dy$

$V = \int_0^1 dV \approx 1.2566 \ldots$ (exactly 0.4π)

b. Graph, solid in part a, sliced perpendicular to the x-axis, generating plane washer slices

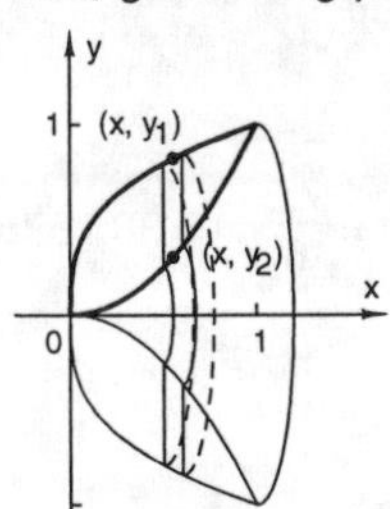

$dV = \pi(y_1^2 - y_2^2)\, dx = \pi(x^{2/3} - x^4)\, dx$

$V = \int_0^1 dV \approx 1.2566 \ldots$ (exactly 0.4π), which is the same answer as in part a, Q.E.D.

c. Various Axes Problem

i. Graph, region between $y = x^2$ and $y = 4$, intersecting at (2, 4) and (–2, 4), rotated about the y-axis, showing back half of solid only

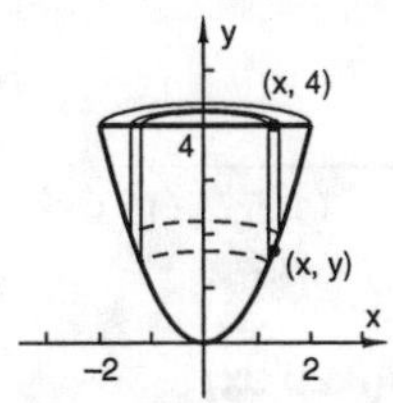

$dV = 2\pi x(4 - y) \cdot dx = 2\pi x(4 - x^2)\, dx$

$V \approx 25.1327 \ldots$ (exactly 8π)

(Washers can also be used.)

ii. Graph, region rotated about the x-axis, showing back half of solid only

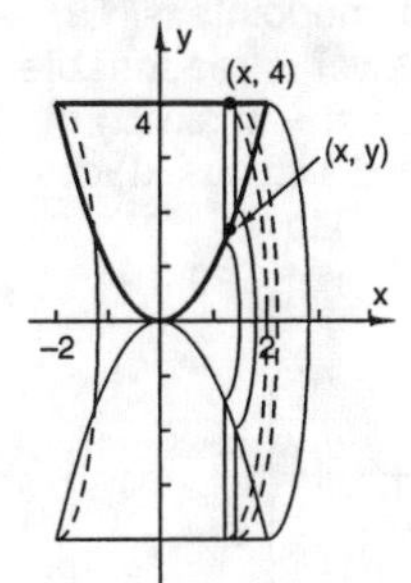

$dV = \pi(4^2 - y^2)\, dx = \pi(16 - x^4)\, dx$

$V = \int_{-2}^2 dV \approx 160.8495 \ldots$ (exactly 51.2π)

(Cylindrical shells can also be used.)

iii. Graph, region rotated about the line y = 5, showing back half of solid only

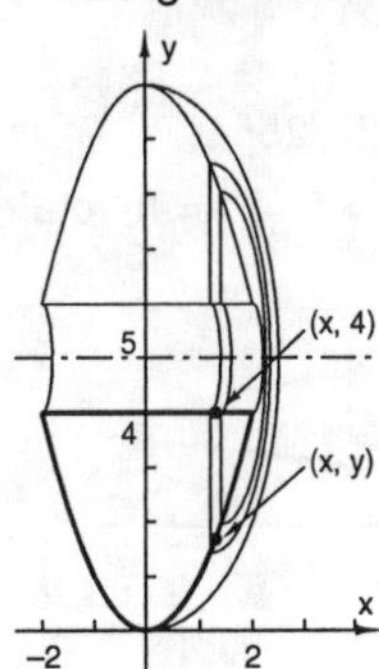

$dV = \pi[(5 - y)^2 - 1^2)\, dx = \pi((5 - x^2)^2 - 1)\, dx$

$V = \int_{-2}^2 dV \approx 174.2536 \ldots$ (exactly $55\frac{7}{15}\pi$)

(Cylindrical shells can also be used.)

iv. Graph, region rotated about the line x = 3, showing back half of solid only

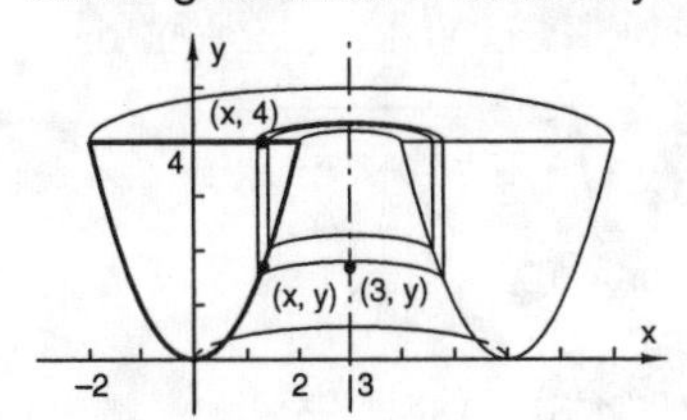

$dV = 2\pi(3 - x) \cdot (4 - y) \cdot dx$

$= 2\pi(3 - x)(4 - x^2)\, dx$

$V = \int_{-2}^2 dV \approx 201.0619 \ldots$ (exactly 64π)

(Washers can also be used.)

R7.a. $y = x^2$ from $x = -1$ to $x = 2$.

$dy = 2x\,dx$

$dL = \sqrt{dx^2 + dy^2} = \sqrt{1 + (2x)^2}\,dx$

$L = \int_{-1}^{2} dL \approx 6.1257\ldots$

b. $y = x^{3/2}$ from $x = 0$ to $x = 9$.

$dy = 1.5x^{1/2}\,dx$

$dL = \sqrt{dx^2 + dy^2} = \sqrt{1 + (1.5x^{1/2})^2}\,dx$

$L = \int_0^9 (1 + 2.25x)^{1/2}\,dx$

$= \frac{1}{2.25}\int_0^9 (1 + 2.25x)^{1/2}\,(2.25\,dx)$

$= \frac{2}{6.75}(1 + 2.25x)^{3/2}\Big|_0^9$

$= \frac{2}{6.75}(21.25^{3/2} - 1) = 28.7281\ldots$

Distance between the endpoints is $\sqrt{9^2 + 27^2} = 28.4604\ldots$, so the answer is reasonable.

c. $x = t\cos \pi t \Rightarrow dx = (\cos \pi t - \pi t \sin \pi t)\,dt$

$y = t \sin \pi t \Rightarrow dy = (\sin \pi t + \pi t \cos \pi t)\,dt$

Graph, t increases from 0 to 4.

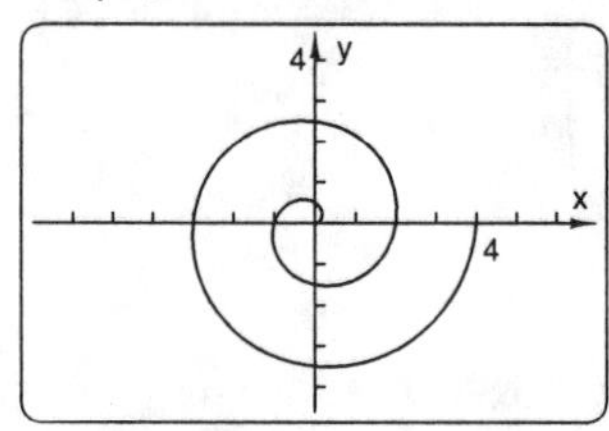

$dL = \sqrt{dx^2 + dy^2}$

$= \sqrt{(\cos \pi t - \pi t \sin \pi t)^2 + (\sin \pi t + \pi t \cos \pi t)^2}\,dt$

$= \sqrt{1 + (\pi t)^2}\,dt$

$L = \int_0^4 \sqrt{1 + \pi^2 t^2}\,dt \approx 25.7255\ldots$

R8.a. Graph, $y = x^{1/3}$, from $x = 0$ to $x = 8$, rotated about the y-axis

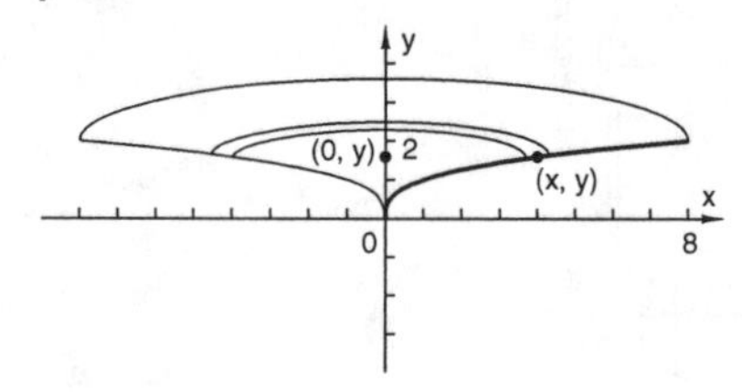

$dy = \frac{1}{3}x^{-2/3}\,dx$

$dL = \sqrt{dx^2 + dy^2} = \sqrt{1 + (\frac{1}{3}x^{-2/3})^2}\,dx$

$dS = 2\pi x \cdot dL = 2\pi x\sqrt{1 + (\frac{1}{3}x^{-2/3})^2}\,dx$

$S = 2\pi \int_0^8 x\sqrt{1 + (\frac{1}{3}x^{-2/3})^2}\,dx$

$= 2\pi \int_0^8 x^{1/3}(x^{4/3} + \frac{1}{9})^{1/2}\,dx$

$= \frac{3}{2}\pi \int_0^8 (x^{4/3} + \frac{1}{9})^{1/2}\,(\frac{4}{3}x^{1/3}\,dx)$

$= \pi(x^{4/3} + \frac{1}{9})^{3/2}\Big|_0^8$

$= \frac{\pi}{27}(145^{3/2} - 1) = 203.0436\ldots$.

The disk of radius 8 has area $64\pi = 201.0619\ldots$, which is close.

b. Graph, $y = \tan x$, from $x = 0$ to $x = 1$, rotated about the line $y = -1$

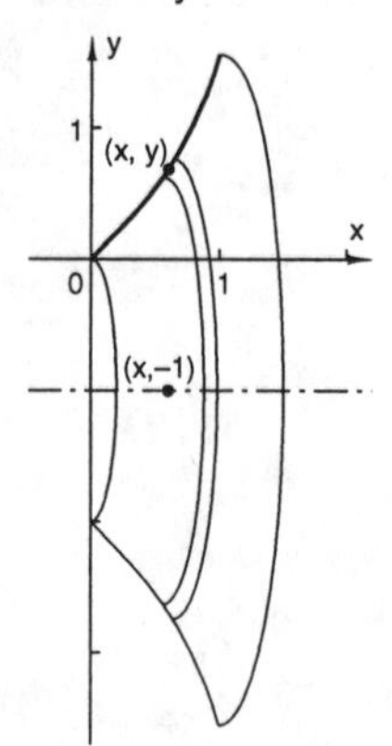

$dy = \sec^2 x\,dx$

$dL = \sqrt{dx^2 + dy^2} = \sqrt{1 + \sec^4 x}\,dx$

$dS = 2\pi(y + 1)\cdot dL$

$= 2\pi(\tan x + 1)\sqrt{1 + \sec^4 x}\,dx$

$S = \int_0^1 dS \approx 20.4199\ldots$

c. Graph, $x = t\cos(\pi t)$ and $y = t\sin(\pi t)$, from $t = 0$ to $t = 4$, rotated about the y-axis. Note that the "seashell" may not be very practical, because it is divided into separate chambers.

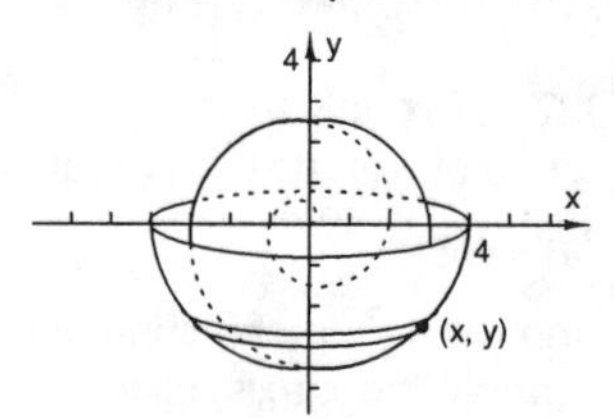

From Problem R7 part c, $dL = \sqrt{1 + (\pi t)^2}\,dt$.

$dS = 2\pi|x|\cdot dL = 2\pi|t\cos \pi t|\sqrt{1 + (\pi t)^2}\,dt$

$= 2\pi t\sqrt{\cos^2 \pi t + \pi^2 t^2 \cos^2 \pi t}\,dt$ (Note $t \ge 0$.)

$S = \int_0^4 dS \approx 272.0945\ldots$

R9.a. $r = \theta \Rightarrow dr = d\theta$

$dL = \sqrt{dr^2 + (r\,d\theta)^2} = \sqrt{1 + \theta^2}\,d\theta$

$L = \int_0^{5\pi/2} dL \approx 32.4706\ldots$

b. $dA = \frac{1}{2}r^2\,d\theta = \frac{1}{2}\theta^2\,d\theta$

Area of the region between the curves equals the area traced out from $t = 2\pi$ to $t = 5\pi/2$ minus the area traced out from $t = 0$ to $t = \pi/2$.

$A = \int_{2\pi}^{5\pi/2} \frac{1}{2}\theta^2\,d\theta - \int_0^{\pi/2} \frac{1}{2}\theta^2\,d\theta$

$= \frac{1}{6}\theta^3\Big|_{2\pi}^{5\pi/2} - \frac{1}{6}\theta^3\Big|_0^{\pi/2}$

$= \frac{1}{6}\pi^3(2.5^3 - 2^3 - 0.5^3 + 0^3) = \frac{7.5}{6}\pi^3 = 38.7578\ldots$

Concepts Problems

C1. Oil Viscosity Problem

a. Graph, $\mu(t) = 130 - 12T + 15T^2 - 4T^3$ from T = 0 to T = 3, showing maxima at T = 0 and $T \approx 2.0$, and minima at $T \approx 0.5$ and T = 3

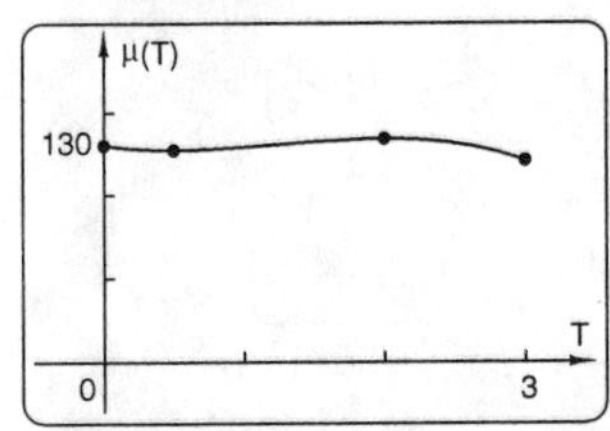

Maximize $\mu(T)$.

$\mu'(T) = -12 + 30T - 12T^2 = -6(2T - 1)(T - 2)$

$\mu'(T) = 0$ at $T = \frac{1}{2}, 2$

$\mu(0) = 130$; $\mu(\frac{1}{2}) = 127.25$; $\mu(2) = 134$; $\mu(3) = 121$

Maximum viscosity occurs at T = 2, or 200°.

b. Minimum viscosity occurs at endpoint, T = 3, or 300°.

C2. "Straight Point" Problem

Graph, $f(x) = (x - 1)^4 + x$, showing that the graph straightens out at x = 1 but does not change concavity.

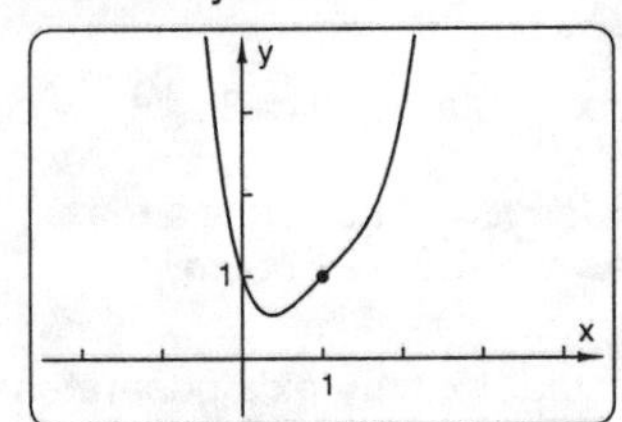

$f'(x) = 4(x - 1)^3 + 1$; $f''(x) = 12(x - 1)^2$, so $f'(1) = 1$ and $f''(1) = 0$.

$f''(x) > 0$ for all $x \neq 1$. In particular, $f''(x)$ does not change sign at x = 1.

Thus the graph is *straight* at x = 1, but not horizontal. Zooming in on (1, 1) shows that the graph resembles y = x when x is close to 1, although it is actually concave upward slightly.

C3. Infinite Derivative Problem

Graphs, $f(x) = x^{2/3}$ and $g(x) = x^{-1/3}$, showing a cusp at x = 0 for function f and a vertical asymptote for function g at x = 0.

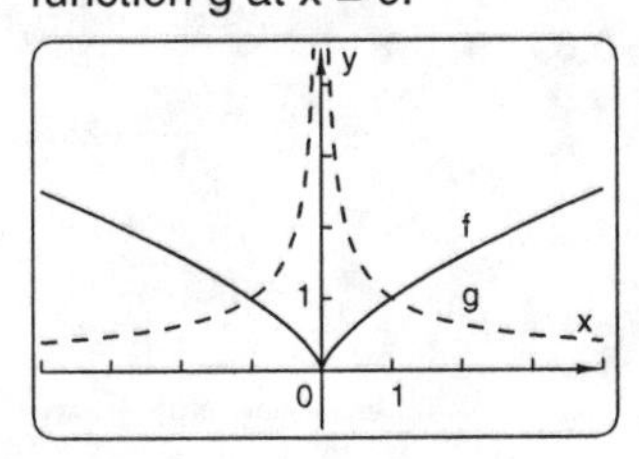

C4. Chapter Logo Problem

a. $y = 3 + 1.25[1 + \cos(\frac{\pi}{3}(x - 5))]^2$

$y' = 2.5(1 + \cos(\frac{\pi}{3}(x - 5)))(-\sin(\frac{\pi}{3}(x - 5))\frac{\pi}{3})$

$= \frac{-2.5\pi}{3}(1 + \cos(\frac{\pi}{3}(x-5)))(\sin(\frac{\pi}{3}(x - 5)))$

$dL = \sqrt{1 + (\frac{-2.5\pi}{3}(1 + \cos X)\sin X)^2}\, dx$

(where X temporarily stands for $\frac{\pi}{3}(x - 5)$)

$L = \int_5^{7.5} dL \approx 5.7726 \ldots$.

b. $y'' = \frac{-2.5\pi}{3}[(1 + \cos X)\cos X + (-\sin X)\sin X]\frac{dX}{dx}$

$= \frac{-2.5\pi}{3}[2\cos^2 X - 1 + \cos X]\frac{\pi}{3}$

$= \frac{-2.5\pi^2}{9}(\cos X + 1)(2\cos X - 1)$

$y'' = 0 \Leftrightarrow \cos X = -1$ or $\cos X = 0.5$

$X = \pi + 2\pi n$ or $X = = \pm\pi/3 + 2\pi n$

x = 8 + 6n, 4 + 6n, or 6 + 6n

The only zero of y'' within the domain is x = 6, so the point of inflection must be at x = 6.

c. $dS = 2\pi(x - 4)\, dL$, where dL is as in part a

$S = \int_5^{7.5} dS \approx 78.2373 \ldots$

d. $x = 7.5 \Rightarrow y = 3 + 1.25(1 + \cos\frac{5\pi}{6})^2$

$= 3 + 1.25\,(1 - \sqrt{3}/2)^2$

$= 3 + 1.25(1.75 - \sqrt{3}) = 3.0224 \ldots$

$dV = 2\pi(x - 4)\cdot(y - 3.0224 \ldots)\cdot dx$

$V = \int_5^{7.5} 2\pi(x - 4)1.25[(1 + \cos X)^2 - (1.75 - \sqrt{3})]\, dx$

$\approx 58.8652 \ldots$

C5. Area by Planimeter Project

The *World Book Encyclopedia* lists the area of Texas as 267,339 square miles. Individual answers will vary.

C6. Hole in the Cylinder Project

Let the cylinder lie on the x-axis and the hole lie on the y-axis, so that the z-axis is perpendicular to both the cylinder and the hole. The cylinder is thus described by $y^2 + z^2 \leq 25$, and the hole by $x^2 + z^2 \leq 9$.

Slice the hole with planes perpendicular to the z-axis. Then for $-3 \leq z \leq 3$, the cross section at z of the hole is a rectangle with height $2y = 2\sqrt{25 - z^2}$ and width $2x = 2\sqrt{9 - z^2}$. Area of cross section rect. is $4\sqrt{225 - 34z^2 + z^4}$, so $dV = 4\sqrt{225 - 34z^2 + z^4}\, dz$. Thus, the volume of the hole (and thus of the uranium that once filled the hole) is

$V = \int_{-3}^{3} 4\sqrt{225 - 34z^2 + z^4}\, dz$

$\approx 269.3703 \ldots \text{ cm}^3$.

According to the *CRC Handbook,* the density of uranium is 19.1 g/cm³. So the mass of the uranium drilled out is

m = (269.3703 ...)(19.1) = 5144.97 ... g.

Value is 200(5144.97 ...) ≈ $1,029,000.

C7. Three-Hole Project

Draw x- and y-axes with origin at the center of the circle on one face of the cube (diagram).

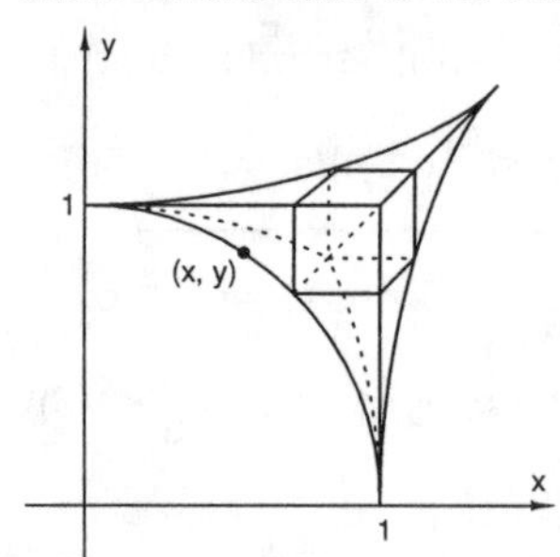

The solid remaining consists of eight identical corner pieces. Each corner piece consists of a cube and three identical spikes. The spikes have square cross sections when sliced perpendicular to the appropriate axes.

The hole perpendicular to the xy-plane cuts a circle in that plane with equation

$x^2 + y^2 = 1$.

The cube shown in the diagram begins at x = y, so that $2x^2 = 1$, from which $x = \sqrt{2}/2$. Each cube is thus $(1 - \sqrt{2}/2)$ cm on a side, and thus has volume

$V_c = (1 - \sqrt{2}/2)^3 = 0.0251262 \ldots \text{ cm}^3$.

Consider the leftmost spike in the diagram above. Pick a sample point (x, y) on the part of the circle in that spike. The cross section perpendicular to the x-axis for this spike is a square of side

$(1 - y) = 1 - \sqrt{1 - x^2}$.

Thus, $dV_s = (1 - \sqrt{1 - x^2})^2\, dx$.

Since the spike goes from x = 0 to $x = \sqrt{2}/2$,

$V_s = \int_0^{\sqrt{2}/2} dV_s \approx 0.0109642 \ldots$.

(The integral can be evaluated algebraically using trigonometry substitution, as in Chapter 9. The exact value is $V_s = \frac{11\sqrt{2}}{12} - \frac{\pi}{4} - \frac{1}{2}$.)

The 24 spikes (three for each of the eight corners) are identical.

Thus the total volume remaining is $V = 8V_c + 24V_s$

$= 8(1 - \sqrt{2}/2)^3 + 24\left(\frac{11\sqrt{2}}{12} - \frac{\pi}{4} - \frac{1}{2}\right)$

$= 8 + 8\sqrt{2} - 6\pi = 0.46415 \ldots \text{ cm}^3$.

Chapter Test

T1. $f(x) = x^3 - 7.8x^2 + 20.25x - 13$

$f'(x) = 3x^2 - 15.6x + 20.25 = 3(x - 2.5)(x - 2.7)$

f'(x) changes from positive to negative at x = 2.5 and from negative back to positive at x = 2.7. So there is a local maximum at x = 2.5 and a local minimum at x = 2.7.

$f''(x) = 6x - 15.6 = 6(x - 2.6)$

$f''(x) = 0$ at $x = 2.6$;

$f'(2.6) = -0.03$, so the graph is not horizontal at the inflection point.

T2. Graph, example

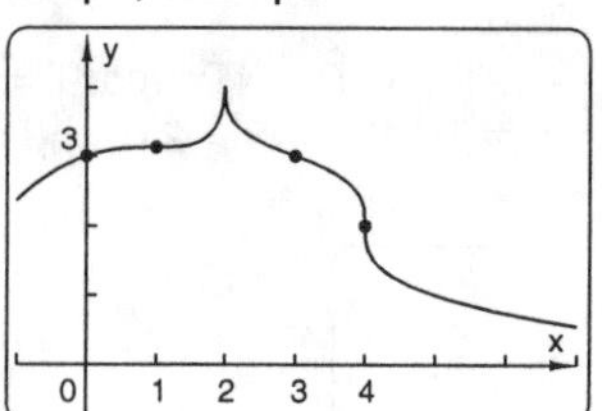

T3. $y = x^3 \Rightarrow dy = 3x^2\, dx$

$dL = \sqrt{dx^2 + dy^2} = \sqrt{1 + (3x^2)^2}\, dx$

$L = \int_0^2 \sqrt{1 + 9x^4}\, dx = 8.6303 \ldots$

T4. $dS = 2\pi x \cdot dL = 2\pi x\sqrt{1 + 9x^4}\, dx$

$S = \int_0^2 2\pi x\sqrt{1 + 9x^4}\, dx = 77.3245 \ldots$

T5. $V(x) = \pi x^2(8 - y) = 8\pi x^2 - \pi x^5$

Graph shows max. V(x) at $x \approx 1.5$.

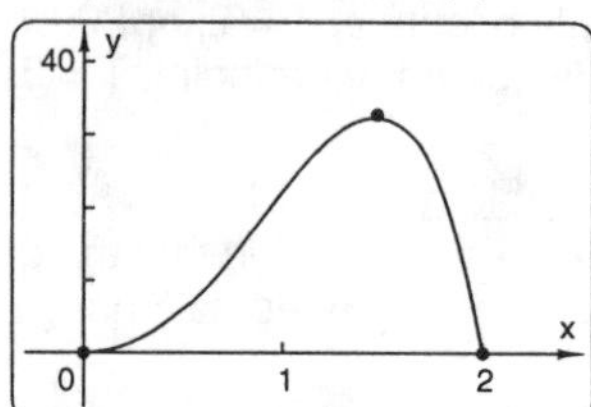

$V'(x) = 16\pi x - 5\pi x^4 = 0$ at $x = 0$ or $3.2^{1/3}$

$V(0) = V(2) = 0$

$V(3.2^{1/3}) = 4.8 \cdot 3.2^{2/3}\pi > 0$, so this is a max.

Max. cylinder has $V = 4.8 \cdot 3.2^{2/3}\pi \text{ cm}^3$

$= 32.7459 \ldots \text{ cm}^3$.

T6. Slicing perpendicular to the y-axis generates circular plane slices of radius x.

$dV = \pi x^2\, dy = \pi y^{2/3}\, dy$

$V = \int_0^8 \pi y^{2/3}\, dy = 0.6\pi y^{5/3} \Big|_0^8$

$= 19.2\pi = 60.3185 \ldots$

T7. Slicing parallel to the y-axis generates cylindrical shells of radius x extending from the sample point (x, y) to the line y = 8.

$dV = 2\pi x \cdot (8 - y) \cdot dx = 2\pi x(8 - x^3)\, dx$

$V = \int_0^2 2\pi(8x - x^4)\, dx = 2\pi(4x^2 - 0.2x^5) \Big|_0^2$

$= 19.2\pi = 60.3185 \ldots$, which agrees with Problem T6.

T8. $V_{cyl} = \pi \cdot 2^2 \cdot 8 = 32\pi$

$\frac{V_{solid}}{V_{cyl}} = \frac{19.2\pi}{32\pi} = 0.6$

So $V_{solid} = 0.6V_{cyl}$.

T9. a. Graph, $x = 5\cos t$, $y = 2\sin t$

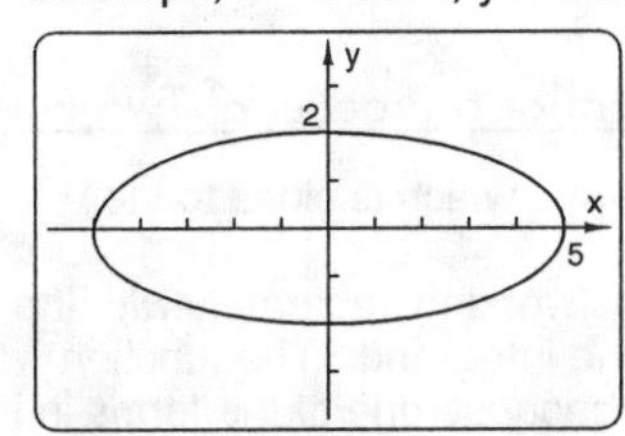

b. $dx = -5\sin t\,dt$, $dy = 2\cos t\,dt$

$dL = \sqrt{dx^2 + dy^2}$

$= \sqrt{(-5\cos t)^2 + (2\sin t)^2}\,dt$

$L = \int_0^{2\pi} dL \approx 23.0131 \ldots$.

c. Slicing perpendicular to the x-axis generates circular slices of radius y, where sample point (x, y) is on the upper branch of the ellipse.

$dV = \pi y^2\,dx = 4\pi\sin^2 t(-5\sin t\,dt)$

$= -20\pi\sin^3 t\,dt$.

Leftmost slice is at $t = \pi$ and rightmost slice is at $t = 0$.

$V = \int_\pi^0 -20\pi\sin^3 t\,dt \approx 26.6666 \ldots \pi$ (numerically)

V can be evaluated algebraically by transforming two of the three sin t factors into cosines.

$V = \int_\pi^0 -20\pi(1 - \cos^2 t)\sin t\,dt$

$= \int_\pi^0 -20\pi\sin t\,dt + \int_\pi^0 20\pi\cos^2 t\sin t\,dt$

$= 20\pi\cos t - \frac{20}{3}\pi\cos^3 t\,\Big|_\pi^0 = 26\frac{2}{3}\pi$

The x-radius is 5 and the y-radius is 2.

$\frac{4}{3}\pi(\text{x-radius})(\text{y-radius})^2 = \frac{4}{3}\pi(5)(2)^2$

$= 26\frac{2}{3}\pi$, Q.E.D.

(In general, if a = x-radius and b = y-radius, the parametric functions are $x = a\cos t$, $y = b\sin t$. Repeating the algebraic solution above gives $V = \frac{4}{3}\pi ab^2$.)

T10. $r = 5e^{0.1\theta}$

$dr = 0.5e^{0.1\theta}\,d\theta$

$dL = \sqrt{dr^2 + (r\,d\theta)^2}$

$= \sqrt{(0.5e^{0.1\theta})^2 + (5e^{0.1\theta})^2}\,d\theta$

$= e^{0.1\theta}\sqrt{25.25}\,d\theta$.

The spiral starts at $r = 5 = 5e^{0.1\cdot 0}$ and makes three complete revolutions, so $0 \le \theta \le 6\pi$.

$L = \int_0^{6\pi} e^{0.1\theta}\sqrt{25.25}\,d\theta = e^{0.1\theta}\sqrt{25.25}\,\Big|_0^{6\pi}$

$= \sqrt{25.25}\cdot 10\cdot(e^{0.6\pi} - 1) = 280.6961 \ldots$

T11. $dA = \frac{1}{2}r^2\,d\theta = 12.5e^{0.2\theta}\,d\theta$

The area between the second and third revolutions equals the area swept out for the third revolution minus the area swept out for the second revolution. In Quadrant I, the third revolution extends from $\theta = 4\pi$ to $\theta = 4.5\pi$, and the second revolution extends from $\theta = 2\pi$ to $\theta = 2.5\pi$.

$A = \int_{4\pi}^{4.5\pi} 12.5e^{0.2\theta}\,d\theta - \int_{2\pi}^{2.5\pi} 12.5e^{0.2\theta}\,d\theta$

$= 62.5e^{0.2\theta}\,\Big|_{4\pi}^{4.5\pi} - 62.5e^{0.2\theta}\,\Big|_{2\pi}^{2.5\pi}$

$= 62.5(e^{0.9\pi} - e^{0.8\pi} - e^{0.5\pi} + e^{0.4\pi})$

$= 203.7405 \ldots$.

Chapter 9

Exploratory Problem Set 9-1, page 436 — Introduction to the Integral of a Product of Two Functions

1. $V = 2\pi \int_0^{\pi/2} x \cdot \cos x \, dx \approx 3.5864 \ldots$
2. $f(x) = x \sin x \Rightarrow f'(x) = x \cos x + \sin x$
3. $\int f'(x)\, dx = \int x \cos x \, dx + \int \sin x \, dx$
4. $\int x \cos x \, dx = \int f'(x)\, dx - \int \sin x \, dx$
   $= f(x) + \cos x + C$ (by definition of indefinite integral)
   $= x \sin x + \cos x + C$
5. $V = 2\pi \int_0^{\pi/2} x \cos x \, dx = 2\pi x \sin x + 2\pi \cos x \, \Big|_0^{\pi/2}$
   $= \pi^2 - 2\pi$
6. $V = \pi^2 - 2\pi = 3.5864 \ldots$, which is close to the approximation.
7. The method involves working separately with the different "parts" of the integrand. The function x sin x was chosen because one of the terms in its derivative is x cos x, which is the original integrand. See Section 9-2.

Problem Set 9-2, page 439 — Integration by Parts—Way to Integrate Products

Q1. $y' = x \sec^2 x + \tan x$ Q2. $\frac{1}{11}x^{11} + C$

Q3. Graph: $y = e^{-x}$ Q4. $\frac{1}{3}\sin 3x + C$

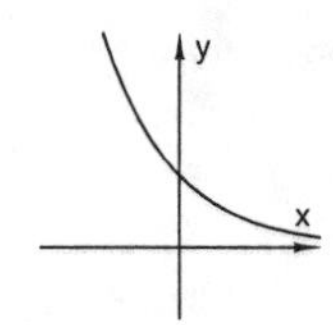

Q5. $5\cos^2 5x - 5\sin^2 5x$ Q6. Graph: $y = 2/x$

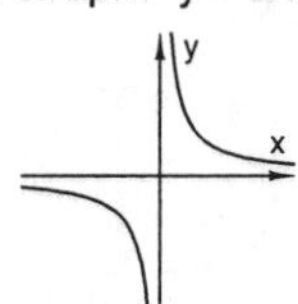

Q7. $r'(x) = t(x)$ Q8. $\lim_{h\to 0} \frac{f(x+h) - f(x)}{h}$

Q9. $2\pi \int_a^b [f(x) - g(x)](x - c)\, dx$

Q10. $\approx 110/6$

1. $\int x \sin x \, dx$ $u = x$ $dv = \sin x \, dx$
   $du = dx$ $v = -\cos x$
   $= -x\cos x - \int (-\cos x)\, dx$
   $= -x\cos x + \sin x + C$
2. $\int x \cos 3x \, dx$ $u = x$ $dv = \cos 3x \, dx$
   $du = dx$ $v = \frac{1}{3}\sin 3x$
   $= \frac{1}{3}x \sin 3x - \int \frac{1}{3}\sin 3x \, dx$
   $= \frac{1}{3}x \sin 3x + \frac{1}{9}\cos 3x + C$
3. $\int x e^{4x}\, dx$ $u = x$ $du = e^{4x}\, dx$
   $du = dx$ $v = \frac{1}{4}e^{4x}$
   $= \frac{1}{4}xe^{4x} - \frac{1}{4}\int e^{4x}\, dx$
   $= \frac{1}{4}xe^{4x} - \frac{1}{16}e^{4x} + C$
4. $\int 6x\, e^{-3x}\, dx$ $u = 6x$ $dv = e^{-3x}\, dx$
   $du = 6\, dx$ $v = -\frac{1}{3}e^{-3x}$
   $= (6x)(-\frac{1}{3}e^{-3x}) - \int (6)(-\frac{1}{3}e^{-3x})\, dx$
   $= -2xe^{-3x} - \frac{2}{3}e^{-3x} + C$
5. $\int (x+4)e^{-5x}\, dx$ $u = x + 4$ $dv = e^{-5x}\, dx$
   $du = dx$ $v = -\frac{1}{5}e^{-5x}$
   $= -(x+4)\cdot\frac{1}{5}e^{-5x} + \frac{1}{5}\int e^{-5x}\, dx$
   $= -\frac{4}{5}e^{-5x} - \frac{1}{5}x\, e^{-5x} - \frac{1}{25}e^{-5x} + C$
   $= -\frac{21}{25}e^{-5x} - \frac{1}{5}x\, e^{-5x} + C$
6. $\int (x+7)e^{2x}\, dx$ $u = x + 7$ $dv = e^{2x}\, dx$
   $du = dx$ $v = \frac{1}{2}e^{2x}$
   $= (x+7)\cdot\frac{1}{2}e^{2x} - \frac{1}{2}\int e^{2x}\, dx$
   $= \frac{7}{2}e^{2x} + \frac{1}{2}xe^{2x} - \frac{1}{4}e^{2x} + C$
7. $\int x^3 \ln x \, dx$ $u = \ln x$ $dv = x^3\, dx$
   $du = x^{-1}\, dx$ $v = \frac{1}{4}x^4$
   $= \frac{1}{4}x^4 \ln x - \frac{1}{4}\int x^3\, dx$
   $= \frac{1}{4}x^4 \ln x - \frac{1}{16}x^4 + C$
8. $\int x^5 \ln 3x \, dx$ $u = \ln 3x$ $dv = x^5\, dx$
   $du = x^{-1}\, dx$ $v = \frac{1}{6}x^6$
   $= \frac{1}{6}x^6 \ln 3x - \frac{1}{6}\int x^5\, dx$
   $= \frac{1}{6}x^6 \ln 3x - \frac{1}{36}x^6 + C$
9. $\int x^2 e^x\, dx$ $u = x^2$ $dv = e^x\, dx$
   $du = 2x\, dx$ $v = e^x$
   $= x^2e^x - \int 2x\, e^x\, dx$ $u = 2x$ $dv = e^x\, dx$
   $du = 2\, dx$ $v = e^x$
   $= x^2e^x - [2x\, e^x - \int 2e^x\, dx]$
   $= x^2e^x - 2xe^x + 2e^x + C$

10. $\int x^2 \sin x\,dx$ $\quad u = x^2 \quad dv = \sin x\,dx$
$\quad du = 2x\,dx \quad v = -\cos x$

$= -x^2 \cos x - \int (-2x \cos x)\,dx$ $\quad u = 2x \quad dv = -\cos x\,dx$
$\quad du = 2\,dx \quad v = -\sin x$

$= -x^2 \cos x - [-2x \sin x - \int (-2 \sin x)\,dx]$
$= -x^2 \cos x + 2x \sin x + 2 \cos x + C$

11. Integral of the Natural Logarithm Problem
Let $u = \ln x$,
Let $dv = dx \Rightarrow du = x^{-1}\,dx$, $v = x$

$\int \ln x\,dx$ $\quad u = \ln x \quad dv = dx$
$\quad du = x^{-1}\,dx \quad v = x$

$= x \ln x - \int x \cdot x^{-1}\,dx$
$= x \ln x - x + C$

Problem Set 9-3, pages 443 to 445 — Rapid Repeated Integration by Parts

Q1. $f'(t) = te^t + e^t$ Q2. $\frac{1}{6}r^6 + C$
Q3. $2m \cos 2m + \sin 2m$ Q4. $\tan x + C$
Q5. $\frac{1}{18}(x^3 + 11)^6 + C$ Q6. $\frac{1}{4}x^4 + 11x + C$
Q7. 1 Q8. 1/2
Q9. $V = \pi \int_a^b [f(x)^2 - g(x)^2]\,dx$
Q10. Sketch

1. $\int x^3 e^{2x}\,dx$

u	sign	dv
x^3	+	e^{2x}
$3x^2$	−	$\frac{1}{2}e^{2x}$
$6x$	+	$\frac{1}{4}e^{2x}$
6	−	$\frac{1}{8}e^{2x}$
0	+	$\frac{1}{16}e^{2x}$

$= \frac{1}{2}x^3e^{2x} - \frac{3}{4}x^2e^{2x} + \frac{3}{4}xe^{2x} - \frac{3}{8}e^{2x} + C$

2. $\int x^5 e^{-x}\,dx$

u	sign	dv
x^5	+	e^{-x}
$5x^4$	−	$-e^{-x}$
$20x^3$	+	e^{-x}
$60x^2$	−	$-e^{-x}$
$120x$	+	e^{-x}
120	−	$-e^{-x}$
0	+	e^{-x}

$= -x^5e^{-x} - 5x^4e^{-x} - 20x^3e^{-x} - 60x^2e^{-x} - 120xe^{-x}$
$- 120e^{-x} + C$

3. $\int x^4 \sin x\,dx$

u	sign	dv
x^4	+	$\sin x$
$4x^3$	−	$-\cos x$
$12x^2$	+	$-\sin x$
$24x$	−	$\cos x$
24	+	$\sin x$
0	−	$-\cos x$

$= -x^4 \cos x + 4x^3 \sin x + 12x^2 \cos x - 24x \sin x$
$- 24 \cos x + C$

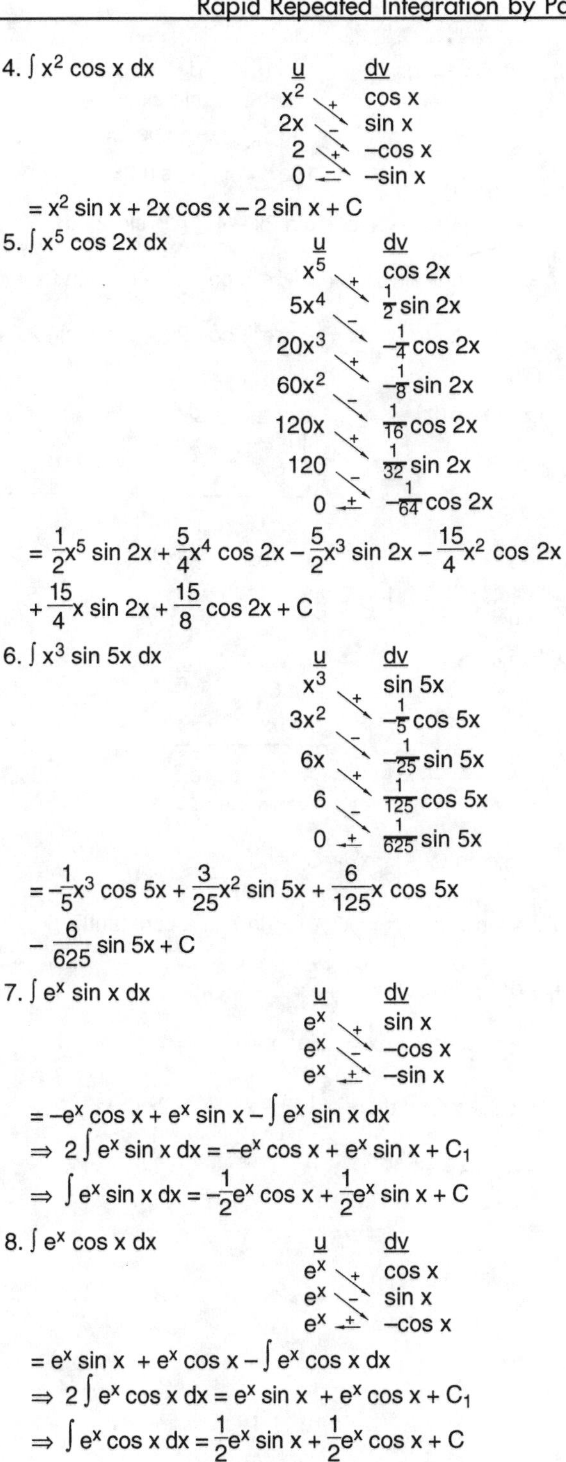

4. $\int x^2 \cos x\,dx$

u	sign	dv
x^2	+	$\cos x$
$2x$	−	$\sin x$
2	+	$-\cos x$
0	−	$-\sin x$

$= x^2 \sin x + 2x \cos x - 2 \sin x + C$

5. $\int x^5 \cos 2x\,dx$

u	sign	dv
x^5	+	$\cos 2x$
$5x^4$	−	$\frac{1}{2}\sin 2x$
$20x^3$	+	$-\frac{1}{4}\cos 2x$
$60x^2$	−	$-\frac{1}{8}\sin 2x$
$120x$	+	$\frac{1}{16}\cos 2x$
120	−	$\frac{1}{32}\sin 2x$
0	+	$-\frac{1}{64}\cos 2x$

$= \frac{1}{2}x^5 \sin 2x + \frac{5}{4}x^4 \cos 2x - \frac{5}{2}x^3 \sin 2x - \frac{15}{4}x^2 \cos 2x$
$+ \frac{15}{4}x \sin 2x + \frac{15}{8} \cos 2x + C$

6. $\int x^3 \sin 5x\,dx$

u	sign	dv
x^3	+	$\sin 5x$
$3x^2$	−	$-\frac{1}{5}\cos 5x$
$6x$	+	$-\frac{1}{25}\sin 5x$
6	−	$\frac{1}{125}\cos 5x$
0	+	$\frac{1}{625}\sin 5x$

$= -\frac{1}{5}x^3 \cos 5x + \frac{3}{25}x^2 \sin 5x + \frac{6}{125}x \cos 5x$
$- \frac{6}{625} \sin 5x + C$

7. $\int e^x \sin x\,dx$

u	sign	dv
e^x	+	$\sin x$
e^x	−	$-\cos x$
e^x	+	$-\sin x$

$= -e^x \cos x + e^x \sin x - \int e^x \sin x\,dx$
$\Rightarrow 2\int e^x \sin x\,dx = -e^x \cos x + e^x \sin x + C_1$
$\Rightarrow \int e^x \sin x\,dx = -\frac{1}{2}e^x \cos x + \frac{1}{2}e^x \sin x + C$

8. $\int e^x \cos x\,dx$

u	sign	dv
e^x	+	$\cos x$
e^x	−	$\sin x$
e^x	+	$-\cos x$

$= e^x \sin x + e^x \cos x - \int e^x \cos x\,dx$
$\Rightarrow 2\int e^x \cos x\,dx = e^x \sin x + e^x \cos x + C_1$
$\Rightarrow \int e^x \cos x\,dx = \frac{1}{2}e^x \sin x + \frac{1}{2}e^x \cos x + C$

9. $\int e^{3x}\cos 5x\,dx$

u	dv
e^{3x} (+)	$\cos 5x$
$3e^{3x}$ (−)	$\frac{1}{5}\sin 5x$
$9e^{3x}$ (+)	$-\frac{1}{25}\cos 5x$

$$= \frac{1}{5}e^{3x}\sin 5x + \frac{3}{25}e^{3x}\cos 5x - \frac{9}{25}\int e^{3x}\cos 5x\,dx \Rightarrow$$

$$\frac{34}{25}\int e^{3x}\cos 5x\,dx = \frac{1}{5}e^{3x}\sin 5x + \frac{3}{25}e^{3x}\cos 5x + C_1$$

$$\Rightarrow \int e^{3x}\cos 5x\,dx = \frac{5}{34}e^{3x}\sin 5x + \frac{3}{34}e^{3x}\cos 5x + C$$

10. $\int e^{4x}\sin 2x\,dx$

u	dv
e^{4x} (+)	$\sin 2x$
$4e^{4x}$ (−)	$-\frac{1}{2}\cos 2x$
$16e^{4x}$ (+)	$-\frac{1}{4}\sin 2x$

$$= -\frac{1}{2}e^{4x}\cos 2x + e^{4x}\sin 2x - 4\int e^{4x}\sin 2x\,dx$$

$$\Rightarrow 5\int e^{4x}\sin 2x\,dx = -\frac{1}{2}e^{4x}\cos 2x + e^{4x}\sin 2x + C_1$$

$$\Rightarrow \int e^{4x}\sin 2x\,dx = -\frac{1}{10}e^{4x}\cos 2x + \frac{1}{5}e^{4x}\sin 2x + C$$

11. $\int x^7\ln 3x\,dx$

u	dv
$\ln 3x$ (+)	x^7
$1/x$	$\frac{1}{8}x^8$
- - - - - -	- - - - - -
1 (−)	$\frac{1}{8}x^7$
0 (+)	$\frac{1}{64}x^8$

$$= \frac{1}{8}x^8\ln 3x - \frac{1}{64}x^8 + C$$

12. $\int x^5\ln 6x\,dx$

u	dv
$\ln 6x$ (+)	x^5
$1/x$	$\frac{1}{6}x^6$
- - - - - -	- - - - - -
1 (−)	$\frac{1}{6}x^5$
0 (+)	$\frac{1}{36}x^6$

$$= \frac{1}{6}x^6\ln 6x - \frac{1}{36}x^6 + C$$

13. $\int x^4\ln 7\,dx = \frac{\ln 7}{5}x^5 + C$ (ln 7 is a constant!)

14. $\int e^{7x}\cos 5\,dx = \frac{\cos 5}{7}e^{7x} + C$

15. $\int \sin^5 x\cos x\,dx = \frac{1}{6}\sin^6 x + C$

16. $\int x(3-x^2)^{2/3}\,dx = -\frac{1}{2}\int (3-x^2)^{2/3}(-2x\,dx)$

$$= -\frac{3}{10}(3-x^2)^{5/3} + C$$

17. $\int x^3(x+5)^{1/2}\,dx$

u	dv
x^3 (+)	$(x+5)^{1/2}$
$3x^2$ (−)	$\frac{2}{3}(x+5)^{3/2}$
$6x$ (+)	$\frac{4}{15}(x+5)^{5/2}$
6 (−)	$\frac{8}{105}(x+5)^{7/2}$
0 (+)	$\frac{16}{945}(x+5)^{9/2}$

$$= \frac{2}{3}x^3(x+5)^{3/2} - \frac{4}{5}x^2(x+5)^{5/2} + \frac{16}{35}x(x+5)^{7/2} - \frac{32}{315}(x+5)^{9/2} + C$$

18. $\int x^2\sqrt{2-x}\,dx$
$= \int x^2(2-x)^{1/2}\,dx$

u	dv
x^2 (+)	$(2-x)^{1/2}$
$2x$ (−)	$-\frac{2}{3}(2-x)^{3/2}$
2 (+)	$\frac{4}{15}(2-x)^{5/2}$
0 (−)	$-\frac{8}{105}(2-x)^{7/2}$

$$= -\frac{2}{3}x^2(2-x)^{3/2} - \frac{8}{15}x(2-x)^{5/2} - \frac{16}{105}(2-x)^{7/2} + C$$

19. $\int \ln x^5\,dx = \int 5\ln x\,dx = 5x\ln x - 5x + C$

20. $\int e^{\ln 7x}\,dx = \int 7x\,dx = \frac{7}{2}x^2 + C$

21. $\int x^5 e^{x^2}\,dx$

u	dv
x^4 (+)	xe^{x^2}
$4x^3$	$\frac{1}{2}e^{x^2}$
- - - - - -	- - - - - -
$2x^2$ (−)	xe^{x^2}
$4x$	$\frac{1}{2}e^{x^2}$
- - - - - -	- - - - - -
2 (+)	xe^{x^2}
0 (−)	$\frac{1}{2}e^{x^2}$

$$= \frac{1}{2}x^4e^{x^2} - x^2e^{x^2} + e^{x^2} + C$$

22. $\int x^5 e^{x^3}\,dx$
$= \frac{1}{3}x^3e^{x^3} - \frac{1}{3}e^{x^3} + C$

u	dv
x^3 (+)	$x^2e^{x^3}$
$3x^2$	$\frac{1}{3}e^{x^3}$
- - - - - -	- - - - - -
1 (−)	$x^2e^{x^3}$
0 (+)	$\frac{1}{3}e^{x^3}$

23. $\int x(\ln x)^3\,dx$

u	dv
$(\ln x)^3$ (+)	x
$3(\ln x)^2/x$	$\frac{1}{2}x^2$
- - - - - -	- - - - - -
$3(\ln x)^2$ (−)	$\frac{1}{2}x$
$6(\ln x)/x$	$\frac{1}{4}x^2$
- - - - - -	- - - - - -
$6\ln x$ (+)	$\frac{1}{4}x$
$6/x$	$\frac{1}{8}x^2$
- - - - - -	- - - - - -
6 (−)	$\frac{1}{8}x$
0 (+)	$\frac{1}{16}x^2$

$$= \frac{1}{2}x^2(\ln x)^3 - \frac{3}{4}x^2(\ln x)^2 + \frac{3}{4}x^2\ln x - \frac{3}{8}x^2 + C$$

24. $\int x^3 (\ln x)^2\,dx$

u		dv
$(\ln x)^2$	+	x^3
$2(\ln x)/x$		$\frac{1}{4}x^4$
$2\ln x$	−	$\frac{1}{4}x^3$
$2/x$		$\frac{1}{16}x^4$
2	+	$\frac{1}{16}x^3$
0	−	$\frac{1}{64}x^4$

$= \frac{1}{4}x^4(\ln x)^2 - \frac{1}{8}x^4 \ln x + \frac{1}{32}x^4 + C$

25. $\int x^3(x^2+1)^4\,dx$

u		dv
x^2	+	$x(x^2+1)^4$
$2x$		$\frac{1}{10}(x^2+1)^5$
$\frac{1}{5}$	−	$x(x^2+1)^5$
0	+	$\frac{1}{12}(x^2+1)^6$

$= \frac{1}{10}x^2(x^2+1)^5 - \frac{1}{60}(x^2+1)^6 + C$

26. $\int x^3\sqrt{x^2-3}\,dx$
$= \int x^3(x^2-3)^{1/2}$

u		dv
x^2	+	$x(x^2-3)^{1/2}$
$2x$		$\frac{1}{3}(x^2-3)^{3/2}$
$\frac{2}{3}$	−	$x(x^2-3)^{3/2}$
0	+	$\frac{1}{5}(x^2-3)^{5/2}$

$= \frac{1}{3}x^2(x^2-3)^{3/2} - \frac{2}{15}(x^2-3)^{5/2} + C$

27. $\int \cos^2 x\,dx$

u		dv
$\cos x$	+	$\cos x$
$-\sin x$	−	$\sin x$

$= \cos x \sin x - \int (-\sin^2 x)\,dx$
$= \cos x \sin x + \int (1 - \cos^2 x)\,dx$
$= \cos x \sin x + x - \int \cos^2 x\,dx$
$\Rightarrow 2\int \cos^2 x\,dx = \cos x \sin x + x + C_1$
$\Rightarrow \int \cos^2 x\,dx = \frac{1}{2}\cos x \sin x + \frac{1}{2}x + C$

28. $\int \sin^2 0.4x\,dx$

u		dv
$\sin 0.4x$	+	$\sin 0.4x$
$0.4\cos 0.4x$	−	$-2.5\cos 0.4x$

$= -2.5 \sin 0.4x \cos 0.4x + \int \cos^2 0.4x\,dx$
$= -2.5 \sin 0.4x \cos 0.4x + \int (1 - \sin^2 0.4x)\,dx$
$= -2.5 \sin 0.4x \cos 0.4x + \int dx - \int \sin^2 0.4x\,dx$
$\Rightarrow 2\int \sin^2 0.4x\,dx = -2.5 \sin 0.4x \cos 0.4x + x + C_1$
$\Rightarrow \int \sin^2 0.4x\,dx = -1.25 \sin 0.4x \cos 0.4x + 0.5x + C$

29. $\int \sec^3 x\,dx$

u		dv
$\sec x$	+	$\sec^2 x$
$\sec x \tan x$	−	$\tan x$

$= \sec x \tan x - \int \sec x \tan^2 x\,dx$
$= \sec x \tan x - \int \sec x(\sec^2 x - 1)\,dx$
$= \sec x \tan x - \int \sec^3 x\,dx + \ln|\sec x + \tan x| \Rightarrow$
$2\int \sec^3 x\,dx = \sec x \tan x + \ln|\sec x + \tan x| + C_1$
$\int \sec^3 x\,dx = \frac{1}{2}\sec x \tan x + \frac{1}{2}\ln|\sec x + \tan x| + C$

30. $\int \sec^2 x \tan x\,dx = \int (\sec x)^1 \cdot (\sec x \tan x\,dx)$
$= \frac{1}{2}\sec^2 x + C$

31. $\int \log_3 x\,dx = \frac{1}{\ln 3}\int \ln x\,dx = \frac{1}{\ln 3}(x \ln x - x) + C$
$= x \log_3 x - \frac{1}{\ln 3}x + C$

32. $\int \log_{10} x\,dx = \frac{1}{\ln 10}\int \ln x\,dx = \frac{1}{\ln 10}(x \ln x - x) + C$
$= x \log_{10} x - \frac{1}{\ln 10}x + C$

33. $\int \sin x\,dx = -\cos x + C$

34. $\int \cos x\,dx = \sin x + C$

35. $\int \csc x\,dx = -\ln|\csc x + \cot x| + C$

36. $\int \sec x\,dx = \ln|\sec x + \tan x| + C$

37. $\int \tan x\,dx = -\ln|\cos x| + C$

38. $\int \cot x\,dx = \ln|\sin x| + C$

39. $\int x^2 \cos x\,dx$
For the first integral, Wanda integrated $\cos x$ and differentiated x^2, but in the second integral she plans to differentiate $\int \cos x\,dx$ and integrate $2x$, effectively canceling out what she did in the first part. She will get $\int x^2 \cos x\,dx = x^2 \sin x - x^2 \sin x + \int x^2 \cos x\,dx$, which is true, but not very useful!

40. $\int x^2 \cos x\,dx$
Amos's choice of u and dv transforms $\int x^2 \cos x\,dx$ into $\frac{1}{3}x^3 \cos x + \frac{1}{3}\int x^3 \sin x\,dx$, which is more complicated than the original expression.

41. After two integrations by parts,
$\int e^x \sin x\,dx = -e^x \cos x + e^x \sin x - \int e^x \sin x\,dx$,
but after two more integrations,
$\int e^x \sin x\,dx = -e^x \cos x + e^x \sin x + e^x \cos x$
$- e^x \sin x + \int e^x \sin x\,dx$.
Two integrations produced the original integral with the opposite sign (which is useful), and two more integrations reversed the sign again to give the original integral with the same sign (which is not useful).

42. $\int \cos^2 x\,dx = \frac{1}{2}\int (1 + \cos 2x)\,dx$
$= \frac{1}{2}(x + \frac{1}{2}\sin 2x) + C$
By the double argument properties from trigonometry, $\frac{1}{2}(x + \frac{1}{2}\sin 2x) + C = \frac{1}{2}(x + \sin x \cos x) + C$, which is equivalent to the answer in Problem 27 found using integrating by parts.

43. <u>Area Problem</u>

Graph, $y = xe^{-x}$

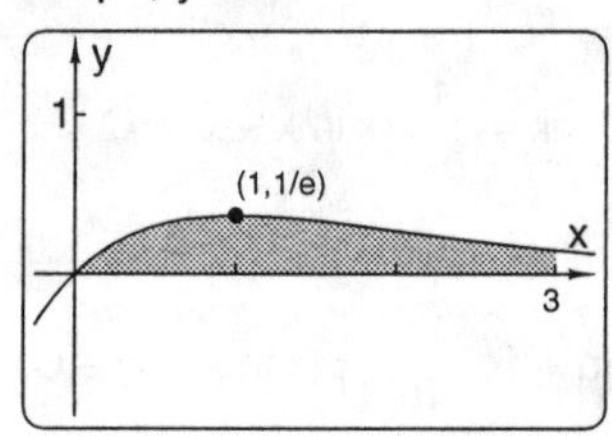

$y' = -xe^{-x} + e^{-x} = e^{-x}(1 - x)$

Critical points at x = 0,1,3; max. at x = 1.

$A = \int_0^3 x\, e^{-x}\, dx = -x\, e^{-x} \Big|_0^3 + \int_0^3 e^{-x}\, dx$

$= -3e^{-3} - e^{-x} \Big|_0^3$

$= -3e^{-3} - e^{-3} + 1 = -4e^{-3} + 1 = 0.8008 \ldots$

44. <u>Unbounded Region Area Problem</u>

$y = 12x^2 e^{-x}$

Area from x = 0 to x = b is

$A_b = \int_0^b 12x^2 e^{-x}\, dx$

$= -12x^2e^{-x} - 24xe^{-x} - 24e^{-x} \Big|_0^b$

$= -12b^2e^{-b} - 24be^{-b} - 24e^{-b} + 24.$

The first two terms approach zero as $b \to \infty$ by L'Hospital's rule. The third term also approaches 0.

$\therefore \lim_{b \to \infty} A_b = 24$

45. <u>Volume Problem</u>

$y = \ln x$

$dV = \pi y^2 dx = \pi\, (\ln x)^2\, dx$

$V = \int_1^5 \pi\, (\ln x)^2\, dx$

u		dv
$(\ln x)^2$	+	1
$2\,(\ln x)/x$		x
$2 \ln x$	−	1
$2/x$		x
2	+	↑
0	−	x

$= \pi x(\ln x)^2 - 2\pi x \ln x + 2\pi x \Big|_1^5$

$= 5\pi(\ln 5)^2 - 10\pi \ln 5 + 10\pi - 0 + 0 - 2\pi = 15.2589 \ldots$

46. <u>Proof Problem</u>

Consider $\int u\, dv$, and write $\int dv = v + C$.

Then $\int u\, dv = u(v + C) - \int (v + C)\, du$

$= uv + Cu - \int v\, du - \int C\, du = uv + Cu - \int v\, du - Cu$

$= uv - \int v\, du.$

Thus, the constant cancels out later, Q.E.D.

47. <u>Areas and Integration by Parts</u>

For integration by parts, $\int u\, dv = uv - \int v\, du$.

Applying limits of integration gives

$\int_c^d u\, dv = uv \Big|_{u=a}^{u=b} - \int_a^b v\, du$

$\int_c^d u\, dv = (bd - ac) - \int_a^b v\, du.$

The quantity (bd − ac) is the area of the "L-shaped" region, which is the area of the larger rectangle minus the area of the smaller one. Thus, the integral of u dv equals the area of the L-shaped region minus the area represented by the integral of v du.

48. <u>Integral of ln Generalization Problem</u>

$\int \ln ax\, dx = \int (\ln a + \ln x)\, dx = x \ln a + x \ln x - x + C$

$= x \ln ax - x + C$

49. <u>Introduction to Reduction Formulas Problem</u>

$\int \sin^7 x\, dx$

u		dv
$\sin^6 x$	+	$\sin x$
$6 \sin^5 x \cos x$	−	$-\cos x$

$= -\sin^6 x \cos x + 6\int \sin^5 x \cos^2 x\, dx$

$= -\sin^6 x \cos x + 6\int \sin^5 x\, (1 - \sin^2 x)\, dx$

$= -\sin^6 x \cos x + 6\int \sin^5 x\, dx - 6\int \sin^7 x\, dx$

$7 \int \sin^7 x\, dx = -\sin^6 x \cos x + 6\int \sin^5 x\, dx$

$\int \sin^7 x\, dx = -\frac{1}{7} \sin^6 x \cos x + \frac{6}{7} \int \sin^5 x\, dx$

The fractions are 1/(old exponent) and (old exponent − 1)/(old exponent). The new exponent is 2 less than the old exponent. So

$\int \sin^7 x\, dx$

$= -\frac{1}{7}\sin^6 x \cos x + \frac{6}{7}\left(-\frac{1}{5}\sin^4 x \cos x + \frac{4}{5}\int \sin^3 x\, dx\right)$

$= -\frac{1}{7}\sin^6 x \cos x - \frac{6}{35}\sin^4 x \cos x$

$\quad + \frac{24}{35}\left(-\frac{1}{3} \sin^2 x \cos x + \frac{2}{3}\int \sin x\, dx\right)$

$= -\frac{1}{7} \sin^6 x \cos x - \frac{6}{35} \sin^4 x \cos x$

$\quad - \frac{24}{105} \sin^2 x \cos x - \frac{48}{105} \cos x + C$

50. <u>Journal Problem</u>

Journal entries will vary.

<u>Problem Set 9-4, pages 449 to 451</u> <u>Reduction Formulas and Computer Software</u>

Q1. $uv - \int v\, du$

Q2. Graph, $y = 3 \cos x$

Q3. Graph, $y = \cos 2x$

Q4. $y' = 1 + \ln 5x$

Q5. $\frac{1}{6}\sin^6 x + C$

Q6. $\ln |x| + C$

Q7. $\frac{1}{2}(e^6 - e^2)$

Q8. Graph, example

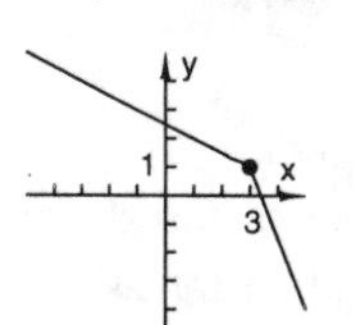

Q9. $\frac{1}{1 + x^2}$

Q10. $\ln |\sec x + \tan x| + C$

1. $\int \sin^9 x\,dx$

u		dv
$\sin^8 x$	+	$\sin x$
$8\sin^7 x\cos x$	−	$-\cos x$

$= -\sin^8 x\cos x + 8\int \sin^7 x\cos^2 x\,dx$
$= -\sin^8 x\cos x + 8\int \sin^7 x(1-\sin^2 x)\,dx$
$= -\sin^8 x\cos x + 8\int \sin^7 x\,dx - 8\int \sin^9 x\,dx$
$9\int \sin^9 x\,dx = -\sin^8 x\cos x + 8\int \sin^7 x\,dx$
$\int \sin^9 x\,dx = -\frac{1}{9}\sin^8 x\cos x + \frac{8}{9}\int \sin^7 x\,dx$

2. $\int \cos^{10} x\,dx$

u		dv
$\cos^9 x$	+	$\cos x$
$-9\cos^8 x\sin x$	−	$\sin x$

$= \cos^9 x\sin x + 9\int \cos^8 x\sin^2 x\,dx$
$= \cos^9 x\sin x + 9\int \cos^8 x(1-\cos^2 x)\,dx$
$= \cos^9 x\sin x + 9\int \cos^8 x\,dx - 9\int \cos^{10} x\,dx$
$10\int \cos^{10} x\,dx = \int \cos^9 x\,dx + 9\int \cos^8 x\,dx$
$\int \cos^{10} x\,dx = \frac{1}{10}\cos^9 x\sin x + \frac{9}{10}\int \cos^8 x\,dx$

3. $\int \cot^{12} x\,dx = \int \cot^{10} x\cot^2 x\,dx$
$= \int \cot^{10} x(\csc^2 x - 1)\,dx$
$= \int \cot^{10} x\csc^2 x\,dx - \int \cot^{10} x\,dx$
$= -\frac{1}{11}\cot^{11} x - \int \cot^{10} x\,dx$

4. $\int \tan^{20} x\,dx = \int \tan^{18} x\tan^2 x\,dx$
$= \int \tan^{18} x(\sec^2 x - 1)\,dx$
$= \int \tan^{18} x\sec^2 x\,dx - \int \tan^{18} x\,dx$
$= \frac{1}{19}\tan^{19} x - \int \tan^{18} x\,dx$

5. $\int \sec^{13} x\,dx$

u		dv
$\sec^{11} x$	+	$\sec^2 x$
$11\sec^{10} x\sec x\tan x$	−	$\tan x$

$= \sec^{11} x\tan x - 11\int \sec^{11} x\tan^2 x\,dx$
$= \sec^{11} x\tan x - 11\int \sec^{11} x(\sec^2 x - 1)\,dx$
$= \sec^{11} x\tan x - 11\int \sec^{13} x\,dx + 11\int \sec^{11} x\,dx$
$12\int \sec^{13} x\,dx = \sec^{11} x\tan x + 11\int \sec^{11} x\,dx$
$\int \sec^{13} x\,dx = \frac{1}{12}\sec^{11} x\tan x + \frac{11}{12}\int \sec^{11} x\,dx$

6. $\int \csc^{100} x\,dx$

u		dv
$\csc^{98} x$	+	$\csc^2 x$
$-98\csc^{97} x\csc x\cot x$	−	$-\cot x$

$= -\csc^{98} x\cot x - 98\int \csc^{98} x\cot^2 x\,dx$
$= -\csc^{98} x\cot x - 98\int \csc^{98} x(\csc^2 x - 1)\,dx$
$= -\csc^{98} x\cot x - 98\int \csc^{100} x\,dx + 98\int \csc^{98} x\,dx$
$99\int \csc^{100} x\,dx = -\csc^{98} x\cot x + 98\int \csc^{98} x\,dx$
$\int \csc^{100} x\,dx = -\frac{1}{99}\csc^{98} x\cot x + \frac{98}{99}\int \csc^{98} x\,dx$

7. $\int \cos^n x\,dx$

u		dv
$\cos^{n-1} x$	+	$\cos x$
$-(n-1)\cos^{n-2} x\sin x$	−	$\sin x$

$= \cos^{n-1} x\sin x + (n-1)\int \cos^{n-2} x\sin^2 x\,dx$
$= \cos^{n-1} x\sin x + (n-1)\int \cos^{n-2} x(1-\cos^2 x)\,dx$
$= \cos^{n-1} x\sin x + (n-1)\int \cos^{n-2} x\,dx - (n-1)\int \cos^n x\,dx$
$n\int \cos^n x\,dx = \cos^{n-1} x\sin x + (n-1)\int \cos^{n-2} x\,dx$
$\int \cos^n x\,dx = \frac{1}{n}\cos^{n-1} x\sin x + \frac{n-1}{n}\int \cos^{n-2} x\,dx$

8. $\int \sin^n x\,dx$

u		dv
$\sin^{n-1} x$	+	$\sin x$
$(n-1)\sin^{n-2} x\cos x$	−	$-\cos x$

$= -\sin^{n-1} x\cos x + (n-1)\int \sin^{n-2} x\cos^2 x\,dx$
$= -\sin^{n-1} x\cos x + (n-1)\int \sin^{n-2} x(1-\sin^2 x)\,dx$
$= -\sin^{n-1} x\cos x + (n-1)\int \sin^{n-2} x\,dx$
$- (n-1)\int \sin^n x\,dx$
$n\int \sin^n x\,dx = -\sin^{n-1} x\cos x + (n-1)\int \sin^{n-2} x\,dx$
$\int \sin^n x\,dx = -\frac{1}{n}\sin^{n-1} x\cos x + \frac{n-1}{n}\int \sin^{n-2} x\,dx$

9. $\int \tan^n x\,dx = \int \tan^{n-2} x\tan^2 x\,dx$
$= \int \tan^{n-2} x(\sec^2 x - 1)\,dx$
$= \int \tan^{n-2} x\sec^2 x\,dx - \int \tan^{n-2} x\,dx$
$= \frac{1}{n-1}\tan^{n-1} x - \int \tan^{n-2} x\,dx$

10. $\int \cot^n x\,dx = \int \cot^{n-2} x\cot^2 x\,dx$
$= \int \cot^{n-2} x(\csc^2 x - 1)\,dx$
$= \int \cot^{n-2} x\csc^2 x\,dx - \int \cot^{n-2} x\,dx$
$= -\frac{1}{n-1}\cot^{n-1} x - \int \cot^{n-2} x\,dx.$

11. $\int \csc^n x\,dx$

u		dv
$\csc^{n-2} x$	+	$\csc^2 x$
$-(n-2)\csc^{n-3} x\csc x\cot x$	−	$-\cot x$

$= -\csc^{n-2} x\cot x - (n-2)\int \csc^{n-2} x\cot^2 x\,dx$
$= -\csc^{n-2} x\cot x - (n-2)\int \csc^{n-2} x(\csc^2 x - 1)\,dx$
$= -\csc^{n-2} x\cot x - (n-2)\int \csc^n x\,dx$
$+ (n-2)\int \csc^{n-2} x\,dx$
$(n-1)\int \csc^n x\,dx = -\csc^{n-2} x\cot x$
$+ (n-2)\int \csc^{n-2} x\,dx$
$\int \csc^n x\,dx = -\frac{1}{n-1}\csc^{n-2} x\cot x$
$+ \frac{n-2}{n-1}\int \csc^{n-2} x\,dx$

12. $\int \sec^n x\,dx$

u		dv
$\sec^{n-2} x$	+	$\sec^2 x$
$(n-2)\sec^{n-3} x\sec x\tan x$	−	$\tan x$

$= \sec^{n-2} x\tan x - (n-2)\int \sec^{n-2} x\tan^2 x\,dx$
$= \sec^{n-2} x\tan x - (n-2)\int \sec^{n-2} x(\sec^2 x - 1)\,dx$
$= \sec^{n-2} x\tan x - (n-2)\int \sec^n x\,dx$
$+ (n-2)\int \sec^{n-2} x\,dx$
$(n-1)\int \sec^n x\,dx = \sec^{n-2} x\tan x$
$+ (n-2)\int \sec^{n-2} x\,dx$
$\int \sec^n x\,dx = \frac{1}{n-1}\sec^{n-2} x\tan x$
$+ \frac{n-2}{n-1}\int \sec^{n-2} x\,dx$

13. $\int \sin^5 x\,dx$

$= -\frac{1}{5}\sin^4 x \cos x - \frac{4}{5}(\frac{1}{3}\sin^2 x \cos x + \frac{2}{3}\cos x) + C$

$= -\frac{1}{5}\sin^4 x \cos x - \frac{4}{15}\sin^2 x \cos x - \frac{8}{15}\cos x + C$

14. $\int \cos^5 x\,dx$

$= \frac{1}{5}\cos^4 x \sin x + \frac{4}{5}(\frac{1}{3}\cos^2 x \sin x + \frac{2}{3}\sin x) + C$

$= \frac{1}{5}\cos^4 x \sin x + \frac{4}{15}\cos^2 x \sin x + \frac{8}{15}\sin x + C$

15. $\int \cot^6 x\,dx$

$= -\frac{1}{5}\cot^5 x - (-\frac{1}{3}\cot^3 x - (-\cot x - x)) + C$

$= -\frac{1}{5}\cot^5 x + \frac{1}{3}\cot^3 x - \cot x - x + C$

16. $\int \tan^7 x\,dx$

$= \frac{1}{6}\tan^6 x - (\frac{1}{4}\tan^4 x - (\frac{1}{2}\tan^2 x + \ln|\cos x|)) + C$

$= \frac{1}{6}\tan^6 x - \frac{1}{4}\tan^4 x + \frac{1}{2}\tan^2 x + \ln|\cos x| + C$

17. $\int \sec^4 x\,dx = \frac{1}{3}\sec^2 x \tan x + \frac{2}{3}\tan x + C$

18. $\int \csc^4 x\,dx = -\frac{1}{3}\csc^2 x \cot x - \frac{2}{3}\cot x + C$

19. Cosine Area Problem

a. $y = \cos x$ is on top; $y = \cos^3 x$ is in the middle; $y = \cos^5 x$ is on the bottom.

b. For $y = \cos x$, area ≈ 2.0000 ...
For $y = \cos^3 x$, area ≈ 1.3333 ...
For $y = \cos^5 x$, area ≈ 1.06666 ...

c. $A_1 = \int_{-\pi/2}^{\pi/2} \cos x\,dx = \sin x \Big|_{-\pi/2}^{\pi/2}$

$\sin(\pi/2) - \sin(-\pi/2) = \underline{2}$

$A_3 = \int_{-\pi/2}^{\pi/2} \cos^3 x\,dx$

$= \frac{1}{3}\cos^2 x \sin x + \frac{2}{3}\sin x \Big|_{-\pi/2}^{\pi/2}$

$= \frac{1}{3}\cos^2(\pi/2)\sin(\pi/2) + \frac{2}{3}\sin(\pi/2)$

$- \frac{1}{3}\cos^2(-\pi/2)\sin(-\pi/2) - \frac{2}{3}\sin(-\pi/2)$

$= 0 + \frac{2}{3} - 0 + \frac{2}{3} = \frac{4}{3} = 1.3333$ ...

Observe that $A_3 = \frac{2}{3}A_1$.

$A_5 = \int_{-\pi/2}^{\pi/2} \cos^5 x\,dx$

$= \frac{1}{5}\cos^4 x \sin x \Big|_{-\pi/2}^{\pi/2} + \frac{4}{5}\int_{-\pi/2}^{\pi/2} \cos^3 x\,dx$

$= 0 + \frac{4}{5}A_3 = \frac{4}{5}\cdot\frac{4}{3} = \frac{4}{5}\cdot\frac{2}{3}\cdot 2 = \frac{16}{15} = 1.066666$ ...

d. Based on the graphs, the area under cos x should be greater than that under $\cos^3 x$, which in turn is greater than the area under $\cos^5 x$. This is exactly what happens with the calculated answers: $A_1 > A_3 > A_5$

e. Graph

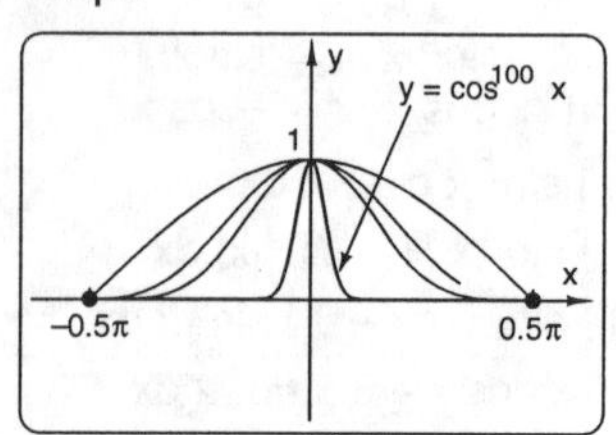

f. Yes, $\lim_{n\to\infty} \int_{-\pi/2}^{\pi/2} \cos^n x\,dx = 0$.

Following the pattern in part c, for odd n,

$A_n = \frac{(n-1)(n-3)(n-5)\ \dots\ (4)(2)(1)}{(n)(n-2)(n-4)\ \dots\ (5)(3)} \cdot 2,$

the denominator gets large faster than the numerator. However, since both go to infinity, this observation is not decisive. The following epsilon proof by Cavan Fang establishes the fact rigorously, using the definition of limit in the form, "For any $\varepsilon > 0$ there is an $N > 0$ such that whenever $n > N$, $A_n < \varepsilon$."

Proof:

Pick $0 < \varepsilon < 2\pi$.

Then $0 < \cos\frac{\varepsilon}{4} < 1$, so there exists $N > 0$ such that

$\cos^N \frac{\varepsilon}{4} < \frac{\varepsilon}{2\pi}$.

Note that if $\frac{\varepsilon}{4} < x < \frac{\pi}{2}$, then $\cos x < \cos\frac{\varepsilon}{4}$

$\Rightarrow \cos^N x < \frac{\varepsilon}{2\pi}$.

Now, for any $n > N$,

$\int_{-\pi/2}^{\pi/2} \cos^n x\,dx = 2\int_0^{\varepsilon/4} \cos^n x\,dx + 2\int_{\varepsilon/4}^{\pi/2} \cos^n x\,dx.$

But $2\int_0^{\varepsilon/4} \cos^n x\,dx < 2\int_0^{\varepsilon/4} dx = \frac{\varepsilon}{2}$. $\quad (\cos^n x < 1)$

And $2\int_{\varepsilon/4}^{\pi/2} \cos^n x\,dx < 2\int_{\varepsilon/4}^{\pi/2} \cos^N x\,dx$ $(n > N)$

$< 2\int_{\varepsilon/4}^{\pi/2} \frac{\varepsilon}{2\pi}\,dx < \frac{\varepsilon}{\pi}\int_0^{\pi/2} dx = \frac{\varepsilon}{2}$. $\quad (\cos^N x < \frac{\varepsilon}{2\pi})$

So $\int_{-\pi/2}^{\pi/2} \cos^n x\,dx$

$= 2\int_0^{\varepsilon/4} \cos^n x\,dx + 2\int_{\varepsilon/4}^{\pi/2} \cos^n x\,dx < \varepsilon.$

$\therefore \lim_{n\to\infty} \int_{-\pi/2}^{\pi/2} \cos^n x\,dx = 0$, Q.E.D.

20. Integral of $\cos^5 x$ Another Way

$\int \cos^5 x\,dx = \int \cos^4 x \cos x\,dx$

$= \int (1 - \sin^2 x)^2 \cos x\,dx$

$= \int (1 - 2\sin^2 x + \sin^4 x)\cos x\,dx$

$= \int \cos x\,dx - 2\int \sin^2 x \cos x\,dx + \int \sin^4 x \cos x\,dx$

$= \sin x - \frac{2}{3}\sin^3 x + \frac{1}{5}\sin^5 x + C$

From Problem 19, $A_5 = \int_{-\pi/2}^{\pi/2} \sin^5 x\,dx$

$= 2(\sin x - \frac{2}{3}\sin^3 x + \frac{1}{5}\sin^5 x)\Big|_0^{\pi/2}$

$= 2 - \frac{4}{3} + \frac{2}{5} = \frac{16}{15} = 1.0666$ ..., which agrees.

21. Integral of Secant Cubed Problem

$\int \sec^3 x\,dx$

u		dv
sec x	+	$\sec^2 x$
sec x tan x	−	tan x

$= \sec x \tan x - \int \sec x \tan^2 x\,dx$

$= \sec x \tan x - \int \sec x(\sec^2 x - 1)\,dx$

$= \sec x \tan x - \int \sec^3 x\,dx + \int \sec x\,dx$

$2\int \sec^3 x\,dx = \sec x \tan x + \ln|\sec x + \tan x| + C_1$

$\int \sec^3 x\,dx = \frac{1}{2}\sec x \tan x + \frac{1}{2}\ln|\sec x + \tan x| + C$

Note that the answer is half the derivative of secant plus half the integral of secant.

22. Reduction Formula for $\int \sin^n ax\,dx$

$\int \sin^n ax\,dx$

u		dv
$\sin^{n-1} ax$	+	sin ax
$a(n-1)\sin^{n-2} ax \cos ax$	−	$-\frac{1}{a}\cos ax$

$= -\frac{1}{a}\sin^{n-1} ax \cos ax + (n-1)\int \sin^{n-2} ax \cos^2 ax\,dx$

$= -\frac{1}{a}\sin^{n-1} ax \cos ax$

$+ (n-1)\int \sin^{n-2} ax(1 - \sin^2 ax)\,dx$

$= -\frac{1}{a}\sin^{n-1} ax \cos ax + (n-1)\int \sin^{n-2} ax\,dx$

$-(n-1)\int \sin^n ax\,dx$

$n\int \sin^n ax\,dx$

$= -\frac{1}{a}\sin^{n-1} ax \cos ax + (n-1)\int \sin^{n-2} ax\,dx$

$\int \sin^n ax\,dx$

$= -\frac{1}{an}\sin^{n-1} ax \cos ax + \frac{n-1}{n}\int \sin^{n-2} ax\,dx$

$\int \sin^5 3x\,dx =$

$-\frac{1}{15}\sin^4 3x \cos 3x - \frac{4}{45}\sin^2 3x \cos 3x - \frac{8}{45}\cos 3x + C$

23. $\int \sin^3 ax\,dx = -\frac{1}{3a}\sin^2 ax \cos ax + \frac{2}{3}\int \sin ax\,dx$

(From Problem 22)

$= -\frac{1}{3a}\sin^2 ax \cos ax - \frac{2}{3a}\cos ax + C$

$= -\frac{1}{3a}\cos ax(\sin^2 ax + 2) + C$, Q.E.D.

Or: $\frac{d}{dx}\left(-\frac{1}{3a}(\cos ax)(\sin^2 ax + 2)\right)$

$= -\frac{1}{3a}(-a \sin ax)(\sin^2 ax + 2)$

$-\frac{1}{3a}(\cos ax)(2a \sin ax \cos ax)$

$= \frac{1}{3}(\sin^3 ax + 2\sin ax - 2\sin ax \cos^2 ax)$

$= \frac{1}{3}(\sin^3 ax + 2\sin ax(1 - \cos^2 ax))$

$= \frac{1}{3}(\sin^3 ax + 2\sin ax(\sin^2 ax))$

$= \sin^3 ax$

$\therefore \int \sin^3 ax\,dx = -\frac{1}{3a}(\cos ax)(\sin^2 ax + 2) + C$, Q.E.D.

24. Use integration by parts, or use the technique of Problem 20, as shown here.

$\int \cos^3 ax\,dx = \int \cos^2 ax \cos ax\,dx$

$= \int (1 - \sin^2 ax)\cos ax\,dx$

$= \int \cos ax\,dx - \int \sin^2 ax \cos ax\,dx$

$= \frac{1}{a}\sin ax - \frac{1}{3a}\sin^3 ax + C$

$= \frac{1}{3a}(\sin ax)(3 - \sin^2 ax) + C$

$= \frac{1}{3a}(\sin ax)(2 + \cos^2 ax) + C$, Q.E.D.

Or: Differentiate, as in the alternate solution for Problem 23.

Problem Set 9-5, pages 453 to 455

Integrating Special Powers of Trigonometric Functions

Q1. $f'(1) = -4$

Q2. $g'(2) = 1/2$

Q3. $h'(3) = -12$

Q4. $t'(4) = \pi/24$

Q5. $p'(5) = 6e^5$

Q6. $x = 8^3 = 512$

Q7. Graph

Q8. integration by parts

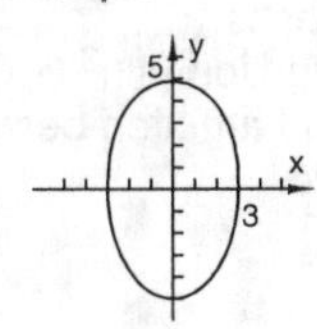

Q9. Graph

Q10. reduction

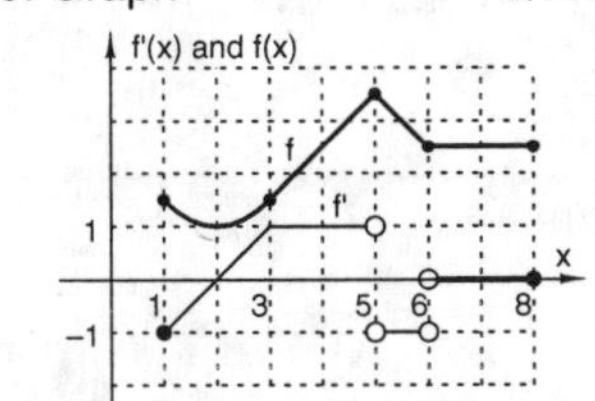

1. $\int \sin^5 x\,dx = \int (1 - \cos^2 x)^2 \sin x\,dx$

$= \int (1 - 2\cos^2 x + \cos^4 x)\sin x\,dx$

$= -\cos x + \frac{2}{3}\cos^3 x - \frac{1}{5}\cos^5 x + C$

2. $\int \cos^7 x\,dx = \int (1 - \sin^2 x)^3 \cos x\,dx$

$= \int (1 - 3\sin^2 x + 3\sin^4 x - \sin^6 x)\cos x\,dx$

$= \sin x - \sin^3 x + \frac{3}{5}\sin^5 x - \frac{1}{7}\sin^7 x + C$

3. $\int \cos^7 9x\,dx = \int (1 - \sin^2 9x)^3 \cos 9x\,dx$

$= \int (1 - 3\sin^2 9x + 3\sin^4 9x - \sin^6 9x)\cos 9x\,dx$

$= \frac{1}{9}\sin 9x - \frac{1}{9}\sin^3 9x + \frac{1}{15}\sin^5 9x - \frac{1}{63}\sin^7 9x + C$

4. $\int \sin^3 10x\,dx = \int (1 - \cos^2 10x)\sin 10x\,dx$

$= -\frac{1}{10}\cos 10x + \frac{1}{30}\cos^3 10x + C$

5. $\int \sin^4 3x \cos 3x\,dx = \frac{1}{15}\sin^5 3x + C$

6. $\int \cos^8 7x \sin 7x\,dx = -\frac{1}{63}\cos^9 7x + C$

7. $\int \cos^6 8x \sin^3 8x\,dx$

$= \int \cos^6 8x(1 - \cos^2 8x)\sin 8x\,dx$

$= \int (\cos^6 8x - \cos^8 8x)\sin 8x\,dx$

$= -\frac{1}{56}\cos^7 8x + \frac{1}{72}\cos^9 8x + C$

8. $\int \sin^4 2x \cos^3 2x\, dx$
$= \int \sin^4 2x\,(1 - \sin^2 2x) \cos 2x\, dx$
$= \int (\sin^4 2x - \sin^6 2x) \cos 2x\, dx$
$= \frac{1}{10}\sin^5 2x - \frac{1}{14}\sin^7 2x + C$

9. $\int \sin^5 x \cos^2 x\, dx = \int \sin x\,(1 - \cos^2 x)^2 \cos^2 x\, dx$
$= \int (\cos^2 x - 2\cos^4 x + \cos^6 x) \sin x\, dx$
$= -\frac{1}{3}\cos^3 x + \frac{2}{5}\cos^5 x - \frac{1}{7}\cos^7 x + C$

10. $\int \cos^3 x \sin^2 x\, dx = \int \cos x\,(1 - \sin^2 x) \sin^2 x\, dx$
$= \int (\sin^2 x - \sin^4 x) \cos x\, dx$
$= \frac{1}{3}\sin^3 x - \frac{1}{5}\sin^5 x + C$

11. $\int \cos^2 x\, dx = \frac{1}{2}\int (1 + \cos 2x)\, dx = \frac{1}{2}x + \frac{1}{4}\sin 2x + C$

12. $\int \sin^2 x\, dx = \frac{1}{2}\int (1 - \cos 2x)\, dx = \frac{1}{2}x - \frac{1}{4}\sin 2x + C$

13. $\int \sin^2 5x\, dx = \frac{1}{2}\int (1 - \cos 10x)\, dx$
$= \frac{1}{2}x - \frac{1}{20}\sin 10x + C$

14. $\int \cos^2 6x\, dx = \frac{1}{2}\int (1 + \cos 12x)\, dx$
$= \frac{1}{2}x + \frac{1}{24}\sin 12x + C$

15. $\int \sec^4 x\, dx = \int (\tan^2 x + 1) \sec^2 x\, dx$
$= \frac{1}{3}\tan^3 x + \tan x + C$

16. $\int \csc^6 x\, dx = \int (\cot^2 x + 1)^2 \csc^2 x\, dx$
$= \int (\cot^4 x + 2\cot^2 x + 1) \csc^2 x\, dx$
$= -\frac{1}{5}\cot^5 x - \frac{2}{3}\cot^3 x - \cot x + C$

17. $\int \csc^8 6x\, dx = \int (\cot^2 6x + 1)^3 \csc^2 6x\, dx$
$= \int (\cot^6 6x + 3\cot^4 6x + 3\cot^2 6x + 1) \csc^2 6x\, dx$
$= -\frac{1}{42}\cot^7 6x - \frac{1}{10}\cot^5 6x - \frac{1}{6}\cot^3 6x - \frac{1}{6}\cot 6x + C$

18. $\int \sec^4 100x\, dx = \int (\tan^2 100x + 1) \sec^2 100x\, dx$
$= \frac{1}{300}\tan^3 100x + \frac{1}{100}\tan 100x + C$

19. $\int \tan^{10} x \sec^2 x\, dx = \frac{1}{11}\tan^{11} x + C$

20. $\int \cot^8 x \csc^2 x\, dx = -\frac{1}{9}\cot^9 x + C$

21. $\int \sec^{10} x \tan x\, dx = \int \sec^9 x\,(\sec x \tan x\, dx)$
$= \frac{1}{10}\sec^{10} x + C$

22. $\int \csc^8 x \cot x\, dx = \int \csc^7 x\,(\csc x \cot x\, dx)$
$= -\frac{1}{8}\csc^8 x + C$

23. $\int \sec^{10} 20\, dx = \sec^{10} 20 \int dx = (\sec^{10} 20)x + C$

24. $\int \csc^8 12\, dx = \csc^8 12 \int dx = (\csc^8 12)x + C$

25. $\int (\cos^2 x - \sin^2 x)\, dx = \int \cos 2x\, dx = \frac{1}{2}\sin 2x + C$

26. $\int (\cos^2 x + \sin^2 x)\, dx = \int dx = x + C$

27. $\int (\sin x)^{-2}\, dx = \int \csc^2 x\, dx = -\cot x + C$

28. $\int (\cos 3x)^{-2}\, dx = \int \sec^2 3x\, dx = \frac{1}{3}\tan 3x + C$

29. $\int \sec^3 x\, dx = \frac{1}{2}\sec x \tan x + \frac{1}{2}\ln|\sec x + \tan x| + C$

30. $\int \csc^3 x\, dx = -\frac{1}{2}\csc x \cot x - \frac{1}{2}\ln|\csc x + \cot x| + C$

31. Area Problem I

a. $\int \cos 5x \sin 3x\, dx$

u		dv
$\sin 3x$	+	$\cos 5x$
$3\cos 3x$	−	$\frac{1}{5}\sin 5x$
$-9\sin 3x$	+	$-\frac{1}{25}\cos 5x$

$= \frac{1}{5}\sin 5x \sin 3x + \frac{3}{25}\cos 5x \cos 3x$
$+ \frac{9}{25}\int \cos 5x \sin 3x\, dx$

$\frac{16}{25}\int \cos 5x \sin 3x\, dx$
$= \frac{1}{5}\sin 5x \sin 3x + \frac{3}{25}\cos 5x \cos 3x + C_1$

$\int \cos 5x \sin 3x\, dx$
$= \frac{5}{16}\sin 5x \sin 3x + \frac{3}{16}\cos 5x \cos 3x + C$

b. $\int_0^{2\pi} \cos 5x \sin 3x\, dx$
$= \frac{5}{16}\sin 5x \sin 3x + \frac{3}{16}\cos 3x \cos 5x \Big|_0^{2\pi} = 0.$

Since the integral finds the area above – minus the area below, this calculation shows the two areas are equal.

32. Area Problem II

a. Graph, $f(x) = \sin^3 x$

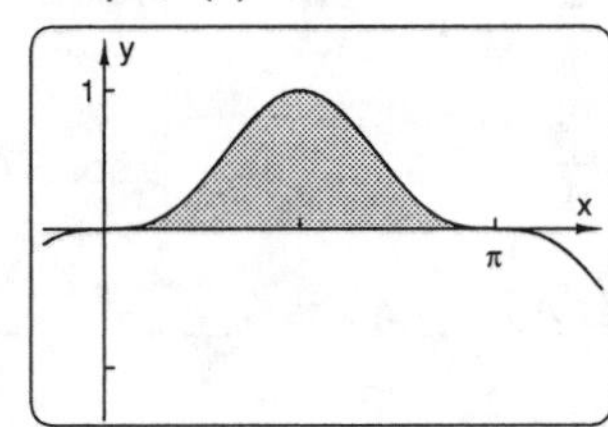

b. $A = \int_0^{\pi} \sin^3 x\, dx = \frac{1}{3}\cos^3 x - \cos x \Big|_0^{\pi} = \frac{4}{3}$

c. Numerically, $A \approx 1.3333\ldots$. (Checks.)

d. $A = 0$ because $\sin^3 x$ is an odd function ($\sin^3(-x) = -\sin^3 x$), and the integral of an odd function between symmetrical limits is equal to zero.

33. Volume Problem No. I

$dV = \pi y^2\, dx = \pi \sin^2 x\, dx$

$V = \pi\int_0^{\pi} \sin^2 x\, dx = \frac{\pi}{2}\int_0^{\pi} (1 - \cos 2x)\, dx$

$= \frac{\pi}{2}x - \frac{\pi}{4}\sin 2x \Big|_0^{\pi} = \pi^2/2$

34. Volume Problem II

a. $y = \sec^2 x$

$dV = \pi((y + 3)^2 - 3^2)\,dx$
$= \pi(\sec^4 x + 6\sec^2 x)\,dx$
$V = \pi\int_0^1 (\sec^4 x + 6\sec^2 x)\,dx$
$= \pi\int_0^1 [(1 + \tan^2 x)\sec^2 x + 6\sec^2 x]\,dx$
$= \pi\int_0^1 (\tan^2 x\sec^2 x + 7\sec^2 x)\,dx$
$= \frac{\pi}{3}\tan^3 x + 7\pi\tan x \Big|_0^1$
$= \frac{\pi}{3}\tan^3 1 + 7\pi\tan 1$ (= 38.2049 ...)

b. $dV = 2\pi(x + 3)y\,dx = 2\pi(x + 3)(\sec^2 x)\,dx$

$V = 2\pi\int_0^1 x\sec^2 x\,dx + 6\pi\int_0^1 \sec^2 x\,dx$
$= 2\pi x\tan x \Big|_0^1 - 2\pi\int_0^1 \tan x\,dx + 6\pi\tan x \Big|_0^1$
$= 8\pi\tan 1 + 2\pi\ln|\cos x| \Big|_0^1$
$= 8\pi\tan 1 + 2\pi\ln(\cos 1)$ (= 35.2738 ...)

35. Limaçon Area Problem

$dA = \frac{1}{2}r^2\,d\theta = \frac{1}{2}(5 + 4\cos\theta)^2\,d\theta$
$A = \frac{1}{2}\int_0^{\pi/4} (16\cos^2\theta + 40\cos\theta + 25)\,d\theta$
$= 4(\theta + \frac{1}{2}\sin 2\theta) + 20\sin\theta + \frac{25}{2}\theta \Big|_0^{\pi/4}$
$= \pi + 2 + 10\sqrt{2} + \frac{25}{8}\pi = 29.1012\ldots$, which agrees with the numerical answer.

36. Cardioid Area Problem

$dA = \frac{1}{2}r^2\,d\theta = \frac{1}{2}a^2(1 + \cos\theta)^2\,d\theta$
$A = \frac{1}{2}a^2\int_0^{2\pi} (1 + 2\cos\theta + \cos^2\theta)\,d\theta$
$= \frac{1}{2}a^2(\theta + 2\sin\theta + \frac{1}{2}\theta + \frac{1}{4}\sin 2\theta) \Big|_0^{2\pi}$
$= \frac{3}{2}\pi a^2$, which is 1.5 times A_{circle}.

37. Journal Problem

Journal entries will vary.

Problem Set 9-6, pages 459 to 462 — Integration by Trigonometric Substitution

Q1. $\frac{1}{3}\sin 3x + C$ Q2. $-\frac{1}{4}\cos 4x + C$

Q3. $-\frac{1}{5}\ln|\cos 5x| + C$ Q4. $\frac{1}{6}\ln|\sin 6x| + C$

Q5. $\frac{1}{7}\ln|\sec 7x + \tan 7x| + C$

Q6. $5\sec^2 5x$ Q7. $y' = 4\cos 4x$

Q8. d Q9. See text stmt. of f.t.c.

Q10. See text definition of indefinite integral, Sect. 5-4.

Note: A radical without a sign in front of it means the *positive* root. Since trigonometric functions can be positive or negative, the radical should technically be replaced by the *absolute value* of the appropriate trigonometric function. Fortunately, this turns out to be unnecessary. If x has been replaced by ($a\sin\theta$), ($a\tan\theta$), or ($a\sec\theta$), it is assumed that θ is the corresponding inverse trigonometric *function.* So θ is restricted to the range of that inverse trigonometric function. Thus, respectively,

$\sqrt{a^2 - x^2} = a|\cos\theta|$, and $\theta \in$ Quadrant I or IV
$\sqrt{a^2 + x^2} = a|\sec\theta|$, and $\theta \in$ Quadrant I or IV
$\sqrt{x^2 - a^2} = a|\tan\theta|$, and $\theta \in$ Quadrant I or II.

For the first two, the absolute value is unnecessary, because $\cos\theta \geq 0$ and $\sec\theta \geq 0$ in the respective quadrants. For the secant substitution, if x is negative, then θ is in Quadrant II, where $\tan\theta < 0$. Thus, the radical equals the *opposite* of ($a\tan\theta$), and one should write

$\sqrt{x^2 - a^2} = -a\tan\theta$.

Where the integral of $\sec\theta$ occurs, one gets

$\ln|a + \sqrt{x^2 + a^2}|$ for $x > 0$
$-\ln|a - \sqrt{x^2 + a^2}|$ for $x < 0$.

The second form can be transformed into the first by taking advantage of the property $-\ln n = \ln(1/n)$. Thus,

$-\ln|a - \sqrt{a^2 - x^2}| = \ln\left|\frac{1}{a - \sqrt{a^2 - x^2}}\right|$
$= \ln|a + \sqrt{a^2 - x^2}|$,

which can be shown by rationalizing the denominator of the fraction. Since the major focus of this section is on the correct substitution to use and the ensuing calculus, and since algebraic techniques are of less importance now that technology is used for evaluating integrals, the student is not expected to carry along the absolute value just to eliminate it later.

1. $\int\sqrt{49 - x^2}\,dx$

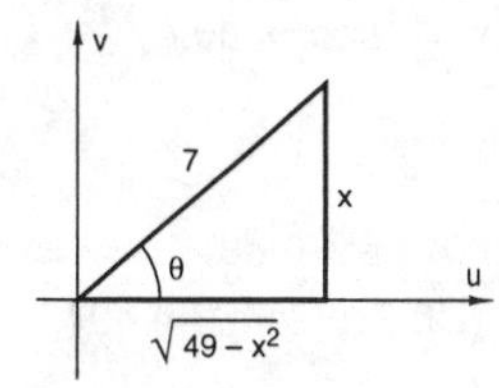

Let $\frac{x}{7} = \sin\theta$. $x = 7\sin\theta$, $dx = 7\cos\theta\,d\theta$,
$\sqrt{49 - x^2} = 7\cos\theta$, $\theta = \sin^{-1}\frac{x}{7}$
$\therefore \int\sqrt{49 - x^2}\,dx = 7\int\cos\theta\,(7\cos\theta\,d\theta)$
$= 49\int\cos^2\theta\,d\theta = \frac{49}{2}\int(1 + \cos 2\theta)\,d\theta$
$= \frac{49}{2}\theta + \frac{49}{4}\sin 2\theta + C = \frac{49}{2}\theta + \frac{49}{2}\sin\theta\cos\theta + C$
$= \frac{49}{2}\sin^{-1}\frac{x}{7} + \frac{49}{2}\cdot\frac{1}{7}x\cdot\frac{1}{7}\sqrt{49 - x^2} + C$
$= \frac{49}{2}\sin^{-1}\frac{x}{7} + \frac{1}{2}x\sqrt{49 - x^2} + C$

2. $\int \sqrt{100 - x^2}\, dx$

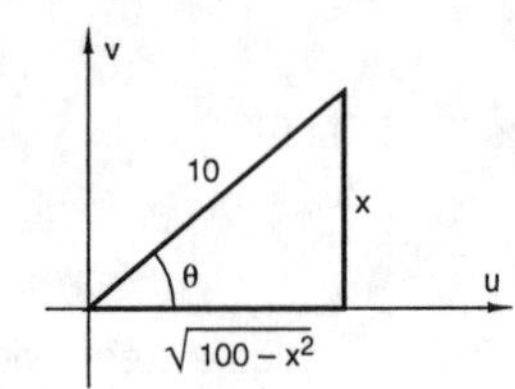

Let $\frac{x}{10} = \sin\theta$. $x = 10\sin\theta$, $dx = 10\cos\theta\, d\theta$,

$\sqrt{100 - x^2} = 10\cos\theta$, $\theta = \sin^{-1}\frac{x}{10}$

$\therefore \int \sqrt{100 - x^2}\, dx = \int 10\cos\theta\,(10\cos\theta\, d\theta)$

$= 100\int \cos^2\theta\, d\theta = \frac{100}{2}\int (1 + \cos 2\theta)\, d\theta$

$= 50\,\theta + 25\sin 2\theta + C$

$= 50\,\theta + 50\sin\theta\cos\theta + C$

$= 50\sin^{-1}\frac{x}{10} + 50\cdot\frac{1}{10}\,x\cdot\frac{1}{10}\sqrt{100 - x^2} + C$

$= 50\sin^{-1}\frac{x}{10} + \frac{1}{2}x\sqrt{100 - x^2} + C$

3. $\int \sqrt{x^2 + 16}\, dx$

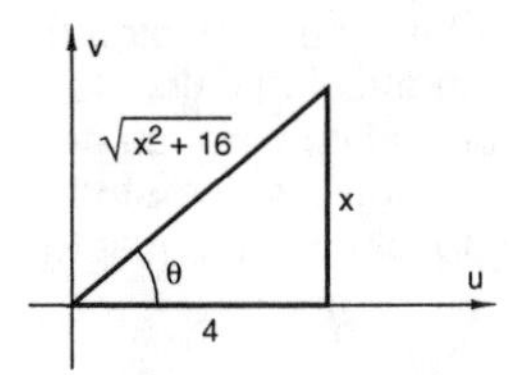

Let $\frac{x}{4} = \tan\theta$. $x = 4\tan\theta$, $dx = 4\sec^2\theta\, d\theta$,

$\sqrt{x^2 + 16} = 4\sec\theta$, $\theta = \tan^{-1}\frac{x}{4}$

$\therefore \int \sqrt{x^2 + 16}\, dx = \int 4\sec\theta\,(4\sec^2\theta\, d\theta)$

$= 16\int \sec^3\theta\, d\theta$ (Cf. Problem 9-4 #21.)

$= \frac{16}{2}\sec\theta\tan\theta + \frac{16}{2}\ln|\sec\theta + \tan\theta| + C_1$

$= \frac{1}{2}x\sqrt{x^2 + 16} + 8\ln\left|\frac{\sqrt{x^2 + 16}}{4} + \frac{x}{4}\right| + C_1$

$= \frac{1}{2}x\sqrt{x^2 + 16} + 8\ln|\sqrt{x^2 + 16} + x| - 8\ln 4 + C_1$

$= \frac{1}{2}x\sqrt{x^2 + 16} + 8\ln|\sqrt{x^2 + 16} + x| + C$

4. $\int \sqrt{81 + x^2}\, dx$

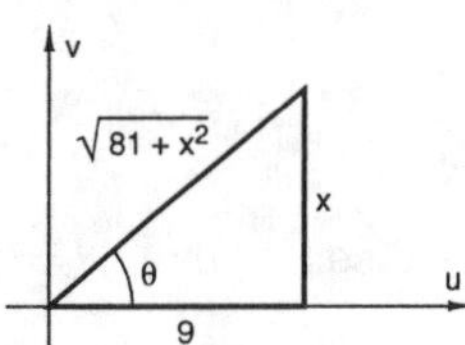

Let $\frac{x}{9} = \tan\theta$. $x = 9\tan\theta$, $dx = 9\sec^2\theta\, d\theta$,

$\sqrt{81 + x^2} = 9\sec\theta$, $\theta = \tan^{-1}\frac{x}{9}$

$\therefore \int \sqrt{81 + x^2}\, dx = \int 9\sec\theta\,(9\sec^2\theta\, d\theta)$

$= 81\int \sec^3\theta\, d\theta$ (Cf. Problem 9-4 #21.)

$= \frac{81}{2}\sec\theta\tan\theta + \frac{81}{2}\ln|\sec\theta + \tan\theta| + C_1$

$= \frac{1}{2}x\sqrt{81 + x^2} + \frac{81}{2}\ln\left|\frac{\sqrt{81 + x^2}}{9} + \frac{x}{9}\right| + C_1$

$= \frac{1}{2}x\sqrt{81 + x^2} + \frac{81}{2}\ln|\sqrt{81 + x^2} + x| - \frac{81}{2}\ln 9 + C_1$

$= \frac{1}{2}x\sqrt{81 + x^2} + \frac{81}{2}\ln|\sqrt{81 + x^2} + x| + C$

5. $\int \sqrt{9x^2 - 1}\, dx$

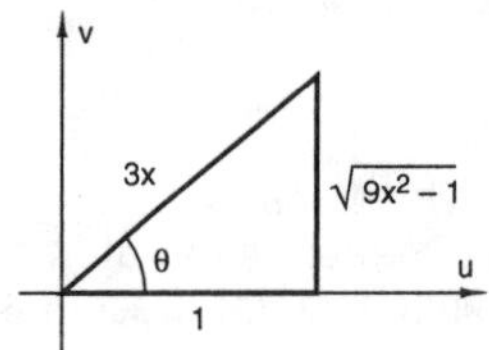

Let $\frac{3x}{1} = \sec\theta$. $x = \frac{1}{3}\sec\theta$, $dx = \frac{1}{3}\sec\theta\tan\theta\, d\theta$,

$\sqrt{9x^2 - 1} = \tan\theta$, $\theta = \sec^{-1} 3x$

$\therefore \int \sqrt{9x^2 - 1}\, dx = \int \tan\theta\,(\frac{1}{3}\sec\theta\tan\theta\, d\theta)$

$= \frac{1}{3}\int \sec\theta\tan^2\theta\, d\theta$

$= \frac{1}{3}\int (\sec^3\theta - \sec\theta)\, d\theta$

$= \frac{1}{6}\sec\theta\tan\theta + \frac{1}{6}\ln|\sec\theta + \tan\theta|$

$- \frac{1}{3}\ln|\sec\theta + \tan\theta| + C$

$= \frac{1}{6}\sec\theta\tan\theta - \frac{1}{6}\ln|\sec\theta + \tan\theta| + C$

$= \frac{1}{2}x\sqrt{9x^2 - 1} - \frac{1}{6}\ln|3x + \sqrt{9x^2 - 1}| + C$

6. $\int \sqrt{16x^2 - 1}\, dx$

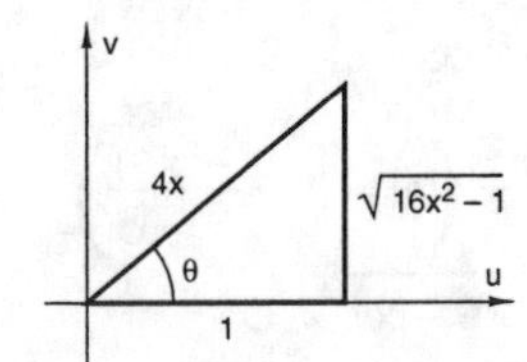

Let $\frac{4x}{1} = \sec\theta$. $x = \frac{1}{4}\sec\theta$, $dx = \frac{1}{4}\sec\theta\tan\theta\, d\theta$,

$\sqrt{16x^2 - 1} = \tan\theta$, $\theta = \sec^{-1} 4x$

$\therefore \int \sqrt{16x^2 - 1}\, dx = \int \tan\theta\, (\frac{1}{4}\sec\theta\tan\theta\, d\theta)$

$= \frac{1}{4}\int \sec\theta\tan^2\theta\, d\theta$

$= \frac{1}{4}\int (\sec^3\theta - \sec\theta)\, d\theta$

$= \frac{1}{8}\sec\theta\tan\theta + \frac{1}{8}\ln|\sec\theta + \tan\theta|$

$- \frac{1}{4}\ln|\sec\theta + \tan\theta| + C$

$= \frac{1}{8}\sec\theta\tan\theta - \frac{1}{8}\ln|\sec\theta + \tan\theta| + C$

$= \frac{1}{2}x\sqrt{16x^2 - 1} - \frac{1}{8}\ln|4x + \sqrt{16x^2 - 1}| + C$

7. $\int \frac{dx}{\sqrt{17 - x^2}}$

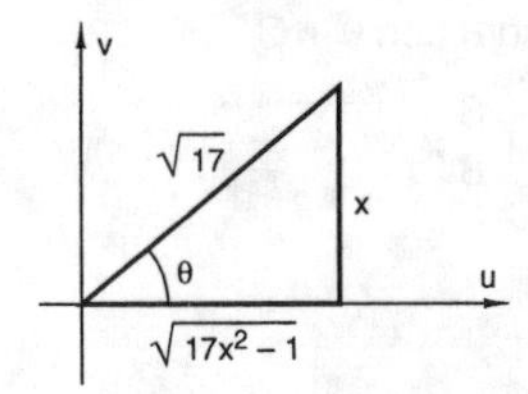

Let $x/\sqrt{17} = \sin\theta$. $x = \sqrt{17}\sin\theta$, $dx = \sqrt{17}\cos\theta\, d\theta$,

$\sqrt{17 - x^2} = \sqrt{17}\cos\theta$, $\theta = \sin^{-1}\frac{x}{\sqrt{17}}$

$\therefore \int \frac{dx}{\sqrt{17 - x^2}} = \int \frac{\sqrt{17}\cos\theta\, d\theta}{\sqrt{17}\cos\theta}$

$= \int d\theta = \theta + C = \sin^{-1}\frac{x}{\sqrt{17}} + C$

8. $\int \frac{dx}{\sqrt{13 - x^2}}$

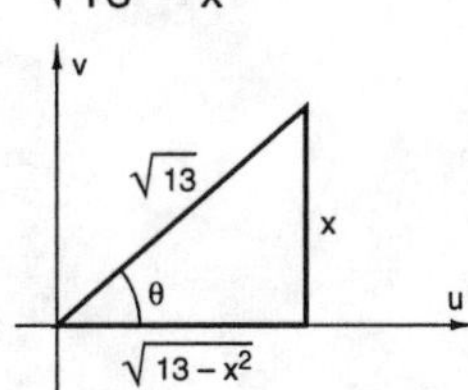

Let $x/\sqrt{13} = \sin\theta$. $x = \sqrt{13}\sin\theta$, $dx = \sqrt{13}\cos\theta$

$d\theta\ \sqrt{13 - x^2} = \sqrt{13}\cos\theta$, $\theta = \sin^{-1}\frac{x}{\sqrt{13}}$

$\therefore \int \frac{dx}{\sqrt{13 - x^2}} = \int \frac{\sqrt{13}\cos\theta\, d\theta}{\sqrt{13}\cos\theta}$

$= \int d\theta = \theta + C = \sin^{-1}\frac{x}{\sqrt{13}} + C$

9. $\int \frac{dx}{\sqrt{x^2 + 1}}$

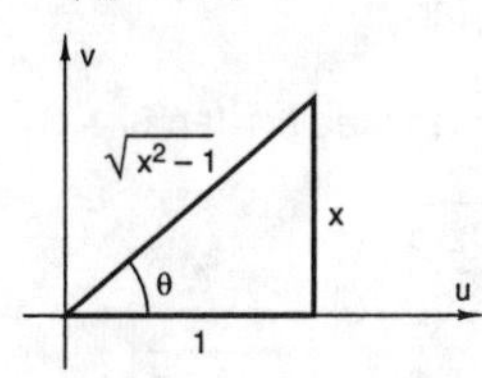

Let $\frac{x}{1} = \tan\theta$. $dx = \sec^2\theta\, d\theta$,

$\sqrt{x^2 + 1} = \sec\theta$, $\theta = \tan^{-1} x$

$\therefore \int \frac{dx}{\sqrt{x^2 + 1}} = \int \frac{\sec^2\theta\, d\theta}{\sec\theta} = \int \sec\theta\, d\theta$

$= \ln|\sec\theta + \tan\theta| + C = \ln|\sqrt{x^2+1} + x| + C$

10. $\int \frac{dx}{\sqrt{x^2 - 121}}$

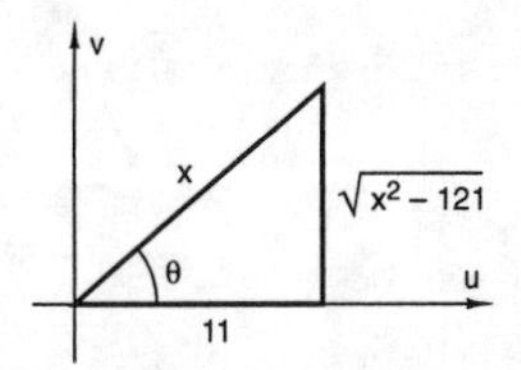

Let $\frac{x}{11} = \sec\theta$. $x = 11\sec\theta$, $dx = 11\sec\theta\tan\theta\, d\theta$,

$\sqrt{x^2 - 121} = 11\tan\theta$, $\theta = \sec^{-1}\frac{x}{11}$

$\therefore \int \frac{dx}{\sqrt{x^2 - 121}} = \int \frac{11\sec\theta\tan\theta\, d\theta}{11\tan\theta}$

$= \int \sec\theta\, d\theta = \ln|\sec\theta + \tan\theta| + C_1$

$= \ln\left|\frac{x}{11} + \frac{\sqrt{x^2 - 121}}{11}\right| + C_1$

$= \ln|x + \sqrt{x^2 - 121}| - \ln 11 + C_1$

$= \ln|x + \sqrt{x^2 - 121}| + C$

11. $\int x^2\sqrt{x^2 - 9}\,dx$

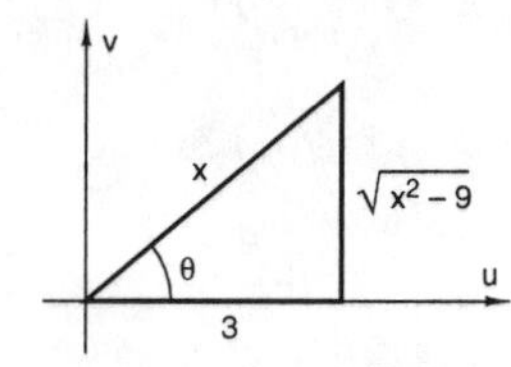

Let $\frac{x}{3} = \sec\theta$. $x = 3\sec\theta$, $dx = 3\sec\theta\tan\theta\,d\theta$,

$\sqrt{x^2 - 9} = 3\tan\theta$, $\theta = \sec^{-1}\frac{x}{3}$

$\therefore \int x^2\sqrt{x^2 - 9}\,dx$

$= \int (9\sec^2\theta)(3\tan\theta)(3\sec\theta\tan\theta\,d\theta)$

$= 81\int \sec^3\theta\tan^2\theta\,d\theta$

$= 81\left(\int \sec^5\theta\,d\theta - \int \sec^3\theta\,d\theta\right)$

$= 81\left(\frac{1}{4}\sec^3\theta\tan\theta + \frac{3}{4}\int \sec^3\theta\,d\theta - \int \sec^3\theta\,d\theta\right)$

$= \frac{81}{4}\sec^3\theta\tan\theta - \frac{81}{4}\int \sec^3\theta\,d\theta$

$= \frac{81}{4}\sec^3\theta\tan\theta - \frac{81}{8}\sec\theta\tan\theta - \frac{81}{8}\ln|\sec\theta + \tan\theta| + C_1$

$= \frac{81}{4}\cdot\frac{x^3}{27}\cdot\frac{\sqrt{x^2-9}}{3} - \frac{81}{8}\cdot\frac{x}{3}\cdot\frac{\sqrt{x^2-9}}{3} - \frac{81}{8}\ln\left|\frac{x}{3} + \frac{\sqrt{x^2-9}}{3}\right| + C_1$

$= \frac{1}{4}x^3\sqrt{x^2-9} - \frac{9}{8}x\sqrt{x^2 - 9} - \frac{81}{8}\ln|x + \sqrt{x^2-9}| + \frac{81}{8}\ln 3 + C_1$

$= \frac{1}{4}x^3\sqrt{x^2-9} - \frac{9}{8}x\sqrt{x^2 - 9} - \frac{81}{8}\ln|x + \sqrt{x^2-9}| + C$

12. $\int x^2\sqrt{9 - x^2}\,dx$

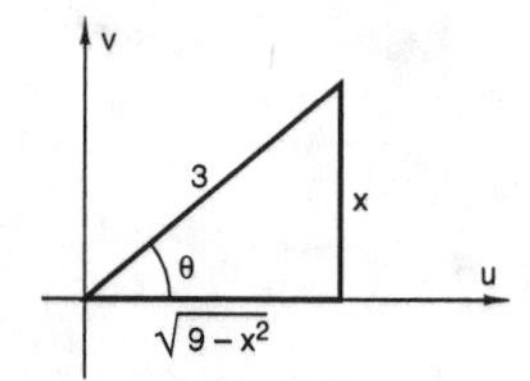

Let $\frac{x}{3} = \sin\theta$. $x = 3\sin\theta$, $dx = 3\cos\theta\,d\theta$,

$\sqrt{9 - x^2} = 3\cos\theta$, $\theta = \sin^{-1}\frac{x}{3}$

$\therefore \int x^2\sqrt{9 - x^2}\,dx$

$= \int (9\sin^2\theta)(3\cos\theta)(3\cos\theta\,d\theta)$

$= 81\int \sin^2\theta\cos^2\theta\,d\theta$

$= 81\int (\cos^2\theta - \cos^4\theta)\,d\theta$

$= 81\int \cos^2\theta\,d\theta - \frac{81}{4}\cos^3\theta\sin\theta - \frac{3\cdot 81}{4}\int \cos^2\theta\,d\theta$

$= \frac{81}{8}\int (1 + \cos 2\theta)\,d\theta - \frac{81}{4}\cos^3\theta\sin\theta$

$= \frac{81}{8}\theta + \frac{81}{16}\sin 2\theta - \frac{81}{4}\cos^3\theta\sin\theta + C$

$= \frac{81}{8}\theta + \frac{81}{8}\sin\theta\cos\theta - \frac{81}{4}\cos^3\theta\sin\theta + C$

$= \frac{81}{8}\theta + \frac{81}{8}\sin\theta\cos\theta\,(1 - 2\cos^2\theta) + C$

$= \frac{81}{8}\sin^{-1}\frac{x}{3} - \frac{81}{8}\cdot\frac{x}{3}\cdot\frac{\sqrt{9 - x^2}}{3}\cdot\left(1 - \frac{2(9 - x^2)}{9}\right) + C$

$= \frac{81}{8}\sin^{-1}\frac{x}{3} - \frac{1}{8}x(2x^2 - 9)\sqrt{9 - x^2} + C$

13. $\int (1 - x^2)^{3/2}\,dx$

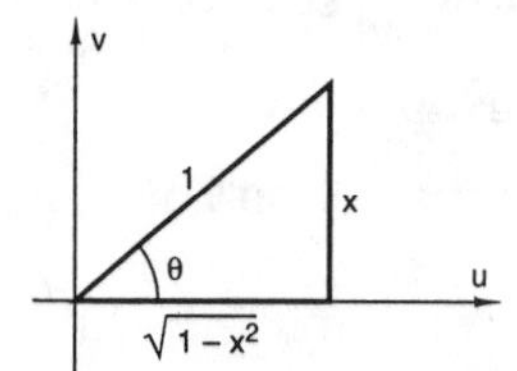

Let $x = \sin\theta$. $dx = \cos\theta\,d\theta$,

$\sqrt{1 - x^2} = \cos\theta$, $\theta = \sin^{-1}x$

$\therefore \int (1 - x^2)^{3/2}\,dx = \int \cos^3\theta\,(\cos\theta\,d\theta)$

$= \int \cos^4\theta\,d\theta$

$= \frac{1}{4}\cos^3\theta\sin\theta + \frac{3}{4}\int \cos^2\theta\,d\theta$

$= \frac{1}{4}\cos^3\theta\sin\theta + \frac{3}{8}\int (1 + \cos 2\theta)\,d\theta$

$= \frac{1}{4}\cos^3\theta\sin\theta + \frac{3}{8}\theta + \frac{3}{16}\sin 2\theta + C$

$= \frac{1}{4}\cos^3\theta\sin\theta + \frac{3}{8}\theta + \frac{3}{8}\sin\theta\cos\theta + C$

$= \frac{1}{4}x(1 - x^2)^{3/2} + \frac{3}{8}\sin^{-1}x + \frac{3}{8}x\sqrt{1 - x^2} + C$

14. $\int (x^2 - 81)^{-3/2}\,dx$

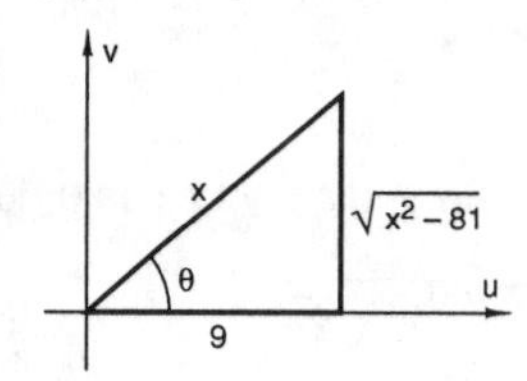

Let $\frac{x}{9} = \sec\theta$. $x = 9\sec\theta$, $dx = 9\sec\theta\tan\theta\,d\theta$,

$\sqrt{x^2 - 81} = 9\tan\theta$, $\theta = \sec^{-1}\frac{1}{9}x$

$\therefore \int (x^2 - 81)^{-3/2}\,dx$

$= \int (9\tan\theta)^{-3}(9\sec\theta\tan\theta\,d\theta)$

$= \frac{1}{81}\int \frac{\sec\theta\,d\theta}{\tan^2\theta}$

$= \frac{1}{81}\int \cot\theta\csc\theta\,d\theta$

$= -\frac{1}{81}\csc\theta + C$

$= \frac{-x}{81\sqrt{x^2 - 81}} + C$

15. $\int \frac{dx}{81 + x^2}$

Let $\frac{x}{9} = \tan\theta$. $x = 9\tan\theta$, $dx = 9\sec^2\theta\, d\theta$,

$\sqrt{81 + x^2} = 9\sec\theta$, $\theta = \tan^{-1}\frac{x}{9}$

$\therefore \int \frac{dx}{81 + x^2} = \int \frac{9\sec^2\theta\, d\theta}{81\sec^2\theta} = \frac{1}{9}\int d\theta = \frac{1}{9}\theta + C$

$= \frac{1}{9}\tan^{-1}\frac{x}{9} + C$

16. $\int \frac{dx}{25x^2 + 1}$

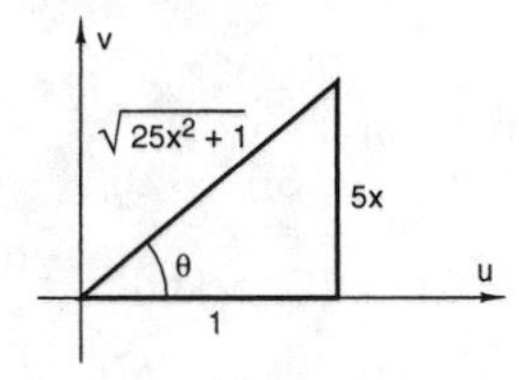

Let $\frac{5x}{1} = \tan\theta$. $x = \frac{1}{5}\tan\theta$, $dx = \frac{1}{5}\sec^2\theta\, d\theta$,

$\sqrt{25x^2 + 1} = \sec\theta$, $\theta = \tan^{-1} 5x$

$\therefore \int \frac{dx}{25x^2 + 1} = \int \frac{\sec^2\theta\, d\theta}{5\cdot\sec^2\theta} = \frac{1}{5}\int d\theta = \frac{1}{5}\theta + C$

$= \frac{1}{5}\tan^{-1} 5x + C$

17.a. $\int \frac{x\, dx}{\sqrt{x^2 + 25}}$

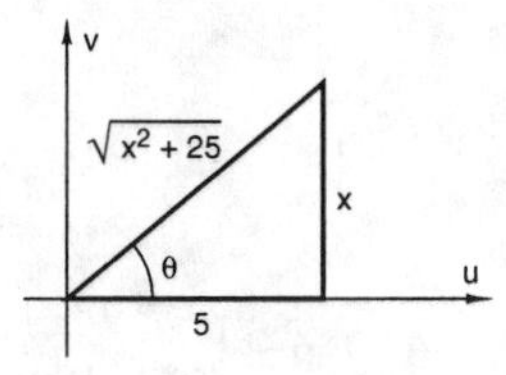

Let $\frac{x}{5} = \tan\theta$. $x = 5\tan\theta$, $dx = 5\sec^2\theta\, d\theta$,

$\sqrt{x^2 + 25} = 5\sec\theta$, $\theta = \tan^{-1}\frac{1}{5}x$

$\therefore \int \frac{x\, dx}{\sqrt{x^2 + 25}} = \int \frac{5\tan\theta\,(5\sec^2\theta\, d\theta)}{5\cdot\sec\theta}$

$= 5\int \tan\theta\sec\theta\, d\theta = 5\sec\theta + C$

$= \sqrt{x^2 + 25} + C$

b. $\int \frac{x\, dx}{\sqrt{x^2 + 25}} = \frac{1}{2}\int (x^2 + 25)^{-1/2}(2x\, dx)$

$= \sqrt{x^2 + 25} + C$, which agrees with part a.

Moral: Always check for an *easy* way to integrate before trying a more powerful technique!

18. a. $\int \frac{x\, dx}{\sqrt{x^2 - 49}}$

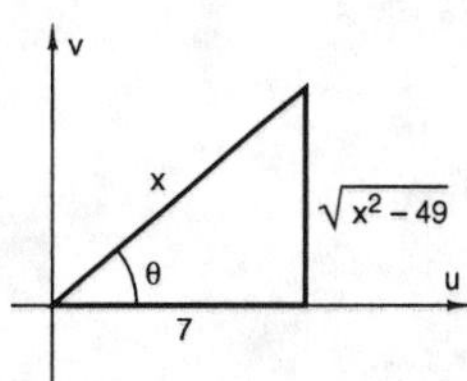

Let $\frac{x}{7} = \sec\theta$. $x = 7\sec\theta$, $dx = 7\sec\theta\tan\theta\, d\theta$,

$\sqrt{x^2 - 49} = 7\tan\theta$, $\theta = \sec^{-1}\frac{x}{7}$

$\therefore \int \frac{x\, dx}{\sqrt{x^2 - 49}} = \int \frac{7\sec\theta\,(7\sec\theta\tan\theta\, d\theta)}{7\tan\theta}$

$= 7\int \sec^2\theta\, d\theta = 7\tan\theta + C$

$= \sqrt{x^2 - 49} + C$

b. $\int \frac{x\, dx}{\sqrt{x^2 - 49}} = \frac{1}{2}\int (x^2 - 49)^{-1/2}(2x\, dx)$

$= \sqrt{x^2 - 49} + C$, which agrees with part a.

19. $\int \frac{dx}{\sqrt{9 - (x - 5)^2}}$

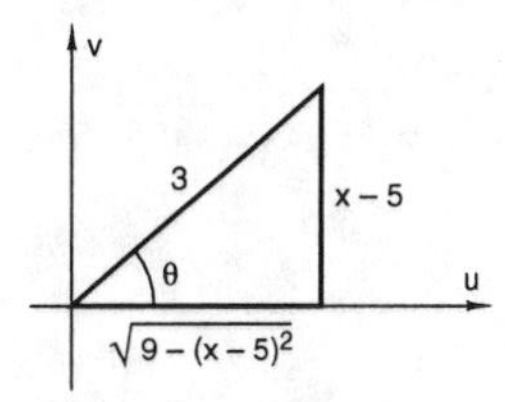

Let $\frac{x - 5}{3} = \sin\theta$. $x - 5 = 3\sin\theta$, $dx = 3\cos\theta\, d\theta$,

$\sqrt{9 - (x - 5)^2} = 3\cos\theta$, $\theta = \sin^{-1}\frac{x - 5}{3}$

$\therefore \int \frac{dx}{\sqrt{9 - (x - 5)^2}} = \int \frac{3\cos\theta\, d\theta}{3\cos\theta}$

$= \int d\theta = \theta + C = \sin^{-1}\frac{x - 5}{3} + C$

20. $\int \frac{dx}{\sqrt{36 - (x + 2)^2}}$

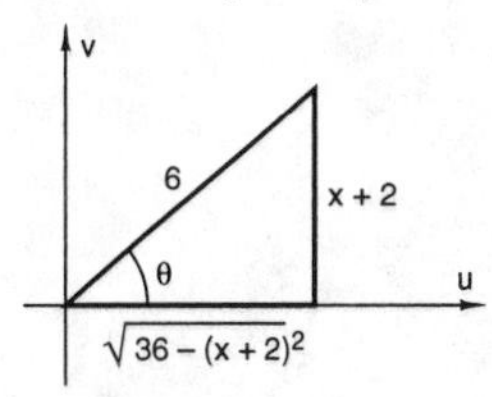

Let $\frac{x + 2}{6} = \sin\theta$. $x + 2 = 6\sin\theta$, $dx = 6\cos\theta\, d\theta$,

$\sqrt{36 - (x + 2)^2} = 6\cos\theta$, $\theta = \sin^{-1}\frac{x + 2}{6}$

$\therefore \int \frac{dx}{\sqrt{36 - (x + 2)^2}} = \int \frac{6\cos\theta d\theta}{6\cos\theta}$

$= \int d\theta = \theta + C = \sin^{-1}\frac{x + 2}{6} + C$

21. $\int \frac{dx}{\sqrt{x^2 + 8x - 20}} = \int \frac{dx}{\sqrt{(x + 4)^2 - 36}}$

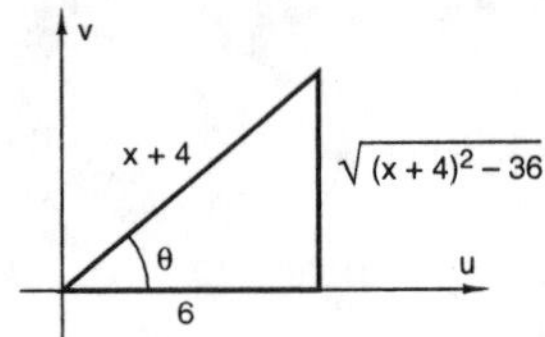

Let $\frac{x + 4}{6} = \sec\theta$. $x + 4 = 6\sec\theta$,

$dx = 6\sec\theta\tan\theta\, d\theta$,

$\sqrt{(x + 4)^2 - 36} = \sqrt{x^2 + 8x - 20} = 6\tan\theta$,

$\theta = \sec^{-1}\frac{x + 4}{6}$

$\therefore \int \frac{dx}{\sqrt{x^2 + 8x - 20}} = \int \frac{6\sec\theta\tan\theta\, d\theta}{6\tan\theta}$

$= \int \sec\theta\, d\theta$

$= \ln|\sec\theta + \tan\theta| + C$

$= \ln\left|\frac{x + 4}{6} + \frac{\sqrt{x^2 + 8x - 20}}{6}\right| + C_1$

$= \ln|x + 4 + \sqrt{x^2 + 8x - 20}| - \ln 6 + C_1$

$= \ln|x + 4 + \sqrt{x^2 + 8x - 20}| + C$

22. $\int \frac{dx}{\sqrt{x^2 - 14x + 50}} = \int \frac{dx}{\sqrt{(x - 7)^2 + 1}}$

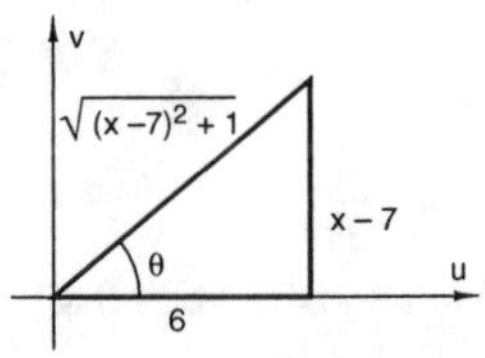

Let $\frac{x - 7}{1} = \tan\theta$. $x - 7 = \tan\theta$, $dx = \sec^2\theta\, d\theta$,

$\sqrt{x^2 - 14x + 50} = \sqrt{(x - 7)^2 + 1} = \sec\theta$,

$\theta = \tan^{-1}(x - 7)$

$\therefore \int \frac{dx}{\sqrt{x^2 - 14x + 50}} = \int \frac{\sec^2\theta\, d\theta}{\sec\theta} = \int \sec\theta\, d\theta$

$= \ln|\sec\theta + \tan\theta| + C$

$= \ln|\sqrt{x^2 - 14x + 50} + x - 7| + C$

23. $\int_{-3}^{8} \sqrt{100 - x^2}\, dx$

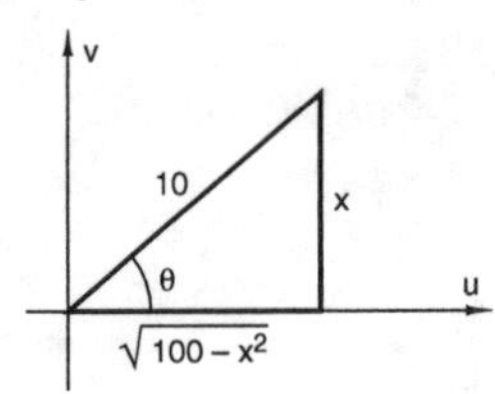

Let $\frac{x}{10} = \sin\theta$. $x = 10\sin\theta$, $dx = 10\cos\theta\, d\theta$,

$\sqrt{100 - x^2} = 10\cos\theta$, $\theta = \sin^{-1}\frac{x}{10}$

$\therefore \int_{-3}^{8} \sqrt{100 - x^2}\, dx$

$= \int_{\sin^{-1}(-0.3)}^{\sin^{-1} 0.8} 10\cos\theta \cdot 10\cos\theta\, d\theta$

$= 100\int_{\sin^{-1}(-0.3)}^{\sin^{-1} 0.8} \cos^2\theta\, d\theta$

$= 50\int_{\sin^{-1}(-0.3)}^{\sin^{-1} 0.8} (1 + \cos 2\theta\, d\theta)$

$= 50\theta + 25\sin 2\theta \Big|_{\sin^{-1}(-0.3)}^{\sin^{-1} 0.8}$

$= 50\sin^{-1} 0.8 + 25\sin(2\sin^{-1} 0.8)$

$- 50\sin^{-1}(-0.3) - 25\sin(2\sin^{-1}(-0.3))$

$= 99.9084\ldots$

Numerical integration: 99.9084... . (Checks.)

24. $\int_{-1}^{4} \sqrt{x^2 + 25}\, dx$

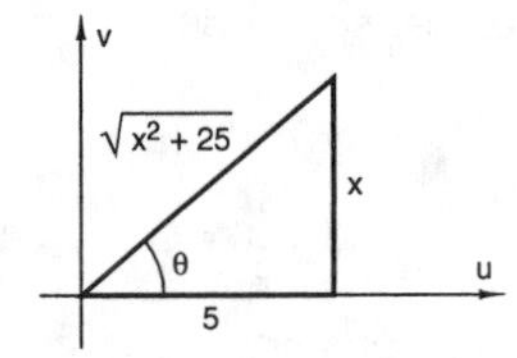

Let $\frac{x}{5} = \tan\theta$. $x = 5\tan\theta$, $dx = 5\sec^2\theta\, d\theta$,

$\sqrt{x^2 + 25} = 5\sec\theta$, $\theta = \tan^{-1} 0.2x$

$\therefore \int_{-1}^{4} \sqrt{x^2 + 25}\, dx$

$= \int_{\tan^{-1}(-0.2)}^{\tan^{-1} 0.8} 5\sec\theta \cdot 5\sec^2\theta\, d\theta$

$= 25\int_{\tan^{-1}(-0.2)}^{\tan^{-1} 0.8} \sec^3\theta\, d\theta$

$= \frac{25}{2}\sec\theta\tan\theta + \frac{25}{2}\ln|\sec\theta + \tan\theta| \Big|_{\tan^{-1}(-0.2)}^{\tan^{-1} 0.8}$

$= \frac{25}{2}\sec(\tan^{-1} 0.8)\cdot 0.8 + \frac{25}{2}\ln|\sec(\tan^{-1} 0.8) + 0.8|$

$- \frac{25}{2}\sec(\tan^{-1}(-0.2))\cdot(-0.2)$

$- \frac{25}{2}\ln|\sec(\tan^{-1}(-0.2)) - 0.2|$

$= 26.9977\ldots$

Numerical integration: 26.9977... .(Checks.)

25. <u>Arc Length of a Parabola Problem</u>

$y = 3x^2$

$dL = \sqrt{1 + y'^2}\,dx = \sqrt{1 + 36x^2}\,dx$

$L = \int_0^5 \sqrt{1 + 36x^2}\,dx$

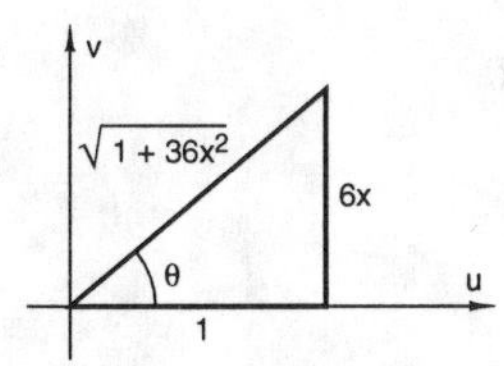

Let $\frac{6x}{1} = \tan\theta$. $x = \frac{1}{6}\tan\theta$, $dx = \frac{1}{6}\sec^2\theta\,d\theta$,

$\sqrt{1 + 36x^2} = \sec\theta$, $\theta = \tan^{-1} 6x$

$\therefore L = \int_{x=0}^{x=5} \sec\theta \cdot \frac{1}{6}\sec^2\theta\,d\theta$

$= \frac{1}{6}\int_{x=0}^{x=5} \sec^3\theta\,d\theta$

$= \frac{1}{12}\sec\theta\tan\theta + \frac{1}{12}\ln\left|\sec\theta + \tan\theta\right| \Big|_{x=0}^{x=5}$

$= \frac{1}{2}\sqrt{1 + 36x^2}\,x + \frac{1}{12}\ln\left|\sqrt{1 + 36x^2} + 6x\right| \Big|_0^5$

$= \frac{5}{2}\sqrt{901} + \frac{1}{12}\ln\left|\sqrt{901} + 30\right| = 75.3828\ldots$

Numerical integration: $L = 75.3828\ldots$. (Check.)

26. <u>Area of an Ellipse Problem</u>

a. $9x^2 + 25y^2 = 225 \Rightarrow y = \pm\frac{3}{5}\sqrt{25 - x^2}$

Slice the region vertically. Pick a sample point (x, y) on the positive branch of the graph, within the strip.

$dA = 2y\,dx = \frac{6}{5}\sqrt{25 - x^2}\,dx$

$A = \frac{6}{5}\int_{-3}^{4} \sqrt{25 - x^2}\,dx$

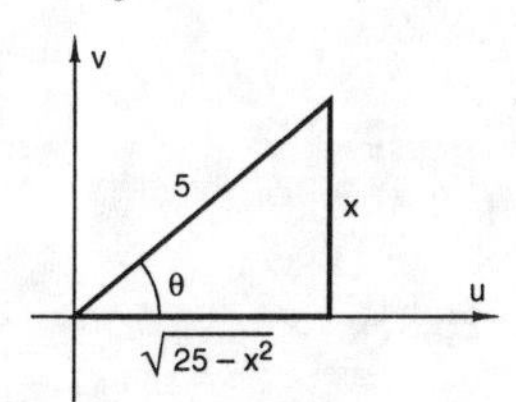

Let $\frac{x}{5} = \sin\theta$. $x = 5\sin\theta$, $dx = 5\cos\theta\,d\theta$,

$\sqrt{25 - x^2} = 5\cos\theta$, $\theta = \sin^{-1}\frac{x}{5}$

$\therefore A = \frac{6}{5}\int_{x=-3}^{x=4} 5\cos\theta \cdot 5\cos\theta\,d\theta$

$= 30\int_{x=-3}^{x=4} \cos^2\theta\,d\theta = 15\int_{x=-3}^{x=4} (1 + \cos 2\theta)\,d\theta$

$= 15\,\theta + \frac{15}{2}\sin 2\theta \Big|_{x=-3}^{x=4}$

$= 15\,\theta + 15\sin\theta\cos\theta \Big|_{x=-3}^{x=4}$

$= 15\sin^{-1}\frac{x}{5} + \frac{3}{5}x\sqrt{25 - x^2} \Big|_{x=-3}^{x=4}$

$= 15\sin^{-1} 0.8 + \frac{3}{5}(4)\sqrt{9}$

$- 15\sin^{-1}(-0.6) - \frac{3}{5}(-3)\sqrt{16}$

$= 15(\sin^{-1} 0.8 - \sin^{-1}(-0.6)) + 14.4$

$= \frac{15\pi}{2} + 14.4 =$ <u>37.9619 ...</u>

Numerical integration: $A = 37.9619\ldots$. (Check.)

b. $A = \frac{6}{5}\int_{-5}^{5} \sqrt{25 - x^2}\,dx$

$x = 5 \Rightarrow \theta = \pi/2$, $x = -5 \Rightarrow \theta = -\pi/2$

$\therefore A = 30\int_{-\pi/2}^{\pi/2} \cos^2\theta\,d\theta$

$= 15\,\theta + \frac{15}{2}\sin 2\theta \Big|_{-\pi/2}^{\pi/2}$

$= \frac{15\pi}{2} + \frac{15}{2}\sin\pi + \frac{15\pi}{2} - \frac{15}{2}\sin(-\pi)$

$= 15\pi = 47.1238\ldots$

The area is π(x-radius)(y-radius).

27. <u>Circle Area Formula Problem</u>

$x^2 + y^2 = r^2 \Rightarrow y = \pm\sqrt{r^2 - x^2}$, $x = 0$ at $y = \pm r$

Slice the region inside the circle perpendicular to the x-axis. Pick sample point (x, y) on the positive branch of the circle, within the strip.

$dA = 2y\,dx = 2\sqrt{r^2 - x^2}\,dx$

$A = 2\int_{-r}^{r} \sqrt{r^2 - x^2}\,dx$

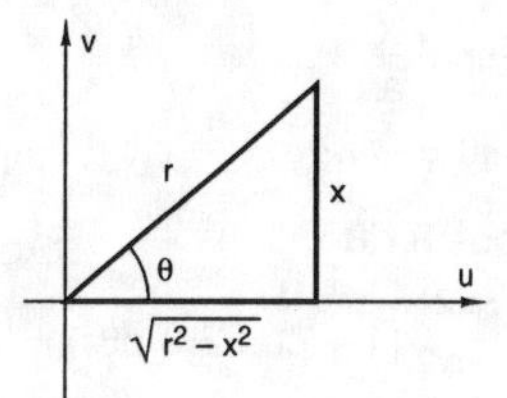

Let $\frac{x}{r} = \sin\theta$. $x = r\sin\theta$, $dx = r\cos\theta\,d\theta$,

$\sqrt{r^2 - x^2} = r\cos\theta$, $\theta = \sin^{-1}\frac{x}{r}$

$x = r \Rightarrow \theta = \pi/2$, $x = -r \Rightarrow \theta = -\pi/2$.

$\therefore A = 2\int_{-\pi/2}^{\pi/2} r\cos\theta \cdot r\cos\theta\,d\theta$

$= 2r^2\int_{-\pi/2}^{\pi/2} \cos^2\theta\,d\theta = r^2\int_{-\pi/2}^{\pi/2} (1 + \cos 2\theta)\,d\theta$

$= r^2\theta + \frac{1}{2}r^2\sin 2\theta \Big|_{-\pi/2}^{\pi/2}$

$= r^2\cdot\frac{\pi}{2} + \frac{1}{2}r^2\sin\pi + r^2\cdot\frac{\pi}{2} - \frac{1}{2}r^2\sin(-\pi) = \pi r^2$

$\therefore A = \pi r^2$, Q.E.D.

28. Ellipse Area Formula Problem

$\left(\frac{x}{a}\right)^2 + \left(\frac{y}{b}\right)^2 = 1 \Rightarrow y = \pm\frac{b}{a}\sqrt{a^2 - x^2}$

Slice the region inside the ellipse perpendicular to the x-axis. Pick sample point (x, y) on the positive branch of the ellipse, within the strip.

$dA = 2y\,dx = \frac{2b}{a}\sqrt{a^2 - x^2}\,dx$

$A = \frac{2b}{a}\int_{-a}^{a}\sqrt{a^2 - x^2}\,dx$

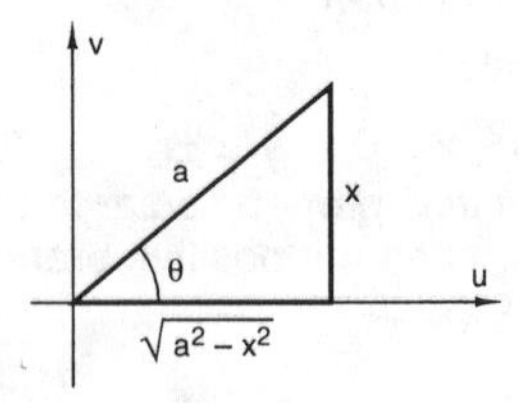

Let $\frac{x}{a} = \sin\theta$. $x = a\sin\theta$, $dx = a\cos\theta\,d\theta$,

$\sqrt{a^2 - x^2} = a\cos\theta$, $\theta = \sin^{-1}\frac{x}{a}$

$x = a \Rightarrow \theta = \pi/2$, $x = -a \Rightarrow \theta = -\pi/2$

$\therefore A = \frac{2b}{a}\int_{-\pi/2}^{\pi/2} a\cos\theta \cdot a\cos\theta\,d\theta$

$= 2ab\int_{-\pi/2}^{\pi/2}\cos^2\theta\,d\theta = ab\int_{-\pi/2}^{\pi/2}(1 + \cos 2\theta)\,d\theta$

$= ab\theta + \frac{ab}{2}\sin 2\theta\,\Big|_{-\pi/2}^{\pi/2}$

$= \frac{ab\pi}{2} + \frac{ab}{2}\sin\pi + \frac{ab\pi}{2} - \frac{ab}{2}\sin(-\pi) = \pi ab.$

$\therefore$ $\underline{A = \pi ab}$

Note that if $a = b = r$, then $\pi ab = \pi r^2$, the area of a circle.

29. Ellipsoid Problem

$dV = \pi x^2 dy = \pi\frac{a^2}{b^2}(b^2 - y^2)\,dy$, $-b \le y \le b$

$V = \pi\frac{a^2}{b^2}\int_{-b}^{b}(b^2 - y^2)\,dy$

$= \pi\frac{a^2}{b^2}\left(b^2y - \frac{y^3}{3}\right)\Big|_{-b}^{b} = \frac{4}{3}\pi a^2b.$

$\therefore V = \frac{4}{3}\pi a^2b$

Rotating instead about the x-axis is equivalent to interchanging the a and b, giving $V = \frac{4}{3}\pi ab^2$.

30. Hyperbola Area Problem

$x^2 - y^2 = 9 \Rightarrow y = \pm\sqrt{x^2 - 9}$

Slice the region perpendicular to the x-axis. Pick a sample point (x, y) on the positive branch of the hyperbola, within the strip.

$dA = 2y\,dx = 2\sqrt{x^2 - 9}\,dx$

$A = 2\int_3^5\sqrt{x^2 - 9}\,dx$

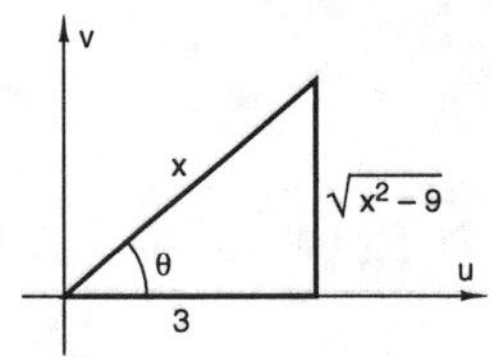

Let $\frac{x}{3} = \sec\theta$. $x = 3\sec\theta$, $dx = 3\sec\theta\tan\theta\,d\theta$,

$\sqrt{x^2 - 9} = 3\tan\theta$, $\theta = \sec^{-1}\frac{x}{3}$

$\therefore A = 2\int_{x=3}^{x=5} 3\tan\theta \cdot 3\sec\theta\tan\theta\,d\theta$

$= 18\int_{x=3}^{x=5}\tan^2\theta\sec\theta\,d\theta$

$= 18\int_{x=3}^{x=5}(\sec^3\theta - \sec\theta)\,d\theta$

$= 9\sec\theta\tan\theta + 9\ln|\sec\theta + \tan\theta|$

$- 18\ln|\sec\theta + \tan\theta|\,\Big|_{x=3}^{x=5}$

$= 9\sec\theta\tan\theta - 9\ln|\sec\theta + \tan\theta|\,\Big|_{x=3}^{x=5}$

$= x\sqrt{x^2 - 9} - 9\ln\left|\frac{1}{3}x + \frac{1}{3}\sqrt{x^2 - 9}\right|\,\Big|_3^5$

$= 20 - 9\ln 3 = 10.1124\ldots$.

Numerical integration: $A = 10.1124\ldots$. (Checks.)

31. Hyperboloid Problem

$dV = 2\pi x(2y)\,dx = 4\pi x\sqrt{x^2 - 9}\,dx$

$V = 4\pi\int_3^5\sqrt{x^2 - 9}\,x\,dx$

$= 2\pi\int_3^5\sqrt{x^2 - 9}\,(2x\,dx)$

$= 2\pi\cdot\frac{2}{3}(x^2 - 9)^{3/2}\,\Big|_3^5$

$= \frac{4}{3}\pi\cdot 64 = \frac{256}{3}\pi = 268.0825\ldots$

32. Average Radius Problem

From Problems 30 and 31, $A = 20 - 9\ln 3$, $V = \frac{256}{3}\pi$

$V = 2\pi\bar{x}\cdot A \Rightarrow \bar{x} = \frac{128}{3(20 - 9\ln 3)} = 4.2192\ldots$

$\bar{x}$ is a little more than halfway through the region.

33. Area of an Ellipse, Parametrically

$x = a\cos t \Rightarrow dx = -a\sin t\,dt$

$y = b\sin t$

$dA = 2y\,dx = 2(b\sin t)(-a\sin t\,dt) = -2ab\sin^2 t\,dt$

$x = -a \Rightarrow t = \pi$, $x = a \Rightarrow t = 0$.

$\therefore A = -2ab\int_\pi^0\sin^2 t\,dt = -ab\int_\pi^0(1 - \cos 2t)\,dt$

$= -abt + \frac{ab}{2}\sin 2t\,\Big|_\pi^0 = 0 + 0 + ab(\pi) - 0 = \pi ab$

$\therefore A = \pi ab$, as in Problem 28.

With this method, you get $\int\sin^2 t\,dt$, just as with trigonometry substitution, but here you get the integral *directly,* not indirectly.

34. Length of a Spiral in Polar Coordinates

$r = 0.5\theta \Rightarrow dr/d\theta = 0.5$

$dL = \sqrt{r^2 + (dr/d\theta)^2}\, d\theta = \sqrt{0.25\theta^2 + 0.25}\, d\theta$

$= 0.5\sqrt{\theta^2 + 1}\, d\theta$

$L = 0.5 \int_0^{6\pi} \sqrt{\theta^2 + 1}\, d\theta$

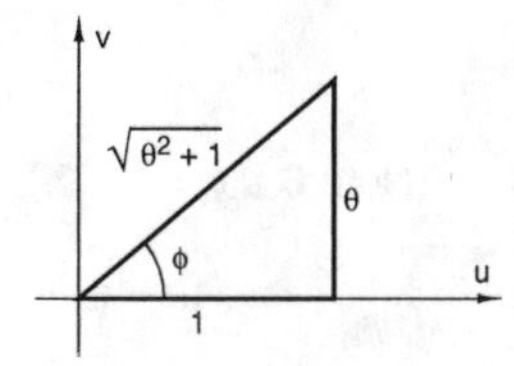

Let $\theta = \tan\phi \Rightarrow d\theta = \sec^2\phi\, d\phi$

$\sqrt{\theta^2 + 1} = \sec\phi,\ \phi = \tan^{-1}\theta$

$\therefore L = 0.5 \int_{\theta=0}^{\theta=6\pi} \sec\phi \cdot \sec^2\phi\, d\phi$

$= 0.5 \int_{\theta=0}^{\theta=6\pi} \sec^3\phi\, d\phi$

$= 0.25 \sec\phi \tan\phi + 0.25 \ln|\sec\phi + \tan\phi| \Big|_{\theta=0}^{\theta=6\pi}$

$= 0.25\theta\sqrt{\theta^2 + 1} + 0.25 \ln|\sqrt{\theta^2 + 1} + \theta| \Big|_0^{6\pi}$

$= 1.5\pi\sqrt{36\pi^2 + 1} + 0.25 \ln|\sqrt{36\pi^2 + 1} + 6\pi|$

= 89.8589 .... same as numerical integration.

35. Trigonometric Substitution for Negative Values of x

See the note preceding the solutions for this section. For the sine and tangent substitution, the range of the inverse sine and inverse tangent make the corresponding radical positive. For the secant substitution, the situation is more complicated, but still gives an answer of the same algebraic form as if x had been only positive.

Problem Set 9-7, pages 464 to 468 — Integration of Rational Functions by Partial Fractions

Q1. $(x + 5)(x - 5)$

Q2. $x^2 + 2x - 15$

Q3. $(x + 2)(x - 6)$

Q4. $x^2 + 14x + 49$

Q5. $(x + 4)^2$

Q6. $x^2 - 64$

Q7. e^x

Q8. Integral ≈ 114

Q9. $b^2 - 4ac = -1500$, so $x^2 + 50x + 1000$ is prime.

Q10. $b^2 - 4ac = -144$, so $x^2 + 36$ is prime.

1. $\int \frac{11x - 15}{x^2 - 3x + 2} dx = \int \left(\frac{4}{x - 1} + \frac{7}{x - 2}\right) dx$

$= 4 \ln|x - 1| + 7 \ln|x - 2| + C$

2. $\int \left(\frac{7x + 25}{x^2 - 7x - 8}\right) dx = \int \left(\frac{-2}{x + 1} + \frac{9}{x - 8}\right) dx$

$= -2 \ln|x + 1| + 9 \ln|x - 8| + C$

3. $\int \frac{(5x - 11)\, dx}{x^2 - 2x - 8} = \int \left(\frac{7/2}{x + 2} + \frac{3/2}{x - 4}\right) dx$

$= \frac{7}{2} \ln|x + 2| + \frac{3}{2} \ln|x - 4| + C$

4. $\int \frac{(3x - 12)\, dx}{x^2 - 5x - 50} = \int \left(\frac{9/5}{x + 5} + \frac{6/5}{x - 10}\right) dx$

$= \frac{9}{5} \ln|x + 5| + \frac{6}{5} \ln|x - 10| + C$

5. $\int \frac{21\, dx}{x^2 + 7x + 10} = \int \left(\frac{-7}{x + 5} + \frac{7}{x + 2}\right) dx$

$= -7 \ln|x + 5| + 7 \ln|x + 2| + C$

6. $\int \frac{10x\, dx}{x^2 - 9x - 36} = \int \left(\frac{2}{x + 3} + \frac{8}{x - 12}\right) dx$

$= 2 \ln|x + 3| + 8 \ln|x - 12| + C$

7. $\int \frac{9x^2 - 25x - 50}{(x + 1)(x - 7)(x + 2)} dx$

$= \int \left(\frac{2}{x + 1} + \frac{3}{x - 7} + \frac{4}{x + 2}\right) dx$

$= 2 \ln|x + 1| + 3 \ln|x - 7| + 4 \ln|x + 2| + C$

8. $\int \frac{7x^2 + 22x - 54}{(x - 2)(x + 4)(x - 1)} dx$

$= \int \left(\frac{3}{x - 2} + \frac{-1}{x + 4} + \frac{5}{x - 1}\right) dx$

$= 3 \ln|x - 2| - \ln|x + 4| + 5 \ln|x - 1| + C$

9. $\int \frac{4x^2 + 15x - 1}{x^3 + 2x^2 - 5x - 6} dx$

$= \int \left(\frac{-1}{x + 3} + \frac{2}{x + 1} + \frac{3}{x - 2}\right) dx$

$= -\ln|x + 3| + 2 \ln|x + 1| + 3 \ln|x - 2| + C$

10. $\int \frac{-3x^2 + 22x - 31}{x^3 - 8x^2 + 19x - 12} dx$

$= \int \left(\frac{-2}{x - 1} + \frac{-4}{x - 3} + \frac{3}{x - 4}\right) dx$

$= -2 \ln|x - 1| - 4 \ln|x - 3| + 3 \ln|x - 4| + C$

11. $\int \frac{3x^3 + 2x^2 - 12x + 9}{x - 1} dx$

$= \int \left(3x^2 + 5x - 7 + \frac{2}{x - 1}\right) dx$

$= x^3 + \frac{5}{2}x^2 - 7x + 2 \ln|x - 1| + C$

12. $\int \frac{x^3 - 7x^2 + 5x + 40}{x^2 - 2x - 8} dx$

$= \int (x - 5 + \frac{3x}{x^2 - 2x - 8}) dx$

$= \int (x - 5 + \frac{1}{x + 2} + \frac{2}{x - 4}) dx$

$= \frac{1}{2}x^2 - 5x + \ln|x + 2| + 2\ln|x - 4| + C$

13. $\int \frac{4x^2 + 6x + 11}{(x^2 + 1)(x + 4)} dx$

$= \int (\frac{x + 2}{x^2 + 1} + \frac{3}{x + 4}) dx$

$= \frac{1}{2}\int \frac{2x\,dx}{x^2 + 1} + 2\int \frac{dx}{x^2 + 1} + \int \frac{3\,dx}{x + 4}$

$= \frac{1}{2}\ln|x^2 + 1| + 2\tan^{-1} x + 3\ln|x + 4| + C$

14. $\int \frac{4x^2 - 15x - 1}{x^3 - 5x^2 + 3x + 1} dx$

$= \int (\frac{3}{x - 1} + \frac{x - 2}{x^2 - 4x - 1}) dx$

$= 3\ln|x - 1| + \frac{1}{2}\ln|x^2 - 4x - 1| + C$

Note that

$\frac{x - 2}{x^2 - 4x - 1} = \frac{1/2}{x - 2 + \sqrt{5}} + \frac{1/2}{x - 2 - \sqrt{5}}$,

but $\frac{1}{2}\ln|x - 2 + \sqrt{5}| + \frac{1}{2}\ln|x - 2 - \sqrt{5}|$

$= \frac{1}{2}\ln|x^2 - 4x - 1|$,

so the answer comes out the same.

15. $\int \frac{4x^2 + 18x + 6}{(x + 5)(x + 1)^2} dx$

$= \int (\frac{1}{x + 5} + \frac{3}{x + 1} + \frac{-2}{(x + 1)^2}) dx$

$= \ln|x + 5| + 3\ln|x + 1| + 2(x + 1)^{-1} + C$

16. $\int \frac{3x^2 - 53x + 245}{x^3 - 14x^2 + 49x} dx$

$= \int (\frac{5}{x} + \frac{-2}{x - 7} + \frac{3}{(x - 7)^2}) dx$

$= 5\ln|x| - 2\ln|x - 7| - 3(x - 7)^{-1} + C$

17. $\int \frac{dx}{x^3 - 6x^2 + 12x - 8} = \int \frac{dx}{(x - 2)^3}$

$= -\frac{1}{2}(x - 2)^{-2} + C$

18. $\int \frac{1}{x^4 + 4x^3 + 6x^2 + 4x + 1} dx = \int \frac{dx}{(x + 1)^4}$

$= -\frac{1}{3}(x + 1)^{-3} + C$

19. Rumor Problem

a. $\frac{dy}{dt} = 2y\frac{1000 - y}{1000} \Rightarrow \frac{1000\,dy}{y(1000 - y)} = 2\,dt$

$\int \frac{1000\,dy}{y(1000 - y)} = \int 2\,dt$

$\int (\frac{1}{y} + \frac{1}{1000 - y}) dy = \int 2\,dt$

$\ln|y| - \ln|1000 - y| = 2t + C$

$\ln\left|\frac{y}{1000 - y}\right| = 2t + C$

$\frac{y}{1000 - y} = e^{2t + C}$ (Note $0 \le y < 1000$.)

$\frac{1000}{y} = 1 + e^{-2t - C} = 1 + ke^{-2t}$ ($k = e^{-C}$)

$y = \frac{1000}{1 + ke^{-2t}}$

Initial condition $y = 10$ when $t = 0 \Rightarrow k = 99$

$y = \frac{1000}{1 + 99e^{-2t}}$

b. $y(1) = \frac{1000}{1 + 99e^{-2}} = 69.4531 \ldots \approx 69$ students have heard the rumor after one hour.

$y(4) = \frac{1000}{1 + 99e^{-8}} = 967.8567 \ldots \approx 968$ students have heard by lunchtime.

$y(8) = \frac{1000}{1 + 99e^{-16}} = 999.9888 \ldots \approx 1000$ students—everyone knows by the end of the day!

c. Maximize $y' = 2y\frac{1000 - y}{1000} = \frac{1}{500}(1000y - y^2)$

$y'' = \frac{1}{500}(1000y' - 2yy') = 0$ when $y = 500$.

This is the max. point because $y'' > 0$ for $y < 500$ and $y'' < 0$ for $y > 500$ (and $y' > 0$ for all t).

So 500 students have heard the news when the rate of spreading (y') is greatest. This occurs when

$500 = \frac{1000}{1 + 99e^{-2t}}$

$99e^{-2t} + 1 = 2$

$e^{-2t} = \frac{1}{99}$

$t = \frac{1}{2}\ln 99 = 2.2975 \ldots$ hours.

d. Graph, which follows the slope field pattern

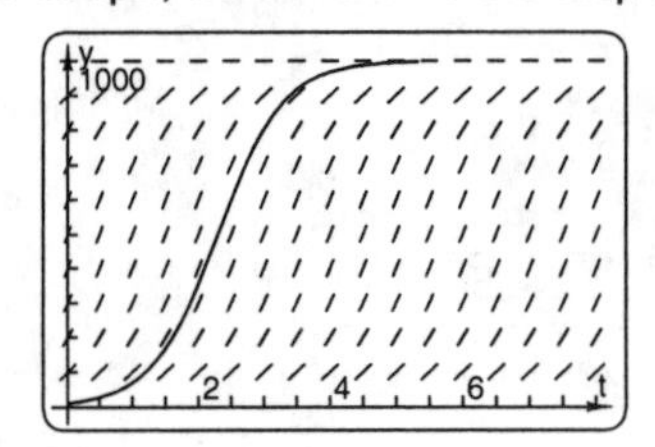

20. Epidemic Problem

a. Assume that an infected person and an uninfected person have about the same chance of meeting any other infected person, (i.e., infected people are not quarantined). An infected person can meet N – P uninfected people out of the total population, so of an average infected person's three contacts per day, (N–P)/N of them will be with uninfected persons (actually (N–P)/(N–1), since the total population that someone can meet is N – 1—people don't meet themselves outside the Twilight Zone—but (N–P)/N is reasonably close enough for now). So there are P infected people, each meeting an average of 3(N–P)/N uninfected people per day for a grand total of 3P(N–P)/N contacts between infected and uninfected people per day.

b. If 10% of the contacts with infected people per day result in infection, then the number of new infections per day should be 0.1(contacts between infected and uninfected people),

i.e., $\frac{dP}{dt} = 0.1\cdot\frac{3P(N-P)}{N} = 0.3P\frac{N-P}{N}$.

c. $\frac{dP}{dt} = 0.3P\frac{N-P}{N} \Rightarrow \frac{N\,dP}{P(N-P)} = 0.3\,dt$

$\int\frac{N\,dP}{P(N-P)} = \int 0.3\,dt$

$\int(\frac{1}{P} + \frac{1}{N-P})\,dP = \int 0.3\,dt$

$\ln|P| - \ln|N-P| = 0.3t + C$

$\ln|\frac{P}{N-P}| = 0.3t + C$

$\frac{P}{N-P} = e^{0.3t+C}$ (Note $0 \le P < N$.)

$\frac{N}{P} = 1 + e^{-0.3t-C} = 1 + ke^{-0.3t}$ $(k = e^{-C})$

$P(t) = \frac{N}{1 + ke^{-0.3t}}$

Initial cond. $P(0) = P_0 \Rightarrow P_0 = \frac{N}{1+k} \Rightarrow k = \frac{N}{P_0} - 1$

$\therefore P(t) = \frac{N}{1 + (N/P_0 - 1)e^{-0.3t}}$

d. $N = 1000$ and $P_0 = 10 \Rightarrow P(t) = \frac{1000}{1 + 99e^{-0.3t}}$

$P(7) = \frac{1000}{1 + 99e^{-2.1}} = 76.2010\ldots \approx 76$ people infected after 1 week

e. Solve $P(t) = 990$.

$990 = \frac{1000}{1 + 99e^{-0.3t}}$

$1 + 99e^{-0.3t} = \frac{100}{99}$

$e^{0.3t} = 99^2$

$t = \frac{2}{0.3}\ln 99 = 30.6341\ldots \approx 31$ days.

21. Area Problem

$A = \int_2^b \frac{25}{x^2 + 3x - 4}\,dx = \int_2^b (\frac{5}{x-1} + \frac{-5}{x+4})\,dx$

$= 5\ln|x-1| - 5\ln|x+4|\,\Big|_2^b = 5\ln\Big|\frac{x-1}{x+4}\Big|\,\Big|_2^b$

$= 5\ln\frac{b-1}{b+4} - 5\ln\frac{1}{6} = 5\ln\frac{b-1}{b+4} + 5\ln 6$

$A(7) = 5\ln\frac{6}{11} + 5\ln 6 = \underline{5.9281\ldots}$

$\lim_{b\to\infty} A(b) = \lim_{b\to\infty} 5\ln\frac{1}{1} + 5\ln 6$ (l'Hospital's rule)

$= 5\ln 6 = 8.9587\ldots$,

so the area does approach a finite limit.

22. Volume Problem

$dV = 2\pi xy\,dx = \frac{50\pi x}{x^2 + 3x - 4}\,dx$

$V = \int_2^b \frac{50\pi x}{x^2 + 3x - 4}\,dx = \int_2^b (\frac{10\pi}{x-1} + \frac{40\pi}{x+4})\,dx$

$= 10\pi\ln|x-1| + 40\pi\ln|x+4|\,\Big|_2^b$

$= 10\pi\ln|b-1| + 40\pi\ln|b+4| - 40\pi\ln 6$

$V(7) = 40\pi\ln 11 - 30\pi\ln 6 = \underline{132.4590\ldots}$

$\lim_{b\to\infty} V(b) = \infty$ since both ln terms become infinite, and are added.

(Note that if the region were rotated about the x-axis, the limit of the volume *would* be finite. The answer would be $5\pi(\frac{35}{6} - 2\ln 6) = 35.3400\ldots$.

23. Equivalent Answers Problem

a. $\int\frac{x-3}{x^2 - 6x + 8}\,dx = \int(\frac{1/2}{x-2} + \frac{1/2}{x-4})\,dx$

$= \frac{1}{2}\ln|x-2| + \frac{1}{2}\ln|x-4| + C$

b. $x^2 - 6x + 8 = (x-3)^2 - 1$

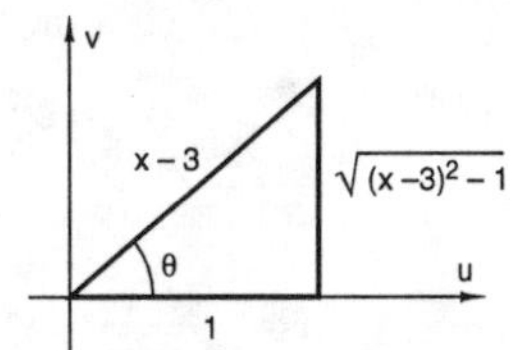

Let $x - 3 = \sec\theta$. $dx = \sec\theta\tan\theta\,d\theta$,

$\sqrt{(x-3)^2 - 1} = \tan\theta$, $\theta = \sec^{-1}(x-3)$

$\therefore \int\frac{x-3}{x^2 - 6x + 8}\,dx = \int\frac{x-3}{(x-3)^2 - 1}\,dx$

$= \int\frac{\sec\theta}{\tan^2\theta}(\sec\theta\tan\theta\,d\theta) = \int\frac{\sec^2\theta}{\tan\theta}\,d\theta$

$= \ln|\tan\theta| + C$

$= \ln\sqrt{(x-3)^2 - 1} + C$

$= \ln\sqrt{x^2 - 6x + 8} + C$

c. $\int\frac{x-3}{x^2 - 6x + 8}\,dx = \frac{1}{2}\int\frac{2x-6}{x^2 - 6x + 8}\,dx$

$= \frac{1}{2}\ln|x^2 - 6x + 8| + C$

d. From part a,

$\frac{1}{2}\ln|x-2| + \frac{1}{2}\ln|x-4| + C$

$= \frac{1}{2}\ln|(x-2)(x-4)| + C$

$= \frac{1}{2}\ln|x^2 - 6x + 8| + C,$

which is the answer in part c. This equals

$\ln|x^2 - 6x + 8|^{1/2} + C$

$= \ln\sqrt{x^2 - 6x + 8} + C,$

which is the answer from part b.

So all three answers are equivalent, Q.E.D.

24. Logistic Curve Problem, Algebraically

a. When the population is very much smaller than the maximum, $(m - p)$ behaves like a constant, and $dp/dt = k(m-p)\cdot p$ is approximately proportional to p. But when p is approaching m, then $(m - p)$ goes to zero, so $dp/dt = kp(m - p)$ goes to zero.

b. $dp/dt = kp(m - p) = k(mp - p^2)$.

So dp/dt is a quadratic function of p.

Thus, the turning point is at $p = -\frac{m}{2(-1)} = m/2$.

If $k > 0$, the graph of dp/dt versus p opens downward, and the turning point is a maximum.

So the population grows fastest when $p = m/2$.

c. $\frac{dp}{dt} = kp(m-p) \Rightarrow \frac{dp}{p(m-p)} = k\,dt$

$\int \frac{dp}{p(m-p)} = \int k\,dt$

$\int \left(\frac{1/m}{p} + \frac{1/m}{m-p}\right) dp = \int k\,dt$

$\frac{1}{m}\ln|p| - \frac{1}{m}\ln|m-p| = kt + C_1$

d. $\ln\left|\frac{p}{m-p}\right| = kmt + C_2$ $\quad (C_2 = mC_1)$

$\frac{p}{m-p} = e^{kmt + C_2} = C_3e^{kmt}$ $\quad (C_3 = e^{C_2})$

(Note $m > p > 0 \Rightarrow \frac{p}{m-p} > 0$.)

$\frac{m-p}{p} = be^{-kmt} \Rightarrow \frac{m}{p} - 1 = be^{-kmt}$ $\quad (b = 1/C_3)$

$\frac{m}{p} = 1 + be^{-kmt} \Rightarrow p = \frac{m}{1 + be^{-kmt}}$

At time $t = 0$, $p = p_0$.

$\therefore p_0 = \frac{m}{1+b} \Rightarrow m = p_0(1+b)$

$\therefore p = \frac{p_0(1+b)}{1 + be^{-kmt}}$

Letting $K = km$, $p = p_0\frac{1+b}{1+be^{-Kt}}$, Q.E.D.

e. Let p denote millions of people. Then $p_0 = 179.3$.

Substitute $p(10) = 203.2$.

$203.2 = 179.3\frac{1+b}{1+be^{-10K}}$

$\Rightarrow 203.2 + 203.2be^{-10K} = 179.3 + 179.3b$

$\Rightarrow b(203.2e^{-10K} - 179.3) = -23.9$

$\Rightarrow b = \frac{-23.9}{203.2e^{-10K} - 179.3}$

By substituting $p(20) = 226.5$ and transforming,

$b = \frac{-47.2}{226.5e^{-20K} - 179.3}$.

Equating the two values of b and solving numerically for K gives

$K = 0.0259109\ldots$

$\therefore b = \frac{-23.9}{203.2e^{-0.259102\ldots} - 179.3} = 1.0630436\ldots$

$\therefore p = 179.3\frac{2.063036\ldots}{1 + 1.063036\ldots e^{-0.0259109\ldots}}$

f. $p(30) = 179.3\cdot\frac{2.0630\ldots}{1 + 1.0630\ldots\cdot e^{-30\cdot 0.0259\ldots}}$

$= 248.4892\ldots \approx 248.5$ million people.

g. $k > 0 \Rightarrow \lim_{t\to\infty} p = \lim_{t\to\infty} p_0\frac{1+b}{1+be^{-Kt}} = p_0(1+b)$

$= 179.3\cdot(1 + 1.0630\ldots)$

$= 369.9024\ldots \approx 369.9$ million people.

h. If $p(10)$ had been 204.2, then K would have been given by

$\frac{-24.9}{204.2e^{-10K} - 179.3} = \frac{-47.2}{226.5e^{-20K} - 179.3}$

$\Rightarrow K = 0.0343965\ldots$

$\Rightarrow b = \frac{-24.9}{204.2e^{-0.0343965\ldots} - 179.3} = 0.721075\ldots$

So the ultimate population would have been

$\lim_{t\to\infty} p = p_0(1+b) = 179.3(1 + 0.7210\ldots)$

$= 308.5888\ldots \approx 308.6$ million people.

An *increase* of 1 million in one of the initial conditions causes a *decrease* of over 61 million in the predicted maximum population! So this model does have a fairly sensitive dependence on the initial conditions.

Problem Set 9-8, page 471 — Integrals of the Inverse Trigonometric Functions

Q1. integration by parts

Q2. partial fractions

Q3. $\theta = \tan^{-1} x$

Q4. $\theta = \sec^{-1} x$

Q5. $\theta = \sin^{-1} x$

Q6. $\frac{1}{16}(x^2 + 1)^8 + C$

Q7. Max. is 7 (f(1)).

Q8. Min. is 3 (f(5)).

Q9. undefined

Q10. 0

1. $\int \tan^{-1} x\,dx$

u		dv
$\tan^{-1} x$	+	1
$\frac{dx}{1+x^2}$	−	x

$= x\tan^{-1} x - \int\frac{x\,dx}{x^2+1}$

$= x\tan^{-1} x - \frac{1}{2}\int\frac{2x\,dx}{x^2+1}$

$= x\tan^{-1} x - \frac{1}{2}\ln|x^2+1| + C$, (Checks.)

2. $\int \cot^{-1} x\, dx$

$$\begin{array}{cc} u & dv \\ \cot^{-1} x & 1 \\ -\dfrac{dx}{1+x^2} & x \end{array}$$

$= x \cot^{-1} x + \int \dfrac{x\,dx}{x^2+1}$

$= x \cot^{-1} x + \dfrac{1}{2}\int \dfrac{2x\,dx}{x^2+1}$

$= x \cot^{-1} x + \dfrac{1}{2} \ln |x^2 + 1| + C$, (Checks.)

3. $\int \cos^{-1} x\, dx$

$$\begin{array}{cc} u & dv \\ \cos^{-1} x & 1 \\ -\dfrac{dx}{\sqrt{1-x^2}} & x \end{array}$$

$= x \cos^{-1} x + \int \dfrac{x\,dx}{\sqrt{1-x^2}}$

$= x \cos^{-1} x - \dfrac{1}{2}\int (1-x^2)^{-1/2}(-2x\,dx)$

$= x \cos^{-1} x - \dfrac{1}{2}\cdot 2(1-x^2)^{1/2} + C$

$= x \cos^{-1} x - \sqrt{1-x^2} + C$, (Checks.)

4. $\int \sin^{-1} x\, dx$

$$\begin{array}{cc} u & dv \\ \sin^{-1} x & 1 \\ \dfrac{dx}{\sqrt{1-x^2}} & x \end{array}$$

$= x \sin^{-1} x - \int \dfrac{x\,dx}{\sqrt{1-x^2}}$

$= x \sin^{-1} x + \dfrac{1}{2}\int (1-x^2)^{-1/2}(-2x\,dx)$

$= x \sin^{-1} x + \dfrac{1}{2}\cdot 2(1-x^2)^{1/2} + C$

$= x \sin^{-1} x + \sqrt{1-x^2} + C$

5. $\int \sec^{-1} x\, dx$

$$\begin{array}{cc} u & dv \\ \sec^{-1} x & 1 \\ \dfrac{dx}{|x|\sqrt{x^2-1}} & x \end{array}$$

$= x \sec^{-1} x - \int \dfrac{x\,dx}{|x|\sqrt{x^2-1}}$

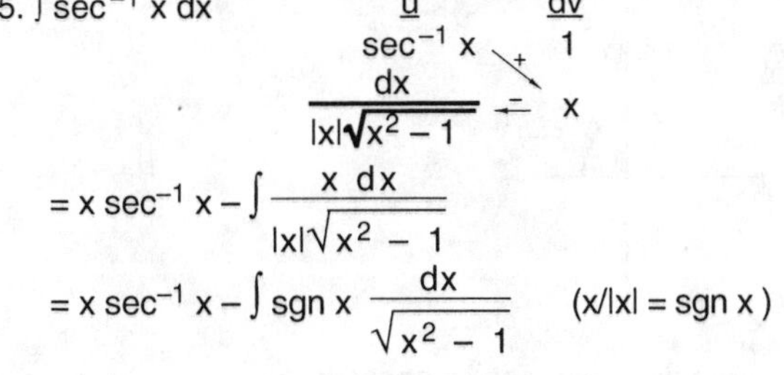

$= x \sec^{-1} x - \int \operatorname{sgn} x \dfrac{dx}{\sqrt{x^2-1}}$ $\quad$ ($x/|x| = \operatorname{sgn} x$)

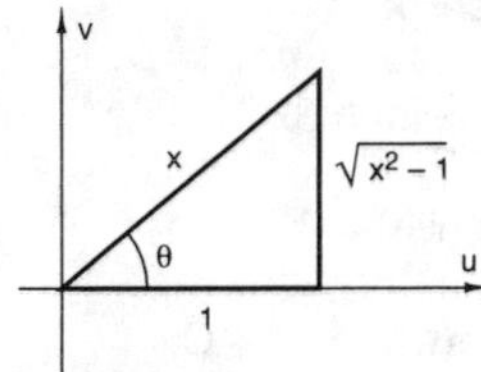

Let $\dfrac{x}{1} = \sec\theta$

$dx = \sec\theta \tan\theta\, d\theta$

$\sqrt{x^2-1} = \tan\theta$

$\theta = \sec^{-1} x$.

$\therefore \int \sec^{-1} x\, dx$

$= x \sec^{-1} x - \int \operatorname{sgn} x \dfrac{\sec\theta \tan\theta\, d\theta}{\tan\theta}$

$= x \sec^{-1} x - \int \operatorname{sgn} x \sec\theta\, d\theta$

$= x \sec^{-1} x - \operatorname{sgn} x \ln |\sec\theta + \tan\theta| + C$

$= x \sec^{-1} x - \operatorname{sgn} x \ln |x + \sqrt{x^2-1}\,| + C$, (Checks.)

Note: This answer can be transformed to

$x \sec^{-1} x - \ln(|x| + \sqrt{x^2-1}\,) + C$.

6. $\int \csc^{-1} x\, dx$

$$\begin{array}{cc} u & dv \\ \csc^{-1} x & 1 \\ -\dfrac{dx}{|x|\sqrt{x^2-1}} & x \end{array}$$

$= x \csc^{-1} x + \int \dfrac{x\,dx}{|x|\sqrt{x^2-1}}$

$= x \csc^{-1} x + \int \operatorname{sgn} x \dfrac{dx}{\sqrt{x^2-1}}$

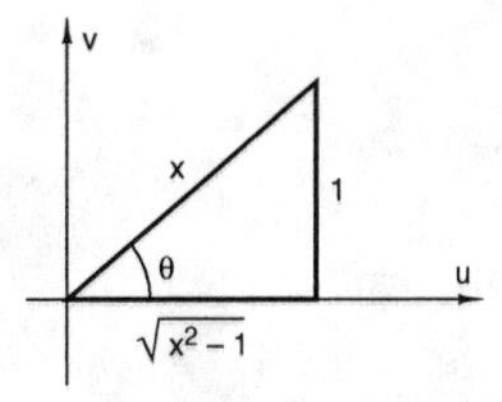

Let $x = \csc\theta$. $dx = -\csc\theta \cot\theta\, d\theta$,

$\sqrt{x^2-1} = \cot\theta$, $\theta = \csc^{-1} x$.

$\therefore \int \csc^{-1} x\, dx$

$= x \csc^{-1} x - \int \operatorname{sgn} x \dfrac{\csc\theta \cot\theta\, d\theta}{\cot\theta}$

$= x \csc^{-1} x - \int \operatorname{sgn} x \csc\theta\, d\theta$

$= x \csc^{-1} x + \operatorname{sgn} x \ln |\csc\theta + \cot\theta| + C$

$= x \csc^{-1} x + \operatorname{sgn} x \ln |x + \sqrt{x^2-1}| + C$,

which checks.

Note: This answer can be transformed to

$x \sec^{-1} x + \ln(|x| + \sqrt{x^2-1}\,) + C$.

7. Answer Verification Problem

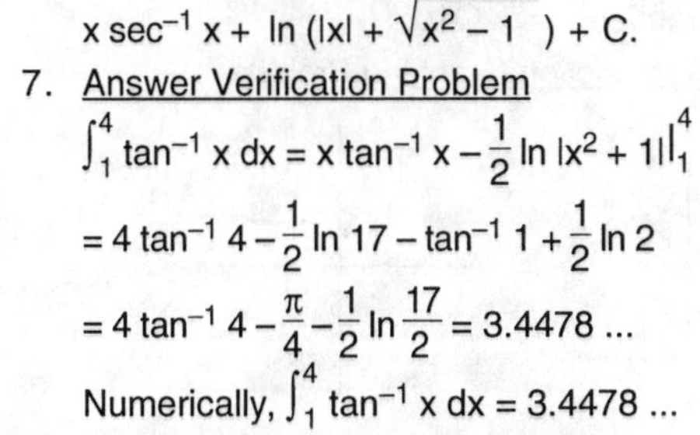

$\int_1^4 \tan^{-1} x\, dx = x \tan^{-1} x - \dfrac{1}{2} \ln |x^2 + 1| \Big|_1^4$

$= 4 \tan^{-1} 4 - \dfrac{1}{2} \ln 17 - \tan^{-1} 1 + \dfrac{1}{2} \ln 2$

$= 4 \tan^{-1} 4 - \dfrac{\pi}{4} - \dfrac{1}{2} \ln \dfrac{17}{2} = 3.4478\ldots$

Numerically, $\int_1^4 \tan^{-1} x\, dx = 3.4478\ldots$

8. Simpson's Rule Review Problem

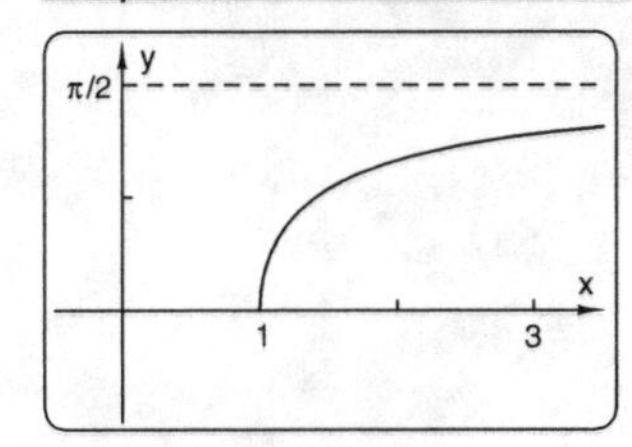

Simpson's rule for $y = \sec^{-1} x$: $n = 10 \Rightarrow \Delta x = 0.2$

$A \approx \dfrac{0.1}{3}(y_1 + 4y_{1.2} + 2y_{1.4} + 4y_{1.6} + \ldots + 4y_{2.8} + y_3)$

$= \underline{1.919692\ldots}$

$A = \int_1^3 \sec^{-1} x\, dx$

$= x \sec^{-1} x - \operatorname{sgn} x \ln(x + \sqrt{x^2-1}\,) \Big|_1^3$

$= 3 \sec^{-1} 3 - 1 \cdot \ln(3 + \sqrt{8}) - \sec^{-1} 1 + 1 \cdot \ln 1$

$= \underline{1.930131\ldots}$, which differs from the Simpson's rule answer by 0.0104 ..., or about 0.5%

9. Area Problem

By vertical slices,

$A = \int_0^1 (\frac{\pi}{2} - \sin^{-1} x)\, dx$

$= \frac{\pi}{2} x - x \sin^{-1} x - \sqrt{1 - x^2} \Big|_0^1$

$= \frac{\pi}{2} - \sin^{-1} 1 - \sqrt{0} - 0 + 0 + \sqrt{1} = \underline{1}.$

By horizontal slices,

$A = \int_0^{\pi/2} \sin y\, dy = -\cos y \Big|_0^{\pi/2} = -\cos \frac{\pi}{2} + \cos 0 = \underline{1},$

which is the same answer as by vertical slices.

10. Volume Problem

By cylindrical shells, $dV = 2\pi x \tan^{-1} x\, dx$.

$V = 2\pi \int_0^1 x \tan^{-1} x\, dx$

$\int x \tan^{-1} x\, dx$

u		dv
$\tan^{-1} x$	+	x
$\frac{dx}{1 + x^2}$	−	$\frac{1}{2}x^2$

$= \frac{1}{2} x^2 \tan^{-1} x - \frac{1}{2} \int \frac{x^2}{1 + x^2}\, dx$

$= \frac{1}{2} x^2 \tan^{-1} x - \frac{1}{2} \int (1 - \frac{1}{1 + x^2})\, dx$

$= \frac{1}{2} x^2 \tan^{-1} x - \frac{1}{2} x + \frac{1}{2} \tan^{-1} x + C$

$\therefore V = \pi x^2 \tan^{-1} x - \pi x + \pi \tan^{-1} x \Big|_0^1$

$= \pi \tan^{-1} 1 - \pi + \pi \tan^{-1} 1 - 0 + 0 - 0$

$= 2\pi \tan^{-1} 1 - \pi = 2\pi \frac{\pi}{4} - \pi$

$= \frac{1}{2} \pi^2 - \pi = 1.7932 \ldots$

Compare this with a cylinder ($\pi r^2 h$) minus a cone ($\pi r^2 h/3$), both of radius 1 and altitude $\pi/4$, which has volume $2\pi(\pi/4)/3 = \pi^2/6 = 1.6449 \ldots$; the volume is slightly less than V, which is expected since the cylinder minus cone is generated by rotating a line that lies below the graph.

Problem Set 9-9, pages 478 to 484 — Calculus of the Hyperbolic and Inverse Hyperbolic Functions

Q1. $\theta = \tan^{-1} \frac{x}{\sqrt{5}}$

Q2. $x e^x - e^x + C$

Q3. $\frac{1}{3} \tan 3x + C$

Q4. $2x^{1/2} + C$

Q5. $\ln |x| + C$

Q6. reduction formula

Q7. False.

Q8. $\sqrt{dx^2 + dy^2}$

Q9. Partial fractions.

Q10. $(1 - x^2)^{-1/2}$

1. Hyperbolic Function Graphing Problem

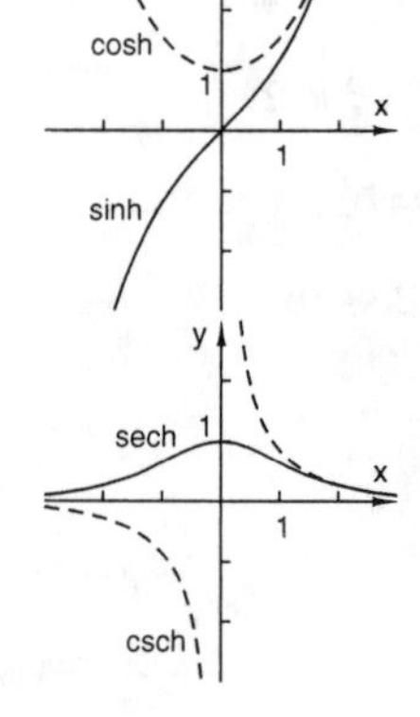

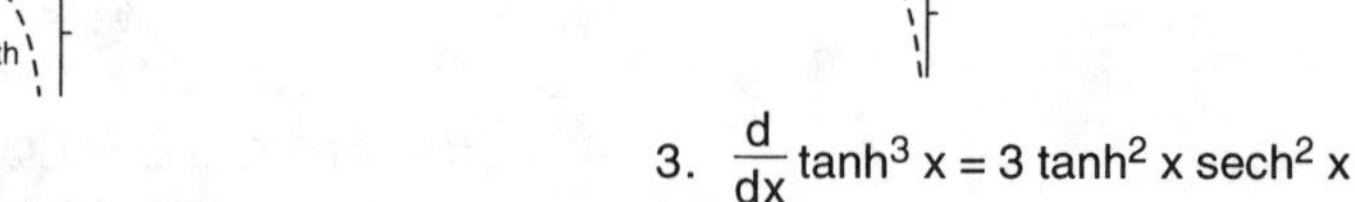

2. Inverse Hyperbolic Function Graphing Problem

3. $\frac{d}{dx} \tanh^3 x = 3 \tanh^2 x \operatorname{sech}^2 x$

4. $\frac{d}{dx} 5 \operatorname{sech} 3x = -15 \operatorname{sech} 3x \tanh 3x$

5. $\int \cosh^5 x \sinh x\, dx = \frac{1}{6} \cosh^6 x + C$

6. $\int (\sinh x)^{-3} \cosh x\, dx = -\frac{1}{2} (\sinh x)^{-2} + C$

$= -\frac{1}{2} \operatorname{csch}^2 x + C$

or $\int (\sinh x)^{-3} \cosh x\, dx = \int \operatorname{csch}^2 x \coth x\, dx$

$= -\frac{1}{2} \coth^2 x + C = -\frac{1}{2} (\operatorname{csch}^2 x + 1) + C$

$= -\frac{1}{2} \operatorname{csch}^2 x + C$

7. $\frac{d}{dx} (\operatorname{csch} x \sin x)$

$= -\operatorname{csch} x \coth x \sin x + \operatorname{csch} x \cos x$

8. $\frac{d}{dx}(\tan x \tanh x) = \sec^2 x \tanh x + \tan x \operatorname{sech}^2 x$

9. $\int \operatorname{sech}^2 4x\, dx = \frac{1}{4}\tanh 4x + C$

10. $\int \operatorname{sech} 7x \tanh 7x\, dx = -\frac{1}{7}\operatorname{sech} 7x + C$

11. $\frac{d}{dx}(x^3 \coth x) = 3x^2 \coth x - x^3 \operatorname{csch}^2 x$

12. $\frac{d}{dx}(x^{2.5} \operatorname{csch} 4x)$
$= 2.5x^{1.5}\operatorname{csch} 4x - 4x^{2.5}\operatorname{csch} 4x \coth 4x$

13. $\int_1^3 \tanh x\, dx = \ln(\cosh x)\Big|_1^3$
$= \ln(\cosh 3) - \ln(\cosh 1) = 1.875547\ldots$

14. $\int_{-4}^4 \sinh x\, dx = \cosh x\Big|_{-4}^4 = 0$
(Note sinh is an odd function.)

15. $\frac{d}{dx}\frac{\sinh 5x}{\ln 3x}$
$= \frac{5\cosh 5x \ln 3x - x^{-1}\sinh 5x}{(\ln 3x)^2}$

16. $\frac{d}{dx}\frac{\cosh 6x}{\cos 3x}$
$= \frac{6\sinh 6x \cos 3x + 3\cosh 6x \sin 3x}{\cos^2 3x}$

17. $\int x \sinh x\, dx$

u		dv
x	+	sinh x
1	−	cosh x
0	+	sinh x

$= x\cosh x - \sinh x + C$
$\therefore \int_0^1 x \sinh x\, dx$
$= x\cosh x - \sinh x\Big|_0^1 = \cosh 1 - \sinh 1$
$= e^{-1} = 0.36787\ldots$

18. $\int x^2 \cosh x\, dx$

u		dv
x^2	+	cosh x
2x	−	sinh x
2	+	cosh x
0	−	sinh x

$= x^2 \sinh x - 2x\cosh x + 2\sinh x + C$
$\therefore \int_a^b x^2 \cosh x\, dx$
$= x^2 \sinh x - 2x\cosh x + 2\sinh x\Big|_a^b$
$= b^2 \sinh b - 2b\cosh b + 2\sinh b$
$\quad - a^2 \sinh a + 2a\cosh a - 2\sinh a$

19. $\frac{d}{dx}(3\sinh^{-1} 4x) = \frac{12}{\sqrt{16x^2 + 1}}$

20. $\frac{d}{dx}(5\tanh^{-1} x^3) = \frac{15x^2}{1 - x^6}$

21. $\int \tanh^{-1} 5x\, dx = x\tanh^{-1} 5x + \frac{1}{10}\ln|1 - (5x)^2| + C$

22. $\int 4\cosh^{-1} 6x\, dx = 4x\cosh^{-1} 6x - \frac{4}{6}((6x)^2 - 1)^{1/2} + C$
$= 4x\cosh^{-1} 6x - \frac{2}{3}\sqrt{36x^2 - 1} + C$

23. Let $x = 3\sinh t$, $dx = 3\cosh t\, dt$,
$\sqrt{x^2 + 9} = \sqrt{9\cdot\sinh^2 t + 9} = 3\cosh t$,
$t = \sinh^{-1}\frac{x}{3}$.
$\therefore \int\sqrt{x^2 + 9}\, dx = \int 3\cosh t \cdot 3\cosh t\, dt$
$= 9\int \cosh^2 t\, dt$

u		dv
cosh t	+	cosh t
sinh t	−	sinh t

$= 9\cosh t \sinh t - 9\int \sinh^2 t\, dt$
$= 9\cosh t \sinh t - 9\int(\cosh^2 t - 1)\, dt$
$= 9\cosh t \sinh t - 9\int \cosh^2 t + 9\int dt$
$\therefore 18\int \cosh^2 t\, dt = 9\cosh t \sinh t + 9t + C_1$
$\therefore 9\int \cosh^2 t\, dt = 4.5\cosh t \sinh t + 4.5t + C$
$= 4.5\cdot\frac{\sqrt{x^2 + 9}}{3}\cdot\frac{x}{3} + 4.5\sinh^{-1}\frac{x}{3} + C$
$= 0.5x\sqrt{x^2 + 9} + 4.5\sinh^{-1}\frac{x}{3} + C$

24. Let $x = 5\cosh t$.
Let $dx = 5\sinh t\, dt$,
$\sqrt{x^2 - 25} = \sqrt{25\cdot\cosh^2 t - 25} = 5\sinh t$,
$t = \cosh^{-1}\frac{x}{5}$.
$\therefore \int\sqrt{x^2 - 25}\, dx = \int 5\sinh t \cdot 5\sinh t\, dt$
$= 25\int \sinh^2 t\, dt$

u		dv
sinh t	+	sinh t
cosh t	−	cosh t

$= 25\sinh t\cosh t - 25\int \cosh^2 t\, dt$
$= 25\sinh t\cosh t - 25\int(\sinh^2 t + 1)\, dt$
$= 25\sinh t\cosh t - 25\int \sinh^2 t\, dt - 25\int dt$
$\therefore 50\int \sinh^2 t\, dt = 25\sinh t\cosh t - 25t + C_1$
$\therefore 25\int \sinh^2 t\, dt = 12.5\sinh t\cosh t - 12.5t + C$
$= 12.5\cdot\frac{\sqrt{x^2 - 25}}{5}\cdot\frac{x}{5} - 12.5\cosh^{-1}\frac{x}{5}$
$= 0.5x\sqrt{x^2 - 25} - 12.5\cosh^{-1}\frac{x}{5} + C$

25. Hanging Chain or Cable Problem

a. Figure 9-9g shows that the horizontal force is given by the vector (h, 0) and the vertical force is the vector (0, v), so their sum, the tension vector, is the vector (h, v), which has slope $\frac{v}{h}$. Since the tension vector points along the graph, the graph's slope, y', also equals $\frac{v}{h}$.

b. v = weight of chain below (x, y) = s·w
$\Rightarrow y' = \frac{v}{h} = \frac{s\cdot w}{h} = \frac{w}{h}\cdot s$

c. $ds = \sqrt{dx^2 + dy^2} = \sqrt{dx^2(1 + (dy/dx)^2)}$
$= \sqrt{1 + (y')^2}\, dx$
$\Rightarrow d(y') = \frac{w}{h}\, ds = \frac{w}{h}\sqrt{1 + (y')^2}\, dx$

d. $\int (1 + (y')^2)^{-1/2}\, d(y')$
$= \int (1 + \sinh^2 t)^{-1/2}\, d(\sinh t)$
$= \int (\cosh^2 t)^{-1/2} (\cosh t\, dt)$
$= \int dt = t + C = \sinh^{-1} y' + C_1$
$\int \frac{w}{h}\, dx = \frac{w}{h} x + C_2$
$\Rightarrow \sinh^{-1} y' = \frac{w}{h} x + C$

e. At x = 0, y' = 0, so
$\sinh^{-1} 0 = \frac{w}{h} 0 + C$
$\Rightarrow C = 0$

f. $\sinh^{-1} y' = \frac{w}{h} x \Rightarrow y' = \sinh \frac{w}{h} x$

g. $\frac{dy}{dx} = \sinh \frac{w}{h} x \Rightarrow \int dy = \int \sinh \frac{w}{h} x\, dx$
$\Rightarrow y = \frac{h}{w} \cosh \frac{w}{h} x + C$

26. Can You Duplicate This Graph?

a. y = 2 when x = 0 $\Rightarrow 2 = k \cosh \frac{1}{k} 0 + C$
$\Rightarrow 2 = k + C \Rightarrow C = 2 - k$
y = 5 when x = 4 $\Rightarrow 5 = k \cosh \frac{4}{k} + 2 - k$
Grapher SOLVE $\Rightarrow k \approx 3.0668 \ldots$
$y = 3.0668 \ldots \cosh \frac{1}{3.0668 \ldots} x + 2 - 3.0668 \ldots$
$y = 3.0668 \ldots \cosh \frac{1}{3.0668 \ldots} x - 1.0668 \ldots$

b. y(20) = 1040.9739 ...

c. y = 4:
$4 = 3.0668 \ldots \cosh \frac{1}{3.0668 \ldots} x - 1.0668 \ldots$
$\cosh \frac{1}{3.0668 \ldots} x = \frac{5.0668 \ldots}{3.0668 \ldots}$

$x = 3.0668 \ldots \cosh^{-1} \frac{5.0668 \ldots}{3.0668 \ldots} = 3.3355 \ldots$
By symmetry, $x = \pm 3.3355 \ldots$
The answer can be found numerically using SOLVE.

d. $y' = \sinh \frac{1}{k} x$; y'(3) = 1.1418 ...

e. $A = \int_{-1}^{3} (k \cosh \frac{1}{k} x + 2 - k)\, dx$
$= k^2 \sinh \frac{1}{k} x + (2 - k)x \Big|_{-1}^{3}$
$= (3.0668 \ldots)^2 (\sinh \frac{3}{3.0668 \ldots} - \sinh \frac{-1}{3.0668 \ldots})$
$+ 4(2 - 3.0668 \ldots)$
$= 9.5937 \ldots$

f. $L = \int_{-1}^{3} \sqrt{1 + y'^2}\, dx = \int_{-1}^{3} \sqrt{1 + \sinh^2 (x/k)}\, dx$
$= \int_{-1}^{3} \cosh \frac{1}{k} x\, dx = k \sinh \frac{1}{k} x \Big|_{-1}^{3}$
$= k(\sinh \frac{3}{k} + \sinh \frac{1}{k}) = 4.5196 \ldots$

27. Power Line Problem

a. The vertex is midway between the poles, so y = 110 ft when x = 150 ft.
$y = \frac{h}{w} \cosh \frac{w}{h} x + C$
$= \frac{400 \text{ lbs}}{0.8 \text{ lb/ft}} \cosh \frac{0.8}{400} x + C$
$110 = 500 \cosh \frac{1}{500} 150 + C$
$\Rightarrow C = 110 - 500 \cosh 0.3$
$y = 500 \cosh \frac{1}{500} x + 110 - 500 \cosh 0.3$
The cable comes closest to the ground at x = 0;
y(0) = 500 cosh 0 + 110 − 500 cosh 0.3
= 610 − 500 cosh 0.3 = 87.3307 ... ≈ 87.3 ft

b. $y' = \sinh \frac{1}{500} x$
$L = \int_{-150}^{150} \sqrt{1 + \sinh^2 (x/500))}\, dx$
$= \int_{-150}^{150} \cosh \frac{1}{500} x\, dx$
$= 500 \sinh \frac{1}{500} x \Big|_{-150}^{150}$
= 500 sinh 0.3 − 500 sinh (−0.3)
= 1000 sinh 0.3 = 304.5202 ... ≈ 304.5 ft
Half weight of cable = vert. tension at (150, 110)
= h·y'(150) (cf. #25)
Weight = $2 \cdot 400 \sinh \frac{1}{500} 150 = 800 \sinh 0.3$
= 243.6162 ... ≈ 243.6 lb.
(Note Since w·L = weight, either of these methods could give both the weight and the length.)

c. $T = \sqrt{h^2 + v^2}$; h is constant and v is greatest at the ends, so the max. tension is at x = 150 ft.
$T(150) = \sqrt{h^2 + (hy'(150))^2}$
$= 400 \sqrt{1 + \sinh^2 0.3} = 400 \cosh 0.3$
= 418.1354 ... ≈ 418.1 lb.

d. The general equation is $y = \frac{h}{w} \cosh \frac{w}{h} x + C$.
If y(0) = 100 and y(150) = 110, find h such that y(150) − y(0) = 10; solve:
$\frac{h}{w} \cosh \frac{w}{h} 150 - \frac{h}{w} = 10$, or
$\cosh \frac{120}{h} - 1 = \frac{8}{h}$
By grapher, h = 901.3301 ... ≈ 901.3 lb

28. Hanging Chain Experiment

The answers will depend on the dimensions of the chain used. Note that the answer is independent of the *kind* of chain. You might show students how a heavy chain and a light chain of equal length will hang in the same catenary if they are suspended from the same points.
Assume that the dimensions are the same as in Example 5.

a. Vertex: (0, 20). Supports: (±90, 120)

b. $y = 51.78 \ldots \cosh \frac{1}{51.78 \ldots} x - 31.78 \ldots$

c. Note: To conserve class time, you might have students plot only each 20 cm for x, as shown here for Example 5. Use the TABLE feature.

x	y
0	20.0
±20	23.9
±40	36.2
±60	58.8
±80	95.1

d. A clever way to make sure the measurements are vertical is to hold a book against the board with its bottom edge along the chalk tray. Then hold the meter stick against the vertical edge of the book. It is crucial that the points be plotted accurately to get the dramatic impact of "perfect fit."

e. For a quadratic function with vertex on the y-axis, $y = ax^2 + c$. Using the data for Example 5,

$20 = a(0) + c \Rightarrow c = 20$

$120 = a(90^2) + 20 \Rightarrow a = \frac{1}{81}$

$y = \frac{1}{81}x^2 + 20.$

x	y
0	20.0
±20	24.9
±40	40.0
±60	64.4
±80	99.0

For graph, see Figure 9-9b. The parabola is more curved at the vertex.

f. For Example 5,

$dL = \sqrt{1 + (y')^2}\,dx = \sqrt{1 + \sinh^2 \frac{1}{51.78\ldots}x}\,dx$

$= \cosh \frac{1}{51.78\ldots}x\,dx$

$L = \int_{-90}^{90} \cosh \frac{1}{51.78\ldots}x\,dx$

$= 51.78\ldots \sinh \frac{1}{51.78\ldots}x \Big|_{-90}^{90} = 285.349\ldots$

≈ 285.3 cm

The actual length should be close to this.

29. Bowl Problem

a. $y = \sinh x$

$dS = 2\pi x\,dL = 2\pi x\sqrt{1 + \cosh^2 x}\,dx$

$S = 2\pi \int_0^1 x\sqrt{1 + \cosh^2 x}\,dx$

$= 5.07327\ldots$ by numerical integration

≈ 5.07 ft^2.

b. Cost = (57)(5.07327 ...) = 289.1766 ... ≈ \$289.18

c. Slice perpendicular to the y-axis.

$dV = \pi x^2\,dy = \pi(\sinh^{-1} y)^2\,dy$

Top of bowl is at $y = \sinh 1 - \frac{1}{24} = 1.133534\ldots$

$\therefore V = \pi \int_0^{1.133\ldots} (\sinh^{-1} y)^2\,dy$

$= 1.25317\ldots$ by numerical integration

≈ 1.253 ft^3

30. Gateway Arch Problem

a. $y = -k \cosh \frac{1}{k}x + C$

Inner catenary: $y_{inner}(0) = 612$, $y_{inner}(260) = 0$

$612 = -k_i \cosh \frac{0}{k_i} + C_i \Rightarrow C_i = 612 + k_i$

$0 = -k_i \cosh \frac{260}{k_i} + 612 + k_i$

$\Rightarrow k_i = 97.1522\ldots$ (numerically)

$y_{inner} = 97.1522\ldots(-\cosh \frac{1}{97.1522\ldots}x + 1) + 612$

Outer catenary: $y_{outer}(0) = 630$, $y_{outer}(315) = 0$

$630 = -k_o \cosh \frac{0}{k_o} + C_o \Rightarrow C_o = 630 + k_o$

$0 = -k_o \cosh \frac{315}{k_o} + 630 + k_o$

$\Rightarrow k_o = 127.7114\ldots$ (numerically)

$y_{outer} = 127.7114\ldots(-\cosh \frac{1}{127.7114\ldots}x + 1) + 630$

b. Graphs, which are the same as in Figure 9-9k.

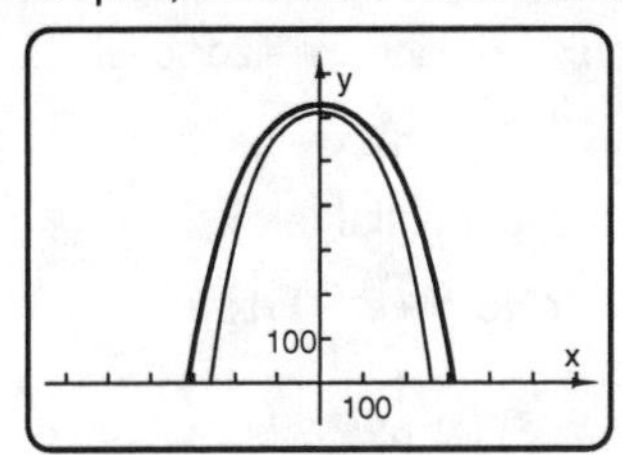

c. $A = \int_{-315}^{315} y_{outer}\,dx - \int_{-260}^{260} y_{inner}\,dx$

$= -k_o^2 \sinh \frac{x}{k_o} + k_o x + 630x \Big|_{-315}^{315}$

$\quad + k_i^2 \sinh \frac{x}{k_i} - k_i x - 612x \Big|_{-260}^{260}$

$= 54323.2729\ldots \approx 54323$ ft^2.

d. $\frac{dy_{outer}}{dx} = -\sinh \frac{1}{k_o}x$, so

$L = \int_{-315}^{315} \sqrt{1 + \sinh^2 \frac{1}{k_o}x}\,dx = \int_{-315}^{315} \cosh \frac{1}{k_o}x\,dx$

$= k_o \sinh \frac{1}{k_o}x \Big|_{-315}^{315}$

$= 2 \cdot 127.7114\ldots \cdot \sinh \frac{315}{127.7114\ldots}$

$= 1493.7422\ldots \approx 1494$ ft.

e. $y_{outer}'(-315) = -\sinh \frac{-315}{k_o} = \sinh \frac{315}{127.7144\ldots}$

$= 5.8481\ldots$ is the spider's starting slope.

f. A.V. can fly through at altitude $y_{inner}(x)$ if $x \geq 50 + 120/2 = 110$.

$y_{inner}(110) = 542.7829\ldots$, so the plane can fly through at heights between 0 and 542 feet.

(Because of the curvature of the arch, the closest distance is slightly *less* than 50 feet when the horizontal distance is 50 feet. The plane can fly through at slightly higher altitudes by banking slightly.)

31. Derivative Verification Problem

a. $H(x) = \text{csch } x \Rightarrow h'(x) = -\text{csch } x \coth x$

$H'(1) = -\text{csch } 1 \coth 1 = -1.1172855 \ldots$

b. $H'(1) \approx \dfrac{\text{csch}(1.01) - \text{csch}(0.99)}{0.02} = -1.11738505 \ldots$

The answers differ by 0.0000995 ..., which is about 0.0089% of the actual answer.

32. Integral Verification Problem

$\int_1^2 \text{sech } x \, dx = \sin^{-1}(\tanh x) \Big|_1^2$

$= \sin^{-1}(\tanh 2) - \sin^{-1}(\tanh 1)$

$= 0.435990 \ldots$

Numerically, $\int_1^2 \text{sech } x \, dx = 0.435990 \ldots$ (Checks.)

33. Integration by Parts Problem

By parts:

$\int e^x \sinh 2x \, dx$

u	dv
sinh 2x (+)	e^x
2 cosh 2x (−)	e^x
4 sinh 2x (+)	e^x

$= e^x \sinh 2x - 2e^x \cosh 2x + 4\int e^x \sinh 2x \, dx$

$\Rightarrow -3\int e^x \sinh 2x \, dx = e^x \sinh 2x - 2e^x \cosh 2x + C_1$

$\Rightarrow \int e^x \sinh 2x \, dx = \frac{2}{3}e^x \cosh 2x - \frac{1}{3}e^x \sinh 2x + C$

By transforming to exponential form:

$\int e^x \sinh 2x \, dx = \frac{1}{2}\int e^x(e^{2x} - e^{-2x}) \, dx$

$= \frac{1}{2}\int (e^{3x} - e^{-x}) \, dx = \frac{1}{6}e^{3x} + \frac{1}{2}e^{-x} + C$

Transforming to exponential form is easier! (Note that the two answers can be shown to be equivalent either by transforming the first to exponential form or by transforming the second to hyperbolic form, as shown below.)

$\frac{1}{6}e^{3x} + \frac{1}{2}e^{-x} + C = e^x\left(\frac{1}{6}e^{2x} + \frac{1}{2}e^{-2x}\right) + C$

$= e^x\left(\frac{1}{3}e^{2x} + \frac{1}{3}e^{-2x} - \frac{1}{6}e^{2x} + \frac{1}{6}e^{-2x}\right) + C$

$= \frac{2}{3}e^x \frac{e^{2x} + e^{-2x}}{2} - \frac{1}{3}e^x \frac{e^{2x} - e^{-2x}}{2} + C$

$= \frac{2}{3}e^x \cosh 2x - \frac{1}{3}e^x \sinh 2x + C$

34. Integration Surprise Problem!

$\int e^x \sinh x \, dx$

u	dv
e^x (+)	sinh x
e^x (−)	cosh x
e^x (+)	sinh x

$= e^x \cosh x - e^x \sinh x + \int e^x \sinh x \, dx$

$\Rightarrow 0\int e^x \sinh x \, dx = e^x(\sinh x - \cosh x) + C.$

The original integral reappeared with the *same* coefficient, so when it was added again to the left-hand side, it exactly canceled out the desired integral. Use the exponential form of sinh x.

$\int e^x \sinh x \, dx = \frac{1}{2}\int e^x(e^x - e^{-x}) \, dx = \frac{1}{2}\int (e^{2x} - 1) \, dx$

$= \frac{1}{4}e^{2x} - \frac{1}{2}x + C.$

35. Derivations of the Pythagorean Properties of Hyperbolic Functions

a. $\cosh^2 x - \sinh^2 x = \left(\frac{e^x + e^{-x}}{2}\right)^2 - \left(\frac{e^x - e^{-x}}{2}\right)^2$

$= \frac{e^{2x} + 2 + e^{-2x}}{4} - \frac{e^{2x} - 2 + e^{-2x}}{4} = 1$

$\therefore \cosh^2 x - \sinh^2 x = 1$, Q.E.D.

b. $\frac{1}{\cosh^2 x}(\cosh^2 x - \sinh^2 x) = \frac{1}{\cosh^2 x}$

$\Rightarrow 1 - \tanh^2 x = \text{sech}^2 x$

c. $\frac{1}{\sinh^2 x}(\cosh^2 x - \sinh^2 x) = \frac{1}{\sinh^2 x}$

$\Rightarrow \coth^2 x - 1 = \text{csch}^2 x$

36. Double-Argument Properties of Hyperbolic Functions

a. Substitute 2x for x in the definition of sinh x.

b. $\sinh 2x = \frac{1}{2}(e^{2x} - e^{-2x})$

$= 2 \cdot \frac{1}{2}(e^x - e^{-x}) \cdot \frac{1}{2} \cdot (e^x + e^{-x})$

$= 2 \sinh x \cosh x.$

c. $\cosh 2x = \frac{1}{2}(e^{2x} + e^{-2x})$

$= \frac{1}{4}(e^{2x} + 1 + e^{-2x}) + \frac{1}{4}(e^{2x} - 1 + e^{-2x})$

$= \left(\frac{1}{2}(e^x + e^{-x})\right)^2 + \left(\frac{1}{2}(e^x - e^{-x})\right)^2$

$= \cosh^2 x + \sinh^2 x.$

d. $\cosh^2 x - \sinh^2 x = 1 \Rightarrow \cosh^2 x = 1 + \sinh^2 x$

$\Rightarrow \cosh 2x = \cosh^2 x + \sinh^2 x$

$= (1 + \sinh^2 x) + \sinh^2 x = 1 + 2\sinh^2 x$

e. $1 + 2\sinh^2 x = \cosh 2x \Rightarrow 2\sinh^2 x = \cosh 2x - 1$

$\Rightarrow \sinh^2 x = \frac{1}{2}(\cosh 2x - 1)$

37. Hyperbolic Radian Problem

a. On the circle, $u^2 + v^2 = 1$

$\Rightarrow 2u \, du + 2v \, dv = 0 \Rightarrow dv = (-u/v) \, du$

$dL = \sqrt{du^2 + dv^2} = \sqrt{du^2 + (u/v)^2 du^2}$

$= \sqrt{\frac{u^2 + v^2}{v^2}} \, du = \frac{1}{v} du = \frac{1}{\sqrt{1 - u^2}} \, du$

$L = \int_{\cos 2}^{1} \frac{du}{\sqrt{1 - u^2}}$

$= -\cos^{-1} u \Big|_{\cos 2}^{1} = -\cos^{-1} 1 + 2 = 2$

On the hyperbola, curve from u = 1 to u = cosh 2 has length greater than the line segment from (1, 0) to (cosh 2, 0). This segment has length L = cosh 2 − 1 = 2.762 .... So the length of the curve is greater than 2, Q.E.D.

b. The area of the triangle that circumscribes the sector is 0.5(2 sinh 2 cosh 2) = sinh 2 cosh 2. The area of the sector is the area of this triangle minus the area of the region between the upper and lower branches of the hyperbola from u = 1 to u = cosh 2.

Slice this region vertically. Pick sample point (u, v) on the upper branch, within the strip.

Let t be the argument of sinh and cosh at the sample point. $0 \le t \le 2$.

$dA = 2v \, du = 2 \sinh t \, d(\cosh t) = 2\sinh^2 t \, dt$

$A = 2\int_0^2 \sinh^2 t \, dt \approx 11.644958 \ldots$

Thus the area of the sector is

cosh 2 sinh 2 − 11.644958 ... = 2, Q.E.D.

c. By definition of the circular functions, x is the length of the arc from (1, 0) to (cos x sin x). So the total arc has length 2x. The circumference of a unit circle is 2π and its area is π. Thus

$A_{sector} = \dfrac{2x}{2\pi}\pi = x$, Q.E.D.

d. Slice as in part (b).

Let $I = \int \sinh^2 t\, dt$

U	dV
sinh t (+)	sinh t
cosh t (−)	cosh t

$= \sinh t \cosh t - \int \cosh^2 t\, dt$

$= \sinh t \cosh t - \int (1 + \sinh^2 t)\, dt$

$= \sinh t \cosh t - t - \int \sinh^2 t\, dt$

$\therefore 2\int \sinh^2 t\, dt = \sinh t \cosh t - t + C$

$\int \sinh^2 t\, dt = 0.5 \sinh t \cosh t - 0.5t + C_1$

Slicing as in part b., the area A between the upper and lower branches of the hyperbola is

$A = 2\int_0^x \sinh^2 t\, dt = 2(0.5 \sinh x \cosh x - 0.5x) - 0$

$= \sinh x \cosh x - x.$

Thus the area of the sector is

$\cosh x \sinh x - (\sinh x \cosh x - x) = x$, Q.E.D.

38. Algebraic Derivatives of the Other Five Inverse Hyperbolic Functions

a. $y = \sinh^{-1} x \Rightarrow \sinh y = x \Rightarrow \cosh y\, y' = 1$

$y' = \dfrac{1}{\cosh y} = \dfrac{1}{\sqrt{\sinh^2 y + 1}} = \dfrac{1}{\sqrt{x^2 + 1}}$, Q.E.D.

b. $y = \tanh^{-1} x \Rightarrow \tanh y = x \Rightarrow \text{sech}^2 y\, y' = 1$

$y' = \dfrac{1}{\text{sech}^2 y} = \dfrac{1}{1 - \tanh^2 y} = \dfrac{1}{1 - x^2}$, Q.E.D.

c. $y = \coth^{-1} x \Rightarrow \coth y = x \Rightarrow -\text{csch}^2 y\, y' = 1$

$y' = \dfrac{1}{-\text{csch}^2 y} = \dfrac{1}{-(\coth^2 y - 1)} = \dfrac{1}{1 - x^2}$, Q.E.D.

d. $y = \text{sech}^{-1} x \Rightarrow \text{sech}\, y = x \Rightarrow$

$-\text{sech}\, y \tanh y\, y' = 1$

$y' = \dfrac{1}{-\text{sech}\, y \tanh y} = \dfrac{1}{-\text{sech}\, y\sqrt{1 - \text{sech}^2 y}}$

$= -\dfrac{1}{x\sqrt{1 - x^2}}$, Q.E.D.

e. $y = \text{csch}^{-1} x \Rightarrow \text{csch}\, y = x \Rightarrow$

$-\text{csch}\, y \coth y\, y' = 1$

$y' = \dfrac{1}{-\text{csch}\, y \coth y} = \dfrac{1}{-\text{csch}\, y\sqrt{1 + \text{csch}^2 y}}$

$= -\dfrac{1}{|x|\sqrt{1 + x^2}}$, Q.E.D.

Problem Set 9-10, pages 488 to 492 — Improper Integrals

Q1. Graph: $y = e^{-x}$

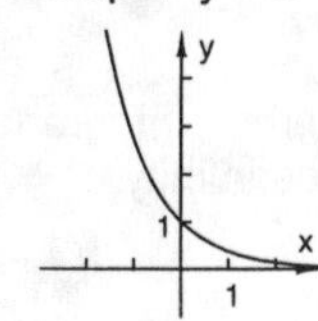

Q2. $y = x^3$

Q3. $y = \tan x$

Q4. $y = \sinh x$ or $x^3 + x$

Q5. $y = e^x$

Q6. $\sinh x + C$

Q7. $\sinh x$

Q8. $-\sin x$

Q9. $\sin x + C$

Q10. $y = 32$ (at $x = 5$)

1. a. Graph, $y = 1/x^2$. Might converge. Integrand approaches zero as x approaches infinity.

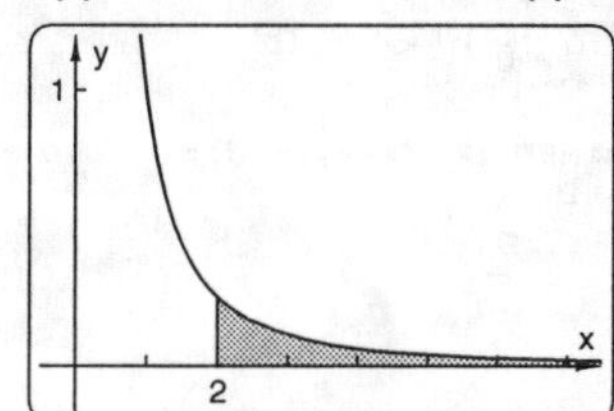

b. $\int_2^\infty (1/x^2)\, dx = \lim_{b\to\infty} \int_2^b (x^{-2})\, dx$

$= \lim_{b\to\infty} -x^{-1}\Big|_2^b = \lim_{b\to\infty} (-1/b + 1/2) = \dfrac{1}{2}$

Integral converges to $\dfrac{1}{2}$.

2. a. Graph, $y = 1/x^4$. Might converge. Integrand approaches zero as x approaches infinity.

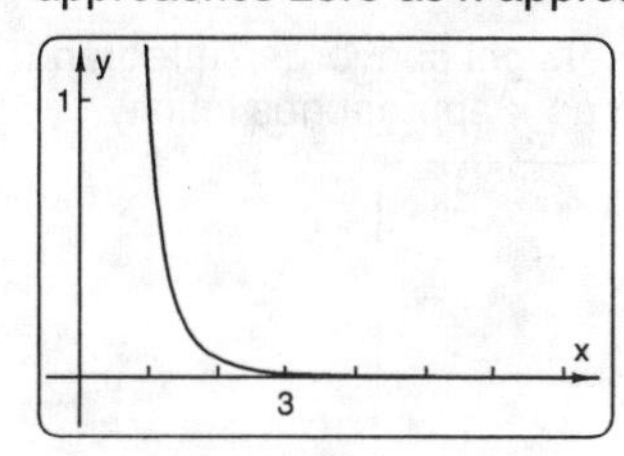

b. $\int_3^\infty 1/x^4\, dx = \lim_{b\to\infty} \int_3^b x^{-4}\, dx$

$= \lim_{b\to\infty} -\dfrac{1}{3}x^{-3}\Big|_3^b = \lim_{b\to\infty} \left(-\dfrac{1}{3b^3} + \dfrac{1}{81}\right) = \dfrac{1}{81}$

Integral converges to $\dfrac{1}{81}$.

3. a. Graph, $y = 1/x$. Might converge. Integrand approaches zero as x approaches infinity.

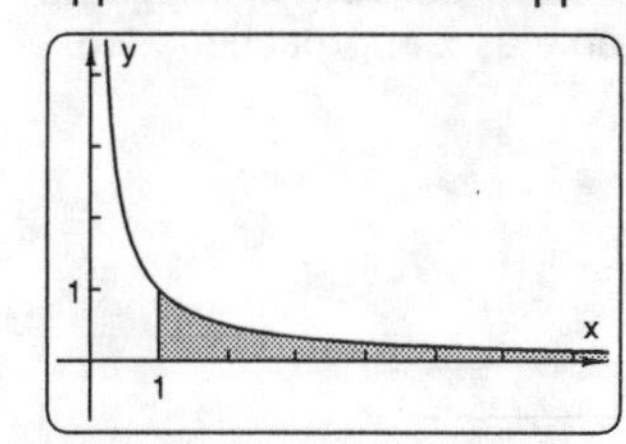

b. $\int_1^\infty (1/x)\, dx = \lim_{b\to\infty} \int_1^b (1/x)\, dx$

$= \lim_{b\to\infty} \ln|x|\Big|_1^b = \lim_{b\to\infty} (\ln b - 0) = \infty$

Integral diverges.

4. a. Graph, $y = 1/x$. Might converge. Integrand becomes infinite only as x approaches zero.

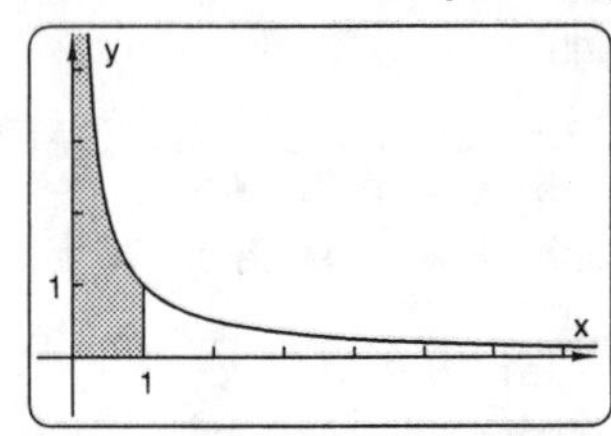

b. $\int_0^1 (1/x)\,dx = \lim_{a\to 0^+} \int_a^1 (1/x)\,dx$

$= \lim_{a\to 0^+} \ln|x| \Big|_a^1 = \lim_{a\to 0^+} (0 - \ln a) = \infty$

Integral diverges.

5. a. Graph, $y = 1/x^{0.2}$. Might converge. Integrand approaches zero as x approaches infinity.

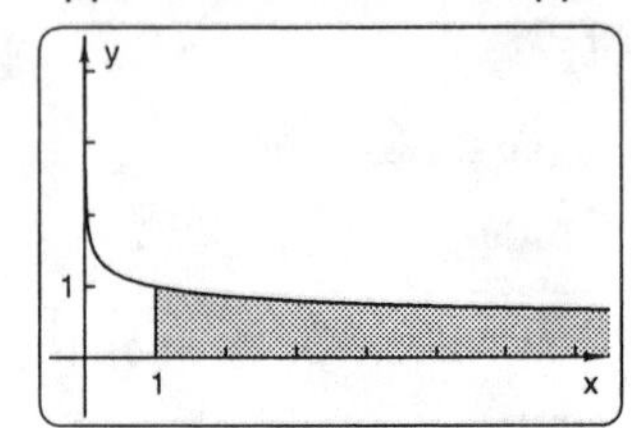

b. $\int_1^\infty 1/x^{0.2}\,dx = \lim_{b\to\infty} \int_1^b x^{-0.2}\,dx$

$= \lim_{b\to\infty} 1.25x^{0.8} \Big|_1^b = \lim_{b\to\infty} (1.25b^{0.8} - 1.25) = \infty$

Integral diverges.

6. a. Graph, $y = 1/x^{1.2}$. Might converge. Integrand approaches zero as x approaches infinity.

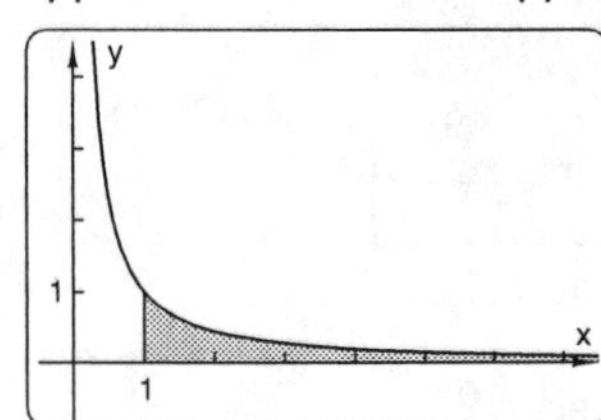

b. $\int_1^\infty 1/x^{1.2}\,dx = \lim_{b\to\infty} \int_1^b x^{-1.2}\,dx$

$= \lim_{b\to\infty} -5x^{-0.2} \Big|_1^b = \lim_{b\to\infty} (-5b^{-0.2} + 5) = 5$

Integral converges to 5.

7. a. Graph, $y = 1/x^{0.2}$. Might converge. Integrand becomes infinite only as x approaches zero.

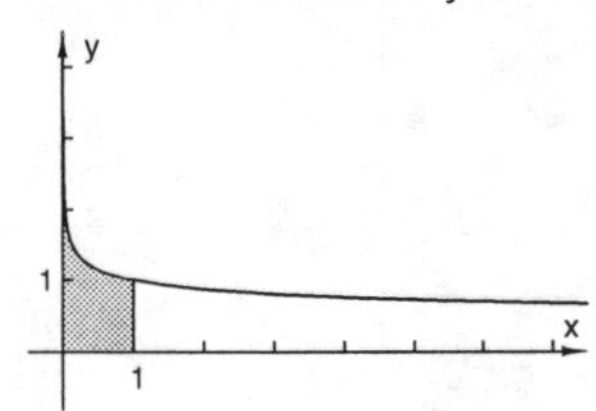

b. $\int_0^1 1/x^{0.2}\,dx = \lim_{a\to 0^+} \int_a^1 x^{-0.2}\,dx$

$= \lim_{a\to 0^+} 1.25x^{0.8} \Big|_a^1 = \lim_{a\to 0^+} (1.25 - 1.25a^{0.8}) = 1.25$

Integral converges to 1.25.

8. a. Graph, $y = 1/x^{1.2}$. Might converge. Integrand becomes infinite only as x approaches zero.

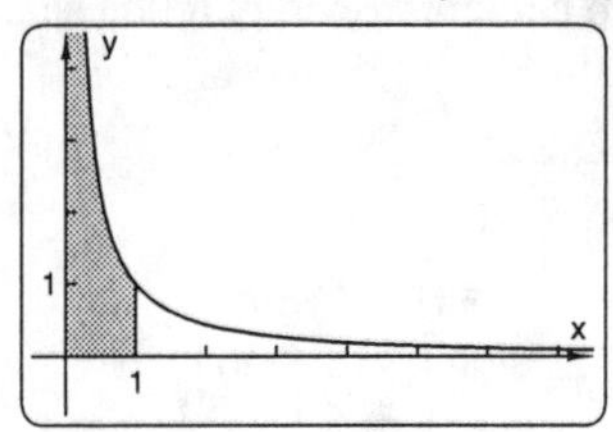

b. $\int_0^1 1/x^{1.2}\,dx = \lim_{a\to 0^+} \int_a^1 x^{-1.2}\,dx$

$= \lim_{a\to 0^+} -5x^{-0.2} \Big|_a^1 = \lim_{a\to 0^+} (-5 + 5a^{-0.2}) = \infty$

Integral diverges.

9. a. Graph, $y = 1/(1 + x^2)$. Might converge. Integrand approaches zero as x approaches infinity.

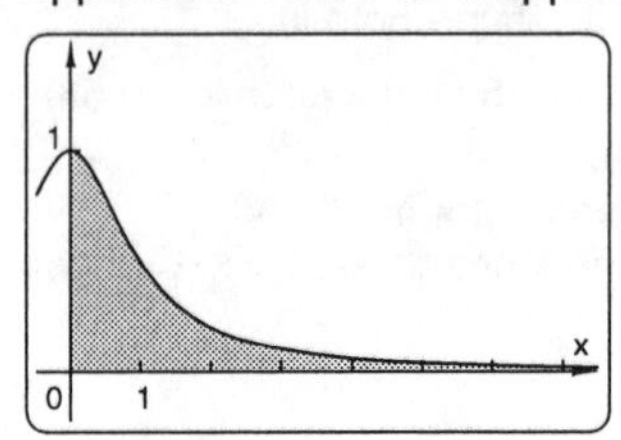

b. $\int_0^\infty 1/(1 + x^2)\,dx = \lim_{b\to\infty} \int_0^b 1/(1 + x^2)\,dx$

$= \lim_{b\to\infty} \tan^{-1} x \Big|_0^b = \lim_{b\to\infty} (\tan^{-1} b - 0) = \frac{\pi}{2}$

Integral converges to $\pi/2$.

10. a. Graph, $y = 1/(1 + x)$. Might converge. Integrand approaches zero as x approaches infinity.

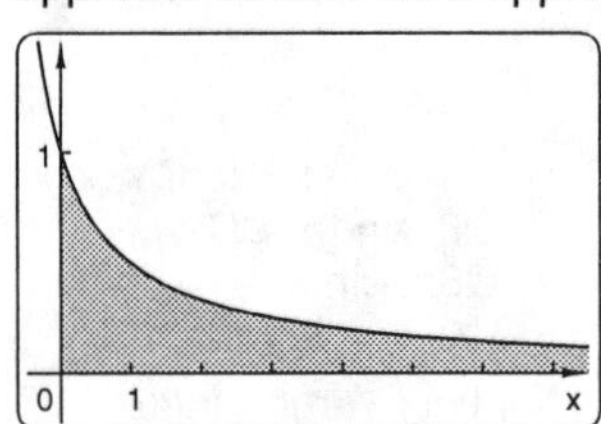

b. $\int_0^\infty 1/(1 + x)\,dx = \lim_{b\to\infty} \int_0^b 1/(1 + x)\,dx$

$= \lim_{b\to\infty} \ln|x + 1| \Big|_0^b = \lim_{b\to\infty} (\ln(b + 1) - 0) = \infty$

Integral diverges.

11. a. Graph, $y = 1/(x \ln x)$. Might converge. Integrand becomes infinite only as x approaches 0 or 1.

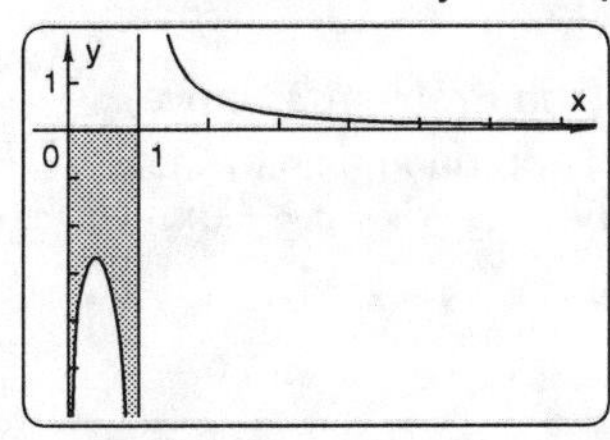

b. To determine whether this converges, split the integral into two pieces. Each piece must converge in order for the integral to converge.
The integral can be written

$\int_0^1 1/(x \ln x)\, dx = \int_0^c 1/(x \ln x)\, dx + \int_c^1 1/(x \ln x)\, dx$

$= \lim_{a \to 0^+} \int_a^c 1/(x \ln x)\, dx + \lim_{b \to 1^-} \int_c^b 1/(x \ln x)\, dx$

$= \lim_{a \to 0^+} \ln|\ln x| \Big|_a^c + \lim_{b \to 1^-} \ln|\ln x| \Big|_c^b$

$= \lim_{a \to 0^+} (\ln|\ln c| - \ln|\ln a|) + \lim_{b \to 1^-} (\ln|\ln b| - \ln|\ln c|)$

$= \infty + \infty.$

For the integral to converge, *both* limits must exist. Since neither exists, the integral diverges.

12. a. Graph, $y = 1/(x(\ln x)^2)$. Might converge. Integrand approaches 0 as x approaches infinity.

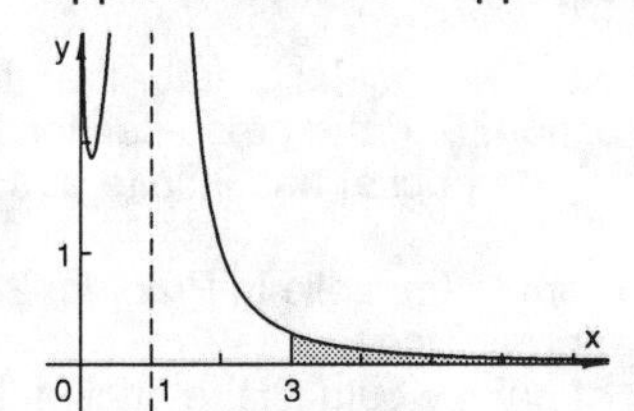

b. The indefinite integral can be written

$\int (\ln x)^{-2} (dx/x) = -(\ln x)^{-1} + C.$

$\int_3^\infty 1/(x(\ln x)^2)\, dx = \lim_{b \to \infty} \int_3^b 1/(x(\ln x)^2)\, dx$

$= \lim_{b \to \infty} -(\ln x)^{-1} \Big|_3^b = \lim_{b \to \infty} (-(\ln b)^{-1} + (\ln 3)^{-1})$

$= (\ln 3)^{-1}$

integral converges to $(\ln 3)^{-1} = 0.910239$ ...

13. a. Graph, $y = e^{-0.4x}$. Might converge. Integrand approaches zero as x approaches infinity.

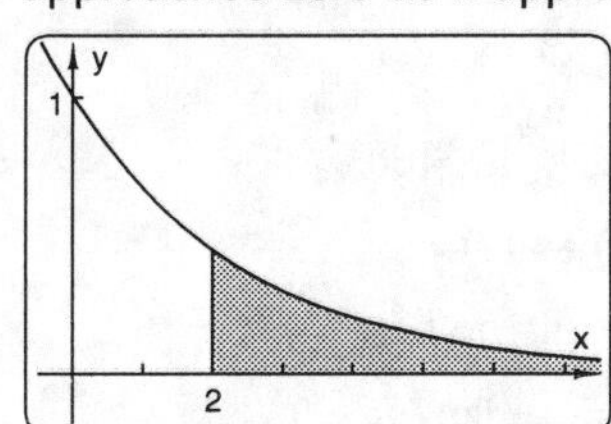

b. $\int_2^\infty e^{-0.4x}\, dx = \lim_{b \to \infty} \int_2^b e^{-0.4x}\, dx$

$= \lim_{b \to \infty} -2.5e^{-0.4x} \Big|_2^b = \lim_{b \to \infty} (-2.5e^{0.4b} + 2.5e^{-0.8})$

$= 2.5e^{-0.8}$.

Integral converges to $2.5e^{-0.8} = 1.1233$ ... .

14. a. Graph, $y = e^{0.02x}$. Diverges. Integrand does not approach zero as x approaches infinity.

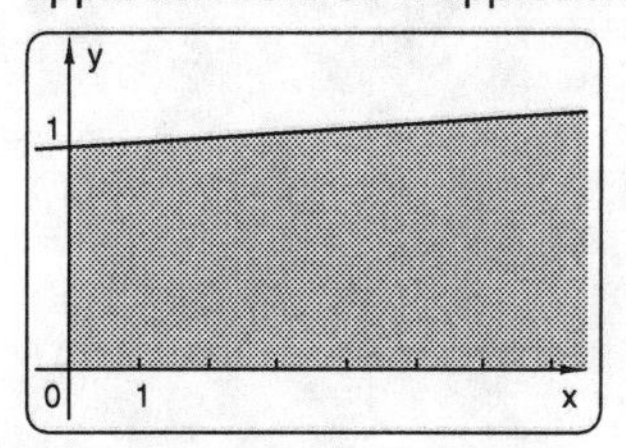

b. (Not applicable).

15. a. Graph, $y = \sqrt{x}$. Does not converge. Integrand is undefined for $x < 0$.

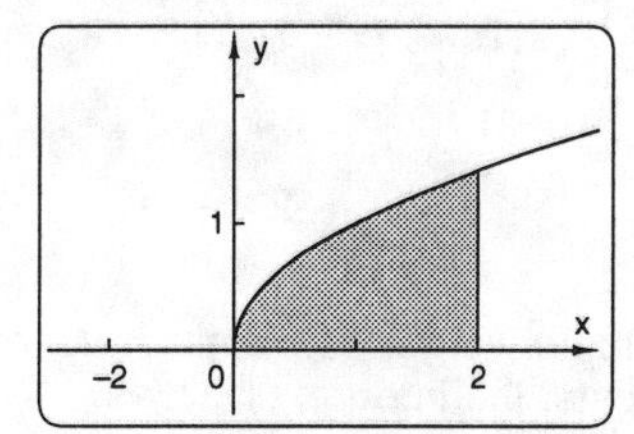

b. (Not applicable)

16. a. Graph, $y = (x - 3)^{-2/3}$. Might converge. Integrand becomes infinite only as x approaches 3.

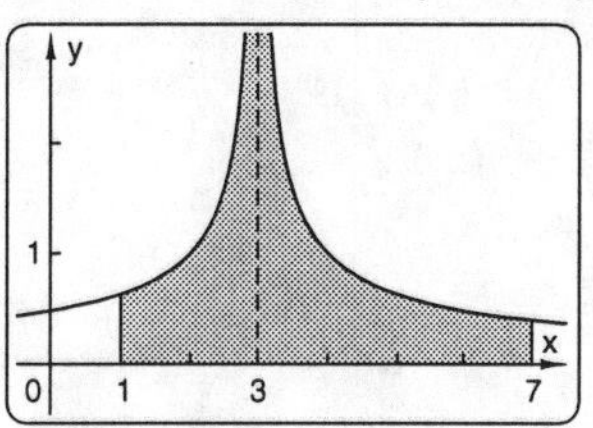

b. $\int_1^7 (x - 3)^{-2/3}\, dx$

$= \lim_{b \to 3^-} \int_1^b (x - 3)^{-2/3}\, dx + \lim_{a \to 3^+} \int_a^7 (x - 3)^{-2/3}\, dx$

$= \lim_{b \to 3^-} 3(x - 3)^{1/3} \Big|_1^b + \lim_{a \to 3^+} 3(x - 3)^{1/3} \Big|_a^7$

$= \lim_{b \to 3^-} (3(b - 3)^{1/3} - 3(-2)^{1/3})$

$+ \lim_{a \to 3^+} (3(4)^{1/3} - 3(a - 3)^{1/3}$

$= 3 \cdot 2^{1/3} + 3 \cdot 4^{1/3}$

Integral converges to $3 \cdot 2^{1/3} + 3 \cdot 4^{1/3} = 8.5419$ ...

17. a. Graph, $y = xe^{-x}$. Might converge. Integrand seems to approach zero as x approaches infinity.

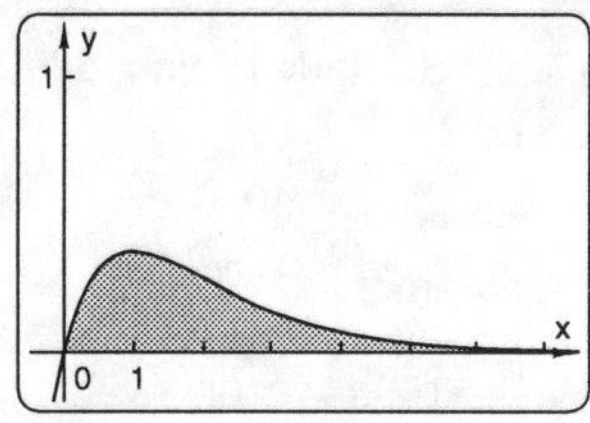

b. Integrate by parts: $\int xe^{-x}\, dx = -e^{-x}(x + 1) + C$

$\int_0^\infty xe^{-x}\, dx = \lim_{b \to \infty} \int_0^b xe^{-x}\, dx$

$= \lim_{b \to \infty} -e^{-x}(x + 1) \Big|_0^b = \lim_{b \to \infty} (-e^{-b}(b + 1) + 1) = 1.$

(The first term is zero by l'Hospital's rule.)
Integral converges to 1.

18. a. Graph, $y = (x-1)^{-2}$. Might converge. Integrand becomes infinite only as x approaches 1.

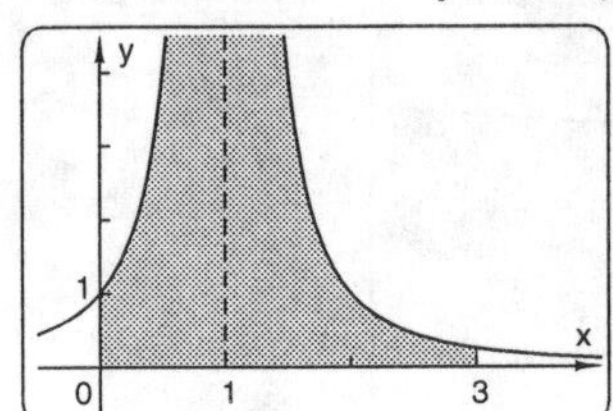

b. $\int_0^3 (x-1)^{-2}\,dx$

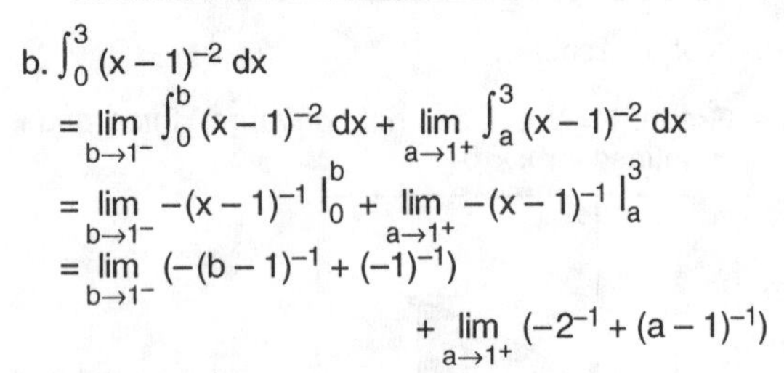

$= \lim_{b\to1^-} \int_0^b (x-1)^{-2}\,dx + \lim_{a\to1^+} \int_a^3 (x-1)^{-2}\,dx$

$= \lim_{b\to1^-} -(x-1)^{-1}\Big|_0^b + \lim_{a\to1^+} -(x-1)^{-1}\Big|_a^3$

$= \lim_{b\to1^-} (-(b-1)^{-1} + (-1)^{-1})$

$+ \lim_{a\to1^+} (-2^{-1} + (a-1)^{-1})$

$= \infty + \infty.$

For the integral to converge, *both* limits must exist. Since neither exists, the integral diverges.

19. a. Graph, $y = \cos x$. Diverges. Integrand does not approach zero as x approaches infinity.

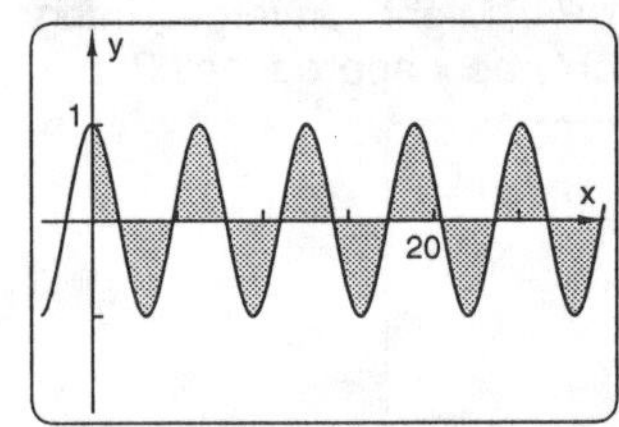

b. (Not applicable.)

20. a. Graph, $y = \sin x$. Diverges. Integrand does not approach zero as x approaches infinity.

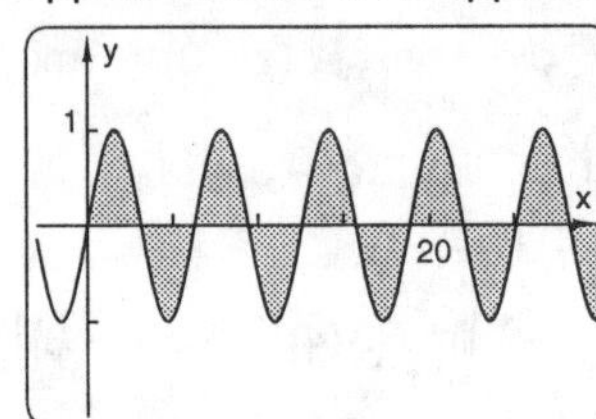

b. (Not applicable)

21. Divergence by Oscillation Problem

As $b \to \infty$, $\int_0^b \cos x\,dx$ oscillates between -1 and 1 and never approaches a limit. Similarly $\int_0^b \sin x\,dx$ oscillates between 0 and 2.

22. p-Integral Problem

a. $I_{1.001} = \int_1^\infty 1/x^{1.001}\,dx = \lim_{b\to\infty} \int_1^b x^{-1.001}\,dx$

$= \lim_{b\to\infty} -1000x^{-0.001}\Big|_1^b = \lim_{b\to\infty} (-1000b^{-0.001} + 1000)$

$= 1000$ (converges), Q.E.D.

$I_{0.999} = \int_1^\infty 1/x^{0.999}\,dx = \lim_{b\to\infty} \int_1^b x^{-0.999}\,dx$

$= \lim_{b\to\infty} 1000x^{0.001}\Big|_1^b = \lim_{b\to\infty} (1000b^{0.001} - 1000)$

$= \infty$ (diverges), Q.E.D.

b. $I_1 = \int_1^\infty 1/x\,dx = \infty$ (see Problem 3), so I_1 diverges.

c. "I_p converges if $p > 1$ and diverges if $p \le 1$."

23. Volume of an Unbounded Solid Problem

a. $y = 1/x = x^{-1}$

$dA = y\,dx = x^{-1}\,dx$

$A = \int_1^\infty x^{-1}\,dx = \infty$ (see Problem 3, above).

The area does *not* approach a finite limit.

b. By plane slices, $dV = \pi y^2\,dx = \pi x^{-2}\,dx$.

$V = \lim_{b\to\infty} \int_1^b \pi x^{-2}\,dx = \lim_{b\to\infty} -\pi x^{-1}\Big|_1^b$

$= \lim_{b\to\infty} (-\pi b^{-1} + \pi) = \pi$

The volume converges to π.

c. By cylindrical shells, $dV = 2\pi xy\,dx$

$= 2\pi x(x^{-1})\,dx = 2\pi\,dx.$

$V = \lim_{b\to\infty} \int_1^b 2\pi\,dx = \lim_{b\to\infty} 2\pi x\Big|_1^b$

$= \lim_{b\to\infty} (2\pi b - 2\pi) = \infty.$

Volume diverges.

d. False. The volume could approach a constant as in part b. or become infinite as in part c.

24. Infinite Paint Bucket Problem

$y = -1/x \Rightarrow x = -y^{-1}$

Slice the vertical cross section horizontally.

$dA = x\,dy = -y^{-1}\,dy$

$A = \lim_{a\to-\infty} \int_a^{-1} -y^{-1}\,dy = \lim_{a\to-\infty} -\ln|y|\Big|_a^{-1}$

$= \lim_{a\to-\infty} (-\ln|-1| + \ln|a|) = \infty$

The area of the bucket's surface is greater that the area of the cross section, and the cross-sectional area diverges. Thus, the bucket has infinite surface area.

The bucket is congruent to the solid in Problem 23b, which has volume approaching π.

Thus, π cubic units of paint would fill the bucket, but could not coat the whole surface!

25. The Gamma Function and Factorial Function

a. $f(x) = \int_0^\infty t^x e^{-t}\,dt$

$f(1) = \lim_{b\to\infty} \int_0^b te^{-t}\,dt = \lim_{b\to\infty} (-te^{-t} - e^{-t})\Big|_0^b$

$= \lim_{b\to\infty} (-be^{-b} - e^{-b} + 0 + 1) = 1$

Using l'Hospital's rule on be^{-b} gives

$\lim_{b\to\infty} be^{-b} = \lim_{b\to\infty} \frac{b}{e^b} = \lim_{b\to\infty} \frac{1}{e^b} = 0.$

$f(2) = \lim_{b\to\infty} \int_0^\infty t^2e^{-t}\,dt$

$= \lim_{b\to\infty} -t^2e^{-t}\Big|_0^b + 2\int_0^\infty te^{-t}\,dt$

$= \lim_{b\to\infty} (-b^2e^{-b} + 0) + 2(1) = 2$

Using l'Hospital's rule on b^2e^{-b} gives

$\lim_{b\to\infty} b^2e^{-b} = \lim_{b\to\infty} \frac{2b}{e^b} = \lim_{b\to\infty} \frac{2}{e^b} = 0$

$f(3) = \lim_{b\to\infty} \int_0^\infty t^3e^{-t}\,dt$

$= \lim_{b\to\infty} -t^3e^{-t}\Big|_0^b + 3\int_0^\infty t^2e^{-t}\,dt$

$= \lim_{b\to\infty} (-b^3e^{-b} + 0) + 3(2) = 6$

Using l'Hospital's rule on b^3e^{-b} gives

$\lim_{b\to\infty} b^3e^{-b} = \lim_{b\to\infty} \frac{3b^2}{e^b} = \lim_{b\to\infty} \frac{6b}{e^b} = \lim_{b\to\infty} \frac{6}{e^b} = 0$

b. Conjecture:
$f(4) = 4\,f(3) = 24 = 4!$
$f(5) = 5\,f(4) = 120 = 5!$
$f(6) = 6\,f(5) = 720 = 6!$

c. $f(x) = \int_0^\infty t^x e^{-t}\,dt$

u		dv
t^x	+	e^{-t}
xt^{x-1}	−	$-e^{-t}$

$= \lim_{b\to\infty} -t^x e^{-t} \Big|_0^b + x\int_0^\infty t^{x-1} e^{-t}\,dt$
$= \lim_{b\to\infty} (-b^x e^{-b} + 0) + x\,f(x-1)$
$= 0 + 0 + x\,f(x-1) = x\,f(x-1)$, Q.E.D.
$\lim_{b\to\infty} (-b^x e^{-b}) = 0$ can be proved by mathematical induction using l'Hospital's rule.

d. Part a. shows that $f(1) = 1 = 1!$.
Part c. shows that $f(n) = n\,f(n-1) = n(n-1)\,f(n-2) = n(n-1)(n-2)\ \ldots\ (2)(1) = n!$, Q.E.D.

e. $\int_0^b t^3e^{-t}\,dt = -b^3e^{-b} - 3b^2e^{-b} - 6be^{-b} - 6e^{-b} + 6$
$|b^3e^{-b} + 3b^2e^{-b} + 6be^{-b} + 6e^{-b}| < 0.000001$
for $b > 23.4050\ \ldots$, say $b \approx 24$.

f. $0.5! = \int_0^\infty t^{0.5}e^{-t}\,dt \approx \int_0^{24} t^{0.5}e^{-t}\,dt \approx 0.886227311\ \ldots$
From the graphs, $t^{0.5}e^{-t} < t^3e^{-t}$ for $x \ge 24$.
The error in 0.5! from stopping at b = 24 is the area under the "tail" of the graph from b = 24.
$\text{Error} = \int_{24}^\infty t^{0.5}e^{-t}\,dt < \int_{24}^\infty t^3e^{-t}\,dt < 0.000001.$
The difference between the tabulated value of 0.5! and the value calculated here is
0.8862269255
−0.866227311 ...
= −0.000000386,
which is less in absolute value than 0.000001. Note, however, that the difference is *negative*, because the calculated value is larger than the tabulated value. This observation means that either the tabulated value is incorrect or there is more inaccuracy in the numerical integration algorithm than there is in the error caused by dropping the tail of the integral. (Using a smaller tolerance in the numerical integrator gives a value of 0.8862269252 ... .)

g. Using the tabulated value of 0.5!,
1.5! = 1.5(0.5!) = 1.3293 ...
2.5! = 2.5(1.5!) = 3.3233 ...
3.5! = 3.5(2.5!) = 11.6317 ...

h. $0! = \int_0^\infty t^0e^{-t}\,dt = \lim_{b\to\infty} (-e^{-t} \Big|_0^b)$
$= \lim_{b\to\infty} (-e^{-b} + 1) = 1$, Q.E.D.

i. (−1)! = 0!/0, which is infinite. So (−2)! and (−3)!, which equal (−1)!/(−1) and (−2)!/(−2), are also infinite. However,
(−0.5)! = 0.5!/(0.5) = 1.77245 ...
(−1.5)! = (−0.5)!/(−0.5) = −3.54490 ...
(−2.5)! = (−1.5)!/(−1.5) = 2.36327 ...,
all of which are finite.

j. $0.5! = \dfrac{\sqrt{\pi}}{2} = 0.886226925\ \ldots$, which agrees with the tabulated value.

26. Spaceship Work Problem
$dW = F\,dr = 1000r^{-2}\,dr$
At the earth's surface, r = 1.
$W = \int_1^\infty 1000r^{-2}\,dr = \lim_{b\to\infty} (-1000r^{-1} \Big|_1^b)$
$= \lim_{b\to\infty} (-1000b^{-1} + 1000) = 1000$ radius-pounds
Thus, the amount of work does *not* increase without bound as r goes to infinity.

27. Piecewise Continuity Problem
a. $y = 2^x - \dfrac{|x-2|}{x-2} = 2^x + 1$ if $x < 2$ and $2^x - 1$ if $x > 2$.
$\int_1^3 y\,dx = \int_1^2 (2^x + 1)\,dx + \int_2^3 (2^x - 1)\,dx$
b. $= \lim_{b\to 2^-} \int_1^b (2^x + 1)\,dx + \lim_{a\to 2^+} \int_a^3 (2^x - 1)\,dx$
c. $= \lim_{b\to 2^-} (2^x/\ln 2 + x) \Big|_1^b + \lim_{a\to 2^+} (2^x/\ln 2 - x) \Big|_a^3$
$= \lim_{b\to 2^-} (2^b/\ln 2 + b - 2/\ln 2 - 1)$
$+ \lim_{a\to 2^+} (2^3/\ln 2 - 3 - 2^a/\ln 2 + a)$
$= 4/\ln 2 + 2 - 2/\ln 2 - 1 + 8/\ln 2 - 3 - 4/\ln 2 + 2$
$= 6/\ln 2$
Integral converges to 6/ln 2 = 8.6561 ... .
d. The integral is defined by dividing the interval into Riemann partitions and adding up the subintervals. But the Riemann partitions may be chosen so that the discontinuities are at endpoints of subintervals. Then the subintervals corresponding to each continuous piece may be added up separately.
e. False. Some discontinuous functions (notably, piecewise continuous functions) are integrable.

28. Journal Problem
Journal entries will vary.

Problem Set 9-11, pages 493 to 496 — Miscellaneous Integrals and Derivatives

1. $y = \sec 3x \tan 3x$
$y' = (3 \sec 3x \tan 3x) \tan 3x + \sec 3x\,(3 \sec^2 3x)$
$= 3 \sec 3x \tan^2 3x + 3 \sec^3 3x$

2. $y = \sinh 5x \tanh 5x$
$y' = (5 \cosh 5x) \tanh 5x + \sinh 5x\,(5 \operatorname{sech}^2 5x)$
$= 5 \sinh 5x + 5 \sinh 5x \operatorname{sech}^2 5x$ or
$5 \sinh 5x + 5 \cosh 5x \tanh 5x$

3. $\int x \cosh 4x\,dx$

u		dv
x	+	cosh 4x
1	−	$\frac{1}{4}\sinh 4x$
0	+	$\frac{1}{16}\cosh 4x$

$= \frac{1}{4}x \sinh 4x - \frac{1}{16}\cosh 4x + C.$

4. $\int x \cos x\,dx$

u		dv
x	+	cos x
1	−	sin x
0	+	−cos x

$= x \sin x + \cos x + C.$

5. $f(x) = (3x + 5)^{-1} \Rightarrow f'(x) = -3(3x + 5)^{-2}$

6. $f(x) = (5 - 2x^{-1}) \Rightarrow f'(x) = 2(5 - 2x)^{-2}$

7. $\int (3x + 5)^{-1}\,dx = \frac{1}{3}\ln|3x + 5| + C$

8. $\int (5 - 2x)^{-1}\,dx = -\frac{1}{2}\ln|5 - 2x| + C$

9. $t(x) = \tan^5 4x$
$t'(x) = 5\tan^4 4x\,(4\sec^2 4x) = 20\tan^4 4x\sec^2 4x$

10. $h(x) = \text{sech}^3\, 7x$
$h'(x) = 3\,\text{sech}^2\, 7x\,(-7\,\text{sech}\, 7x\tanh 7x)$
$= -21\,\text{sech}^3\, 7x\tanh 7x.$

11. $\int \sin^2 x\,dx = \frac{1}{2}\int (1 - \cos 2x)\,dx = \frac{1}{2}x - \frac{1}{4}\sin 2x + C$
$= \frac{1}{2}x - \frac{1}{2}\sin x\cos x + C$ (or integrate by parts)

12. $\int \cos^2 x\,dx = \frac{1}{2}\int (1 + \cos 2x)\,dx = \frac{1}{2}x + \frac{1}{4}\sin 2x + C$
$= \frac{1}{2}x + \frac{1}{2}\sin x\cos x + C$ (or integrate by parts)

13. $y = \dfrac{6x - 11}{x + 2}$
$y' = \dfrac{6(x + 2) - (6x - 11)(1)}{(x + 2)^2} = \dfrac{23}{(x + 2)^2}$

14. $y = \dfrac{5x + 9}{x - 4}$
$y' = \dfrac{5(x - 4) - (5x + 9)(1)}{(x - 4)^2} = \dfrac{-29}{(x - 4)^2}$

15. $\int \dfrac{6x - 11}{x + 2}\,dx = \int \left(6 - \dfrac{23}{x + 2}\right)dx$
$= 6x - 23\ln|x + 2| + C$

16. $\int \dfrac{5x + 9}{x - 4}\,dx = \int \left(5 + \dfrac{29}{x - 4}\right)dx$
$= 5x + 29\ln|x - 4| + C$

17. $f(t) = \sqrt{1 + t^2} = (1 + t^2)^{1/2}$
$f'(t) = \frac{1}{2}(1 + t^2)^{-1/2}(2t) = \dfrac{t}{\sqrt{1 + t^2}}$

18. $g(t) = \sqrt{t^2 - 1} = (t^2 - 1)^{1/2}$
$g'(t) = \frac{1}{2}(t^2 - 1)^{-1/2}(2t) = \dfrac{t}{\sqrt{t^2 - 1}}$

19. $\int \sqrt{1 + t^2}\,dt = \int \sqrt{1 + \tan^2\theta}\,d(\tan\theta)$
$= \int \sec^3\theta\,d\theta = \frac{1}{2}\sec\theta\tan\theta + \frac{1}{2}\ln|\sec\theta + \tan\theta| + C$
$= \frac{1}{2}t\sqrt{1 + t^2} + \frac{1}{2}\ln\left|\sqrt{1 + t^2} + t\right| + C$

20. $\int \sqrt{t^2 - 1}\,dt = \int \sqrt{\sec^2\theta - 1}\,d(\sec\theta)$
$= \int \sec\theta\tan^2\theta\,d\theta = \int (\sec^3\theta - \sec\theta)\,d\theta$
$= \frac{1}{2}\sec\theta\tan\theta + \frac{1}{2}\ln|\sec\theta + \tan\theta|$
$- \ln|\sec\theta + \tan\theta| + C$
$= \frac{1}{2}\sec\theta\tan\theta - \frac{1}{2}\ln|\sec\theta + \tan\theta| + C$
$= \frac{1}{2}t\sqrt{t^2 - 1} - \frac{1}{2}\ln\left|t + \sqrt{t^2 - 1}\right| + C$

21. $y = x^3 e^x$
$y' = 3x^2e^x + x^3e^x = x^2e^x(3 + x)$

22. $y = x^4 e^{-x}$
$y' = 4x^3e^{-x} - x^4e^{-x} = x^3e^{-x}(4 - x)$

23. $\int x^3 e^x\,dx$

u	sign	dv
x^3	+	e^x
$3x^2$	−	e^x
$6x$	+	e^x
6	−	e^x
0	+	e^x

$= x^3e^x - 3x^2e^x + 6xe^x - 6e^x + C$

24. $\int x^4 e^{-x}\,dx$

u	sign	dv
x^4	+	e^{-x}
$4x^3$	−	$-e^{-x}$
$12x^2$	+	e^{-x}
$24x$	−	$-e^{-x}$
24	+	e^{-x}
0	−	$-e^{-x}$

$= -x^4e^{-x} - 4x^3e^{-x} - 12x^2e^{-x} - 24xe^{-x} - 24e^{-x} + C$

25. $f(x) = \sin^{-1} x \Rightarrow f'(x) = \dfrac{1}{\sqrt{1 - x^2}} = (1 - x^2)^{-1/2}$

26. $g(x) = \tan^{-1} x \Rightarrow g'(x) = \dfrac{1}{x^2 + 1}.$

27. $\int \sin^{-1} x\,dx$

u	sign	dv
$\sin^{-1} x$	+	1
$(1 - x^2)^{-1/2}$	−	x

$= x\sin^{-1} x - \int (1 - x^2)^{-1/2}(x\,dx)$
$= x\sin^{-1} x - (-0.5)(2)(1 - x^2)^{1/2} + C$
$= x\sin^{-1} x + \sqrt{1 - x^2} + C.$

28. $\int \tan^{-1} x\,dx$

u	sign	dv
$\tan^{-1} x$	+	1
$\dfrac{1}{1+x^2}$	−	x

$= x\tan^{-1} x - \int \dfrac{1}{1 + x^2}(x\,dx)$
$= x\tan^{-1} x - \frac{1}{2}\ln|1 + x^2| + C$

29. $\int \dfrac{1}{x^2 + 4x - 5}\,dx = \int \left(\dfrac{-1/6}{x + 5} + \dfrac{1/6}{x - 1}\right)dx$
$= -\frac{1}{6}\ln|x + 5| + \frac{1}{6}\ln|x - 1| + C$

30. $\int \dfrac{1}{x^2 - 6x - 7}\,dx = \int \left(\dfrac{-1/8}{x + 1} + \dfrac{1/8}{x - 7}\right)dx$
$= -\frac{1}{8}\ln|x + 1| + \frac{1}{8}\ln|x - 7| + C$

31. $\int \dfrac{1}{\sqrt{x^2 + 4x - 5}}\,dx = \int \dfrac{1}{\sqrt{(x + 2)^2 - 9}}\,dx$
$= \int \dfrac{1}{\sqrt{(3\sec\theta)^2 - 9}}(3\sec\theta\tan\theta\,d\theta)$
$= \int \dfrac{1}{3\tan\theta}(3\sec\theta\tan\theta\,d\theta) = \int \sec\theta\,d\theta$
$= \ln|\sec\theta + \tan\theta| + C$
$= \ln\left|\frac{1}{3}(x + 2) + \frac{1}{3}\sqrt{(x + 2)^2 - 9}\right| + C_1$
$= \ln\left|x + 2 + \sqrt{x^2 + 4x - 5}\right| + C$

32. $\int \frac{1}{\sqrt{x^2 - 6x - 7}}\,dx = \int \frac{1}{\sqrt{(x-3)^2 - 16}}\,dx$

$= \int \frac{1}{\sqrt{(4\sec\theta)^2 - 16}}(4\sec\theta\tan\theta\,d\theta)$

$= \int \frac{1}{4\tan\theta}(4\sec\theta\tan\theta\,d\theta) = \int \sec\theta\,d\theta$

$= \ln|\sec\theta + \tan\theta| + C$

$= \ln\left|\frac{1}{4}(x-3) + \frac{1}{4}\sqrt{(x-3)^2 - 16}\right| + C_1$

$= \ln\left|x - 3 + \sqrt{x^2 - 6x - 7}\right| + C$

33. $f(x) = \tanh x \Rightarrow f'(x) = \text{sech}^2\, x$

34. $f(x) = \coth x \Rightarrow f'(x) = -\text{csch}^2\, x$

35. $\int \tanh x\,dx = \int \frac{\sinh x\,dx}{\cosh x} = \ln|\cosh x| + C$
(Absolute values are optional.)

36. $\int \coth x\,dx = \int \frac{\cosh x\,dx}{\sinh x} = \ln|\sinh x| + C$
(Absolute values are *necessary!*)

37. $y = e^{2x}\cos 3x$
$y' = (2e^{2x})\cos 3x + e^{2x}(-3\sin 3x)$
$= e^{2x}(2\cos 3x - 3\sin 3x)$

38. $y = e^{-3x}\cos 4x$
$y' = (-3e^{-3x})\cos 4x + e^{-3x}(-4\sin 4x)$
$= -e^{-3x}(3\cos 4x + 4\sin 4x)$

39. $\int e^{2x}\cos 3x\,dx$

u	sign	dv
e^{2x}	+	$\cos 3x$
$2e^{2x}$	−	$\frac{1}{3}\sin 3x$
$4e^{2x}$	+	$-\frac{1}{9}\cos 3x$

$= \frac{1}{3}e^{2x}\sin 3x + \frac{2}{9}e^{2x}\cos 3x - \frac{4}{9}\int e^{2x}\cos 3x\,dx$

$\frac{13}{9}\int e^{2x}\cos 3x\,dx = \frac{1}{3}e^{2x}\sin 3x + \frac{2}{9}e^{2x}\cos 3x + C_1$

$\int e^{2x}\cos 3x\,dx = \frac{3}{13}e^{2x}\sin 3x + \frac{2}{13}e^{2x}\cos 3x + C$

40. $\int e^{-3x}\cos 4x\,dx$

u	sign	dv
e^{-3x}	+	$\cos 4x$
$-3e^{-3x}$	−	$\frac{1}{4}\sin 4x$
$9e^{-3x}$	+	$-\frac{1}{16}\cos 4x$

$= \frac{1}{4}e^{-3x}\sin 4x - \frac{3}{16}e^{-3x}\cos 4x - \frac{9}{16}\int e^{-3x}\cos 4x\,dx$

$\frac{25}{16}\int e^{-3x}\cos 4x\,dx = \frac{1}{4}e^{-3x}\sin 4x - \frac{3}{16}e^{-3x}\cos 4x + C_1$

$\int e^{-3x}\cos 4x\,dx = \frac{4}{25}e^{-3x}\sin 4x - \frac{3}{25}e^{-3x}\cos 4x + C$

Note: As a check for integrals such as Problems 39 and 40, the numerators of the coefficients equal the 3 and 4 in the arguments of e^{-3x} and $\cos 4x$. The denominators equal $3^2 + 4^2$, or 25.

41. $g(x) = x^3 \ln 5x$
$g'(x) = (3x^2)\ln 5x + x^3(5/5x) = x^2(3\ln 5x + 1)$

42. $h(x) = x^2 \ln 8x$
$h'(x) = (2x)\ln 8x + x^2(8/8x) = x(2\ln 8x + 1)$

43. $\int x^3 \ln 5x\,dx$

u	sign	dv
$\ln 5x$	+	x^3
$\frac{1}{x}$		$\frac{1}{4}x^4$
- - - -		- - - -
		$\frac{1}{4}x^3$
1	−	$\frac{1}{4}x^3$
0	+	$\frac{1}{16}x^4$

$= \frac{1}{4}x^4 \ln 5x - \frac{1}{16}x^4 + C.$

44. $\int x^2 \ln 8x\,dx$

u	sign	dv
$\ln 8x$	+	x^2
$\frac{1}{x}$		$\frac{1}{3}x^3$
- - - -		- - - -
1	−	$\frac{1}{3}x^2$
0	+	$\frac{1}{9}x^3$

$= \frac{1}{3}x^3 \ln 8x - \frac{1}{9}x^3 + C$

45. $y = \frac{x}{(x+2)(x+3)(x+4)}$
$\ln y = \ln x - \ln(x+2) - \ln(x+3) - \ln(x+4)$
$y' = y(x^{-1} - (x+2)^{-1} - (x+3)^{-1} - (x+4)^{-1})$

46. $y = \frac{x}{(x-1)(x-2)(x-3)}$
$\ln y = \ln x - \ln(x-1) - \ln(x-2) - \ln(x-3)$
$y' = y(x^{-1} - (x-1)^{-1} - (x-2)^{-1} - (x-3)^{-1})$

47. $\int \frac{x}{(x+2)(x+3)(x+4)}\,dx$
$= \int \left(\frac{-1}{x+2} + \frac{3}{x+3} - \frac{2}{x+4}\right)dx$
$= -\ln|x+2| + 3\ln|x+3| - 2\ln|x+4| + C$

48. $\int \frac{x}{(x-1)(x-2)(x-3)}\,dx$
$= \int \left(\frac{1/2}{x-1} - \frac{2}{x-2} + \frac{3/2}{x-3}\right)dx$
$= \frac{1}{2}\ln|x-1| - 2\ln|x-2| + \frac{3}{2}\ln|x-3| + C$

49. $y = \cos^3 x \sin x$
$y' = (-3\cos^2 x \sin x)\sin x + \cos^3 x(\cos x)$
$= -3\cos^2 x \sin^2 x + \cos^4 x$

50. $y = \sin^5 x \cos x$
$y' = (5\sin^4 x \cos x)\cos x + \sin^5 x(-\sin x)$
$= 5\sin^4 x \cos^2 x - \sin^6 x$

51. $\int \cos^3 x(\sin x\,dx) = -\frac{1}{4}\cos^4 x + C$

52. $\int \sin^5 x(\cos x\,dx) = \frac{1}{6}\sin^6 x + C$

53. $\int \cos^3 x\,dx = \int (1 - \sin^2 x)\cos x\,dx$
$= \int \cos x\,dx - \int \sin^2 x(\cos x\,dx) = \sin x - \frac{1}{3}\sin^3 x + C$

or: $\int \cos^3 x\,dx = \frac{1}{3}\cos^2 x \sin x + \frac{2}{3}\int \cos x\,dx$
$= \frac{1}{3}\cos^2 x \sin x + \frac{2}{3}\sin x + C$

54. $\int \sin^5 x\,dx = \int (1-\cos^2 x)^2 (\sin x\,dx)$
$= \int (1 - 2\cos^2 x + \cos^4 x)(\sin x\,dx)$
$= \int \sin x\,dx - 2\int \cos^2 x \sin x\,dx + \int \cos^4 x \sin x\,dx$
$= -\cos x + \frac{2}{3}\cos^3 x - \frac{1}{5}\cos^5 x + C$
or: $\int \sin^5 x\,dx = -\frac{1}{5}\sin^4 x \cos x + \frac{4}{5}\int \sin^3 x\,dx$
$= -\frac{1}{5}\sin^4 x\cos x - \frac{4}{15}\sin^2 x \cos x + \frac{8}{15}\int \sin x\,dx$
$= -\frac{1}{5}\sin^4 x\cos x - \frac{4}{15}\sin^2 x\cos x - \frac{8}{15}\cos x + C$

55. $\int \cos^4 x\,dx = \frac{1}{4}\cos^3 x \sin x + \frac{3}{4}\int \cos^2 x\,dx$
$= \frac{1}{4}\cos^3 x\sin x + \frac{3}{8}\cos x \sin x + \frac{3}{8}\int dx$
$= \frac{1}{4}\cos^3 x \sin x + \frac{3}{8}\cos x\sin x + \frac{3}{8}x + C$

56. $\int \sin^6 x\,dx = -\frac{1}{6}\sin^5 x\cos x + \frac{5}{6}\int \sin^4 x\,dx$
$= -\frac{1}{6}\sin^5 x\cos x - \frac{5}{24}\sin^3 x\cos x + \frac{15}{24}\int \sin^2 x\,dx$
$= -\frac{1}{6}\sin^5 x\cos x - \frac{5}{24}\sin^3 x \cos x$
$- \frac{15}{48}\sin x\cos x + \frac{15}{48}\int dx$
$= -\frac{1}{6}\sin^5 x\cos x - \frac{5}{24}\sin^3 x\cos x$
$- \frac{5}{16}\sin x \cos x + \frac{5}{16}x + C$

57. $g(x) = (x^4+3)^3$
$g'(x) = 3(x^4+3)^2(4x^3) = 12x^3(x^4+3)^2$

58. $f(x) = (x^3-1)^4$
$f'(x) = 4(x^3-1)^3(3x^2) = 12x^2(x^3-1)^3$

59. $\int (x^4+3)^3\,dx = \int (x^{12} + 9x^8 + 27x^4 + 27)\,dx$
$= \frac{1}{13}x^{13} + x^9 + \frac{27}{5}x^5 + 27x + C$

60. $\int (x^3-1)^4\,dx = \int (x^{12} - 4x^9 + 6x^6 - 4x^3 + 1)\,dx$
$= \frac{1}{13}x^{13} - \frac{4}{10}x^{10} + \frac{6}{7}x^7 - x^4 + x + C$

61. $\int (x^4+3)^3 x^3\,dx = \frac{1}{16}(x^4+3)^4 + C$

62. $\int (x^3-1)^4 x^2\,dx = \frac{1}{15}(x^3-1)^5 + C$

63. $\int (x^4+3)\,dx = \frac{1}{5}x^5 + 3x + C$

64. $\int (x^3-1)\,dx = \frac{1}{4}x^4 - x + C$

65. $f(x) = \int_1^x (t^4+3)^3\,dt \Rightarrow f'(x) = (x^4+3)^3$

66. $h(x) = \int_5^x (t^3-1)^4\,dt \Rightarrow h'(x) = (x^3-1)^4$

67. $\int_1^2 x e^x\,dx$

u		dv
x	+	e^x
1	−	e^x
0	+	e^x

$= xe^x - e^x \Big|_1^2 = 2e^2 - e^2 - e + e = e^2 = 7.3890\ldots$

68. $\int_0^2 x e^{-x}\,dx$

u		dv
x	+	e^{-x}
1	−	$-e^{-x}$
0	+	e^{-x}

$= -xe^{-x} - e^{-x}\Big|_0^2 = -2e^{-2} - e^{-2} + 0 + 1$
$= -3e^{-2} + 1 = 0.59399\ldots$

69. $r(x) = xe^x \Rightarrow r'(x) = xe^x + e^x$

70. $s(x) = xe^{-x} \Rightarrow s'(x) = -xe^{-x} + e^{-x}$

71. $q(x) = \dfrac{\ln x + 2}{x}$
$q'(x) = \dfrac{(1/x)\cdot x - (\ln x + 2)\cdot 1}{x^2} = \dfrac{-1 - \ln x}{x^2}$

72. $r(x) = \dfrac{(\ln x)^3 + 4}{x}$
$r'(x) = \dfrac{3(\ln x)^2(1/x)\cdot x - ((\ln x)^3 + 4)\cdot 1}{x^2}$
$= \dfrac{3(\ln x)^2 - (\ln x)^3 - 4}{x^2}$

73. $\int \dfrac{\ln x + 2}{x}\,dx = \int (\ln x + 2)\dfrac{dx}{x}$
$= \frac{1}{2}(\ln x + 2)^2 + C$

74. $\int \dfrac{(\ln x)^3 + 4}{x}\,dx = \int (\ln x)^3 \dfrac{dx}{x} + \int \dfrac{4}{x}\,dx$
$= \frac{1}{4}(\ln x)^4 + 4\ln|x| + C$
(The absolute values are optional because ln x appears in the original integrand.)

75. $f(x) = e^{x^2} \Rightarrow f'(x) = 2xe^{x^2}$

76. $f(x) = e^{x^3} \Rightarrow f'(x) = 3x^2e^{x^3}$

77. $\int xe^{x^2}\,dx = \frac{1}{2}e^{x^2} + C$

78. $\int x^2e^{x^3}\,dx = \frac{1}{3}e^{x^3} + C$

79. $\int x^3 e^{x^2}\,dx$

u		dv
x^2	+	$x e^{x^2}$
2x		$\frac{1}{2}e^{x^2}$ (Prob. 77)
2	−	$\frac{1}{2}x e^{x^2}$
0	+	$\frac{1}{4}e^{x^2}$

$= \frac{1}{2}x^2e^{x^2} - \frac{1}{2}e^{x^2} + C$

80. $\int x^5 e^{x^3}\,dx$

u		dv
x^3	+	$x^2 e^{x^3}$
$3x^2$		$\frac{1}{3}e^{x^3}$ (Prob. 78)
1	−	$x^2 e^{x^3}$
0	+	$\frac{1}{3}e^{x^3}$

$= \frac{1}{3}x^3e^{x^3} - \frac{1}{3}e^{x^3} + C$

81. $\int e^{ax} \cos bx\, dx$

u		dv
e^{ax}	+	$\cos bx$
$a e^{ax}$	−	$\frac{1}{b}\sin bx$
$a^2 e^{ax}$	+	$-\frac{1}{b^2}\cos bx$

$= \frac{1}{b}e^{ax}\sin bx + \frac{a}{b^2}e^{ax}\cos bx - \frac{a^2}{b^2}\int e^{ax}\cos bx\, dx$

$\frac{a^2 + b^2}{b^2}\int e^{ax}\cos bx\, dx$

$= \frac{1}{b}e^{ax}\sin bx + \frac{a}{b^2}e^{ax}\cos bx + C_1$

$\int e^{ax}\cos bx\, dx$

$= \frac{b}{a^2 + b^2}e^{ax}\sin bx + \frac{a}{a^2 + b^2}e^{ax}\cos bx + C$ (for a, b not both 0)

$\int e^{ax}\cos bx\, dx = x + C$ (for $a = b = 0$)

82. $\int e^{ax} \sin bx\, dx$

u		dv
e^{ax}	+	$\sin bx$
$a e^{ax}$	−	$-\frac{1}{b}\cos bx$
$a^2 e^{ax}$	+	$-\frac{1}{b^2}\sin bx$

$= -\frac{1}{b}e^{ax}\cos bx + \frac{a}{b^2}e^{ax}\sin bx - \frac{a^2}{b^2}\int e^{ax}\sin bx\, dx$

$\frac{a^2 + b^2}{b^2}\int e^{ax}\sin bx\, dx$

$= -\frac{1}{b}e^{ax}\cos bx + \frac{a}{b^2}e^{ax}\sin bx + C_1$

$\int e^{ax}\sin bx\, dx$

$= \frac{a}{a^2 + b^2}e^{ax}\sin bx - \frac{b}{a^2 + b^2}e^{ax}\cos bx + C$ (for a, b not both 0)

$\int e^{ax}\sin bx\, dx = C$ (for $a = b = 0$)

83. $\int \sin^2 cx\, dx = \frac{1}{2}\int (1 - \cos 2cx)\, dx$

$= \frac{1}{2}x - \frac{1}{4c}\sin 2cx + C$ (for $c \ne 0$)

$\int \sin^2 cx\, dx = C$ (for $c = 0$)

84. $\int \cos^2 cx\, dx = \frac{1}{2}\int (1 + \cos 2cx)\, dx$

$= \frac{1}{2}x + \frac{1}{4c}\sin 2cx + C$ (for $c \ne 0$)

$\int \cos^2 cx\, dx = x + C$ (for $c = 0$)

85. $f(x) = \frac{ax + b}{cx + d}$

$f'(x) = \frac{a(cx + d) - c(ax + b)}{(cx + d)^2} = \frac{ad - bc}{(cx + d)^2}$

(for c, d not both 0)
(undefined for $c = d = 0$)

86. $f(x) = (ax + b)^n$

$f'(x) = na(ax + b)^{n-1}$ (for a, b not both 0, or $n \ge 1$)

$f'(x) = 0$ (for $a = b = 0$ and $0 \le n \le 1$)

(undefined for $a = b = 0$, $n < 0$)

87. $\int \frac{ax + b}{cx + d}\, dx = \int \left(\frac{a}{c} + \frac{b - (a/c)d}{cx + d}\right) dx$

$= \frac{ax}{c} + \frac{bc - ad}{c^2}\ln|cx + d| + C$ (for $c \ne 0$)

$\int \frac{ax + b}{cx + d}\, dx = \frac{a}{2d}x^2 + \frac{b}{d}x + C$ (for $c = 0$, $d \ne 0$)

(undefined for $c = d = 0$)

88. $\int (ax + b)^n\, dx = \frac{(ax + b)^{n+1}}{a(n + 1)} + C$ (for $n \ne -1$, $a \ne 0$)

$\int (ax + b)^n\, dx = \frac{1}{a}\ln|ax + b| + C$ (for $n = -1$, $a \ne 0$)

$\int (ax + b)^n\, dx = b^n x + C$ (for $a = 0$)

89. $\int \frac{x\, dx}{\sqrt{x^2 + a^2}} = \frac{1}{2}\int (x^2 + a^2)^{-1/2}(2x\, dx)$

$= \frac{1}{2}\cdot 2(x^2 + a^2)^{1/2} + C = \sqrt{x^2 + a^2} + C$

90. $\int \frac{x\, dx}{\sqrt{a^2 - x^2}} = -\frac{1}{2}\int (a^2 - x^2)^{-1/2}(-2x\, dx)$

$= -\frac{1}{2}\cdot 2(a^2 - x^2)^{1/2} + C = -\sqrt{a^2 - x^2} + C$ (for $a \ne 0$)

(undefined for $a = 0$)

91. $\int \frac{dx}{\sqrt{x^2 + a^2}} = \int \frac{d(a \tan \theta)}{\sqrt{a^2 \tan^2 \theta + a^2}}$

$= \int \frac{a \sec^2 \theta\, d\theta}{a \sec \theta} = \int \sec \theta\, d\theta$

$= \ln|\sec \theta + \tan \theta| + C_1$

$= \ln\left|\frac{1}{a}\sqrt{x^2 + a^2} + \frac{1}{a}x\right| + C_1$

$= \ln\left|\sqrt{x^2 + a^2} + x\right| + C$

92. $\int \frac{dx}{\sqrt{a^2 - x^2}} = \int \frac{d(a \sin \theta)}{\sqrt{a^2 - a^2 \sin^2 \theta}}$

$= \int \frac{a \cos \theta\, d\theta}{a \cos \theta} = \int d\theta = \theta + C = \sin^{-1}\frac{x}{a} + C$ (for $a \ne 0$)

(undefined for $a = 0$)

93. $f(x) = x^2 \sin ax \Rightarrow f'(x) = 2x \sin ax + ax^2 \cos ax$

94. $f(x) = x^2 \cos ax \Rightarrow f'(x) = 2x \cos ax - ax^2 \sin ax$

95. $\int x^2 \sin ax\, dx$

u		dv
x^2	+	$\sin ax$
$2x$	−	$-\frac{1}{a}\cos ax$
2	+	$-\frac{1}{a^2}\sin ax$
0	−	$\frac{1}{a^3}\cos ax$

$= -\frac{1}{a}x^2 \cos ax + \frac{2}{a^2}x \sin ax + \frac{2}{a^3}\cos ax + C$ (for $a \ne 0$)

$\int x^2 \sin ax\, dx = C$ (for $a = 0$)

96. $\int x^2 \cos ax\, dx$

u		dv
x^2	+	$\cos ax$
$2x$	−	$\frac{1}{a}\sin ax$
2	+	$-\frac{1}{a^2}\cos ax$
0	−	$-\frac{1}{a^3}\sin ax$

$= \frac{1}{a}x^2 \sin ax + \frac{2}{a^2}x \cos ax - \frac{2}{a^3}\sin ax + C$ (for $a \ne 0$)

$\int x^2 \cos ax\, dx = \frac{1}{3}x^3 + C$ (for $a = 0$)

97. $\int \sinh ax\, dx = \frac{1}{a}\cosh ax + C$ (for $a \ne 0$)

$\int \sinh ax\, dx = C$ (for $a = 0$)

98. $\int \cosh ax\, dx = \frac{1}{a}\sinh ax + C$ (for $a \ne 0$)

$\int \cosh ax\, dx = x + C$ (for $a = 0$)

99. $\int \cos^{-1} ax\, dx$

u	dv
$\cos^{-1} ax$ (+)	1
$\dfrac{-a}{\sqrt{1-(ax)^2}}$ (−)	x

$= x\cos^{-1} ax + \int \dfrac{ax\, dx}{\sqrt{1-(ax)^2}}$

$= x\cos^{-1} ax - \dfrac{1}{2a}\int (1-(ax)^2)^{-1/2}(-2a^2x\, dx)$

$= x\cos^{-1} ax - \dfrac{1}{a}\sqrt{1-(ax)^2} + C$ (for $a \neq 0$)

$\int \cos^{-1} ax\, dx = \dfrac{\pi}{2}x + C$ (for $a = 0$)

100. $\int \sin^{-1} ax\, dx$

u	dv
$\sin^{-1} ax$ (+)	1
$\dfrac{a}{\sqrt{1-(ax)^2}}$ (−)	x

$= x\sin^{-1} ax - \int \dfrac{ax\, dx}{\sqrt{1-(ax)^2}}$

$= x\sin^{-1} ax + \dfrac{1}{2a}\int (1-(ax)^2)^{-1/2}(-2a^2x\, dx)$

$= x\sin^{-1} ax + \dfrac{1}{a}\sqrt{1-(ax)^2} + C$ (for $a \neq 0$)

$\int \sin^{-1} ax\, dx = C$ (for $a = 0$)

101. $\int \dfrac{1}{1+\sqrt{x}}\, dx$ $\quad u = 1 + \sqrt{x}$

$x = (u-1)^2$
$dx = 2(u-1)\, du$

$= \int \dfrac{2(u-1)\, du}{u} = \int 2\, du - \int (2/u)\, du = 2u - 2\ln|u| + C$

$= 2(1+\sqrt{x}) - 2\ln|1+\sqrt{x}| + C$

(or $2\sqrt{x} - 2\ln|1+\sqrt{x}| + C_1$)

Absolute values are optional because $1 + \sqrt{x} > 0$.

102. $\int \dfrac{1}{1-\sqrt{x}}\, dx$ $\quad$ Let $u = 1 - \sqrt{x}$.

$x = (1-u)^2$
$dx = 2(u-1)\, du$

$= \int \dfrac{2(u-1)\, du}{u} = \int 2\, du - \int (2/u)\, du = 2u - 2\ln|u| + C$

$= 2(1-\sqrt{x}) - 2\ln|1-\sqrt{x}| + C$

(or $-2\sqrt{x} - 2\ln|1-\sqrt{x}| + C_1$).

103. $\int \dfrac{1}{1+\sqrt[4]{x}}\, dx$ $\quad$ Let $u = 1 + \sqrt[4]{x}$.

$x = (1-u)^4$
$dx = 4(u-1)^3\, du$

$= \int \dfrac{4(u-1)^3\, du}{u} = \int (4u^2 - 12u + 12 - 4/u)\, du$

$= \dfrac{4}{3}u^3 - 6u^2 + 12u - 4\ln|u| + C$

$= \dfrac{4}{3}(1+\sqrt[4]{x})^3 - 6(1+\sqrt[4]{x})^2 + 12(1+\sqrt[4]{x}) - 4\ln(1+\sqrt[4]{x}) + C$

or $\dfrac{4}{3}(\sqrt[4]{x})^3 - 2(\sqrt[4]{x})^2 + 4\sqrt[4]{x} - 4\ln|1+\sqrt[4]{x}| + C_1$, by expanding the powers or by starting with $u = \sqrt[4]{x}$.

Absolute values are optional because $1 + \sqrt[4]{x} > 0$.

104. $\int \dfrac{1}{\sqrt{x} + \sqrt[3]{x}}\, dx$ $\quad$ Let $u = x^{1/6}$.

$x = u^6$
$dx = 6u^5\, du$

$= \int \dfrac{6u^5\, du}{u^3 + u^2} = \int \dfrac{6u^3\, du}{u+1}$

$= \int \left(6u^2 - 6u + 6 - \dfrac{6}{u+1}\right) du$ (by long division)

$= 2u^3 - 3u^2 + 6u - 6\ln|u+1| + C$

$= 2\sqrt{x} - 3\sqrt[3]{x} + 6\sqrt[6]{x} - 6\ln(\sqrt[6]{x} + 1) + C$

105. $\int \dfrac{1}{\sqrt{e^x + 1}}\, dx$ $\quad$ Let $u = \sqrt{e^x + 1}$

$e^x = u^2 - 1$
$x = \ln(u^2 - 1)$
$dx = \dfrac{2u\, du}{u^2 - 1}$

$= \int \dfrac{2\, du}{u^2 - 1} = \int \left(\dfrac{1}{u-1} - \dfrac{1}{u+1}\right) du$

(by partial fractions)

$= \ln|u-1| - \ln|u+1| + C$

$= \ln(\sqrt{e^x + 1} - 1) - \ln(\sqrt{e^x + 1} + 1) + C$

106. $\int \dfrac{1}{\sqrt{e^x - 1}}\, dx$ $\quad$ Let $u = \sqrt{e^x - 1}$

$e^x = u^2 + 1$
$x = \ln(u^2 + 1)$
$dx = \dfrac{2u\, du}{u^2 + 1}$

$= \int \dfrac{2\, du}{u^2 + 1} = 2\tan^{-1} u + C = 2\tan^{-1}\sqrt{e^x - 1} + C.$

107.a. Let $t = x/2$ and substitute, getting
$\cos x = 2\cos^2(x/2) - 1$ and
$\sin x = 2\sin(x/2)\cos(x/2)$.

b. $\cos x = \dfrac{2}{\sec^2(x/2)} - 1$

$= \dfrac{2 - \sec^2(x/2)}{\sec^2(x/2)}$

$= \dfrac{2 - (1 + \tan^2(x/2))}{1 + \tan^2(x/2)}$

$= \dfrac{1 - \tan^2(x/2)}{1 + \tan^2(x/2)}$, Q.E.D.

$\sin x = 2\dfrac{\sin(x/2)}{\cos(x/2)}\cos^2(x/2)$

$= 2\tan(x/2)\dfrac{1}{\sec^2(x/2)}$

$= \dfrac{2\tan(x/2)}{1 + \tan^2(x/2)}$, Q.E.D.

c. $u = \tan(x/2) \Rightarrow 2\tan^{-1} u = x \Rightarrow dx = \dfrac{2\, du}{1 + u^2}$

$\cos x = \dfrac{1 - u^2}{1 + u^2}$ and $\sin x = \dfrac{2u}{1 + u^2}$ from b.

d. $\int \dfrac{1}{1 + \cos x}\, dx$

$= \int \dfrac{1}{1 + \dfrac{1 - u^2}{1 + u^2}} \cdot \dfrac{2\, du}{1 + u^2}$

$= \int \dfrac{2\, du}{(1 + u^2) + (1 - u^2)} = \int du$

e. $\int \dfrac{1}{1 + \cos x}\, dx = \int du = u + C = \tan(x/2) + C$

108. Another Indefinite Integral of Secant

a. $\int \sec x\,dx = \int \frac{1}{\cos x}\,dx = \int \frac{1+u^2}{1-u^2}\cdot\frac{2\,du}{1+u^2}$

$= \int \frac{2}{1-u^2}\,du$

b. $\int \sec x\,dx = \int \left(\frac{1}{1-u}+\frac{1}{1+u}\right)du$

$= -\ln|1-u| + \ln|1+u| + C$

$= \ln\left|\frac{1+u}{1-u}\right| + C = \ln\left|\frac{1+\tan(x/2)}{1-\tan(x/2)}\right| + C$

c. $\int \sec x\,dx = \ln\left|\frac{1+\tan(x/2)}{1-1\cdot\tan(x/2)}\right| + C$

$= \ln\left|\frac{\tan(\pi/4)+\tan(x/2)}{1-\tan(\pi/4)\tan(x/2)}\right| + C$

$= \ln|\tan(\pi/4 + x/2)| + C$

d. i. $\int_0^1 \sec x\,dx = \ln|\tan(\pi/4 + x/2)|\,\Big|_0^1$

$= \ln|\tan(\pi/4 + 1/2)| - \ln|\tan \pi/4|$

$= \ln|\tan(\pi/4 + 1/2)| = 1.226191\ldots$

ii. $\int_0^1 \sec x\,dx = \ln|\sec x + \tan x|\,\Big|_0^1$

$= \ln|\sec 1 + \tan 1| - \ln|1 + 0| = 1.226191\ldots$, which agrees with the answer in part i.

109. $\int \frac{1}{1-\cos x}\,dx = \int \frac{1}{1-\frac{1-u^2}{1+u^2}}\cdot\frac{2\,du}{1+u^2}$

$= \int \frac{2\,du}{(1+u^2)-(1-u^2)} = \int \frac{du}{u^2} = \frac{-1}{u} + C$

$= -\cot(x/2) + C$

110. $\int \frac{1}{1+\sin x}\,dx = \int \frac{1}{1+\frac{2u}{1+u^2}}\cdot\frac{2\,du}{1+u^2}$

$= \int \frac{2\,du}{(1+u^2)+2u} = \int \frac{du}{(u+1)^2} = \frac{-1}{u+1} + C$

$= \frac{-1}{\tan(x/2)+1} + C$

111. $\int \frac{\cos x}{1-\cos x}\,dx = \int \frac{\frac{1-u^2}{1+u^2}}{1-\frac{1-u^2}{1+u^2}}\cdot\frac{2\,du}{1+u^2}$

$= \int \frac{1-u^2}{u^2(1+u^2)}\,du = \int \left(\frac{1}{u^2} - \frac{2}{1+u^2}\right)du$

$= -\frac{1}{u} - 2\tan^{-1} u + C$

$= -\frac{1}{\tan(x/2)} - 2\tan^{-1}(\tan(x/2)) + C$

$= -\cot(x/2) - x + C$

Or: $\int \frac{\cos x}{1-\cos x}\,dx = \int \left(-1 + \frac{1}{1-\cos x}\right)dx$

$= -\int dx + \int \frac{1}{1-\cos x}\,dx$

$= -x - \cot(x/2) + C$ (using Problem 109)

Problem Set 9-12, page 497 — Integrals in Journal

1. Table of Integrals Problem
   Journal entries will vary.

Problem Set 9-13, pages 498 to 502 — Chapter Review and Test

Review Problems

R0. Journal entries will vary.

R1. $f(x) = x\cos x$

$f'(x) = x(-\sin x) + (1)\cos x = \cos x - x\sin x$

$\Rightarrow x\cos x\,dx + C = \int f'(x)\,dx = \int \cos x - x\sin x\,dx$

$= \sin x - \int x\sin x\,dx$

$\Rightarrow \int x\sin x\,dx = \sin x - x\cos x + C$

$\int_1^4 x\sin x\,dx = \sin x - x\cos x\Big|_1^4$

$= \sin 4 - 4\cos 4 - \sin 1 + \cos 1 = 1.5566\ldots$

Numerically, $\int_1^4 x\sin x\,dx \approx 1.5566\ldots$

R2. $\int 5x\sin 2x\,dx$ $u = 5x$ $dv = \sin 2x\,dx$

$du = 5\,dx$ $v = -\frac{1}{2}\cos 2x$

$= 5x\left(-\frac{1}{2}\cos 2x\right) + \int \frac{1}{2}\cos 2x\,(5\,dx)$

$= -\frac{5}{2}x\cos 2x + \frac{5}{4}\sin 2x + C$

R3. a. $\int x^3\cos 2x\,dx$

u		dv
x^3	+	$\cos 2x$
$3x^2$	−	$\frac{1}{2}\sin 2x$
$6x$	+	$-\frac{1}{4}\cos 2x$
6	−	$-\frac{1}{8}\sin 2x$
0	+	$\frac{1}{16}\cos 2x$

$= \frac{1}{2}x^3\sin 2x + \frac{3}{4}x^2\cos 2x - \frac{3}{4}x\sin 2x - \frac{3}{8}\cos 2x + C$

b. $\int e^{4x}\sin 3x\,dx$

u		dv
e^{4x}	+	$\sin 3x$
$4e^{4x}$	−	$-\frac{1}{3}\cos 3x$
$16e^{4x}$	+	$-\frac{1}{9}\sin 3x$

$= -\frac{1}{3}e^{4x}\cos 3x + \frac{4}{9}e^{4x}\sin 3x - \frac{9}{16}\int e^{4x}\sin 3x\,dx$

$\Rightarrow \frac{25}{16}\int e^{4x}\sin 3x\,dx = -\frac{1}{3}e^{4x}\cos 3x + \frac{4}{9}e^{4x}\sin 3x + C_1$

$\Rightarrow \int e^{4x}\sin 3x\,dx = -\frac{3}{25}e^{4x}\cos 3x + \frac{4}{25}e^{4x}\sin 3x + C$

c. $\int x (\ln x)^2\, dx$

u		dv
$(\ln x)^2$	+	x
$2 \ln x \cdot \frac{1}{x}$		$\frac{1}{2}x^2$
$\ln x$		x
$\frac{1}{x}$		$\frac{1}{2}x^2$
1	+	$\frac{1}{2}x$
0	−	$\frac{1}{4}x^2$

$= \frac{1}{2} x^2 (\ln x)^2 - \frac{1}{2} x^2 \ln x + \frac{1}{4} x^2 + C.$

d. Slice parallel to the y-axis. Pick a sample point (x, y) on the graph, within the slice.
$dV = 2\pi x \cdot y \cdot dx = 2\pi x\, (x \ln x)\, dx = 2\pi x^2 \ln x\, dx$

$V = 2\pi \int_1^2 x^2 \ln x\, dx$

u		dv
$\ln x$	+	x^2
$\frac{1}{x}$		$\frac{1}{3}x^3$
1	−	$\frac{1}{3}x^2$
0	+	$\frac{1}{9}x^3$

$= 2\pi(\frac{1}{3}x^3 \ln x - \frac{1}{9}x^3)\Big|_1^2 = \frac{16}{3}\pi \ln 2 - \frac{16}{9}\pi + \frac{2}{9}\pi$

$= \frac{16}{3}\pi \ln 2 - \frac{14}{9}\pi = 6.7268 \ldots .$

R4. a. $\int \cos^{30} dx$

u		dv
$\cos^{29} x$	+	$\cos x$
$-29 \cos^{28} x \sin x$	−	$\sin x$

$= \cos^{29} x \sin x + 29 \int \cos^{28} x \sin^2 x\, dx$

$= \cos^{29} x \sin x + 29 \int \cos^{28} x\, (1 - \cos^2 x)\, dx$

$\Rightarrow 30 \int \cos^{30} dx = \cos^{29} x \sin x + 29 \int \cos^{28} x\, dx$

$\Rightarrow \int \cos^{30} dx = \frac{1}{30} \cos^{29} x \sin x + \frac{29}{30} \int \cos^{28} x\, dx$

b. $\int \sec^6 x\, dx = \frac{1}{5} \sec^4 x \tan x + \frac{4}{5} \int \sec^4 x\, dx$

$= \frac{1}{5} \sec^4 x \tan x + \frac{4}{15} \sec^2 x \tan x + \frac{8}{15} \int \sec^2 x\, dx$

$= \frac{1}{5} \sec^4 x \tan x + \frac{4}{15} \sec^2 x \tan x + \frac{8}{15} \tan x + C$

c. $\int \tan^n x\, dx = \int \tan^{n-2} x\ (\tan^2 x\, dx)$

$= \int \tan^{n-2} x\, (\sec^2 x - 1)\, dx$

$= \int \tan^{n-2} x \sec^2 x\, dx - \int \tan^{n-2} x\, dx$

$= \frac{1}{n-1} \tan^{n-1} x - \int \tan^{n-2} x\, dx$

R5. a. $\int \cos^5 x\, dx = \int (1 - \sin^2 x)^2 (\cos x\, dx)$

$= \int (1 - 2\sin^2 x + \sin^4 x)(\cos x\, dx)$

$= \sin x - \frac{2}{3} \sin^3 x + \frac{1}{5} \sin^5 x + C$

b. $\int \sec^6 x\, dx = \int (\tan^2 x + 1)^2 (\sec^2 x\, dx)$

$= \int (\tan^4 x + 2\tan^2 x + 1)(\sec^2 x\, dx)$

$= \frac{1}{5} \tan^5 x + \frac{2}{3} \tan^3 x + \tan x + C$

c. $\int \sin^2 7x\, dx = \int \frac{1}{2}(1 - \cos 14x)\, dx$

$= \frac{1}{2} x - \frac{1}{28} \sin 14x + C$

d. $\int \sec^3 x\, dx$

u		dv
$\sec x$	+	$\sec^2 x$
$\sec x \tan x$	−	$\tan x$

$= \sec x \tan x - \int \tan^2 x \sec x\, dx$

$= \sec x \tan x - \int (\sec^2 - 1) \sec x\, dx$

$= \sec x \tan x + \int \sec x\, dx - \int \sec^3 x\, dx$

$2 \int \sec^3 x\, dx = \sec x \tan x + \ln |\sec x + \tan x| + C$

$\int \sec^3 x\, dx = \frac{1}{2} \sec x \tan x + \frac{1}{2} \ln |\sec x + \tan x| + C$

e. $\int \tan^9 32\, dx = (\tan^9 32) \int dx = (\tan^9 32)x + C$

f. $r = 9 + 8 \sin \theta$

$dA = \frac{1}{2} r^2\, d\theta = \frac{1}{2}(9 + 8 \sin \theta)^2\, d\theta$

$A = \frac{1}{2} \int_0^{\pi/4} (64 \sin^2 \theta + 144 \sin \theta + 81)\, d\theta$

$= \frac{1}{2} \int_0^{\pi/4} (32(1 - \cos 2\theta) + 144 \sin \theta + 81)\, d\theta$

$= 16(\theta - \frac{1}{2} \sin 2\theta) - 72 \cos \theta + \frac{81}{2}\theta \Big|_0^{\pi/4}$

$= 4\pi - 8 - 36\sqrt{2} + \frac{81}{8}\pi + 72$

$= \frac{113}{8}\pi + 64 - 36\sqrt{2} = 57.4633 \ldots$

R6. a. $\int \sqrt{x^2 - 49}\, dx$

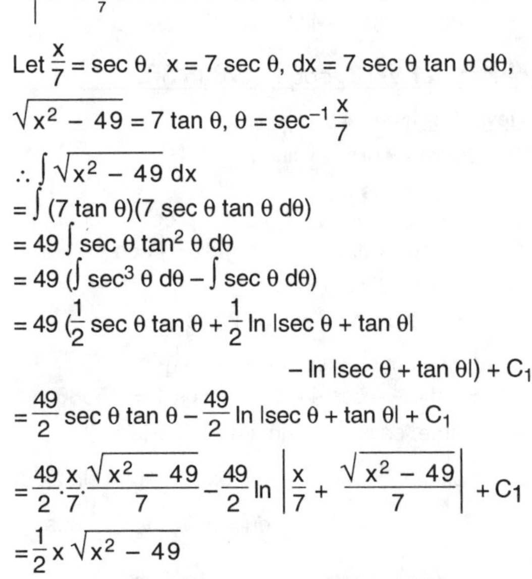

Let $\frac{x}{7} = \sec \theta$. $x = 7 \sec \theta$, $dx = 7 \sec \theta \tan \theta\, d\theta$,

$\sqrt{x^2 - 49} = 7 \tan \theta$, $\theta = \sec^{-1} \frac{x}{7}$

$\therefore \int \sqrt{x^2 - 49}\, dx$

$= \int (7 \tan \theta)(7 \sec \theta \tan \theta\, d\theta)$

$= 49 \int \sec \theta \tan^2 \theta\, d\theta$

$= 49 (\int \sec^3 \theta\, d\theta - \int \sec \theta\, d\theta)$

$= 49 (\frac{1}{2} \sec \theta \tan \theta + \frac{1}{2} \ln |\sec \theta + \tan \theta|$

$- \ln |\sec \theta + \tan \theta|) + C_1$

$= \frac{49}{2} \sec \theta \tan \theta - \frac{49}{2} \ln |\sec \theta + \tan \theta| + C_1$

$= \frac{49}{2} \cdot \frac{x}{7} \cdot \frac{\sqrt{x^2 - 49}}{7} - \frac{49}{2} \ln \left| \frac{x}{7} + \frac{\sqrt{x^2 - 49}}{7} \right| + C_1$

$= \frac{1}{2} x \sqrt{x^2 - 49}$

$- \frac{49}{2} \ln |x + \sqrt{x^2 - 49}\,| + \frac{49}{2} \ln 7 + C_1$

$= \frac{1}{2} x \sqrt{x^2 - 49} - \frac{49}{2} \ln |x + \sqrt{x^2 - 49}\,| + C$

b. $\int \sqrt{x^2 - 10x + 34}\,dx = \int \sqrt{(x-5)^2 + 9}\,dx$

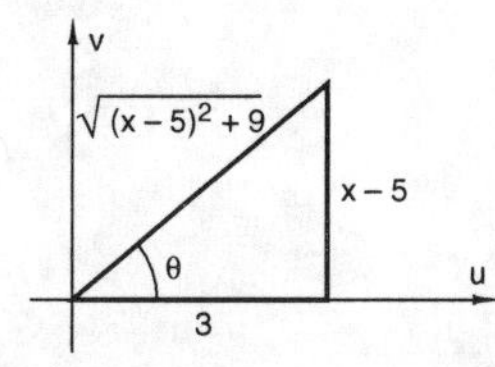

Let $\frac{x-5}{3} = \tan\theta$. $x = 5 + 3\tan\theta$, $dx = 3\sec^2\theta\,d\theta$,

$\sqrt{(x-5)^2 + 9} = 3\sec\theta$, $\theta = \tan^{-1}\frac{x-5}{3}$

$\therefore \int \sqrt{(x-5)^2 + 9}\,dx$

$= \int (3\sec\theta)(3\sec^2\theta\,d\theta) = 9\int \sec^3\theta\,d\theta$

$= \frac{9}{2}\sec\theta\tan\theta + \frac{9}{2}\ln|\sec\theta + \tan\theta| + C_1$

$= \frac{9}{2}\frac{\sqrt{(x-5)^2+9}}{3}\frac{x-5}{3} + \frac{9}{2}\ln\left|\frac{\sqrt{(x-5)^2+9}}{3} + \frac{x-5}{3}\right|$

$+ C_1$

$= \frac{1}{2}\sqrt{(x-5)^2+9}\cdot(x-5)$

$+ \frac{9}{2}\ln|\sqrt{(x-5)^2+9} + x - 5| - \frac{9}{2}\ln 3 + C_1$

$= \frac{1}{2}(x-5)\sqrt{x^2 - 10x + 34}$

$+ \frac{9}{2}\ln|\sqrt{x^2 - 10x + 34} + x - 5| + C$

c. $\int \sqrt{1 - 0.25x^2}\,dx$

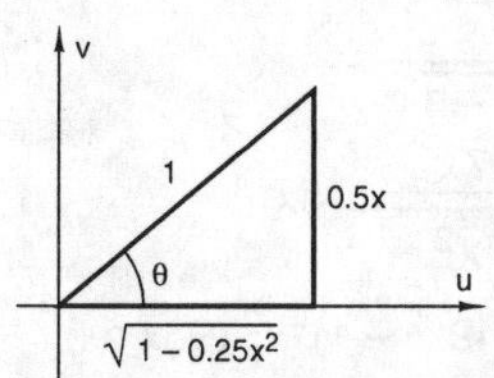

Let $\frac{0.5x}{1} = \sin\theta$, $x = 2\sin\theta$, $dx = 2\cos\theta\,d\theta$,

$\sqrt{1 - 0.25x^2} = \cos\theta$, $\theta = \sin^{-1}\frac{x}{2}$

$\int \sqrt{1 - 0.25x^2}\,dx = \int (\cos\theta)(2\cos\theta\,d\theta)$

$= \int 2\cos^2\theta\,d\theta = \int (1 + \cos 2\theta)\,d\theta$

$= \theta + \frac{1}{2}\sin 2\theta + C = \theta + \sin\theta\cos\theta + C$

$= \sin^{-1}\frac{x}{2} + \frac{1}{2}x\sqrt{1 - 0.25x^2} + C$

d. Slice region vertically. Pick sample point (x, y) on the upper branch of the circle, within the strip.

$dA = 2y\,dx = 2\sqrt{25 - x^2}\,dx$

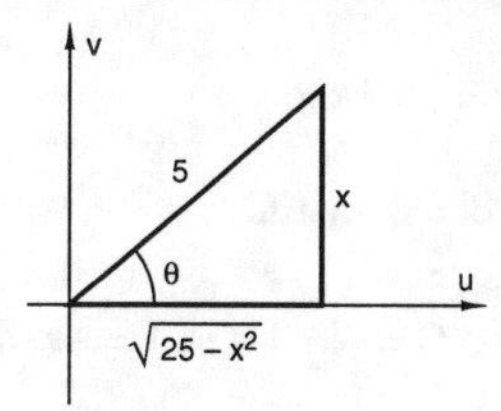

Let $\frac{x}{5} = \sin\theta$. $x = 5\sin\theta$, $dx = 5\cos\theta\,d\theta$,

$\sqrt{25 - x^2} = 5\cos\theta$, $\theta = \sin^{-1}\frac{x}{5}$

$A = \int_3^4 2\sqrt{25 - x^2}\,dx = 2\int_{x=3}^{x=4} 5\cos\theta\,(5\cos\theta\,d\theta)$

$= 25\int_{x=3}^{x=4} (1 + \cos 2\theta)\,d\theta = 25\theta + 12.5\sin 2\theta\,\Big|_{x=3}^{x=4}$

$= 25\theta + 25\sin\theta\cos\theta\,\Big|_{x=3}^{x=4}$

$= 25\sin^{-1}\frac{x}{5} + 25\cdot\frac{x}{5}\cdot\frac{1}{5}\sqrt{25 - x^2}\,\Big|_3^4$

$= 25\sin^{-1}0.8 + 4\sqrt{9} - 25\sin^{-1}0.6 - 3\sqrt{16}$

$= 25(\sin^{-1}0.8 - \sin^{-1}0.6) = 7.0948\ldots$

R7. a. $\int \frac{(6x+1)\,dx}{x^2 - 3x - 4} = \int \frac{(6x+1)\,dx}{(x+1)(x-4)}$

$= \int \left(\frac{1}{x+1} + \frac{5}{x-4}\right)dx$

$= \ln|x+1| + 5\ln|x-4| + C.$

b. $\int \frac{5x^2 - 21x - 2}{(x-1)(x+2)(x-3)}\,dx$

$= \int \left(\frac{3}{x-1} + \frac{4}{x+2} - \frac{2}{x-3}\right)dx$

$= 3\ln|x-1| + 4\ln|x+2| - 2\ln|x-3| + C$

c. $\int \frac{5x^2 + 3x + 45}{x^3 + 9x}\,dx = \int \frac{5x^2 + 3x + 45}{x(x^2+9)}\,dx$

$= \int \left(\frac{5}{x} + \frac{3}{x^2+9}\right)dx = 5\ln|x| + \tan^{-1}\frac{x}{3} + C$

(The second integral may be found by inspection or by trigonometry substitution.)

d. $\int \frac{5x^2 + 27x + 32}{x\,(x+4)^2}\,dx$

$= \int \left(\frac{2}{x} + \frac{3}{x+4} - \frac{1}{(x+4)^2}\right)dx$

$= 2\ln|x| + 3\ln|x+4| + (x+4)^{-1} + C$

$= \ln|x^2(x+4)^3| + \frac{1}{x+4} + C$

e. $\frac{dy}{dx} = 0.1\,(y-3)\,(y-8)$

$\int \frac{dy}{(y-3)\,(y-8)} = \int 0.1\,dx$

$\int (\frac{-1/5}{y-3} + \frac{1/5}{y-8})\,dy = \int 0.1\,dx$

$-\frac{1}{5}\ln|y-3| + \frac{1}{5}\ln|y-8| = 0.1x + C_1$

$-\ln|y-3| + \ln|y-8| = 0.5x + C$

Substituting (0, 7) gives $C = -\ln 4 + \ln 1 = -\ln 4$.

$\ln\left|\frac{y-8}{y-3}\right| = 0.5x - \ln 4$

$\left|\frac{y-8}{y-3}\right| = e^{0.5x - \ln 4} = 0.25e^{0.5x}$

$-\frac{y-8}{y-3} = 0.25e^{0.5x}$

(0, 7) on the graph $\Rightarrow (y-8)/(y-3) < 0$

$y = 3 + \frac{5}{1 + 0.25e^{0.5x}}$

Graph, showing that solution fits slope field.

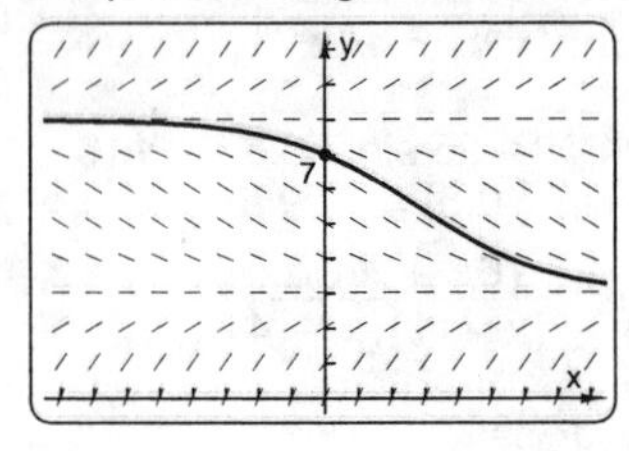

R8. a. Graph, $y = \cos^{-1} x$.

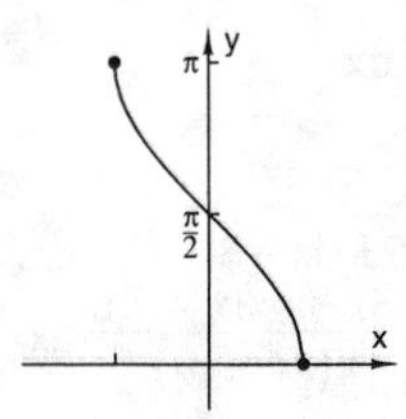

b. $f(x) = \sec^{-1} 3x$

$f'(x) = \frac{3}{|3x|\sqrt{(3x)^2 - 1}} = \frac{1}{|x|\sqrt{9x^2 - 1}}$

c. $\int \tan^{-1} 5x\,dx$

u	dv
$\tan^{-1} 5x$	1 (+)
$\frac{5}{1 + 25x^2}$	x (−)

$= x\tan^{-1} 5x - \int \frac{5x}{1 + 25x^2}\,dx$

$= x\tan^{-1} 5x - \frac{1}{10}\int \frac{1}{1 + 25x^2}\,(50x\,dx)$

$= x\tan^{-1} 5x - \frac{1}{10}\ln|1 + 25x^2| + C$

(Absolute values are optional because $1 + 25x^2 > 0$.)

d. "Obvious" way:

Slice the region vertically. Pick a sample point (x, y) on the graph, within the strip.

$dA = y\,dx = \cos^{-1} x\,dx$

$A = \int_0^1 \cos^{-1} x\,dx = x\cos^{-1} x - \sqrt{1 - x^2}\,\Big|_0^1$

$= \cos^{-1} 1 - \sqrt{0} - 0 + \sqrt{1} = 1$

Easier way:

Slice horizontally. Pick a sample point (x, y) on the graph within the strip.

$dA = x\,dy = \cos y\,dy$

$A = \int_0^{\pi/2} \cos y\,dy = \sin y\,\Big|_0^{\pi/2} = 1 - 0 = 1$

R9. a. Graph, $f(x) = \sinh x$.

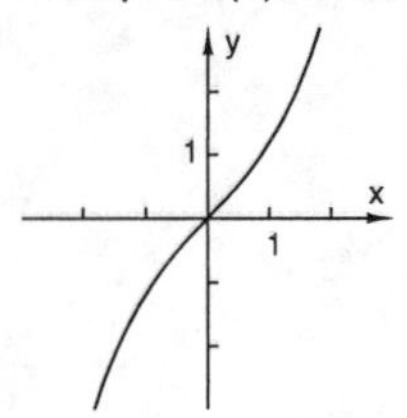

b. Graph, $g(x) = \cosh^{-1} x\ (y \ge 0)$.

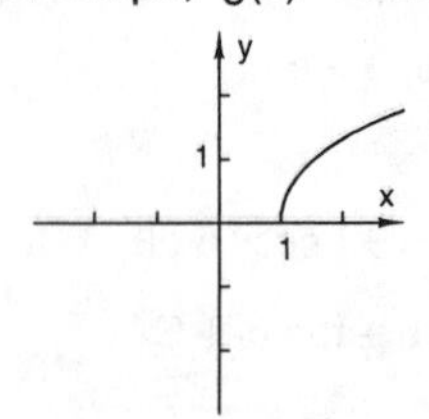

c. $h(x) = x^2\operatorname{sech} x$

$h'(x) = -x^2\operatorname{sech} x\tanh x + 2x\operatorname{sech} x$

d. $f(x) = \sinh^{-1} 5x$

$f'(x) = \frac{5}{\sqrt{25x^2 + 1}}$

e. $\int \tanh 3x\,dx = \int \frac{1}{\cosh 3x}\sinh 3x\,dx$

$= \frac{1}{3}\ln|\cosh 3x| + C$

(Absolute values are optional because $\cosh 3x > 0$.)

f. $\int \cosh^{-1} 7x\,dx$

u	dv
$\cosh^{-1} 7x$	1 (+)
$\frac{7}{\sqrt{49x^2 - 1}}$	x (−)

$= x\cosh^{-1} 7x - \int \frac{7x}{\sqrt{49x^2 - 1}}\,dx$

$= x\cosh^{-1} 7x - \frac{1}{14}\int (49x^2 - 1)^{-1/2}\,(98x\,dx)$

$= x\cosh^{-1} 7x - \frac{1}{14}\cdot 2(49x^2 - 1)^{1/2} + C$

$= x\cosh^{-1} 7x - \frac{1}{7}\sqrt{49x^2 - 1} + C$

g. $\cosh^2 x - \sinh^2 x$

$= \frac{1}{2}(e^x + e^{-x})^2 - \frac{1}{2}(e^x - e^{-x})^2$

$= \frac{1}{4}(e^{2x} + 2 + e^{-2x}) - \frac{1}{4}(e^{2x} - 2 + e^{-2x})$

= 1, Q.E.D.

h. The general equation is $y = k\cosh\frac{1}{k}x + C$.

$y = 5$ at $x = 0 \Rightarrow 5 = k\cosh 0 + C \Rightarrow C = 5 - k$

$y = 7$ at $x = 3 \Rightarrow 7 = k\cosh\frac{3}{k} + 5 - k$

$\Rightarrow 2 = k\cosh\frac{3}{k} - k$

$\Rightarrow k = 2.5269\ldots$ (solving numerically)

$y = 2.5269\ldots\cosh\frac{t}{2.5269\ldots} + 5 - 2.5269\ldots$.

$y(10) = 68.5961\ldots$

$20 = 2.5269\ldots\cosh\frac{x}{2.5269\ldots} + 5 - 2.5269\ldots$

$\Rightarrow x = \pm 6.6324\ldots$ (solving numerically)

R10. a. $\int_3^{\infty} (x-2)^{-1.2}\,dx = \lim_{b\to\infty} \int_3^b (x-2)^{-1.2}\,dx$

$= \lim_{b\to\infty} -5(x-2)^{-0.2} \Big|_3^b = \lim_{b\to\infty} (-5(b-2)^{-0.2} + 5) = 5.$

Converges to 5.

b. $\int_{\pi/2}^{0} \tan x\,dx = \lim_{a\to\pi/2^-} \int_a^0 \tan x\,dx$

$= \lim_{a\to\pi/2^-} \ln|\sec x| \Big|_a^0$

$= \lim_{a\to\pi/2^-} (\ln|\sec 0| - \ln|\sec a|) = -\infty$

Integral diverges.

c. $\int_{-1}^{1} x^{-2/3}\,dx$

$= \lim_{b\to 0^-} \int_{-1}^{b} x^{-2/3}\,dx + \lim_{a\to 0^+} \int_a^1 x^{-2/3}\,dx$

$= \lim_{b\to 0^-} 3x^{1/3} \Big|_{-1}^{b} + \lim_{a\to 0^+} 3x^{1/3} \Big|_a^1$

$= \lim_{b\to 0^-} (3b^{1/3} - (-3)) + \lim_{a\to 0^+} (3 - 3a^{1/3}) = 6$

Converges to 6.

d. $\int_0^4 (\sqrt{x} - \frac{|x-1|}{x-1})\,dx$

$= \lim_{b\to 1^-} \int_0^b (\sqrt{x}+1)\,dx + \lim_{a\to 1^+} \int_a^4 (\sqrt{x}-1)\,dx$

$= \lim_{b\to 1^-} (\frac{2}{3}x^{3/2} + x) \Big|_0^b + \lim_{a\to 1^+} (\frac{2}{3}x^{3/2} - x) \Big|_a^4$

$= \lim_{b\to 1^-} (\frac{2}{3}b^{3/2} + b - 0) + \lim_{a\to 1^+} (\frac{2}{3}4^{3/2} - 4 - \frac{2}{3}a^{3/2} + a)$

$= \frac{2}{3}\cdot 1^{3/2} + 1 + \frac{2}{3}\cdot 4^{3/2} - 4 - \frac{2}{3}\cdot 1^{3/2} + 1$

$= 1 + \frac{16}{3} - 4 + 1 = \frac{10}{3}$

Converges to $\frac{10}{3} = 3.333\ldots$

e. $\int_1^{\infty} x^{-p}\,dx$ converges if $p > 1$, and diverges otherwise.

R11. a. $f(x) = x\sin^{-1} x \Rightarrow f'(x) = \sin^{-1} x + \frac{x}{\sqrt{1-x^2}}$

b. $I = \int x \sin^{-1} x\,dx$

u		dv
$\sin^{-1} x$	+	x
$\frac{1}{\sqrt{1-x^2}}$	−	$\frac{1}{2}x^2$

$= \frac{1}{2}x^2 \sin^{-1} x - \frac{1}{2}\int \frac{x^2\,dx}{\sqrt{1-x^2}}$

Let $I_1 = \int \frac{x^2\,dx}{\sqrt{1-x^2}}$

Let $x = \sin\theta$.

$\therefore dx = \cos\theta\,d\theta$, $\sqrt{1-x^2} = \cos\theta$, $\theta = \sin^{-1} x$.

$I_1 = \int \frac{\sin^2\theta\cos\theta\,d\theta}{\cos\theta} = \int \sin^2\theta\,d\theta$

$= \frac{1}{2}\int (1-\cos 2\theta)\,d\theta = \frac{1}{2}\theta - \frac{1}{4}\sin 2\theta + C$

$= \frac{1}{2}\theta - \frac{1}{2}\sin\theta\cos\theta + C$

$= \frac{1}{2}\sin^{-1} x - \frac{1}{2}x\sqrt{1-x^2} + C$

$\therefore I = \frac{1}{2}x^2\sin^{-1} x - \frac{1}{4}\sin^{-1} x + \frac{1}{4}x\sqrt{1-x^2} + C$

c. $\frac{d}{dx}\tanh e^x = e^x \cdot \operatorname{sech}^2 e^x$.

d. $\int (x^3 - x)^{-1}\,dx = \int \frac{1}{x^3 - x}\,dx$

$= \int \frac{1}{x(x-1)(x+1)}\,dx$

$= \int (-\frac{1}{x} + \frac{1/2}{x-1} + \frac{1/2}{x+1})\,dx$

$= -\ln|x| + \frac{1}{2}\ln|x-1| + \frac{1}{2}\ln|x+1| + C$

e. $f(x) = (1-x^2)^{1/2}$

$f'(x) = \frac{1}{2}(1-x^2)^{-1/2}(-2x) = -x(1-x^2)^{-1/2}$

f. $I = \int (1-x^2)^{1/2}\,dx$

Let $x = \sin\theta$.

$\therefore dx = \cos\theta\,d\theta$, $(1-x^2)^{1/2} = \cos\theta$, $\theta = \sin^{-1} x$.

$\therefore I = \int \cos\theta\cdot\cos\theta\,d\theta = \int \cos^2\theta\,d\theta$

$= \frac{1}{2}\int (1+\cos 2\theta)\,d\theta = \frac{1}{2}\theta + \frac{1}{4}\sin 2\theta + C$

$= \frac{1}{2}\theta + \frac{1}{2}\sin\theta\cos\theta + C$

$= \frac{1}{2}\sin^{-1} x + \frac{1}{2}x\sqrt{1-x^2} + C$

g. $g(x) = (\ln x)^2 \Rightarrow g'(x) = 2\ln x \cdot \frac{1}{x}$

h. $\int x \ln x\,dx$

u		dv
$\ln x$	+	x
$\frac{1}{x}$		$\frac{1}{2}x^2$
1	−	$\frac{1}{2}x$
0	+	$\frac{1}{4}x^2$

$= \frac{1}{2}x^2 \ln x - \frac{1}{4}x^2 + C$

R12. For $\int (9-x^2)^{-1/2}\,x\,dx$, the $x\,dx$ can be transformed to the differential of the inside function by multiplying by a *constant.*

$-\frac{1}{2}\int (9-x^2)^{-1/2}(-2x\,dx) = -(9-x^2)^{1/2} + C$, and thus has no inverse sine.

For $\int (9-x^2)^{-1/2}\,dx$, transforming the dx to the differential of the inside function, $-2x\,dx$, requires multiplying by a *variable.* Since the integral of a product does not equal the product of the two integrals, you can't divide on the outside of the integral by $-2x$. So a more sophisticated technique must be used, in this case, trigonometry substitution. As a result, an inverse sine appears in the answer:

$\int (9-x^2)^{-1/2}\,dx = \sin^{-1}\frac{x}{3} + C$

Concepts Problems

C1. Integral of sech x Problem

$\int \text{sech } x\, dx = \int \sqrt{1 - \tanh^2 x}\, dx$

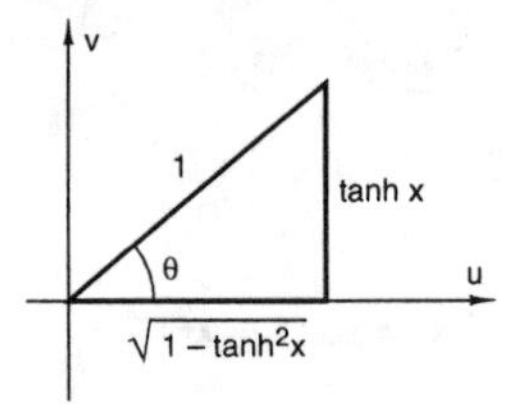

Let $\tanh x = \sin\theta$.

$\therefore x = \tanh^{-1}(\sin\theta)$ and $\theta = \sin^{-1}(\tanh x)$

$dx = \dfrac{1}{1 - \sin^2\theta} \cdot \cos\theta\, d\theta = \dfrac{1}{\cos\theta}\, d\theta$

$\sqrt{1 - \tanh^2 x} = \sqrt{1 - \sin^2\theta} = \cos\theta$

$\therefore \int \text{sech } x\, dx = \int \cos\theta \cdot \dfrac{1}{\cos\theta}\, d\theta = \int d\theta$

$= \theta + C = \sin^{-1}(\tanh x) + C$, Q.E.D.

$\int_0^1 \text{sech } x\, dx = \sin^{-1}(\tanh x)\Big|_0^1$

$= \sin^{-1}(\tanh 1) - \sin^{-1}(\tanh 0)$

$= \sin^{-1}(\tanh 1) = 0.86576948 \ldots$

Numerical integration gives 0.86576948 ..., which agrees with the exact answer.

C2. Integral of csch x Problem

From $\sinh 2A = 2 \sinh A \cosh A$, let $A = x/2$, so:

$\sinh x = 2 \sinh(x/2) \cosh(x/2)$

$\Rightarrow \text{csch } x = \dfrac{1}{\sinh x} = \dfrac{1}{2\cdot\sinh(x/2)\cdot\cosh(x/2)}$

$\text{csch } x = \dfrac{1}{2\cdot\sinh(x/2)\cdot\cosh(x/2)} \cdot \dfrac{\text{sech}^2(x/2)}{\text{sech}^2(x/2)}$

$= \dfrac{\text{sech}^2(x/2)}{2\cdot\tanh(x/2)} = \dfrac{\frac{1}{2}\text{sech}^2(x/2)}{\tanh(x/2)}$

$\therefore \int \text{csch } x\, dx = \int \dfrac{1}{\tanh(x/2)} \cdot (\frac{1}{2}\text{sech}^2(x/2)\, dx)$

$= \ln|\tanh(x/2)| + C$, Q.E.D.

$\int_1^2 \text{csch } x\, dx = \ln|\tanh(x/2)|\Big|_1^2$

$= \ln|\tanh 1| - \ln|\tanh(1/2)| = 0.49959536 \ldots$

Numerical integration gives 0.49959536 ... .

C3. Another Integral of csc x

From $\sin 2A = 2 \sin A \cos A$, let $A = x/2$, so:

$\sin x = 2 \sin(x/2) \cos(x/2)$

$\csc x = \dfrac{1}{\sin x} = \dfrac{1}{2\sin(x/2)\cos(x/2)}$

$= \dfrac{1}{2\sin(x/2)\cos(x/2)} \cdot \dfrac{\sec^2(x/2)}{\sec^2(x/2)}$

$= \dfrac{\sec^2(x/2)}{2\tan(x/2)} = \dfrac{\frac{1}{2}\sec^2(x/2)}{\tan(x/2)}$

$\therefore \int \csc x\, dx = \int \dfrac{1}{\tan(x/2)} \cdot (\frac{1}{2}\sec^2(x/2)\, dx)$

$= \ln|\tan(x/2)| + C$, Q.E.D.

or:

Let $u = \tan(x/2)$, as in Problem Set 9-11 #107.

Then $dx = \dfrac{2\, du}{1 + u^2}$ and $\csc x = \dfrac{1 + u^2}{2u}$

$\therefore \int \csc x\, dx = \int \dfrac{1 + u^2}{2u} \cdot \dfrac{2\, du}{1 + u^2}$

$= \int (1/u)\, du = \ln|u| + C = \ln|\tan(x/2)| + C$, Q.E.D.

Confirmation:

$\int_{0.5}^1 \csc x\, dx = \ln|\tan(x/2)|\Big|_{0.5}^1$

$= \ln \tan\frac{1}{2} - \ln \tan\frac{1}{4} = 0.7605 \ldots$

Numerical Integration gives 0.7605 ... .

Note that $\tan(x/2) = \dfrac{2\sin(x/2)\cos(x/2)}{2\cos^2(x/2)}$

$= \dfrac{\sin x}{1 + \cos x} = \dfrac{1}{\csc x + \cot x}$, so

$\ln|\tan(x/2)| = -\ln|\csc x + \cot x|$

C4. Another Definition of π Problem

$A = \int_{-\infty}^{\infty} \dfrac{1}{1 + x^2}\, dx$

$= \lim_{a\to-\infty} \int_a^0 \dfrac{1}{1 + x^2}\, dx + \lim_{b\to\infty} \int_0^b \dfrac{1}{1 + x^2}\, dx$

$= \lim_{a\to-\infty} \tan^{-1} x\Big|_a^0 + \lim_{b\to\infty} \tan^{-1} x\Big|_0^b$

$= \lim_{a\to-\infty} (0 - \tan^{-1} a) + \lim_{b\to\infty} (\tan^{-1} b - 0)$

$= -(-\pi/2) + (\pi/2) = \pi$

C5. Upper Bound Problem

Prove that $f(x) = \ln x$ is unbounded above.

Proof:

Assume $f(x) = \ln x$ is not unbounded above.

Then there is a number $M > 0$ such that $\ln x < M$ for all $x > 0$.

Let $x = e^{M+1}$.

Then $\ln x = \ln e^{M+1} = M + 1$.

$\therefore \ln x > M$, which is a contradiction.

$\therefore$ the assumption is false, and $\ln x$ is unbounded above, Q.E.D.

Chapter Test

T1. $\int \sin^5 x \cos x\, dx = \frac{1}{6}\sin^6 x + C$

T2. $\int x^3 \sinh 6x\, dx$

sign	u	dv
+	x^3	$\sinh 6x$
−	$3x^2$	$\frac{1}{6}\cosh 6x$
+	$6x$	$\frac{1}{36}\sinh 6x$
−	6	$\frac{1}{216}\cosh 6x$
+	0	$\frac{1}{1296}\sinh 6x$

$= \frac{1}{6}x^3 \cosh 6x - \frac{1}{12}x^2 \sinh 6x + \frac{1}{36} x \cosh 6x - \frac{1}{216}\sinh 6x + C$

T3. $\int \cos^{-1} x\, dx$

sign	u	dv
+	$\cos^{-1} x$	1
−	$-\frac{1}{\sqrt{1-x^2}}$	x

$= x\cos^{-1} x + \int \frac{x}{\sqrt{1-x^2}}\, dx$

$= x\cos^{-1} x - \frac{1}{2}\int (1-x^2)^{-1/2}(-2x\, dx)$

$= x\cos^{-1} x - \frac{1}{2}(2)(1-x^2)^{1/2} + C$

$= x\cos^{-1} x - \sqrt{1-x^2} + C.$

T4. $\int \sec^3 x\, dx = \frac{1}{2}\sec x \tan x + \frac{1}{2}\ln|\sec x + \tan x| + C$

T5. $\int e^{2x}\cos 5x\, dx$

sign	u	dv
+	e^{2x}	$\cos 5x$
−	$2e^{2x}$	$\frac{1}{5}\sin 5x$
+	$4e^{2x}$	$-\frac{1}{25}\cos 5x$

$= \frac{1}{5}e^{2x}\sin 5x + \frac{2}{25}e^{2x}\cos 5x - \frac{4}{25}\int e^{2x}\cos 5x\, dx$

$\frac{29}{25}\int e^{2x}\cos 5x\, dx = \frac{1}{5}e^{2x}\sin 5x + \frac{2}{25}e^{2x}\cos 5x + C$

$\int e^{2x}\cos 5x\, dx = \frac{5}{29}e^{2x}\sin 5x + \frac{2}{29}e^{2x}\cos 5x + C$

T6. $\int \ln 3x\, dx$

sign	u	dv
+	$\ln 3x$	1
−	$1/x$	x

$= x\ln 3x - \int dx = x\ln 3x - x + C.$

T7. $f(x) = \operatorname{sech}^3(e^{5x})$
$f'(x) = 3\operatorname{sech}^2(e^{5x})\cdot(-\operatorname{sech}(e^{5x})\tanh(e^{5x}))\cdot 5e^{5x}$
$= -15e^{5x}\operatorname{sech}^3(e^{5x})\tanh(e^{5x})$

T8. $g(x) = \sin^{-1} x \Rightarrow g'(x) = \frac{1}{\sqrt{1-x^2}}$

T9. $f(x) = \tanh^{-1} x \Rightarrow \tanh f(x) = x,\ |x| \le 1$
$\operatorname{sech}^2 f(x)\cdot f'(x) = 1$
$(1-\tanh^2 f(x))\cdot f'(x) = 1$
$(1-x^2)\cdot f'(x) = 1$
$f'(x) = \frac{1}{1-x^2},\ |x| < 1$

$f'(0.6) = \frac{1}{1-0.36} = \frac{1}{0.64} = 1.5625$

Numerically, $f'(0.6) \approx 1.5625$ ... (depending on the tolerance of the calculator).

T10. General equation is $y = k\cosh\frac{1}{k}x + C$.
$y = 1$ at $x = 0 \Rightarrow 1 = k\cosh 0 + C \Rightarrow C = 1 - k$
$y = 3$ at $x = 5 \Rightarrow 3 = k\cosh\frac{5}{k} + 1 - k$
Solving numerically, $k \approx 6.5586\ \ldots$.
$y = 6.5586 \ldots \cosh\frac{1}{6.5586\ldots}x + 1 - 6.5586\ldots$

T11. a. $I = \int \frac{x-3}{x^2-6x+5}\, dx = \int \frac{x-3}{(x-3)^2-4}\, dx$

Let $\frac{x-3}{2} = \sec\theta$. $x - 3 = 2\sec\theta$,
$dx = 2\sec\theta\tan\theta\, d\theta$,
$\sqrt{(x-3)^2-4} = 2\tan\theta,\ \theta = \sec^{-1}\frac{x-3}{2}$

$\therefore I = \int \frac{(2\sec\theta)(2\sec\theta\tan\theta)\, d\theta}{4\tan^2\theta}$

$= \int \frac{1}{\tan\theta}\cdot\sec^2\theta\, d\theta = \ln|\tan\theta| + C_1$

$= \ln\left|\frac{1}{2}\sqrt{(x-3)^2-4}\right| + C_1$

$= \ln\left|\sqrt{(x-3)^2-4}\right| + C$

$= \frac{1}{2}\ln|x^2-6x+5| + C$

b. $\int \frac{x-3}{x^2-6x+5}\, dx = \int \left(\frac{1/2}{x-1} + \frac{1/2}{x-5}\right) dx$

$= \frac{1}{2}\ln|x-1| + \frac{1}{2}\ln|x-5| + C$

$= \frac{1}{2}\ln|(x-1)(x-5)| + C = \frac{1}{2}\ln|x^2-6x+5| + C,$
which agrees with part a.

c. $\int \frac{x-3}{x^2-6x+5}\, dx$

$= \frac{1}{2}\int \frac{1}{x^2-6x+5}\cdot(2x-6)\, dx$

$= \frac{1}{2}\ln|x^2-6x+5| + C$, as in parts a. and b.

d. See parts a., b., and c.

T12. $\int \cos^2 x\, dx = \int \frac{1}{2}(1+\cos 2x)\, dx$
$= \frac{1}{2}x + \frac{1}{4}\sin 2x + C$

T13. a. $\int \cos^5 x\,dx = \int (1-\sin^2 x)^2 \cos x\,dx$

$= \int (1 - 2\sin^2 x + \sin^4 x)\cos x\,dx$

$= \sin x - \frac{2}{3}\sin^3 x + \frac{1}{5}\sin^5 x + C$

b. $\int \cos^5 x\,dx = \frac{1}{5}\cos^4 x \sin x + \frac{4}{5}\int \cos^3 x\,dx$

$= \frac{1}{5}\cos^4 x \sin x + \frac{4}{15}\cos^2 x \sin x + \frac{8}{15}\int \cos x\,dx$

$= \frac{1}{5}\cos^4 x \sin x + \frac{4}{15}\cos^2 x \sin x + \frac{8}{15}\sin x + C$

c. $\frac{1}{5}\cos^4 x \sin x + \frac{4}{15}\cos^2 x \sin x + \frac{8}{15}\sin x$

$= \frac{1}{5}(1-\sin^2 x)^2 \sin x$

$\qquad + \frac{4}{15}(1-\sin^2 x)\sin x + \frac{8}{15}\sin x$

$= \frac{1}{5}\sin x - \frac{2}{5}\sin^3 x + \frac{1}{5}\sin^5 x$

$\qquad + \frac{4}{15}\sin x - \frac{4}{15}\sin^3 x + \frac{8}{15}\sin x$

$= (\frac{1}{5} + \frac{4}{15} + \frac{8}{15})\sin x - (\frac{2}{5} + \frac{4}{15})\sin^3 x + \frac{1}{5}\sin^5 x$

$= \sin x - \frac{2}{3}\sin^3 x + \frac{1}{5}\sin^5 x$

T14. $\int_0^\infty x e^{-0.1x}\,dx$

u	dv
x (+)	$e^{-0.1x}$
1 (−)	$-10e^{-0.1x}$
0	$100e^{-0.1x}$

$= \lim_{b\to\infty} (-10xe^{-0.1x} - 100e^{-0.1x}) \Big|_0^b$

$= \lim_{b\to\infty} (-10be^{-0.1b} - 100e^{-0.1b} + 0 + 100)$

$= \lim_{b\to\infty} -\frac{10b}{e^{0.1b}} + 100$

$= \lim_{b\to\infty} -\frac{10}{0.1e^{0.1b}} + 100$ (by l'Hospital's rule)

$= 100$

Chapter 10

Exploratory Problem Set 10-1, pages 505 to 506 — Introduction to Distance and Displacement for Motion Along a Line

1. $v(t) = 100(0.8)^t - 30 = 100\,e^{t\ln 0.8} - 30 = 0$
$\Rightarrow e^{t\ln 0.8} = 0.3 \Rightarrow t = \dfrac{\ln 0.3}{\ln 0.8} = 5.3955...$
v becomes negative after $t_0 \approx 5.40$ minutes.

2. $s_{up} = \int_0^{t_0} v\,dt = \int_0^{t_0} (100\,e^{t\ln 0.8} - 30)\,dt$
$= 151.8341...$ (numerically) ≈ 151.8 ft.
$s_{down} = -\int_{t_0}^{10} v\,dt = -\int_{t_0}^{10} (100\,e^{t\ln 0.8} - 30)\,dt$
$= 51.8110...$ (numerically) ≈ 51.8 ft
Distance $= s_{up} + s_{down} = 203.6452... \approx 203.6$ ft.

3. Displacement $= s_{up} - s_{down} = 100.0231...$
≈ 100.0 ft.
Since the displacement is positive, Calvin is upstream of his starting point.

4. Displacement $= \int_0^{10} (100\,e^{t\ln 0.8} - 30)\,dt$
$= 100.0231...$ (numerically) ≈ 100.0 ft.

5. Distance $= \int_0^{10} |v|\,dt = \int_0^{10} |100\,e^{t\ln 0.8} - 30|\,dt$
$= 203.6452...$ (numerically) ≈ 203.6 ft.

Problem Set 10-2, pages 509 to 513 — Distance, Displacement, and Acceleration for Linear Motion

Q1. 120 mi
Q2. 25 mph
Q3. 1.25 hr
Q4. $f'(x) = 1/x$
Q5. $x\ln x - x + C$
Q6. $f'(t) = \sec^2 t$
Q7. $g'(t) = \text{sech}^2\, t$
Q8. $\frac{1}{3}x^3 + C$
Q9. $\frac{1}{\ln 2}2^x + C$
Q10. $\ln 2\, e^{x\ln 2} = 2^x \ln 2$

1. a. $v(t) = t^2 - 10t + 16$ on $[0, 6]$
$v(t) = (t-2)(t-8) = 0 \Leftrightarrow t = 2$ or 8 sec.
$v(t) > 0$ for t in $[0, 2)$. $v(t) < 0$ for t in $(2, 6]$.

b. For $[0, 2)$, displ. $= \int_0^2 (t^2 - 10t + 16)\,dt = 14\frac{2}{3}$
Distance $= 14\frac{2}{3}$ ft.
For $(2, 6]$, displ.. $= \int_2^6 (t^2 - 10t + 16)\,dt = -26\frac{2}{3}$
Distance $= 26\frac{2}{3}$ ft.

c. Displ. $= \int_0^6 (t^2 - 10t + 16)\,dt = -12$ ft.
Dist. $= \int_0^6 |t^2 - 10t + 16|\,dt = 41\frac{1}{3}$ ft.

d. Displ. $= 14\frac{2}{3} + (-26\frac{2}{3}) = -12$ ft.
Dist. $= 14\frac{2}{3} + 26\frac{2}{3} = 41\frac{1}{3}$ ft.

e. $a(t) = v'(t) = 2t - 10$
$a(3) = 2(3) - 10 = -4$ (ft./sec)/sec

2. a. $v(t) = \tan 0.2t$ on $[10, 20]$
$v(t) = 0 \Leftrightarrow t = ...\ 0, 5\pi, 10\pi, ... = 5\pi$ in $[10, 20]$.
$v(t)$ is infinite $\Leftrightarrow t = ...\ 2.5\pi, 7.5\pi, ...$, none of which is in $[10, 20]$.
$v(t) < 0$ for t in $[10, 5\pi)$. $v(t) > 0$ for t in $(5\pi, 20]$.

b. For $[10, 5\pi)$, displ. $= \int_{10}^{5\pi} \tan 0.2t\,dt$
$= 5\ln|\sec \pi| - 5\ln|\sec 2| = -4.3835...$
Distance $= 4.3835... \approx 4.38$ cm
For $(5\pi, 20]$, displ. $= \int_{5\pi}^{20} \tan 0.2t\,dt$
$= 5\ln|\sec 4| - 5\ln|\sec \pi| = 2.1259...$
Distance $= 2.1259... \approx 2.13$ cm

c. Displ. $= \int_{10}^{20} \tan 0.2t\,dt = -2.2576... \approx -2.26$ cm
Dist. $= \int_{10}^{20} |\tan 0.2t|\,dt = 6.5095... \approx 6.51$ cm

d. Displ. $= -4.3835... + 2.1259... = -2.1259...$
≈ -2.13 cm.
Dist. $= -(-4.3835...) + 2.1259... = 6.5095...$
≈ 6.51 cm.

e. $a(t) = v'(t) = \sec^2 t$
$a(15) = \sec^2 3 = 1.0203... \approx 1.02$ (cm/sec)/sec

3. a. $v(t) = \sec \frac{\pi}{24}t - 2$ on $[1, 11]$
$v(t) = 0$ when $\cos \frac{\pi}{24}t = 0.5 \Leftrightarrow t = 8$ in $[1, 11]$
$v(t) < 0$ for t in $[1, 8)$. $v(t) > 0$ for t in $(8, 11]$.

b. For $[1, 8)$, displ. $= \int_1^8 (\sec \frac{\pi}{24}t - 2)\,dt$
$= \frac{24}{\pi}\ln|\sec\frac{\pi}{3} + \tan\frac{\pi}{3}| - 16$
$\quad - \frac{24}{\pi}\ln|\sec\frac{\pi}{24} + \tan\frac{\pi}{24}| + 2$
$= -4.9420...$
Distance ≈ 4.94 km.
For $(8, 11]$, displ. $= \int_8^{11} (\sec \frac{\pi}{24}t - 2)\,dt$
$= \frac{24}{\pi}\ln|\sec\frac{11}{24}\pi + \tan\frac{11}{24}\pi| - 22$
$\quad - \frac{24}{\pi}\ln|\sec\frac{\pi}{3} + \tan\frac{\pi}{3}| + 16$
$= 4.7569...$
Distance ≈ 4.76 km.

c. Displ. $= \int_1^{11} (\sec \frac{\pi}{24}t - 2)\,dt = -0.1850... \approx -0.19$ km
Dist. $= \int_1^{11} |\sec \frac{\pi}{24}t - 2|\,dt = 9.6990... \approx 9.70$ km

d. Displ. $= -4.9420... + 4.7569... = -0.1850...$
≈ -0.19 km.
Dist. $= -(-4.9420...) + 4.7569... = 9.6990...$
≈ 9.70 km.

e. $a(t) = v'(t) = \frac{\pi}{24}\sec\frac{\pi}{24}t\,\tan\frac{\pi}{24}t$
$a(6) = 0.1851... \approx 0.19$ (km/h)/h (exactly $\frac{\pi}{24}\sqrt{2}$)

4\. a. $v(t) = t^3 - 5t^2 + 8t - 6$ on $[0, 5]$
$v(t) = (t - 3)(t^2 - 2t + 2) = 0 \Leftrightarrow t = 3$ in $[0, 5]$
$v < 0$ for t in $[0,3)$. $v > 0$ for t in $(3,5]$.

b. For $[0, 3)$, displ. $= \int_0^3 (t^3 - 5t^2 + 8t - 6)\,dt = -6\frac{3}{4}$

Distance $= 6\frac{3}{4}$ mi.

For $(3, 5]$, displ. $= \int_3^5 (t^3 - 5t^2 + 8t - 6)\,dt = 24\frac{2}{3}$

Distance $= 24\frac{2}{3}$ mi.

c. Displ. $= \int_0^5 (t^3 - 5t^2 + 8t - 6)\,dt = 17\frac{11}{12}$ mi.

Dist. $= \int_0^5 |t^3 - 5t^2 + 8t - 6|\,dt = 31\frac{5}{12}$ mi.

d. Displ. $= -6\frac{3}{4} + 24\frac{2}{3} = 17\frac{11}{12}$ mi.

Dist. $= -(-6\frac{3}{4}) + 24\frac{2}{3}$ mi. $= 31\frac{5}{12}$ mi.

e. $a(t) = v'(t) = 3t^2 - 10t + 8$
$a(2.5) = 1.75$ (mi/min)/min

5\. $a(t) = t^{1/2}$, $v(0) = -18$, on $[0, 16]$

$v(t) = \int t^{1/2}\,dt = \frac{2}{3}t^{3/2} + C$; $v(0) = -18 \Rightarrow C = -18$

$v(t) = \frac{2}{3}t^{3/2} - 18$

Displ. $= \int_0^{16} (\frac{2}{3}t^{3/2} - 18)\,dt = -14\frac{14}{15}$ ft.

Dist. $= \int_0^{16} |\frac{2}{3}t^{3/2} - 18|\,dt = 179\frac{7}{15}$ ft.

6\. $a(t) = t^{-1}$, $v(1) = 0$, on $[0.4, 1.6]$
$v(t) = \int t^{-1}\,dt = \ln t + C$ $(t > 0)$; $v(1) = 0 \Rightarrow C = 0$
$v(t) = \ln t$
Displ. $= \int_{0.4}^{1.6} \ln t\,dt = -0.0814... \approx -0.081$ cm
Dist. $= \int_{0.4}^{1.6} |\ln t|\,dt = 0.3854... \approx 0.385$ cm

7\. $a(t) = 6 \sin t$, $v(0) = -9$, on $[0, \pi]$
$v(t) = \int 6 \sin t\,dt = -6 \cos t + C$; $v(0) = -9 \Rightarrow C = -3$
$v(t) = -6 \cos t - 3$
Displ. $= \int_0^{\pi} (-6 \cos t - 3)\,dt = -9.4247... \approx -9.42$ km
(Exact: -3π km)
Dist. $= \int_0^{\pi} |-6 \cos t - 3|\,dt = 13.5338... \approx 13.53$ km

(Exact: $6\sqrt{3} + \pi$)

8\. $a(t) = \sinh t$, $v(0) = -2$, on $[0, 5]$
$v(t) = \int \sinh t\,dt = \cosh t + C$; $v(0) = -2 \Rightarrow C = -3$
$v(t) = \cosh t - 3$
Displ. $= \int_0^5 (\cosh t - 3)\,dt = 59.2032... \approx 59.20$ mi.
(Exact: $\sinh 5 - 15$)
Dist. $= \int_0^5 |\cosh t - 3|\,dt = 64.1228... \approx 64.12$ mi.
$v(t) = \cosh t - 3 = 0$ at $t = \pm\cosh^{-1} 3$ hr.
$v > 0$ on $(\cosh^{-1} 3, 5]$, $v < 0$ on $[0, \cosh^{-1} 3)$

9\. Meg's Velocity Problem

a. $v = t^{1/2} - 2 = 0 \Leftrightarrow t = 4$ sec;
$v < 0$ if $t < 4$, $v > 0$ if $t > 4$

b. Displ. $= \int_1^9 (t^{1/2} - 2)\,dt = 1\frac{1}{3}$ ft.

c. Dist. $= \int_1^9 |t^{1/2} - 2|\,dt = 4$ ft

10\. Periodic Motion Problem

a. $v = \sin 2t = 0$ at $t = \ldots, -\pi, -\frac{1}{2}\pi, 0, \frac{1}{2}\pi, \pi, \frac{3}{2}\pi, \ldots$

$\sin 2t \geq 0$ on $[0, \frac{1}{2}\pi]$ so

Dist. $= \int_0^{\pi/2} \sin 2t\,dt = 1$ cm

b. Displ. $= \int_0^{4.5\pi} \sin 2t\,dt = 1$ cm

Dist. $= \int_0^{4.5\pi} \sin 2t\,dt = 9$ cm

11\. Car on the Hill Problem

a. $v = 60 - 2t$
Displ. $= \int_{10}^{40} (60 - 2t)\,dt = 300$ ft.

b. Dist. $= \int_{10}^{40} |60 - 2t|\,dt = 500$ ft.

12\. Rocket Problem

a. $a(t) = \begin{cases} 40 \cos 0.015t - 9.8, & t \text{ in } [0, 100] \\ -9.8, & t > 100 \end{cases}$

For t in $[0, 100]$, $v(t) = \int (40 \cos 0.015t - 9.8)\,dt$
$= \frac{40}{0.015} \sin 0.015t - 9.8t + C$
$v(0) = 0 \Rightarrow C = 0$
For $t > 100$, $v(t) = \int -9.8\,dt = -9.8t + C$
$v(100) = \frac{40}{0.015} \sin 1.5 - 980 = 1679.986...$
$\Rightarrow C = 1679.986... + 980 = 2659.986...$

$v(t) = \begin{cases} \frac{40}{0.015} \sin 0.015t - 9.8t, & t \text{ in } [0, 100] \\ -9.8t + 2659.986..., & t > 100 \end{cases}$

Graphs.

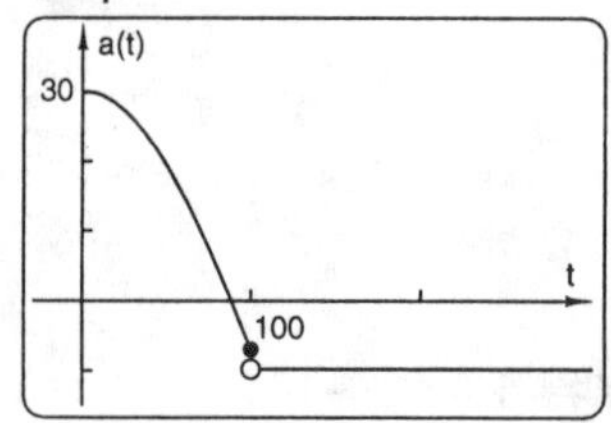

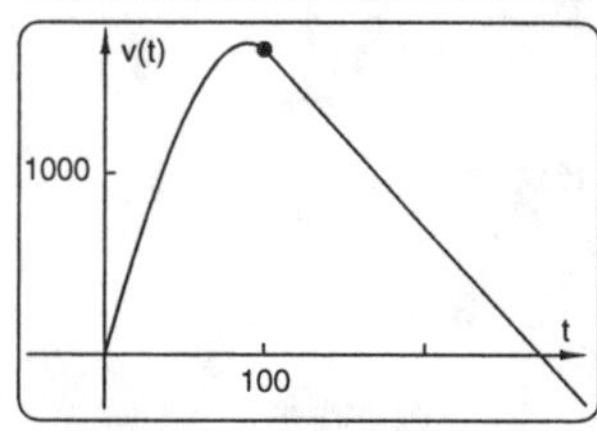

b. $a = 0$ at $t = \frac{1}{0.015} \cos^{-1} \frac{9.8}{40} = 88.2184... \approx 88.2$ sec
$v = 0$ at $t = 2{,}659.986.../9.8 = 271.4272...$
≈ 271.4 sec.

c. Displ. $= \int_0^{300} v(t)\,dt$

$= \int_0^{100} (\frac{40}{0.015} \sin 0.015t - 9.8t)dt$

$+ \int_{100}^{300} (-9.8t + 2{,}659.986...)\,dt$

$\approx 116{,}202.27... + 139{,}997.32... \approx 256{,}200$ m

Dist. $= 116{,}202.27... + \int_{100}^{300} |-9.8t + 2{,}659.986...|\,dt$
$= 116{,}202.27... + 147{,}998.09... \approx 264{,}200$ m
The distance is greater than the displacement, which agrees with the fact that the velocity becomes negative at $t = 271.4...$ sec.

d. $v(300) = -9.8(300) + 2{,}659.986... = -280.0133...$
so the rocket is moving downward (falling) at about 280 m/sec.

13. Subway Problem

a.

t_{end} sec	a_{avg} mph/sec	v_{end} mph	v_{avg} mph	s_{end} mi
0	----	0	----	0
5	2.95	14.75	7.375	0.0102...
10	3.8	33.75	24.25	0.0439...
15	1.75	42.5	38.125	0.0968...
20	0.3	44	43.25	0.1569...
25	0	44	44	0.2180...
30	0	44	44	0.2791...
35	0	44	44	0.3402...
40	–0.2	43	43.5	0.4006...
45	–0.9	38.5	40.75	0.4572...
50	–2.6	25.5	32	0.5017...
55	–3.5	8	16.75	0.525
60	–1.6	0	4	0.5305...

b. $v_{end} = 0$ at $t = 60 \Rightarrow$ the train is at rest.

c. The train is just starting at t = 0; its acceleration must be greater than zero to get it moving, even though it is stopped at t = 0. Acceleration and velocity are different quantities; the velocity can be zero, but changing, which means the acceleration is nonzero.

d. Zero acceleration means the velocity is constant, but not necessarily zero.

e. The last entry in the last column is the displacement at time t = 60. Thus it is 0.5305... . ≈ 0.53 mi between stations.

14. Spaceship Problem

a.

t_{end} sec	a_{avg} mph/sec	v_{end} mph	v_{avg} mph	s_{end} mi
0	----	6000	----	400
10	8.5	6085	6042.5	416.7847...
20	22	6305	6195	433.9930...
30	33	6635	6470	451.9652...
40	39.5	7030	6832.5	470.9444...
50	42.5	7455	7242.5	491.0625...
60	53	7985	7720	512.5069...
70	71	8695	8340	535.6736...
80	83.5	9530	9112.5	560.9861...
90	47.5	10005	9767.5	588.1180...
100	3	10035	10020	615.9513...

b. According to these calculations, the spaceship is only about 620 mi. from the launch pad and moving at only about 10,000 mph. So the specifications are definitely not met, and the project should be sent back to the drawing board.

15. Physics Formula Problem

a. $a = \dfrac{dv}{dt} \Rightarrow v = \int a\,dt = at + C;$

$v = v_0$ when $t = 0 \Rightarrow C = 0 \Rightarrow v = v_0 + at$

b. $v = \dfrac{ds}{dt} \Rightarrow s = \int v\,dt = \int (v_0 + at)\,dt = v_0t + \dfrac{1}{2}at^2 + C$

$s = s_0$ when $t = 0 \Rightarrow C = s_0 \Rightarrow s = v_0t + \dfrac{1}{2}at^2 + s_0$

16. Elevator Project

Use s(t) for displacement. Assume v(0) = s(0) = 0.

a. $a(t) = \begin{cases} 2, & \text{if } 0 \le t < 6 \\ 0, & \text{if } t \ge 6 \end{cases}$

$v(t) = \begin{cases} 2t, & \text{if } 0 \le t < 6 \\ 12, & \text{if } t > 6 \end{cases}$

$s(t) = \begin{cases} t^2, & \text{if } 0 \le t < 6 \\ 12t - 36, & \text{if } t > 6 \end{cases}$

–36 comes from the initial condition s(6) = 36.

Graphs.

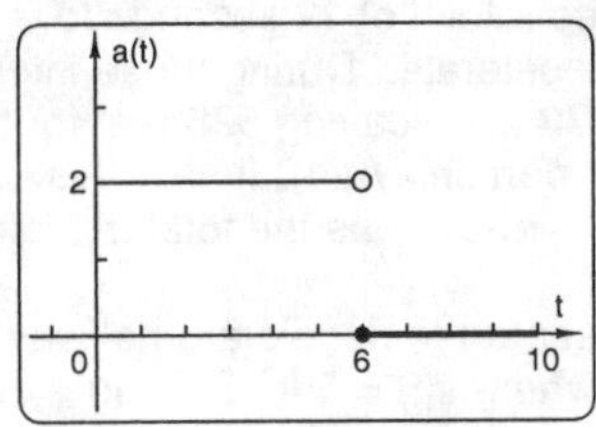

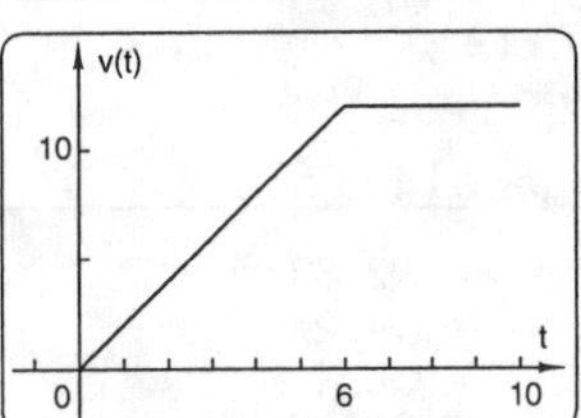

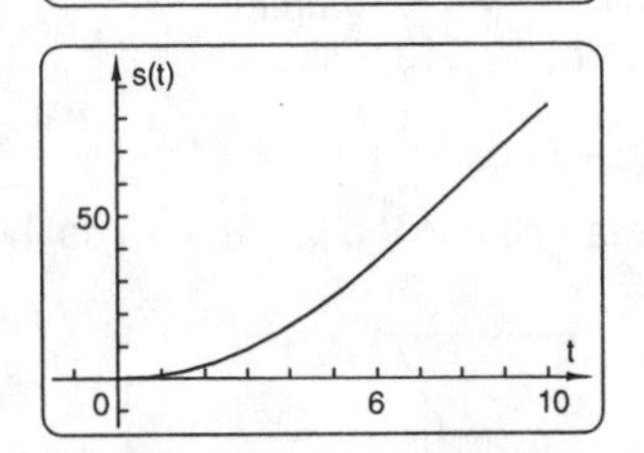

b. The acceleration suddenly jumps from 0 to 2 at t = 0, and drops back to 0 at t = 6. The velocity graph has cusps in both places.

c. $a(t) = 2 - 2\cos\frac{\pi}{3}t$

$\lim_{t \to 0^+} a(t) = \lim_{t \to 0^+} (2 - 2\cos\frac{\pi}{3}t) = 2 - 2\cos 0 = 0$

$\lim_{t \to 6^-} a(t) = \lim_{t \to 6^-} (2 - 2\cos\frac{\pi}{3}t) = 2 - 2\cos 2\pi = 0$

Since a(t) is continuous at t = 0 and 6, there are no sudden changes in acceleration.

d. $a(t) = \begin{cases} 2 - 2\cos\frac{\pi}{3}t, & \text{if } 0 \le t \le 6 \\ 0, & \text{if } t \ge 6 \end{cases}$

$v(t) = \begin{cases} 2t - \frac{6}{\pi}\sin\frac{\pi}{3}t, & \text{if } 0 \le t \le 6 \\ 12, & \text{if } t \ge 6 \end{cases}$

e. Graph. There are no step discontinuities in a(t), and thus the graph of v(t) is smooth.

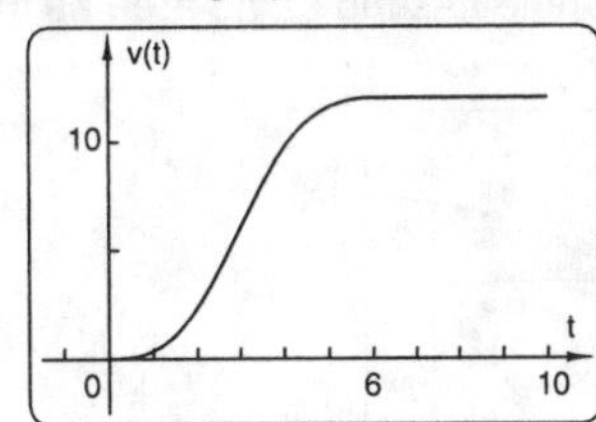

f. For t in [0, 6], $s(t) = \int (2t - \frac{6}{\pi}\sin\frac{\pi}{3}t)\,dt$

$= t^2 + \frac{18}{\pi^2}\cos\frac{\pi}{3}t + C$

$s(0) = 0 \Rightarrow C = -\frac{18}{\pi^2} = -1.8237...$

$s(6) = 36 + 1.8237 - 1.8237 = 36$

Elevator goes 36 ft.

g. The elevator will take another 36 ft to slow down and stop. So the deceleration should start where the elevator is 564 ft up, about the 47th floor.

h. The elevator takes a total of 12 seconds to accelerate and decelerate. During these intervals it travels a total of 72 feet, leaving 528 feet for the constant velocity portion. At 12 ft/sec, this part of the trip will take 44 sec. Thus the total trip takes 56 sec.

i. The elevator must start to decelerate halfway through the trip, where s(t) = 6 ft. Solving

$\int_0^b (2t - \frac{6}{\pi}\sin\frac{\pi}{3}t)\,dt = 6$

numerically for b gives b ≈ 3.1043... ≈ 3.1 sec.

a(3.1043...) = 3.9880... ≈ 4.0 ft/sec^2.

By symmetry, the deceleration process must start at this time, meaning the acceleration jumps to −3.9880... ft/sec^2. The graph looks like this:

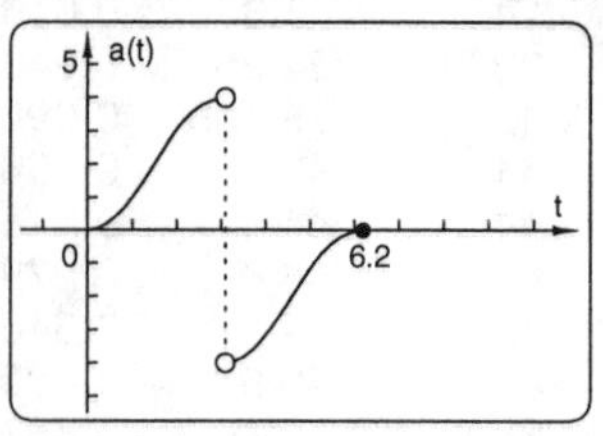

Thus, the passengers get a large jerk at the midpoint of the trip.

One way to remedy the problem is to reduce the acceleration so that the elevator goes only 6 feet instead of 36 feet in the first 6 seconds. That is,

$a(t) = \frac{1}{3} - \frac{1}{3}\cos\frac{\pi}{3}t$

You may think of other ways.

Problem Set 10-3, pages 514 to 516 — Average Value Problems in Motion and Elsewhere

Q1. 50 mph
Q2. 30 mi
Q3. 20 min
Q4. 2π
Q5. No local max.
Q6. 1.5
Q7. f(x) = 16 (at x = 1)
Q8. infinite
Q9. Mean value theorem
Q10. ellipse

1. a. $y_{av} = \frac{1}{4}\int_1^5 (x^3 - x + 5)\,dx = \frac{1}{4}(164) = 41$

b. Graph. The rectangle has the same area as the shaded region.

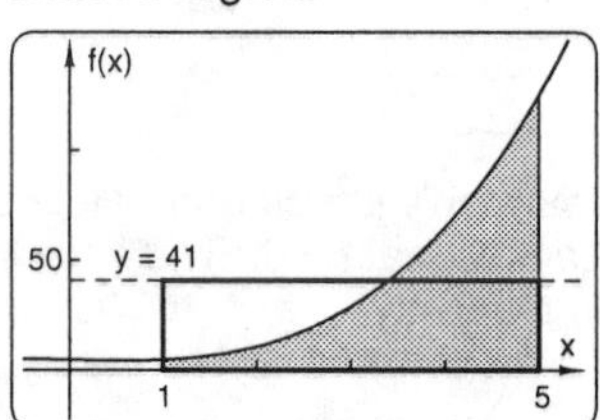

2. a. $y_{av} = \frac{1}{8}\int_1^9 (x^{1/2} - x + 7)\,dx = 4\frac{1}{6}$

b. Graph. The rectangle has the same area as the shaded region.

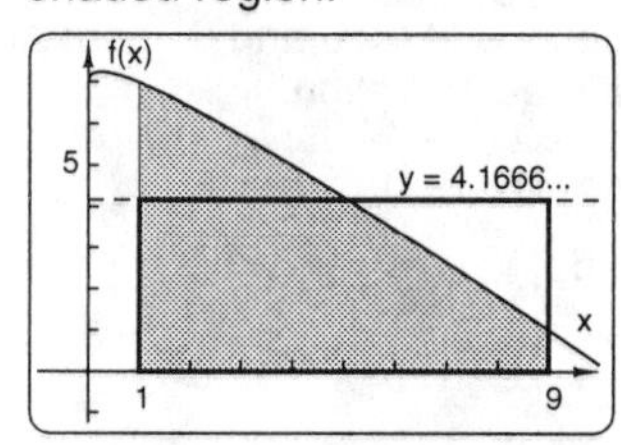

3. a. $y_{av} = \frac{1}{6}\int_1^7 3\sin 0.2x\,dx = 2.0252...$

b. Graph. The rectangle has the same area as the shaded region.

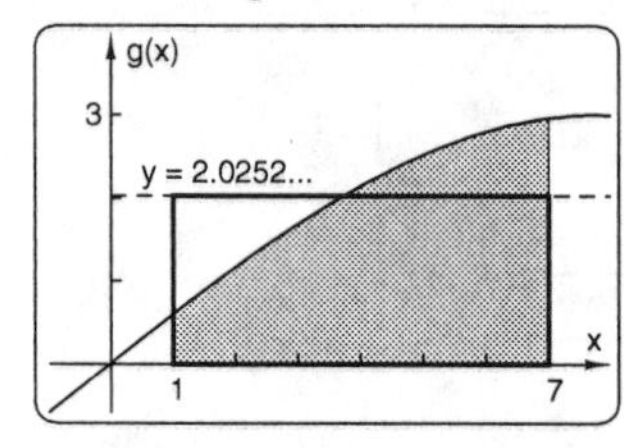

4. a. $y_{av} = \frac{1}{1}\int_{0.5}^{1.5} \tan x\,dx = = 2.5181...$

b. Graph. The rectangle has the same area as the shaded region.

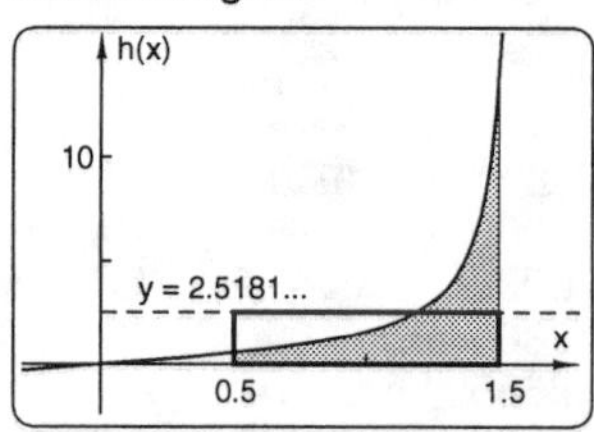

5. a. $y_{av} = \frac{1}{8}\int_1^9 \sqrt{t}\,dt = 2\frac{1}{6}$

b. Graph. The rectangle has the same area as the shaded region.

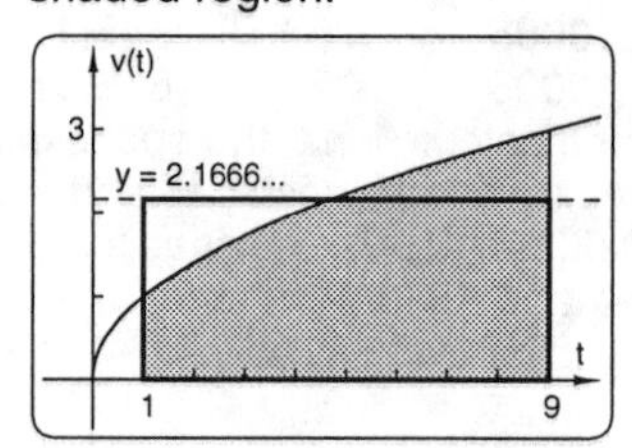

6. a. $y_{av} = \frac{1}{3}\int_0^3 100(1 - e^{-t})\,dt = \frac{100}{3}(2 + e^{-3}) = 68.3262...$

b. Graph. The rectangle has the same area as the shaded region.

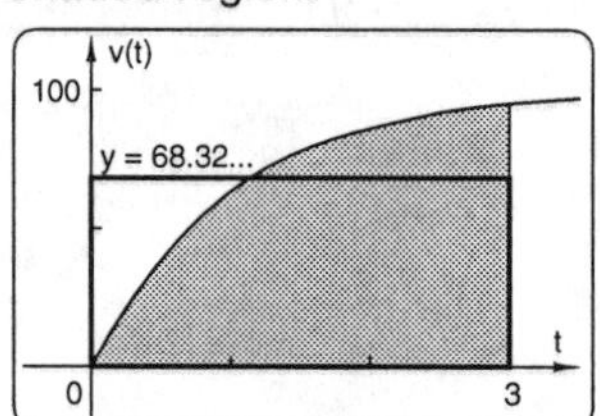

7. $y_{av} = \frac{1}{k}\int_0^k ax^2\,dx = \frac{1}{3}ak^2$

8. $y_{av} = \frac{1}{k}\int_0^k ax^3\,dx = \frac{1}{4}ak^3$

9. $y_{av} = \frac{1}{k}\int_0^k ae^x\,dx = \frac{1}{k}a(e^k - 1)$

10. $y_{av} = \frac{1}{k}\int_0^k \tan x\,dx = \frac{1}{k}\ln|\sec k|$

11. Average Velocity from Acceleration Problem

$a(t) = 6t^{-1/2}$
$v(t) = 12t^{1/2} + C;\ v(0) = 60 \Rightarrow C = 60$
$v(t) = 12t^{1/2} + 60$
$s(t) = 8t^{3/2} + 60t + s_0$
$v(25) = 120$ ft/sec
Displ. $= s(25) - s(0) = 2500$ ft.
$v_{av} = 2500/25 = 100$ ft/sec

12. Ida's Speeding Ticket Problem

The general equation of a parabola with vertex (h, k) is $v - k = a(t - h)^2$. Vertex is at (t, v) = (2, 50), so $v - 50 = a(t - 2)^2$. v = 30 when t = 0, so
$-20 = a(-2)^2 \Rightarrow a = -5$
$v = 50 - 5(t - 2)^2$
$v_{av} = \frac{1}{4}\int_0^4 (50 - 5(t-2)^2)\,dt = 43\frac{1}{3}$ mph

This is just $13\frac{1}{3}$ mph above the speed limit.

If Ida wins her appeal, her fine will be
$7\cdot 13\frac{1}{3} = \$93\frac{1}{3} \approx \$93.33$, which is \$46.67 less than what she now faces.

13. Average Velocity for Constant Acceleration Problem

Consider an object with constant acceleration a, for a time interval $[t_0, t_1]$.
$v(t) = \int a\,dt = at + C$
At $t = t_0$, $v(t) = v_0 \Rightarrow v_0 = at_0 + C \Rightarrow C = v_0 - at_0$
$\therefore v(t) = at + v_0 - at_0 = v_0 + a(t - t_0)$

$$v_{av} = \frac{\int_{t_0}^{t_1} (v_0 + a(t - t_0))\,dt}{t_1 - t_0}$$

$$= \frac{1}{t_1 - t_0}\left(v_0t_1 + \frac{1}{2}a(t_1 - t_0)^2 - v_0t_0 - \frac{1}{2}a(t_0 - t_0)^2\right)$$

$= v_0 + \frac{1}{2}a(t_1 - t_0)$.

The average of v_0 and v_1 is
$\frac{1}{2}(v_0 + v_1) = \frac{1}{2}(v_0 + v_0 + a(t_1 - t_0)) = v_0 + \frac{1}{2}a(t_1 - t_0)$
$\therefore v_{av}$ = the average of v_0 and v_1, Q.E.D.

14. Average Velocity for Other Accelerations Problem

Counterexample: Problem 11 above, the car's acceleration is $a = 6/\sqrt{t}$. The initial velocity is v(0) = 60 ft/sec; the final velocity after 25 seconds is v(25) = 120 ft/sec; and the average velocity is $v_{av} = 100$ ft/sec. But the average of the initial and final velocities is $\frac{1}{2}(v(0) + v(25)) = 90 \text{ ft/sec} \neq v_{av}$.

15. Average Voltage Problem

$v = A\sin 120\pi t$ and $y = |A\sin 120\pi t|$

$$y_{av} = \frac{1}{1/60}\int_0^{1/60} |A\sin 120\pi t|\,dt$$
$$= 60\int_0^{1/120} A\sin 120\pi t\,dt - 60\int_{1/120}^{1/60} A\sin 120\pi t\,dt$$
$$= -\frac{A}{2\pi}\cos 120\pi t\,\Big|_0^{1/120} + \frac{A}{2\pi}\cos 120\pi t\,\Big|_{1/120}^{1/60}$$
$$= \frac{A}{2\pi}(-\cos\pi + \cos 0 + \cos 2\pi - \cos\pi) = \frac{2A}{\pi}$$

If $y_{av} = 110$, then $\frac{2A}{\pi} = 110 \Rightarrow A = 55\pi = 172.78...$ V.

16. Root Mean Square Deviation Problem

a. $d = k\sin x$

$$d^2_{av} = \frac{1}{2\pi}\int_0^{2\pi} k^2\sin^2 x\,dx$$
$$= \frac{k^2}{2\pi}\left(\frac{1}{2}x - \frac{1}{4}\sin 2x\right)\Big|_0^{2\pi} = \frac{k^2}{2\pi}(\pi - 0 - 0 + 0) = \frac{k^2}{2}$$

$\therefore$ rms $= k/\sqrt{2} = 0.7071...k$.

b. $\cos 2x = 1 - 2\sin^2 x \Rightarrow \sin^2 x = \frac{1}{2} - \frac{1}{2}\cos 2x$

Thus, $\sin^2 x$ is a sinusoid. Graph.

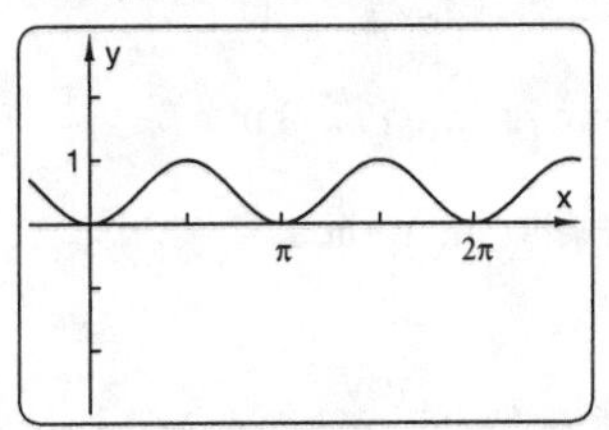

c. By symmetry, the average of $y = \sin^2 x$ over $[0, 2\pi]$ is $\frac{1}{2}$. Thus, the average of $y = k^2\sin^2 x$ is $\frac{1}{2}k^2$.

$\therefore$ rms $= k/\sqrt{2}$, as in part a.

d. By symmetry, it suffices to find the average and rms for one arch of the graph, i.e., over $[0,\pi]$.

$$y_{av} = \frac{1}{\pi}\int_0^{\pi} |\sin x|\,dx$$
$$= \frac{1}{\pi}\int_0^{\pi} \sin x\,dx \quad (\text{since } \sin x \geq 0 \text{ in } [0,\pi])$$
$$= -\frac{1}{\pi}\cos x\,\Big|_0^{\pi} = \frac{2}{\pi}$$
$$d^2_{av} = \frac{1}{\pi}\int_0^{\pi} (|\sin x| - 2/\pi)^2\,dx \approx 0.094715...$$

$\therefore$ rms $\approx 0.094715...^{1/2} = 0.3077...$

The maximum distance between high and low points for this curve is 1; a sinusoidal curve with max distance 1 between high and low points has equation $y = \frac{1}{2}\sin x$, with rms = $\sqrt{2/4}$) =0.3535... (using part a). This number is greater than the rms for $|\sin x|$, so $|\sin x|$ is smoother.

Q1. displacement
Q2. distance
Q3. distance
Q4. displacement
Q5. speeding up
Q6. smaller
Q7. $xe^x - e^x + C$
Q8. $\cos x - x \sin x$
Q9. $\frac{1}{x}\frac{dx}{dt}$
Q10. -2

1. Bacteria Spreading Problem

Know: $\frac{dA}{dt} = 12$ mm²/hr. Want: $\frac{dr}{dt}$

$A = \pi r^2 \Rightarrow \frac{dA}{dt} = 2\pi r\frac{dr}{dt} \Rightarrow \frac{dr}{dt} = \frac{6}{\pi r}$

Graph.

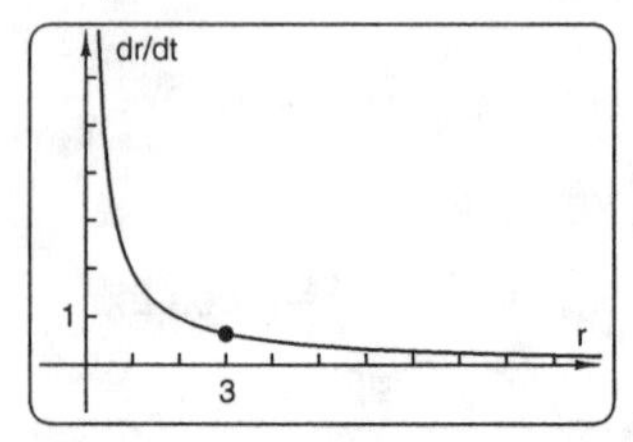

$\frac{dr}{dt} = \frac{2}{\pi} = 0.6366...$ mm/hr when r = 3 mm.

$\frac{dr}{dt}$ varies inversely with the radius.

2. Balloon Problem

Know: $\frac{dr}{dt} = 2$ cm/sec. Want: $\frac{dV}{dt}$

$V = \frac{4}{3}\pi r^3 \Rightarrow \frac{dV}{dt} = 4\pi r^2\frac{dr}{dt}$

$\frac{dV}{dt} = 72\pi = 226.1946...$ cm³/sec at r = 3 cm

$\frac{dV}{dt} = 288\pi = 904.7786...$ cm³/sec at r = 6 cm.

Graph, showing that the larger the balloon gets, the faster Phil must blow air to maintain the 2 cm/sec rate of change of radius.

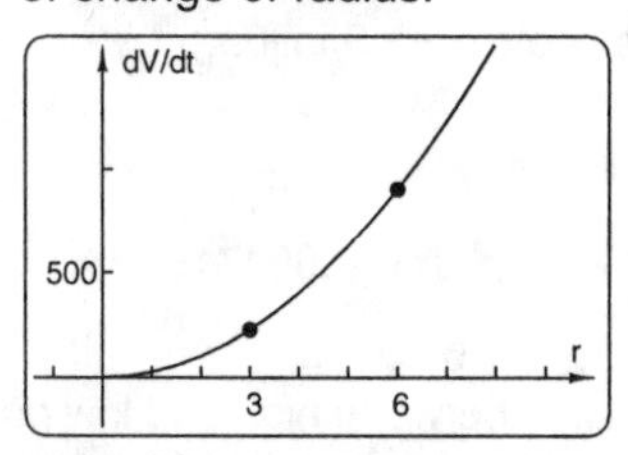

3. Ellipse Problem

Know: $\frac{dA}{dt} = -144$ cm²/sec. Want: $\frac{da}{dt}$

$A = \pi ab$ and $a = 2b \Rightarrow A = \frac{1}{2}\pi a^2$

$\frac{dA}{dt} = \pi a\frac{da}{dt} \Rightarrow \frac{da}{dt} = \frac{1}{\pi a}\frac{dA}{dt}$

$b = 12 \Rightarrow a = 24 \Rightarrow \frac{da}{dt} = -\frac{6}{\pi} = -1.9098...$

≈ -1.91 cm/sec.

Length of major axis is 2a, so major axis is decreasing at $12/\pi$ cm/sec.

4. Bathtub Problem

a. Know: $\frac{dV}{dt} = ky$. Want: $\frac{dy}{dt}$

$dV = 2x\cdot 5\cdot dy = 10x\,dy$

$y = x^4 \Rightarrow x = y^{1/4}$

$\therefore dV = 10y^{1/4}\,dy$

$\frac{dV}{dt} = 10y^{1/4}\frac{dy}{dt}$ (divide by dt)

$ky = 10y^{1/4}\frac{dy}{dt} \Rightarrow \frac{dy}{dt} = 0.1ky^{3/4}$

If depth is 6 in., then y = 0.5.

$\frac{dy}{dt} = 0.1k(0.5^{3/4}) = 0.05946...k.$

b. With a person sitting in the tub, dy/dt would be faster. dV/dt would be the same because the depth is the same. But each cubic foot of water that flows out lowers the water level farther.

5. Base Runner Problem

Let y = Milt's distance from home plate.
Let x = Milt's displacement from third base.

Know: $\frac{dx}{dt} = -20$ ft/sec. Want: $\frac{dy}{dt}$

$y^2 = x^2 + 90^2 \Rightarrow 2y\frac{dy}{dt} = 2x\frac{dx}{dt}$

$\Rightarrow \frac{dy}{dt} = \frac{x}{y}\cdot\frac{dx}{dt} = \frac{-20x}{\sqrt{x^2 + 90^2}}$

Graph.

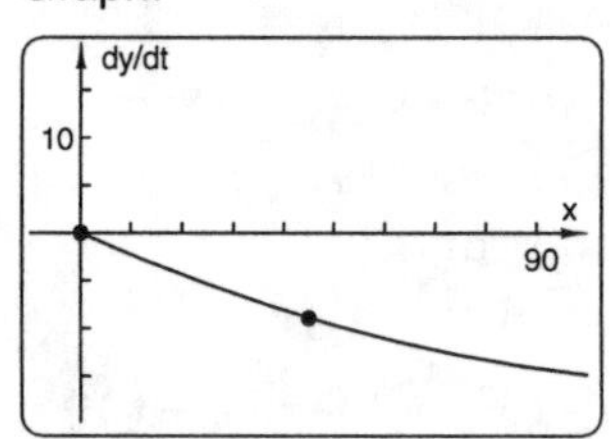

At x = 45, $\frac{dy}{dt} = -8.944...$

≈ -8.9 ft/sec (exact: $-4\sqrt{5}$)

At x = 0, $\frac{dy}{dt} = 0$ ft/sec, which is reasonable since Milt is moving perpendicular to his line from home plate.

6. Tugboat Problem

Let y = displacement from stern to dock along pier.
Let x = displacement from bow to pier along dock.

Know: $\frac{dy}{dt} = -3$ m/sec. Want: $\frac{dx}{dt}$

$x^2 + y^2 = 200^2$

$2x\frac{dx}{dt} + 2y\frac{dy}{dt} = 0 \Rightarrow \frac{dx}{dt} = -\frac{y}{x}\frac{dy}{dt} = \frac{3y}{\sqrt{200^2 - y^2}}$

At y = 120, $\frac{dx}{dt} = \frac{360}{160} = 2.25$ m/sec.

Graph.

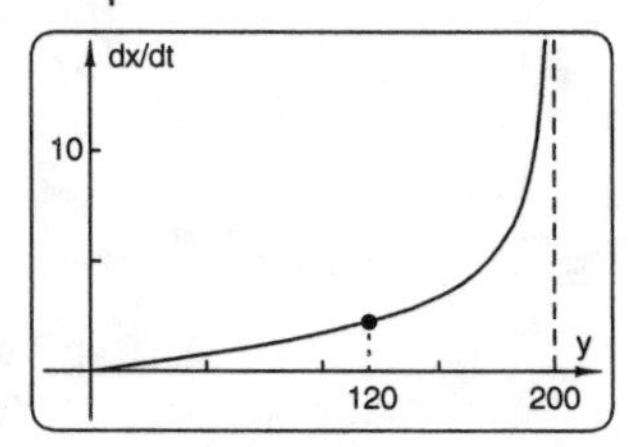

7. Rectangle Problem I
Let L = length.
Let W = width.
Know: $\frac{dL}{dt} = 3, \frac{dW}{dt} = -2$. Want: $\frac{dA}{dt}$
$A = LW \Rightarrow \frac{dA}{dt} = \frac{dL}{dt}\cdot W + L\cdot\frac{dW}{dt}$
At L = 50 and W = 20,
$\frac{dA}{dt} = 3(20) - 2(50) = -40$
Area is decreasing at 40 ft^2/min.

8. Rectangle Problem II
a.

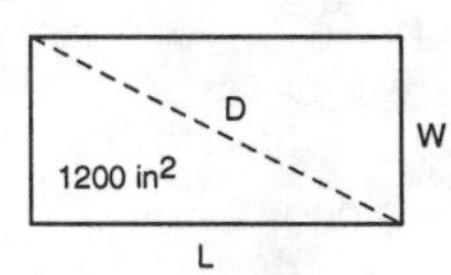

Know: $\frac{dL}{dt}$. Want: $\frac{dW}{dt}$
$LW = 1200 \Rightarrow \frac{dL}{dt}\cdot W + L\frac{dW}{dt} = 0$
$\Rightarrow \frac{dW}{dt} = \frac{-W}{1200/W}\cdot\frac{dL}{dt} = -\frac{1}{1200}W^2\cdot\frac{dL}{dt}$
b. $-2 = -\frac{1}{1200}W^2(6) \Rightarrow W = 20$ in. $\Rightarrow L = 60$ in.
c. $D^2 = L^2 + W^2 \Rightarrow 2D\frac{dD}{dt} = 2L\frac{dL}{dt} + 2W\frac{dW}{dt}$
$\Rightarrow \frac{dD}{dt} = \frac{1}{\sqrt{L^2 + W^2}}\left(L\frac{dL}{dt} + W\frac{dW}{dt}\right)$
At L = 60 and W = 20,
$\frac{dD}{dt} = \frac{1}{\sqrt{60^2 + 20^2}}\left(60(6) + 20(-2)\right)$
$= \frac{320}{\sqrt{4000}} = 1.6\sqrt{10} = 5.0596...$
Diagonal is decreasing at about 5.06 in/min.

9. Luke and Leia's Trash Compactor Problem
a. Let L = length.
Let W = width.
Let H = depth (meters)
Know: $\frac{dW}{dt} = 0.1$ m/sec, $\frac{dL}{dt} = -0.3$ m/sec
Want: $\frac{dH}{dt}$
$LWH = 20 \Rightarrow \frac{dL}{dt}\cdot WH + L\cdot\frac{dW}{dt}\cdot H + LW\cdot\frac{dH}{dt} = 0$
$\frac{dH}{dt} = -\frac{H}{W}\cdot\frac{dW}{dt} - \frac{H}{L}\cdot\frac{dL}{dt}$
$= -\frac{20}{LW^2}(0.1) - \frac{20}{L^2W}(-0.3)$
b. $\frac{dH}{dt} = -\frac{20\cdot 0.1}{5\cdot 2^2} + \frac{20\cdot 0.3}{5^2\cdot 2} = 0.02$
Depth is increasing at 0.02 m/sec.

10. Darth Vader's Problem
Let L = distance between spaceships
Know: $\frac{dx}{dt} = 80$ km/sec, $\frac{dy}{dt} = -50$ km/sec
Want: $\frac{dL}{dt}$
$L^2 = x^2 + y^2 \Rightarrow 2L\frac{dL}{dt} = 2x\frac{dx}{dt} + 2y\frac{dy}{dt}$
$\Rightarrow \frac{dL}{dt} = \frac{1}{\sqrt{x^2 + y^2}}(80x - 50y)$
$\frac{dL}{dt} = \frac{1}{1300}(80\cdot 500 - 50\cdot 1200) = \frac{-200}{13} = -15.3846...$
Distance is decreasing at about 15.4 km/sec.

11. Point on a Parabola Problem
a. Know: $\frac{dx}{dt} = kx$. Want: $\frac{dy}{dt}$
$y = x^2 \Rightarrow \frac{dy}{dt} = 2x\frac{dx}{dt} = 2kx^2$
b. $\frac{dx}{dt} = kx \Rightarrow 10 = k\cdot 5 \Rightarrow k = 2$
c. $\frac{dy}{dt} = 2(2\cdot 7^2) = 196$

12. Point on a Tangent Graph Problem
Know: $\frac{dx}{dt} = 5$/min. Want: $\frac{dy}{dt}$
$y = \tan x \Rightarrow \frac{dy}{dt} = \sec^2 x\frac{dx}{dt} = 5\sec^2 x$
$\frac{dy}{dt} = 5\sec^2 1 = 17.1275...$ units/min.

13. Barn Ladder Problem
a. Let x = distance from bottom of ladder to wall.
Let y = distance from top of ladder to floor.
$20^2 = x^2 + y^2 \Rightarrow 0 = 2x\frac{dx}{dt} + 2y\frac{dy}{dt} \Rightarrow \frac{dy}{dt} = -\frac{x}{y}\frac{dx}{dt}$
Note that the velocity of the weight is $-dy/dt$, so
$v = \frac{x}{\sqrt{400 - x^2}}\frac{dx}{dt}$
b. $v = \frac{4}{\sqrt{384}}\cdot(-3) = -\frac{\sqrt{6}}{4} = -0.6123...$ ft/sec
c. Here x = 20, $\frac{dx}{dt} = 2$, so $v = \frac{40}{0} \to \infty$ (!!)

14. Kinetic Energy Problem
Know: $\frac{dK}{dt} = 100{,}000$ MJ/sec; $\frac{dm}{dt} = -20$ kg/sec.
Want: $\frac{dV}{dt}$ (Note 1 megaJoule—MJ— is the energy required to accelerate a 1-kg mass by 1 km/sec through a distance of 1 km; it can be expressed 1 MJ = 1 kg·km^2/sec^2.)
$K = \frac{1}{2}mV^2 \Rightarrow \frac{dK}{dt} = \frac{1}{2}V^2\frac{dm}{dt} + mV\frac{dV}{dt}$
$\Rightarrow \frac{dV}{dt} = \frac{1}{mV}\frac{dK}{dt} - \frac{V}{2m}\frac{dm}{dt}$
$\frac{dV}{dt} = \frac{100000}{5000\cdot 10} - \frac{10(-20)}{2\cdot 5000} = 2.02$ (km/sec)/sec.

15. Conical Water Tank Problem

a. Let h = depth of water.
Let r = radius of water at surface.
Let V = volume of water.

Know: $\frac{dh}{dt} = 5$ m/hr. Want: $\frac{dV}{dt}$

$V = \frac{1}{3}\pi r^2 h$

By similar triangles, $\frac{r}{h} = \frac{3}{5} \Rightarrow r = \frac{3}{5}h$

$\therefore V = \frac{1}{3}\pi\left(\frac{3}{5}h\right)^2 h = \frac{3}{25}\pi h^3$

$\frac{dV}{dt} = \frac{9}{25}\pi h^2 \frac{dh}{dt}$

At h = 3, $\frac{dV}{dt} = \frac{81}{5}\pi = 16.2\,\pi = 50.8938...$

$\approx 50.9\ m^3/hr$

b. i. Know: $\frac{dV}{dt} = -2\ m^3/hr$. Want: $\frac{dh}{dt}$.

$\frac{dV}{dt} = \frac{9}{25}\pi h^2 \frac{dh}{dt} \Rightarrow \frac{dh}{dt} = \frac{25}{9\pi h^2}\frac{dV}{dt}$

$\frac{dh}{dt} = \frac{-50}{144\pi} = -0.1105...$

≈ -0.11 m/hr at h = 4 m

ii. $\frac{dh}{dt} \to -\infty$ as $h \to 0$ m

c. i. Know: $\frac{dV}{dt} = k\sqrt{h}$.

$\frac{dV}{dt} = -0.5$ at $h = 4 \Rightarrow k = -0.25$

$\frac{dV}{dt} = -0.25\sqrt{h}$

ii. $\frac{dV}{dt} = -0.25\sqrt{0.64} = -0.2\ m^3/hr$ at h = 0.64 m

iii. $\frac{dV}{dt} = -0.2$ at $h = 0.64\ m \Rightarrow$

$\frac{dh}{dt} = \frac{25}{9\pi(0.64)^2}(-0.2) = -0.4317... \approx -0.43$ m/hr

16. Conical Tank Generalization Problem

Let h = depth of water.
Let f = radius of water at surface.
Let V = volume of water.

Know: $\frac{dV}{dt}$, possibly a variable. Want: $\frac{dh}{dt}$.

$V = \frac{1}{3}\pi r^2 h$

By similar triangles, $\frac{r}{h} = \frac{a}{b} \Rightarrow r = \frac{a}{b}h$

$V = \frac{1}{3}\pi\left(\frac{a}{b}h\right)^2 h = \frac{a^2}{3b^2}\pi h^3 \Rightarrow \frac{dV}{dt} = \frac{a^2}{b^2}\pi h^2 \frac{dh}{dt}$

$\Rightarrow \frac{dh}{dt} = \frac{b^2}{a^2\pi h^2}\frac{dV}{dt}$.

17. Cone of Light Problem

Let h = altitude.
Let r = radius.
Let V = volume of cone.

Know: $\frac{dh}{dt} = -6$ ft/min; $\frac{dr}{dt} = 7$ ft/min.

Want: $\frac{dV}{dt}$

$V = \frac{1}{3}\pi r^2 h \Rightarrow \frac{dV}{dt} = \frac{2}{3}\pi r \frac{dr}{dt} h + \frac{1}{3}\pi r^2 \frac{dh}{dt}$

$\frac{dV}{dt} = \frac{48}{3}\pi(7) + \frac{64}{3}\pi(-6) = -16\pi\ ft^3/min = -50.2654...$

Volume is decreasing at about 50.3 ft^3/min.

18. Slag Heap Problem

Let h = altitude
Let r = radius
Let c = circumference.
Let V = volume of heap.

Know: $\frac{dc}{dt} = 7$ ft/day. Want: $\frac{dV}{dt}$

$V = \frac{1}{3}\pi r^2 h$

By trigonometry, h = r tan 40°.

$\therefore V = \frac{1}{3}\pi r^3 \tan 40°$

$c = 2\pi r \Rightarrow r = \frac{c}{2\pi}$

$\therefore V = \frac{1}{3}\pi\left(\frac{c}{2\pi}\right)^3 \tan 40° = \frac{\tan 40°}{24\pi^2}c^3$

$\frac{dV}{dt} = \frac{\tan 40°}{8\pi^2}c^2\frac{dc}{dt} = \frac{7\tan 40°}{8\pi^2}c^2$

At c = 3,000, $\frac{dV}{dt} = \frac{7\tan 40°}{8\pi^2}3{,}000^2$

$= 669{,}521.2216... \approx 670{,}000\ ft^3/day$

19. Cone in Hemisphere Problem

Let r = radius of hemisphere.
Let S = total surface area of hemisphere.
Let V = volume of cone.

Know: $\frac{dS}{dt} = 18\ in^2/sec$. Want: $\frac{dV}{dt}$

$S = \frac{1}{2}\cdot 4\pi r^2 + \pi r^2 = 3\pi r^2 \Rightarrow \frac{dS}{dt} = 6\pi r\frac{dr}{dt}$

$\frac{dr}{dt} = \frac{1}{24\pi}\frac{dS}{dt} = \frac{3}{4\pi}$ at r = 4 in.

$V = \frac{1}{3}\pi r^2 h = \frac{1}{3}\pi r^3$ (since r = h) $\Rightarrow \frac{dV}{dt} = \pi r^2\frac{dr}{dt}$

$\frac{dV}{dt} = 16\pi\cdot\frac{3}{4\pi} = 12\ in^3/sec$ at r = 4 in.

20. Planetary Motion Problem

a. Let ω = angular velocity in radians per day.

$\omega_E = \frac{2\pi}{365}$, $\omega_M = \frac{2\pi}{687}$

$\frac{d\theta}{dt} = \omega_E - \omega_M = \frac{644\pi}{250755} = 0.008068...$

≈ 0.00807 rad/day

b. $T = \left(\frac{1}{365} - \frac{1}{687}\right)^{-1} = 778.7422... \approx 778.7$ days

The next time after (Mon.) 10 Oct. 1988 when the two planets were closest was 779 days later, on (Tue.) 27 Nov. 1990 (or Wed. 28 Nov., if the planets were aligned later than about 6:11 a.m. back on 10 Oct. 1988).

c. By the law of cosines,

$D^2 = 93^2 + 141^2 - 2\cdot 93\cdot 141\cos\theta$

$D = \sqrt{28{,}530 - 26{,}226\cos\theta}$ million miles

d. $\frac{dD}{dt} = \frac{26{,}226 \sin\theta}{2\sqrt{28{,}530 - 26{,}226\cos\theta}}\frac{d\theta}{dt}$

$= \frac{26{,}226\cdot(\frac{1}{365} - \frac{1}{687})\cdot 2\pi\sin\theta}{2\sqrt{28{,}530 - 26{,}226\cos\theta}}$ million mi/day

rate $= \frac{1{,}000{,}000\cdot 26{,}226\cdot(\frac{1}{365} - \frac{1}{687})\cdot 2\pi\sin\theta}{24\cdot 2\sqrt{28{,}530 - 26{,}226\cos\theta}}$

$= \frac{1{,}092{,}750{,}000\cdot(\frac{1}{365} - \frac{1}{687})\pi\cdot\sin\theta}{\sqrt{28530 - 26226\cos\theta}}$ mi/h

To find out how fast D is changing *today*, first determine how many days after 10 October 1988 it is today, then multiply that number by

$\frac{d\theta}{dt} = (\frac{1}{365} - \frac{1}{687})2\pi$ to find θ.

e. To maximize $\frac{dD}{dt}$, plot the variable part of $\frac{dD}{dt}$,

$y = \frac{\sin\theta}{\sqrt{28530 - 26226\cos\theta}}$.

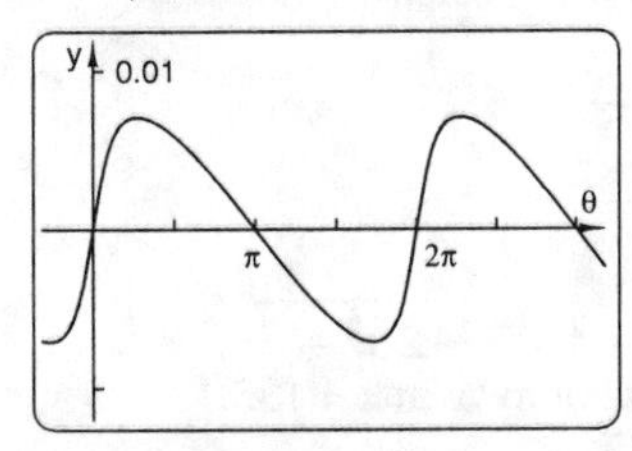

From the graph, it is clear that the maximum occurs well before $\theta = \pi/2$ (90°). Using the maximize feature, the maximum occurs at $\theta \approx 0.8505...$, or 48.7...°.
(The exact value is $\cos^{-1}(93/141)$. One can find this by finding (d/dt)(dD/dt) and setting it equal to zero. One can also see this by decomposing the Earth's motion vector into two components—one toward/away from Mars, and the other perpendicular to the first. The rate of change in D is maximized when all the Earth's motion is along the Earth-to-Mars component, which occurs when the Earth-Mars-Sun triangle has a right angle at the Earth.
In this case, $\cos\theta = \frac{93}{141}$.)

f. $\theta = (\frac{1}{365} - \frac{1}{687})2\pi t$ if t = days since 10 Oct. 1988.

$D = \sqrt{28530 - 26226\cos(\frac{1}{365} - \frac{1}{687})2\pi t}$

Graph. It is not a sinusoid. The high and low points are not symmetric.

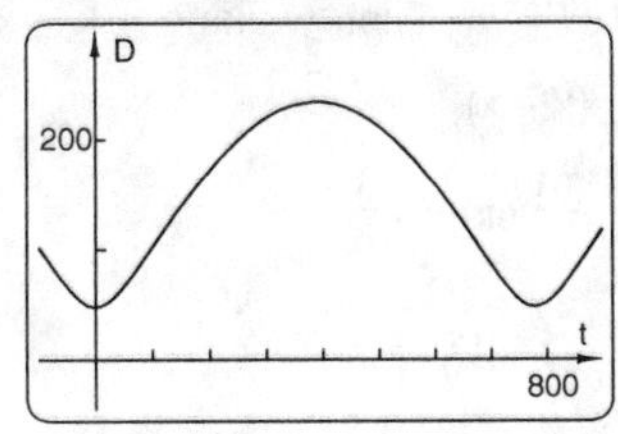

21. Speeding Piston Problem

a. The connecting rod, the crankshaft, and the y-axis form a triangle with angle $\phi = \theta - \pi/2$ included between sides of 6 cm and (y − 8) cm.

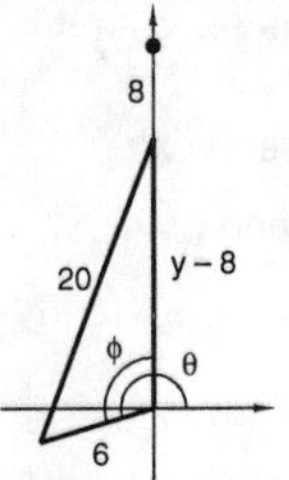

By the law of cosines,
$20^2 = (y-8)^2 + 6^2 - 2\cdot 6\cdot(y-8)\cos(\theta - \pi/2)$
$20^2 = (y-8)^2 + 6^2 - 12(y-8)\sin\theta$
$(y-8)^2 - 12\sin\theta\,(y-8) - 364 = 0$
Solve for y using the quadratic formula.
$y - 8 = 6\sin\theta + \sqrt{36\cdot\sin^2\theta + 364}$
(The solution with the negative radical gives the ambiguous triangle below the origin.)
$y = 8 + 6\sin\theta + 2\sqrt{9\cdot\sin^2\theta + 91}$

b. $v = \frac{dy}{dt} = 6\cos\theta\frac{d\theta}{dt} + \frac{18\sin\theta\cos\theta}{\sqrt{9\cdot\sin^2\theta + 91}}\frac{d\theta}{dt}$

$v = 6\cos\theta\frac{d\theta}{dt} + \frac{9\sin 2\theta}{\sqrt{9\cdot\sin^2\theta + 91}}\frac{d\theta}{dt}$

c. $a = \frac{d^2y}{dt^2}$

$= -6\sin\theta\left(\frac{d\theta}{dt}\right)^2 + 18\frac{91\cos 2\theta - 9\sin^4\theta}{(9\sin^2\theta + 91)^{3/2}}\left(\frac{d\theta}{dt}\right)^2$

$a = \left(18\frac{91\cos 2\theta - 9\sin^4\theta}{(9\sin^2\theta + 91)^{3/2}} - 6\sin\theta\right)\left(\frac{d\theta}{dt}\right)^2$

(There are many other correct forms of the answer, depending on how you use the double-argument properties and Pythagorean properties from trigonometry.)
Note that the angular velocity is constant at 6000π radians per minute, so

$\frac{d\theta}{dt} = 100\pi$ rad/sec.

d. Graph, showing acceleration. Note that a line at a = −980 is so close to the x-axis that it does not show up.

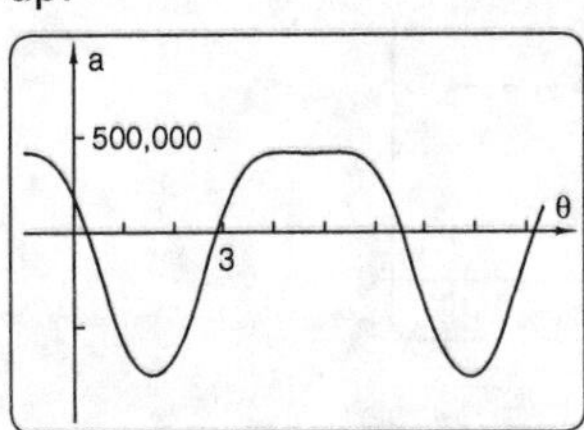

Solving graphically and numerically, $a < -980$ for $\theta \in (0.2712..., 2.8703...)$. The piston is going down ($v < 0$) for $\theta \in (\pi/2, 3\pi/2)$. So the piston is going down with acceleration greater than gravity for θ between π/2 and 2.8703... .

Q1. $x = 81$

Q2. $y' = -x(100 - x^2)^{-1/2}$

Q3. $-\frac{1}{3}(100 - x^2)^{3/2} + C$

Q4. $y' = 3\cdot(1 - 9x^2)^{-1/2}$

Q5. $\frac{1}{2}xe^{2x} - \frac{1}{4}e^{2x} + C$

Q6. $y' = \text{sech}^2\, x$

Q7. 1.5

Q8. $t = 1$ and $t = 4$

Q9. $t = 4$

Q10. $t = 2$

1. Swim and Run Problem

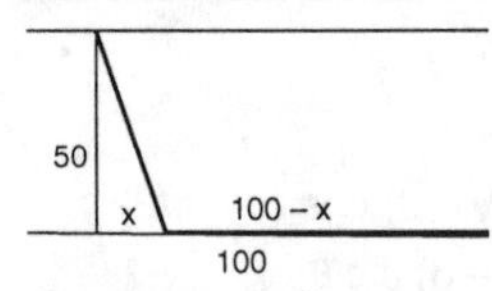

$T = \frac{1}{2}\sqrt{50^2 + x^2} + \frac{1}{5}(100 - x)$

Graph, showing minimum T at $x \approx 22$ m.

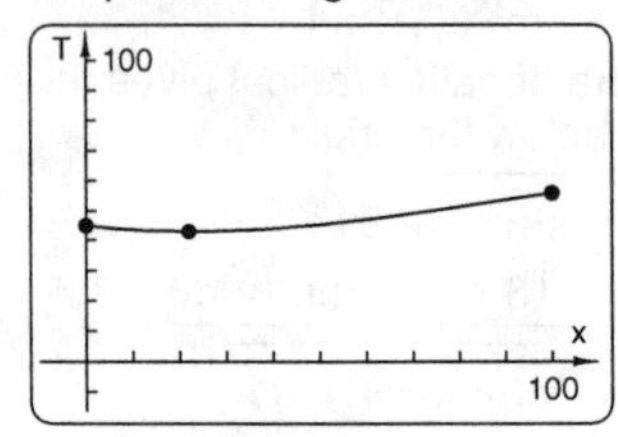

Algebraic solution:

$T' = \frac{1}{4}(50^2 + x^2)^{-1/2}\cdot 2x - \frac{1}{5}$

$T' = 0 \Leftrightarrow \frac{1}{2}(50^2 + x^2)^{-1/2}x = \frac{1}{5}$

$5x = 2(50^2 + x^2)^{1/2}$

$25x^2 = 4\cdot 50^2 + 4x^2$

$x = \pm 100/\sqrt{21} = \pm 21.8217...$

Swim toward a point about 21.8 m downstream.

2. Scuba Diver Problem

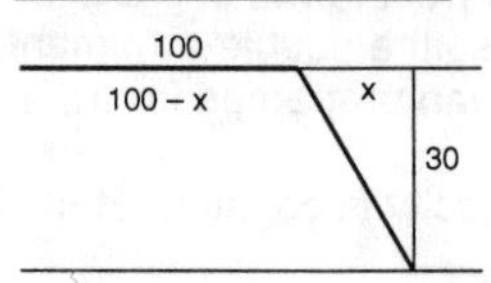

$T = \frac{1}{13}(100 - x) + \frac{1}{12}\sqrt{30^2 + x^2}$

Graph, showing minimum T at $x \approx 72$

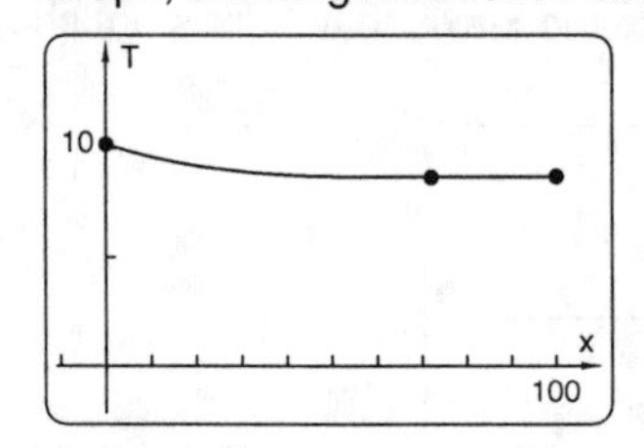

Algebraic solution:

$T' = -\frac{1}{13} + \frac{1}{24}(30^2 + x^2)^{-1/2}\cdot 2x$

$T' = 0 \Leftrightarrow \frac{1}{13} = \frac{1}{12}x(30^2 + x^2)^{-1/2}$

$13x = 12(30^2 + x^2)^{1/2}$

$169x^2 = 144\cdot 30^2 + 144x^2$

$x = \pm 72.$

Swim for $100 - 72 = 28$m, then dive.

3. Pipeline Problem

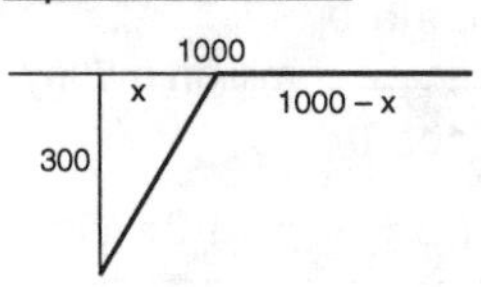

$C = 40(1000 - x) + 50\sqrt{300^2 + x^2}$

Graph, showing minimum C at $x \approx 400$.
(Exactly $x = 400$.)

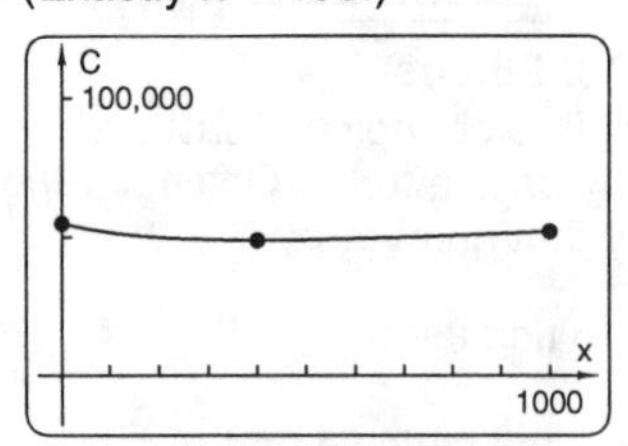

Go 600 m along road, then start crossing field 400 m up the road from the well.

4. Elevated Walkway Problem

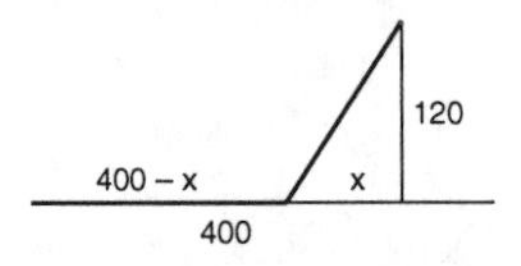

$W = 3000(400 - x) + 4000\sqrt{120^2 + x^2}$

Graph, showing minimum W at $x \approx 136$.

(Exactly $x = 360/\sqrt{7} = 136.067...$)

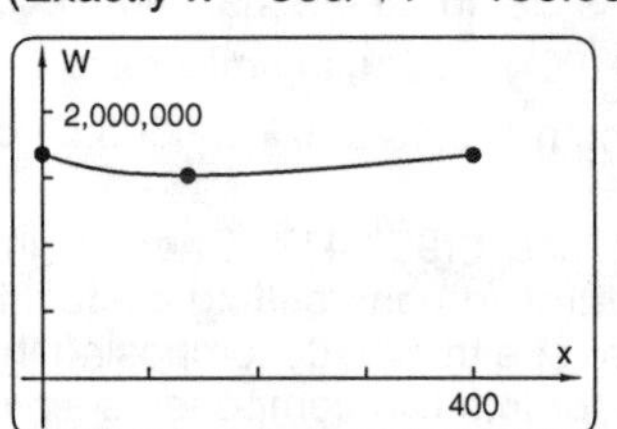

Go $400 - 136.067... \approx 263.9$ m parallel to the street, then cross the street.

5. Minimum Path Discovery Problem

a. For minimal path, $x = 100/\sqrt{21}$.

$\therefore \sin\theta = \dfrac{x}{\sqrt{50^2 + x^2}} = 0.4 = 2/5$, Q.E.D.

b. For minimal path, $x = 400$.

$\sin\theta = \dfrac{x}{\sqrt{300^2 + x^2}} = 0.8 = 40/50$, Q.E.D.

6. Minimum Path Generalization Problem

Dist. swimming $= \sqrt{p^2 + x^2}$; Dist. walking $= k - x$

$T = \frac{1}{s}\sqrt{p^2 + x^2} + \frac{1}{w}(k - x)$

$T' = \dfrac{x}{s\sqrt{p^2 + x^2}} - \dfrac{1}{w} = \dfrac{1}{s}\sin\theta - \dfrac{1}{w}$

$T' = 0 \Leftrightarrow \sin\theta = \frac{s}{w}$, Q.E.D.

7. Scuba Diver Problem Revisited

$\sin\theta = \frac{12}{13}$

$x = 30\tan(\sin^{-1}\frac{12}{13}) = 72$

Swim 100 – 72 = 28 m, then dive.

The algebraic solution is easier than before because no algebraic calculus needs to be done.

Mathematicians find general solutions to gain insight, and to find patterns and methods to allow easier solution of similar problems.

8. Elevated Walkway Problem Revisited

$\sin\theta = \frac{x}{\sqrt{400^2 + x^2}} = \frac{3000}{4000} = \frac{3}{4}$

$16x^2 = 9(400^2 + x^2)$

$7x^2 = 9\cdot400^2 \Leftrightarrow x = \pm360/\sqrt{7} = 136.067...$

Go 400 – 136.067... ≈ 263.9 m parallel to the street, then cross the street.

The algebraic solution is easier than before because no algebraic calculus needs to be done.

Mathematicians find general solutions to gain insight, and to find patterns and methods to allow easier solution of similar problems.

9. Pipeline Problem, Near-Miss

x	C(x), approx.
300	49,213
390	49,002
400	49,000
410	49,002
500	49,155

The table shows that a near-miss will have virtually no effect on the minimal cost. For instance, missing the optimal value of x will make about $2 difference in cost, and missing by 100 m makes only $150 to $200 difference.

10. Calvin and Phoebe's Commuting Problem

$T(x) = \frac{1}{5}(500 - x) + \frac{1}{3}\sqrt{1200^2 + x^2}$

Graph, showing a local minimum at x ≈ 900 ft, which is out of the domain. (Exact: 900 ft)

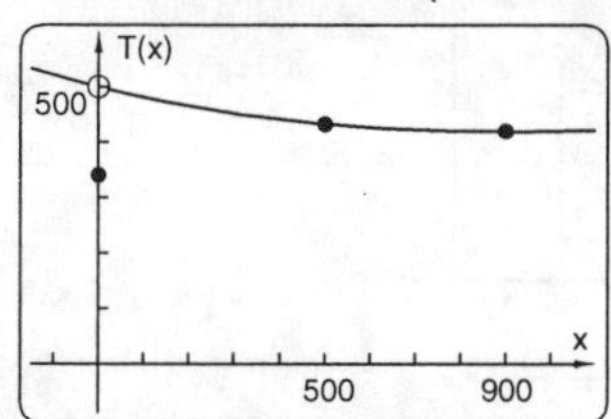

The minimum occurs at an endpoint of the domain. Since Calvin can walk entirely along pavement when x = 0, there is a removable discontinuity in the above function, and T(0) = 100 + 240 = 340 sec. Since T(500) = 433.333... , which is greater than 340, the minimum time is at x = 0. Calvin's time is minimized by staying on the sidewalks. If road construction (for instance) prevented Calvin from walking on Heights Street, his time would be minimized by walking directly to Phoebe's house.

11. Robinson Crusoe Problem

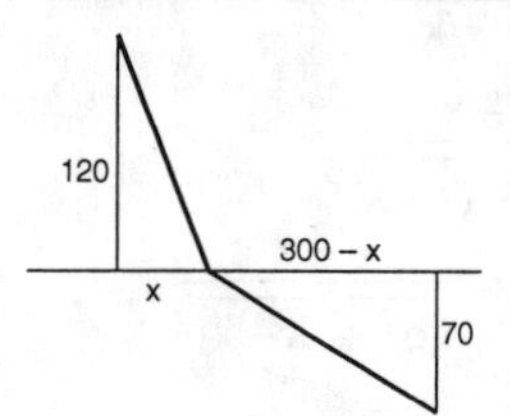

$T = \frac{1}{50}\sqrt{120^2 + x^2} + \frac{1}{130}\sqrt{70^2 + (300 - x)^2}$

Graph, showing minimum T at x ≈ 48 yd.

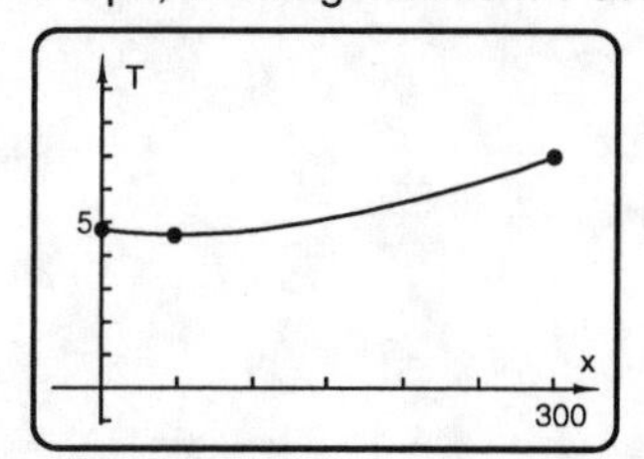

Algebraically:

$T' = \frac{x}{50\sqrt{120^2 + x^2}} - \frac{300 - x}{130\sqrt{70^2 + (300 - x)^2}}$

Setting T' = 0 and simplifying leads to a fourth-degree equation, which must be solved numerically. Minimum is at x = 47.8809... ≈ 47.9 yd.

12. Robinson Crusoe Follow-up Problem

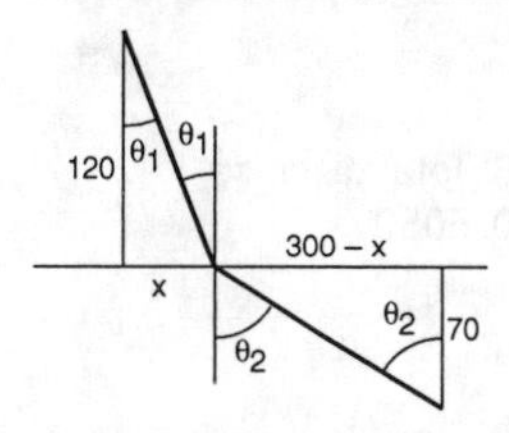

From Problem 11,

$T' = \frac{x}{50\sqrt{120^2 + x^2}} - \frac{300 - x}{130\sqrt{70^2 + (300 - x)^2}}$

By trigonometry,

$\sin\theta_1 = \frac{x}{\sqrt{120^2 + x^2}}, \ \sin\theta_2 = \frac{300 - x}{\sqrt{70^2 + (300 - x)^2}}$

$\therefore T' = \frac{1}{50}\sin\theta_1 - \frac{1}{130}\sin\theta_2$

For minimal path, T' = 0. Thus,

$\frac{1}{50}\sin\theta_1 = \frac{1}{130}\sin\theta_2$

$\frac{\sin\theta_1}{\sin\theta_2} = \frac{50}{130}$, Q.E.D.

13. Robinson Crusoe Generalization Problem

$T = \frac{1}{v_1}\sqrt{a^2 + x^2} + \frac{1}{v_2}\sqrt{b^2 + (k-x)^2}$

$T' = \frac{x}{v_1\sqrt{a^2 + x^2}} - \frac{k-x}{v_2\sqrt{b^2 + (k-x)^2}}$

$\sin\theta_1 = \frac{x}{\sqrt{a^2 + x^2}}$, $\sin\theta_2 = \frac{k-x}{\sqrt{b^2 + (k-x)^2}}$

$\therefore T' = \frac{1}{v_1}\sin\theta_1 - \frac{1}{v_2}\sin\theta_2$

For minimal path, $T' = 0$. Thus,

$\frac{1}{v_1}\sin\theta_1 = \frac{1}{v_2}\sin\theta_2$

$\frac{\sin\theta_1}{\sin\theta_2} = \frac{v_1}{v_2}$, Q.E.D.

14. Snell's Law of Refraction Problem

a. The light rays take the minimal time to get from one point to another, just as Robinson Crusoe wanted to take the minimal time to get from hut to wreck.

b. Light always takes the path requiring the least time between two points.

c. When you look at the object, your mind tells you the light rays go straight. Actually, they are bent, as shown in the diagram. So the object is deeper than it appears to be.

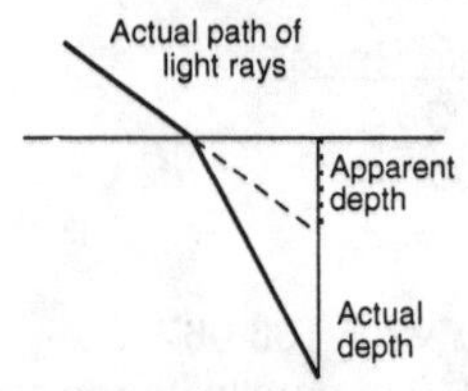

15. Journal Problem

Journal entries will vary.

Problem Set 10-6, pages 530 to 532 — Maximum and Minimum Problems in Motion and Elsewhere

Q1. $f'(x) = \sin x + x\cos x$

Q2. $g''(x) = x^{-1}$

Q3. $xe^x - e^x + C$

Q4. Snell's law

Q5. x

Q6. Sketch, paraboloid.

Q7. Graph, $y = x_{1/3}$

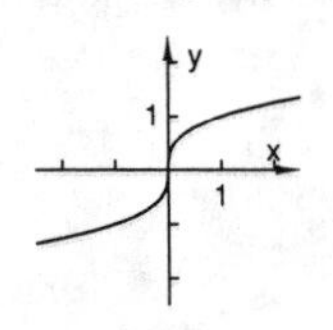

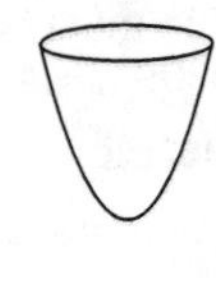

Q8. Total distance

Q9. Newton and Leibniz

Q10. 5050

1. Rocket Problem

$D = t + \frac{1}{t}$ $D' = 1 - t^{-2}$

Graphs, showing zero derivative and local minimum of D at t = 1, and maximum at D = 3.

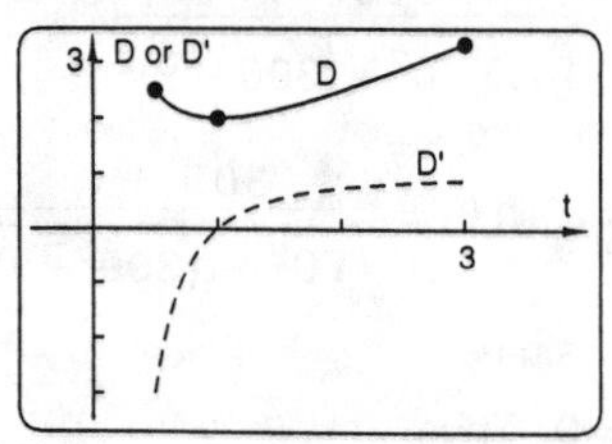

$D' = 0 \Leftrightarrow t^2 = 1 \Leftrightarrow t = \pm 1$, confirming the graph.

Minimum is $D(1) = 2$, or 2,000 mi.

Maximum is $D(3) = 3\frac{1}{3}$, or about 3333 mi.

2. Truck Problem

Fuel cost per mile $= k \cdot v^2$

At $v = 30$, cost $= 0.10$.

$0.10 = k \cdot 30^2 \Rightarrow k = \frac{1}{9000}$

Driver cost is $10t = 10 \cdot \frac{100}{v} = \frac{1000}{v}$

$\therefore C = \frac{1000}{v} + \frac{v^2}{9000} \cdot 100 = \frac{1000}{v} + \frac{v^2}{90}$

$C' = -\frac{1000}{v^2} + \frac{v}{45}$

$C' = 0$ at $v = 10\sqrt[3]{45} = 35.5689...$

Graphs, showing minimum C at $v \approx 36$, C' is multiplied by 10, so that it is easier to see its behavior around $C' = 0$

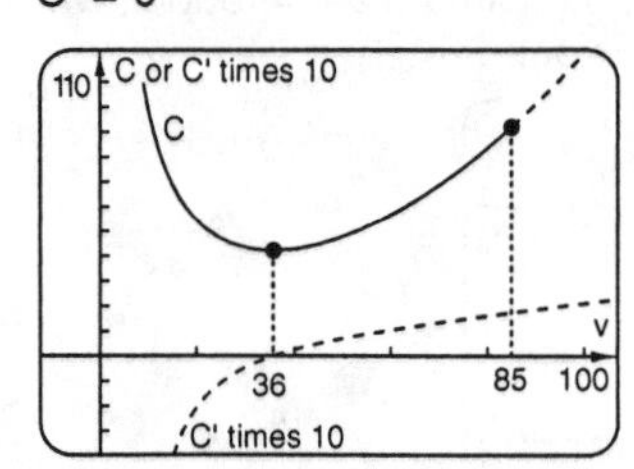

3. Number Problem I

Maximize $f(x) = x - x^2$

$f'(x) = 1 - 2x$; $f'(x) = 0$ at $x = 0.5$;

$f''(x) = -2$, so graph is concave downward everywhere.

Maximum of $f(x)$ is at $x = 0.5$.

4. Number Problem II

Maximize $f(x) = x - x^2$ for $x \geq 2$.

Graph, showing maximum at endpoint $x = 2$.

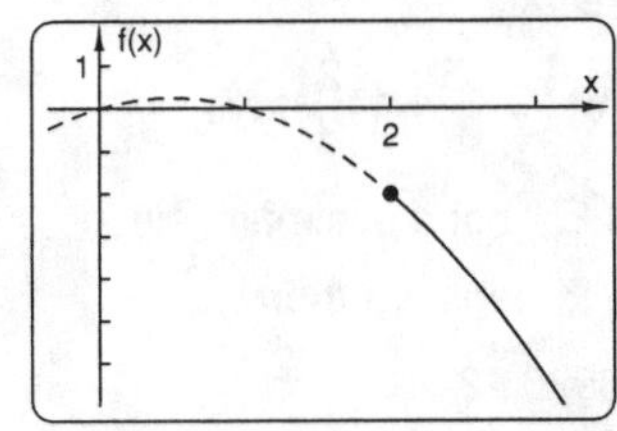

Since f(2) is the maximum and it is negative, there is no number greater that 2 that exceeds its square.

5. Fran's Optimal Study Time Problem

a. $S = \dfrac{100t}{t+1}$; $F = \dfrac{9}{t+9}$; $G = \dfrac{900t}{(t+1)(t+9)}$

Graph, showing maximum of G at t = 3 hours.

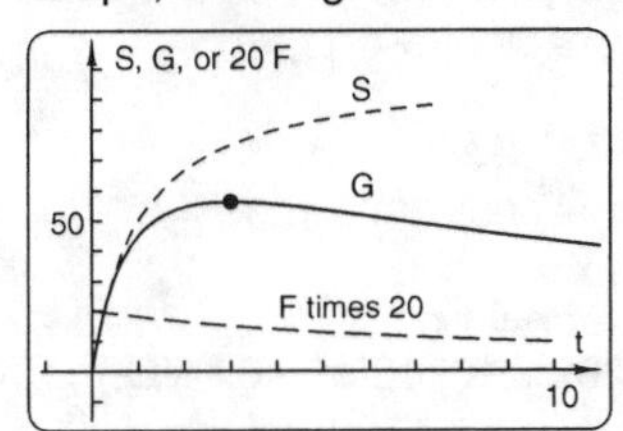

b. $G = \dfrac{900\,t}{(t+1)(t+9)} = \dfrac{900t}{t^2+10t+9}$

$G' = \dfrac{900(t^2+10t+9) - 900t(2t+10)}{(t^2+10t+9)^2}$

$= \dfrac{900(9-t^2)}{(t^2+10t+9)^2}$

$G' = 0 \Leftrightarrow t = \pm 3$

Since G' changes from positive to negative at t = 3, there is a local maximum there, as in the graph.

Fran should study for 3 hours.

c. Optimum grade = G(3) = 56.25 ≈ 56 (not good!)

i. G(4) = 55.3846... ≈ 55, about 1 point less.

ii. G(2) = 54.5454... , ≈ 55, about 1 point less.

6. Motor Oil Viscosity Problem

a. $\mu = 130 - 12T + 15T^2 - 4T^3$, $0 \leq T \leq 3$

$\dfrac{d\mu}{dT} = -12 + 30T - 12T^2 = -6(2T-1)(T-2)$

$\dfrac{d\mu}{dT} = 0$ at T = 0.5 or T = 2

$\mu(0) = 130$

$\mu(0.5) = 127.25$

$\mu(2) = 134$

$\mu(3) = 121$

Max. viscosity occurs at T = 2, or 200°.

b. Min. viscosity = 121 centipoise at T = 3, or 300°.

c. $\dfrac{d\mu}{dt} = \dfrac{d\mu}{dT} \cdot \dfrac{dT}{dt}$

Since $T = \sqrt{t}$, $\dfrac{dT}{dt} = \dfrac{1}{2\sqrt{t}} = \dfrac{1}{2T}$

When T = 1, $\dfrac{dT}{dt} = 0.5$ and $\dfrac{d\mu}{dT} = 6$.

$\therefore \dfrac{d\mu}{dt} = 0.5(6) = 3$

Viscosity is increasing at 3 centipoise/min.

7. Cylinder-in-the-Cone Problem I

a. Put a coordinate system with origin at the center of the cone's base. Pick a sample point (x, y) where the cylinder touches the element of the cone. Thus, x is the radius of the cylinder and y is its altitude.

The volume and surface area are:

$V = \pi x^2 y$

$A = 2\pi x^2 + 2\pi xy$

The cone element has equation $y = -0.6x + 6$.

$V = \pi x^2(-0.6x + 6) = \pi(-0.6x^3 + 6x^2)$

$A = 2\pi x^2 + 2\pi x(-0.6x + 6) = \pi(0.8x^2 + 12x)$

Graphs of V and A.

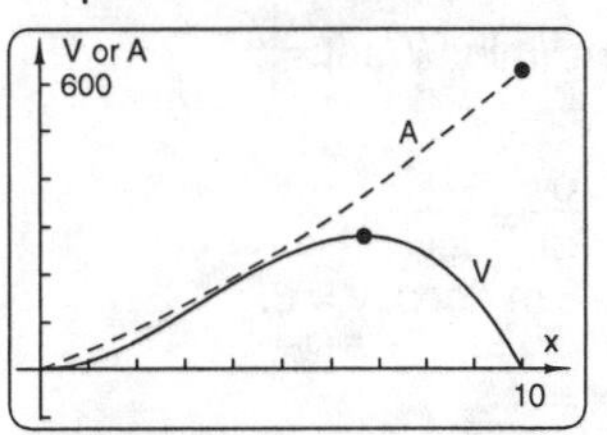

b. From the graphs, the maximum volume occurs where the radius x ≈ 6.7 in. The maximum area occurs at x = 10, where all of the area is in the two bases of the cone.

Algebraically,

$V' = \pi(-1.8x^2 + 12x)$

$V' = 0 \Leftrightarrow x = 0$ or $x = 6\frac{2}{3}$

Maximum V is at $x = 6\frac{2}{3}$ in., as shown on graph, and y = 2 in.

$A' = \pi(1.6x + 12)$

$A' = 0 \Leftrightarrow x = -7.5$, which is out of the domain.

$A(0) = 0$ and $A(10) = 200\pi$, so maximum A is at x = 10 in., as shown on graph, and y = 0 in.

The maximum volume and maximum area do not occur at the same radius.

Note that the radius of the cone is large compared to its altitude. Thus, the increase in areas of the two bases of the cylinder offsets the decrease in its lateral area as x increases, making the maximum area that of the degenerate cylinder of altitude zero.

8. Cylinder-in-the-Cone Problem II

a. Put a coordinate system with origin at the center of the cone's base. Pick a sample point (x, y) where the cylinder touches the element of the cone. Thus, x is the radius of the cylinder and y is its altitude.

Know: $\dfrac{dy}{dt} = 2$ in./min. Want: $\dfrac{dV}{dt}$

$V = \pi x^2 y$

The cone element has equation $y = -3x + 18$, from which $x = 6 - \frac{1}{3}y$

$V = \pi(6 - \frac{1}{3}y)^2 \cdot y = \pi(36y - 4y^2 + \frac{1}{9}y^3)$

$\dfrac{dV}{dy} = \pi(36 - 8y + \frac{1}{3}y^2) = \frac{1}{3}\pi(y-6)(y-18)$

$\dfrac{dV}{dt} = \dfrac{dV}{dy} \cdot \dfrac{dy}{dt} = \frac{2}{3}\pi(y-6)(y-18)$

When y = 12, $\dfrac{dV}{dt} = -24\pi$.

V is decreasing at $24\pi = 75.3982...$ ≈ 75.4 in³/min.

b. If $t \in [0, 9]$ then $y \in [0, 18]$

$\frac{dV}{dt} = 0 \Leftrightarrow y = 6$ or $y = 18$.

$V(0) = 0$; $V(6) = 96\pi$; $V(18) = 0$.

Maximum V is 96π in^3 at t = 3 min.

c. If $t \in [4, 6]$, then $y \in [8, 12]$.

No critical points for V are in [8, 12].

$V(8) = 88.8888...\pi$; $V(12) = 48\pi$.

Maximum V is $88.8888...\pi$

≈ 279.3 in^3 at t = 4 min.

9. Quartic Parabola Tank Problem

Know: $\frac{dV}{dt} = -0.7$ m^3/min. Want: $\frac{dy}{dt}$

$dV = \pi x^2\, dy$

$\therefore \frac{dV}{dt} = \pi x^2 \frac{dy}{dt} \Rightarrow \frac{dy}{dt} = \frac{-0.7}{\pi x^2}$

When the water is 3 m deep, y = 8.

Since $y = x^4 + 5$, $x = \sqrt[4]{3}$.

$\frac{dy}{dt} = \frac{-0.7}{\pi\sqrt{3}} = -0.1286... \approx 0.129$ m/min.

10. Cylinder in Paraboloid Problem

a. Pick a sample point (x, y) where the cylinder touches the parabola. Thus, the radius of the cylinder is x and its altitude is y.

Know: $\frac{dx}{dt} = 0.3$ Want: $\frac{dV}{dt}$

$V = \pi x^2 y = \pi x^2(4 - x^2) = \pi(4x^2 - x^4)$

$\frac{dV}{dt} = \pi(8x - 4x^3)\cdot\frac{dx}{dt} = 1.2\pi(2x - x^3)$

When $x = 1.5$, $\frac{dV}{dt} = -0.45\pi$

b. $\frac{dV}{dx} = 4\pi(2x - x^3)$

$\frac{dV}{dx} = 0 \Leftrightarrow x = 0, \pm\sqrt{2}$ ($-\sqrt{2}$ is out of domain)

$V(0) = V(2) = 0$; $V(\sqrt{2}) = 4\pi$

Max volume = 4π units^3 at radius = $\sqrt{2}$ units

11. Pig Sale Problem

a. $w = 1000 + 15t$ (lbs); $p = 0.90 - 0.01t$ (\$/lb)

$A = (1000 + 15t)(0.90 - 0.01t)$

$= 900 + 3.5t - 0.15t^2$ (\$)

b. $\frac{dA}{dt} = 3.5 - 0.3t = 0$ at $t = \frac{35}{3} = 11\frac{2}{3}$ days

Maximum A at $t = 11\frac{2}{3}$, not a minimum, since $\frac{dA}{dt}$ goes from positive to negative there.

c. $A(11\frac{2}{3}) = 920\frac{5}{12} \approx \$920.42$

12. Bridge Problem

a. $0 \le D \le 130 \Rightarrow 0 \le 20x + 10 \le 130 \Rightarrow -\frac{1}{2} \le x \le 6$

$0 \le W \le 310 \Rightarrow 0 \le 10(x^2 - 8x + 22) \le 310$

$\Rightarrow -1 \le x \le 9$

Given $x \ge 1$, the domain of x is [1, 6].

b. Minimize/Maximize W on $x \in [1, 6]$

$\frac{dW}{dx} = 10(2x - 8) = 0$ at $x = 4$

$W(1) = 150$; $W(4) = 60$; $W(6) = 100$

Min W = 60 ft (at x = 4 mi);

Max W = 150 ft (at x = 1 mi).

c. $C = k\cdot D\cdot W = k\cdot(20x + 10)\cdot 10(x^2 - 8x + 22)$

$= 100k(2x^3 - 15x^2 + 36x + 22)$ $(k > 0)$

$\frac{dC}{dt} = 100k(6x^2 - 30x + 36) = 600k(x - 2)(x - 3)$

$\frac{dC}{dt} = 0 \Leftrightarrow x = 2$ or $x = 3$.

$C(1) = 4500k$; $C(2) = 5000k$; $C(3) = 4900k$;

$C(6) = 13{,}000k$.

Cheapest bridge at x = 1 mi.

d. No. The shortest bridge at x = 4 mi would cost C(4) = 5400k, which is 900k more than the cheapest bridge at x = 1.

Problem Set 10-7, pages 541 to 548 — Vector Functions for Motion in a Plane

Q1. $-x\cos x + \sin x + C$

Q2. $2x\,e^{3x} + 3x^2\,e^{3x}$

Q3. $\frac{2^x}{\ln 2} + C$

Q4. $5^3 = 125$

Q5. $\frac{1}{4}x^4 + 7$

Q6. $\frac{6\sec^2 6t}{3e^{3t}} = \frac{2}{x}\sec^2 \ln x^2$

Q7. parametric

Q8. $x\ln x - x + C$

Q9. spiral

Q10. x^2

1. Parabolic Path Problem I

a. $\vec{r}(t) = (10\sin 0.6t)\vec{i} + (4\cos 1.2t)\vec{j}$

$\vec{v}(t) = (6\cos 0.6t)\vec{i} + (-4.8\sin 1.2t)\vec{j}$

$\vec{a}(t) = (-3.6\sin 0.6t)\vec{i} + (-5.76\cos 1.2t)\vec{j}$

b. $\vec{r}(0.5) = (10\sin 0.3)\vec{i} + (4\cos 0.6)\vec{j}$

$= 2.9552...\vec{i} + 3.3013...\vec{j}$

$\vec{v}(0.5) = (6\cos 0.3)\vec{i} + (-4.8\sin 0.6)\vec{j}$

$= 5.7320...\vec{i} - 2.7102...\vec{j}$

$\vec{a}(0.5) = (-3.6\sin 0.3)\vec{i} + (-5.76\cos 0.6)\vec{j}$

$= -1.0638...\vec{i} - 4.7539...\vec{j}$

Graph, showing $\vec{r}$, $\vec{v}$, and $\vec{a}$ at t = 0.5.

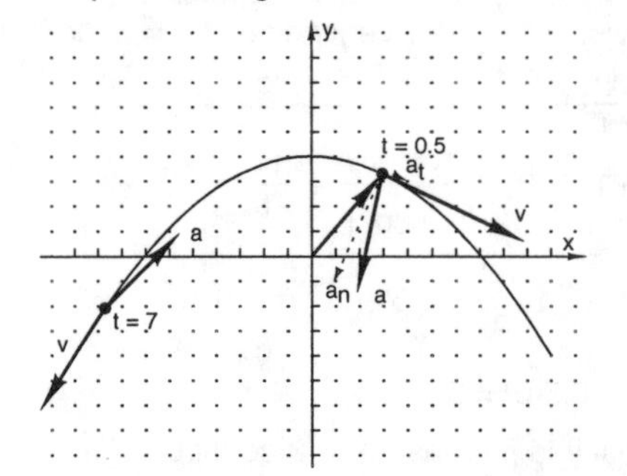

These vectors make sense because the head of $\vec{r}$ is on the graph, $\vec{v}$ is tangent to the graph, and $\vec{a}$ points to the concave side of the graph.

c. The object is speeding up. The angle between $\vec{a}$ and $\vec{v}$ is acute.

d. $|\vec{v}(0.5)| = \sqrt{(6\cos 0.3)^2 + (-4.8\sin 0.6)^2}$
$= 6.3404...$
$\vec{a}(0.5)\cdot\vec{v}(0.5) = (-3.6\sin 0.3)(6\cos 0.3) + (-5.76\cos 0.6)(-4.8\sin 0.6)$
$= 6.7863...$, so the angle is acute.
$P = \dfrac{\vec{a}(0.5)\cdot\vec{v}(0.5)}{|\vec{v}(0.5)|} = 1.0703...$
$\vec{a}_t(0.5) = P\dfrac{\vec{v}(0.5)}{|\vec{v}(0.5)|}$
$= P\dfrac{(6\cos 0.3)\vec{i} + (-4.8\sin 0.6)\vec{j}}{|\vec{v}(0.5)|}$
$= 0.9676...\vec{i} - 0.4575...\vec{j}$
$\vec{a}_n(0.5) = \vec{a}(0.5) - \vec{a}_t(0.5)$
$= -2.0314...\vec{i} - 4.2964...\vec{j}$
Graph, part b.

e. Object is speeding up at $|\vec{a}_t(0.5)| = P$
$= 1.0703... \approx 1.07$ (ft/sec)/sec.

f. $\vec{r}(7) = (10\sin 4.2)\vec{i} + (4\cos 8.4)\vec{j}$
$= -8.7157...\vec{i} - 2.0771...\vec{j}$
$\vec{v}(7) = (6\cos 4.2)\vec{i} + (-4.8\sin 8.4)\vec{j}$
$= -2.9415...\vec{i} - 4.1020...\vec{j}$
$\vec{a}(7) = (-3.6\sin 4.2)\vec{i} + (-5.76\cos 8.4)\vec{j}$
$= 3.1376...\vec{i} + 2.9911...\vec{j}$
Graph, part b.
Object is slowing down. The angle between $\vec{a}$ and $\vec{v}$ is obtuse.
(Note $P = \dfrac{\vec{a}(7)\cdot\vec{v}(7)}{|\vec{v}(7)|} = -4.2592...$, so the object is slowing down at $4.2592... \approx 4.26$ (ft/sec)/sec.)

g. $\vec{r}(0) = (10\sin 0)\vec{i} + (4\cos 0)\vec{j} = 0\vec{i} + 4\vec{j}$
$\vec{v}(0) = (6\cos 0)\vec{i} + (-4.8\sin 0)\vec{j} = 6\vec{i} + 0\vec{j}$
$\vec{a}(0) = (-3.6\sin 0)\vec{i} + (-5.76\cos 0)\vec{j}$
$= 0\vec{i} - 5.76\vec{j}$
$\vec{a}(0)\cdot\vec{v}(0) = (0)(6) + (-5.76)(0) = 0$
$\therefore \vec{a}(0)$ and $\vec{v}(0)$ are perpendicular, Q.E.D.
This means the object is neither slowing down nor speeding up at t = 0.

2. Parabolic Path Problem II

a. $\vec{r}(t) = (8\cos 0.8t)\vec{i} + (6\sin 0.4t)\vec{j}$
$\vec{v}(t) = (-6.4\sin 0.8t)\vec{i} + (2.4\cos 0.4t)\vec{j}$
$\vec{a}(t) = (-5.12\cos 0.8t)\vec{i} + (-0.96\sin 0.4t)\vec{j}$

b. $\vec{r}(1) = (8\cos 0.8)\vec{i} + (6\sin 0.4)\vec{j}$
$= 5.5736...\vec{i} + 2.3365...\vec{j}$
$\vec{v}(1) = (-6.4\sin 0.8)\vec{i} + (2.4\cos 0.4)\vec{j}$
$= -4.5910...\vec{i} + 2.2105...\vec{j}$
$\vec{a}(1) = (-5.12\cos 0.8)\vec{i} + (-0.96\sin 0.4)\vec{j}$
$= -3.5671...\vec{i} - 0.3738...\vec{j}$
Graph, showing $\vec{r}$, $\vec{v}$, and $\vec{a}$ at t = 1.

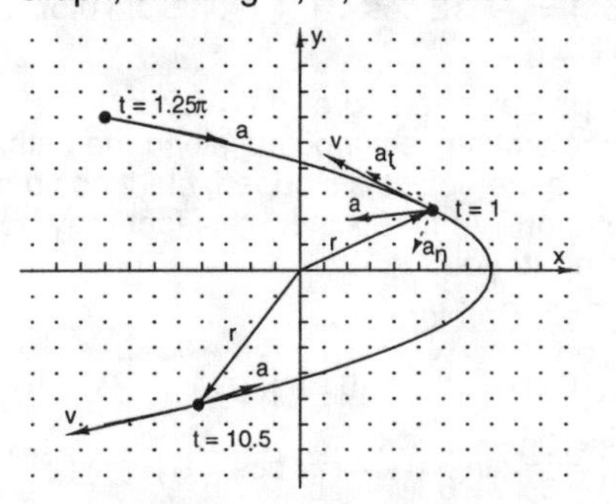

These vectors make sense because the head of $\vec{r}$ is on the graph, $\vec{v}$ is tangent to the graph, and $\vec{a}$ points to the concave side of the graph.

c. The object is speeding up. The angle between $\vec{a}$ and $\vec{v}$ is acute.

d. $|\vec{v}(1)| = \sqrt{(-6.4\sin 0.8)^2 + (2.4\cos 0.4)^2}$
$= 5.0955...$
$\vec{a}(1)\cdot\vec{v}(1) = (-5.12\cos 0.8)(-6.4\sin 0.8) + (-0.96\sin 0.4)(2.4\cos 0.4)$
$= 15.5506...$, so the angle is acute.
$P = \dfrac{\vec{a}(1)\cdot\vec{v}(1)}{|\vec{v}(1)|} = 3.0518...$
$\vec{a}_t(1) = P\dfrac{\vec{v}(1)}{|\vec{v}(1)|}$
$= P\dfrac{(-6.4\sin 0.8)\vec{i} + (2.4\cos 0.4)\vec{j}}{|\vec{v}(1)|}$
$= -2.7496...\vec{i} + 1.3239...\vec{j}$
$\vec{a}_n(1) = \vec{a}(1) - \vec{a}_t(1)$
$= -0.8174...\vec{i} - 1.6977...\vec{j}$
Graph, part b., showing $\vec{a}_t$ and $\vec{a}_n$ at t = 1.

e. Object is speeding up at
$|\vec{a}_t(1)| = P(1) = 3.0518... \approx 3.05$ (ft/sec)sec.

f. $\vec{r}(10.5) = (8\cos 8.4)\vec{i} + (6\sin 4.2)\vec{j}$
$= -4.1543...\vec{i} - 5.2294...\vec{j}$
$\vec{v}(10.5) = (-6.4\sin 8.4)\vec{i} + (2.4\cos 4.2)\vec{j}$
$= -5.4694...\vec{i} - 1.1766...\vec{j}$
$\vec{a}(10.5) = (-5.12\cos 8.4)\vec{i} + (-0.96\sin 4.2)\vec{j}$
$= 2.6587...\vec{i} + 0.8367...\vec{j}$
Graph, part b., showing $\vec{r}$, $\vec{v}$, and $\vec{a}$ at t = 10.5.
The object is slowing down at t = 10.5. The angle between $\vec{a}$ and $\vec{v}$ is obtuse at that time.
(Note $P = \dfrac{\vec{a}(10.5)\cdot\vec{v}(10.5)}{|\vec{v}(10.5)|} = -2.7552...$, so the object is slowing down at about 2.8 (ft/sec)/sec.)

g. The object is stopped when

$\vec{v}(t) = (-6.4 \sin 0.8t)\vec{i} + (2.4 \cos 0.4t)\vec{j} = \vec{0}$

$\Leftrightarrow -6.4 \sin 0.8t = 0$ and $2.4 \cos 0.4t = 0$

Using $-6.4 \sin 0.8t = -1.28 \sin 0.4t \cos 0.4t$, one sees that $\vec{v}(t) = \vec{0}$ exactly when $\cos 0.4t = 0$; the first time this happens at $t = 1.25\pi$ sec.

$\vec{r}(1.25\pi) = (8 \cos \pi)\vec{i} + (6 \sin 0.5\pi)\vec{j} = -8\vec{i} + 6\vec{j}$

$\vec{a}(1.25\pi) = (-5.12 \cos \pi)\vec{i} + (-0.96 \sin 0.5\pi)\vec{j}$

$= 5.12\vec{i} - 0.96\vec{j}$.

Graph, part b., showing $\vec{a}$ at $t = 1.25\pi$.

The acceleration vector points along the path at $t = 1.25\pi$. So the object is stopped, but it has a nonzero acceleration. At first glance, this fact may be surprising to you!

3. <u>Elliptical Path Problem</u>

a. $\vec{r}(t) = (10 \cos \frac{\pi}{6} t)\vec{i} + (6 \sin \frac{\pi}{6} t)\vec{j}$

$\vec{v}(t) = (-\frac{10\pi}{6} \sin \frac{\pi}{6} t)\vec{i} + (\frac{6\pi}{6} \cos \frac{\pi}{6} t)\vec{j}$

$\vec{r}(t) + \vec{v}(t) = (10 \cos \frac{\pi}{6} t - \frac{10\pi}{6} \sin \frac{\pi}{6} t)\vec{i}$

$+ (6 \sin \frac{\pi}{6} t + \frac{6\pi}{6} \cos \frac{\pi}{6} t)\vec{j}$

Graph, showing path of $\vec{r} + \vec{v}$.

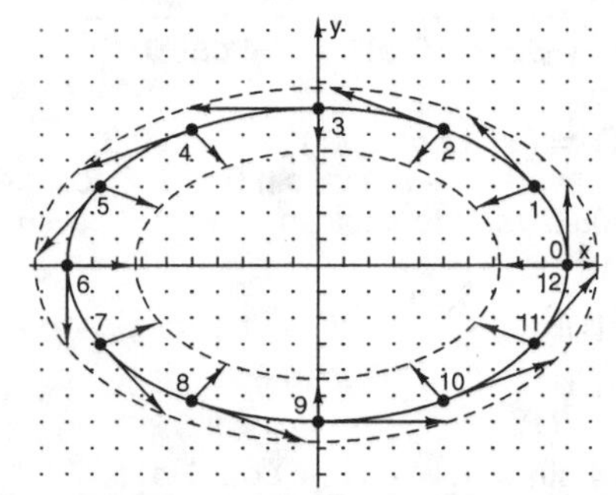

b. Graph, part a., showing vectors $\vec{v}$.

c. For $\vec{r} + \vec{v}$,

$\frac{x}{10} = \cos \frac{\pi}{6} t - \frac{\pi}{6} \sin \frac{\pi}{6} t$

$\frac{y}{6} = \sin \frac{\pi}{6} t + \frac{\pi}{6} \cos \frac{\pi}{6} t$

$(\frac{x}{10})^2 = \cos^2 \frac{\pi}{6} t - \frac{\pi}{3} \cos \frac{\pi}{6} t \sin \frac{\pi}{6} t + (\frac{\pi}{6})^2 \sin^2 \frac{\pi}{6} t$

$(\frac{y}{6})^2 = \sin^2 \frac{\pi}{6} t + \frac{\pi}{3} \sin \frac{\pi}{6} t \cos \frac{\pi}{6} t + (\frac{\pi}{6})^2 \cos^2 \frac{\pi}{6} t$

$\therefore (\frac{x}{10})^2 + (\frac{y}{6})^2 = \cos^2 \frac{\pi}{6} t + \sin^2 \frac{\pi}{6} t + (\frac{\pi}{6})^2 \sin^2 \frac{\pi}{6} t$

$+ (\frac{\pi}{6})^2 \cos^2 \frac{\pi}{6} t$

$(\frac{x}{10})^2 + (\frac{y}{6})^2 = 1 + (\frac{\pi}{6})^2$

$$\frac{x^2}{100(1 + \pi^2/36)} + \frac{y^2}{36(1 + \pi^2/36)} = 1.$$

This is the equation of an ellipse centered at the origin with x-radius 11.2878... and y-radius 6.7727...

d. $\vec{a}(t) = (-\frac{10\pi^2}{36} \cos \frac{\pi}{6} t)\vec{i} + (-\frac{6\pi^2}{36} \sin \frac{\pi}{6} t)\vec{j}$

$\vec{r}(t) + \vec{a}(t) = (10 - \frac{10\pi^2}{36}) \cos \frac{\pi}{6} t\ \vec{i} + (6 - \frac{6\pi^2}{36}) \sin \frac{\pi}{6} t\ \vec{j}$

Graph, part a., showing elliptical path followed by the heads of the acceleration vectors.

e. The direction of each acceleration vector is the opposite of the corresponding position vector, and thus directed toward the origin.

Note that $\vec{a}(t) = -\frac{\pi^2}{36} \vec{r}(t)$.

4. <u>Spiral Path Problem</u>

a. $\vec{r}(t) = (0.5t \cos t)\vec{i} + (0.5t \sin t)\vec{j}$

$\vec{v}(t) = (0.5 \cos t - 0.5t \sin t)\vec{i}$

$+ (0.5 \sin t + 0.5t \cos t)\vec{j}$

$\vec{a}(t) = (-\sin t - 0.5t \cos t)\vec{i} + (\cos t - 0.5t \sin t)\vec{j}$

b. $\vec{r}(8.5) = 4.25 \cos 8.5\ \vec{i} + 4.25 \sin 8.5\ \vec{j}$

$= -2.5585...\vec{i} + 3.3935...\vec{j}$

$\vec{v}(8.5) = (0.5 \cos 8.5 - 4.25 \sin 8.5)\vec{i}$

$+ (0.5 \sin 8.5 + 4.25 \cos 8.5)\vec{j}$

$= -3.6945...\vec{i} - 2.1593...\vec{j}$

$\vec{a}(8.5) = (-\sin 8.5 - 4.25 \cos 8.5)\vec{i}$

$+ (\cos 8.5 - 4.25 \sin 8.5)\vec{j}$

$= 1.7600...\vec{i} - 3.9955...\vec{j}$

$\vec{r}(12) = 6 \cos 12\ \vec{i} + 6 \sin 12\ \vec{j}$

$= 5.0631...\vec{i} - 3.2194...\vec{j}$

$\vec{v}(12) = (0.5 \cos 12 - 6 \sin 12)\vec{i}$

$+ (0.5 \sin 12 + 6 \cos 12)\vec{j}$

$= 3.6413...\vec{i} + 4.7948...\vec{j}$

$\vec{a}(12) = (-\sin 12 - 6 \cos 12)\vec{i}$

$+ (\cos 12 - 6 \sin 12)\vec{j}$

$= -4.5265...\vec{i} + 4.0632...\vec{j}$

Graph, showing that $\vec{r}(8.5)$ and $\vec{r}(12)$ really do terminate on the path.

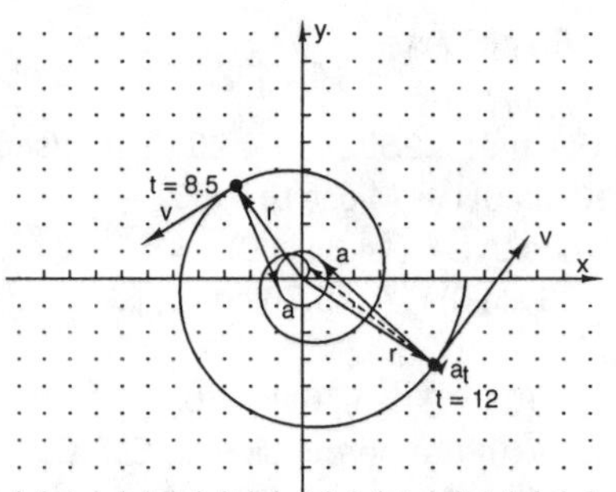

c. Graph, part b., showing $\vec{v}(8.5)$, $\vec{v}(12)$, $\vec{a}(8.5)$, and $\vec{a}(12)$. The velocity vectors point along the path as it spirals outward, and the acceleration vectors point inward to the concave side of the graph.

d. In both cases, the angle between $\vec{a}$ and $\vec{v}$ appears to be acute. Check using dot products.

$\vec{a}(8.5) \cdot \vec{v}(8.5) = 2.125$, which is positive.

$\vec{a}(12) \cdot \vec{v}(12) = 3$, which is also positive.

Thus, the angles are acute, and the object is speeding up at both times.

e. At t = 12 hr, $\vec{a}(12) \cdot \vec{v}(12) = 3$

$|\vec{v}(12)| = \sqrt{36.25} = 6.0207...$

$\vec{a}_t(12) = \frac{\vec{a}(12) \cdot \vec{v}(12)}{|\vec{v}(12)|} \cdot \frac{\vec{v}(12)}{|\vec{v}(12)|}$

$= \frac{3}{36.25} (3.6413...\vec{i} + 4.7948...\vec{j})$

$= 0.3013...\vec{i} + 0.3968...\vec{j}$

$\vec{a}_n(12) = \vec{a}(12) - \vec{a}_t(12)$

$= -4.8279...\vec{i} + 3.6664...\vec{j}$

Graph, part b., showing $\vec{a}_n$ and $\vec{a}_t$ at t = 12.

f. Speed = $|\vec{v}(12)| = \sqrt{36.25} = 6.0207... \approx 6.02$ mph.

Speed is increasing by $P(12) = \dfrac{3}{\sqrt{36.25}} = 0.4982...$

≈ 0.498 mph/hr.

g. Graph, part b., showing $\vec{r}(t) + \vec{a}(t)$

The heads seem to lie on a unit circle.

Algebraic verification:

$\vec{r}(t) + \vec{a}(t) = -\sin t\ \vec{i} + \cos t\ \vec{j}$, which is a circle.

5. Parabolic Path Problem III

a. $\vec{r}(x) = x\vec{i} + y\vec{j} = x\vec{i} + x^2\vec{j}$

$\vec{v}(x) = \dfrac{dx}{dt}\vec{i} + \dfrac{dy}{dt}\vec{j} = \dfrac{dx}{dt}\vec{i} + 2x\dfrac{dx}{dt}\vec{j}$

b. $\dfrac{dx}{dt} = -3 \Rightarrow \vec{v}(x) = -3\vec{i} - 6x\vec{j}$

$\vec{v}(2) = -3\vec{i} - 12\vec{j}$

At $x = 2$, speed = $|\vec{v}(2)| = \sqrt{153} = 12.3693...$

≈ 12.4 cm/sec.

c. Graph, showing $\vec{r}(2)$ and $\vec{v}(2)$.

This is reasonable because $\vec{v}(2)$ points along the curve to the left, indicating that x is decreasing.

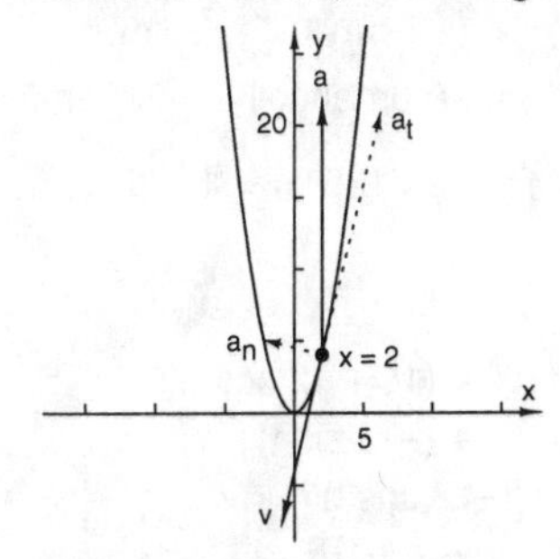

d. From part b., $\vec{v}(x) = -3\vec{i} - 6x\vec{j}$

$\therefore\ \vec{a}(x) = 0\vec{i} - 6\dfrac{dx}{dt}\vec{j} = 18\vec{j}$

$\vec{a}(2) = 18\vec{j}$. Graph, part c.

e. $\vec{a}_t(2) = \dfrac{\vec{a}(2)\cdot\vec{v}(2)}{|\vec{v}(2)|}\cdot\dfrac{\vec{v}(2)}{|\vec{v}(2)|} = \dfrac{-216(-3\vec{i} - 12\vec{j})}{153}$

$= \dfrac{72}{17}\vec{i} + \dfrac{288}{17}\vec{j} = 4.2352...\vec{i} + 16.9411...\vec{j}$

$\vec{a}_n(2) = \vec{a}(2) - \vec{a}_t(2)$

$= -\dfrac{72}{17}\vec{i} + \dfrac{18}{17}\vec{j} = -4.2352...\vec{i} + 1.0588...\vec{j}$

$\vec{a}_t(2)$ is parallel to the curve. $\vec{a}_n(2)$ is normal to the curve and points inward to the concave side.

f. When $x = 2$, the object is slowing down. This is true because the angle between $\vec{a}(2)$ and $\vec{v}(2)$ is obtuse, as shown by the graph and by the fact that the dot product is negative. Also, $\vec{a}_t(2)$ points in the opposite direction of $\vec{v}(2)$.

g. $dL = \sqrt{1 + (dy/dx)^2}\,dx = \sqrt{1 + 4x^2}\,dx$

$\dfrac{dL}{dt} = \sqrt{1 + 4x^2}\dfrac{dx}{dt} = 5$

At $x = 2$, $5 = \sqrt{1 + 4(2)^2}\dfrac{dx}{dt} = \sqrt{17}\dfrac{dx}{dt}$

$\Rightarrow \dfrac{dx}{dt} = \dfrac{5}{\sqrt{17}} = 1.2126... \approx 1.21$ cm/sec.

6. Velocity Vector Limit Problem

$\vec{r}(1) = 8.8615...\vec{i} + 4.8410...\vec{j}$

$\vec{q}(2) = -2.9659...\vec{i} + 4.3406...\vec{j}$

$\vec{q}(1.5) = -0.2065...\vec{i} + 6.6362...\vec{j}$

$\vec{q}(1.1) = 2.5579...\vec{i} + 7.4880...\vec{j}$

$\vec{v}(t) = (12\cos t\cos 0.5t - 6\sin t\sin 0.5t)\vec{i}$
$\qquad + (12\cos t\sin 0.5t + 6\sin t\cos 0.5t)\vec{j}$

$\vec{v}(1) = 3.2693...\vec{i} + 7.5391...\vec{j}$

Graph, showing average velocity vectors approaching the instantaneous velocity vector $\vec{v}(1)$ as t approaches 1. The instantaneous velocity vector is tangent to the graph, and points in the direction of motion.

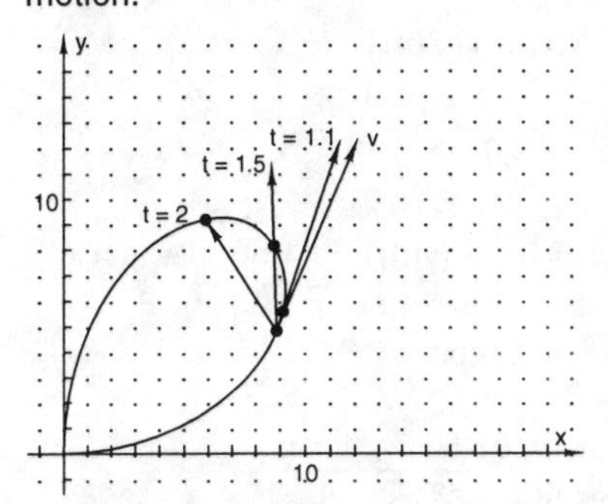

7. $\vec{r}(t) = (10\sin 0.6t)\vec{i} + (4\cos 1.2t)\vec{j}$

$dL = \sqrt{(dx/dt)^2 + (dy/dt)^2}\,dt$

$= \sqrt{(6\cos 0.6t)^2 + (-4.8\sin 1.2t)^2}\,dt$

$L = \int_0^2 dL \approx 12.0858...$ ft (numerically)

8. $\vec{r}(t) = (10\cos\frac{\pi}{6}t)\vec{i} + (6\sin\frac{\pi}{6}t)\vec{j}$

$dL = \sqrt{(dx/dt)^2 + (dy/dt)^2}\,dt$

$= \sqrt{\left(\frac{-10\pi}{6}\cdot\sin\frac{\pi}{6}t\right)^2 + \left(\frac{6\pi}{6}\cdot\cos\frac{\pi}{6}t\right)^2}\,dt$

One complete cycle of the curve is $0 \le t \le 12$, so

$L = \int_0^{12} dL = 51.0539...$ (numerically) ≈ 51.1 ft.

9. Baseball Problem

a. $\vec{a}(t) = 0\vec{i} - 32\vec{j}$

$\vec{v}(t) = \int (0\vec{i} - 32\vec{j})\,dt = C_1\vec{i} + (-32t + C_2)\vec{j}$

$\vec{v}(0) = -130\vec{i} + 0\vec{j} \Leftrightarrow C_1 = -130$ and $C_2 = 0$

$\therefore\ \vec{v}(t) = -130\vec{i} - 32t\vec{j}$.

b. $\vec{r}(t) = \int (-130\vec{i} - 32t\vec{j})\,dt$

$= (-130t + C_3)\vec{i} + (-16t^2 + C_4)\vec{j}$

$\vec{r}(0) = 60.5\vec{i} + 8\vec{j} \Leftrightarrow C_3 = 60.5$ and $C_4 = 8$

$\therefore\ \vec{r}(t) = (-130t + 60.5)\vec{i} + (-16t^2 + 8)\vec{j}$.

c. When the ball passes over the plate, $x(t) = 0$, so $t = 60.5/130 = 0.4653...$.

At that time, $y(t) = 4.5346...$, which is slightly above the strike zone.

d. At $t = 0$, $dx/dt = 200\cos 15^\circ$, $dy/dt = 200\sin 15^\circ$.

As in part a., $\vec{v}(t) = C_1\vec{i} + (-32t + C_2)\vec{j}$

$= (200\cos 15^\circ)\vec{i} + (-32t + 200\sin 15^\circ)\vec{j}$

As in part b.,

$\vec{r}(t) = (200t\cos 15^\circ)\vec{i}$
$\qquad + (-16t^2 + 200t\sin 15^\circ + 3)\vec{j}$

e. When $x = 400$, $t = 2 \sec 15^\circ = 2.0705...$ sec
$y(2.0705...) = 41.5846...$.
Phyllis makes the home run, because $41.5... > 10$.
Graph.

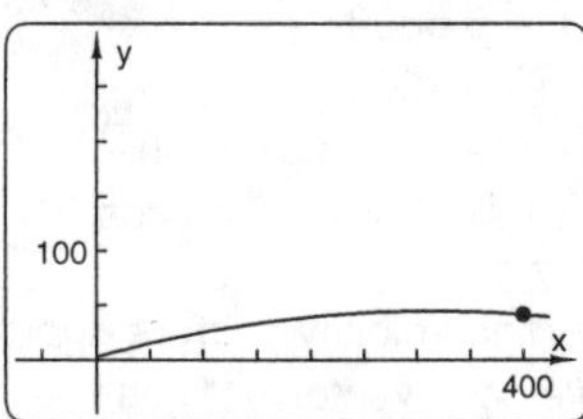

10. Sinusoidal Path Problem

a. $\vec{a}(t) = 3\vec{i} + y''(t)\vec{j}$
$\vec{v}(t) = (3t + C_1)\vec{i} + (y'(t))\vec{j}$
$\vec{v}(0) = 0\vec{i} + 0\vec{j} \Rightarrow C_1 = 0$
$\vec{r}(t) = (1.5t^2 + C_2)\vec{i} + (y(t))\vec{j}$
$\vec{r}(0) = 0\vec{i} + 0\vec{j} \Rightarrow C_2 = 0$
$\therefore \vec{r}(t) = (1.5t^2)\vec{i} + (y(t))\vec{j} = (1.5t^2)\vec{i} + (\sin x(t))\vec{j}$
$\vec{r}(t) = (1.5t^2)\vec{i} + (\sin 1.5t^2)\vec{j}$

b. $\vec{v}(t) = (3t)\vec{i} + (3t \cos 1.5t^2)\vec{j}$
If $x = 6$, $t = 2$
$\vec{v}(2) = 6\vec{i} + 5.7610...\vec{j}$
Speed $= |\vec{v}(2)| = \sqrt{6^2 + 5.76...^2} = 8.3180...$
≈ 8.32 m/min.

11. Figure Skating Problem

a. $d = a + b \cos t$
$t = 0$: $240 = a + b \cos 0 = a + b$
$t = \pi$: $-60 = a + b \cos \pi = a - b$
$2a = 180 \Rightarrow a = 90$
$2b = 300 \Rightarrow b = 150$
$\therefore d = 90 + 150 \cos t$

b. $\vec{r}(t) = (90 \cos t + 150 \cos^2 t)\vec{i}$
$+ (90 \sin t + 150 \sin t \cos t)\vec{j}$
$\vec{v}(t) = (-90 \sin t - 300 \cos t \sin t)\vec{i}$
$+ (90 \cos t + 150 \cos^2 t - 150 \sin^2 t)\vec{j}$
$\vec{v}(t) = (-90 \sin t - 150 \sin 2t)\vec{i}$
$+ (90 \cos t + 150 \cos 2t)\vec{j}$
$\vec{v}(1) = -212.1270...\vec{i} - 13.7948...\vec{j}$
Speed $= \sqrt{(-212.1...)^2 + (-13.7...)^2}$
$= 212.5750... \approx 212.6$ cm/sec.

c. $\vec{a}(t) = (-90 \cos t - 300 \cos 2t)\vec{i}$
$+ (-90 \sin t - 300 \sin 2t)\vec{j}$
$\vec{a}(1) = 76.2168...\vec{i} - 348.5216...\vec{j}$
$P(1) = \dfrac{\vec{a}(1) \cdot \vec{v}(1)}{|\vec{v}(1)|} = -53.4392...$
$\vec{a}_t(1) = P(1)\dfrac{\vec{v}(1)}{|\vec{v}(1)|} = 53.3266...\vec{i} + 3.4678...\vec{j}$
$\vec{a}_n(1) = \vec{a}(1) - \vec{a}_t(1)$
$= 22.8902...\vec{i} - 351.9894...\vec{j}$
Annie is slowing down. The angle between the acceleration and velocity vector is obtuse, as revealed by the negative dot product. She is slowing down at $53.4392... \approx 53.4$ cm/sec.

12. River Bend Problem

a. $\vec{r} = (0.5t + \sin t)\vec{i} + (4 \cos 0.5t)\vec{j}$
$\vec{v}(t) = (0.5 + \cos t)\vec{i} + (-2 \sin 0.5t)\vec{j}$
$\vec{a}(t) = (-\sin t)\vec{i} + (-\cos 0.5t)\vec{j}$
$\vec{v}(14) = 0.6367...\vec{i} - 1.3139...\vec{j}$
$\vec{a}(14) = -0.9906...\vec{i} - 0.7539...\vec{j}$
Speed $= |\vec{v}(14)| = 1.4601...$ mph
$P(14) = \dfrac{\vec{a}(14) \cdot \vec{v}(14)}{|\vec{v}(14)|} = \dfrac{0.3598...}{1.4601...} = 0.2464...$
$\vec{a}_t(14) = P(14)\dfrac{\vec{v}(14)}{|\vec{v}(14)|} = 0.1074...\vec{i} - 0.2217...\vec{j}$
$\vec{a}_n(14) = \vec{a}(14) - \vec{a}_t(14)$
$= -1.0980...\vec{i} - 0.5312...\vec{j}$
The log is speeding up at $t = 14$. You can tell by the fact that $P(14)$ is positive, and thus the angle between $\vec{a}(14)$ and $\vec{v}(14)$ is acute, which means that $\vec{a}_t(14)$ points in the same direction as $\vec{v}(14)$. It is speeding up at $0.2464... \approx 0.246$ mph/hr.

b. $dL = \sqrt{dx^2 + dy^2}$
$= \sqrt{(0.5 + \cos t)^2 + (-2 \sin 0.5t)^2}\ dt$
$L = \int_0^{14} dL \approx 22.7185...$ (numerically) ≈ 22.7 mi.
Average speed $\approx \dfrac{1}{14}(22.7185...) = 1.6227...$
≈ 1.62 mph.

13. Roller Coaster Problem

a. $\vec{r}(t) = (5t - 12 \sin t)\vec{i} + (15 + 12 \cos t)\vec{j}$
$\vec{v}(t) = (5 - 12 \cos t)\vec{i} + (-12 \sin t)\vec{j}$
$\vec{a}(t) = (12 \sin t)\vec{i} + (-12 \cos t)\vec{j}$.

b. $\vec{v}(2.5) = 14.6137...\vec{i} - 7.1816...\vec{j}$
$\vec{a}(2.5) = 7.1816...\vec{i} + 9.6137...\vec{j}$.
Graph, showing $\vec{v}(2.5)$ and $\vec{a}(2.5)$.

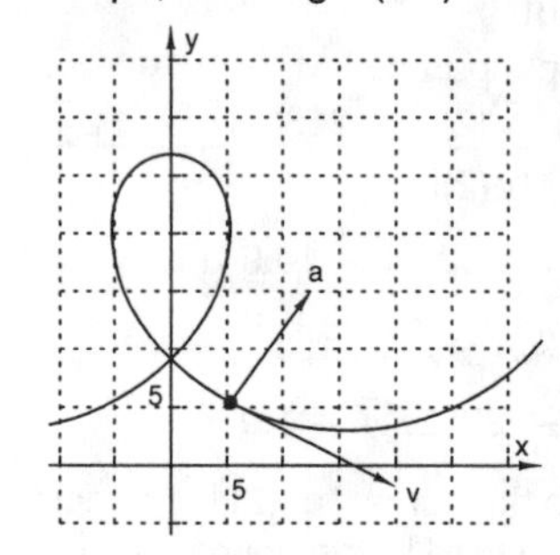

c. $P(2.5) = \dfrac{\vec{a}(2.5) \cdot \vec{v}(2.5)}{|\vec{v}(2.5)|}$
$= \dfrac{60 \sin 2.5}{\sqrt{169 - 120 \cos 2.5}} = 2.2052...$
$\vec{a}_t(2.5) = P(2.5)\dfrac{\vec{v}(2.5)}{|\vec{v}(2.5)|}$
$= 1.9791...\vec{i} - 0.9726...\vec{j}$
$\vec{a}_n(2.5) = \vec{a}(2.5) - \vec{a}_t(2.5)$
$= 5.2024...\vec{i} + 10.5863...\vec{j}$

d. $\vec{v}(2.5)$ is reasonable because its graph points along the path in the direction of motion. $\vec{a}(2.5)$ is reasonable because it points toward the concave side of the path. The rollercoaster is traveling at $|\vec{v}(2.5)| = 16.2830...$ ft/sec. Its speed is increasing at $P(2.5) = 2.2052...$ ft/sec^2, as shown by the fact that P(2.5) is positive, meaning that the angle between $\vec{a}(2.5)$ and $\vec{v}(2.5)$ is acute.

e. The path is at a high point when the y-component of $\vec{r}$ is a maximum. This happens when $\cos t = 1$, or $t = 0 + 2\pi n$.

$\vec{a}(0+2\pi n) = 0\vec{i} - 12\vec{j}$, pointing straight down.

Similarly, the path is at a low point when $\cos t = -1$, or $t = \pi + 2\pi n$.

$\vec{a}(\pi + 2\pi n) = 0\vec{i} + 12\vec{j}$, pointing straight up, Q.E.D.

f. $dL = \sqrt{dx^2 + dy^2}$

$= \sqrt{(5 - 12\cos t)^2 + (-12\sin t)^2}\, dt$

$L = \int_0^{2\pi} dL \approx 78.7078...$ (numerically) ≈ 78.7 ft.

14. Dot Product Problem

Recall that $|\vec{i}| = |\vec{j}| = 1$.

The angle between $\vec{i}$ and $\vec{i}$ is 0, so

$\vec{i}\cdot\vec{i} = |\vec{i}||\vec{i}|\cos 0 = 1$.

Similarly, $\vec{j}\cdot\vec{j} = 1$.

The angle between $\vec{i}$ and $\vec{j}$ is $\frac{\pi}{2}$, so

$\vec{i}\cdot\vec{j} = |\vec{i}||\vec{j}|\cos\frac{\pi}{2} = 0$.

$\therefore \vec{v}_1\cdot\vec{v}_2 = (x_1\vec{i} + y_1\vec{j})\cdot(x_2\vec{i} + y_2\vec{j})$

$= x_1x_2\vec{i}\cdot\vec{i} + x_1y_2\vec{i}\cdot\vec{j} + y_1x_2\vec{j}\cdot\vec{i} + y_1y_2\vec{j}\cdot\vec{j}$

$= x_1x_2(1) + x_1y_2(0) + y_1x_2(0) + y_1y_2(1)$

$= x_1x_2 + y_1y_2$, Q.E.D.

15. Three-Dimensional Vector Problem

$\vec{r}(t) = (10\sin 0.8t)\vec{i} + (10\cos 0.6t)\vec{j} + (6t^{0.5})\vec{k}$

$\vec{v}(t) = (8\cos 0.8t)\vec{i} + (-6\sin 0.6t)\vec{j} + (3t^{-0.5})\vec{k}$

$\vec{a}(t) = (-6.4\sin 0.8t)\vec{i}$

$\quad + (-3.6\cos 0.6t)\vec{j} + (-1.5t^{-1.5})\vec{k}$

$\vec{v}(1) = (8\cos 0.8)\vec{i} + (-6\sin 0.6)\vec{j} + 3\vec{k}$

$\vec{a}(1) = (-6.4\sin 0.8)\vec{i} + (-3.6\cos 0.6)\vec{j} - 1.5\vec{k}$

To determine whether the object is speeding up or slowing down, find the dot product.

$\vec{a}(1)\cdot\vec{v}(1) = (-6.4\sin 0.8)(8\cos 0.8)$

$\quad + (-3.6\cos 0.6)(-6\sin 0.6) + (-1.5)(3)$

$= -20.0230...$

$\therefore$ the object is slowing down, because the angle between $\vec{a}(1)$ and $\vec{v}(1)$ is obtuse.

16. Curvature Project

a. This is an example of the chain rule.

b. dy/dx equals the slope of the velocity vector, and $\tan\phi$ also equals the slope of this vector. Thus, $\tan\phi = dy/dx$.

By the chain rule, $dy/dx = (dy/dt)/(dx/dx)$, Q.E.D.

c. $\tan\phi = \frac{dy/dt}{dx/dt} = \frac{y'(t)}{x'(t)} \Rightarrow \frac{d}{ds}(\tan\phi) = \frac{d}{ds}\left(\frac{y'(t)}{x'(t)}\right)$

$\Rightarrow \sec^2\phi\,\frac{d\phi}{ds} = \frac{x'y'' - x''y'}{x'^2}\,\frac{dt}{ds}$

$\therefore \frac{d\phi}{ds} = \frac{x'y'' - x''y'}{x'^2(\sec^2\phi)(ds/dt)}$

But $\sec^2\phi = 1 + \tan^2\phi = 1 + y'^2/x'^2$, $ds/dt = |\vec{v}|$.

$\therefore \frac{d\phi}{ds} = \frac{x'y'' - x''y'}{x'^2(1 + y'^2/x'^2)|\vec{v}|}$

$= \frac{x'y'' - x''y'}{(x'^2 + y'^2)|\vec{v}|} = \frac{x'y'' - x''y'}{|\vec{v}|^3}$, Q.E.D.

d. $x = 5\cos t \Rightarrow x' = -5\sin t \Rightarrow x'' = -5\cos t$

$y = 3\sin t \Rightarrow y' = 3\cos t \Rightarrow y'' = -3\sin t$

$|\vec{v}| = \sqrt{25\sin^2 t + 9\cos^2 t}$

$\therefore \frac{d\phi}{dt} = \frac{15\sin^2 t + 15\cos^2 t}{(25\sin^2 t + 9\cos^2 t)^{3/2}}$

$= \frac{15}{(16\sin^2 t + 9)^{3/2}}$,

which is maximized for $\sin^2 t = 0$ at $(\pm 5, 0)$, the ends of the major axis; and is minimized for $\sin^2 t = 1$ at $(0, \pm 3)$, the ends of the minor axis, Q.E.D.

e. $x = r\cos t \Rightarrow x' = -r\sin t \Rightarrow x'' = -r\cos t$

$y = r\sin t \Rightarrow y' = r\cos t \Rightarrow y'' = -r\sin t$

$|\vec{v}| = \sqrt{r^2\cos^2 t + r^2\sin^2 t} = r$

$\therefore \frac{d\phi}{ds} = \frac{r^2\sin^2 t + r^2\cos^2 t}{|r|^3} = \frac{1}{|r|}$,

a constant equal to the reciprocal of the radius.

f. $x = 5\cos^2 t \Rightarrow x' = -10\cos t\sin t = -5\sin 2t$

$\Rightarrow x'' = -10\cos 2t$

$y = 3\sin^2 t \Rightarrow y' = 6\sin t\cos t = 3\sin 2t$

$\Rightarrow y'' = 6\cos 2t$

$|\vec{v}| = \sqrt{25\sin^2 2t + 9\sin^2 2t} = \sqrt{34}\,|\sin 2t|$

$\therefore \frac{d\phi}{ds} = \frac{-30\sin 2t\cos 2t + 30\sin 2t\cos 2t}{\sqrt{34}\,|\sin 2t|}$

$= 0$, Q.E.D.

g. At (5,0), $\sin t = 0$, so $\frac{d\phi}{ds} = \frac{15}{9^{3/2}} = \frac{5}{9}$.

Radius of curvature $= \frac{9}{5} = 1.8$

h. The osculating circle has radius 1.8 and center on the x-axis at $x = 4 - 1.8 = 3.2$. Equations are:

$x = 3.2 + 1.8\cos t$

$y = 1.8\sin t$

Graph, showing osculating circle. The name is appropriate because the circle "kisses" the ellipse at the point (5, 0).

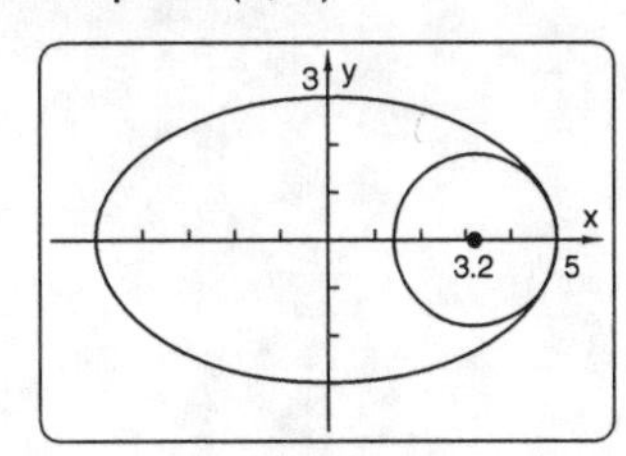

Review Problems

R0. Journal entries will vary.

R1. Popeye and Olive Problem

$v = \sqrt{t} - 3 = 0$ at $t = 9$ seconds.
$v > 0$ for $t > 9$ sec.
Displacement from $t = 0$ to $t = 9$ is
$\int_0^9 (\sqrt{t} - 3)\,dt = -9.$
They have moved 9 ft. closer to the sawmill.
From $t = 0$ to $t = 25$:

$\text{Displ.} = \int_0^{25} (\sqrt{t} - 3)\,dt = 8\frac{1}{3}$ ft.

$\text{Dist.} = \int_0^{25} |\sqrt{t} - 3|\,dt = 26\frac{1}{3}$ ft.

R2.a. i. $v(t) = 2^t - 8$
Graph, showing $v(t) > 0$ for $t > 3$.

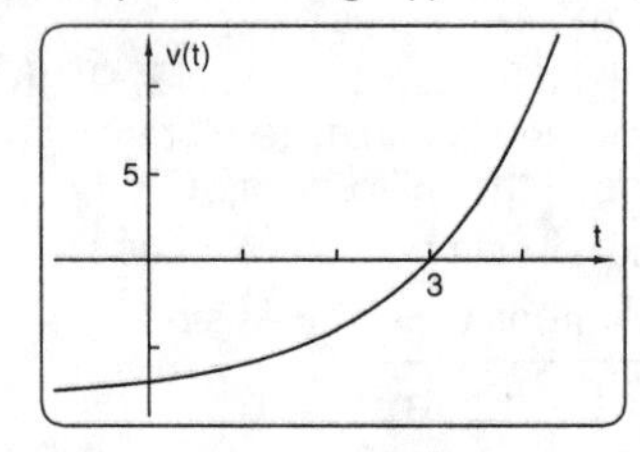

ii. $\text{Displ.} = \int_1^4 (2^t - 8)\,dt \approx -3.8022... \approx -3.8$ cm
(Exactly $14/\ln 2 - 24$)

iii. $\text{Dist.} = \int_1^4 |2^t - 8|\,dt \approx 10.8853... \approx 10.9$ cm
(Exactly $2/\ln 2 + 8$)

b. Acceleration Data Problem

t_{end}	a	a_{avg}	v_{end}	
0	2	----	30	speeding up
5	8	5	55	speeding up
10	1	4.5	77.5	speeding up
15	0	0.5	80	neither
20	−10	−5	55	slowing down
25	−20	−15	−20	slowing down

(Note that the object is speeding up, slowing down, or neither, exactly when $a_{end} > 0$, $a_{end} < 0$, or $a_{end} = 0$, respectively, in the original table.)

R3. a. Average Velocity Problem

i. $v_{avg} = \frac{1}{3}\int_0^3 \sin(\pi t/6)\,dt = 2/\pi = 0.6366...$

ii. $v_{avg} = \frac{1}{6}\int_3^9 \sin(\pi t/6)\,dt = 0$

iii. $v_{avg} = \frac{1}{12}\int_0^{12} \sin(\pi t/6)\,dt = 0$

b. Average Value Problem

i. $f(x) = 6x^2 - x^3 = x^2(6 - x) = 0$ at $x = 0, 6$
$\text{Avg.} = \frac{1}{6}\int_0^6 (6x^2 - x^3)\,dx = 18$

ii. Graph. The rectangle has the same area as the shaded region.

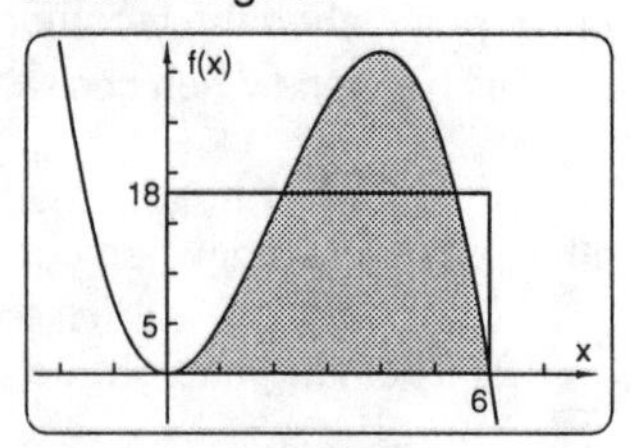

iii. The average of the two values of f(x) at the endpoints is zero, not 18.

R4. Rover's Tablecloth Problem

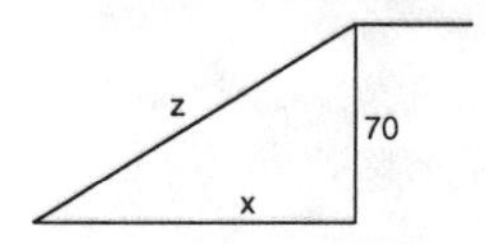

Let x = Rover's distance from the table.
Let z = slant length of tablecloth.

Know: $\frac{dx}{dt} = 20$ cm/sec

Want: $\frac{dz}{dt}$ at $z = 200$

$z^2 = x^2 + 70^2$

$2z\frac{dz}{dt} = 2x\frac{dx}{dt}$

$\frac{dz}{dt} = \frac{x}{z}\frac{dx}{dt} = \frac{20x}{z}$

At $z = 200$, $x = \sqrt{200^2 - 70^2} = 30\sqrt{39}$

$\therefore \frac{dz}{dt} = \frac{20 \cdot 30\sqrt{39}}{200} = 3\sqrt{39} = 18.7349...$

The glass moves at the same speed as the tablecloth, or about 18.7 cm/sec, which is about 1.3 cm/sec slower than Rover.

R5. a. Campus Cut-Across Problem

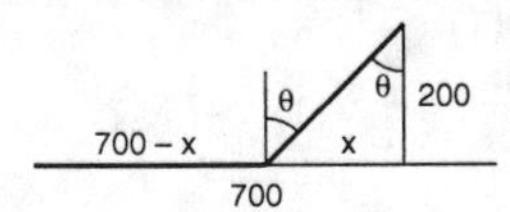

Let x = distance from intersection to cutoff.

$0 \le x \le 700$

Let T = total time taken.

$T = \frac{1}{5.7}\sqrt{200^2 + x^2} + \frac{1}{6.2}(700 - x)$

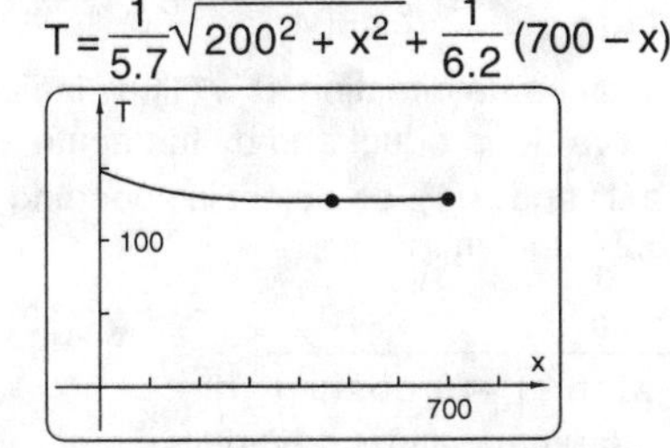

$T' = \frac{1}{5.7} \cdot \frac{1}{2}(200^2 + x^2)^{-1/2}(2x) - \frac{1}{6.2}$

$= \frac{1}{5.7} \cdot x(200^2 + x^2)^{-1/2} - \frac{1}{6.2}$

$T' = 0 \Leftrightarrow 6.2x = 5.7(200^2 + x^2)^{1/2}$

$38.44x^2 = 32.49(200^2) + 32.49x^2$

$x^2 = \frac{32.49(200^2)}{5.95} \Leftrightarrow x = \pm 467.3544...$

Or: Let θ = angle of incidence.

Minimal path occurs for $\theta = \sin^{-1}(5.7/6.2)$.

$x = 200 \tan \theta = 467.3544...$.

Note that at x = 0, Juana goes entirely along the sidewalk.

$T(0) = \frac{1}{6.2} \cdot 900 = 145.1612...$

$T(467.3544...) = 126.7077...$

$T(700) = 127.7212...$

Heading for a point about 467 ft from the intersection gives the minimum time, although it takes only a second longer to head straight for the English building.

b. Resort Island Causeway Problem

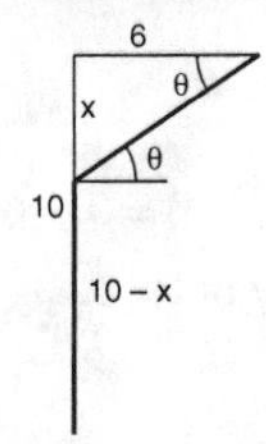

Let x = distance from closest point on the beach to the cutoff point. $0 \le x \le 10$

Let C = total cost of the road.

$C = 5(10 - x) + 13\sqrt{36 + x^2}$

Graph, showing minimum C at $x \approx 2.5$.

Let θ be the angle of incidence.

By the minimal path property, the cost is minimized when

$\sin \theta = \frac{x}{\text{dist. bridge}} = \frac{5}{13}$

$x = 6 \tan(\sin^{-1}(5/13)) = 2.5$

$C(2.5) = 122$

$C(10) = 151.6047...$

The minimum cost is $122,000 by going 7.5 km along the beach, then cutting across to the island. This path saves about $29,600 over the path straight to the island.

R6.a. i. $a(t) = 6t - t^2$, t in [0, 10]

$a'(t) = 6 - 2t$

$a'(t) = 0 \Leftrightarrow t = 3$

$a(0) = 0$; $a(3) = 9$; $a(10) = -40$

Max. acceleration = 9 at t = 3.

Min. acceleration = –40 at t = 10.

ii. $v(t) = \int (6t - t^2)\,dt = 3t^2 - \frac{1}{3}t^3 + C$

$v(0) = 0 \Rightarrow C = 0$

$\therefore v(t) = 3t^2 - \frac{1}{3}t^3$

$v'(t) = a(t) = t(6 - t)$

$v'(t) = 0 \Leftrightarrow t = 0 \text{ or } t = 6$

$v(0) = 0$; $v(6) = 36$; $v(10) = -33\frac{1}{3}$

Max. velocity = 36 at t = 6.

Min. velocity = $-33\frac{1}{3}$ at t = 10.

iii. $s(t) = \int v(t)\,dt = t^3 - \frac{1}{12}t^4 + C$

Since s(t) measures distance from the starting point, s(0) = 0, which implies that C = 0.

$\therefore s(t) = t^3 - \frac{1}{12}t^4$

$s'(t) = v(t) = \frac{1}{3}t^2(9 - t)$

$s'(t) = 0 \Leftrightarrow t = 0 \text{ or } t = 9$

$s(0) = 0$; $s(9) = 182\frac{1}{4}$; $s(10) = 166\frac{2}{3}$

Max. displacement = $182\frac{1}{4}$ at t = 9.

Min. displacement = 0 at t = 0.

b. Inflation Problem

i. Let t = number of days Saul has been saving.
Let P(t) = number of pillars in Saul's account.
Let V(t) = real value (in constant day zero pillars) of money in account after t days.
$P(t) = 50t$ (assuming continuous depositing)
$V(t) = P(t)(0.5^{0.005t}) = 50t(0.5^{0.005t})$

ii. Graph, showing maximum V(t) at t ≈ 289 days

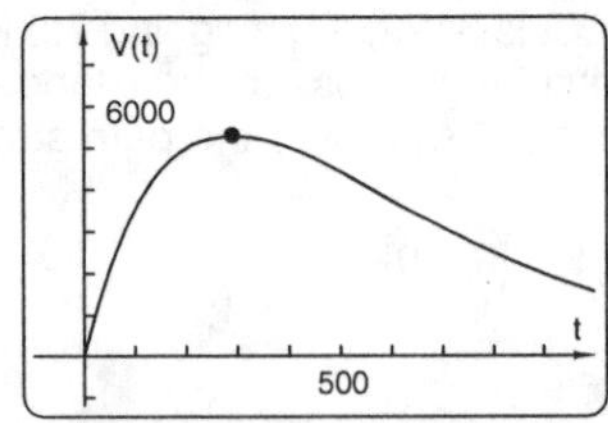

$V'(t) = 50(0.5^{0.005t}) + 50t(0.005(0.5^{0.005t}))\ln 0.5$
$V'(t) = 0 \Leftrightarrow 1 = -0.005t \ln 0.5$
$t = -\dfrac{200}{\ln 0.5} = 288.5390...$
Saul's greatest purchasing power will be after about 289 days.

R7. a. i. and ii. Graphs.

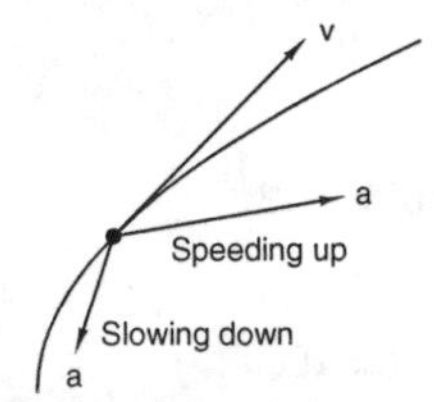

b. i. $\vec{r}(t) = (5\cosh t)\vec{i} + (3\sinh t)\vec{j}$
$\vec{v}(t) = (5\sinh t)\vec{i} + (3\cosh t)\vec{j}$
$\vec{a}(t) = (5\cosh t)\vec{i} + (3\sinh t)\vec{j}$
$\vec{r}(1) = (5\cosh 1)\vec{i} + (3\sinh 1)\vec{j}$
$= 7.7154...\,\vec{i} + 3.5256...\,\vec{j}$
$\vec{v}(1) = 5.8760...\,\vec{i} + 4.6292...\,\vec{j}$
$\vec{a}(1) = 7.7154...\,\vec{i} + 3.5256...\,\vec{j}$

ii. Graph, showing $\vec{r}(1)$, $\vec{v}(1)$, and $\vec{a}(1)$.
Note that $\vec{a}(1) = \vec{r}(1)$, so that the acceleration vector points directly away from the origin when it is drawn from the head of $\vec{r}(1)$. (For an elliptical path, the acceleration vector points directly toward the origin.)

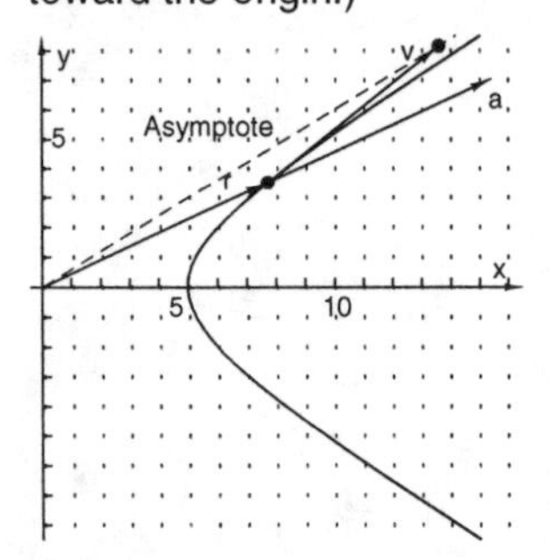

iii. Speed $= |\vec{v}(1)| = \sqrt{25\sinh^2 1 + 9\cosh^2 1}$
$= 7.4804... \approx 7.48$ units/min.
$\vec{a}(1)\cdot\vec{v}(1) = 34\sinh 1\cosh 1 = 61.6566...$
The object is speeding up at t = 1, as shown by the positive dot product and by the acute angle between $\vec{a}(1)$ and $\vec{v}(1)$.

$\vec{a}_t(1) = \dfrac{\vec{a}(1)\cdot\vec{v}(1)}{|\vec{v}(1)|}\,\dfrac{\vec{v}(1)}{|\vec{v}(1)|}$
$= \dfrac{34\sinh 1\cosh 1}{25\sinh^2 1 + 9\cosh^2 1}\vec{v}(1)$
$= 1.1018...\vec{v}(1)$
$= 6.4744...\vec{i} + 5.1007...\vec{j}$
$(\vec{a}_n(1) = 1.2409...\vec{i} - 1.5751...\vec{j})$
$|\vec{a}_t(1)| = \dfrac{|\vec{a}(1)\cdot\vec{v}(1)|}{|\vec{v}(1)|} = \dfrac{61.6566...}{7.4804...} = 8.2423...$
$\vec{a}_t(1)$ points in same direction as $\vec{v}(1)$ as indicated by the positive dot product and by the acute angle between $\vec{a}(1)$ and $\vec{v}(1)$, so object is speeding up at about 8.24 units/min^2.

iv. Distance $= \int_0^1 ds$
$= \int_0^1 \sqrt{25\sinh^2 t + 9\cosh^2 t}\, dt$
$= 4.5841...$ (numerically) ≈ 4.58 units

v. $\vec{r}(t) + \vec{v}(t) = (5\cosh t + 5\sinh t)\vec{i}$
$+ (3\sinh t + 3\cosh t)\vec{j}$
Note that the y-coordinate is 0.6 times the x-coordinate, so the head lies on y = 0.6x, one asymptote of the hyperbola.

Concepts Problems

C1. One-Problem Test on Linear Motion and Other Concepts

a. $v = t^3 - 7t^2 + 15t - 9$, for t in [0, 4]
Graph.

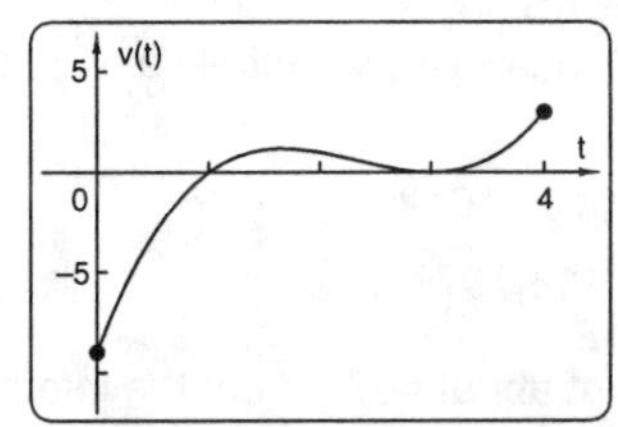

b. $v = (t-1)(t-3)^2$
$v = 0 \Leftrightarrow t = 1, 3$
Particle is stopped at 1 sec and 3 sec.

c. $v' = 3t^2 - 14t + 15 = (3t-5)(t-3)$
$v' = 0$ at $t = \frac{5}{3}, 3$
$v(0) = -9$; $v(\frac{5}{3}) = \frac{32}{27} = 1\frac{5}{27}$; $v(3) = 0$; $v(4) = 3$.
Max. velocity at t = 4, min. velocity at t = 0.

d. $v''(t) = 6t - 14$
$v''(t) = 0 \Leftrightarrow t = \frac{7}{3}$
$v''(t)$ changes from negative to positive at $t = \frac{7}{3}$, so there is a point of inflection at that point.

e. At $t = \frac{7}{3}$, the particle's acceleration stops decreasing and starts increasing. Thus, the minimum acceleration is at that time.

f. $y = \int v(t)\, dt = \frac{1}{4}t^4 - \frac{7}{3}t^3 + \frac{15}{2}t^2 - 9t + C$
$y(0) = 4 \Rightarrow C = 4$
$\therefore y = \frac{1}{4}t^4 - \frac{7}{3}t^3 + \frac{15}{2}t^2 - 9t + 4$

g. Graph.

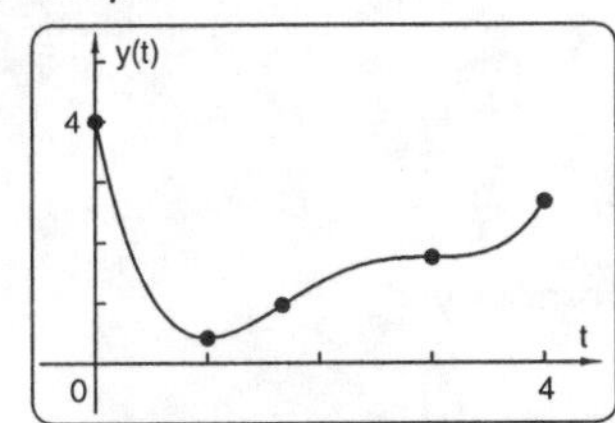

h. $y'(t) = v(t) = 0$ when $t = 1, 3$.

$y(0) = 4$; $y(1) = \frac{5}{12}$; $y(3) = \frac{7}{4}$; $y(4) = \frac{8}{3}$

Max. y at t = 0; min. y at t = 1.

i. $y'' = v' = (3t - 5)(t - 3) = 0$ at $t = \frac{5}{3}, 3$

y'' changes sign at $t = \frac{5}{3}$ and at t = 3, so there are points of inflection at these values of t.

j. At $t = \frac{5}{3}$, the particle stops accelerating and starts decelerating, so the velocity at that time is a local maximum. At t = 3, the particle stops decelerating and starts accelerating, so the velocity is a local minimum.

k. y is never negative because its minimum value is 5/12 at t = 1.

l. Displ. $= \int_0^4 v(t) = y(4) - y(0) = \frac{8}{3} - 4 = -\frac{4}{3}$ ft.

m. Dist. $= \int_0^4 |v(t)|\, dt = 5\frac{5}{6}$ ft.

n. $v_{avg} = \frac{1}{4}\int_0^4 v\, dt = \frac{1}{4}\cdot(\text{displ.}) = -\frac{1}{3}$ ft/sec.

o. $|v|_{avg} = \frac{1}{4}\int_0^4 |v|\, dt = \frac{1}{4}\cdot(\text{dist.}) = \frac{35}{24}$ ft/sec.

C2. New York to Los Angeles Problem

Assume the maximum g a human can withstand is A, and that the distance from New York to Los Angeles is D km.

Recall that 1g = 9.81 (m/s)/s

For the fastest trip, the passenger accelerates at A g for the first D/2 km, then decelerates at –A g for the last D/2 km.

Starting at rest, the velocity t seconds after leaving New York, when accelerating at the maximum rate, is:

$v(t) = A\cdot 9.81\, t$

and the distance from New York is

$s(t) = \frac{1}{2} A\cdot 9.81\, t^2$

The passenger reaches the halfway point of the trip when $s(t) = 1000\cdot\frac{1}{2}D$ (D is km, s is m!)

so the first half of the trip takes $t = \sqrt{\frac{1000\, D}{9.81\, A}}$ seconds. By symmetry, the second half takes exactly as long, so the minimum time for the trip is $t = 2\sqrt{\frac{1000D}{9.81\, A}}$ seconds.

For example, suppose that it is 4000 km from New York to Los Angeles, and that the human body can withstand A = 5g. Then the minimal time is

$t = 2\sqrt{\frac{1000(4000)}{9.81(5)}} = 571.1372...$, or about 9.5 min.

C3. Spider and Clock Problem

Let x = distance from center along clock hand.

Let L = length of web.

Let θ = central angle.

Know: $\frac{dx}{dt} = -0.7$ cm/sec; $\frac{d\theta}{dt} = \frac{\pi}{30}$ rad/sec.

Want: $\frac{dL}{dt}$ at t = 10 sec.

By the law of cosines,

$L^2 = x^2 + 25^2 - 2\cdot x\cdot 25\cdot\cos\theta$

$2L\frac{dL}{dt} = 2x\frac{dx}{dt} - 50\cos\theta\frac{dx}{dt} + 50x\sin\theta\frac{d\theta}{dt}$

At t = 10: x = 18 cm, $\theta = \frac{\pi}{3}$, $\cos\theta = \frac{1}{2}$, $\sin\theta = \frac{\sqrt{3}}{2}$

So $L = \sqrt{18^2 + 25^2 - 25\cdot 18} = \sqrt{499}$

$2L\frac{dL}{dt} = 2x\frac{dx}{dt} - 50\cos\theta\frac{dx}{dt} + 50x\sin\theta\frac{d\theta}{dt}$

$\frac{dL}{dt} = \frac{1}{\sqrt{499}}\left(-18\cdot 0.7 + 25\cdot\frac{1}{2}\cdot 0.7 + 25\cdot 18\cdot\frac{\sqrt{3}}{2}\cdot\frac{2\pi}{60}\right)$

= 1.6545... cm/sec.

C4. Submerging Cone Problem

a. Let t = time since vertex of cone touched water.

Let y = distance from vertex of cone to bottom of cylinder. $0 \le y \le 15$

Let h = altitude of submerged part of cone.

Let r = radius of submerged part of cone.

Let D = depth of water in the cylinder.

Know: $\frac{dy}{dt} = -2$ cm/min. Want: $\frac{dD}{dt}$

Volume of water is $15\cdot 7^2\pi = 735\pi$ cm³.

Volume of submerged cone is $\frac{1}{3}\pi r^2 h$.

Volume of cone plus water is $\pi\cdot 7^2\cdot D$.

$\therefore 49\pi D = 735\pi + \frac{1}{3}\pi r^2 h$

$49D = 735 + \frac{1}{3} r^2 h$

But h + y = D, and $r = \frac{5}{12}h$, so

$49D = 735 + \frac{1}{3}\cdot\frac{25}{144}(D - y)^3$

$49\frac{dD}{dt} = \frac{25}{144}(D - y)^2\left(\frac{dD}{dt} - \frac{dy}{dt}\right)$

Find D when y = 10.

$49D = 735 + \frac{25}{432}(D - 10)^3$

Solving numerically gives D ≈ 15.1624...

Substitute this for D, 10 for y, and –2 for dy/dt.

$49\frac{dD}{dt} = \frac{25}{144}(5.1624...)^2\left(\frac{dD}{dt} + 2\right)$

Solving algebraically or numerically gives

$\frac{dD}{dt} = 0.2085... \approx 0.21$ cm/min.

b. When the cone is completely submerged, the total volume is

$735\pi + \frac{1}{3}\pi\cdot 5^2\cdot 12 = 835\pi$

In this case, $D = \frac{835\pi}{49\pi} = 17.0408...$.

When the cone just goes under,

y = 17.0408... – 12 = 5.0408...

Thus, when y = 1, the cone is already completely submerged, and the depth D is not changing.

C5. Horse Race Theorem

Let $h(t) = f(t) - g(t)$, so $h'(t) = f'(t) - g'(t)$

Then $h(a) = h(b) = 0$, since $f(a) = g(a)$, $f(b) = g(b)$.

By the mean value theorem (or Rolle's theorem), there exists an $x = c$ in (a, b) such that

$$h'(c) = \frac{h(b) - h(a)}{b - a} = 0.$$

But because $h'(c) = f'(c) - g'(c)$ at time c, $f'(c) = g'(c)$, so the knights have the same velocity at this time.

C6. Hemispherical Railroad Problem

Let L = length of track.

Let z = vertical coordinate of a point on the track.

Let $T(\theta)$ = number of minutes to reach the top.

$v = 30 - 60 \sin \theta$

Domain of θ is $0 \le \theta \le \frac{\pi}{6}$ since v would be negative for acute angles $\theta > \pi/6$.

Since θ is constant, v is constant. Thus,

$$T(\theta) = \frac{L}{v} = \frac{L}{30 - 60 \sin \theta}$$

To find L for any value of θ, consider z to be an independent variable. By trigonometry,

$\frac{dL}{dz} = \csc \theta$, and thus $dL = \csc \theta \, dz$.

$L = \int_{z=0}^{1000} \csc \theta \, dz = 1000 \csc \theta$ (θ is constant)

(Another way to find L is to "unroll" the track into a vertical plane. Since the track always makes an angle of θ with the horizontal, this will result in a right triangle with hypotenuse = L, altitude = 1000, and base angle θ. Then $\sin \theta = 1000/L$, so that $L = 1000 \csc \theta$.)

$$\therefore T(\theta) = \frac{1000 \csc \theta}{30 - 60 \sin \theta} = \frac{100}{3} (\sin \theta - 2 \sin^2 \theta)^{-1} \; T'(\theta)$$

$$= -\frac{100}{3} (\sin \theta - 2 \sin^2 \theta)^{-2} (\cos \theta - 4 \sin \theta \cos \theta)$$

$T'(\theta) = 0 \Leftrightarrow \cos \theta (1 - 4 \sin \theta) = 0$

$\cos \theta = 0$ only for values of θ outside the domain.

$\therefore 1 - 4 \sin \theta = 0 \Leftrightarrow \theta = \sin^{-1} 0.25$

$T(\theta)$ approaches positive infinity as θ approaches either end of the domain. So $T(\theta)$ is a minimum for $\theta = \sin^{-1} 0.25$.

Optimal trip takes $T(\sin^{-1} 0.25)$

$$= \frac{100}{3} (0.25 - 2(0.25)^2)^{-1} = 266\tfrac{2}{3} \text{ sec}$$

or 4 minutes, $26\frac{2}{3}$ seconds.

Chapter Test

T1. Truck Passing Problem

$v = \sqrt{t} + 60$

Displ. $= \int_0^{25} (\sqrt{t} + 60) \, dt = 1583\frac{1}{3}$ feet

T2. Power Line Problem

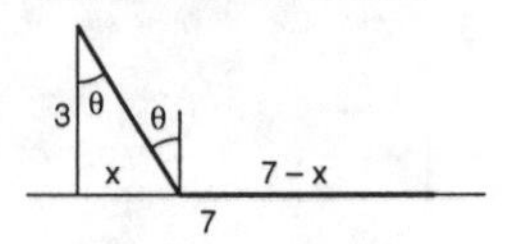

By the minimal path property

$\sin \theta = \frac{360}{800} = 0.45$

$\therefore \theta = \sin^{-1} 0.45$

$x = 3 \tan \theta = 3 \tan (\sin^{-1} 0.45) = 1.5117...$

So the cheapest path is $7 - x = 5.4882...$ mi along the road, then turning toward Ima's house.

This path costs

$360 \cdot 5.4882... + 800 \cdot \sqrt{9 + 1.5117...^2}$

$= 4663.2685... \approx \$4663$, which is about \$257 cheaper than the proposal!

T3. $f(x) = x^3 - 4x + 5$, $x \in [1, 3]$

$f'(x) = 3x^2 - 4$

$f'(x) = 0 \Leftrightarrow x = \pm\sqrt{4/3} = \pm 1.1547...$

(The negative value is out of the domain.)

$f(1) = 2$

$f(1.1547...) = 1.9207...$, the minimum

$f(3) = 20$, the maximum.

Average $= \frac{1}{2} \int_1^3 (x^3 - 4x + 5) \, dx = 7$

Graph, showing min. at $x = 1.1547...$, max. at $x = 3$, and average of 7. The area of the rectangle of altitude 7 equals the area of the region under the graph.

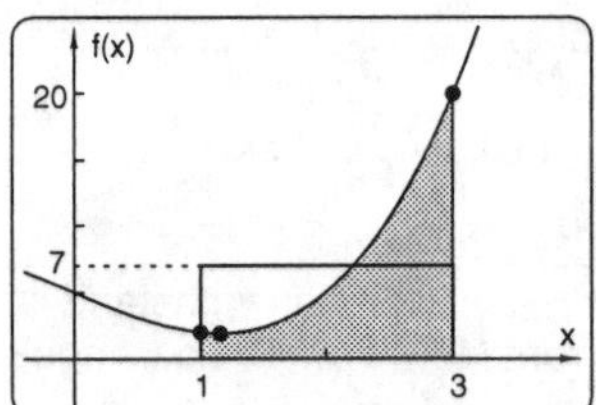

T4. a. $v(t) = 10(0.5 - 2^{-t})$

Dist. $= \int_0^2 |v(t)| \, dt = 3.6067... \approx 3.61$ ft

(exactly $2.5/\ln 2$).

Displ. $= \int_0^2 v(t) \, dt = -0.8202... \approx -0.82$ ft

(Exactly $10 - 7.5/\ln 2$).

b. $a(0) = v'(0) = 2^{-0} \ln 2 = \ln 2 = 0.6931...$

≈ 0.69 (ft/sec)/sec.

c. $v(0) = -5$

Since v(0) is negative and a(0) is positive, the object is slowing down.

T5.

t	a	a_{avg}	v_{end}	v_{avg}	$displ_{end}$
0	4	----	50	----	0
7	6	5	85	67.5	472.5
14	10	8	141	113	1263.5
21	13	11.5	221.5	181.25	2532.25

The object traveled about 2532.25 cm.

Average velocity was about

$\frac{1}{21} \cdot (2532.25) = 120.583... \approx 120.6$ cm/sec

T6. $\vec{r}(t) = (10 \cos 0.4t)\vec{i} + (10 \sin 0.6t)\vec{j}$

$\vec{v}(t) = (-4 \sin 0.4t)\vec{i} + (6 \cos 0.6t)\vec{j}$

T7. $\vec{a}(t) = (-1.6 \cos 0.4t)\vec{i} + (-3.6 \sin 0.6t)\vec{j}$

T8. $\vec{r}(2) = (10 \cos 0.8)\vec{i} + (10 \sin 1.2)\vec{j}$
$= 6.9670...\vec{i} + 9.3203...\vec{j}$
Graph, showing $\vec{r}(2)$

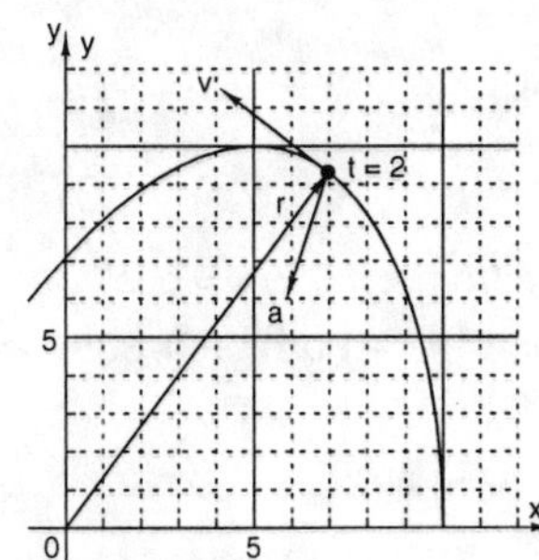

T9. $\vec{v}(2) = (-4 \sin 0.8)\vec{i} + (6 \cos 1.2)\vec{j}$
$= -2.8694...\vec{i} + 2.1741...\vec{j}$
Graph, Problem T8.
The velocity vector is tangent to the path, pointing in the direction of motion.

T10. $\vec{a}(2) = (-1.6 \cos 0.8)\vec{i} + (-3.6 \sin 1.2)\vec{j}$
$= -1.1147...\vec{i} - 3.3553...\vec{j}$
Graph, Problem T8.

T11. $\vec{a}(2) \cdot \vec{v}(2)$
$= 6.4 \cos 0.8 \sin 0.8 - 21.6 \cos 1.2 \sin 1.2$
$= -4.0963... \approx -4.10 \text{ (mph)}^2\text{/hr}$
$|\vec{v}(2)| = \sqrt{16 \sin^2 0.8 + 36 \cos^2 1.2}$
$= 3.6000...$ mph
$P = \dfrac{\vec{a}(2) \cdot \vec{v}(2)}{|\vec{v}(2)|} = -1.1378... \approx -1.14$ mph/hr
$\vec{a}_t(2) = \dfrac{P(2)}{|\vec{v}(2)|}\vec{v}(2) = 0.9069...\vec{i} - 0.6871...\vec{j}$
$\vec{a}_n(2) = \vec{a}(2) - \vec{a}_t(2)$
$= -2.0216...\vec{i} - 2.6681...\vec{j}$
Sketch.

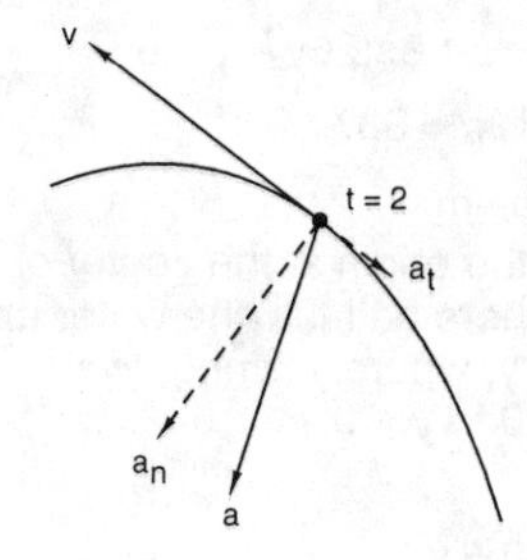

T12. The tangential component $\vec{a}_t(2)$ has direction the opposite of $\vec{v}(2)$, so $\vec{v}$ is decreasing and the object is slowing down at t = 2.

T13. Object is slowing down at $|\vec{a}_t(2)| = |P(2)|$
$= 1.1378...$ mph/h

T14. $\vec{a}_n(2)$ points inward to the concave side because $\vec{a}_n$ is the component of acceleration that pulls the object out of the straight path into a curve.

T15. $dL = \sqrt{dx^2 + dy^2} = |\vec{v}(t)|\, dt$
$= \sqrt{16 \cdot \sin^2 0.4t + 36 \cdot \cos^2 0.6t}\ dt$
$L = \int_0^2 dL = 10.0932...$ (numerically) ≈ 10.09 mi

Chapter 11

Exploratory Problem Set 11-1, page 557 — Review of Work—Force Times Displacement

1. Graph, showing strip and sample point (x, F)

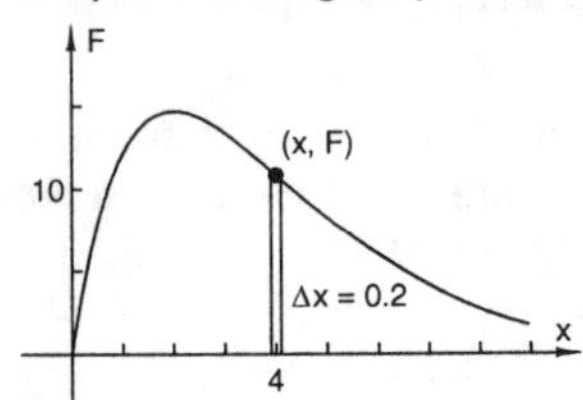

$F \approx F(4) = 80e^{-2} = 10.8268... \approx 10.83$ lb in the strip
$W \approx F(4)\cdot\Delta x = 16e^{-2} = 2.1653... \approx 2.17$ ft-lb

2. $dW = 20xe^{-0.5x}\,dx$
3. $W = \int_0^7 20xe^{-0.5x}\,dx = 69.1289...$
   (exactly $80 - 360e^{-3.5}$)
4. $W \approx 69.13$ ft-lb
5. The amount of work done from x = 0 to x = b is
   $W = \int_0^b 20x^{-0.5x}\,dx = -40be^{-0.5b} - 80e^{-0.5b} + 80$
   $\lim_{b\to\infty} W = 0 + 0 + 80 = 80$ ft-lb
   (Use l'Hospital's rule for $be^{-0.5b}$.)

Problem Set 11-2, pages 561 to 563 — Work Done by a Variable Force

Q1. Area = 2 Q2. Area = $10\frac{2}{3}$
Q3. $v(t) = \ln|\sec t| + C$ Q4. $a(t) = t^{-1}$
Q5. Fundamental Theorem of Calculus Q6. Riemann
Q7. Avg. = 0 Q8. Integration by parts
Q9. Implicit differentiation Q10. Heaviside method

1. Leaking Bucket Problem
   Ignore the weight of the rope.
   Let y = the distance from the bottom of the well.
   Slope of linear function is –8/50 = –0.16.
   Weight = 20 – 0.16y
   $dW = (\text{weight})\,dy = (20 - 0.16y)\,dy$
   $W = \int_0^{50} (20 - 0.16y)\,dy = 800$ ft-lb
2. Spaceship Problem
   a. Let y = no. of miles up.
      Slope of linear function is $-20/70 = -\frac{2}{7}$
      Weight $= 30 - \frac{2}{7}y$ (tons)
      $dW = (30 - \frac{2}{7}y)\,dy$
      $W = \int_0^{70} (30 - \frac{2}{7}y)\,dy = 1400$ mi-tons
   b. $W_{total} = 90 \text{ tons} \cdot 70 \text{ mi} = 6300$ mi-tons
      Excess energy becomes kinetic energy of rocket and spent fuel.
3. Spring Problem
   Hooke's law: $F = k\cdot s$
   $dW = ks\,ds$
   $W = \int_0^{10} ks\,ds = 50k$
4. Table-Moving Problem
   a. $F = -x^3 + 6x^2 - 12x + 16$
      Graph, starting at high force of 16 lb, leveling off, then dropping to F = 0 at x = 4.

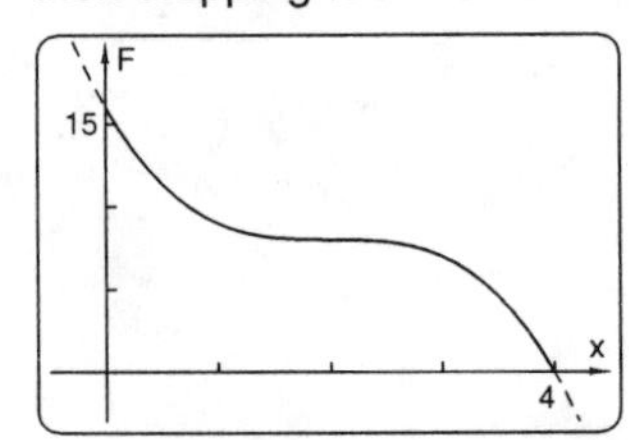

   b. $dW = F\,dx = (-x^3 + 6x^2 - 12x + 16)\,dx$
      $W = \int_0^4 (-x^3 + 6x^2 - 12x + 16)\,dx = 32$ ft-lb
5. Conical Reservoir Problem

   $dV = \pi x^2\,dy$
   $\therefore dW = (17 - y)(62.4)(\pi x^2\,dy)$
   By similar triangles, x = 1.5y.
   $\therefore dW = (17 - y)(62.4)(\pi \cdot 2.25y^2\,dy)$
   $= 140.4\pi(17y^2 - y^3)\,dy$
   $W = \int_0^{10} dW = 1{,}396{,}752.0937...$
   ≈ 1.4 million ft-lb (Exactly $444{,}600\pi$)
6. Paraboloidal Tank Problem
   $dV = \pi x^2\,dy$
   At x = 4, y = 16.
   $\therefore dW = (26 - y)(54.8)(\pi x^2\,dy)$
   Since $y = x^2$,
   $dW = (26 - y)(54.8)(\pi y\,dy) = 54.8\pi(26y - y^2)\,dy$
   $W = \int_0^{16} dW = 337{,}891.2751... \approx 337{,}891$ ft-lb
7. Spherical Water Tower Problem
   a. Draw x- and y-axes with the origin at the center of the sphere. To fill the sphere half full, the water must be pumped from –120 to y, where y is negative. Integration is from y = –20 to y = 0.
      $dV = \pi x^2\,dy$
      $x^2 + y^2 = 20^2 \Rightarrow x^2 = 400 - y^2$
      $\therefore dW = (y - (-120))(62.4)(\pi(400 - y^2)\,dy)$
      $= 62.4\pi(y + 120)(400 - y^2)\,dy$
      $W = \int_{-20}^0 dW = 117621229.... \approx 117.6$ million ft-lb
      (exactly $62.4\pi \cdot 600000$)

b. For filling the tank, the limits of integration are from −20 to 20.
$\int_{-20}^{20} dW = 250{,}925{,}288.4... \approx 250.9$ million ft-lb
(exactly $62.4\pi\cdot 1{,}280{,}000$)
This answer can be found quickly through lifting the entire weight of the water through the distance the center of the sphere moves, namely 120 ft.
$W = (62.4)(\frac{4}{3})\pi\cdot 20^3)(120) = 62.4\pi\cdot 1{,}280{,}000.$
(Note that the amount of work to fill the entire tank is more than twice the amount needed to half-fill it. The work to fill the top hemisphere is greater than that to fill the bottom hemisphere because the same amount of water has to be lifted through a greater displacement.)

8. Flooded Ship Problem
Slice the water horizontally. Pick sample point (x, y) on the curve $y = 0.0002x^4$ within the slice.
$dV = 15\cdot 2x\cdot dy = 30(5000y)^{1/4}\,dy = 300(0.5y)^{1/4}\,dy$
$\therefore\ dW = (30 - y)(67)(300(0.5y)^{1/4}\,dy)$
$= 20100(30 - y)(0.5y)^{1/4}\,dy$
$W = \int_0^{16} dW \approx 9{,}134{,}602$ ft-lb
(Exactly $(20100)(0.5)^{1/4}(540\frac{4}{9})$)

9. Carnot Cycle Problem
a. If x is the distance between the piston and the cylinder head and F is the force exerted by the hot gases, then $dW = F\,dx$.
$F = pA$, where p is the pressure and A is the area of the piston.
$\therefore\ dW = pA\,dx.$
$A\,dx = dV$
$\therefore\ dW = p\,dV$
$p = k_1 V^{-1.4}$
Initial condition $V = 1$ at $p = 1000 \Rightarrow k_1 = 1000$
$\therefore\ dW = 1000\,V^{-1.4}\,dV$
$W = \int_1^{10} 1000\,V^{-1.4}\,dV \approx 1504.7320...$
≈ 1504.7 in-lb (Exactly $2500(1 - 10^{-0.4})$)
b. Initial condition $p = 15$ at $V = 10 \Rightarrow k_2 = 15\cdot 10^{1.4}$
$dW = 15\cdot 10^{1.4}\,V^{-1.4}\,dV$
$W = \int_{10}^{1} 15\cdot 10^{1.4}\,V^{-1.4}\,dV \approx -566.9574...$
So about 567 in-lb of work is done in compressing the gases (exactly $37.5\cdot 10^{1.4}(10^{-0.4} - 1)$).
(Mathematically, the work is negative because the force is positive and dx is negative. Physically, the work is negative because energy is taken out of the surroundings to put into the gases. Positive work indicates that energy is put into the surroundings by the expanding gases.)
c. Net amount of work $\approx 1504.7320... - 566.9574$
$= 937.7746... \approx 937.8$ in-lb.
d. Carnot (kar-nō´), Nicolas Léonard Sadi. 1796–1832, French physicist; pioneer in the field of thermodynamics.

Problem Set 11-3, pages 565 to 567 — Mass of a Variable-Density Object

Q1. 2 cm^3
Q2. 3 cm^3
Q3. $y = 24$
Q4. Graph, $y = \sin x$

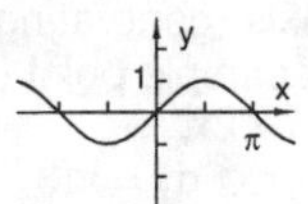

Q5. Graph, $y = \ln x$

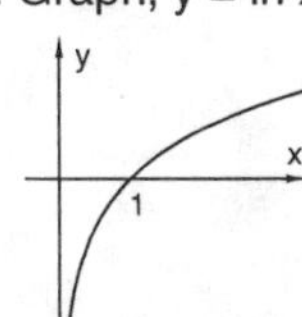

Q6. Graph, $y = 2^x$

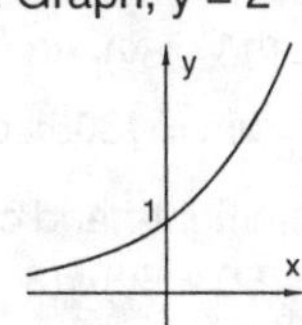

Q7. Graph, $y = x^2$

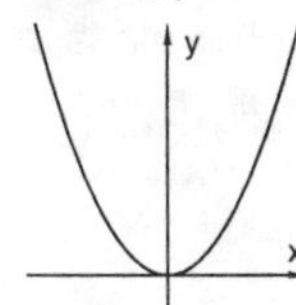

Q8. (mass)/(volume)
Q9. (force)(displ.)
Q10. $\dfrac{1}{\sqrt{1 - x^2}}$

1.a. Graph, $y = \ln x$, rotated about $x = 0$, showing back half of solid only.

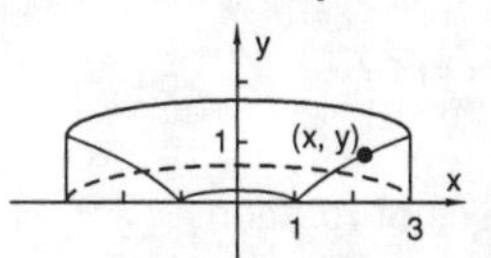

Slice the region parallel to the axis of rotation, generating cylindrical shells. Pick sample point (x, y) on the curve, within the slice.
$\rho = kx^{-1}$
$dm = \rho\,dV = (kx^{-1})(2\pi x \ln x\,dx) = 2\pi k \ln x\,dx$
$m = \int_1^3 2\pi k \ln x\,dx \approx 8.1419...\,k$
(exactly $2\pi k(3 \ln 3 - 2)$)
b. Slice perpendicular to the axis of rotation, generating plane washers.
$\rho = 5 + 2y$
$dm = \rho\,dV = (5 + 2y)\cdot\pi(3^2 - x^2)\,dy$
$= \pi(5 + 2y)(9 - e^{2y})\,dy$
$m = \int_0^{\ln 3} dm \approx 108.1103...$
(exactly $\pi(36 \ln 3 + 9 (\ln 3)^2 - 16)$)

2. Graph, $y = \sin x$, rotated about the y-axis, showing back half of solid only.

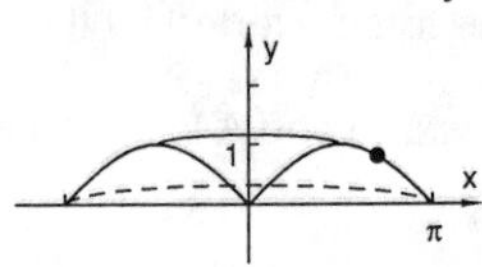

Slice the region parallel to the axis of rotation, generating cylindrical shells.

$\rho = kx$

$dm = \rho\ dV = kx \cdot 2\pi xy\ dx = 2\pi kx^2 \sin x\ dx$

$m = \int_0^{\pi} dm \approx 36.8798...\ k$ (exactly $2\pi(\pi^2 - 4)k$)

3. a. Graph, $y = 9 - x^2$, rotated about the y-axis.

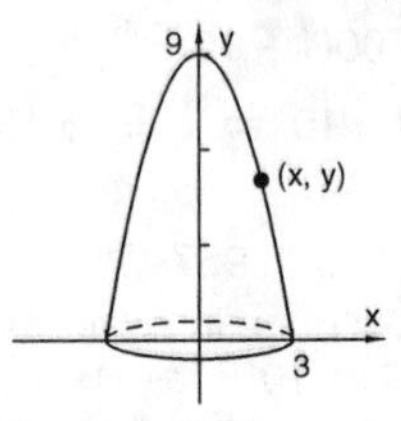

Slice the region perpendicular to the axis of rotation, generating plane disks.

$\rho = k$, $dm = k\ dV = k \cdot \pi x^2\ dy = k \cdot \pi(9 - y)\ dy$

$m = \int_0^9 dm = 40.5\pi k$

Or: Slice parallel to the axis of rotation.

$dm = k \cdot 2\pi xy\ dx = 2\pi kx(9 - x^2)\ dx$

$m = \int_0^3 dm = 40.5\pi k$

Or: Volume of paraboloid is half the volume of the circumscribed cylinder, or $0.5(\pi \cdot 3^2)(9) = 40.5\pi$, so $m = 40.5\pi k$.

b. Slice perpendicular to the axis of rotation.

$\rho = ky^2$

$dm = \rho\ dV = ky^2 \cdot \pi(9 - y)\ dy$

$m = \int_0^9 dm = 546.75\pi k$

c. Slice parallel to the axis of rotation.

$\rho = k(1 + x)$

$dm = \rho \cdot 2\pi xy\ dx = 2\pi kx(1 + x)(9 - x^2)\ dx$

$m = \int_0^3 dm = 105.3\pi k$

d. The solid in part b. has the largest mass.

4. a. Graphs, $y_1 = \sqrt{x}$ and $y_2 = 0.5x$

Graphs intersect at (0, 0) and (4, 2).

Rotate the region about the x-axis. Graph, showing back half of solid only.

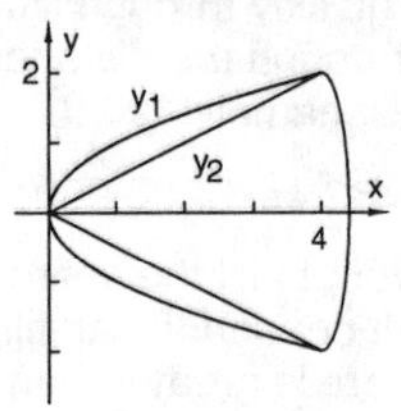

Slice perpendicular to the axis of rotation, generating plane washers.

Pick sample points (x, y_1) and (x, y_2).

$\rho = kx$

$dm = \rho\ dV = kx \cdot \pi(y_1^2 - y_2^2)\ dx$

$= kx\pi(x - 0.25x^2)\ dx$

$m = \frac{16}{3}\pi k = 16.7551...\ k$

b. Slice parallel to the axis of rotation, generating cylindrical shells.

Pick sample points (x_1, y) and (x_2, y).

$\rho = ky^2$

$dm = \rho\ dV = ky^2 \cdot 2\pi y(x_2 - x_1)\ dy$

$= 2\pi ky^3(2y - y^2)\ dy$

$m = \int_0^2 dm = \frac{64}{15}\pi k = 13.4041...\ k$

5. Two-Cone Problem

a. Prediction: Cone on the left, with higher density at base, has greater mass, because higher density is in the larger part of the cone.

b. Set up a coordinate system with the origin at the center of the base. Slice each cone perpendicular to its axis, generating plane disks.

Pick sample point (x, y) on the element of the cone, $y = 6 - 2x$.

$dV = \pi x^2\ dy = \pi(3 - 0.5y)^2\ dy$

For the left-hand cone, $\rho = 80 - 5y$.

$dm = (80 - 5y) \cdot \pi(3 - 0.5y)^2\ dy$

$m = \int_0^6 dm = 1305\pi$ oz.

For the right-hand cone, $\rho = 50 + 5y$.

$dm = (50 + 5y) \cdot \pi(3 - 0.5y)^2\ dy$

$m = \int_0^6 dm = 1035\pi$ oz.

∴ the cone on the left has the higher mass, as predicted in part a.

6. Two-Cylinder Problem
   a. Prediction: Cylinder on the left, with higher density at walls, has higher mass, because higher density is in the larger part of the cylinder.
   b. Set up a coordinate system with the origin at the center of the bottom base. Slice each cylinder parallel to its axis, generating cylindrical shells. Pick sample point (x, 6).
   $dV = 2\pi x \cdot 6 \cdot dx = 12\pi x\ dx$

   For the left-hand cylinder, $\rho = 50 + 10x$.
   $dm = (50 + 10x) \cdot 12\pi x\ dx = 12\pi(50x + 10x^2)\ dx$
   $m = \int_0^3 dm = 3780\pi$ oz.

   For the right-hand cylinder, $\rho = 80 - 10x$.
   $dm = (80 - 10x) \cdot 12\pi x\ dx = 12\pi(80x - 10x^2)\ dx$
   $m = \int_0^3 dm = 3240\pi$ oz.

   $\therefore$ the cylinder on the left has the higher mass, as predicted in part a.
7. $y_1 = 4 - 2x^2$ and $y_2 = 3 - x^2$, rotated about the x-axis. Graphs intersect at (1, 2) in Quadrant I.
   Slice perpendicular to the axis of rotation, generating plane washers.
   Pick sample points (x, y_1) and (x, y_2).
   $\rho = kx^2$, $dV = \pi(y_1^2 - y_2^2)\ dx$
   $dm = \rho\ dV = \pi kx^2(7 - 10x^2 + 3x^4)\ dx$
   $m = \int_0^1 dm = \frac{16}{21}\pi k = 2.3935\ldots k$
8. Rotate the region in Problem 7 about the y-axis. Slice the region parallel to the axis of rotation, generating cylindrical shells.
   Pick sample points (x, y_1) and (x, y_2).
   $\rho = e^{-x}$, $dV = 2\pi x(y_1 - y_2)\ dx = 2\pi x(1 - x^2)\ dx$
   $dm = \rho\ dV = 2\pi xe^{-x}(1 - x^2)\ dx$
   $m = \int_0^1 dm = 0.9444\ldots$ (exactly $2\pi(14e^{-1} - 5)$)
9. Uranium Fuel Pellet Problem
   Set up axes with the origin at the center of the lower base and the y-axis coaxial with the cylinder's axis. Slice perpendicular to the axis of the cylinder, generating plane disks of constant radius 0.5.
   ρ is given in the table, $dV = \pi 0.5^2\ dy = \frac{\pi}{4}\ dy$
   $dm = \rho\ dV = \frac{\pi}{4}\rho\ dy$
   $m = \frac{\pi}{4}\int_0^2 \rho\ dy$
   Simpson's rule cannot be used because there is an odd number of increments. Use trapezoidal rule.
   $m \approx \frac{\pi}{4}(0.4)(\frac{1}{2}(10) + 9.9 + 9.8 + 9.6 + 9.4 + \frac{1}{2}(9.0))$
   $= 4.82\pi \approx 15.14$ g
10. a. Graph, $y_1 = 4 - x^2$, $y_2 = 4x - x^2$, intersecting at the point (1, 3), rotated about the y-axis, showing back half of solid only

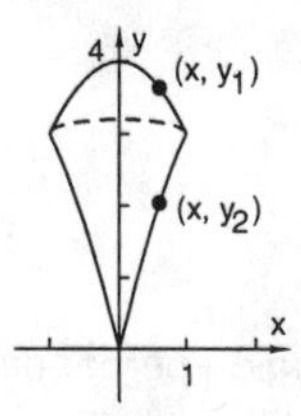

   Slice parallel to the axis of rotation, generating cylindrical shells.
   Pick sample points (x, y_1) and (x, y_2).
   $\rho = kx$, $dV = 2\pi x(y_1 - y_2)\ dx = 2\pi x(4 - 4x)\ dx$
   $dm = \rho\ dV = 2\pi kx^2(4 - 4x)\ dx$
   $m = \int_0^1 dm = \frac{2}{3}\pi k = 2.0943\ldots k$
   b. Graph, rotated about the x-axis, showing back half of solid only.

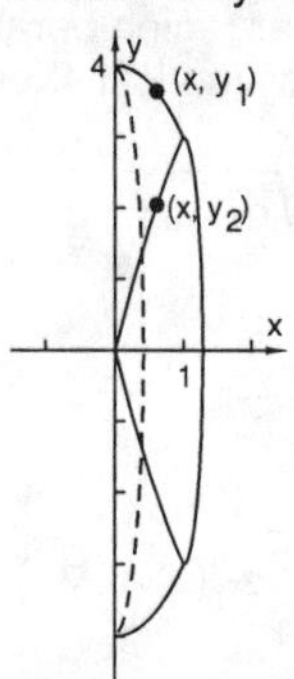

   Slice perpendicular to the axis of rotation, generating plane washers.
   Pick sample points (x, y_1) and (x, y_2).
   $\rho = kx$, $dV = \pi(y_1^2 - y_2^2)\ dx$
   $dm = \rho\ dV = \pi kx(16 - 24x^2 + 8x^3)\ dx$
   $m = \int_0^1 dm = 3.6\pi k = 11.3097\ldots k$
   c. Region is rotated about the y-axis as in part a. Slice perpendicular to the axis of rotation, generating plane disks
   Pick sample points (x_1, y) and (x_2, y).
   Below $y = 3$, disks have radius x_2.
   Above $y = 3$, disks have radius x_1.
   $\rho = ky$
   For x in [0, 3], $dV = \pi x_2^2\ dx = \pi(2 - \sqrt{4-y})^2\ dy$
   For x in [3, 4], $dV = \pi x_1^2\ dx = \pi(4 - y)\ dy$
   $m = \int_0^3 ky \cdot \pi(2 - \sqrt{4-y})^2\ dy + \int_3^4 ky \cdot \pi(4 - y)\ dy$
   $= 1\frac{14}{15}\pi k + 1\frac{2}{3}\pi k = 3.6\pi k = 11.3097\ldots k$
   (Coincidentally, this answer equals the answer to part b.)

11. a. Graph, with origin at center of sphere

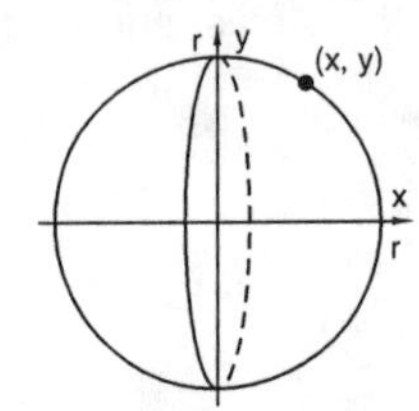

Slice the upper semicircular region perpendicular to the x-axis and rotate it to get plane disks.
Pick a sample point (x, y).
Equation of the circle in the xy-plane is
$x^2 + y^2 = r^2$.

$\rho = k|x|$, $dV = \pi y^2\,dx = \pi(r^2 - x^2)\,dx$

$dm = \rho\,dV = k|x|\,\pi(r^2 - x^2)\,dx$

$m = \pi k\int_{-r}^{r} |x|(r^2 - x^2)\,dx = 2\pi k\int_0^r (r^2x - x^3)\,dx$

$= 2\pi k(\frac{1}{2}r^2x^2 - \frac{1}{4}x^4)\Big|_0^r = \frac{1}{2}\pi r^4 k$

b. Slice the right-hand semicircular region parallel to the y-axis and rotate it to get cylindrical shells coaxial to the y-axis.

$\rho = kx$, $dV = 2\pi x\cdot 2y\cdot dx = 4\pi x\sqrt{r^2 - x^2}\,dx$

$dm = \rho\,dV = 4\pi k x^2\sqrt{r^2 - x^2}\,dx$

$m = 4\pi k\int_0^r x^2\sqrt{r^2 - x^2}\,dx$

Let $x = r\sin\theta$.

Then $dx = r\cos\theta\,d\theta$, $\sqrt{r^2 - x^2} = r\cos\theta$.

$x = r \Rightarrow \theta = \sin^{-1} 1 = \pi/2$.

$\therefore m = 4\pi k\int_0^{\pi/2} r^2\sin^2\theta\cdot r\cos\theta\cdot r\cos\theta\,d\theta$

$= 4\pi r^4 k\int_0^{\pi/2} \sin^2\theta\cos^2\theta\,d\theta$

$= \pi r^4 k\int_0^{\pi/2} \sin^2 2\theta\,d\theta$ (half-argument property)

$= \frac{1}{2}\pi r^4 k\int_0^{\pi/2} (1 - \cos 4\theta)\,d\theta$ (half-arg. prop.)

$= \frac{1}{2}\pi r^4 k(\theta - \frac{1}{4}\sin 4\theta)\Big|_0^{\pi/2} = \frac{1}{4}\pi^2 r^4 k$

c. Slice into spherical shells. Pick a sample point on the x-axis within the shell.
Then x is the radius of the shell and $4\pi x^2$ is the area of the shell at the sample point.

$\therefore dV = 4\pi x^2\,dx$

$\rho = kx$

$dm = \rho\,dV = 4\pi k x^3\,dx$

$m = 4\pi k\int_0^r x^3\,dx$

$= \pi k x^4\Big|_0^r = \pi k r^4$

12. Mass of the Earth Problem
Assume the earth is spherical, with radius 3960 mi = 3960·5280·12·2.54 cm = 637,300,224 cm, and slice into spherical shells with radius x and $dV = 4\pi x^2\,dx$.

$\rho = 12 - \frac{8x}{637300224}$ g/cm^3

$dm = \rho\,dV = (48\pi x^2 - \frac{32\pi x^3}{637300224})\,dx$

$m = \int_0^{637300224} dV$

$= (16\pi x^3 - \frac{8\pi x^4}{637300224})\Big|_0^{637300224}$

$= 8\pi\cdot 637{,}300{,}224^3 \approx 6.505 \times 10^{27}$ g

Mass is about 6.505×10^{21} metric tons!

13. Graph, $y = e^x$, from $x = 0$ to $\pi/2$, rotated about the y-axis, showing back half of solid only.

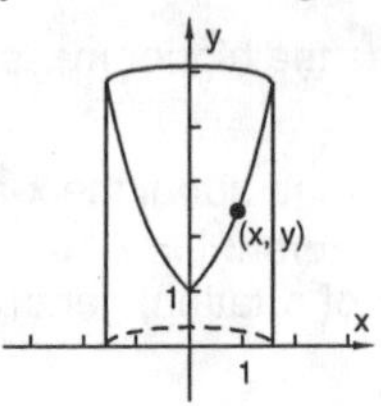

Slice parallel to the axis of rotation, generating cylindrical shells.
Pick sample point (x, y).

$\rho = \cos x$, $dV = 2\pi x\cdot y\cdot dx = 2\pi x e^x\,dx$

$dm = \rho\,dV = \cos x\; 2\pi x e^x\,dx$

$m = \int_0^{\pi/2} dm \approx 8.6261\ldots$ (exactly $\pi e^{\pi/2}(\frac{\pi}{2} - 1)$)

14. Buckminster's Elliptical Dome Problem
a = 4 mi, b = 1 mi, c = 0.5 mi.

a. $(\frac{x}{a})^2 + (\frac{y}{b})^2 + (\frac{z}{c})^2 = 1$, where a = 4, b = 1, c = 0.5.
The cross section at $z = z_0 < c$ has equation
$(\frac{x}{a})^2 + (\frac{y}{b})^2 = 1 - (\frac{z_0}{c})^2$
This is the equation of an ellipse with
x-radius $a\sqrt{1 - (z_0/c)^2}$ and
y-radius $b\sqrt{1 - (z_0/c)^2}$.

b. Slice horizontally into plane elliptical disks.
The area of the cross section is
π(x-radius)(y-radius) $= \pi ab(1 - (z/c)^2)$
$= 4\pi(1 - (z/0.5)^2) = 4\pi(1 - 4z^2)$

$\rho = 0.08(5280)^3 e^{-0.2z}$ lb/mi^3

$dm = \rho\,dV = 0.08\cdot 5280^3 e^{-0.2z}\cdot 4\pi(1 - 4z^2)\,dz$
$= 0.32\cdot 5280^3 \pi e^{-0.2z}(1 - 4z^2)\,dz$
$m = \int_0^{0.5} dm \approx 0.32\cdot 5280^3\cdot 1.008953\ldots$

$\approx 4.7525\ldots \times 10^{10}$ lb or about 23,762,540 tons
(exactly $0.32\cdot 5280^3\pi(1100e^{-0.1} - 995)$).

c. Volume of semi-ellipsoid $= \frac{2}{3}\pi abc = \frac{4}{3}\pi$ mi^3

Weight $= 0.08 \cdot 5280^3 \cdot \frac{4}{3}\pi \approx 49{,}326{,}507{,}160$ lb,

1801427783 lb more ($\approx$ 3.8% more than actual)

d. $V = 2\int_0^c \pi ab(1 - (z/c)^2)\,dz$

$= 2\pi ab(z - \frac{1}{3}\cdot c(z/c)^3)\,\Big|_0^c$

$= 2\pi ab(\frac{2}{3}c) = \frac{4}{3}\pi abc$, Q.E.D.

Problem Set 11-4, pages 573 to 577

Moments, Centroids, Center of Mass, and the Theorem of Pappus

Q1. $-5^2 = -25$

Q2. $(-11)^2 = 121$

Q3. $\sin 2x = 2\sin x \cos x$

Q4. $\cos^2 x = \frac{1}{2}(1 + \cos 2x)$

Q5. $\frac{-1/3}{(x-2)} + \frac{1/3}{(x-5)}$

Q6. $\frac{1}{3}\ln|x-5| - \frac{1}{3}\ln|x-2| + C$

Q7. $\frac{1/3}{(x-2)^2} + \frac{-1/3}{(x-5)^2}$

Q8. $f(a) = f(b) = 0$

Q9. $g(x) = \int f(x)\,dx \Leftrightarrow g'(x) = f(x)$

Q10. $f'(2) > 0$: increasing

1. Paraboloid Problem

a. Graph, $y = 9 - x^2$, rotated about the y-axis

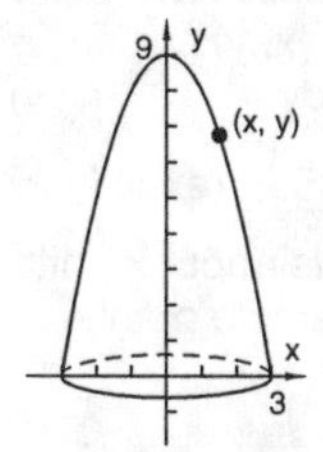

Slice the region perpendicular to the axis of rotation, generating plane disks.

$dV = \pi x^2\,dy = \pi(9 - y)\,dy$

$V = \int_0^9 \pi(9 - y)\,dy = 40.5\pi$

b. Each point in a disk is about y units from the xz-plane where y is at the sample point (x, y).

$dM_{xz} = y\,dV = \pi(9y - y^2)\,dy$

$M_{xz} = \int_0^9 \pi(9y - y^2)\,dy = 121.5\pi$

c. $\bar{y}\cdot V = M_{xz} \Rightarrow \bar{y} = \frac{121.5\pi}{40.5\pi} = 3$

$\bar{x} = \bar{z} = 0$ by symmetry.

Centroid is at (0, 3, 0).

2. Ellipsoid Problem

a. $(\frac{x}{12})^2 + (\frac{y}{5})^2 = 1 \Rightarrow y^2 = 25(1 - \frac{1}{144}x^2)$

Slice the ellipsoidal region above the x-axis perpendicular to the x-axis, generating plane disks as the region rotates.

Pick sample point (x, y).

$dV = \pi y^2\,dx = 25\pi(1 - \frac{1}{144}x^2)\,dx$

$V = 25\pi\int_0^{12}(1 - \frac{1}{144}x^2)\,dx$

$= 25\pi(x - \frac{1}{432}x^3)\,\Big|_0^{12} = 200\pi$

This answer equals $\frac{2}{3}\cdot\pi\cdot 12\cdot 5^2$, which is expected because the volume of a (whole) ellipsoid is $V = \frac{4}{3}\pi abc$.

b. Each point in a disk is about x units from the yz-plane where x is at the sample point (x, y).

$dM_{yz} = x\,dV = 25\pi x(1 - \frac{1}{144}x^2)\,dx$

$M_{yz} = \int_0^{12} dM_{yz} = 900\pi$

c. $\bar{x}\cdot V = M_{yz} \Rightarrow \bar{x} = \frac{900\pi}{200\pi} = 4.5$

$\bar{y} = \bar{z} = 0$ by symmetry

Centroid is at (4.5, 0, 0).

3. Paraboloid Mass Problem

a. See graph in Problem 1.

Each point in a disk is about y units from the xz-plane where y is at the sample point (x, y), so each point has about the same density.

$\rho = ky^{1/3}$, $dm = \rho\,dV = k\pi(9y^{1/3} - y^{4/3})\,dy$

$m = \int_0^9 dm = 170.1375\ldots k$

(exactly $= \frac{9^3}{28}\pi\sqrt[3]{9}\,k$)

b. Each point in a disk is about y units from the xz-plane where y is at the sample point (x, y).

$dM_{xz} = y\,dm = k\pi(9y^{4/3} - y^{7/3})\,dy$

$M_{xz} = \int_0^9 dM_{xz} = 612.4952\ldots k$ (exactly $\frac{9^4}{28}\pi\sqrt[3]{9}\,k$)

c. $\bar{y}\cdot m = M_{xz} \Rightarrow \bar{y} = \frac{612.4952\ldots k}{170.1375\ldots k} = 3.6$ (exactly)

$\bar{x} = \bar{z} = 0$ by symmetry.

Center of mass is at (0, 3.6, 0).

d. False. The centroid is at (0, 3, 0) but the center of mass is at (0, 3.6, 0).

4. Ellipsoid Mass Problem

a. Slice the ellipsoid as in Problem 2.

Each point in a disk is about x units from the yz-plane where x is at the sample point (x, y), so each point has about the same density as at the sample point.

$\rho = kx$, $dV = \pi y^2\,dx = 25\pi(1 - \frac{1}{144}x^2)\,dx$

$dm = \rho\,dV = 25\pi kx(1 - \frac{1}{144}x^2)\,dx$

$m = \int_0^{12} dm = 2827.4333\ldots k$ (exactly $900\pi k$)

b. Each point in a disk is about x units from the yz-plane, where x is at the sample point (x, y).

$dM_{yz} = x\,dm = 25\pi kx^2(1 - \frac{1}{144}x^2)\,dx$

$M_{yz} = \int_0^{12} dM_{yz} = 5760\pi k$

c. $\bar{x} \cdot m = M_{yz} \Rightarrow \bar{x} = \dfrac{5760\pi k}{900\pi k} = 6.4$

$\bar{y} = \bar{z} = 0$ by symmetry.
Center of mass is at (6.4, 0, 0).

d. False. The centroid is at (4.5, 0, 0), but the center of mass is at (6.4, 0, 0).

5. Exponential Region and Solid Problem

a. $y = e^x$
Slice the region parallel to the y-axis.
$dA = y\,dx = e^x\,dx$
$A = \int_0^2 e^x\,dx = e^2 - 1 = 6.3890...$
Each point in a strip is about x units from the y-axis where x is at the sample point (x, y).
$\therefore\ dM_y = x\,dA = xe^x\,dx$
$M_y = \int_0^2 xe^x\,dx = e^2 + 1 = 8.3890...$
$\bar{x} \cdot A = M_y \Rightarrow \bar{x} = \dfrac{e^2 + 1}{e^2 - 1} = 1.3130...$ $(= \coth 1)$

b. Strips in part a. generate plane disks. Each point in a disk is about x units from the yz-plane where x is at the sample point (x, y).
$dV = \pi y^2\,dx = \pi e^{2x}\,dx$
$V = \int_0^2 \pi e^{2x}\,dx = \dfrac{\pi}{2}(e^4 - 1) = 84.1917...$
$dM_{yz} = x\,dV = \pi x e^{2x}\,dx$
$M_{yz} = \int_0^2 dM_{yz} = \dfrac{3}{4}\pi e^4 + \dfrac{1}{4}\pi = 129.4292...$
$\bar{x} \cdot V = M_{yz} \Rightarrow \bar{x} = \dfrac{3e^4+1}{2(e^4-1)} = 1.5373...$

c. False. For the solid, $\bar{x}$ is farther from the yz-plane.

6. Secant Curve Region Problem

a. Slice the region parallel to the y-axis.
$dA = \sec x\,dx$
$A = \int_0^{\pi/3} \sec x\,dx = \ln(2 + \sqrt{3}) = 1.3169...$
$dM_y = x\,dA = x \sec x\,dx$
$M_y = \int_0^{\pi/3} x \sec x\,dx = 0.7684...$ (numerically)
$\bar{x} \cdot A = M_y \Rightarrow \bar{x} = \dfrac{0.7684...}{1.3169...} = 0.5835...$

b. Strips in part a. generate plane disks. Each point in a disk is about x units from the yz-plane where x is at the sample point (x, y).
$dV = \pi y^2\,dx = \pi \sec^2 x\,dx$
$V = \int_0^{\pi/3} \pi \sec^2 x\,dx = \pi\sqrt{3} = 5.4413...$
$dM_{yz} = x\,dV = \pi x \sec^2 x\,dx$
$M_{yz} = \int_0^{\pi/3} \pi x \sec^2 x\,dx = 3.5206...$
(exactly $\dfrac{\pi^2\sqrt{3}}{3} + \pi \ln \dfrac{1}{2}$)
$\bar{x} \cdot V = M_{yz} \Rightarrow \bar{x} = 0.6470...$
(exactly $\dfrac{\pi}{3} - \dfrac{\ln 2}{\sqrt{3}}$)

c. False. For the solid, $\bar{x}$ is farther from the yz-plane.

7. Centroid of a Triangle Experiment

Construct axes with the origin at a vertex and the x-axis along the base, b.
Slice the triangle parallel to the x-axis.
Width of a strip is $b - \dfrac{b}{h}y$
$dA = (b - \dfrac{b}{h}y)\,dy$
$dM_x = y\,dA = (by - \dfrac{b}{h}y^2)\,dy$
$M_x = \int_0^h (by - \dfrac{b}{h}y^2)\,dy = \dfrac{1}{2}by^2 - \dfrac{b}{3h}y^3 \Big|_0^h = \dfrac{1}{6}bh^2$
$\bar{y} \cdot A = M_x \Rightarrow \bar{y} = \dfrac{\frac{1}{6}bh^2}{\frac{1}{2}bh} = \dfrac{1}{3}h$, Q.E.D.

8. Centroid Cut-Out Experiment

a. $y = x^{2/3}$ from $x = 0$ to $x = 8$
Slice the region vertically. Pick a sample point (x, y) on the graph within the strip. (See the graph in part e.)
$dA = y\,dx = x^{2/3}\,dx$
$A = \int_0^8 x^{2/3}\,dx = 19.2$

b. Slice the region parallel to the x-axis so that each point in a strip will be about y units from the x-axis, where y is at the sample point (x, y).
$dM_x = y(8 - x)\,dy = (8y - y^{5/2})\,dy$
$M_x = \int_0^4 (8y - y^{5/2})\,dy = 27.4285...$ (exactly $27\frac{3}{7}$)

c. Each point in a strip of part a. is about x units from the y-axis, where x is at the sample point.
$dM_y = x\,dA = x^{5/3}\,dx$
$M_y = \int_0^8 x^{5/3}\,dx = 96$

d. $\bar{x} \cdot A = M_y \Rightarrow \bar{x} = \dfrac{96}{19.2} = 5$
$\bar{y} \cdot A = M_x \Rightarrow \bar{y} = \dfrac{27.4285...}{19.2} = 1.4285...$
(exactly $1\frac{3}{7}$)
Centroid is at (5, 1.4285...).

e. Graph, showing balance point

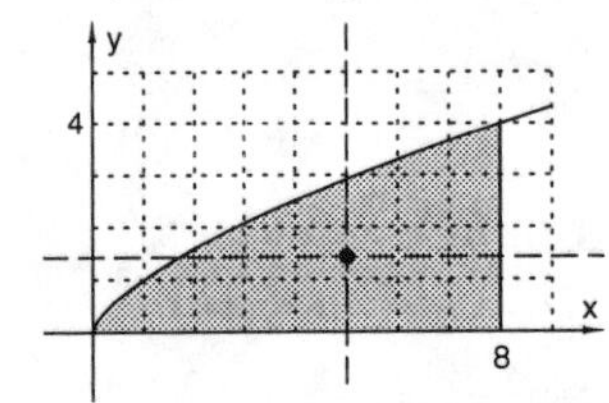

The photograph on page 572 of the text shows the author's student Audrey Diehl with her solution to this problem in 1996.

9. Second Moment of Area Problem

a. Slice the region parallel to the y-axis so that each point in a strip will be about x units from the y-axis, where x is at the sample point (x, y).

$dA = y\,dx = \sin x\,dx$

$A = \int_0^{\pi} \sin x\,dx = 2$ (exactly)

(This may be "well-known" by now.)

$dM_y = x\,dA = x \sin x\,dx$

$M_y = \int_0^{\pi} x \sin x\,dx = 3.1415... = \pi$ (exactly)

$\bar{x} \cdot A = M_y \Rightarrow \bar{x} = \frac{\pi}{2}$, Q.E.D.

(Or just note the symmetry.)

b. $dM_{2y} = x^2\,dA = x^2 \sin x\,dx$

$M_{2y} = \int_0^{\pi} x^2 \sin x\,dx = 5.8696...$ (exactly $\pi^2 - 4$)

c. $\bar{\bar{x}}^2 \cdot A = M_{2y} \Rightarrow \bar{\bar{x}} = \sqrt{\frac{\pi^2-4}{2}} = 1.7131...$

10. Second Moments for Plane Regions Problem

a. Set up axes with x-axis along the base, B.

$dM_{2B} = y^2\,dA = y^2 B\,dy$

$M_{2B} = \int_0^H y^2 B\,dy = \frac{1}{3} BH^3$

b. Set up axes with x-axis through the centroid.

$dM_{2c} = y^2\,dA = y^2 B\,dy$

$M_{2c} = \int_{-0.5H}^{0.5H} y^2 B\,dy = \frac{1}{12} BH^3$

c. Set up axes with x-axis along the base, B.

$dM_{2B} = y^2\,dA = y^2 (B - \frac{B}{H} y)\,dy$

$M_{2B} = \int_0^H (By^2 - \frac{B}{H} y^3)\,dy = \frac{1}{12} BH^3$

d. Use the axes in part c. The distance from the centroidal axis to a sample point (x, y) is $y - \frac{1}{3}H$.

$dM_{2c} = (y - \frac{1}{3}H)^2\,dA = (y - \frac{1}{3}H)^2 (B - \frac{B}{H} y)\,dy$

$M_{2c} = B \int_{-H/3}^{2H/3} (-\frac{1}{H} y^3 + \frac{5}{3} y^2 - \frac{7}{9} Hy + \frac{1}{9} H^2)\,dy$

$= -\frac{B}{4H} y^4 + \frac{5}{9} By^3 - \frac{7}{18} BHy^2 + \frac{1}{9} BH^2 y \Big|_0^H = \frac{1}{36} BH^3$

11. Second Moments for Solid Figures

a. Slice into cylindrical shells so that each point in a shell will be about r units from the axis.

Altitude of shell is a constant, H.

$dM = r^2\,dV = r^2\, 2\pi r H\,dr$

$M = \int_0^R 2\pi H r^3\,dr = \frac{1}{2} \pi H R^4$

$\bar{r}^2 \cdot V = M \Rightarrow \bar{r}^2 = \dfrac{\frac{1}{2}\pi H R^4}{\pi R^2 H} \Rightarrow \bar{r} = \frac{1}{\sqrt{2}} R$

b. Slice the cone into cylindrical shells so that each point in a shell will be about r units from the axis.

Altitude of a shell is $H - \frac{H}{R} r$.

$dM = r^2\,dV = r^2\, 2\pi r (H - \frac{H}{R} r)\,dr$

$M_h = 2\pi H \int_0^R (r^3 - \frac{1}{R} r^4)\,dr = \frac{1}{10} \pi H R^4$

$\bar{r}^2 \cdot V = M \Rightarrow \bar{r}^2 = \dfrac{\frac{1}{10}\pi H R^4}{\frac{1}{3}\pi R^2 H} \Rightarrow \bar{r} = \sqrt{0.3}\,R$

c. Slice the sphere into cylindrical shells so that each point in a shell is about r units from the axis.

Equation of the sphere is $r^2 + y^2 = R^2$.

Altitude of a shell is 2y.

$dM = r^2\,dV = r^2\, 2\pi r \cdot 2\sqrt{R^2 - r^2}\,dr$

$M = 4\pi \int_0^R r^3 \sqrt{R^2 - r^2}\,dr$

Let $r = R \sin\theta$.

$dr = R\cos\theta\,d\theta$, $\sqrt{R^2 - r^2} = R\cos\theta$

$r = 0 \Rightarrow \theta = 0$, $r = R \Rightarrow \theta = \frac{\pi}{2}$

$M = 4\pi \int_0^{\pi/2} R^3 \sin^3\theta \cdot R\cos\theta \cdot R\cos\theta\,d\theta$

$= 4\pi R^5 \int_0^{\pi/2} (\cos^2\theta - \cos^4\theta)\sin\theta\,d\theta$

$= 4\pi R^5 [-\frac{1}{3}\cos^3\theta + \frac{1}{5}\cos^5\theta] \Big|_0^{\pi/2}$

$= 4\pi R^5 [-0 + 0 + \frac{1}{3} - \frac{1}{5}] = \frac{8}{15}\pi R^5$

$\bar{r}^2 \cdot V = M \Rightarrow \bar{r}^2 = \dfrac{\frac{8}{15}\pi R^5}{\frac{4}{3}\pi R^3} \Rightarrow \bar{r} = \sqrt{0.4}\,R$

12. Rotation of Solids Problem

Assume the clay has uniform density ρ.

Cylinder: $H = 2R_C$, $V = \pi R_C^2 H = 2\pi R_C^3 = 1000$

$R_C = (\frac{500}{\pi})^{1/3}$ cm

Second moment of volume $= \frac{1}{2}\pi(2R_c)R_c^4$

$= \pi R_C^5$ (from Problem 11a)

Second moment of mass

$= \rho\pi R_C^5 = 500\rho(\frac{500}{\pi})^{2/3} = 14684.1932...\,\rho$

Sphere: $V = \frac{4}{3}\pi R_S^3 = 1000 \Rightarrow R_S = (\frac{750}{\pi})^{1/3}$ cm

Second moment of volume $= \frac{8}{15}\pi R_S^5$ (from #11c)

Second moment of mass

$= \rho \frac{8}{15}\pi R_S^5 = 400\rho(\frac{750}{\pi})^{2/3} = 15{,}393.3892...\,\rho$

Sphere has higher moment of mass.

13. Beam Moment Problem

a. Set up axes with x-axis through the centroid.

$dM_2 = y\,dA = y^2 \cdot B\,dy$

$M_2 = B\int_{-0.5H}^{0.5H} y^2\,dy = \frac{1}{3} y^3 \Big|_{-0.5H}^{0.5H} = \frac{1}{12} BH^3$, Q.E.D.

(Same answer as in Problem 10b.)

b. i. $B = 2$, $H = 12$; $M_2 = 288$; stiffness = 288k

ii. $B = 12$, $H = 2$; $M_2 = 8$; stiffness = 8k

Board up on edge is 36 times stiffer.

c. i. Set up axes with x-axis through the centroid.

From y = 0 to y = 2, $dM_2 = y^2 \cdot 2\,dy$.

From y = 2 to y = 4, $dM_2 = y^2 \cdot 4\,dy$.

By symmetry, $M_2 = 2\int_0^4 dM_2$

$= 2\int_0^2 2y^2\,dy + 2\int_2^4 4y^2\,dy = 160$

Stiffness = 160k

ii. From $y = 0$ to $y = 4$, $dM_2 = y^2 \cdot 1\ dy$.
From $y = 4$ to $y = 6$, $dM_2 = y^2 \cdot 4\ dy$.

By symmetry, $M_2 = 2\int_0^6 dM_2$
$= 2\int_0^4 y^2\ dy + 2\int_4^6 4y^2\ dy = 448$
Stiffness = 448k (2.8 times stiffer!)

d. Increasing the depth does seem to increase stiffness greatly, but making the beam *very* tall would also make the web *very* thin, perhaps too thin to withstand much force.

14. Introduction to the Theorems of Pappus

a. $dA = y\ dx = x^3\ dx$
$A = \int_0^2 x^3\ dx = 4$

b. $dV = 2\pi x \cdot y \cdot dx = 2\pi x^4\ dx$
$V = \int_0^2 2\pi x^4\ dx = 12.8\pi$

c. $dM_y = x\ dA = x^4\ dx$
$M_y = \int_0^2 x^4\ dx = 6.4$
The volume integral is 2π times the moment integral.

d. $\bar{x} \cdot A = M_y \Rightarrow \bar{x} = \frac{6.4}{4} = 1.6$

e. The centroid travels $2\pi\bar{x} = 3.2\pi$.
(Area)(Distance traveled by centroid)
$= (4)(3.2\pi) = 12.8\pi$, which equals the volume. Thus, the theorem of Pappus is confirmed.

15. Theorem of Pappus Problem

a. Toroid Problem
Area of small circle: $A = \pi r^2$
The centroid of the small circle is its center, so the distance from the axis of rotation to the centroid is R. Thus, Pappus's Theorem implies:
$V = 2\pi RA = 2\pi R(\pi r^2) = 2\pi^2 r^2 R$

b. Centroid of a Semicircle
Area of a semicircle $= \frac{1}{2}\pi r^2$
Volume of a sphere $= \frac{4}{3}\pi r^3$
$2\pi\bar{r} \cdot A = V \Rightarrow \bar{r} = \frac{\frac{4}{3}\pi r^3}{2\pi \cdot \frac{1}{2}\pi r^2} = \frac{4}{3\pi} r$

16. Theorem of Pappus Proof
Pick a closed region that does not lie on both sides of the y-axis.
Slice the region parallel to the y-axis so that each point in the strip will be about r units from the y-axis (see graph).

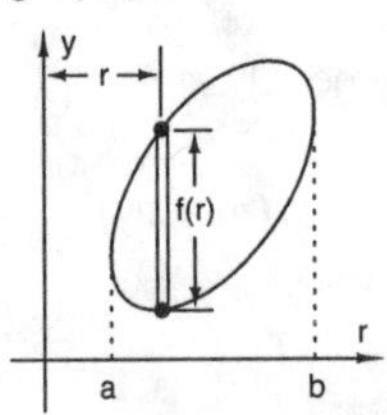

Let f(r) be the length of the strip or the sum of the lengths if the region has "S-shaped" parts.
Let A be the area of the region.
$dM_y = r\ dA = r\ f(r)\ dr$
$M_y = \int_a^b r\ f(r)\ dr$
Rotate the region about the y-axis. The strips generate cylindrical shells.
$dV = 2\pi r\ f(r)\ dr$
$V = \int_a^b 2\pi r\ f(r)\ dr = 2\pi\int_a^b r\ f(r)\ dr = 2\pi M_y$
But M_y also equals $\bar{r} \cdot A$.
$\therefore V = 2\pi\bar{r}A = (2\pi\bar{r})(A)$
= (distance traveled by centroid)(area of region), Q.E.D.

Problem Set 11-5, pages 580 to 583

Q1. centroid
Q2. center of mass
Q3. radius of gyration
Q4. definite integration
Q5. indefinite integration (or antidifferentiation)
Q6. ρ = (mass)÷(volume)
Q7. $x^{1/2}$
Q8. ln |sec x + tan x| + C
Q9. $y' = (x^2 + 1)^{-1}$
Q10. cosh x

1. Trough Problem

a. Slice the trough face horizontally so that each point in a strip is about the same distance below the surface as at the sample point (x, y).
$y = 2x^4 \Rightarrow x = (0.5y)^{1/4}$
$p = k(2 - y)$, $dA = 2x\ dy = 2(0.5y)^{1/4}\ dy$
$dF = p\ dA = 2k(2 - y)(0.5y)^{1/4}\ dy$
$F = \int_0^2 dF = 2.8444...\ k$ (exactly $\frac{128}{45}$ k)

b. $dM_x = y\ dF = y \cdot 2k(2 - y)(0.5y)^{1/4}\ dy$
$M_x = \int_0^2 dM_x = 2.1880...\ k$ (exactly $\frac{256}{117}$ k)

Force Exerted by a Variable Pressure—Center of Pressure

c. $\bar{y} \cdot F = M_x \Rightarrow \bar{y} = \frac{2.1880...\ k}{2.8444...\ k} = 0.7692...$
(exactly $\frac{10}{13}$)
$\bar{x} = 0$ by symmetry.
Center of pressure is at $(0, \frac{10}{13})$.

2. Dam Problem

a. Graph, $y = x^2$, between $y = 0$ and $y = 100$

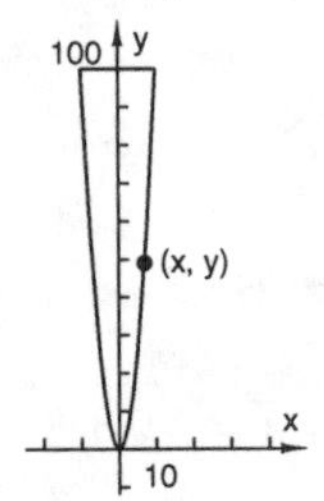

Width at y = 100 ft is $2\sqrt{y} = 20$ ft, Q.E.D.

b. Slice the dam face horizontally so that each point in a strip is the same distance below the surface as the sample point (x, y).

$dA = 2x\,dy = 2y^{1/2}\,dx$

$A = \int_0^{100} 2y^{1/2}\,dx = 1333\frac{1}{3}\text{ ft}^2$

(2/3 the area of the circumscribed rectangle)

c. $p = k(100 - y)$ with $k = 62.4\text{ lb/ft}^3$

$dF = p\,dA = 2k(100 - y)(y^{1/2})\,dy$

$F = \int_0^{100} dF = 53{,}333\frac{1}{3}k = 3{,}328{,}000$

Force is 3,328,000 lb, or 1664 tons.

d. $dM_x = y\,dF = 2ky(100 - y)(y^{1/2})\,dy$

$M_x = \int_0^{100} dM_x = \frac{16000000}{7}k = 142{,}628{,}571.4285...$

$\approx 142.6...$ million lb-ft

e. $\bar{y}\cdot F = M_x \Rightarrow \bar{y} = \frac{300}{7} = 42\frac{7}{8}$

$= 42.8571... \approx 42.86$ ft

3. <u>Ship's Bulkhead Problem</u>

a. Slice the bulkhead horizontally so that each point in a strip is the same distance below the surface as the sample point (x, y).

$\left(\frac{x}{20}\right)^4 + \left(\frac{y - 32}{32}\right)^4 = 1$

$x = 20(1 - (\frac{1}{32}y - 1)^4)^{1/4}$

$dA = 2x\,dy = 40(1 - (\frac{1}{32}y - 1)^4)^{1/4}\,dy$

$A = \int_0^{32} dA \approx 1{,}186.6077... \approx 1186.6\text{ ft}^2$

b. $p = 67(32 - y)$

$dF = p\,dA = 67(32 - y)\cdot 40(1 - (\frac{1}{32}y - 1)^4)^{1/4}\,dy$

$F = \int_0^{32} dF \approx 1{,}199{,}294.1645... \approx 1.199$ million lb

c. $dM_x = y\,dF = y\cdot 67(32 - y)\cdot 40(1 - (\frac{1}{32}y - 1)^4)^{1/4}\,dy$

$M_x = \int_0^{32} dM_x \approx 13{,}992{,}028.2564...$

≈ 13.992 million lb-ft.

d. $\bar{y}\cdot F = M_x \Rightarrow \bar{y} \approx 11.6668...$ ft. $\bar{x} = 0$ by symmetry.

Center of pressure is at about (0,11.67) ft.

e. Moment of area:

$dM = y\,dA = y\cdot 40(1 - (\frac{1}{32}y - 1)^4)^{1/4}\,dy$

$M = \int_0^{32} dM \approx 20{,}071.5364... \approx 20.07\text{ thousand ft}^3$

$\bar{y}\cdot A = M \Rightarrow \bar{y} \approx 16.9150...$ ft. $\bar{x} = 0$ by symmetry.

Centroid is at about (0,16.92) ft.

Centroid is different from center of pressure.

f. Area below waterline:

$A_w = \int_0^{16} dA \approx 548.6345... \approx 548.6\text{ ft}^2$

First moment of area below waterline:

$M_w = \int_0^{16} dM \approx 4749.3398... \approx 4749.3\text{ ft}^3$

$\bar{y}\cdot A_w = M_w \Rightarrow \bar{y} \approx 8.6566...$ ft. $\bar{x} = 0$ by symmetry.

Center of buoyancy is at about (0, 8.66) ft

4. <u>Oil Truck Problem</u>

a. Equation of ellipse is $\left(\frac{x}{6}\right)^2 + \left(\frac{y}{3}\right)^2 = 1$

b. Slice the ellipse horizontally so that each point in a strip is y units from the surface where y is at the sample point and y is negative.

Surface of oil is at $y = 0 \Rightarrow p = -50y$

$x = 2\sqrt{9 - y^2}$, $dA = 2x\,dy = 4\sqrt{9 - y^2}\,dy$

$dF = p\,dA = -50y\cdot 4\sqrt{9 - y^2}\,dy$

$= -200y\sqrt{9 - y^2}\,dy$

$F = \int_{-3}^{0} dF = 1800$ lb (exactly)

5. <u>Airplane Wing Problem I</u>

a. Graph, $y = 60\cos\frac{\pi}{20}x$

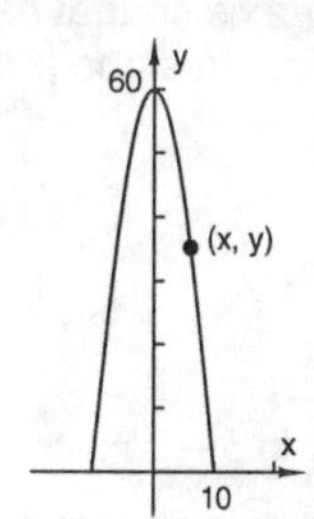

Slice the wing parallel to the y-axis. Pick sample point (x, y) within the strip.

$dA = y\,dx = 60\cos\frac{\pi}{20}x\,dx$

$A = \int_{-10}^{10} dA = \frac{2400}{\pi} = 763.9437... \approx 763.9\text{ ft}^2.$

b. $dF = p\,dA = k(10 - |x|)\cdot 60\cos\frac{\pi}{20}x\,dx$

$F = \int_{-10}^{10} dF = 4{,}863.4168...\,k$ (exactly $\frac{48000}{\pi^2}k$)

c. Make $4863.4168...\,k \ge 96$

$k \ge 0.0197...\text{ tons/ft}^2$ (exactly $0.002\pi^2$)

6. <u>Airplane Wing Problem II</u>

a. $y = 100 - x^2$ intersects the x-axis at $x = \pm 10$.

Slice the wing parallel to the y-axis. Pick sample point (x, y) within the strip.

$p = 90 - 7x.$

$dA = y\,dx = (100 - x^2)\,dx$

$dF = p\,dA = (90 - 7x)(100 - x^2)\,dx$

$F = \int_{-10}^{10} dF = 120{,}000$ lb (exactly)

b. $dM_y = x\,dF = x(90 - 7x)(100 - x^2)\,dx$

$M_y = \int_{-10}^{10} dM_y = -\frac{560000}{3}$ lb-ft

c. $\bar{x}\cdot F = M_y \Rightarrow \bar{x} = -1\frac{5}{9}$ ft

d. $p = ky = \frac{6}{5}y$ (since $p = 60$ at $y = 50$)

$dA = 2x\,dy = 2\sqrt{100 - y}\,dy$

$dF = p\,dA = \frac{12}{5}y\sqrt{100 - y}\,dy$

$F = \int_0^{100} dF = 64{,}000$ lb (exactly)

e. $dM_x = y\,dF = \frac{12}{5}y^2\sqrt{100 - y}\,dy$

$M_x = \int_0^{100} dM_x = 3{,}657{,}142.8...$

≈ 3.657 million lb-ft (exactly $\frac{25600000}{7}$)

f. $\bar{y}\cdot F = M_x \Rightarrow \bar{y} = 57.1428... \approx 57.14$ ft

(exactly $\frac{400}{7}$)

7. Double-Integration Airplane Wing Problem
   a. Slice the region as shown in Figure 11-5f.
   At a sample point (x, t),
   $d(dM_{2x}) = t^2\,dx\,dt$
   $dM_{2x} = \int_{t=0}^{t=y} t^2\,dx\,dt = (\int_{t=0}^{t=y} t^2\,dt)\,dx$
   $= \frac{1}{3}t^3 \Big|_{t=0}^{t=y} dx = \frac{1}{3}y^3\,dx$
   $= \frac{1}{3}(0.25(x-4) - (x-4)^{1/3})^3\,dx.$
   b. $M_{2x} = \int_{x=-4}^{x=4} dM_{2x} = 0.5333...$ (exactly $\frac{8}{15}$)
8. Double-Integration Variable Pressure Problem
   a. Slice the region parallel to the y-axis so that each point in a strip will have the about the same pressure as at the sample point (x, y).
   $y = e^{-x}$
   $p = kx^2$, $dA = (1 - e^{-x})\,dx$
   $dF = p\,dA = kx^2(1 - e^{-x})\,dx$
   $F = \int_0^{\ln 5} dF = 0.9514...\ k$
   (Exactly $(\frac{1}{3}(\ln 5)^3 + \frac{1}{5}(\ln 5)^2 + \frac{2}{5}\ln 5 - \frac{8}{5})k$)
   b. Slice the region parallel to the x-axis so that each point in a strip will have about the same pressure as at the sample point (x, y).
   $x = -\ln y$, $p = ky^{-1}$
   $dA = (\ln 5 - x)\,dy = (\ln 5 + \ln y)\,dy = \ln(5y)\,dy$
   $dF = p\,dA = ky^{-1}\ln(5y)\,dy$
   $x = \ln 5 \Rightarrow y = e^{-\ln 5} = 0.2$
   $F = \int_{0.2}^{1} dF = 1.2951...\ k$ (Exactly $\frac{1}{2}(\ln 5)^2\,k$)
   c. Slice the region parallel to the y-axis. Then slice a strip parallel to the x-axis as shown in Figure 11-5g.
   At sample point (x, t), $p = kx^2t^{-1}$
   $d(dF) = p\,dA = kx^2t^{-1}\,dx\,dt$
   $dF = \int_{t=y}^{t=1} kx^2t^{-1}\,dx\,dt = (\int_{t=y}^{t=1} kt^{-1}\,dt)\,x^2\,dx$
   $= (k \ln t \Big|_{t=y}^{t=1})\,x^2\,dx = k(0 - \ln y)x^2\,dx = kx^3\,dx$
   $F = \int_0^{\ln 5} kx^3\,dx = = \frac{1}{4}k(\ln 5)^4 = 1.6774...\ k$
9. The integrals in Problems 7 and 8 can be written in the form
   $\int_{x=a}^{x=b}\int_{t=c}^{t=d} f(x, t)\,dt\,dx$
   Since two integrals appear, the result is called a double integral. (Hiding inside each integral is a second integral!)
10. Floodgate Problem
   a. $y = 5\tan^2 \frac{\pi}{8}x$
   $y = 5 \Rightarrow \tan^2 \frac{\pi}{8}x = 1 \Rightarrow x = \pm 2$
   Slice the floodgate parallel to the y-axis.
   $dA = (5 - 5\tan^2 \frac{\pi}{8}x)\,dx$
   $A = \int_{-2}^{2} dA = 14.5352... \approx 14.54\ \text{ft}^2$
   (exactly $40 - \frac{80}{\pi}$)
   b. Slice the floodgate parallel to the x-axis so that each point in a strip has about the same pressure as at the sample point (x, y).
   $p = k(20 - y)$ with $k = 62.4\ \text{lb/ft}^2$
   $y = 5\tan^2 \frac{\pi}{8}x \Rightarrow x = \frac{8}{\pi}\tan^{-1}\sqrt{0.2y}$
   $dA = 2x\,dy = \frac{16}{\pi}\tan^{-1}\sqrt{0.2y}\,dy$
   $dF = p\,dA = k(20 - y)\cdot\frac{16}{\pi}\tan^{-1}\sqrt{0.2y}\,dy$
   $F = \int_0^5 dF = 248.2628...\ k$
   $= 15491.6027... \approx 15.49$ thousand lb
   (Exactly $(800 - \frac{5200}{3\pi})\,k$)
   (The force can also be found by slicing parallel to the y-axis as in part a., then slicing the strip horizontally and using a double integral. In this case, the pressure at a sample point (x, t) is
   $p = k(20 - t)$
   $d(dF) = p\,dA = k(20 - t)\,dt\,dx$
   The first integration is from $t = y$ to $t = 5$. The second integration is from $x = -2$ to $x = 2$.)
   c. Let μ (Greek letter mu) = coefficient of friction.
   $\mu \cdot F = 10{,}000 \Rightarrow \mu = \frac{10000}{15491.6027...} = 0.6455...$

Problem Set 11-6, pages 585 to 591 — Other Variable-Factor Products

Q1. $\frac{1}{101}x^{101} + C$
Q2. 0
Q3. $x \ln x - x + C$
Q4. $2 \sin x \cos x = \sin 2x$
Q5. (force)(displacement)
Q6. $y' = 3(1 + 9x^2)^{-1}$
Q7. $x = -2$
Q8. $2 \sec^2 x \tan x$
Q9. $y'' = -9 \cos 3x$
Q10. hyperbola

1. Heat Capacity Problem
   Partition the interval into small subintervals of width dT so that C is about the same at any point in a subinterval. The amount of heat, dH, to raise the temperature by dT is
   $dH = C\,dT = (10 + 0.3\,T^{1/2})\,dT$
   $H = \int_{100}^{900} dH = 13200$ calories (exactly)
2. Phoebe's Speeding Problem
   a. $v(t) = 55 + 6t - t^2$
   $v(0) = 55 + 6\cdot 0 - 0^2 = 55$ mph
   $v(3) = 55 + 6\cdot 3 - 3^2 = 64$ mph
   $v(6) = 55 + 6\cdot 6 - 6^2 = 55$ mph, Q.E.D.
   b. Cost of a short time dt at speed v
   $dC = 3(v - 55)dt = 18t - 3t^2\,dt$
   Total ticket cost is
   $C = \int_0^6 dC = 108$ (exactly)
   Fine should be \$108.00.
3. Tunnel Problem
   a. Cost per foot $P = ax^2 + bx + c$
   $a\cdot 0^2 + b\cdot 0 + c = 500 \Rightarrow c = 500$
   $\left.\begin{array}{l} a\cdot 100^2 + b\cdot 100 + 500 = 820 \\ a\cdot 200^2 + b\cdot 200 + 500 = 1180 \end{array}\right\} \Rightarrow \left\{\begin{array}{l} a = 0.002 \\ b = 3 \end{array}\right.$
   $P(x) = 0.002x^2 + 3x + 500$

b. $P(700) = 0.002 \cdot 700^2 + 3 \cdot 700 + 500 = \$3580/\text{ft}$.

c. Cost to dig a short distance dx is

$dC = P\,dx = (0.002x^2 + 3x + 500)\,dx$

Cost to dig 1000 feet is

$\int_0^{1000} (0.002x^2 + 3x + 500)\,dx = \frac{8}{3} \cdot 1000^2$

Cost is about $2,666,667.

d. Cost to dig 500 feet twice (once from each end) is

$C = 2\int_0^{500} (0.002x^2 + 3x + 500)\,dx = \frac{17}{3} \cdot 500^2$

Cost is about $1,416,667.

Savings is about $1,250,000!

4. Water Pipe Problem

a. velocity · area has the units

$\frac{\text{in}}{\text{sec}} \cdot \text{in}^2$,

which is in^3/sec, correct for flow rate.

b. $v = 4 - x^2 \Rightarrow v' = -2x$

v' changes from positive to negative at $x = 0$.

$\therefore$ there is a maximum flow rate at the center of the pipe where $x = 0$.

(Or simply observe that the graph of v is a parabola opening downward with vertex at $x = -b/(2a) = 0$.)

$v(2) = 4 - 2^2 = 0$, Q.E.D.

c. Slice the water in the pipe into cylindrical shells. Each point in a shell has about the same water velocity as at the sample point x units from the axis.

Let F = flow rate in in^3/sec.

$dF = v\,dA = (4 - x^2) \cdot 2\pi x \cdot dx = 2\pi(4x - x^3)\,dx$

$F = \int_0^2 2\pi(4x - x^3)\,dx = 8\pi = 25.1327...$

$\approx 25.13\ \text{in}^3/\text{sec}$.

d. $25.1327...\ \text{in}^3/\text{sec} \cdot 60\ \text{sec/min} \cdot 1\ \text{gal}/231\ \text{in}^3$

$= 6.5279... \approx 6.53$ gal/min.

e. $4\ \text{in/sec} \cdot \pi \cdot 2^2\ \text{in}^2 = 16\pi = 13.0559...$

≈ 13.06 gal/min.

(Exactly twice the actual rate.)

f. The problem is equivalent to finding the volume of a solid of rotation by cylindrical shells. The velocity takes the place of the altitude of a shell.

5. Wire-Pulling Problem

a. Graph, connected scatter plot

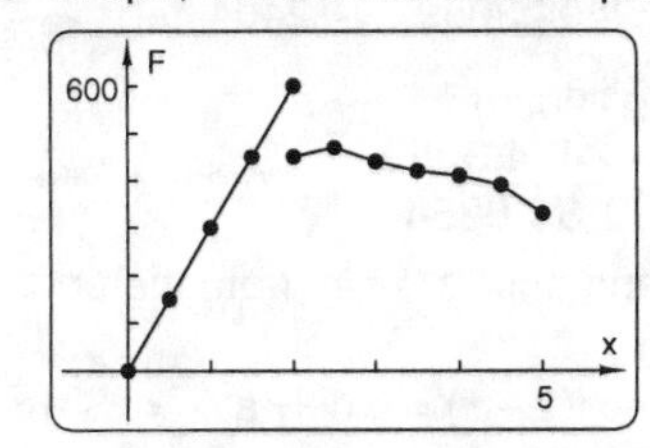

b. F has a step discontinuity at $x = 2$.

c. $dW = F\,dx$

Since the graph is linear, the work equals the area of the triangle.

$W = \frac{1}{2} \cdot 2 \cdot 600 = 600$ in-lb

d. $W = \int_2^5 F\,dx$

By Simpson's rule,

$W \approx \frac{1}{3}(0.5)(450 + 4 \cdot 470 + 2 \cdot 440 + 4 \cdot 420 + 2 \cdot 410 + 4 \cdot 390 + 330)$

$= 1266\frac{2}{3}$ in-lb

e. Total work $\approx 600 + 1266\frac{2}{3} = 1866\frac{2}{3}$ in-lb

f. Yes, a piecewise-continuous function such as this one can be integrable. See Problem 27 in Problem Set 9-10 (Improper Integrals).

6. Variable Attraction Problem

a. Slice the solid into disks parallel to the xz-plane so that each point in a disk has about the same density as at the sample point (x, y).

$y = 4 - x^2 \Rightarrow x^2 = 4 - y$

$dm = \rho\,dV = k \cdot \pi x^2\,dy = k\pi(4 - y)\,dy$

$m = \int_0^4 k\pi(4 - y)\,dy = 8\pi k$ g

b. Each point in a disk of part a. is also about the same distance from the xz-plane as the sample point (x, y).

Let K stand for the constant.

$dF = K \cdot dm \cdot y^{-1/2} = K \cdot k\pi(4 - y)\,dy \cdot y^{-1/2}$

$= Kk\pi(4y^{-1/2} - y^{1/2})\,dy$

$F = \int_0^4 dF = \frac{32}{3}Kk\pi = 33.5103...\ Kk$

7. Moment of Inertia Problem

Slice the solid into cylindrical shells so that each point in a shell is about the same distance from the y-axis as the sample point (x, y).

$dM_{2y} = x^2\,dm = x^2 \cdot \rho\,dV = x^2 \cdot k \cdot 2\pi xy\,dx$

$= 2\pi k\,x^3(4 - x^2)\,dx$

$M_{2y} = \int_0^2 dM_{2y} = \frac{32}{3}\pi k = 33.5103...\ \text{kg-cm}^2$

8. Degree-Days Problem

a. $T(D) = 20 \sin 2\pi D$

$T(0) = 20 \sin 0 = 0$

$T(1/4) = 20 \sin \pi/2 = 20$, which checks.

b. Partition the time interval into short increments of width dD so that T is about the same at any time in the increment as it is at the sample point (D, T).

Let H = no. of degree-days.

$dH = T\,dD = 20 \sin 2\pi D\,dD$

$H = \int_0^{1/4} dH = \frac{10}{\pi} = 3.1830... \approx 3.18$ degree-days

9. Rocket Car Problem

a. $m = 2000 - 5t$ (mass in kg, time in seconds)

b. $a = F/m = 7000(2000 - 5t)^{-1} = 1400(400 - t)^{-1}$

c. $a = \frac{dv}{dt} = \frac{1400}{400 - t}$

$\int dv = \int \frac{1400}{400 - t}\,dt$

$v = -1400 \ln|400 - t| + C$

Assume the car starts at rest at $t = 0$.

$0 = -1400 \ln 400 + C \Rightarrow C = 1400 \ln 400$

$v(t) = 1400 \ln \frac{400}{|400 - t|}$

d. $v(20) = 1400 \ln \frac{20}{19} = 71.8106... \approx 71.81$ m/sec

$v = \frac{ds}{dt} = 1400 \ln \frac{400}{400 - t}$

$s = \int_0^{20} 1400 \ln \frac{400}{400 - t}\,dt = 711.9673...$

≈ 712.0 m (exactly $28000(1 - 19 \ln \frac{20}{19})$)

10. Field Worth Problem

Slice the tract parallel to the tracks so that each point in the strip will have about the same value per square kilometer as at the sample point (x, y).

Let v = thousands of dollars per square kilometer.

Let W = thousands of dollars the land is worth.

$v = kx = 200x \quad (v = 200 \text{ at } x = 1)$

$dW = v\,dA = 200x\,[(4 - x^2) - (4x - x^2)]\,dx$

$= 800(x - x^2)\,dx$

The curves intersect at x = 1.

$W = \int_0^1 800(x - x^2)\,dx = 133\frac{1}{3}$

The land is worth about $133,333.

If all the land were worth $200 thousand per km²,

$W = 200\,A = 200\int_0^1 (4 - 4x)\,dx = 400.$

The land would be worth $400,000.

Actual value is about $267 thousand less.

11. Sinusoidal Land Tract Problem

a. Slice the tract parallel to the y-axis so that each point in a strip will be about the same value per square unit as at the sample point (x, y).

$y = \cos x$

Let v = value of land per square unit.

Let W = worth of the land.

$v = kx,\ dA = y\,dx = \cos x\,dx$

$dW = v\,dA = kx\cos x\,dx$

$W = \int_0^{\pi/2} dA = (\frac{\pi}{2} - 1)\,k = 0.5707...\ k$

b. Slice the track parallel to the x-axis so that each point in a strip will be about the same value per square unit as at the sample point (x, y).

$v = ky$

$dW = v\,dA = v\cdot x\,dy = ky\cdot\cos^{-1} y\,dy$

$W = \int_0^1 dW = \frac{\pi}{8}k = 0.3926...\ k$

12. Painted Wall Problem

Graph, $y = 9 - x^2$

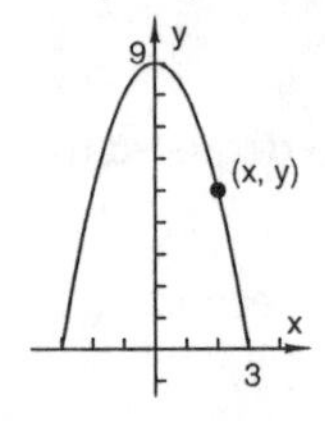

Slice the wall parallel to the ground so that each point in the slice will cost about the same to paint per square meter.

Let r = rate in dollars per square meter.

Let C = cost in dollars to paint the wall.

$r = ky^2 = 3y^2 \quad (r = 12 \text{ when } y = 2)$

$dA = 2x\,dy = 2\sqrt{9 - y}\,dy$

$dC = r\,dA = 3y^2 \cdot 2\sqrt{9 - y}\,dy$

$C = \int_0^9 dC \approx \$1999.54$ (exactly $1999\frac{19}{35}$)

13. City Land Value Problem:

a. Let v = value of land per square kilometer.

Let W = worth of the land in dollars.

Let r = distance from center of town.

Slice the city into circular rings of width dr so that each point in a ring will be about r units from the center, where r is to a sample point.

$v = 10 - 3r,\ dA = 2\pi r\,dr$

$dW = v\,dA = (10 - 3r)\cdot 2\pi r\,dr$

$W = \int_0^3 dW = 36\pi = 113.0973...$

≈ 113.1 million dollars.

b. $v = 10e^{kr},\ v(3) = 1 \Rightarrow k = -\frac{1}{3}\ln 10 \Rightarrow$

$v = 10e^{-(\ln 10)r/3}$

$dW = v\,dA = 10e^{-(\ln 10)r/3}\cdot 2\pi r\,dr$

$W = \int_0^3 dW = 71.4328... \approx 71.4$ million dollars.

(Exactly $\frac{18\pi}{(\ln 10)^2}(9 - \ln 10)$)

c. By Simpson's rule,

$W = \int_0^3 v\cdot 2\pi r\,dr \approx \frac{1}{3}(0.3)(2\pi)(10 + 4\cdot 12 + 2\cdot 15$

$+ 4\cdot 14 + 2\cdot 13 + 4\cdot 10 + 2\cdot 8 + 4\cdot 5 + 2\cdot 3 + 4\cdot 2 + 1)$

$= 52.2\pi = 163.9911... \approx 164.0$ million dollars.

d. This problem is equivalent to volume by cylindrical shells, where the value of the land per square unit takes the place of the altitude of the cylinder. It is also equivalent to the water flow in Problem 4 of this problem set.

14. Diving Board Problem

a. $p = 150[(x - 8)^{1/2} - 0.5(x - 8)]$

$dF = p\,dA = 2p\,dx = 300[(x - 8)^{1/2} - 0.5(x - 8)]\,dx$

$F = \int_8^{10} dF = 265.6854... \approx 266$ lb

(exactly $400\sqrt{2} - 300$)

b. Average pressure = total force / total area

$= \frac{265.6854...}{4} = 66.4213... \approx 66.4$ lb/ft²

(exactly $100\sqrt{2} - 75$).

c. $dM_{yz} = x\,dF = 2px\,dx$

$= 300x[(x - 8)^{1/2} - 0.5(x - 8)]\,dx$

$M_{yz} = \int_8^{10} dM_{yz} = 2404.3059... \approx 2404$ lb-ft

(exactly $3680\sqrt{2} - 2800$)

d. $\bar{x}\cdot F = M_{yz} \Rightarrow \bar{x} = \frac{2404.3059...}{265.6854...} = 9.0494...$ ft

Calvin should stand about $11\frac{1}{2}$ in. from the end.

15. Skewness Problem

a. $f(x) = 9 - x^2 = (3 - x)(3 + x) = 0$ only at $x = \pm 3$.

$g(x) = -\frac{1}{3}x^3 - x^2 + 3x + 9$

$= -\frac{1}{3}(x - 3)(x + 3)^2 = 0$ only at $x = \pm 3$

b. $A_f = \int_{-3}^{3} (9 - x^2)\,dx = 36$

$A_g = \int_{-3}^{3} (-\frac{1}{3}x^3 - x^2 + 3x + 9)\,dx = 36$

To simplify algebraic integration, you could use

$A_f = 2\int_0^3 (9 - x^2)\,dx$

$A_g = 2\int_0^3 (9 - x^2)\,dx$, where the odd terms integrate to zero between symmetrical limits.

Thus, the two integrals are identical.

c. The high point of f comes at $x = 0$.
The high point of g comes where $g'(x) = 0$.
$g'(x) = -x^2 - 2x + 3 = -(x + 3)(x - 1)$
$g'(x) = 0 \Leftrightarrow x = -3$ or $x = 1$.
The high point is at $x = 1$.

d. Slice the region under the g graph parallel to the y-axis so that each point in a strip will be about the same distance from the y-axis as the sample point (x, y).
$dM_y = x\, dA = x\, g(x)\, dx = (-\frac{1}{3}x^4 - x^3 + 3x^2 + 9x)\, dx$
$M_y = \int_{-3}^{3} dM_y = 21.6$
$\bar{x} \cdot A = M_y \Rightarrow \bar{x} = \frac{21.6}{36} = 0.6$

e. False. For the symmetrical region under the f graph, the centroid is on the line through the high point. But for the asymmetrical region under the g graph, the high point is at $x = 1$ and the centroid is at $x = 0.6$.

f. False.
Area to left $= \int_{-3}^{0.6} g(x)\, dx = 17.1072$ (exactly)
Area to right $= \int_{0.6}^{3} g(x)\, dx = 18.8928$ (exactly)
(or $36 - 17.1072 = 18.8928$)

g. Let S stand for skewness.
$dS = (x - \frac{3}{5})^3\, dA = (x - \frac{3}{5})^3\, g(x)\, dx$
$S = \int_{-3}^{3} (x - \frac{3}{5})^3 (-\frac{1}{3}x^3 - x^2 + 3x + 9)\, dx$
$= -17.7737...$ (exactly $\frac{-64 \cdot 3^5}{7 \cdot 125}$)

h. By symmetry, the centroid of the area under f is on the y-axis, so $\bar{x} = 0$. Then
$dS = x^3\, dA = x^3(9 - x^2)\, dx$
$S = \int_{-3}^{3} x^3(9 - x^2)\, dx = 0$ (odd function integrated between symmetrical limits)
The "skewness" being zero reflects the symmetry of this region. It is not skewed at all.

i. For example, graph $g(-x) = \frac{1}{3}x^3 - x^2 - 3x + 9$.

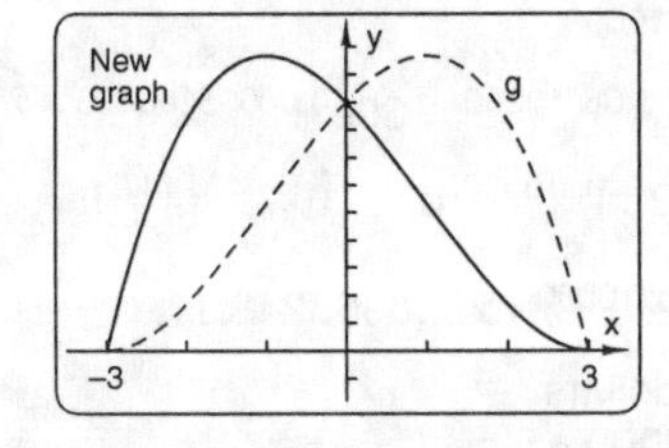

16. Moment of Arc Length Problem
a. $y = x^2$
$dL = \sqrt{dx^2 + dy^2} = \sqrt{1 + 4x^2}\, dx$
$dM_y = x\, dL = x\sqrt{1 + 4x^2}\, dx$
b. $M_y = \int_0^2 dM_y = 5.7577...$ (Exactly $\frac{1}{12}(17\sqrt{17} - 1)$)
c. $L = \int_0^2 \sqrt{1 + 4x^2}\, dx = 4.6467...$
(exactly $\frac{1}{4}\ln(\sqrt{17} + 4) + \sqrt{17}$)
d. $\bar{x} \cdot L = M_y \Rightarrow \bar{x} = \frac{5.7577...}{4.6467...} = 1.2390...$
e. $dS = 2\pi x\, dL = 2\pi x\sqrt{1 + 4x^2}\, dx$
$S = \int_0^2 dS = 36.1769...$ (exactly $\frac{\pi}{6}(17\sqrt{17} - 1)$)
f. Integral for S is 2π times the integral for M_y!

17. Another Theorem of Pappus Problem
In Problem 16, $R = \bar{x} = 1.2390...$ and $L = 4.6467...$.
$2\pi RL = 2\pi(1.2390...)(4.6467...) = 36.1769...$,
which equals S, Q.E.D.

18. Application of Pappus's Other Theorem
The centroid of the small circle is at its center, R units away from the axis.
The arc length L of the small circle is $2\pi r$.
Surface area $S = 2\pi R(2\pi r) = 4\pi^2 rR$

Problem Set 11-7, pages 592 to 596 — Chapter Review and Test

Review Problems

R0. Journal entries will vary.

R1. Work Problem
Slice the region parallel to the force axis so that each point in a strip has about the same force as at the sample point (x, F).
$dW = F\, dx = 30\, e^{-0.2x}\, dx$
$W = \int_0^{10} 30\, e^{-0.2x}\, dx = 150(1 - e^{-2}) = 129.6997...$
≈ 129.7 ft-lb

R2. a. Magnet Problem
$dW = F\, dx = kx^{-2}\, dx$
$W = \int_3^1 kx^{-2}\, dx = -\frac{2}{3}k$ ft-lb
(Mathematically, the answer is negative because dx is negative. Physically, the answer is negative because the magnets *absorb* energy from their surroundings rather than releasing energy to their surroundings.)

b. Conical Cup Problem

Construct axes with the origin at the vertex of the cone. An element of the cone in the xy-plane has the equation $y = \frac{7}{3}x$ or $x = \frac{3}{7}y$.

Slice the water horizontally into disks so that each point in a disk is lifted about the same distance as the sample point (x, y) on the element of the cone.

$F = 0.036\ dV = 0.036 \cdot \pi x^2\ dy = 0.036 \cdot \pi\ \frac{9}{49}\ y^2\ dy$

Each disk is lifted (10 – y) cm.

$dW = (10 - y)\ dF = (10 - y)(0.036)\pi\ \frac{9}{49}\ y^2\ dy$

$W = \int_0^7 dW = 3.591\pi = 11.2814... \approx 11.28$ in-lb

R3. Variable Density Problem

a. Graph, showing the region in Quadrant I under the graph of $y = 8 - x^3$ rotated about the y-axis

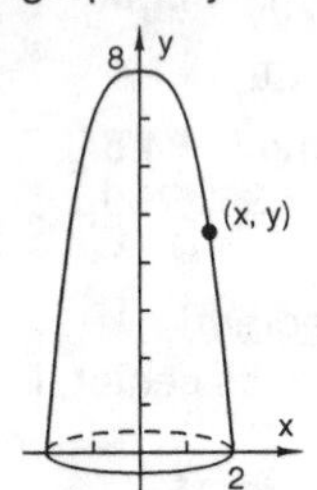

Slice the region parallel to the x-axis, generating disks, so that each point in a disk is about the same distance from the xz-plane as the sample point (x, y).

$\rho = ky,\ \ dV = \pi x^2\ dy = \pi(8 - y)^{2/3}\ dy$

$m = \int_0^8 k\pi y(8 - y)^{2/3}\ dy = 57.6\pi k$

b. Slice the region parallel to the y-axis, generating cylindrical shells, so that each point in a shell is about the same distance from the y-axis as the sample point (x, y).

$\rho = e^x,\ \ dV = 2\pi xy\ dx = 2\pi(8x - x^4)\ dx$

$m = \int_0^2 2\pi e^x(8x - x^4)\ dx = 64\pi$

R4. a. Triangle Centroid Problem

The width of a strip at the sample point (x, y) is

$w = b - \frac{b}{h}y \Rightarrow dA = (b - \frac{b}{h}y)\ dy.$

$dM_x = y\ dA = (by - \frac{b}{h}y^2)\ dy$

$M_x = \int_0^h (by - \frac{b}{h}y^2)\ dy$

$= \frac{1}{2}by^2 - \frac{b}{3h}y^3 \Big|_0^h = \frac{1}{2}bh^2 - \frac{b}{3h}h^3 - 0 + 0 = \frac{1}{6}bh^2$

$\bar{y} \cdot A = \bar{y} \cdot \frac{1}{2}bh = M_x \Rightarrow \bar{y} = \dfrac{\frac{1}{6}bh^2}{\frac{1}{2}bh} = \frac{1}{3}h,$ Q.E.D.

b. Second Moment of Volume Problem

Graph showing the region under $y = e^x$ rotated about the y-axis (showing back side of solid only).

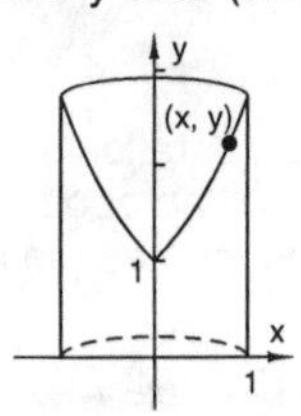

Slice the region parallel to the y-axis, generating cylindrical shells so that each point in a shell will be about the same distance from the y-axis as the sample point (x, y).

$dV = 2\pi x \cdot y \cdot dx = 2\pi x\ e^x\ dx$

$dM_{2y} = x^2\ dV = 2\pi x^3\ e^x\ dx$

$M_{2y} = \int_0^1 2\pi x^3\ e^x\ dx = 3.5401...$

(exactly $12\pi - 4\pi e$)

R5. Wind Force Problem

Draw axes with the x-axis at ground level and the y-axis through the upper vertex of the triangle. Slice the face of the building horizontally so that the wind pressure at any point in a strip is about equal to the pressure at the sample point (x, y).

$dA = (150 - \frac{150}{400}y)\ dy$

$dF = p\ dA = 200 \cdot 150(1 - e^{-0.01y})(1 - \frac{1}{400}y)\ dy$

$F = \int_0^{400} dF = 3736263.2708... \approx 3.736$ million lb

(exactly $30000(125 - 25e^{-4})$)

R6. Oil Well Problem

a. Let x = no. of feet at which drill is operating.

Let r(x) = no. of dollars per foot to drill at x feet.

$r(x) = a \cdot b^x$

$r(0) = 30 \Rightarrow a = 30$

$50 = 30 \cdot b^{10000} \Rightarrow b = (\frac{5}{3})^{1/10000}$

$\therefore\ r(x) = 30(\frac{5}{3})^{x/10000}$

(or $r(x) = 30e^{-\ln 0.6 \cdot x/10000} = 30e^{0.00005108256...\ x}$)

b. $dC = r(x)\ dx = 30(\frac{5}{3})^{x/10000}\ dx$

$C = \int_0^{50000} 30(\frac{5}{3})^{x/10000}\ dx = 6965243.17...$

≈ 6.965 million dollars

(exactly $-30 \cdot \frac{10000}{\ln 0.6}((\frac{5}{3})^5 - 1)$)

Concepts Problems

C1. Cubical Parabola Region Problem

a. Either slice the region parallel to the y-axis,

$dA = (8 - y)\,dx = (8 - x^3)\,dx$

$A = \int_0^2 (8 - x^3)\,dx = 12$

or slice parallel to the x-axis.

$A = \int_0^8 y^{1/3}\,dy = 12$

b. i. Use slices parallel to the x-axis so that each point in a strip will be about the same distance from the x-axis as the sample point (x, y).

$dM_x = y\,dA = y\,(y^{1/3}\,dy)$

$M_x = \int_0^8 y^{4/3}\,dy = \frac{384}{7} = 54.8571...$

ii. Use slices parallel to the y-axis so that each point in a strip will be about the same distance from the y-axis as the sample point (x, y).

$dM_y = x\,dA = x\,(8 - x^3)\,dx$

$M_y = \int_0^2 (8x - x^4)\,dx = 9.6$

c. $\bar{x}\cdot A = M_y \Rightarrow \bar{x} = \frac{9.6}{12} = 0.8$

$\bar{y}\cdot A = M_x \Rightarrow \bar{y} = \frac{384/7}{12} = \frac{32}{7} = 4.5714...$

Centroid is at (0.8, 4.5714...)

d. i. With slices parallel to the x-axis,

$dV = 2\pi y\cdot x\cdot dy = 2\pi y^{4/3}\,dy$

$V = \int_0^8 2\pi y^{4/3}\,dy = \frac{768}{7}\pi = 344.6775...$

With slices perpendicular to the x-axis,

$dV = \pi(8^2 - y^2)\,dx = \pi(64 - x^6)\,dx$

$V = \int_0^2 \pi(64 - x^6)\,dx = \frac{768}{7}\pi = 344.6775...$

ii. With slices parallel to the y-axis,

$dV = 2\pi x\cdot(8 - y)\cdot dx = 2\pi x(8 - x^3)\,dx$

$V = \int_0^2 2\pi(8x - x^4)\,dx = 19.2\pi = 60.3185...$

With slices perpendicular to the y-axis,

$dV = \pi x^2\,dy = \pi y^{2/3}\,dy$

$V = \int_0^8 \pi y^{2/3}\,dy = 19.2\pi = 60.3185...$

iii. With slices parallel to the line x = 3,

$dV = 2\pi(3 - x)\cdot(8 - y)\cdot dx = 2\pi(3 - x)(8 - x^3)\,dx$

$V = \int_0^2 2\pi(3 - x)(8 - x^3)\,dx = 52.8\pi = 165.8760...$

With slices perpendicular to the line x = 3,

$dV = \pi(3^2 - (3 - x)^2)\,dy = \pi(9 - (3 - y^{1/3})^2)\,dy$

$V = \int_0^8 \pi(9 - (3 - y^{1/3})^2)\,dy = 52.8\pi = 165.8760...$

e. i. The centroid is 32/7 units from the x-axis.

$\therefore V = 2\pi\cdot\frac{32}{7}\cdot 12 = \frac{768}{7}\pi = 344.6775...$ (checks)

ii. The centroid is 0.8 units from the y-axis.

$V = 2\pi\cdot 0.8\cdot 12 = 19.2\pi = 60.3185...$ (checks)

iii. The centroid is 3 – 0.8 = 2.2 units from the line x = 3.

$V = 2\pi\cdot 2.2\cdot 12 = 52.8\pi = 165.8760...$ (checks)

f. Use horizontal slices so that each point in a disk will be about the same distance from the xz-plane as the sample point (x, y).

$dM_{xz} = y\,dV = y\,(\pi x^2\,dy) = y\cdot\pi y^{2/3}\,dy$

$M_{xz} = \int_0^8 \pi y^{5/3}\,dy = 96\pi = 301.5928...$

g. $\bar{y}\cdot V = M_{xz} \Rightarrow \bar{y} = \frac{96\pi}{19.2\pi} = 5$

$\bar{x} = \bar{z} = 0$ by symmetry.

Centroid is at (0,5,0).

h. No. For the solid, $\bar{y} = 5$, but for the region, $\bar{y} = 4.5714...$.

i. Use slices of the region parallel to the y-axis so that each point in a resulting cylindrical shell will be about the same distance from the y-axis as the sample point (x, y).

$\rho = kx^2,\ dV = 2\pi x(8 - y)\,dx = 2\pi(8x - x^4)\,dx$

$dm = \rho\,dV = kx^2\cdot 2\pi(8x - x^4)\,dx = 2\pi k(8x^3 - x^6)\,dx$

$m = \int_0^2 2\pi k(8x^3 - x^6)\,dx = \frac{192}{7}\pi k = 86.1693...\ k$

j. Use cylindrical shells as in part i. so that each point in a shell will be about the same distance from the y-axis as the sample point (x, y).

$dM_2 = x^2\cdot dm = 2\pi k(8x^5 - x^8)\,dx$

$M_2 = \int_0^2 2\pi k(8x^5 - x^8)\,dx = \frac{512}{9}\pi k = 178.7217...$

k. Use vertical slices of the region so that each point in a strip will have about the same pressure acting on it as at the sample point (x, y).

$p = 3 - x,\ dA = (8 - y)\,dx = (8 - x^3)\,dx$

$dF = p\,dA = (3 - x)(8 - x^3)\,dx$

$F = \int_0^2 (3 - x)(8 - x^3)\,dx = 26.4$

(Note the similarity to the integral in part d.iii.)

l. $F = kz^{-2}$

$F = 26.4$ at $z = 1 \Rightarrow k = 26.4 \Rightarrow F = 26.4z^{-2}$

$dW = F\,dz = 26.4z^{-2}\,dz$

$W = \int_1^3 26.4z^{-2}\,dz = 17.6$

m. Use horizontal slices so that each point in a resulting disk will be at about the same temperature as the sample point (x, y).

$dH = CT\,dm = 0.3(10 - y)(5.8\pi y^{2/3}\,dy)$

$H = \int_0^8 1.74(10 - y)(\pi y^{2/3})\,dy = 167.04\pi$

$= 524.7716... \approx 524.8$ cal.

C2. Moment vs. Volume Problem

Let f(x) be the height of a vertical strip at x (or combined heights, if the region being rotated is not convex). Let x = a and x = b be the left and right boundaries of the region.

$dV = 2\pi x\,dA = 2\pi x\,f(x)\,dx \Rightarrow V = 2\pi\int_a^b x\,f(x)\,dx$

$dM_y = x\,dA = x\,f(x)\,dx \Rightarrow M_y = \int_a^b x\,f(x)\,dx$

Note that $V = 2\pi\,M_y$, thus showing that the two problems are mathematically equivalent, Q.E.D.

C3. Paraboloid Moment Conjecture Problem

$dM_{xz} = y\, dV_{xz} = y\, \pi x^2\, dy = \pi y(9 - y)\, dy$

$M_{xz} = \pi \int_0^9 \pi y(9 - y)\, dy = 121.5\pi$

$dM_{2y} = x^2\, dV_y = x^2\, 2\pi xy\, dx = 2\pi x^3(9 - x^2)\, dx$

$M_{2y} = \int_0^3 2\pi x^3(9 - x^2)\, dx = 121.5\pi$, Q.E.D.

This is not true in general. Counterexample: Rotate the region under $y = 2 - 2x^2$.

$dM_{xz} = y\, dV_{xz} = y\, \pi x^2\, dy = \pi y(1 - \frac{1}{2}y)\, dy$

$M_{xz} = \int_0^2 \pi y(1 - \frac{1}{2}y)\, dy = \frac{2}{3}\pi$

$dM_{2y} = x^2\, dV_y = x^2\, 2\pi xy\, dx = 2\pi x^3(2 - 2x^2)\, dx$

$M_{2y} = \int_0^1 2\pi x^3(2 - 2x^2)\, dx = \frac{1}{3}\pi$, not $\frac{2}{3}\pi$.

General proof: For any paraboloid of height H and base radius R, let h = distance (along the axis) from the base and r = radius. Then a generating parabola is given by

$h = H - \frac{H}{R^2} \cdot r^2$.

$dM_{base} = h\, dV = h\, \pi r^2\, dh = h\, \pi(H - h)\frac{R^2}{H}\, dh$

$M_{base} = \frac{R^2}{H}\pi \int_{h=0}^{h=H} (Hh - h^2)\, dh$

$= \frac{R^2}{H}\pi(\frac{H}{2}h^2 - \frac{1}{3}h^3)\Big|_{h=0}^{h=H} = \frac{1}{6}\pi R^2H^2$

$dM_{2axis} = r^2\, dV = r^2\, 2\pi rh\, dr = r^2\, 2\pi r(H - \frac{H}{R^2}r^2)\, dr$

$M_{2axis} = 2\pi H \int_{r=0}^{r=R} (r^3 - \frac{1}{R^2}r^5)\, dr$

$= 2\pi H(\frac{1}{4}r^4 - \frac{1}{6R^2}r^6)\Big|_{r=0}^{r=R} = \frac{1}{6}\pi R^4H$

In the original example, $H = R^2$, so the two moments turned out to be equal.

C4. Infinitesimals of Higher Order

a. Assume $m \neq 0$.

The area of the trapezoid is

$A = \frac{b_1+b_2}{2} \cdot h = \frac{ma+mb}{2}(b - a) = \frac{1}{2}m(b^2 - a^2)$

Integrating, $\int_a^b y\, dx \approx \int_a^b mx\, dx$

$= \frac{1}{2}mx^2\Big|_a^b = \frac{1}{2}m(b^2 - a^2) = A$, Q.E.D.

The length is $L = (b - a)\sqrt{1 + m^2}$.

Integrating, $\int_a^b dL \approx \int_a^b dx = (b - a) \neq L$, Q.E.D.

b. Note $r = mh$.

The volume of the cone is

$V = \frac{1}{3}\pi r^2 h = \frac{1}{3}\pi m^2 h^3$

Integrating $dV \approx \pi y^2\, dx = \pi m^2 x^2\, dx$,

$\int_0^h \pi m^2 x^2\, dx = \frac{1}{3}\pi m^2 h^3 = V$, Q.E.D.

The surface area is $S = \pi r\sqrt{r^2 + h^2} = \pi m h^2\sqrt{1 + m^2}$.

Integrating $dS \approx 2\pi y\, dx = 2\pi mx\, dx$

$\int_0^h 2\pi mx\, dx = \pi m h^2 \neq S$, Q.E.D.

c. Exact area of a strip:

$\Delta A = \frac{1}{2}(mx + m(x + \Delta x))\Delta x = y\Delta x + \frac{1}{2}\Delta y \Delta x$

Exact volume of frustum:

$\Delta V = \frac{\pi}{3}(m^2(x + \Delta x)^2 + m^2x(x + \Delta x) + m^2x^2)\Delta x$

$= \frac{\pi}{3}m^2\Delta x(3x^2 + 3x(\Delta x) + (\Delta x)^2)$

$= \pi(y^2\Delta x + y\Delta y\Delta x + \frac{1}{3}(\Delta y)^2\Delta x)$

d. $dA - y\, dx = (y\, dx + \frac{1}{2}\, \Delta y\, dx) - y\, dx = \frac{1}{2}\Delta y\, dx$

$dV - \pi y^2\, dx$

$= \pi(y^2\, dx + y\, \Delta y\, dx + \frac{1}{3}\, \Delta y^2 dx) - \pi y^2 dx$

$= \pi y\, \Delta y\, dx + \frac{1}{3}\, \Delta y^2\, dx$

Both differences contain only higher-order infinitesimals.

e. If $dQ = \Delta Q$ leaves out only infinitesimals of higher order, then $\int_a^b dQ$ is exactly equal to Q.

f. Reasons:

i. 0.5 and Δy are constant with respect to the summation, so they can be pulled out.

ii. The sum of all the subsegments Δx of [a, b] must be b – a, the whole interval.

iii. Δy has limit zero as Δx goes to zero.

Chapter Test

T1. Using exponential regression,

$F \approx 29.9829... (1.0626...)^x$

$dW = F\, dx$

$W = \int_0^{10} F\, dx \approx 412.4652... \approx 412.5$ ft-lb

(By trapezoidal rule, $W \approx 413$ ft-lb. Simpson's rule cannot be used because there is an odd number of increments.)

T2. a. Graph, $y = e^x$ from x = 0 to x = 2

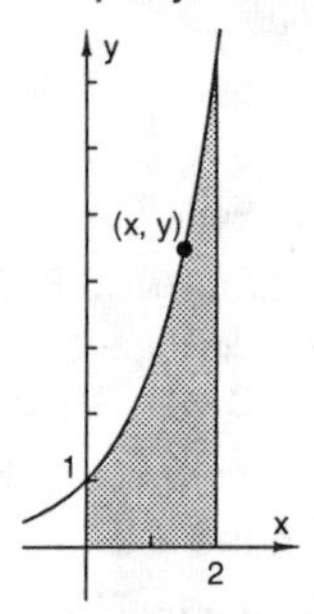

Slice the region parallel to the y-axis so that each point in a strip will be the about the same distance from the y-axis as the sample point (x, y).

$dM_y = x\, dA = x\, e^x\, dx$

$M_y = \int_0^2 x\, e^x\, dx = e^2 + 1 = 8.3890... \approx 8.39$ in^3

b. $dM_{2y} = x^2\, dA = x^2\, e^x\, dx$

$M_{2y} = \int_0^2 x^2\, e^x\, dx = 2e^2 - 2 = 12.7781... \approx 12.78$ in^4

c. $A = \int_0^2 e^x\, dx = e^2 - 1 = 6.3890... \approx 6.39$ in^2

$\bar{x} \cdot A = M_y \Rightarrow \bar{x} = \frac{e^2 + 1}{e^2 - 1} = 1.3130... \approx 1.31$ in

T3. Graph, $y = x^{1/2}$ from $x = 0$ to $x = 16$, rotated about the x-axis

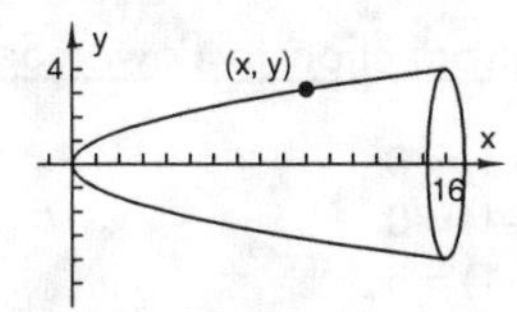

Slice the region parallel to the x-axis so that each point in a resulting cylindrical shell will be about the same distance from the x-axis as the sample point (x, y).

$\rho = 3y$, $dm = \rho\, dV = 3y \cdot 2\pi(16 - x)y\, dy$
$= 6\pi y^2(16 - y^2)\, dy$
$m = \int_0^4 6\pi(16y^2 - y^4)\, dy = 819.2\pi$
$= 2573.5927... \approx 2573.6$ g

T4. a. Slice the end of the trough parallel to the x-axis so that each point in a strip has about the same pressure acting on it as the sample point (x, y), where $x \ge 0$.

$p = 62.4(8 - y)$, $dA = 2x\, dy = 2y^{1/3}\, dy$
$dF = p\, dA = 62.4(8 - y) \cdot 2y^{1/3}\, dy$
$F = \int_0^8 62.4(8 - y) \cdot 2y^{1/3}\, dy$
$= 62.4(\frac{64 \cdot 9}{7}) = 5134.6285... \approx 5134.6$ lb

b. $dM_x = y\, dF = 62.4(8 - y) \cdot 2y^{4/3}\, dy$
$F = \int_0^8 62.4(8 - y) \cdot 2y^{4/3}\, dy = \frac{9 \cdot 2^{10}}{35} \cdot 62.4$
$= 16430.8114... \approx 16.43$ thousand lb-ft
$\bar{y} \cdot F = M_x \Rightarrow \bar{y} = \frac{16430.8114...}{5134.6285...} = 3.2$ ft

$\bar{x} = 0$ by symmetry
Center of pressure is at (0, 3.2).

T5. Theater in the Round Problem

a. Slice the seating area into concentric rings of width dr. Each point in a ring will be about the same distance from the center as the sample point.
Let W = worth of the seating.
Let v = value per square foot.
$dW = v\, dA = 150r^{-1} \cdot 2\pi r\, dr = 300\pi\, dr$
$W = \int_{30}^{b} 300\pi dr = 300\pi(b - 30)$ dollars

b. $300\pi(b - 30) = 60000 \Rightarrow$
$b = 30 + \frac{200}{\pi} = 93.6619... \approx 93.7$ ft

Chapter 12

Problem Set 12-1, page 599 — Introduction to Power Series

1. Graphs, $f(x) = \dfrac{6}{1 - x}$,
   $P_5(x) = 6 + 6x + 6x^2 + 6x^3 + 6x^4 + 6x^5$

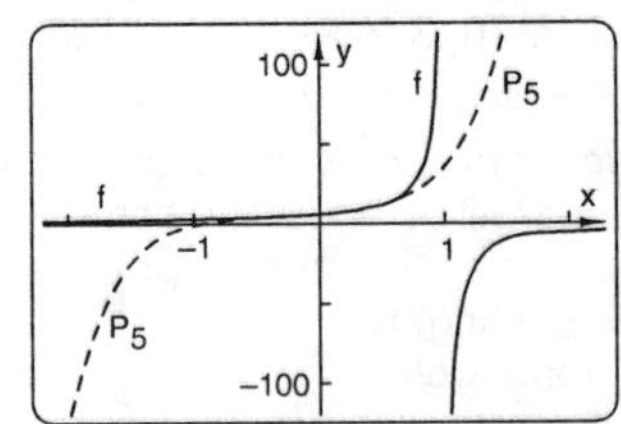

2. Graph, $P_6(x) = P_5(x) + 6x^6$

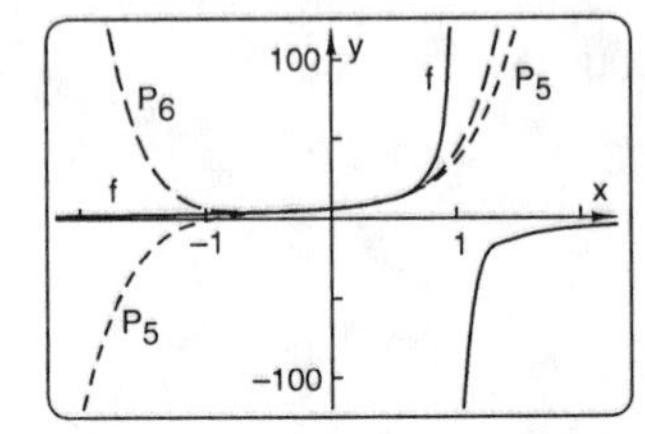

   The graphs of $P_5(x)$ and $P_6(x)$ fit the graph of f(x) if x is between about –0.9 and about 0.7. The graphs of $P_5(x)$ and $P_6(x)$ bear little or no resemblance to the graph of f if $x > 1$ or if $x \le -1$.

3. $P_5(0.5) = 11.8125$, $P_6(0.5) = 11.90625$, $f(0.5) = 12$
   $\therefore P_6(0.5)$ is closer to $f(0.5)$ than $P_5(0.5)$ is.
   $P_5(2) = 378$, $P_6(2) = 762$, $f(2) = -6$
   $\therefore P_6(2)$ is *not* closer to $f(2)$ than $P_5(2)$ is.

4. Conjecture: P(x) converges to f(x) for $-1 < x < 1$, or perhaps for $-1 \le x \le 1$.

5. $P_0(1) = 6$ $\quad P_0(-1) = 6$
   $P_1(1) = 12$ $\quad P_1(-1) = 0$
   $P_2(1) = 18$ $\quad P_2(-1) = 6$
   $P_3(1) = 24$ $\quad P_3(-1) = 0$
   $P_4(1) = 30$ $\quad P_4(-1) = 6$
   For x = 1, the sums just keep getting larger and larger as more terms are added. For x = –1, the sums oscillate between 0 and 6. In neither case does the series converge. If the answer to Problem 4 had included x = 1 or x = –1, the conjecture would have to be modified.

6. $P_5(0.5) = 11.8125$ and $f(0.5) = 12$
   The values differ by 0.1875, and $6(0.5)^6 = 0.09375$.
   $P_5(-0.5) = 3.9375$ and $f(-0.5) = 4$
   The values differ by 0.0625, and $6(-0.5)^6 = -0.09375$.
   For $P_5(0.5)$, the difference is greater than the value of the next term of the series. This result is to be expected because the rest of the series is formed by adding more positive terms.
   For $P_5(-0.5)$, the difference is less in absolute value than the absolute value of the next term. This result is reasonable since the terms alternate in sign, so that you are adding and subtracting ever smaller quantities.

7. Geometric series. x is the common ratio.

Problem Set 12-2, pages 603 to 606 — Geometric Sequences and Series as Mathematical Models

Q1. ...for any $\varepsilon > 0$ there is a $D > 0$ such that if $x > D$, then f(x) is within ε units of L.
Q2. fund. thm. of calculus
Q3. fund. thm. of calculus
Q4. mean value theorem
Q5. derivative
Q6. $\cos x - x \sin x$
Q7. $x \sin x + \cos x + C$
Q8. $dA = \frac{1}{2} r^2\, d\theta$
Q9. $f(x) \ne e^{-x}$
Q10. $g(x) = 2 \cos x$

1. Series: 200 – 120 + 72 – 43.2 + 25.92 – 15.552 + ...
   Sums: 200, 80, 152, 108.8, 134.72, 119.168, ...
   Graph, showing convergence to 125 (below)

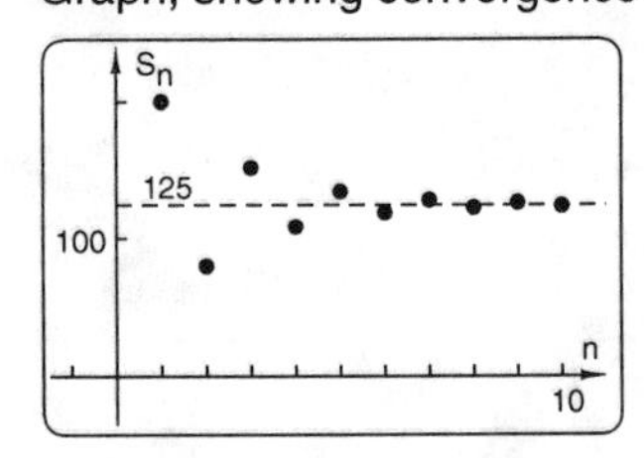

$$S = 200 \cdot \frac{1}{1 + 0.6} = 125$$

$$|125 - S_n| = \left|125 - 200 \cdot \frac{1 - (-0.6)^n}{1 + 0.6}\right|$$

$$= 125 - 200 \cdot \frac{1 - 0.6^n}{1 + 0.6} = 125(0.6^n)$$

$$125(0.6^n) = 0.0001 \Leftrightarrow n = \frac{\ln 0.0001/125}{\ln 0.6} = 27.48...$$

   Make $n \ge 28$.
   S_n will be within 0.0001 unit of 125 for all values of $n \ge 28$.

2. Series: 30 + 33 + 36.3 + 39.93 + 43.923 + 48.3153 + ...
   Sums: 30, 63, 99.3, 139.23, 183.153, 231.4683, ...
   Graph, showing divergence

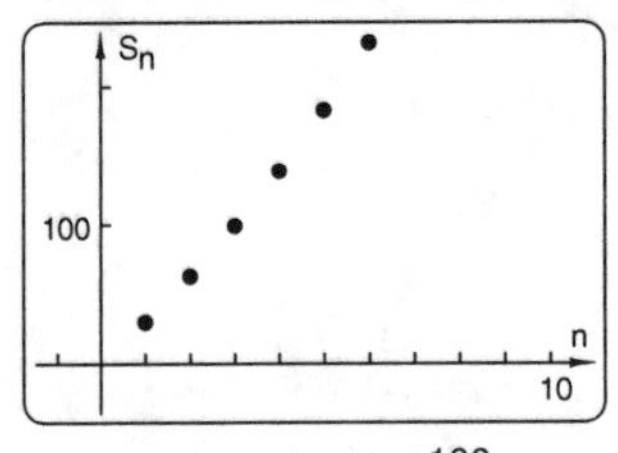

$$S_{100} = 30 \cdot \frac{1 - 1.1^{100}}{1 - 1.1} = 4{,}133{,}883.70...\ \text{(Wow!)}$$

   The formula $S = t_1/(1 - r)$ gives –300 for S, but it has no meaning because the series does not converge.

3. Drug Dosage Problem

a. Series: $\sum_{n=1}^{\infty} 7(0.8^{n-1}) = 7 + 5.6 + 4.48 + 3.584 + \ldots$

Sums: 7, 12.6, 17.08, 20.664, 23.5312, ...

$S = 7 \cdot \frac{1}{1 - 0.8} = 35$

The amount approaches 35µg as a limit, and thus never reaches 50 or 80µg.

b. 2 puffs:

Maximum amount just after a dose:

$S = 14 \cdot \frac{1}{1 - 0.8} = 70\mu g$

$S_n = 14 \cdot \frac{1 - 0.8^n}{1 - 0.8} = 70(1 - 0.8^n)$

$S_n = 50 \Leftrightarrow 70 - 70(0.8^n) = 50$

$n = \frac{\ln (2/7)}{\ln 0.8} = 5.6141$

Minimum amount just before the next dose:

$S = (0.8)(14) \cdot \frac{1}{1 - 0.8} = 56\mu g$

$S_n = 50 \Leftrightarrow 56 - 56(0.8^n) = 50$

$n = \frac{\ln (6/56)}{\ln 0.8} = 10.0096\ldots$

$S_n = 80 \Leftrightarrow 56 - 56(0.8)^n = 80$

$n = \frac{\ln (-24/56)}{\ln 0.8}$, which is not a real number.

S_n is never 80.

The amount will first exceed 50µg after the 6th dose, and will stay above 50µg after the 11th dose. It will never reach 80µg.

3 puffs, repeating the above calculations:

Maximum amount just after a dose:

$S = 105\mu g$

$S_n = 50$ for $n = \frac{\ln (55/105)}{\ln 0.8} = 2.8978\ldots$

$S_n = 80$ for $n = \frac{\ln (25/105)}{\ln 0.8} = 6.4312\ldots$

Minimum amount just before next dose:

$S = 84\mu g$

$S_n = 50$ for $n = \frac{\ln (34/84)}{\ln 0.8} = 4.0532\ldots$

$S_n = 80$ for $n = \frac{\ln (4/84)}{\ln 0.8} = 13.6437\ldots$

The amount will first exceed 50µg after the 3rd dose and will stay above 50µg after the 5th dose.

The amount will first exceed 80 µg after the 7th dose and will stay above 80µg after the 14th dose.

4 puffs:

Maximum amount just after a dose:

$S = 140\mu g$

$S_n = 50$ for $n = \frac{\ln (90/140)}{\ln 0.8} = 1.9800\ldots$

$S_n = 80$ for $n = \frac{\ln (60/140)}{\ln 0.8} = 3.7970\ldots$

Minimum amount just before next dose:

$S = 112\mu g$

$S_n = 50$ for $n = \frac{\ln (62/112)}{\ln 0.8} = 2.6501\ldots$

$S_n = 80$ for $n = \frac{\ln (32/112)}{\ln 0.8} = 5.6141\ldots$

The amount will first exceed 50µg after the 2nd dose and will stay above 50µg after the 3rd dose.

The amount will first exceed 80 µg after the 4th dose and will stay above 80µg after the 6th dose.

(Numerical or graphical solutions are o.k.)

c. Twice a day: $r = 0.8^2 = 0.64$, p = no. of puffs

Amount just after the nth dose:

$S_n = 7p \cdot \frac{1 - 0.64^n}{1 - 0.64}$

For p = 4 puffs, $S = 28 \cdot \frac{1}{1 - 0.64} = 77.7777\ldots$

For p > 4 puffs, S > 80, and is thus unsafe.

Amount just before the nth dose is 0.64 times the amount just after the (n – 1)st dose.

$S_n = 7p(0.64) \cdot \frac{1 - 0.64^{n-1}}{1 - 0.64}$

For p = 4, $S = 17.92 \cdot \frac{1}{1 - 0.64} = 49.7777\ldots$

This amount is just barely below the minimum effective amount.

The graph shows the maximum and minimum amounts for p = 4.

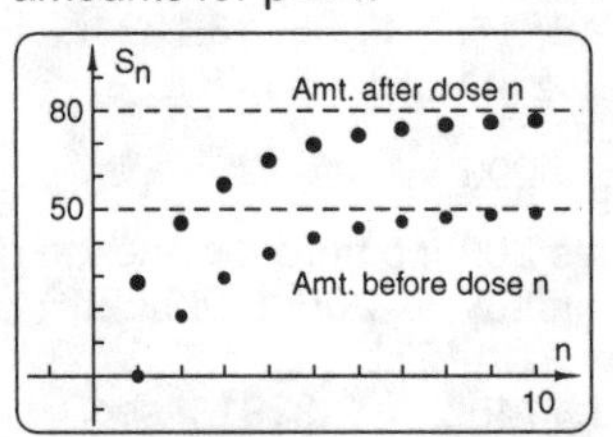

From the graph, you can see that if the maximum amounts after dose n are kept below the allowable 80µg, the minimum amounts before dose n are significantly below the minimum effective amount of 50µg for 3 or 4 days. The situation would be worse for daily doses.

4. Inscribed Squares Problem

a. Perimeters are 16, $16\sqrt{0.5}$, 16(0.5), ... , which is a geometric sequence with $t_1 = 16$ and $r = \sqrt{0.5}$.

b. $S_{10} = 16 \cdot \frac{1 - 0.5^5}{1 - 0.5^{1/2}} = 52.9203\ldots$ cm

c. The total perimeter converges to

$16 \cdot \frac{1}{1 - 0.5^{1/2}} = 54.6274\ldots$ cm

d. The sum of the areas is 16 + 8 + 4 + 2 + ... , which is a convergent geometric series with r = 0.5.

$S = 16 \cdot \frac{1}{1 - 0.5} = 32\text{ cm}^2$

5. Compound Interest Problem

a. Interest rate for 1 month is 0.09/12 = 0.0075.

Months	Dollars
0	1,000,000.00
1	1,007,500.00
2	1,015,056.25
3	1,022,669.17

b. Worth is $(1{,}000{,}000)(1.0075^{12})$ = \$1,093,806.90; interest = \$93,806.90.

c. The first deposit is made at time t = 0, the second at time t = 1, and so forth, so at time t = 12, the term index is 13.

d. Meg earned \$93,806.90 the first year.

$APR = \frac{93806.90}{1000000} \cdot 100 = 9.3806\ldots\%$

e. $(1{,}000{,}000)(1.0075^n) = 2{,}000{,}000$

$n = \frac{\ln 2}{\ln 1.0075} = 92.7657\ldots$

After 93 months.

6. Regular Deposits Problem
   a. Interest rate for 1 month is 0.108/12 = 0.009.
      $S_5 = 100 + 100(1.009) + 100(1.009^2)$
      $+ 100(1.009^3) + 100(1.009)^4 + 100(1.009^5)$
      $= 100 \cdot \dfrac{1 - 1.009^6}{1 - 1.009} = \$613.66$
   b. There are six terms, because the term index of the first term is 0.
   c. 10 years equals 120 months. There will have been 121 deposits after 10 years because the initial deposit was made at time 0. So there are 121 terms.
      $S_{120} = 100 \cdot \dfrac{1 - 1.009^{121}}{1 - 1.009} = \$21{,}742.92$
      The principal is 121(100) = $12,100.
      The interest is 21,742.92 – 12,100 = $9,642.92.
7. Bouncing Ball Problem
   a. Sequence: 20, 18, 16.2, 14.58, 13.122, ...
   b. $S_4 = 20 + 18 + 16.2 + 14.58 = 68.78$ ft
   c. $S = 20 \cdot \dfrac{1}{1 - 0.9} = 200$
      So the ball travels 200 ft before it comes to rest.
   d. For the 20-foot first cycle, $20 = 0.5(32.2)t^2$.
      $t = (20/16.1)^{1/2} = 1.1145...$
      Total time is 2(1.1145...) = 2.2291... sec.
      For the 18-foot second cycle,
      time $= 2(18/16.1)^{1/2} = 2.1147...$ sec.
   e. The times form a geometric series with first term 2.2291... and common ratio equal to $0.9^{1/2} = 0.9486...$. So the series of times converges to
      $S = 2.2291... \cdot \dfrac{1}{1 - 0.9^{1/2}} = 43.4383...$.
      The model predicts that the ball comes to rest after about 43.4 sec.
8. Snowflake Curve Problem
   a.

Iteration	Tot. Length
0	27
1	36
2	48
3	64

   Since each segment is divided into 4 pieces, each of which is 1/3 of the original length, the length at the next iteration can be calculated by multiplying the previous length by 4/3.
   b. The sequence of lengths diverges because the common ratio, 4/3, is greater than 1. Thus the total length of the snowflake curve is infinite!
   c. From geometry, the area of an equilateral triangle of side s is $A = \frac{\sqrt{3}}{4}s^2$.
      Number of triangles added is 3, 12, 48, 192, ...
      Side of each added triangle is 3, 1, 1/3, 1/9, ...
      Added areas form the series
      $\frac{\sqrt{3}}{4}(3(3)^2 + 12(1)^2 + 48(1/3)^2 + 192(1/9)^2 + ...)$
      $= \frac{\sqrt{3}}{4} \cdot 3 \cdot 9^2[4^0(1/3)^2 + 4^1(1/3)^4 + 4^2(1/3)^6 + 4^3(1/3)^8 + ...]$
      $= \frac{\sqrt{3}}{16} \cdot 3 \cdot 9^2[4/9 + (4/9)^2 + (4/9)^3 + (4/9)^4 + ...]$
      $= \frac{\sqrt{3}}{16} \cdot 3 \cdot 9^2(4/9) \cdot \dfrac{1}{1 - 4/9} = 12.15\sqrt{3}$
      Area of preimage is $\frac{\sqrt{3}}{4} \cdot 9^2 = 20.25\sqrt{3}$.
      Total area is $32.4\sqrt{3} = 56.1184...$ cm^2.
9. Derivatives of a Geometric Series
   $f(x) = \dfrac{6}{1 - x}$
   $P(x) = 6 + 6x + 6x^2 + 6x^3 + 6x^4 + 6x^5 + ...$
   $P'(x) = 6 + 12x + 18x^2 + 24x^3 + 30x^4 + ...$
   $P''(x) = 12 + 36x + 72x^2 + 120x^3 + ...$
   $P'''(x) = 36 + 144x + 360x^2 + ...$
   $f'(x) = 6(1 - x)^{-2}$
   $f''(x) = 12(1 - x)^{-3}$
   $f'''(x) = 36(1 - x)^{-4}$
   $P'(0) = 6$ and $f'(0) = 6$,
   $P''(0) = 12$ and $f''(0) = 12$,
   $P'''(0) = 36$ and $f'''(0) = 36$
   Conjecture: $P^{(n)}(0) = f^{(n)}(0)$ for all values of n.

Problem Set 12-3, pages 607 to 608 — Power Series for an Exponential Function

Q1. 0.3333...
Q2. 0.4444...
Q3. $\frac{2}{3}$
Q4. $\frac{4}{9}$
Q5. 13
Q6. 125
Q7. mass · displacement
Q8. centroid
Q9. ln x + C
Q10. 2 sec 2x tan 2x

1. $f(x) = 5e^{2x}$
   $f'(x) = 10e^{2x}$
   $f''(x) = 20e^{2x}$
   $f'''(x) = 40e^{2x}$
   $f^{(4)}(x) = 80e^{2x}$
2. $P_1(x) = c_0 + c_1x$ and $P_1'(x) = c_1$
   $P_1(0) = c_0$ and $f(0) = 5 \Rightarrow c_0 = 5$
   $P_1'(0) = c_1$ and $f'(0) = 10 \Rightarrow c_1 = 10$
   $\therefore P_1(x) = 5 + 10x$
3. $P_2(x) = c_0 + c_1x + c_2x^2$,
   $P_2'(x) = c_1 + 2c_2x$, and $P_2''(x) = 2c_2$.
   $P_2(0) = c_0$ and $f(0) = 5 \Rightarrow c_0 = 5$
   $P_2'(0) = c_1$ and $f'(0) = 10 \Rightarrow c_1 = 10$
   $P_2''(0) = 2c_2$ and $f''(0) = 20 \Rightarrow 2c_2 = 20$
   $\Rightarrow c_2 = 10$
   $\therefore P_2(x) = P_1(x) = 5 + 10x + 10x^2$
   c_0 and c_1 are the same as for $P_1(x)$.

4. $P_3(x) = c_0 + c_1x + c_2x^2 + c_3x^3$
$P_4(x) = c_0 + c_1x + c_2x^2 + c_3x^3 + c_4x^4$
$P_4'''(x) = 6c_3 + 24c_4x$, and $P_4^{(4)}(x) = 24c_4$
$P_4'''(0) = 6c_3$ and $f'''(0) = 40$
$\Rightarrow 6c_3 = 40 \Rightarrow c_3 = \frac{20}{3}$
$P_4^{(4)}(0) = 24c_4$ and $f^{(4)}(0) = 80$
$\Rightarrow 24c_4 = 80 \Rightarrow c_4 = \frac{10}{3}$
c_0, c_1, and c_2 are the same as before.

5. $P_3(x) = 5 + 10x + 10x^2 + \frac{20}{3}x^3$
$P_4(x) = 5 + 10x + 10x^2 + \frac{20}{3}x^3 + \frac{10}{3}x^4$
Graphs of f, P_3, and P_4.

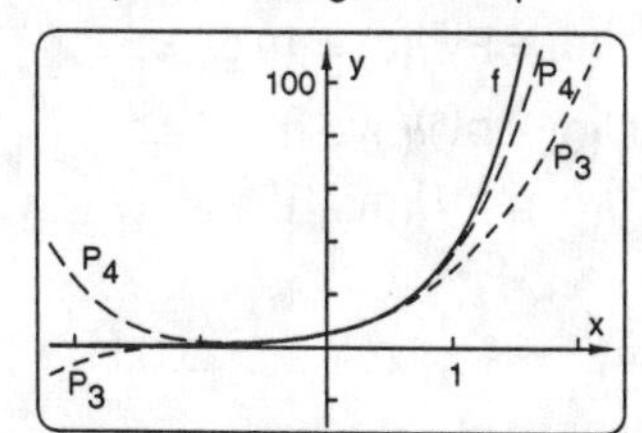

6. P_4 is indistinguishable from f for about $-1 < x < 0.9$.

7. $P_3(1) = 31.6666666...$
$P_4(1) = 35.0000000...$
$f(1) = 5e^2 = 36.9452804...$
$\therefore P_4(1)$ is closer to $f(1)$ than $P_3(1)$, Q.E.D.

8. $c_4 = \frac{80}{24} = \frac{5 \cdot 2^4}{4!}$
The 5 is the coefficient in $5e^{2x}$.
The 2 is the exponential constant.
The 4 is the exponent of x in the last term.

9. $c_3 = \frac{40}{6} = \frac{5 \cdot 2^3}{3!}$, $c_2 = \frac{20}{2} = \frac{5 \cdot 2^2}{2!}$,
$c_1 = \frac{10}{1} = \frac{5 \cdot 2^1}{1!}$, $c_0 = 5 = \frac{5 \cdot 2^0}{0!}$ $(0! = 1)$

10. Conjecture:
$c_5 = \frac{5 \cdot 2^5}{5!} = \frac{160}{120} = \frac{4}{3}$, $c_6 = \frac{5 \cdot 2^6}{6!} = \frac{320}{720} = \frac{4}{9}$

11. $P(x) = \sum_{n=0}^{\infty} \frac{5 \cdot 2^n}{n!} x^n$

Problem Set 12-4, pages 613 to 615 — Power Series for Other Elementary Functions

Q1. Graph, y = sin x

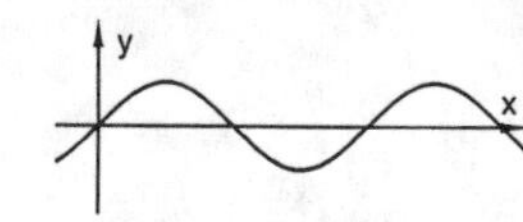

Q2. Graph, y = cos x

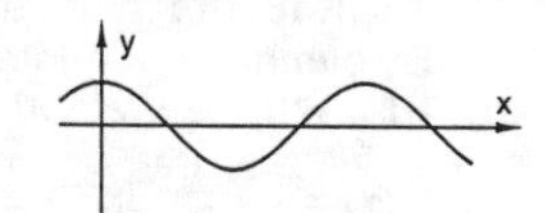

Q3. Graph, $y = e^x$

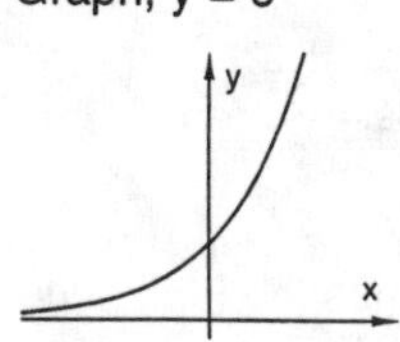

Q4. Graph, y = ln x

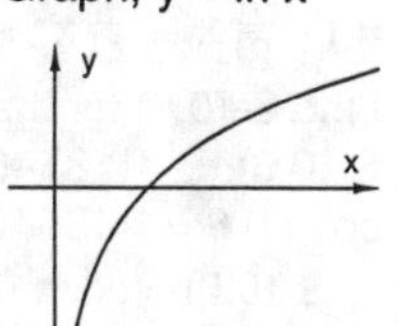

Q5. Graph, y = cosh x

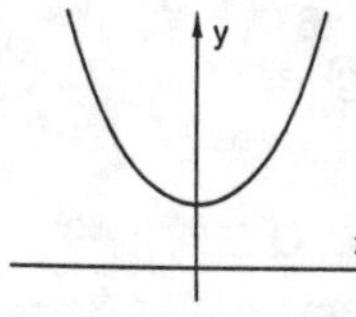

Q6. Graph, $y = \tan^{-1} x$

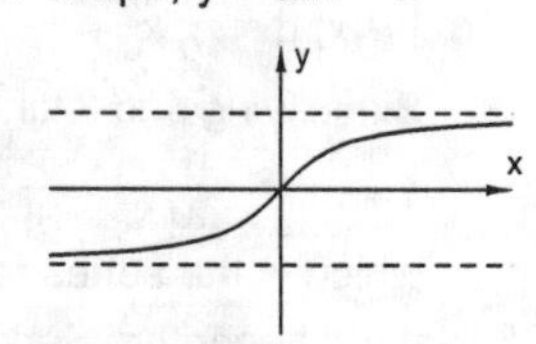

Q7. exponent
Q8. coefficient
Q9. power
Q10. $\frac{2}{3}(9 \cdot 6) = 36$

1. Exponential Function Series Problem

a. $f(x) = e^x$ $\quad f(0) = P(0) = 1$ $\quad c_0 = 1$
$f'(x) = e^x$ $\quad f'(0) = P'(0) = 1$ $\quad c_1 = 1$
$f''(x) = e^x$ $\quad f''(0) = P''(0) = 1$ $\quad 2!c_2 = 1, c_2 = \frac{1}{2!}$
$f'''(x) = e^x$ $\quad f'''(0) = P'''(0) = 1$ $\quad 3!c_3 = 1, c_3 = \frac{1}{3!}$
...
$\therefore P(x) = 1 + x + \frac{1}{2!}x^2 + \frac{1}{3!}x^3 + ...$, Q.E.D.

b. Next two terms: $... + \frac{1}{4!}x^4 + \frac{1}{5!}x^5 + ...$

c. $\sum_{n=0}^{\infty} \frac{1}{n!}x^n$

d. Graph, $y = S_3(x)$ (fourth partial sum) and $y = e^x$.

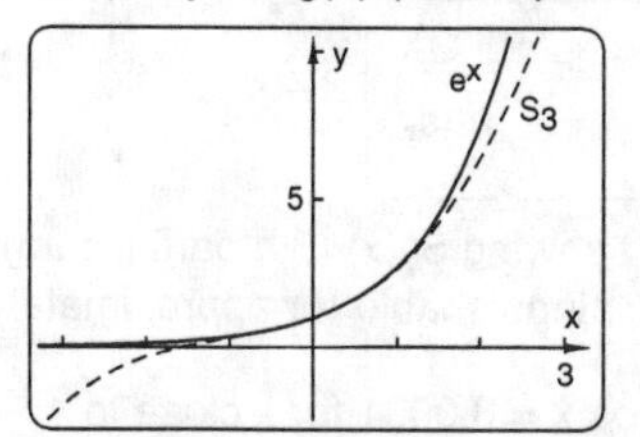

e. The two graphs are indistinguishable for about $-1 < x < 1$.

f. Solve $e^x - S_3(x) = 0.0001$ for x close to 1.
$x \approx 0.2188...$
Solve $e^x - S_3(x) = 0.0001$ for x close to -1.
$x = -0.2237...$
Interval is $-0.2237... < x < 0.2188...$.

g. The ninth partial sum is $S_8(x)$.
Solve $e^x - S_8(x) = 0.0001$ for x close to 1.
$x \approx 1.4648...$
Solve $S_8(x) - e^x = 0.0001$ for x close to -1.
$x = -1.5142...$
Interval is $-1.5142... < x < 1.4648...$.

2. Cosine Function Series Problem

a. $f(x) = \cos x$ $\quad f(0) = P(0) = 1$ $\quad c_0 = 1$

$f'(x) = -\sin x$ $\quad f'(0) = P'(0) = 0$ $\quad c_1 = 0$

$f''(x) = -\cos x$ $\quad f''(0) = P''(0) = -1$ $\quad c_2 = -\frac{1}{2!}$

$f'''(x) = \sin x$ $\quad f'''(0) = P'''(0) = 0$ $\quad c_3 = 0$

$f^{(4)}(x) = \cos x$ $\quad f^{(4)}(0) = P^{(4)}(0) = 1$ $\quad c_4 = \frac{1}{4!}$

$f^{(5)}(x) = -\sin x$ $\quad f^{(5)}(0) = P^{(5)}(0) = 0$ $\quad c_5 = 0$

$f^{(6)}(x) = -\cos x$ $\quad f^{(6)}(0) = P^{(6)}(0) = -1$ $\quad c_6 = -\frac{1}{6!}$

$f^{(7)}(x) = \sin x$ $\quad f^{(7)}(0) = P^{(7)}(0) = 0$ $\quad c_7 = 0$

$f^{(8)}(x) = \cos x$ $\quad f^{(8)}(0) = P^{(8)}(0) = 1$ $\quad c_8 = \frac{1}{8!}$

...

$\therefore P(x) = 1 - \frac{1}{2!}x^2 + \frac{1}{4!}x^4 - \frac{1}{6!}x^6 + \frac{1}{8!}x^8 - \dots$, Q.E.D.

b. $\dots - \frac{1}{10!}x^{10} + \frac{1}{12!}x^{12} - \frac{1}{14!}x^{14} + \dots$

c. $\sum_{n=0}^{\infty} (-1)^n \frac{1}{(2n)!} x^{2n}$

d. Graph, $y = \cos x$ and $y = S_4(x)$ (5th partial sum).

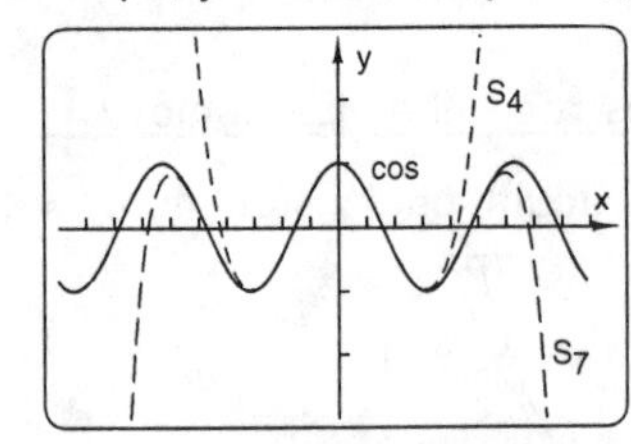

e. Graph, part d., showing $S_7(x)$ (8th partial sum)
Graphs are indistinguishable for approximately $-4 < x < 4$.

f. Solve $S_7(x) - \cos x = 0.0001$ for x close to 4.
$x \approx 3.8355...$
(Note that some solvers may give an error message. In this case, zoom in by table, starting at x = 3 and using increments of 0.1; then x = 3, and increments of 0.1, and so forth.)
By symmetry, the interval is
$-3.8355... < x < 3.8355...$.

g. The series has only even powers of x, and is thus an even function, as is cosine.

3. Sine Series Problem

a. $S_3(0.6) = 0.6 - \frac{1}{3!}(0.6^3) + \frac{1}{5!}(0.6^5) - \frac{1}{7!}(0.6^7)$
$= 0.564642445...$
$\sin 0.6 = 0.564642473...$
$\therefore S_3(0.6) \approx \sin 0.6$, Q.E.D.

b. $\sin 0.6 = 0.564642473...$
Tail $= \sin 0.6 - S_n(0.6)$
First term of the tail is t_{n+1}.
$\sin 0.6 - S_1(0.6) = 0.0006424733...$
$t_2 = 0.000648$
$\sin 0.6 - S_2(0.6) = -0.00000552660...$
$t_3 = -0.00000555428...$
$\sin 0.6 - S_3(0.6) = 0.0000000276807...$
$t_4 = 0.0000000277714...$
In each case the tail is less in magnitude than the absolute value of the first term of the tail, Q.E.D.

c. Make $|t_{n+1}| < 0.5 \times 10^{-20}$.
$\frac{1}{(2n+3)!}(0.6^{2n+3}) < 5 \times 10^{-21}$
Inequality is first true for n = 8.
Use at least 9 terms (n = 8).

4. Hyperbolic Sine and Cosine Series Problem

a. $P(x) = x + \frac{1}{3!}x^3 + \frac{1}{5!}x^5 + \frac{1}{7!}x^7 + \dots$

b. $f(x) = \sinh x$ $\quad f(0) = P(0) = 0$ $\quad c_0 = 0$

$f'(x) = \cosh x$ $\quad f'(0) = P'(0) = 1$ $\quad c_1 = 1$

$f''(x) = \sinh x$ $\quad f''(0) = P''(0) = 0$ $\quad c_2 = 0$

$f'''(x) = \cosh x$ $\quad f'''(0) = P'''(0) = 1$ $\quad c_3 = \frac{1}{3!}$

$f^{(4)}(x) = \sinh x$ $\quad f^{(4)}(0) = P^{(4)}(0) = 0$ $\quad c_4 = 0$

$f^{(5)}(x) = \cosh x$ $\quad f^{(5)}(0) = P^{(5)}(0) = 1$ $\quad c_5 = \frac{1}{5!}$

$f^{(6)}(x) = \sinh x$ $\quad f^{(6)}(0) = P^{(6)}(0) = 0$ $\quad c_6 = 0$

$f^{(7)}(x) = \cosh x$ $\quad f^{(7)}(0) = P^{(7)}(0) = 1$ $\quad c_7 = \frac{1}{7!}$

...

$\therefore P(x) = x + \frac{1}{3!}x^3 + \frac{1}{5!}x^5 + \frac{1}{7!}x^7 + \dots$, Q.E.D.

c. $S_3(0.6) = 0.636653554...$
$\sinh 0.6 = 0.636653582...$
$\therefore S_3(0.6) \approx \sinh 0.6$, Q.E.D.

d. Solve $S_3(x) - \sinh x = 0.0001$ for x close to 1.
$x \approx 1.4870...$.
By symmetry the interval is
$-1.4870... < x < 1.4870...$

e. $P'(x) = 1 + \frac{1}{3!}\cdot 3x^2 + \frac{1}{5!}\cdot 5x^4 + \frac{1}{7!}\cdot 7x^6 + \dots$
$= 1 + \frac{1}{2!}x^2 + \frac{1}{4!}x^4 + \frac{1}{6!}x^6 + \dots$

f. Find $S_3(0.6)$ for the P' series.
$S_3(0.6) = 1.1854648$
$\cosh 0.6 = 1.18546521...$
$\therefore S_3(0.6) \approx \cosh 0.6$, and thus the P'(x) series seems to represent cosh x, Q.E.D.

g. $\int P(x)\,dx = \frac{1}{2}x^2 + \frac{1}{3!}\cdot\frac{1}{4}x^4 + \frac{1}{5!}\cdot\frac{1}{6}x^6 + C$
Simplifying and letting C = 1 gives
$1 + \frac{1}{2!}x^2 + \frac{1}{4!}x^4 + \frac{1}{6!}x^6 + \dots$,
which is the series for cosh x, Q.E.D.

5. Natural Logarithm Series Problem

a. $f(x) = \ln x$ $\quad f(1) = 0$

$f'(x) = x^{-1}$ $\quad f'(1) = 1$

$f''(x) = -x^{-2}$ $\quad f''(1) = -1$

$f'''(x) = 2x^{-3}$ $\quad f'''(1) = 2$

$P(x) = (x-1) - \frac{1}{2}(x-1)^2 + \frac{1}{3}(x-1)^3 - \frac{1}{4}(x-1)^4 + \dots$
$P'(x) = 1 - (x-1) + (x-1)^2 - (x-1)^3 + \dots$
$P''(x) = -1 + 2(x-1) - 3(x-1)^2 + \dots$
$P'''(x) = 2 - 6(x-1) + \dots$
$P(1) = 0 = f(1)$
$P'(1) = 1 = f'(1)$
$P''(1) = -1 = f''(1)$
$P'''(1) = 2 = f'''(2)$, Q.E.D.

b. $\dots \frac{1}{5}(x-1)^5 - \frac{1}{6}(x-1)^6 + \dots$

c. $P(x) = \sum_{n=1}^{\infty} (-1)^{n+1}\cdot\frac{1}{n}(x-1)^n$

d. Graph, $S_{10}(x)$ and ln x

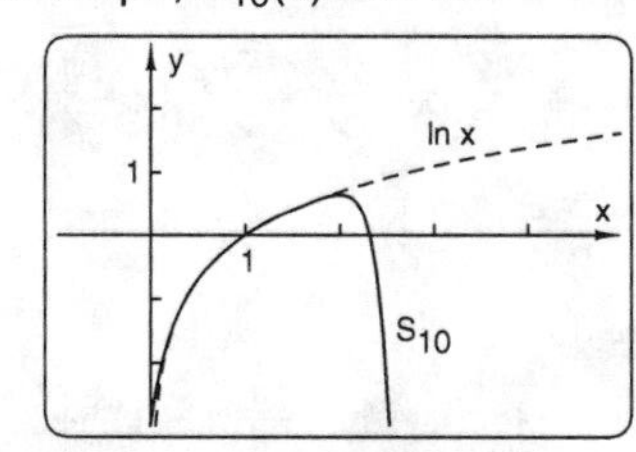

e. $S_{10}(1.2) = 0.182321555...$
ln 1.2 = 0.182321556...

$S_{10}(1.95) = 0.640144911...$
ln 1.95 = 0.667829372...

$S_{10}(3) = -64.8253968...$
ln 3 = 1.0986122...

$S_{10}(x)$ fits ln x in about $0.1 < x < 2$.

$S_{10}(1.2)$ and ln 1.2 agree through the 8th decimal place. The values of $S_{10}(1.95)$ and ln 1.95 agree only to 1 decimal place. The values of $S_{10}(3)$ and ln 3 bear no resemblance to each other.

6. Convergence and Divergence Problem

a. $P(x) = (x-1) - \frac{1}{2}(x-1)^2 + \frac{1}{3}(x-1)^3 - \frac{1}{4}(x-1)^4 + ...$

n	$t_n(3)$
1	2
2	−2
3	2.6666...
4	−4
5	6.4
6	−10.6666...

The absolute values of the terms are getting larger as n increases.

b. $\lim_{x\to\infty} |t_n| = \lim_{x\to\infty} \frac{2^n}{n} \to \frac{\infty}{\infty}$

$= \lim_{x\to\infty} \frac{2^n \ln 2}{1} \to \frac{\infty}{1}$

$= \infty$

The series cannot possibly converge, because the terms do not approach zero as n approaches infinity.

c.

n	$t_n(1.2)$
1	0.2
2	−0.02
3	0.0026666...
4	−0.0004
5	0.000064
6	−0.00001066...

The absolute values of the terms are approaching zero as n increases.

d. Tail = ln 1.2 − $S_n(1.2)$

First term of the tail is t_{n+1}.

ln 1.2 − $S_1(1.2) = -0.01767...$
$t_2 = -0.02$

ln 1.2 − $S_2(1.2) = 0.002321...$
$t_3 = 0.002666...$

ln 1.2 − $S_3(1.2) = -0.0003451...$
$t_4 = -0.0004$

In each case the tail is less in magnitude than the absolute value of the first term of the tail.

7. Inverse Tangent Series Problem

a. $f(x) = \tan^{-1} x$

$P(x) = \sum_{n=0}^{\infty} (-1)^n \frac{1}{2n+1} x^{2n+1}$

$= x - \frac{1}{3}x^3 + \frac{1}{5}x^5 - \frac{1}{7}x^7 + ...$

b. Graph, showing $\tan^{-1} x$, and $S_5(x)$ and $S_6(x)$, the sixth and seventh partial sums.

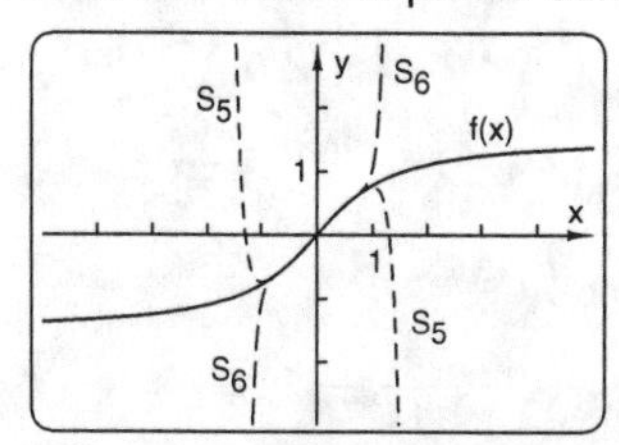

Both partial sums fit the graph of f very well for about $-0.9 < x < 0.9$. For $x > 1$ and $x < -1$, the partial sums bear no resemblance to the graph of f.

Problem Set 12-5, pages 619 to 621 — Taylor and Maclaurin Series, and Operations on These Series

Q1. 4! = 24
Q2. 3! = 6
Q3. 4!/4 = 6
Q4. n = 3
Q5. n = m − 1
Q6. m = 1
Q7. 0! = 1!/1 = 1
Q8. (−1)! = 0!/0 = 1/0 = ∞
Q9. $x/\sqrt{x^2 - 7}$
Q10. cosh x + C

1. $f(u) = e^u = 1 + u + \frac{1}{2!}u^2 + \frac{1}{3!}u^3 + \frac{1}{4!}u^4 + \frac{1}{5!}u^5 + ...$

2. $f(u) = \ln u = (u-1) - \frac{1}{2}(u-1)^2 + \frac{1}{3}(u-1)^3 - \frac{1}{4}(u-1)^4 + ...$

3. $f(u) = \sin u = u - \frac{1}{3!}u^3 + \frac{1}{5!}u^5 - \frac{1}{7!}u^7 + \frac{1}{9!}u^9 - \frac{1}{11!}u^{11} + ...$

4. $f(u) = \cos u = 1 - \frac{1}{2!}u^2 + \frac{1}{4!}u^4 - \frac{1}{6!}u^6 + \frac{1}{8!}u^8 - \frac{1}{10!}u^{10} + ...$

5. $f(u) = \cosh u = 1 + \frac{1}{2!}u^2 + \frac{1}{4!}u^4 + \frac{1}{6!}u^6 + \frac{1}{8!}u^8 + \frac{1}{10!}u^{10} + ...$

6. $f(u) = \sinh u = u + \frac{1}{3!}u^3 + \frac{1}{5!}u^5 + \frac{1}{7!}u^7 + \frac{1}{9!}u^9 + \frac{1}{11!}u^{11} + ...$

7. $f(u) = (1-u)^{-1} = 1 + u + u^2 + u^3 + u^4 + u^5 + ...$

8. $f(u) = \tan^{-1} u = u - \frac{1}{3}u^3 + \frac{1}{5}u^5 - \frac{1}{7}u^7 + \frac{1}{9}u^9 - \frac{1}{11}u^{11} + ...$

9. $x \sin x = x(x - \frac{1}{3!}x^3 + \frac{1}{5!}x^5 - \frac{1}{7!}x^7 + \frac{1}{9!}x^9 - ...)$

$= x^2 - \frac{1}{3!}x^4 + \frac{1}{5!}x^6 - \frac{1}{7!}x^8 + \frac{1}{9!}x^{10} - ...$

10. $x \sinh x = x(x + \frac{1}{3!}x^3 + \frac{1}{5!}x^5 + \frac{1}{7!}x^7 + \frac{1}{9!}x^9 + ...)$

$= x^2 + \frac{1}{3!}x^4 + \frac{1}{5!}x^6 + \frac{1}{7!}x^8 + \frac{1}{9!}x^{10} + ...$

11. $\cosh x^3 = 1 + \frac{1}{2!}(x^3)^2 + \frac{1}{4!}(x^3)^4 + \frac{1}{6!}(x^3)^6 + \frac{1}{8!}(x^3)^8 +$

$= 1 + \frac{1}{2!}x^6 + \frac{1}{4!}x^{12} + \frac{1}{6!}x^{18} + \frac{1}{8!}x^{24} + ...$

12. $\cos x^2 = 1 - \frac{1}{2!}(x^2)^2 + \frac{1}{4!}(x^2)^4 - \frac{1}{6!}(x^2)^6 + \frac{1}{8!}(x^2)^8 -$

$= 1 - \frac{1}{2!}x^4 + \frac{1}{4!}x^8 - \frac{1}{6!}x^{12} + \frac{1}{8!}x^{16} - ...$

13. $\ln x^2 = (x^2 - 1) - \frac{1}{2}(x^2 - 1)^2 + \frac{1}{3}(x^2 - 1)^3 - ...$

(or, $\ln x^2 = 2 \ln x = 2(x - 1) - (x - 1)^2 + \frac{2}{3}(x - 1)^3 - ...$)

14. $e^{-x^2} = 1 + (-x^2) + \frac{1}{2!}(-x^2)^2 + \frac{1}{3!}(-x^2)^3 + \frac{1}{4!}(-x^2)^4 + ...$

$= 1 - x^2 + \frac{1}{2!}x^4 - \frac{1}{3!}x^6 + \frac{1}{4!}x^8 - ...$

15. $\int_0^x e^{-t^2}\,dt = \int_0^x (1 - t^2 + \frac{1}{2!}t^4 - \frac{1}{3!}t^6 + \frac{1}{4!}t^8 - ...)\,dt$

$= x - \frac{1}{3}x^3 + \frac{1}{5}\cdot\frac{1}{2!}x^5 - \frac{1}{7}\cdot\frac{1}{3!}x^7 + \frac{1}{9}\cdot\frac{1}{4!}x^9 - ...$

16. $\int_0^x \sin t^3\,dt = \int_0^x (t^3 - \frac{1}{3!}t^9 + \frac{1}{5!}t^{15} - \frac{1}{7!}t^{21} + \frac{1}{9!}t^{27} - ...)\,dt$

$= \frac{1}{4}x^4 - \frac{1}{10}\cdot\frac{1}{3!}x^{10} + \frac{1}{16}\cdot\frac{1}{5!}x^{16} - \frac{1}{22}\cdot\frac{1}{7!}x^{22} + ...$

17. $\int_0^x t^2 \sin t^5\,dt = \int_0^x t^2(t^5 - \frac{1}{3!}t^{15} + \frac{1}{5!}t^{25} - \frac{1}{7!}t^{35} + ...)\,dt$

$= \int_0^x (t^7 - \frac{1}{3!}t^{17} + \frac{1}{5!}t^{27} - \frac{1}{7!}t^{37} + ...)\,dt$

$= \frac{1}{8}x^8 - \frac{1}{18}\cdot\frac{1}{3!}x^{18} + \frac{1}{28}\cdot\frac{1}{5!}x^{28} - \frac{1}{38}\cdot\frac{1}{7!}x^{38} + ...$

18. $\int_1^x \ln t^3\,dt = 3\int_1^x \ln t\,dt$

$= 3\int_1^x ((t - 1) - \frac{1}{2}(t - 1)^2 + \frac{1}{3}(t - 1)^3 - \frac{1}{4}(t - 1)^4 + ...)\,dt$

$= \frac{3}{2}(x - 1)^2 - \frac{1}{2}(x - 1)^3 + \frac{1}{4}(x - 1)^4 - \frac{3}{20}(x - 1)^5 + ...$

19. $\int_0^x \frac{1}{t}\sinh t^2\,dt = \int_0^x \frac{1}{t}(t^2 + \frac{1}{3!}t^6 + \frac{1}{5!}t^{10} + \frac{1}{7!}t^{14} + ...)\,dt$

$= \int_0^x (t + \frac{1}{3!}t^5 + \frac{1}{5!}t^9 + \frac{1}{7!}t^{13} + ...)\,dt$

$= \frac{1}{2}x^2 + \frac{1}{6}\cdot\frac{1}{3!}x^6 + \frac{1}{10}\cdot\frac{1}{5!}x^{10} + \frac{1}{14}\cdot\frac{1}{7!}x^{14} + ...$

20. $\int_0^x \cos t^{0.5}\,dt = \int_0^x (1 - \frac{1}{2!}t + \frac{1}{4!}t^2 - \frac{1}{6!}t^3 + \frac{1}{8!}t^4 - ...)\,dt$

$= x - \frac{1}{2}\cdot\frac{1}{2!}x^2 + \frac{1}{3}\cdot\frac{1}{4!}x^3 - \frac{1}{4}\cdot\frac{1}{6!}x^4 + \frac{1}{5}\cdot\frac{1}{8!}x^5 - ...$

21. $\frac{1}{x^4 + 1} = 1 - x^4 + x^8 - x^{12} + x^{16} - ...$

22. $\frac{9}{x^2 + 3} = \frac{3}{1 + (x^2/3)} = 3(1 - \frac{1}{3}x^2 + \frac{1}{3^2}x^4 - \frac{1}{3^3}x^6 + ...)$

$= 3 - x^2 + \frac{1}{3}x^4 - \frac{1}{3^2}x^6 + ...$

23. $\int_0^x \frac{1}{t^4 + 1}\,dt = \int_0^x (1 - t^4 + t^8 - t^{12} + t^{16} - ...)\,dt$

$= x - \frac{1}{5}x^5 + \frac{1}{9}x^9 - \frac{1}{13}x^{13} + \frac{1}{17}x^{17} - ...$

24. $\int_0^x \frac{9}{t^2+3}\,dt = \int_0^x (3 - t^2 + \frac{1}{3}t^4 - \frac{1}{3^2}t^6 + ...)\,dt$

$= 3x - \frac{1}{3}x^3 + \frac{1}{3\cdot 5}x^5 - \frac{1}{3^2\cdot 7}x^7 + \frac{1}{3^3\cdot 9}x^9 - ...$

25. $f(x) = \sin x$, about $x = \pi/4$:

$f(x) = \frac{\sqrt{2}}{2} + \frac{\sqrt{2}}{2}(x - \frac{\pi}{4}) - \frac{\sqrt{2}}{2\cdot 2!}(x - \frac{\pi}{4})^2 - \frac{\sqrt{2}}{2\cdot 3!}(x - \frac{\pi}{4})^3$

$+ \frac{\sqrt{2}}{2\cdot 4!}(x - \frac{\pi}{4})^4 + \frac{\sqrt{2}}{2\cdot 5!}(x - \frac{\pi}{4})^5 - ...$

26. $f(x) = \cos x$, about $x = \pi/4$:

$f(x) = \frac{\sqrt{2}}{2} - \frac{\sqrt{2}}{2}(x - \frac{\pi}{4}) - \frac{\sqrt{2}}{2\cdot 2!}(x - \frac{\pi}{4})^2 + \frac{\sqrt{2}}{2\cdot 3!}(x - \frac{\pi}{4})^3$

$+ \frac{\sqrt{2}}{2\cdot 4!}(x - \frac{\pi}{4})^4 - \frac{\sqrt{2}}{2\cdot 5!}(x - \frac{\pi}{4})^5 - ...$

27. $f(x) = \ln x$, about $x = 1$:

$f(x) = (x - 1) - \frac{1}{2}(x - 1)^2 + \frac{1}{3}(x - 1)^3 - \frac{1}{4}(x - 1)^4 + ...$

28. $f(x) = \log x$, about $x = 10$

$f(x) = 1 + \frac{1}{\ln 10}\cdot\frac{(x - 10)}{10} - \frac{1}{2\ln 10}\cdot\frac{(x - 10)^2}{10^2}$

$+ \frac{1}{3\ln 10}\cdot\frac{(x - 10)^3}{10^3} - \frac{1}{4\ln 10}\cdot\frac{(x - 10)^4}{10^4} + ...$

29. $f(x) = (x - 5)^{7/3}$, about $x = 4$:

$f(x) = -1 + \frac{7}{3}(x - 4) - \frac{7\cdot 4}{3^2 2!}(x - 4)^2 + \frac{7\cdot 4\cdot 1}{3^3 3!}(x - 4)^3$

$- \frac{7\cdot 4\cdot 1\cdot(-2)}{3^4 4!}(x - 4)^4 + \frac{7\cdot 4\cdot 1\cdot(-2)(-5)}{3^5 5!}(x - 4)^5 - ...$

30. $f(x) = (x + 6)^{4.2}$, about $x = -5$:

$f(x) = 1 + 4.2(x + 5) + \frac{4.2\cdot 3.2}{2!}(x + 5)^2$

$+ \frac{4.2\cdot 3.2\cdot 2.2}{3!}(x + 5)^3 + \frac{4.2\cdot 3.2\cdot 2.2\cdot 1.2}{4!}(x + 5)^4 + ...$

31. By equating derivatives:

$f(x) = \cos 3x$	$f(0) = P(0) = 1$	$c_0 = 1$
$f'(x) = -3 \sin 3x$	$f'(0) = P'(0) = 0$	$c_1 = 0$
$f''(x) = -9 \cos 3x$	$f''(0) = P''(0) = -9$	$c_2 = -\frac{9}{2!}$
$f'''(x) = 27 \sin 3x$	$f'''(0) = P'''(0) = 0$	$c_3 = 0$
$f^{(4)}(x) = 81 \cos 3x$	$f^{(4)}(0) = P^{(4)}(0) = 81$	$c_4 = \frac{81}{4!}$
$f^{(5)}(x) = -243 \sin 3x$	$f^{(5)}(0) = P^{(5)}(0) = 0$	$c_5 = 0$
$f^{(6)}(x) = -729 \cos 3x$	$f^{(6)}(0) = P^{(6)}(0) = -729c_6$	$= -\frac{729}{6!}$

...

$\therefore \cos 3x = 1 - \frac{9}{2!}x^2 + \frac{81}{4!}x^4 - \frac{729}{6!}x^6 + ...$

By substitution:

$\cos 3x = 1 - \frac{1}{2!}(3x)^2 + \frac{1}{4!}(3x)^4 - \frac{1}{6!}(3x)^6 + ...$

$= 1 - \frac{9}{2!}x^2 + \frac{81}{4!}x^4 - \frac{729}{6!}x^6 + ...$

The two answers are equivalent. Substitution gives the answer much more easily in this case.

32. By equating derivatives:

$f(x) = \ln(1 + x)$	$f(0) = P(0) = 0$	$c_0 = 0$
$f'(x) = (1 + x)^{-1}$	$f'(0) = P'(0) = 1$	$c_1 = 1$
$f''(x) = -(1 + x)^{-2}$	$f''(0) = P''(0) = -1$	$c_2 = -\frac{1}{2}$
$f'''(x) = 2(1 + x)^{-3}$	$f'''(0) = P'''(0) = 2$	$c_3 = \frac{1}{3}$
$f^{(4)}(x) = -6(1 + x)^{-4}$	$f^{(4)}(0) = P^{(4)}(0) = -6$	$c_4 = -\frac{1}{4}$

$\therefore \ln(1 + x) = x - \frac{1}{2}x^2 + \frac{1}{3}x^3 - \frac{1}{4}x^4 + ...$

By substitution, substitute $(1 + x)$ for u in

$\ln u = (u - 1) - \frac{1}{2}(u - 1)^2 + \frac{1}{3}(u - 1)^3 - \frac{1}{4}(u - 1)^4 + ...$

$\ln(1 + x) = x - \frac{1}{2}x^2 + \frac{1}{3}x^3 - \frac{1}{4}x^4 + ...$

The two answers are equivalent. Substitution gives the answer much more easily in this case.

33. <u>Accuracy for ln x Series Value</u>

$S_4(1.5) = 0.40104166...$; $\ln 1.5 = 0.40546510...$

error = 0.00442344...

fifth term $= \frac{1}{5}(1.5-1)^5 = .00625$

Error is smaller in absolute value than first term of tail.

34. <u>Accuracy Interval for ln x Series</u>

Solve numerically for x close to 2:

$S_4(x) - \ln x = 0.0001$

$x \approx 1.2263...$

Solve numerically for x close to 0.1:

$\ln x - S_4(x) = 0.0001$

$x \approx 0.7896...$

Interval is about $0.7896... < x < 1.2263...$.

35. <u>Inverse Tangent Series and an Approximation for π</u>

a. $\tan^{-1} x = x - \frac{1}{3}x^3 + \frac{1}{5}x^5 - \frac{1}{7}x^7 + \frac{1}{9}x^9 - \frac{1}{11}x^{11} + ...$

$\therefore \tan^{-1} 1 = 1 - \frac{1}{3} + \frac{1}{5} - \frac{1}{7} + \frac{1}{9} - \frac{1}{11} + ...$

The tenth partial sum is $S_9(1)$.

$$S_9(1) = \sum_{n=0}^{9} (-1)^n \frac{1}{(2n+1)} = 0.760459904...$$

$4\,S_9(1) = 3.04183961...$

$\pi = 3.14159265...$

The error is about 3%.

b. The fiftieth partial sum is $S_{49}(1)$.

$4\,S_{49}(1) = 3.12159465...$

$\pi = 3.14159265...$

The error is about 0.6%.

(It is interesting to note that although $4\,S_{49}(1)$ differs from π in the second decimal place, many other decimal places later on do match up!)

c. By the composite argument properties from trig,

$$\tan\left(\tan^{-1}\frac{1}{2} + \tan^{-1}\frac{1}{3}\right)$$

$$= \frac{\tan\left(\tan^{-1}\frac{1}{2}\right) + \tan\left(\tan^{-1}\frac{1}{3}\right)}{1 - \tan\left(\tan^{-1}\frac{1}{2}\right) \cdot \tan\left(\tan^{-1}\frac{1}{3}\right)}$$

$$= \frac{\frac{1}{2} + \frac{1}{3}}{1 - \frac{1}{2} \cdot \frac{1}{3}} = 1$$

$\therefore \tan^{-1} 1 = \tan^{-1}\frac{1}{2} + \tan^{-1}\frac{1}{3}$, Q.E.D.

$$4\,S_9 = \sum_{n=0}^{9} (-1)^n \frac{4}{2n+1}\left(\frac{1}{2}\right)^{2n+1} + \sum_{n=0}^{9} (-1)^n \frac{4}{2n+1}\left(\frac{1}{3}\right)^{2n+1}$$

$= 3.14159257...$

$\pi = 3.14159265...$

The answer differs from π by only 1 in the 7th decimal place. The improvement in accuracy is accounted for by the fact that the inverse tangent series converges much more rapidly for x = 1/2 and x = 1/3 than it does for x = 1. In Problem 17 of Problem Set 12-6 you will see that the interval of convergence for the inverse tangent series is $-1 \le x \le 1$. In general, power series converge slowly at the endpoints of the convergence interval.

36. <u>Tangent Series Problem</u>

$\sin x = x - \frac{1}{3!}x^3 + \frac{1}{5!}x^5 - \frac{1}{7!}x^7 + ...$

$\cos x = 1 - \frac{1}{2!}x^2 + \frac{1}{4!}x^4 - \frac{1}{6!}x^6 + ...$

Long division of $x - \frac{1}{3!}x^3 + \frac{1}{5!}x^5 - \frac{1}{7!}x^7 + ...$ by $1 - \frac{1}{2!}x^2 + \frac{1}{4!}x^4 - \frac{1}{6!}x^6 + ...$:

Quotient: $x + \frac{1}{3}x^3 + \frac{2}{15}x^5 + \frac{17}{315}x^7 + ...$

$x - \frac{1}{2!}x^3 + \frac{1}{4!}x^5 - \frac{1}{6!}x^7 + ...$

$\frac{1}{3}x^3 - \frac{4}{5!}x^5 + \frac{6}{7!}x^7 - ...$

$\frac{1}{3}x^3 - \frac{1}{6}x^5 + \frac{1}{72}x^7 - ...$

$\frac{2}{15}x^5 - \frac{64}{7!}x^7 - ...$

$\frac{2}{15}x^5 - \frac{1}{15}x^7 + ...$

$\frac{17}{315}x^7 - ...$

$\therefore \tan x = x + \frac{1}{3}x^3 + \frac{2}{15}x^5 + \frac{17}{315}x^7 + ...$

$S_4(0.2) = 0.202710024...$

$\tan 0.2 = 0.202710035...$

37. <u>Taylor Series Proof Problem</u>

Write $a_i(x) = \frac{f^{(i)}(x)}{i!}(x-a)^i$ the ith term of the general Taylor series, so $f(x) = \sum_{i=0}^{\infty} a_i(x)$.

Assume $\frac{d^n}{dx^n}\sum_{i=0}^{\infty} a_i(x) = \sum_{i=0}^{\infty} \frac{d^n}{dx^n} a_i(x)$

For $i < n$, $\frac{d^n}{dx^n} a_i(x) = \frac{f^{(i)}(x)}{i!}\frac{d^n}{dx^n}(x-a)^i = 0$

For $i \ge n$, $\frac{d^n}{dx^n} a_i(x) = \frac{f^{(i)}(x)}{i!}\frac{d^n}{dx^n}(x-a)^i$

$= \frac{f^{(i)}(x)}{i!} i \cdot (i-1)(i-2)...(i-n+1)(x-a)^{i-n} = 0$

So $\frac{d^n}{dx^n} a_i(a) = 0$ for $i > n$ and $\frac{d^n}{dx^n} a_n(a) = f^{(n)}(a)$.

Thus, $\frac{d^n}{dx^n}\sum_{i=0}^{\infty} a_i(x)$ evaluated at x = a

is $\frac{d^n}{dx^n} a_n(a) = f^{(n)}(a)$.

38. <u>Historical Problem</u>

Brook Taylor: 1685–1731

Colin Maclaurin: 1698–1746

Sir Isaac Newton: 1642–1727

Gottfried Wilhelm von Leibniz: 1646–1716

39. Ratio of Terms Problem

a. $\left|\frac{t_{n+1}}{t_n}\right| = \left|\frac{(-1)^{n+2}\frac{1}{n+1}(x-1)^{n+1}}{(-1)^{n+1}\frac{1}{n}(x-1)^n}\right| = \frac{n}{n+1}|x-1|$

b. $r_{10} = \frac{2}{11}$ for $x = 1.2$

$r_{10} = \frac{9.5}{11}$ for $x = 1.95$

$r_{10} = \frac{20}{11}$ for $x = 3$

c. $r = \lim_{n\to\infty} \frac{n}{n+1}|x-1| = |x-1| \lim_{n\to\infty} \frac{n}{n+1} = |x-1|$

d. $r = 0.2$ for $x = 1.2$
$r = 0.95$ for $x = 1.95$
$r = 2$ for $x = 3$

e. The series converges to ln x whenever the value of x makes $r < 1$, and diverges whenever the value of x makes $r > 1$.

f. The series should converge for $r < 1$.
$r = |x-1| < 1 \Rightarrow -1 < (x-1) < 1 \Rightarrow 0 < x < 2$.

40. Journal Problem
Journal entries will vary.

Problem Set 12-6, pages 626 to 630 — Interval of Convergence for a Series—The Ratio Technique

Q1. sin x
Q2. sinh x
Q3. e^{-x}
Q4. e^x
Q5. $(1-x)^{-1}$ $(-1 < x \le 1)$
Q6. $\frac{1}{2}\sin 2x + C$
Q7. $3\sec^2 3x$
Q8. 1
Q9. e
Q10. Work

1. a. $\sum_{n=1}^{\infty} \frac{n}{4^n}x^n = \frac{1}{4}x + \frac{2}{16}x^2 + \frac{3}{64}x^3 + \frac{4}{256}x^4 + \frac{5}{1024}x^5 + \ldots$

b. $L = \lim_{n\to\infty} \left|\frac{t_{n+1}}{t_n}\right| = \lim_{n\to\infty} \left|\frac{(n+1)x^{n+1}}{4^{n+1}} \cdot \frac{4^n}{nx^n}\right|$

$= \left|\frac{x}{4}\right| \lim_{n\to\infty} \frac{n+1}{n} = \left|\frac{x}{4}\right|$

$L < 1 \Leftrightarrow \left|\frac{x}{4}\right| < 1 \Leftrightarrow -1 < \frac{x}{4} < 1 \Leftrightarrow -4 < x < 4$

Open interval of convergence is (–4, 4).

c. Radius of convergence = 4.

2. a. $\sum_{n=1}^{\infty} \frac{x^n}{n \cdot 2^n} = \frac{1}{2}x + \frac{1}{2 \cdot 4}x^2 + \frac{1}{3 \cdot 8}x^3 + \frac{1}{4 \cdot 16}x^4 + \frac{1}{5 \cdot 32}x^5 + \ldots$

b. $L = \lim_{n\to\infty} \left|\frac{t_{n+1}}{t_n}\right| = \lim_{n\to\infty} \left|\frac{x^{n+1}}{(n+1)\cdot 2^{n+1}} \cdot \frac{n \cdot 2^n}{x^n}\right|$

$= \left|\frac{x}{2}\right| \lim_{n\to\infty} \frac{n}{n+1} = \left|\frac{x}{2}\right|$

$L < 1 \Leftrightarrow \left|\frac{x}{2}\right| < 1 \Leftrightarrow -1 < \frac{x}{2} < 1 \Leftrightarrow -2 < x < 2$

Open interval of convergence is (–2, 2).

c. Radius of convergence = 2

3. a. $\sum_{n=1}^{\infty} \frac{(2x+3)^n}{n}$

$= (2x+3) + \frac{(2x+3)^2}{2} + \frac{(2x+3)^3}{3} + \frac{(2x+3)^4}{4} + \ldots$

b. $L = \lim_{n\to\infty} \left|\frac{(2x+3)^{n+1}}{n+1} \cdot \frac{n}{(2x+3)^n}\right|$

$= |2x+3| \lim_{x\to\infty} \frac{n}{n+1} = |2x+3|$

$L < 1 \Leftrightarrow |2x+3| < 1 \Leftrightarrow -1 < 2x+3 < 1$

$\Leftrightarrow -2 < x < -1$

Open interval of convergence is (–2, –1).

c. Radius of convergence $= \frac{1}{2}$.

4. a. $\sum_{n=1}^{\infty} \frac{(5x-7)^n}{2n}$

$= \frac{(5x-7)}{2} + \frac{(5x-7)^2}{4} + \frac{(5x-7)^3}{6} + \frac{(5x-7)^4}{8} + \ldots$

b. $L = \lim_{n\to\infty} \left|\frac{(5x-7)^{n+1}}{2(n+1)} \cdot \frac{2n}{(5x-7)^n}\right|$

$= |5x-7| \lim_{n\to\infty} \frac{n}{n+1} = |5x-7|$

$L < 1 \Leftrightarrow |5x-7| < 1 \Leftrightarrow -1 < 5x-7 < 1$

$\Leftrightarrow 1.2 < x < 1.6$

Open interval of convergence is (1.2, 1.6).

c. Radius of convergence = 0.2

5. a. $\sum_{n=1}^{\infty} \frac{n^3}{n!}(x-8)^n$

$= (x-8) + \frac{8}{2}(x-8)^2 + \frac{27}{6}(x-8)^3 + \frac{64}{24}(x-8)^4 + \ldots$

b. $L = \lim_{n\to\infty} \left|\frac{(n+1)^3(x-8)^{n+1}}{(n+1)!} \cdot \frac{n!}{n^3(x-8)^n}\right|$

$= |x-8| \lim_{n\to\infty} \left(\left(\frac{n+1}{n}\right)^3 \cdot \frac{1}{n+1}\right) = |x-8| \cdot 1 \cdot 0 = 0$

$L < 0$ for all values of x.

Series converges for all values of x.

c. Radius of convergence is infinite.

6. a. $\sum_{n=1}^{\infty} \frac{n!}{n^4}(x+2)^n$

$= (x+2) + \frac{2}{16}(x+2)^2 + \frac{6}{81}(x+2)^3 + \frac{24}{256}(x+2)^4 + \ldots$

b. $L = \lim_{n\to\infty} \left|\frac{(n+1)! \cdot (x+2)^{n+1}}{(n+1)^4} \cdot \frac{n^4}{n! \cdot (x+2)^n}\right|$

$= |x+2| \lim_{n\to\infty} \left((n+1) \cdot \left(\frac{n}{n+1}\right)^4\right)$

$= |x+2| \lim_{n\to\infty} (n+1) \cdot 1 = \infty$

The series converges only for $|x+2| = 0$

$\Leftrightarrow x = -2$.

c. Radius of convergence = 0

7. $\sin x = \sum_{n=0}^{\infty} \frac{(-1)^n}{(2n+1)!} x^{2n+1}$

Note that $|(-1)^n|$ can be left out of the ratio.

$L = \lim_{n\to\infty} \left|\frac{x^{2n+3}}{(2n+3)!} \cdot \frac{(2n+1)!}{x^{2n+1}}\right|$

$= x^2 \lim_{n\to\infty} \frac{1}{(2n+3)(2n+2)} = x^2 \cdot 0$

$\therefore L < 1$ for all x and the series converges for all x.

8. $\cos x = \sum_{n=0}^{\infty} \frac{(-1)^n}{(2n)!} x^{2n}$

Note that $|(-1)^n|$ can be left out of the ratio.

$L = \lim_{n\to\infty} \left| \frac{x^{2n+2}}{(2n+2)!} \cdot \frac{(2n)!}{x^{2n}} \right|$

$= x^2 \lim_{n\to\infty} \frac{1}{(2n+2)(2n+1)} = x^2 \cdot 0$

$\therefore$ L < 1 for all x and the series converges for all x.

9. $\sinh x = \sum_{n=0}^{\infty} \frac{1}{(2n+1)!} x^{2n+1}$

$L = \lim_{n\to\infty} \left| \frac{x^{2n+3}}{(2n+3)!} \cdot \frac{(2n+1)!}{x^{2n+1}} \right|$

$= x^2 \lim_{n\to\infty} \frac{1}{(2n+3)(2n+2)} = x^2 \cdot 0$

$\therefore$ L < 1 for all x and the series converges for all x.

10. $\cosh x = \sum_{n=0}^{\infty} \frac{1}{(2n)!} x^{2n}$

$L = \lim_{n\to\infty} \left| \frac{x^{2n+2}}{(2n+2)!} \cdot \frac{(2n)!}{x^{2n}} \right|$

$= x^2 \lim_{n\to\infty} \frac{1}{(2n+2)(2n+1)} = x^2 \cdot 0$

$\therefore$ L < 1 for all x and the series converges for all x.

11. $e^x = \sum_{n=0}^{\infty} \frac{1}{n!} x^n$

$L = \lim_{n\to\infty} \left| \frac{x^{n+1}}{(n+1)!} \cdot \frac{n!}{x^n} \right| = |x| \lim_{n\to\infty} \frac{1}{n+1} = |x| \cdot 0$

$\therefore$ L < 1 for all x and the series converges for all x.

12. $e^{-x} = \sum_{n=0}^{\infty} \frac{(-1)^n}{n!} x^n$

$L = \lim_{n\to\infty} \left| \frac{x^{n+1}}{(n+1)!} \cdot \frac{n!}{x^n} \right| = |x| \lim_{n\to\infty} \frac{1}{n+1} = |x| \cdot 0$

$\therefore$ L < 1 for all x and the series converges for all x.

13. $t_n = x^n n!$

$L = \lim_{n\to\infty} \left| \frac{x^{n+1}(n+1)!}{x^n n!} \right| = |x| \lim_{n\to\infty} (n+1) = |x| \cdot \infty$

$L = \infty$ for all $x \neq 0$; $L = 0$ at $x = 0$.

$\therefore$ the series converges only for x = 0.

14. $t_n = \frac{n!}{100^n} x^n$

$L = \lim_{n\to\infty} \left| \frac{(n+1)!x^{n+1}}{100^{n+1}} \cdot \frac{100^n}{n!x^n} \right| = |x| \cdot \infty$

$L = \infty$ for all $x \neq 0$; $L = 0$ at $x = 0$.

$\therefore$ the series converges only for x = 0.

15. $\cosh 10 = \sum_{n=0}^{\infty} \frac{1}{(2n)!} 10^{2n}$

$L = \lim_{n\to\infty} \left| \frac{10^{2n+2}}{(2n+2)!} \cdot \frac{(2n)!}{10^{2n}} \right|$

$= 10^2 \lim_{n\to\infty} \frac{1}{(2n+2)(2n+1)} = 0$

$L = 0 < 1 \Rightarrow$ series converges.

16. $\ln 0.1 = \sum_{n=1}^{\infty} (-1)^{n+1} \frac{1}{n}(-0.9)^n$

$t_n = -(0.9)^n/n$

n	t_n	$\lvert t_{n+1}/t_n \rvert$
1	−0.9	0.45
2	−0.405	0.6
3	−0.243	0.675
4	−0.164025	0.72
5	−0.118098	0.75
9	−0.043046721	0.81
15	−0.0137260754...	0.84375
35	−0.0007151872...	0.875

Ratio seems to approach 0.9.

Proof:

$L = \lim_{n\to\infty} \left| \frac{-(0.9)^{n+1}}{n+1} \cdot \frac{n}{-(0.9)^n} \right| = 0.9 \lim_{n\to\infty} \frac{n}{n+1}$

$= 0.9(1) = 0.9$, Q.E.D.

17. Inverse Tangent Series Problem

a. $P(x) = \sum_{n=0}^{\infty} (-1)^n \frac{1}{2n+1} x^{2n+1}$

Note that $|(-1)^n| = 1$ for all n.

$L = \lim_{n\to\infty} \left| \frac{x^{2n+3}}{2n+3} \cdot \frac{2n+1}{x^{2n+1}} \right|$

$= x^2 \lim_{n\to\infty} \frac{2n+1}{2n+3} = x^2 \cdot 1$ by l'Hospital's rule

$L < 1 \Leftrightarrow x^2 < 1 \Leftrightarrow -1 < x < 1$

Open interval of convergence is (−1, 1).

b. Graphs, $y = \tan^{-1} x$, and $y = S_3(x)$ and $S_4(x)$, the fourth and fifth partial sums, respectively.

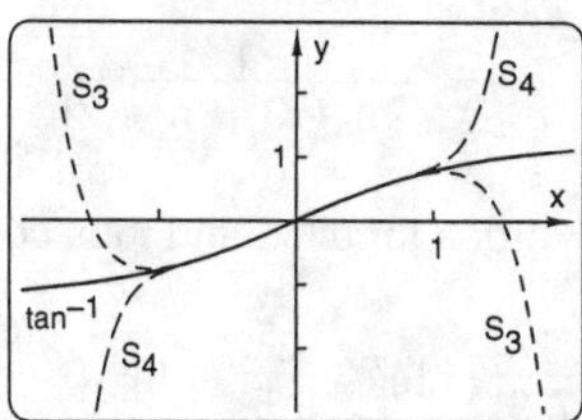

The graphs of the partial sums of P(x) and $\tan^{-1} x$ fit very well for $-1 < x < 1$. The partial sums diverge from $\tan^{-1} x$ for x outside this interval.

c. $S_3(0.1) = 0.09966865238095...$

d. $\tan^{-1} 0.1 = 0.09966865249116...$;
tail = 0.00000000011020...

e. First term of tail $= \frac{1}{9}(0.1)^9 = 0.00000000011111...$, which is larger than the tail.

18. Volume Problem

a. $y = x^2 \sin 2x$, from x = 0 to x = 1.5, rotated about the y-axis.

A slice of the region parallel to the axis of rotation generates a cylindrical shell.

$dV = 2\pi x \cdot y \cdot dx = 2\pi x^3 \sin 2x \, dx$

$V = \int_0^{1.5} 2\pi x^3 \sin 2x \, dx \approx 4.66269394...$

b. Integrate by parts.

u	dv
x^3 (+)	$\sin 2x$
$3x^2$ (−)	$-\frac{1}{2}\cos 2x$
$6x$ (+)	$-\frac{1}{4}\sin 2x$
6 (−)	$\frac{1}{8}\cos 2x$
0 (+)	$\frac{1}{16}\sin 2x$

$$V = 2\pi\left(-\frac{1}{2}x^3\cos 2x + \frac{3}{4}x^2\sin 2x + \frac{3}{4}x\cos 2x - \frac{3}{8}\sin 2x\right)\Big|_0^{1.5}$$

$$= 2\pi\left(-\frac{9}{16}\cos 3 + \frac{21}{16}\sin 3\right)$$

c. $V = 4.66269394...$ from part b.
$V \approx 4.66269394...$ from part a.
The approximate answer from part a. is the same as the exact answer to 8 decimal places.

d. Omitting the 2π, $\int x^3 \sin 2x\,dx$

$$= \int x^3\left((2x) - \frac{1}{3!}(2x)^3 + \frac{1}{5!}(2x)^5 - \frac{1}{7!}(2x)^7 + ...\right)dx$$

$$= \int \left(2x^4 - \frac{2^3}{3!}x^6 + \frac{2^5}{5!}x^8 - \frac{2^7}{7!}x^{10} + ...\right)dx$$

$$= \frac{2}{5}x^5 - \frac{2^3}{7\cdot 3!}x^7 + \frac{2^5}{9\cdot 5!}x^9 - \frac{2^7}{11\cdot 7!}x^{11} + ... + C$$

$$= \sum_{n=0}^{\infty} (-1)^n \frac{2^{2n+1}}{(2n+5)\cdot(2n+1)!}x^{2n+5} + C$$

e. For the series in part (d),

$$L = \lim_{n\to\infty} \left|\frac{2^{2n+3}\cdot x^{2n+7}}{(2n+7)\cdot(2n+3)!} \cdot \frac{(2n+5)\cdot(2n+1)!}{2^{2n+1}\cdot x^{2n+5}}\right|$$

$$= 4x^2 \lim_{n\to\infty}\frac{2n+5}{2n+7} \cdot \lim_{n\to\infty}\frac{1}{(2n+3)(2n+2)}$$

$$= 4x^2 \cdot 1 \cdot 0$$

$\therefore$ the series converges for all x, and thus converges for $x = 1.5$.

f. $$V \approx 2\pi\left(\frac{2}{5}(1.5)^5 - \frac{2^3}{7\cdot 3!}(1.5)^7 + \frac{2^5}{9\cdot 5!}(1.5)^9 - \frac{2^7}{11\cdot 7!}(1.5)^{11} + \frac{2^9}{13\cdot 9!}(1.5)^{13}\right)$$

$= 4.67164363...$
The answer agrees with the other two answers within 1 unit in the second decimal place.

g. $$t_{n+1} = (-1)^n \frac{2\pi\cdot 2^{2n+3}}{(2n+7)\cdot(2n+3)!}(1.5)^{2n+7}$$

By table search, $|t_{n+1}| < 0.5 \times 10^{-10}$ for $n \geq 10$.
Since n starts at 0 for the first term, you would need 11 terms to estimate the volume to 10 decimal places.

19. The Error Function

a. Assume this series can be integrated term by term.

$$f(x) = \int_0^x e^{-t^2}\,dt$$

$$= \int_0^x \left(1 - t^2 + \frac{1}{2!}t^4 - \frac{1}{3!}t^6 + \frac{1}{4!}t^8 - \frac{1}{5!}t^{10} + ...\right)dt$$

$$= x - \frac{1}{3}x^3 + \frac{1}{5\cdot 2!}x^5 - \frac{1}{7\cdot 3!}x^7 + \frac{1}{9\cdot 4!}x^9 - \frac{1}{11\cdot 5!}x^{11} + ...$$

b. Graph, $y = f(x)$ numerically and $y = S_5(x)$, the sixth partial sum.

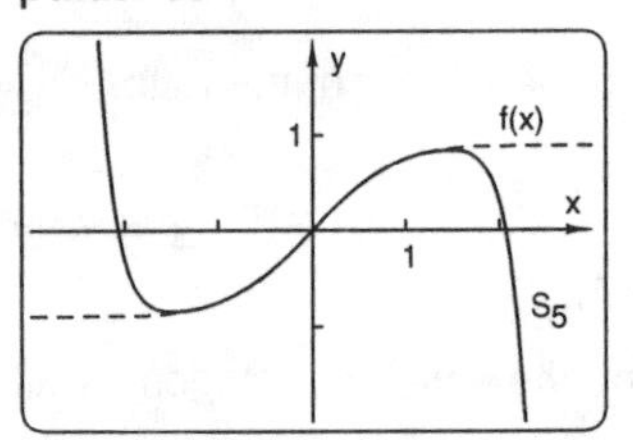

The partial sum is reasonably close for approximately $-1.5 < x < 1.5$.

c. $$t_n = \frac{(-1)^n}{(2n+1)n!}x^{2n+1}$$

Note that $|(-1)^n| = 1$.

$$L = \lim_{n\to\infty}\left|\frac{x^{2n+3}}{(2n+3)(n+1)!}\cdot\frac{(2n+1)n!}{x^{2n+1}}\right|$$

$$= x^2 \lim_{n\to\infty}\frac{2n+1}{2n+3}\cdot\lim_{n\to\infty}\frac{1}{n+1} = x^2\cdot 1\cdot 0 \leq 1 \text{ for all x.}$$

d. Erf x does seem to be approaching 1 as x increases, as shown by the following table generated by numerical integration.

x	erf x
1	0.8427007929...
2	0.9953222650...
3	0.9999779095...
4	0.9999999845...
5	0.9999999999...

20. The Sine-Integral Function

a. Assume this series can be integrated term by term.

$$\frac{\sin t}{t} = \frac{1}{t}\cdot\left(t - \frac{1}{3!}t^3 + \frac{1}{5!}t^5 - \frac{1}{7!}t^7 + \frac{1}{9!}t^9 - \frac{1}{11!}t^{11} + ...\right)$$

$$= 1 - \frac{1}{3!}t^2 + \frac{1}{5!}t^4 - \frac{1}{7!}t^6 + \frac{1}{9!}t^8 - \frac{1}{11!}t^{10} + ...$$

$$= \sum_{n=0}^{\infty}(-1)^n\frac{t^{2n}}{(2n+1)!}$$

$$\text{Si } x = \int_0^x \left(1 - \frac{1}{3!}t^2 + \frac{1}{5!}t^4 - \frac{1}{7!}t^6 + \frac{1}{9!}t^8 - \frac{1}{11!}t^{10} + ...\right)dt$$

$$= x - \frac{1}{3\cdot 3!}x^3 + \frac{1}{5\cdot 5!}x^5 - \frac{1}{7\cdot 7!}x^7 + \frac{1}{9\cdot 9!}x^9 - \frac{1}{11\cdot 11!}x^{11} + ...$$

$$= \sum_{n=0}^{\infty}(-1)^n\frac{1}{(2n+1)(2n+1)!}x^{2n+1}$$

b. Ratio for $\frac{\sin t}{t}$ is

$$L = \lim_{n\to\infty}\left|\frac{t^{2n+2}}{(2n+3)!}\cdot\frac{(2n+1)!}{t^{2n}}\right|$$

$$= t^2 \lim_{n\to\infty}\frac{1}{(2n+3)(2n+2)} = t^2\cdot 0$$

$\therefore L < 1$ for all values of t.
Series for $(\sin t)/t$ converges for all values of t.
Ratio for Si x is

$$L = \lim_{n\to\infty}\left|\frac{x^{2n+3}}{(2n+3)(2n+3)!}\cdot\frac{(2n+1)(2n+1)!}{x^{2n+1}}\right|$$

$$= x^2 \lim_{n\to\infty}\frac{2n+3}{2n+1}\cdot\lim_{n\to\infty}\frac{1}{(2n+3)(2n+2)} = x^2\cdot 1\cdot 0$$

$\therefore L < 1$ for all values of x
Series for Si x converges for all values of x.
The radii of convergence for both series are infinite.

c. The third partial sum is $S_2(x)$.

$S_2(0.6) = 0.6 - \frac{1}{3\cdot3!}(0.6)^3 + \frac{1}{5\cdot5!}(0.6)^5$
$= 0.5881296$

Si 0.6 $= 0.5881288...$

The answers are quite close!

d. Graph, showing $y = S_9(x)$ (the tenth partial sum), and $y = \text{Si } x$ by numerical integration

$S_9(x)$ is reasonably close to Si x for $-3\pi < x < 3\pi$.

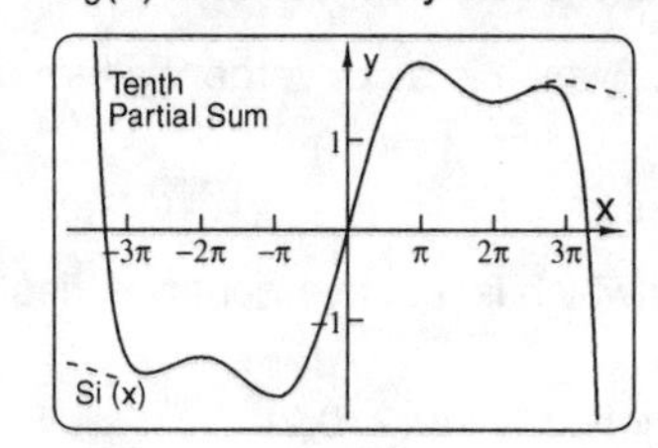

21. <u>The Root Technique</u>

a. Given $L = \lim_{n\to\infty} \sqrt[n]{t_n}$ where $L < 1$

By the definition of limit as $n \to \infty$, there is a number

$k > 0$ for any $\varepsilon > 0$ such that if $n > k$, then $\sqrt[n]{t_n}$ is within ε units of L. Thus,

$\sqrt[n]{t_n} < L + \varepsilon$, Q.E.D.

b. $L < 1 \Rightarrow 1 - L > 0$.

So take any $\varepsilon < 1 - L$

$\Rightarrow L + \varepsilon < L + 1 - L$

$\Rightarrow L + \varepsilon < 1$.

c. For all integers $n > k$,

$0 \le \sqrt[n]{t_n} < L + \varepsilon \Rightarrow 0 \le t_n < (L + \varepsilon)^n$

and $(L + \varepsilon)^n < (L + \varepsilon)^{n-k}$ for all $n > k$, since $L + \varepsilon < 1$,

so $0 \le t_n < (L + \varepsilon)^{n-k}$, Q.E.D.

d. Because $0 \le t_n < (L + \varepsilon)^{n-k}$ for all $n > k$, it follows that the tail after t_n satisfies:

$0 \le t_{n+1} + t_{n+2} + t_{n+3} + ...$

$< (L + \varepsilon)^{n+1-k} + (L + \varepsilon)^{n+2-k} + (L + \varepsilon)^{n+3-k} + ...$

$= (L + \varepsilon)^{n+1-k}(1 + (L + \varepsilon) + (L + \varepsilon)^2 + ...)$

which converges because $L + \varepsilon < 1$.

e. The tail of the series is increasing, and is bounded above by

$(L + \varepsilon)^{n+1-k}(1 + (L + \varepsilon) + (L + \varepsilon)^2 + ...) = \frac{(L + \varepsilon)^{n+1-k}}{1 - (L + \varepsilon)}$

So the series converges, Q.E.D.

22. <u>A Special Limit Problem</u>

$L = \lim_{n\to\infty} \sqrt[n]{n}$

Because ln is a continuous function,

$\ln L = \ln(\lim_{n\to\infty} \sqrt[n]{n}) = \lim_{n\to\infty} \ln \sqrt[n]{n}$

$= \lim_{n\to\infty} \frac{1}{n} \ln n = \lim_{n\to\infty} \frac{\ln n}{n} = \lim_{x\to\infty} \frac{\ln x}{x} \to \frac{\infty}{\infty}$

$= \lim_{x\to\infty} \frac{1/x}{1}$ by l'Hospital's rule

$= 0$

$\therefore L = e^0 = 1$, Q.E.D.

23. $\ln x = \sum_{n=1}^{\infty} \frac{(-1)^{n+1}}{n}(x - 1)^n$

$L = \lim_{n\to\infty} \sqrt[n]{|t_n|} = \lim_{n\to\infty} \sqrt[n]{\frac{(x-1)^n}{n}}$

$= \frac{|x-1|}{\lim_{n\to\infty} \sqrt[n]{n}} = \frac{|x-1|}{1} = |x-1|$

$L < 1 \Leftrightarrow |x - 1| < 1 \Leftrightarrow 0 < x < 2$

Open interval of convergence is (0, 2).

24. $\sum_{n=1}^{\infty} \frac{1}{n^n} x^n$

$L = \lim_{n\to\infty} \sqrt[n]{\frac{|x^n|}{n^n}} = \lim_{n\to\infty} \frac{|x|}{n} = |x| \cdot 0$

$\therefore L < 1$ for all values of x, and thus the series converges for all values of x, Q.E.D.

25. $\sum_{n=1}^{\infty} n^n x^n$

$L = \lim_{n\to\infty} \sqrt[n]{|n^n x^n|} = \lim_{n\to\infty} |nx| = |x| \cdot \infty$

$L = 0$ if $x = 0$, and is infinite if $x \ne 0$.

$\therefore$ the series converges only if $x = 0$.

26. <u>"Which One Wins?" Problem</u>

$\sum_{n=1}^{\infty} \frac{n!}{n^n} x^n$

Use the ratio technique.

$L = \lim_{n\to\infty} \left|\frac{(n+1)!\cdot x^{n+1}}{(n+1)^{n+1}} \cdot \frac{n^n}{n!\cdot x^n}\right|$

$= |x| \lim_{n\to\infty} \frac{n^n}{(n+1)^n} = |x| \lim_{n\to\infty} \frac{1}{(1 + 1/n)^n} = |x| \cdot \frac{1}{e}$

$L < 1 \Leftrightarrow |x| \cdot \frac{1}{e} < 1 \Leftrightarrow -e < x < e$

Open interval of convergence is (−e, e).

Problem Set 12-7, pages 637 to 642 — Convergence of Series at the Ends of the Convergence Interval

Q1. geometric

Q2. multiplying by 2

Q3. common ratio

Q4. ln x

Q5. $1 - \frac{4}{2!}x^2 + \frac{16}{4!}x^4$

Q6. −1/3!

Q7. 2.5

Q8. $1 < x < 7$

Q9. 40.5π

Q10. $(2e^{2t})\vec{i} + (3\cos 3t)\vec{j}$

1. <u>Vocabulary Problem I</u>

a. $\sum_{n=1}^{\infty} \frac{6}{n!} = 6 + \frac{6}{2!} + \frac{6}{3!} + \frac{6}{4!} + \frac{6}{5!} + ...$

$= 6 + 3 + 1 + \frac{1}{4} + \frac{1}{20} + ...$

b. Sequence of partial sums is

$6, 9, 10, 10\frac{1}{4}, 10\frac{3}{10}, ...$

c. $\frac{6}{6!}+\frac{6}{7!}+\frac{6}{8!}+\ldots=\frac{1}{120}+\frac{1}{840}+\frac{1}{6720}+\ldots$

d. Terms are decreasing.

e. Partial sums are increasing.

2. Vocabulary Problem II

Adding a positive term can only increase the sum, even if one is adding smaller and smaller positive terms.

3. Vocabulary Problem III

a. $\sum_{n=1}^{\infty}(-1)^{n+1}\frac{6}{n!}=6-\frac{6}{2!}+\frac{6}{3!}-\frac{6}{4!}+\frac{6}{5!}-\ldots$

$=6-3+1-\frac{1}{4}+\frac{1}{20}-\ldots$

b. Sequence of partial sums is

$6, 3, 4, 3\frac{3}{4}, 3\frac{4}{5}, \ldots$

c. $-\frac{6}{6!}+\frac{6}{7!}-\frac{6}{8!}+\ldots=-\frac{1}{120}+\frac{1}{840}-\frac{1}{6720}+\ldots$

d. The $(-1)^{n+1}$ factor makes the signs of the terms alternate.

e. $S_2=3$, $S_4=3.75$, $S_6=3.791666\ldots$,

The even partial sums are increasing. For the two terms added to get the next even partial sum, the positive term is larger in absolute value than the negative term.

f. $S_1=6$, $S_3=4$, $S_5=3.8$, ...

The odd partial sums are decreasing. For the two terms added to get the next odd partial sum, the positive term is smaller in absolute value than the negative term. Since the odd partial sums are all greater than the even partial sums, the entire sequence is bounded above by the greatest odd partial sum, $S_1=6$.

4. Vocabulary Problem No. 4

"Absolutely" convergent and "conditionally" convergent, respectively.

5. $\sum_{n=1}^{\infty} n(x-3)^n$

$L=\lim_{n\to\infty}\left|\frac{(n+1)(x-3)^{n+1}}{n(x-3)^n}\right|$

$=|x-3|\lim_{n\to\infty}\frac{n+1}{n}=|x-3|\cdot 1$

$L<1 \Leftrightarrow |x-3|<1 \Leftrightarrow 2<x<4$

At $x=2$ the series is

$-1+2-3+4-\ldots$, which diverges because the terms do not approach zero.

At $x=4$ the series is

$1+2+3+4+\ldots$, which diverges because the terms do not approach zero.

Interval of convergence is $(2, 4)$.

6. $\sum_{n=1}^{\infty}\frac{5^n\cdot x^n}{n^2}$

$L=\lim_{n\to\infty}\left|\frac{5^{n+1}\cdot x^{n+1}}{(n+1)^2}\cdot\frac{n^2}{5^n\cdot x^n}\right|$

$=5|x|\lim_{n\to\infty}\left(\frac{n}{n+1}\right)^2=5|x|\cdot 1$

$L<1 \Leftrightarrow 5|x|<1 \Leftrightarrow -0.2<x<0.2$

At $x=-0.2$ the series is

$-1+\frac{1}{4}-\frac{1}{9}+\frac{1}{16}-\ldots$, which is a convergent alternating series.

At $x=0.2$ the series is

$1+\frac{1}{4}+\frac{1}{9}+\frac{1}{16}+\ldots$, which is a convergent p-series with $p=2$.

Interval of convergence is $[-0.2, 0.2]$.

7. $\sum_{n=1}^{\infty}\frac{x^n}{n}$

$L=\lim_{n\to\infty}\left|\frac{x^{n+1}}{n+1}\cdot\frac{n}{x^n}\right|$

$=|x|\lim_{n\to\infty}\frac{n}{n+1}=|x|\cdot 1$

$L<1 \Leftrightarrow |x|<1 \Leftrightarrow -1<x<1$

At $x=-1$ the series is

$-1+\frac{1}{2}-\frac{1}{3}+\frac{1}{4}-\ldots$, which is a convergent alternating series.

At $x=1$ the series is

$1+\frac{1}{2}+\frac{1}{3}+\frac{1}{4}+\ldots$, which is a divergent harmonic series (p-series with $p=1$).

Interval of convergence is $[-1, 1)$.

8. $\sum_{n=4}^{\infty}\frac{(-1)^n(x-6)^n}{n\cdot 2^n}$

$L=\lim_{n\to\infty}\left|\frac{(x-6)^{n+1}}{(n+1)\cdot 2^{n+1}}\cdot\frac{n\cdot 2^n}{(x-6)^n}\right|$

$=\frac{1}{2}|x-6|\lim_{n\to\infty}\frac{n}{n+1}=\frac{1}{2}|x-6|\cdot 1$

$L<1 \Leftrightarrow \frac{1}{2}|x-6|<1 \Leftrightarrow 4<x<8$

At $x=4$ the series is

$\frac{1}{4}+\frac{1}{5}+\frac{1}{6}+\frac{1}{7}+\ldots$, which is a divergent harmonic series (p-series with $p=1$).

At $x=8$ the series is

$\frac{1}{4}-\frac{1}{5}+\frac{1}{6}-\frac{1}{7}+\ldots$, which is a convergent alternating series.

Interval of convergence is $(4, 8]$.

9. $\sum_{n=1}^{\infty} \frac{(-1)^{n+1}\cdot(x+5)^{2n}}{2n}$

$L = \lim_{n\to\infty} \left| \frac{(x+5)^{2n+2}}{2(n+1)} \cdot \frac{2n}{(x+5)^{2n}} \right|$

$= (x+5)^2 \lim_{n\to\infty} \frac{n}{n+1} = (x+5)^2 \cdot 1$

$L < 1 \Leftrightarrow (x+5)^2 < 1 \Leftrightarrow -6 < x < -4$

At $x = -6$ the series is

$\frac{1}{2} - \frac{1}{4} + \frac{1}{6} - \frac{1}{8} + \ldots$, which is a convergent alternating series.

At $x = -4$ the series is

$\frac{1}{2} - \frac{1}{4} + \frac{1}{6} - \frac{1}{8} + \ldots$, which is a convergent alternating series.

Interval of convergence is $[-6, -4]$.

10. $\sum_{n=1}^{\infty} \frac{(x+1)^n}{n^2}$

$L = \lim_{n\to\infty} \left| \frac{(x+1)^{n+1}}{(n+1)^2} \cdot \frac{n^2}{(x+1)^n} \right|$

$= |x+1| \lim_{n\to\infty} \left(\frac{n}{n+1}\right)^2 = |x+1| \cdot 1$

$L < 1 \Leftrightarrow |x+1| < 1 \Leftrightarrow -2 < x < 0$

At $x = -2$ the series is

$-1 + \frac{1}{4} - \frac{1}{9} + \frac{1}{16} - \ldots$, which is a convergent alternating series.

At $x = 0$ the series is

$1 + \frac{1}{4} + \frac{1}{9} + \frac{1}{16} + \ldots$, which is a convergent p-series with $p = 2$.

Interval of convergence is $[-2, 0]$.

11. $\sum_{n=0}^{\infty} \frac{\ln(n+1)}{n+1} x^n$

$L = \lim_{n\to\infty} \left| \frac{\ln(n+2)\cdot x^{n+1}}{n+2} \cdot \frac{n+1}{\ln(n+1)\cdot x^n} \right|$

$= |x| \lim_{n\to\infty} \frac{\ln(n+2)}{\ln(n+1)} \cdot \lim_{n\to\infty} \frac{n+1}{n+2}$

$= |x| \lim_{n\to\infty} \frac{1/(n+2)}{1/(n+1)} \cdot \lim_{n\to\infty} \frac{n+1}{n+2}$ by l'Hopital's rule

$= |x| \lim_{n\to\infty} \frac{n+1}{n+2} \cdot \lim_{n\to\infty} \frac{n+1}{n+2} = |x| \cdot 1 \cdot 1$

$L < 1 \Leftrightarrow |x| < 1 \Leftrightarrow -1 < x < 1$

At $x = -1$ the series is

$\frac{\ln(1)}{1} - \frac{\ln(2)}{2} + \frac{\ln(3)}{3} - \frac{\ln(4)}{4} + \ldots$

By l'Hospital's rule,

$\lim_{n\to\infty} \frac{\ln(n)}{n} = \lim_{n\to\infty} \frac{1/n}{1} = 0$

Since the terms decrease in absolute value and approach 0 for a limit, the series converges by the alternating series test.

At $x = 1$ the series is

$\frac{\ln(1)}{1} + \frac{\ln(2)}{2} + \frac{\ln(3)}{3} + \frac{\ln(4)}{4} + \ldots$

$\int_1^{\infty} \frac{\ln(x)}{x}\,dx = \lim_{b\to\infty} \frac{1}{2}(\ln(x))^2 \Big|_1^b$

$= \lim_{b\to\infty} \left(\frac{1}{2}(\ln(b))^2 - 0\right) = \infty$

Thus, the series diverges by the integral test.

Interval of convergence is $[-1, 1]$.

12. $\sum_{n=1}^{\infty} 5(x-3)^n$

$L = \lim_{n\to\infty} \left| \frac{5(x-3)^{n+1}}{5(x-3)^n} \right| = |x-3|$

$L < 1 \Leftrightarrow |x-3| < 1 \Leftrightarrow 2 < x < 4$

At $x = 2$ the series is

$-5 + 5 - 5 + 5 - \ldots$, which diverges because the terms do not approach zero.

At $x = 4$ the series is

$5 + 5 + 5 + 5 + \ldots$, which diverges because the terms do not approach zero.

Interval of convergence is $[2, 4]$.

13. $\sum_{n=0}^{\infty} \frac{4^n}{x^n}$

$L = \lim_{n\to\infty} \left| \frac{4^{n+1}}{x^{n+1}} \cdot \frac{x^n}{4^n} \right| = \frac{4}{|x|}$

$L < 1 \Leftrightarrow \frac{4}{|x|} < 1 \Leftrightarrow \frac{|x|}{4} > 1 \Leftrightarrow x < -4 \text{ or } x > 4$

At $x = -4$ the series is

$1 - 1 + 1 - 1 + \ldots$, which diverges because the terms do not approach zero.

At $x = 4$ the series is

$1 + 1 + 1 + 1 + 1 + \ldots$, which diverges because the terms do not approach zero.

Intervals of convergence are $(-\infty, -4)$ and $(4, \infty)$.

(Note that the series in Problems 13 and 14 have negative powers of x, and are called Laurent series rather than Taylor series.)

14. $\sum_{n=1}^{\infty} \frac{1}{x^n}$

$L = \lim_{n\to\infty} \left| \frac{x^n}{x^{n+1}} \right| = \frac{1}{|x|}$

$L < 1 \Leftrightarrow \frac{1}{|x|} < 1 \Leftrightarrow \frac{|x|}{1} > 1 \Leftrightarrow x < -1 \text{ or } x > 1$

At $x = -1$ the series is

$-1 + 1 - 1 + 1 - \ldots$, which diverges because the terms do not approach zero.

At $x = 1$ the series is

$1 + 1 + 1 + 1 + \ldots$, which diverges because the terms do not approach zero.

Intervals of convergence are $(-\infty, -1)$ and $(1, \infty)$.

15. Upper Bound by Convergent Improper Integral

a. $S = \sum_{n=1}^{\infty} \frac{1}{n^2}$

$S = 1 + \frac{1}{4} + \frac{1}{9} + \frac{1}{16} + \frac{1}{25} + \ldots$

$S_5 = \frac{5269}{3600} = 1.46361111\ldots$

b. The sixth term of the series has a rectangle between $x = 5$ and $x = 6$ (the height of the rectangles being used is the value of the function at the rightmost edge). So the integral must be from 5 to ∞ to include this rectangle.

c. $\int_5^{\infty} \frac{1}{x^2}\,dx = \lim_{b\to\infty} -x^{-1} \Big|_5^b = \lim_{b\to\infty} \left(-b^{-1} + \frac{1}{5}\right) = \frac{1}{5}$

Tail is bounded above by $\frac{1}{5}$.

d. The sequence of partial sums is increasing (since the terms of the series are positive) and bounded above. Thus, the sequence of partial sums must converge. The series is a finite sum added to the tail, so the series converges.

e. $\sum_{n=1}^{1000} n^{-2} = 1.643934...$

f. $R_{1000} = \sum_{n=1001}^{\infty} n^{-2} < \int_{1000}^{\infty} x^{-2}\,dx$

$= \lim_{b\to\infty} -x^{-1}\Big|_{1000}^{b} = \lim_{b\to\infty} (-b^{-1} + \frac{1}{1000}) = \frac{1}{1000}$

Upper bound for tail is 0.001
(Note that a lower bound for the tail is $\int_{1001}^{\infty} x^{-2}\,dx$, which equals $\frac{1}{1001}$. In general, the remainder after n terms is between $\frac{1}{n}$ and $\frac{1}{n+1}$. See Example 5 in Section 12-8.)

g. False. The first term of the tail is $\frac{1}{1001^2} = \frac{1}{1002001}$, which is not close to the upper bound. As shown in part f., the tail is between 1/1001 and 1/1000.

h. The remainder after 1000 terms is no more than 0.001. The correct total is greater than S_{1000} = 1.643934... but less than S_{1000} + upper bound for error = 1.644934... , so the error is less than $(0.001/1.643934)\cdot 100 = 0.0608...$.
No more than a 0.0608% error.

i. The above shows that the error after n terms is less than $\frac{1}{n}$ (and in fact, greater than $\frac{1}{n+1}$, as shown in part f.

$\frac{1}{n} = 0.0000005 \Leftrightarrow n = 2000000$

It would take at least 2 million terms!

16. Divergence by Comparison with Divergent Improper Integral

a. $S = \sum_{n=1}^{\infty} \frac{1}{n}$

$S_5 = 1 + \frac{1}{2} + \frac{1}{3} + \frac{1}{4} + \frac{1}{5} = \frac{137}{60} = 2.283333...$

b. $R_5 > \int_6^{\infty} \frac{1}{x}\,dx = \lim_{b\to\infty} \ln|x|\Big|_1^b = \lim_{b\to\infty} (\ln b - \ln 1) = \infty$

Thus, the remainder is infinite also, which implies that the series diverges.

c. It would be futile to evaluate the series by computer because there is no (finite) answer in the first place. The only result would be partial sums, which may or may not be useful.

d. False. This problem is a counterexample of the terms going to zero ($n^{-1} \to 0$), but the sum diverging.

17. Integral Test Problem

Assume f(x) is positive and decreasing for all x beyond x = D.

If I converges, then the tail of the series can be bounded above by the number to which the integral converges. Because the terms are positive, the partial sums are increasing. Thus, the sequence of partial sums converges because it is increasing and bounded above. Since the tail of the series converges, so does the series.

If I diverges, the tail of the series can be bounded below by a divergent improper integral. Thus, the tail is infinite, which implies that the series diverges.

18. Follow-Up Problem

If a series S is an upper sum for the integral, and the integral converges to a limit L, then all that is known is that S > L. Unfortunately, this does not rule out the series' diverging, since S could be ∞, and ∞ > L.

19. The Factorial Reciprocal Series Converges

a. $S = \sum_{n=0}^{\infty} \frac{1}{n!}$

It is difficult to find the appropriate function f(x) to integrate, such that $f(n) = \frac{1}{n!}$ at the integer points. So the integral test is impractical for this series. (Note that the gamma function, introduced in Problem 25 of Problem Set 9-10, has this property. But its definition,

$\Gamma(x+1) = x! = \int_0^{\infty} t^x e^{-t}\,dt$

already involves an improper integral, which would have to be integrated again to use the integral test for the series.)

b. $\text{Tail} = \frac{1}{16} + \frac{1}{32} + \frac{1}{64} + \dots$,

which is geometric with first term $\frac{1}{16}$ and common ratio $\frac{1}{2}$. The geometric series approaches

$S_g = \frac{1}{16} \cdot \frac{1}{1 - \frac{1}{2}} = \frac{1}{8}$.

c. An upper bound for the tail of the series is $\frac{1}{8}$.

d. $S_3 = 1 + 1 + \frac{1}{2} + \frac{1}{6} = 2\frac{2}{3}$

An upper bound for the entire series is $2\frac{2}{3} + \frac{1}{8}$

$= 2\frac{19}{24} = 2.791666...$.

e. The sequence of partial sums is increasing (since the terms of the series are positive) and bounded above by 2.7916... . Thus, the sequence of partial sums converges, so the series converges.

20. Comparison Test for the Exp. Function Series

a. The seventh term of $\sum_{n=0}^{\infty} \frac{1}{n!} 0.6^n$ is

$t_6 = \frac{1}{6!} 0.6^6 = 0.0000648$.

b. $S_4 = \sum_{n=0}^{4} \frac{1}{n!} 0.6^n = 1.8214$

$e^{0.6} = 1.8221188...$

S_4 differs from $e^{0.6}$ by 0.00071880... , which is greater than $t_5 = 0.000648$, but not much greater. The difference is greater than t_5 because all subsequent terms are added, not subtracted. It is not much greater than t_5 because the subsequent terms are very small.

c.

n	5	6	7
Tail:	0.000648	0.0000648	0.000005554...
Geom.:	0.000648	0.0000648	0.00000648

Terms of the $e^{0.6}$ series are formed by multiplying the previous term as follows:

$t_n = \frac{0.6}{n} t_{n-1}$

Terms of the geometric series are formed by multiplying the previous term by 0.1:

$t_n = 0.1 t_{n-1}$

For $n \ge 7$, 0.6/n is smaller than 0.1, so the terms of the $e^{0.6}$ series are smaller than the corresponding terms of the geometric series. Thus, the geometric series forms an upper bound for the tail of the $e^{0.6}$ series after term t_6.

d. Geometric series converges to

$0.0000648 \cdot \frac{1}{1 - 0.1} = 0.000072$

e. The tail of the series after t_6 is bounded by 0.000072.

The entire series is bounded by

$S_6(0.6) + 0.000072 = 1.8221128 + 0.000072$
$= 1.8221848$

$e^{0.6} = 1.8221188...$

So the upper bound is just above $e^{0.6}$, Q.E.D.

21. Alternating Series Remainders Property Problem

a. $\sin x = \sum_{n=0}^{\infty} (-1)^n \frac{1}{(2n+1)!} x^{2n+1}$

$t_3 = (-1)^3 \cdot \frac{1}{(2 \cdot 3 + 1)!} \cdot 0.6^{2 \cdot 3+1}$

$= -\frac{1}{7!} 0.6^7 = -0.00000555428571...$

b. $S_1(0.6) = 0.6 - \frac{1}{3!}0.6^3 = 0.564$

$S_2(0.6) = 0.6 - \frac{1}{3!}0.6^3 + \frac{1}{5!}0.6^5 = 0.564648$

c. $R_1 = \sin 0.6 - S_1(0.6) = 0.0006424...$

$R_2 = \sin 0.6 - S_2(0.6) = -0.0000055266...$

$|R_1| = 0.0006424...$

$|t_2| = 0.000648$

$\therefore |R_1| < |t_2|$

$|R_2| = 0.0000055266...$

$|t_3| = 0.0000055542...$

$\therefore |R_2| < |t_3|$

d. The terms are strictly alternating in sign.

The terms are strictly decreasing in absolute value.

The terms approach zero for a limit as $n \to \infty$.

Thus, the series converges by the alternating series test.

Or:

$|R_n| < |t_{n+1}|$ for all $n \ge 1$, as shown by example in part c.

$\lim_{n\to\infty} |t_{n+1}| = 0$, since it takes the form $\frac{0}{\infty}$.

$\therefore \lim_{n\to\infty} |R_n| = 0$, and thus the series converges.

Or: Use the ratio technique.

$L = \lim_{n\to\infty} \left| \frac{0.6^{2n+3}}{(2n+3)!} \cdot \frac{(2n+1)!}{0.6^{2n+1}} \right|$

$= 0.36 \lim_{n\to\infty} \frac{1}{(2n+3)(2n+2)} = 0$

Because $L < 1$, the series converges.

22. Infinite Overhang Problem

a. Assume all the blocks have equal mass = m with the center of mass at the center of the block, and equal length = L.

Write H_n = the distance the nth block overhangs the (n + 1)th block. (n = 1 for the top block.)

Note that according to the rule, H_n = the distance between the rightmost edge of the nth block and the center of mass of the pile of the top n blocks.

Now, the center of mass of the nth block is $\frac{1}{2}L$ units from its rightmost edge; and the center of mass of pile of the top n – 1 blocks is 0 units from (i.e., right on top of) the edge of the nth block according to the rule.

Therefore, the center of mass of the pile of the top n blocks is $\frac{1}{nm}(\frac{1}{2}L \cdot m + 0 \cdot (n-1)m)$ units from the edge of the nth block, i.e., $H_n = \frac{1}{2n}L$. QED.

b. The total distance the top (1st) block overhangs the nth block is $H_1 + H_2 + ... + H_{n-1}$. So for a pile of n blocks, the top block will project entirely beyond the bottom block if

$L < H_1 + ... + H_{n-1} = \frac{1}{2}L + \frac{1}{4}L + \frac{1}{6}L + ... + \frac{1}{2(n-1)}L.$

The first n for which $1 < \frac{1}{2} + \frac{1}{4} + \frac{1}{6} + ... + \frac{1}{2(n-1)}$ is $n = 5$.

c. To make a pile with overhang H, find an n such that $1 + \frac{1}{2} + \frac{1}{3} + ... + \frac{1}{n-1} > \frac{2H}{L}$ (this is possible since the harmonic series diverges to infinity). Then a stack of n blocks will have total overhang

$H_1 + ... + H_{n-1} = \frac{1}{2}L + \frac{1}{4}L + \frac{1}{6}L + ... + \frac{1}{2(n-1)}L$

$= \frac{1}{2}L(1 + \frac{1}{2} + \frac{1}{3} + ... + \frac{1}{n+1})$

$< \frac{1}{2}L \cdot \frac{2H}{L} = H.$

(The achieved overhang is greater than H, so one may pull blocks slightly back—moving blocks back can only make the pile more stable—until the overhang equals H exactly.)

d. The theoretical overhang for a stack of 52 objects is:

$H = H_1 + ... + H_{51} = \frac{1}{2}L + \frac{1}{4}L + \frac{1}{6}L + ... + \frac{1}{102}L$

$= L(\frac{1}{2} + \frac{1}{4} + \frac{1}{6} + ... + \frac{1}{102})$

$= 2.2594...\ L,$

slightly over two-and-a-quarter card lengths.

23. Convergence of Sequences Proof

The Least Upper Bound postulate says that any nonempty set of real numbers that has an upper bound has a least upper bound. In particular, any number less than this least upper bound cannot be an upper bound for the set.

The set of real numbers $\{t_1, t_2, t_3, ...\}$ is non-empty and is bounded above (given). Therefore this set has a least upper bound L. Any number less than L is also less than some t_D in the set.

Claim: $L = \lim_{n\to\infty} t_n$

Proof:

Pick a number $\varepsilon > 0$.

Since L is an upper bound for t_n, $L + \varepsilon$ is also an upper bound.

Since L is the least upper bound for t_n, $L - \varepsilon$ is not an upper bound.

$\therefore$ there exists an integer $D > 0$ such that $t_D > L + \varepsilon$.

But the values of t_n are increasing.

$\therefore t_n > t_D > L - \varepsilon$ for all $n > D$.

Keep $n > D$.

Then $L - \varepsilon < t_n < L + \varepsilon$.

Thus, t_n is within ε units of L for all $n > D$.

$\therefore L = \lim_{n\to\infty} t_n$ by the definition of limit as $n \to \infty$, Q.E.D.

24. Sequences vs. Series Problem

The sequence 1.9, 1.99, 1.999, ... converges since the nth term, t_n, has a limit, 2, as $n \to \infty$.

The series 1.9 + 1.99 + 1.999 + ... does not converge since the sequence of partial sums, 1.9, 3.89, 5.889, ... becomes infinite. For a series to converge, a necessary condition is that $t_n \to 0$ as n approaches infinity.

25. $\sum_{n=0}^{\infty} \frac{3}{4^n} = 3 + \frac{3}{4} + \frac{3}{16} + \frac{3}{64} + ...$

Converges because it is a geometric series with common ratio 1/4, which is less than 1 in absolute value.

26. $\sum_{n=0}^{\infty} \frac{3^n}{4^n} = 1 + \frac{3}{4} + \frac{9}{16} + \frac{27}{64} + ...$

Converges because it is a geometric series with common ratio 3/4, which is less than 1 in absolute value.

27. $\sum_{n=0}^{\infty} \frac{1}{(2n+1)!} = \frac{1}{1!} + \frac{1}{3!} + \frac{1}{5!} + \frac{1}{7!} + ...$

$= 1 + \frac{1}{6} + \frac{1}{120} + \frac{1}{5040} + ...$

Converges by comparison with:

Geometric series with $t_0 = 1$ and $r = 1/6$.

Factorial reciprocal series in Problem 19.

28. $\sum_{n=0}^{\infty} \frac{1}{(-3)^n} = 1 - \frac{1}{3} + \frac{1}{9} - \frac{1}{27} + ...$

Converges by the alternating series test.

(Terms are strictly alternating.

Terms are strictly decreasing in absolute value.

t_n approaches 0 as n approaches infinity.)

29. $\sum_{n=2}^{\infty} \frac{n^3}{n^4 - 1} = \frac{8}{15} + \frac{27}{80} + \frac{64}{255} + \frac{125}{624} + ...$

Diverges. Use the integral test.

$\int_2^{\infty} \frac{x^3}{x^4 - 1}\,dx = \lim_{b\to\infty} \frac{1}{4} \ln |x^4 - 1| \Big|_2^b$

$= \lim_{b\to\infty} (\frac{1}{4} \ln (b^4 - 1) - 0) = \infty$

Or: Compare with a harmonic series.

$\sum_{n=2}^{\infty} \frac{n^3}{n^4-1} > \sum_{n=2}^{\infty} \frac{1}{n} \to \infty$

30. $\sum_{n=0}^{\infty} \sin n = \sin 0 + \sin 1 + \sin 2 + \sin 3 + ...$

$= 0 + 0.8414... + 0.9092... + 0.1411... + ...$

Diverges. t_n does not approach 0 as $n \to \infty$.

31. Journal Problem

Journal entries will vary.

Problem Set 12-8, pages 646 to 649 — Error Analysis for Series

Q1. ratio technique
Q2. |common ratio| < 1
Q3. for all values of x
Q4. radius = 1
Q5. $x - \frac{1}{3}x^3 + \frac{1}{5}x^5 - \frac{1}{7}x^7 + ...$
Q6. Graph, sketch.

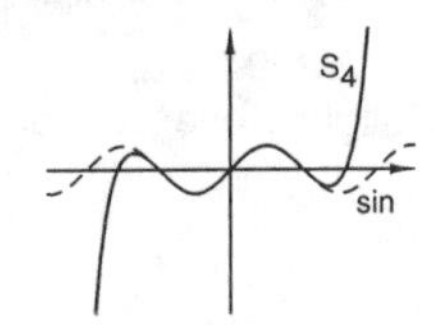

Q7. $\ln |\sec x + \tan x| + C$
Q8. $y' = \sec^2 x$
Q9. $\tan x + C$
Q10. Newton and Leibniz

1\. a. $\cosh x = \sum_{n=0}^{\infty} \frac{1}{(2n)!} x^{2n}$

$S_5(4) = 27.2699118...$

b. $R_5(4) = \frac{f^{(2\cdot5+2)}(c)}{(2\cdot5+2)!} \cdot 4^{2\cdot5+2}$

$f^{(12)}(x) = \cosh x$

$\therefore M = \cosh 4 < \frac{1}{2}(3^4 + 2^{-4}) = 40.5312... < 41$

$|R_5(4)| \le \frac{41}{12!} \cdot 4^{12} = 1.4360...$

$S_5(4)$ is within 2 of cosh 4 in the units digit.

c. cosh 4 = 27.3082328...

$S_5(4)$ = 27.2699118...

$\cosh 4 - S_5(4) = 0.0383...$, which is well within the 1.4360... upper bound found by Lagrange's form.

2. a. $\sinh x = \sum_{n=0}^{\infty} \frac{1}{(2n+1)!} x^{2n+1}$

$S_9(5) = 74.2032007...$

b. $R_9(5) = \frac{f^{(2\cdot 9+3)}(c)}{(2\cdot 9+3)!} \cdot 5^{2\cdot 9+3}$

$f^{(21)}(x) = \cosh x$

$\therefore M = \cosh 5 < \frac{1}{2}(3^5 + 2^{-5}) = 121.5156... < 122$

$|R_9(5)| \le \frac{122}{21!} \cdot 5^{21} = 0.001138...$

$S_9(5)$ is within 2 units of sinh 5 in the third decimal place.

c. $\sinh 5 = 74.2032105...$
$S_9(5) = 74.2032007...$
$\sinh 5 - S_9(5) = 0.00000981...$, which is well within the 0.001138... upper bound found by Lagrange's form.

3. a. $e^x = \sum_{n=0}^{\infty} \frac{x^n}{n!}$

The 15th partial sum is $S_{14}(3) = 20.0855234...$.

b. $R_{14}(3) = \frac{f^{(15)}(c)}{15!} \cdot 3^{15}$

$f^{(15)}(x) = e^x$

$\therefore M = e^3 < 3^3 = 27$

$|R_{14}(3)| \le \frac{27}{15!} \cdot 3^{15} = 0.0002962...$

$S_{14}(3)$ is within 3 units of e^3 in the 4th decimal place.

c. $e^3 = 20.085536923...$
$S_{14}(3) = 20.085523458...$
$e^3 - S_{14}(3) = 0.00001346...$, which is within the 0.0002962... found by Lagrange's form.

4. a. $\ln x = \sum_{n=1}^{\infty} (-1)^{n+1} \cdot \frac{1}{n} (x-1)^n$

$S_8(0.7) = -0.356671944...$

b. $R_8(0.7) = \frac{f^{(9)}(c)}{9!} \cdot (0.7-1)^9$

$f^{(9)}(x) = 8!x^{-9}$

$\therefore M = 8!(0.7)^{-9}$

$|R_8(0.7)| \le \frac{8!(0.7)^{-9}}{9!} \cdot (0.3)^9 = \frac{1}{9}(3/7)^9$

$= 5.4195... \times 10^{-5}$

$S_8(0.7)$ is within 6 units of ln 0.7 in the 5th decimal place.

(Note that for ln x, Lagrange's form of the remainder simplifies to

$|R_n(x)| \le \frac{1}{n+1} \cdot \left(\frac{|x-1|}{x}\right)^{n+1}$

For $x < 0.5$, the fraction $|x-1|/x$ is greater than 1. Lagrange's form of the remainder becomes infinite as $n \to \infty$, and is thus not useful.)

c. $\ln 0.7 = -0.356674943...$
$S_8(0.7) = -0.356671944...$
$|\ln 0.7 - S_8(0.3)| = 2.9998 \times 10^{-6}$, which is within the $5.4195... \times 10^{-5}$ found by Lagrange's form.

5. For sinh 2, all derivatives are bounded by cosh 2.

$\cosh 2 < \frac{1}{2}(3^2 + 2^{-2}) = 4.625$

General term is $t_n = \frac{1}{(2n+1)!} \cdot 2^{2n+1}$

For 6-place accuracy,

$|R_n(2)| \le \frac{4.625}{(2n+3)!} \cdot 2^{2n+3} < 0.5 \times 10^{-6}$

The second inequality is first true for n = 6.
Use at least 7 terms (n = 6).

6. For cosh 3, all derivatives are bounded by cosh 3.

$\cosh 3 < \frac{1}{2}(3^3 + 2^{-3}) = 13.5625$

General term is $t_n = \frac{1}{(2n)!} \cdot 3^{2n}$

For 8-place accuracy,

$|R_n(3)| \le \frac{13.5625}{(2n+2)!} \cdot 3^{2n+2} < 0.5 \times 10^{-8}$

The second inequality is first true for n = 10.
Use at least 11 terms (n = 10).

7. For ln x, $f^{(n)}(0.6) = (-1)^{n+1}(n-1)!(0.6)^{-n} = M$

$|R_n(0.6)| \le \frac{n!(0.6)^{-(n+1)}}{(n+1)!} \cdot |0.6-1|^{n+1} = \frac{1}{n+1} \cdot \left(\frac{2}{3}\right)^{n+1}$

For 7-place accuracy,

$\frac{1}{n+1} \cdot \left(\frac{2}{3}\right)^{n+1} < 0.5 \times 10^{-7}$

This inequality is first true for n = 32.
Use at least 32 terms.

8. For e^{10}, all derivatives are bounded by e^{10}.

$e^{10} < 3^{10} = 59049$

For 5-place accuracy,

$|R_n(10)| \le \frac{59049}{(n+1)!} \cdot 10^{n+1} < 0.5 \times 10^{-5}$

The second inequality is first true for n = 43.
Use 44 terms (n = 43).

9. $\cosh 2 = 3.76219569...$
$S_4(2) = 3.76190476...$
$\cosh 2 - S_4(2) = 0.000290929...$

General term is $t_n = \frac{1}{(2n)!} \cdot 2^{2n}$

$R_4(2) = \frac{f^{(2\cdot 4+2)}(c)}{(2\cdot 4+2)!} \cdot 2^{2\cdot 4+2} = \cosh c \cdot \frac{2^{10}}{10!}$

$\therefore \cosh c \cdot \frac{2^{10}}{10!} = 0.000290929...$

$\cosh c = 1.03098027...$
$c = \cosh^{-1} 1.0309... = 0.2482...$,
which is between 0 and 2.

10. $e^5 = 148.413159...$
$S_{19}(5) = 148.413107...$
$e^5 - S_{19}(5) = 5.1234... \times 10^{-5}$

General term is $\frac{1}{n!} 5^n$

$R_{19}(5) = \frac{f^{(20)}(c)}{20!} \cdot 5^{20} = e^c \cdot \frac{5^{20}}{20!}$

$\therefore e^c \cdot \frac{5^{20}}{20!} = 5.1234... \times 10^{-5}$

$e^c = 1.30702806...$
$c = \ln 1.3070... = 0.2677...$,
which is between 0 and 5.

11. $\cos 2.4 = 1 - \frac{1}{2!}(2.4)^2 + \frac{1}{4!}(2.4)^4 - \frac{1}{6!}(2.4)^6 + \frac{1}{8!}(2.4)^8 - \frac{1}{10!}(2.4)^{10} + \ldots$
$= 1 - 2.88 + 1.3824 - 0.2654208 + 0.0273004\ldots - \ldots$
The terms are strictly alternating. They are decreasing in absolute value after t_1, and they approach zero for a limit as $n \to \infty$.
Therefore, the hypotheses of the alternating series test apply, and $|R_n(2.4)| < |t_{n+1}| = \frac{1}{(2n+2)!}(2.4)^{2n+2}$
For 6-place accuracy make $|R_n(2.4)| < 0.5 \times 10^{-6}$
The inequality is first true for n = 7.
Use 8 terms (n = 7).

12. $e^{-2} = 1 + (-2) + \frac{1}{2!}(-2)^2 + \frac{1}{3!}(-2)^3 + \frac{1}{4!}(-2)^4 + \frac{1}{5!}(-2)^5 + \frac{1}{6!}(-2)^6 + \ldots$
$= 1 - 2 + 2 - 1.3333\ldots + 0.6666\ldots - 0.2666\ldots + \ldots$
The terms are strictly alternating. They are decreasing in absolute value after t_2, and they approach zero for a limit as $n \to \infty$.
Therefore the hypotheses of the alternating series test apply, and $|R_n(-2)| < |t_{n+1}| = \frac{1}{(n+1)!} \cdot 2^{n+1}$
For 7-place accuracy make $|R_n(-2)| < 0.5 \times 10^{-7}$.
The inequality is first true for n = 14.
Use 15 terms (n = 14).

13. p-Series Problem I
$S = \sum_{n=1}^{\infty} \frac{1}{n^3}$ and thus $R_{10} = \sum_{n=11}^{\infty} \frac{1}{n^3}$
$R_{10} > \int_{11}^{\infty} x^{-3}\,dx = \lim_{b\to\infty} -\frac{1}{2}x^{-2}\Big|_{11}^{b}$
$= \lim_{b\to\infty} (-\frac{1}{2}b^{-2} + \frac{1}{2}\cdot 11^{-2}) = 0.004132\ldots$
$R_{10} < \int_{11}^{\infty} (x-1)^{-3}\,dx = \lim_{b\to\infty} -\frac{1}{2}(x-1)^{-2}\Big|_{11}^{b}$
$= \lim_{b\to\infty} (-\frac{1}{2}b^{-2} + \frac{1}{2}\cdot 10^{-2}) = 0.005$
$\therefore 0.004132\ldots < R_{10} < 0.05$
$t_{11} = \frac{1}{1331} = 0.0007513\ldots$
R_{10} is considerably greater than the first term of the tail of the series.
$R_n < \frac{1}{2}n^{-2}$
For 5-place accuracy, make $R_n < 0.5 \times 10^{-5}$.
$\frac{1}{2}n^{-2} < 0.5 \times 10^{-5}$ is first true for n = 317.
Use 317 terms.

14. p-Series Problem II
In this p-series, p = 0.5, which is not greater than or equal to 1. Thus, the series diverges and the remainder is infinite.

15. p-Series Problem III
$R_{99} = \sum_{n=100}^{\infty} \frac{1}{n^{1.05}}$
$R_{99} > \int_{100}^{\infty} x^{-1.05}\,dx = \lim_{b\to\infty} -\frac{1}{0.05}x^{-0.05}\Big|_{100}^{b}$
$= \lim_{b\to\infty} (-20b^{-0.05} + 20\cdot 100^{-0.05}) = 15.8865\ldots$
$R_{99} < \int_{100}^{\infty} (x-1)^{-1.05}\,dx = \lim_{b\to\infty} -\frac{1}{0.05}(x-1)^{-0.05}\Big|_{100}^{b}$
$= \lim_{b\to\infty} (-20(b-1)^{-0.05} + 20\cdot 99^{-0.05})$
$= 15.8945\ldots$
So, Amos, the 4.69030101... you calculated for S_{99} is not close to the actual limit to which the series converges.
(A reasonable estimate for S, the number to which the series converges, is the average of the upper and lower bounds added to the value of S_{99}.
$S \approx 4.69030101\ldots + \frac{1}{2}(15.8945\ldots + 15.8865\ldots)$
$= 20.5808\ldots$)

16. Ratio Technique and p-Series Problem
Let $S = \sum_{n=1}^{\infty} \frac{1}{n^p}$
$L = \lim_{n\to\infty} \left|\frac{1}{(n+1)^p} \cdot \frac{n^p}{1}\right| = \lim_{n\to\infty} \left(\frac{n}{n+1}\right)^p = 1^p = 1$
Thus, L is never less than 1, and the ratio technique does not give conclusive results.

17. Geometric Series as an Upper Bound Problem
$e^2 = \sum_{n=0}^{\infty} \frac{1}{n!} \cdot 2^n$
From Example 1, $S_{10} = 7.38899470\ldots$
By Lagrange form, $|R_{10}| < 0.0004617\ldots$
Use a geometric series as an upper bound.
$t_{11} = \frac{1}{11!}\cdot 2^{11}$ and $t_{12} = \frac{1}{12!}\cdot 2^{12}$
Common ratio $r = \frac{t_{12}}{t_{11}} = \frac{1}{6}$
$\therefore |R_{10}| < \frac{1}{11!}\cdot 2^{11} \cdot \frac{1}{1 - \frac{1}{6}} = 0.00006156\ldots$
The geometric series gives a better estimate of the remainder than does the Lagrange form.

18. Values of e^x from Values of e^{-x} Problem
$e^{-2} = \sum_{n=0}^{\infty} (-1)^n \frac{1}{n!} \cdot 2^n$
$S_{10} = 0.135379188\ldots$
$|R_{10}| < |t_{11}| = \frac{2^{11}}{11!} = 0.000051306\ldots$
This number appears to be a better estimate of the error. However, it represents a 0.03791...% error.
$e^2 \approx 1/S_{10} = 7.38665971\ldots$
A 0.037...% error for this value would be 0.002802... , which is a worse estimate of the error than that by Lagrange or by geometric series.
(In general, an error of ε% in1/f(x) gives a maximum error of
$\frac{\varepsilon}{1 - \varepsilon/100}$ in the value of f(x). So an error of 0.03791...% in $1/e^2$ means an error of
$\frac{0.03791\ldots}{1 - 0.0003791\ldots} = 0.03793\ldots\%$ in e^2.)

19. Sin x for Any Argument Using a Value of x in [0, π/4]

a. $\frac{250}{2\pi} = 39.7887357...$

Thus, 250 radians is 39 complete cycles plus 0.7887... additional cycle, or
$b = (2\pi)(0.7887...) = 4.9557730...$ radians.
$\sin b = -0.970528019...$
$\sin 250 = -0.970528019...$, which (Checks.)
The value of b can be calculated efficiently using the fraction part command. For a typical grapher,
b = fPart(250/2π)2π

b. From Figure 12-8b, you can tell that the value of c is one cycle back from the value of b.
$c = b - 2\pi = -1.32741228...$
Check:
$\sin c = -0.970528019...$
$\sin 250 = -0.970528019...$, (Checks.)
In general:
If b is in $[0, \pi/2]$, then $c = b$.
If b is in $(\pi/2, 3\pi/2]$, then $c = \pi - b$.
If b is in $(3\pi/2, 2\pi]$, then $c = 2\pi - b$.

c. From Figure 12-8b, you can tell that the value of d is a quarter-cycle ahead of the value of c. The value of the sine is the opposite of the corresponding value of cos d.
$d = \frac{\pi}{2} + c = 0.243384039...$
Check:
$-\cos d = -0.970528019...$
$\sin 250 = -0.970528019...$, (Checks.)
In general:

$c \in [-\frac{\pi}{2}, -\frac{\pi}{4})$: $d = \frac{\pi}{2} + c$ and $\sin x = -\cos d$

$c \in [-\frac{\pi}{4}, 0)$: $d = -c$ and $\sin x = -\sin d$

$c \in [0, \frac{\pi}{4})$: $d = c$ and $\sin x = \sin d$

$c \in [\frac{\pi}{4}, \frac{\pi}{2}]$: $d = \frac{\pi}{2} - c$ and $\sin x = \cos d$

d. For x in $[0, \pi/4]$, both the sine and cosine series meet the hypotheses of the alternating series test. Thus, the error in $S_5(x)$ is bounded by $|t_6|$, the first term of the tail. $|t_6|$ is greater for the cosine series than for the sine series. The maximum of $|t_6|$ in the interval is at $x = \pi/4$.

$\therefore |R_5(x)| < |t_6(\pi/4)| = \frac{1}{(2\cdot 6 + 2)!}(\pi/4)^{2\cdot 6+2}$
$= 3.8980... \times 10^{-13}$,
which is small enough to guarantee that sin x will be correct to 10 decimal places.
For direct calculation,

$|R_n(250)| < \frac{1}{(2n + 3)!} \cdot 250^{2n+3} < 0.5 \cdot 10^{-10}$

The second inequality is first true when n is 348.
Since both numerator and denominator may overflow most computers, you can calculate values of ln $|R_n(250)|$ as follows:

$\ln |R_n(250)| = (2n + 3) \ln 250 - \sum_{i=2}^{2n+3} \ln i$

Then compare the values with $\ln (0.5 (10^{-10})$.
So you would need to use 349 terms. Unfortunately, even this procedure would not be practical, since the terms themselves would have to be calculated to 10 or more decimal places, and they are so large that each term overflows most computers' capacities.

e. The program will have the following steps. The particular commands will depend on the grapher or computer used.
- Put in a value of x.
- Find b, as shown in part a., above.
- Find c, as shown in part b., above.
- Find d, as shown in part c., above.
- Chose the function and sign as shown in c.
- Calculate and display the answer.

20. For sin 1, $|R_n(1)| < |t_{n+1}| = \frac{1}{(2n + 3)!} \cdot 1^{2n+3} = \frac{1}{(2n + 3)!}$

Set $\frac{1}{(2n + 3)!} < 0.5 \times 10^{-23}$
This inequality is first true for n = 11.
Use at least 12 terms (n = 11).
Using the technique in Problem 19,

$|R_n(1)| < \frac{1}{(2n + 2)!}(\pi/4)^{2n+2} < 0.5 \cdot 10^{-23}$

The second inequality is first true for n = 10.
You would save only one term by the method of Problem 19.

21. Derivation of the Lagrange Form of the Remainder

a. Apply the mean value theorem to f'(x) on [a, x].
There is a number x = c in (x, a) such that

$f''(c) = \frac{f'(x) - f'(a)}{x - a}$

$\Rightarrow f'(x) = f'(a) + f''(c)(x - a)$, Q.E.D.

b. $\int f'(x)\,dx = \int f'(a)\,dx + \int f''(c)(x - a)\,dx$

$f(x) = f'(a)x + f''(c)\cdot\frac{1}{2}(x - a)^2 + C$

Substituting the initial condition (a, f(a)) gives
$f(a) = f'(a)a + f''(c)(0) + C \Rightarrow C = f(a) - f'(a)a$
$f(x) = f'(a)x + f''(c)\cdot\frac{1}{2}(x - a)^2 + f(a) - f'(a)a$

$f(x) = f(a) + f'(a)(x - a) + \frac{1}{2}f''(c)(x - a)^2$, Q.E.D.

c. Apply the mean value theorem to f''(x) on [a, x].
There is a number x = c in (a, x) such that

$f'''(c) = \frac{f''(x) - f''(a)}{x - a}$

$\Rightarrow f''(x) = f''(a) + f'''(c)(x - a)$

Integrate once to get f'(a).
$\int f''(x)\,dx = \int f''(a)\,dx + \int f'''(c)(x - a)\,dx$

$f'(x) = f''(a)x + f'''(c)\cdot\frac{1}{2}(x - a)^2 + C$

Use (a, f'(a)) as an initial condition.

$f'(a) = f''(a)a + \frac{1}{2}f'''(c)(0) + C \Rightarrow C = f'(a) - f''(a)a$

$f'(x) = f''(a)x + \frac{1}{2}f'''(c)(x - a)^2 + f'(a) - f''(a)a$

$f'(x) = f'(a) + f''(a)(x - a) + \frac{1}{2}f'''(c)(x - a)^2$

Integrate again to get f(x).

$\int f'(x)\,dx = \int f'(a)\,dx + \int f''(a)(x-a)\,dx$

$+\int \frac{1}{2}f'''(c)(x-a)^2\,dx$

$f(x) = f'(a)x + \frac{1}{2}f''(a)(x-a)^2 + \frac{1}{6}f'''(c)(x-a)^3 + C$

Use (a, f"(a)) as an initial condition.

$f(a) = f'(a)a + \frac{1}{2}f''(a)(0) + \frac{1}{6}f'''(c)(0) + C$

$\Rightarrow C = f(a) - f'(a)a$

$f(x) = f'(a)x + \frac{1}{2!}f''(a)(x-a)^2 + \frac{1}{3!}f'''(c)(x-a)^3 + f(a) - f'(a)a$

$f(x) = f(a) + f'(a)(x-a) + \frac{1}{2!}f''(a)(x-a)^2 + \frac{1}{3!}f'''(c)(x-a)^3$, Q.E.D.

d. The technique is mathematical induction.

22. A Pathological Function

a. $f(x) = \begin{cases} e^{-x^{-2}}, & \text{if } x \ne 0 \\ 0, & \text{if } x = 0 \end{cases}$

It is given that $f^{(n)}(0) = 0$ for all n > 0.

$c_0 = f(0) = 0$

$c_1 = f'(0) = 0$

$2!c_2 = f''(0) = 0 \Rightarrow c_2 = 0$

$3!c_3 = f'''(0) = 0 \Rightarrow c_3 = 0...$

$\therefore$ series is $0 + 0x + 0x^2 + 0x^3 + ...$, Q.E.D.

b. Each partial sum of the Maclaurin series equals zero for any value of x. Thus, the sequence of partial sums converges to zero for all x. But f(x) does not equal zero except at x = 0. Thus, the series converges to f(x) only at x = 0.

c. $e^{-x^{-2}} = 1 + (-x^{-2}) + \frac{1}{2!}(-x^{-2})^2 + \frac{1}{3!}(-x^{-2})^3 + ...$

$= 1 - x^{-2} + \frac{1}{2!}x^{-4} - \frac{1}{3!}x^{-6} + ...$

d. The fourth partial sum, $S_3(2) = 0.7786458333...$.

$f(2) = e^{-2^{-2}} = e^{-0.25} = 0.7788007830...$

The partial sum is close to f(2), so it is reasonable to make the conjecture that the Laurent series converges to f(2).

23. The Maclaurin Series for e^x v' Score Converges to e^x

Using the Lagrange form of the remainder, the value of e^x is given *exactly* by

$e^x = \sum_{n=0}^{k} \frac{1}{n!}x^n + R_k(x)$, where

$R_k(x) = \frac{f^{(k+1)}(c)}{(k+1)!}x^{k+1}$ and c is between 0 and x.

$|R_k(x)| \le \frac{M}{(k+1)!}|x|^{k+1}$

Since all derivatives of e^x equal e^x, the value of M for any particular value of x is also e^x, which is less than 3^x, if $x \ge 0$; or 1, if $x < 0$.

$\lim_{k\to\infty} |R_k(x)| < \lim_{k\to\infty} \frac{3^x}{(k+1)!}|x|^{k+1}$

which approaches 0 as $k \to \infty$ by the ratio technique. Since the remainder approaches zero as n approaches infinity, e^x is given exactly by

$e^x = \sum_{n=0}^{\infty} \frac{1}{n!}x^n$, Q.E.D.

Review Problems

R0. Journal entries will vary.

R1. $f(x) = \frac{9}{1-x}$ and $P(x) = 9 + 9x + 9x^2 + 9x^3 + ...$

Graph, f(x), $P_5(x)$, and $P_6(x)$, showing that P(x) is close to f(x) for x between about –0.7 and 0.6, and bears little resemblance to f(x) beyond ±1

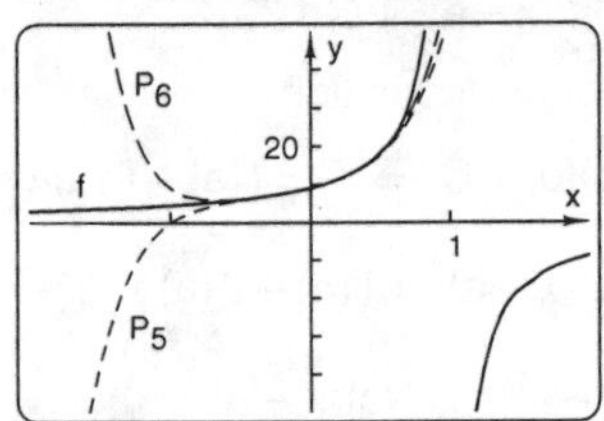

$P_5(0.4) = 14.93856$

$P_6(0.4) = 14.975424$

$f(0.4) = 15$

$\therefore P_6(0.4)$ is closer to f(0.4) than $P_5(0.4)$ is, Q.E.D.

$P_5(x) = 9 + 9x + 9x^2 + 9x^3 + 9x^4 + 9x^5$ $\quad P_5(0) = 9$

$P_5'(x) = 9 + 18x + 27x^2 + 36x^3 + 45x^4$ $\quad P_5'(0) = 9$

$P_5''(x) = 18 + 54x + 108x^2 + 180x^3$ $\quad P_5''(0) = 18$

$P_5'''(x) = 54 + 216x + 540x^2$ $\quad P_5'''(0) = 54$

$f(x) = 9(1-x)^{-1}$ $\quad f(0) = 9$

$f'(x) = 9(1-x)^{-2}$ $\quad f'(0) = 9$

$f''(x = 18(1-x)^{-3}$ $\quad f''(0) = 18$

$f'''(x) = 54(1-x)^{-4}$ $\quad f'''(0) = 54$

$\therefore P_5'(0) = f'(0)$, $P_5''(0) = f'(0)$, and $P_5'''(0) = f'''(0)$

$P_n(x)$ is a subset of a geometric series.

R2. a. Biceps Problem

Series is 3 + 2.7 + 2.43 + 2.187 + ...

After 10 days, $S_{10} = 3 \cdot \frac{1 - 0.9^{10}}{1 - 0.9} = 19.5396...$

About 19.5 mm increase in 10 days

$S = 3 \cdot \frac{1}{1 - 0.9} = 30$

About 30 mm increase eventually

b. Present Value Problem

Let x be the amount invested to have 0.5 million at the end of 19 years.

Interest rate is 10% per year, so the amount at the end of a year is 1.1 times the amount at the beginning of the year.

$x(1.1^{19}) = 0.5$

$x = 0.5(1.1^{-19}) = 0.081753995...$

They must invest $81,754.00 now in order to make the last payment.

The total to invest is the sum

$0.5(1.1^{-1}) + 0.5(1.1^{-2}) + ... + 0.5(1.1^{-19})$

This is the 19th partial sum of the geometric series with first term $0.5(1.1)^{-1}$ and common ratio 1.1^{-1}.

$S_{19} = 0.5(1.1^{-1}) \cdot \dfrac{1 - 1.1^{-19}}{1 - 1.1^{-1}} = 4.182460045...$

They must invest $4,182,460.05 now to make all 19 payments.

R3. $P(x) = c_0 + c_1x + c_2x^2 + c_3x^3 + c_4x^4 + ...$

$f(x) = 7e^{3x} \Rightarrow f(0) = 7 \Rightarrow c_0 = 7$

$f'(x) = 21e^{3x} \Rightarrow f'(0) = 21 \Rightarrow c_1 = 21$

$f''(x) = 63e^{3x} \Rightarrow f''(0) = 63 \Rightarrow 2!c_2 = 63 \Rightarrow c_2 = 31.5$

$f'''(x) = 189e^{3x} \Rightarrow f'''(0) = 189 \Rightarrow c_3 = 189/3! = 31.5$

R4. a. $e^{0.12} = 1.127496851...$

$S_3(0.12) = 1.127488$, which is close to $e^{0.12}$.

b. $\cos 0.12 = 0.9928086358538...$

$S_3(0.12) = 0.9928086358528$, which is close.

c. $\sinh(0.12) = 0.1202882074311...$

$S_3(0.12) = 0.1202882074310...$, which is close.

d. $\ln 1.7 = 0.530628251...$

$S_{20}(1.7) = 0.530612301...$, which is close.

$\ln 2.3 = 0.83290912...$

$S_{20}(2.3) = -4.42067878...$, which is not close.

R5. a. A Maclaurin series is a Taylor series expanded about x = 0.

b. Substitute t = x + 1 into

$\ln t = (t-1) - \frac{1}{2}(t-1)^2 + \frac{1}{3}(t-1)^3 - \frac{1}{4}(t-1)^4 + ...$

$\ln(x+1) = x - \frac{1}{2}x^2 + \frac{1}{3}x^3 - \frac{1}{4}x^4 + ... = \sum_{n=1}^{\infty} \frac{(-1)^{n+1}}{n}x^n$

c. Assume one may integrate this function term by term.

$\int \ln(x+1)\,dx = \frac{1}{2}x^2 - \frac{1}{3\cdot 2}x^3 + \frac{1}{4\cdot 3}x^4 - ... + C$

$= \sum_{n=1}^{\infty} \frac{(-1)^{n+1}}{(n+1)n}x^{n+1}$

d. $\int \ln(x+1)\,dx = (x+1)\ln(x+1) - (x+1) + C_1$

$= x\ln(x+1) + \ln(x+1) - x + C \qquad (C = C_1 - 1)$

$= x^2 - \frac{1}{2}x^3 + \frac{1}{3}x^4 - \frac{1}{4}x^5 + ...$

$+ x - \frac{1}{2}x^2 + \frac{1}{3}x^3 - \frac{1}{4}x^4 + ... - x + C$

$= \frac{1}{2}x^2 - \frac{1}{3\cdot 2}x^3 + \frac{1}{4\cdot 3}x^4 - ... + C,$

which is the same as the series in part c.

e. $\int_0^x t\cos t^2\,dt = \int_0^x t(1 - \frac{1}{2!}(t^2)^2 + \frac{1}{4!}(t^2)^4 - ...)\,dt$

$= \int_0^x (t - \frac{1}{2!}t^5 + \frac{1}{4!}t^9 - \frac{1}{6!}t^{13} + ...)\,dt$

$= \frac{1}{2}x^2 - \frac{1}{6\cdot 2!}x^6 + \frac{1}{10\cdot 4!}x^{10} - \frac{1}{14\cdot 6!}x^{14} + ...$

(Note that the series can be transformed to

$= \frac{1}{2}(x^2 - \frac{1}{3!}(x^2)^3 + \frac{1}{5!}(x^2)^5 - \frac{1}{7!}(x^2)^7 + ...)$

$= \frac{1}{2}\sin(x^2)$.)

f. $\tan^{-1} x = \int_0^x \frac{1}{1+t^2}\,dt$

$= \int_0^x (1 - t^2 + (t^2)^2 - (t^2)^3 + (t^2)^4 - ...)\,dt \quad (|t| \le 1)$

$= x - \frac{1}{3}x^3 + \frac{1}{5}x^5 - \frac{1}{7}x^7 + \frac{1}{9}x^9 - ...$

g. $f(3) = 5 \Rightarrow c_0 = 5$

$f'(3) = 7 \Rightarrow c_1 = 7$

$f''(3) = -6 \Rightarrow c_2 = -6/2! = -3$

$f'''(3) = 0.9 \Rightarrow c_3 = 0.9/3! = 0.15$

$\therefore f(x) = 5 + 7(x-3) - 3(x-3)^2 + 0.15(x-3)^3 + ...$

R6. a. $\sum_{n=1}^{\infty} = (-3)^{-n}(x-5)^n$

$= -\frac{1}{3}(x-5) + \frac{1}{9}(x-5)^2 - \frac{1}{27}(x-5)^3 + ...$

b. $L = \lim_{n\to\infty} \left| \frac{(-3)^{-(n+1)}(x-5)^{n+1}}{(-3)^{-n}(x-5)^n} \right|$

$= \frac{1}{3}|x-5|$

$L < 1 \Leftrightarrow |x-5| < 3 \Leftrightarrow 2 < x < 8.$

Open interval of convergence is (2, 8).

Radius of convergence = 3.

c. $\cosh x = \sum_{n=0}^{\infty} \frac{1}{(2n)!}x^{2n}$

$L = \lim_{n\to\infty} \left| \frac{x^{2n+2}}{(2n+2)!} \cdot \frac{(2n)!}{x^{2n}} \right|$

$= x^2 \lim_{n\to\infty} \frac{1}{(2n+2)(2n+1)}$

$= x^2 \cdot 0$

L < 1 for all x.

Series converges for all x, Q.E.D.

d. $e^{1.2} = 1 + 1.2 + \frac{1}{2!}(1.2)^2 + \frac{1}{3!}(1.2)^3 + \frac{1}{4!}(1.2)^4 + ...$

$S_4(1.2) = 3.2944$ (the fifth partial sum)

$e^{1.2} = 3.32011692...$

Error $= e^{1.2} - S_4(1.2) = 0.02571692...$

First term of the tail is $t_5 = \frac{1}{5!}(1.2)^5 = 0.020736$

The error is greater than t_5, but not much greater.

e. Graphs, $y = \ln x$, $y = S_{10}(x)$, and $y = S_{11}(x)$

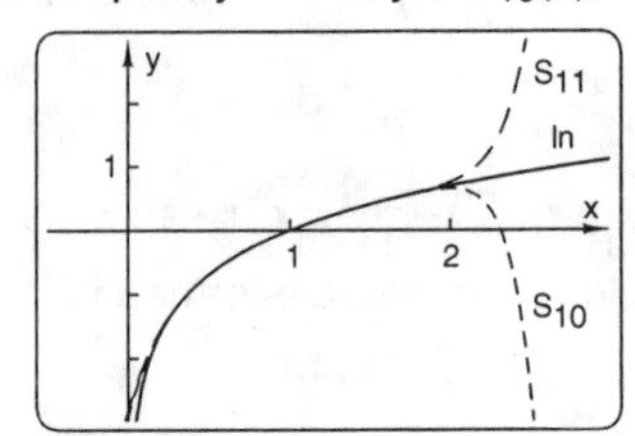

The open interval of convergence is (0, 2). Both partial sums fit ln well within this interval. Above x = 2 the partial sums diverge rapidly to $\pm\infty$. Below x = 0, the partial sums give answers, but there are no real values for ln x.

R7. a. $S_{10} = 1000 \cdot \dfrac{1 - 0.8^{10}}{1 - 0.8} = 4463.129088$ (exactly).

b. $S = 1000\sum_{n=0}^{\infty} 0.8^n = \dfrac{1000}{1 - 0.8} = 5000$

$S - S_{10} = 536.870912$, which differs from the limit by about 10.7%.

c. "Tail"

d. "Remainder"

e. $1 + \frac{1}{8} + \frac{1}{27} + \frac{1}{64} + \ldots = \sum_{n=1}^{\infty} \frac{1}{n^3}$

$R_{10} = \sum_{n=11}^{\infty} \frac{1}{n^3} < \int_{10}^{\infty} \frac{1}{x^3}\,dx = \lim_{b\to\infty} -\frac{1}{2}x^{-2}\Big|_{10}^{b}$

$= \lim_{b\to\infty} (-\frac{1}{2}b^{-2} + \frac{1}{2}\cdot 10^{-2}) = 0.005$

The remainder is bounded above by 0.005.

f. The series converges because the sequence of partial sums is increasing and bounded above by $S_{10} + 0.005$.

g. $2/1! + 4/2! + 8/3! + 16/4! + 32/5! +$
$= 2 + 2 + 1.3333... + 0.6666... + 0.2666... + ...$
$= \sum_{n=1}^{\infty} 2^n/n!$

The terms are decreasing starting at t_2, which can be seen numerically, above, or algebraically by the fact that the next term is formed by multiplying the numerator by 2 and the denominator by more than 2.
R_1 is bounded by the geometric series with first term 2 and common ratio 1.3333.../2 = 2/3.
Since |common ratio| is less than 1, the geometric series converges (to 2/(1 – 2/3) = 6).
Thus, the tail after the first partial sum is bounded above by a convergent geometric series, Q.E.D.

h. Use the Alternating Series test.
The terms alternate in sign, decrease in absolute value, and approach zero for a limit as $n \to \infty$.

i. $|R_{10000}| < |t_{10001}| = 1/10001 = 0.0000999900...$
Upper bound is 1/10001.

j. i. $\sum_{n=1}^{\infty} \dfrac{10^n(x-3)^n}{n^2}$

$L = \lim_{n\to\infty} \left|\dfrac{10^{n+1}(x-3)^{n+1}}{(n+1)^2} \cdot \dfrac{n^2}{10^n(x-3)^n}\right|$

$= 10|x-3| \lim_{n\to\infty} \left(\dfrac{n}{n+1}\right)^2 = 10|x-3| \cdot 1$

$L < 1 \Leftrightarrow 10|x-3| < 1 \Leftrightarrow 2.9 < x < 3.1$

At x = 2.9, the series is

$-1 + \frac{1}{4} - \frac{1}{9} + \frac{1}{16} - \ldots$, which converges by the alternating series test.

At x = 3.1, the series is

$1 + \frac{1}{4} + \frac{1}{9} + \frac{1}{16} + \ldots$, which converges because it is a p-series with p = 2.

Interval of convergence is [2.9, 3.1].

ii. $\sum_{n=1}^{\infty} \dfrac{(-1)^n(x+1)^n}{n\cdot 2^n}$

$L = \lim_{n\to\infty} \left|\dfrac{(x+1)^{n+1}}{(n+1)\cdot 2^{n+1}} \cdot \dfrac{n\cdot 2^n}{(x+1)^n}\right|$

$= \frac{1}{2}|x+1| \lim_{n\to\infty} \dfrac{n}{n+1} = \frac{1}{2}|x+1| \cdot 1$

$L < 1 \Leftrightarrow \frac{1}{2}|x+1| < 1 \Leftrightarrow |x+1| < 2 \Leftrightarrow -3 < x < 1$

At x = –3 the series is

$1 + \frac{1}{2} + \frac{1}{3} + \frac{1}{4} + \ldots$, which is a divergent harmonic series.

At x = 1 the series is

$-1 + \frac{1}{2} - \frac{1}{3} + \frac{1}{4} - \ldots$, which converges by the alternating series test.

Interval of convergence is [–3, 1].

k. i. $\sum_{n=0}^{\infty} \dfrac{10}{n!} = 10 + 10 + 5 + 1.6666... + 0.4166... + ...$

The tail after S_0 is bounded above by the convergent geometric series with first term 10 and common ratio 0.5. Thus, the series converges. (Other justifications are possible.)

ii. $\sum_{n=1}^{\infty} (n^{-3} + 5^{-1}) = 1.2 + 0.325 + 0.2370...$
$+ 0.215625 + 0.208 + 0.2046... + 0.2029... + ...$

Diverges because $t_n \to 0.2$, not 0, as $n\to\infty$.

R8. a. $\cosh 2 = \sum_{n=0}^{\infty} \dfrac{1}{(2n)!} \cdot 2^{2n}$

Fourth partial sum is $S_3(2)$.

The (2n)th derivative of cosh x is cosh x, so all derivatives are bounded by

$\cosh 2 < \frac{1}{2}(3^2 + 2^{-2}) = 4.625$

$|R_3(2)| \le \dfrac{4.625}{8!} \cdot 2^8 = 0.02936...$

Error is less than 0.03.

b. $e^3 = \sum_{n=0}^{\infty} \frac{1}{n!} \cdot 3^n$

All derivatives of e^x are equal to e^x, so all derivatives are bounded by $e^3 < 3^3 = 27$.

For 20-place accuracy,

$|R_n(3)| \le \frac{27}{(n+1)!} \cdot 3^{n+1} < 0.5 \times 10^{-20}$

The second inequality is first true for n = 33.

Use at least 34 terms (n = 33).

c. Using the Lagrange form of the remainder, the value of cosh 4 is given *exactly* by

$\cosh 4 = \sum_{n=0}^{k} \frac{1}{(2n)!} \cdot 4^{2n} + R_k(4)$, where

$R_k(4) = \frac{f^{(2k+2)}(c)}{(2k+2)!} \cdot 4^{2k+2}$ and c is between 0 and 4.

$|R_k(4)| \le \frac{M}{(2k+2)!} |4|^{2k+2}$

Since all even derivatives of cosh x equal cosh x, the value of M for any particular value of x is cosh 4, which is less than $\frac{1}{2}(3^4 + 2^{-4}) = 40.53125$.

Use M = 41.

$\lim_{k\to\infty} |R_k(4)| < \lim_{k\to\infty} \frac{41}{(2k+2)!} \cdot 4^{2k+2}$

$= 41 \lim_{k\to\infty} \frac{4^{2k+2}}{(2k+2)!} = 0$

By the ratio technique, this fraction approaches zero as k approaches infinity. Therefore, since the remainder approaches zero as k approaches infinity, cosh 4 is given exactly by

$\cosh 4 = \sum_{n=0}^{\infty} \frac{1}{(2n)!} \cdot 4^{2n}$, Q.E.D.

d. $\sinh 0.6 = \sum_{n=0}^{\infty} \frac{1}{(2n+1)!} \cdot 0.6^{2n+1}$

$S_3(0.6) = 0.636653554...$

$\sinh 0.6 = 0.636653582...$

$\sinh 0.6 - S_3(0.6) = 2.7862... \times 10^{-8}$

$R_3(0.6) = \frac{f^{(2\cdot3+3)}(c)}{(2\cdot3+3)} = \frac{\cosh c}{9!} \cdot 0.6^9 = 2.7862... \times 10^{-8}$

$\cosh c = 1.00328...$

$c = \cosh^{-1} 1.00328... = 0.0809...$, which is in the interval (0, 0.6).

e. $\ln x = \sum_{n=1}^{\infty} (-1)^{n+1} \frac{1}{n}(x-1)^n$

$|R_n(1.3)| < |t_{n+1}|$

For 20-place accuracy, make

$\frac{1}{n+1}(1.3-1)^{n+1} < 0.5 \times 10^{-20}$

This inequality is first true for n = 35.

Use at least 35 terms.

f. $R_{50} = \sum_{n=51}^{\infty} \frac{1}{p^4} < \int_{50}^{\infty} x^{-4}\,dx = \lim_{b\to\infty} -\frac{1}{3}x^{-3}\Big|_{50}^{b}$

$= \lim_{b\to\infty} (-\frac{1}{3}b^{-3} + \frac{1}{3} \cdot 50^{-3}) = 2.6666... \times 10^{-6}$

An upper bound is $2.6666... \cdot 10^6$.

Concepts Problems

C1. Series with Imaginary Numbers Problem

Recall that $i = \sqrt{-1}$, $i^2 = -1$, $i^3 = -i$, $i^4 = 1$, so $i^{4n} = 1$ and $i^{4n+2} = -1$ for all n.

a. $\cos ix = 1 - \frac{1}{2!}(ix)^2 + \frac{1}{4!}(ix)^4 - \frac{1}{6!}(ix)^6 + \frac{1}{8!}(ix)^8 - ...$

$= 1 - \frac{i^2}{2!}x^2 + \frac{i^4}{4!}x^4 - \frac{i^6}{6!}x^6 + \frac{i^8}{8!}x^8 - ...$

$= 1 - \frac{-1}{2!}x^2 + \frac{1}{4!}x^4 - \frac{-1}{6!}x^6 + \frac{1}{8!}x^8 - ...$

$= 1 + \frac{1}{2!}x^2 + \frac{1}{4!}x^4 + \frac{1}{6!}x^6 + \frac{1}{8!}x^8 + ... = \cosh x$, Q.E.D.

b. $\sin ix = ix - \frac{1}{3!}(ix)^3 + \frac{1}{5!}(ix)^5 - \frac{1}{7!}(ix)^7 + ...$

$= ix - i\frac{i^2}{3!}x^3 + i\frac{i^4}{5!}x^5 - i\frac{i^6}{7!}x^7 + ...$

$= ix - i\frac{-1}{3!}x^3 + i\frac{1}{5!}x^5 - i\frac{-1}{7!}x^7 + ...$

$= i(x + \frac{1}{3!}x^3 + \frac{1}{5!}x^5 + \frac{1}{7!}x^7 + ...) = i \sinh x$, Q.E.D.

c. $e^{ix} = 1 + ix + \frac{1}{2!}(ix)^2 + \frac{1}{3!}(ix)^3 + \frac{1}{4!}(ix)^4 + \frac{1}{5!}(ix)^5 + ...$

$= 1 + ix + \frac{i^2}{2!}x^2 + \frac{i^3}{3!}x^3 + \frac{i^4}{4!}x^4 + \frac{i^5}{5!}x^5 + ...$

$= 1 + ix + \frac{-1}{2!}x^2 + \frac{-i}{3!}x^3 + \frac{1}{4!}x^4 + \frac{i}{5!}x^5 + ...$

$= 1 - \frac{1}{2!}x^2 + \frac{1}{4!}x^4 - ... + i(x - \frac{1}{3!}x^3 + \frac{1}{5!}x^5 - ...)$

$= \cos x + i \sin x$, Q.E.D.

d. Using the formula in part c (Euler's formula):

$e^{i\pi} = \cos \pi + i \sin \pi = -1 + i \cdot 0 = -1$, Q.E.D.

C2. Practical Calculation of Pi Problem

$\tan(4\tan^{-1}\frac{1}{5} - \tan^{-1}\frac{1}{239})$

$= \frac{\tan(4\tan^{-1}\frac{1}{5}) - \tan\tan^{-1}\frac{1}{239}}{1 + \tan(4\tan^{-1}\frac{1}{5}) \cdot \tan\tan^{-1}\frac{1}{239}}$

$= \frac{\tan(4\tan^{-1}\frac{1}{5}) - \frac{1}{239}}{1 + \tan(4\tan^{-1}\frac{1}{5}) \cdot \frac{1}{239}}$

To evaluate $\tan(4\tan^{-1}\frac{1}{5})$, recall that

$\tan 2A = \frac{2\tan A}{1 - \tan^2 A}$.

Therefore,

$\tan(2\tan^{-1}\frac{1}{5}) = \frac{\frac{2}{5}}{1 - (\frac{1}{5})^2} = \frac{5}{12}$

and $\tan(2\cdot2\tan^{-1}\frac{1}{5}) = \frac{\frac{10}{12}}{1 - (\frac{5}{12})^2} = \frac{120}{119}$

Substituting this value gives

$\tan(4\tan^{-1}\frac{1}{5} - \tan^{-1}\frac{1}{239}) = \frac{\frac{120}{119} + \frac{-1}{239}}{1 - \frac{120}{119}\cdot\frac{-1}{239}} = 1$

Thus, $4\tan^{-1}\frac{1}{5} - \tan^{-1}\frac{1}{239} = \tan^{-1} 1 = \frac{\pi}{4}$, Q.E.D.

The two series are:

$4\tan^{-1}\frac{1}{5} = 4\cdot\frac{1}{5} - \frac{4}{3}(\frac{1}{5})^3 + \frac{4}{5}(\frac{1}{5})^5 - \frac{4}{7}(\frac{1}{5})^7 + \ldots$

$\tan^{-1}\frac{1}{239} = 4\cdot\frac{1}{239} - \frac{4}{3}(\frac{1}{239})^3 + \frac{4}{5}(\frac{1}{239})^5 - \ldots$

$|R_n(\frac{1}{5})| < \frac{4}{2n+3}(\frac{1}{5})^{2n+3}$

$|R_n(\frac{1}{239})| < \frac{1}{2n+3}(\frac{1}{239})^{2n+3}$

$|\text{Total remainder}| < \frac{1}{2n+3}(4\cdot(\frac{1}{5})^{2n+3} + (\frac{1}{239})^{2n+3})$

To get π accurate to 50 places, as shown, the remainder for π must be less than 0.5×10^{-50}

For $\pi/4$, remainder must be less than 0.125×10^{-50}.

The inequality

$\frac{1}{2n+3}(4\cdot(\frac{1}{5})^{2n+3} + (\frac{1}{239})^{2n+3}) < 0.125 \times 10^{-50}$

is first true for n = 35.

Use at least 35 terms.

C3. Series Solution of a Differential Equation

a. $y'' + 9xy = 0$; $y = 7$ and $y' = 5$ when $x = 0$.

$y = c_0 + c_1x + c_2x^2 + c_3x^3 + c_4x^4 + c_5x^5 + c_6x^6 + \ldots$

$y' = c_1 + 2c_2x + 3c_3x^2 + 4c_4x^3 + 5c_5x^4 + 6c_6x^5 + \ldots$

$y'' = 2c_2 + 6c_3x + 12c_4x^2 + 20c_5x^3 + 30c_6x^4 + \ldots$

b. Substitute y = 5 in the y-equation: $c_0 = 5$

Substitute y' = 7 in the y'-equation: $c_1 = 7$

c. Constant term: $2c_2 = 0 \Rightarrow c_2 = 0$

x-term: $6c_3 + 9c_0 = 0 \Rightarrow c_3 = \frac{1}{6}(-9\cdot5) = -7.5$

x^2-term: $12c_4 + 9c_1 = 0 \Rightarrow c_4 = \frac{1}{12}(-9\cdot7) = -5.25$

x^3-term: $20c_5 + 9c_2 = 0 \Rightarrow c_5 = \frac{1}{20}(-9\cdot0) = 0$

x^4-term: $30c_6 + 9c_3 = 0 \Rightarrow c_6 = \frac{1}{30}(-9)(-7.5) = 2.25$

d. $y = 5 + 7x + 0x^2 - 7.5x^3 - 5.25x^4 + 0x^5 + 2.25x^6 + \ldots$

$S_6(0.3) = 5 + 7(0.3) - 7.5(0.3)^3 - 5.25(0.3)^4 + 2.25(0.3)^6$

$= 6.85661525$

e. To ascertain convergence or divergence, notice that y can be written as three separate series.

$y = c_0 + \frac{(-9)}{2\cdot3}c_0x^3 + \frac{(-9)^2}{2\cdot3\cdot5\cdot6}c_0x^6 + \ldots$

$+ c_1x + \frac{(-9)}{3\cdot4}c_1x^4 + \frac{(-9)^2}{3\cdot4\cdot6\cdot7}c_1x^7 + \ldots$

$+ c_2x^2 + \frac{(-9)}{4\cdot5}c_2x^5 + \frac{(-9)^2}{4\cdot5\cdot7\cdot8}c_2x^8 + \ldots$

If 0.3 is substituted for x, the first and second series have terms that are strictly alternating, decreasing in absolute value, and approaching 0 for a limit as n approaches infinity. Thus, these series converge by the alternating series test. The third series is zero, since $c_2 = 0$. Thus, the entire series for y converges when x = 0.3.

Chapter Test

T1. $R_{1000} = \sum_{n=1001}^{\infty} 2n^{-3} < \int_{1000}^{\infty} 2x^{-3}\,dx$

$= \lim_{b\to\infty} -x^{-2}\Big|_{1000}^{b} = \lim_{b\to\infty} (-b^{-2} + 1000^{-2}) = 10^{-6}$

The tail is bounded by 10^{-6}.

T2. Since $R_{1000} < 10^{-6}$, S_{1000} should be accurate up to 5 decimal places, and within 1 unit in the 6th place.

T3. $f(x) = \ln x$, $f(1) = 0$, $c_0 = 0$

$f'(x) = x^{-1}$, $f'(1) = 1$, $c_1 = 1$

$f''(x) = -x^{-2}$, $f''(1) = -1$, $2!c_2 = -1$, $c_2 = -\frac{1}{2}$

$f'''(x) = 2x^{-3}$, $f'''(x) = 2$, $3!c_3 = 2$, $c_3 = \frac{1}{3}$

$f^{(4)}(x) = -3!x^{-4}$, $f^{(4)}(1) = -3!$, $4!c_4 = -3!$, $c_4 = -\frac{1}{4}$

...

$\therefore \ln x = (x-1) - \frac{1}{2}(x-1)^2 + \frac{1}{3}(x-1)^3 - \frac{1}{4}(x-1)^4 + \ldots$,

Q.E.D.

T4. $f(x) = \int_0^x \frac{1}{1+t^2}\,dt = \int_0^x (1 - t^2 + t^4 - t^6 + \ldots)\,dt$

$= x - \frac{1}{3}x^3 + \frac{1}{5}x^5 - \frac{1}{7}x^7 + \ldots = \sum_{n=0}^{\infty} (-1)^n \frac{1}{2n+1}x^{2n+1}$

(The same as $\tan^{-1} x$).

T5. $L = \lim_{n\to\infty} \left|\frac{x^{2n+3}}{2n+3}\cdot\frac{2n+1}{x^{2n+1}}\right| = x^2 \lim_{n\to\infty}\frac{2n+1}{2n+3} = x^2 \cdot 1$

$L < 1 \Leftrightarrow x^2 < 1 \Leftrightarrow -1 < x < 1$

At x = −1, the series is

$-1 + \frac{1}{3} - \frac{1}{5} + \frac{1}{7} - \ldots$, which converges by the alternating series test.

At x = 1, the series is

$1 - \frac{1}{3} + \frac{1}{5} - \frac{1}{7} + \ldots$, which converges by the alternating series test.

Interval of convergence is [−1, 1].

T6. $f(0.6) \approx S_{19}(0.6)$ (the 20th partial sum)

$= 0.540419500\ldots$

T7. $f(0.6) \approx 0.540419500\ldots$ numerically

T8. $f(0.6) = \tan^{-1} 0.6 = 0.540419500\ldots$ exactly

The answers to Problems T6 and T7 are correct to at least 10 decimal places.

T9. First term in the tail for $S_{19}(0.6)$ is

$t_{20} = \frac{1}{41}(0.6^{41}) = 1.9562\ldots \times 10^{-11}$, which agrees with the observation that $S_{19}(0.6)$ is correct to at least 10 decimal places.

T10. $\cosh x = 1 + \frac{1}{2!}x^2 + \frac{1}{4!}x^4 + \frac{1}{6!}x^6 + \ldots$

$= \sum_{n=0}^{\infty} \frac{1}{(2n)!}x^{2n}$

T11. All even derivatives of cosh x equal cosh x.

Derivatives are bounded by $\cosh 3 = \frac{1}{2}(e^3 + e^{-3})$

$< \frac{1}{2}(3^3 + 2^{-3}) = 13.5625 = M$

For 10-place accuracy,

$|R_n(3)| \le \frac{13.5625}{(2n+2)!}\cdot 3^{2n+2} < 0.5 \times 10^{-10}$

The second inequality is first true for n = 11.

Use at least 12 terms (n = 11).

T12. $\sin(x^2) = x^2 - \frac{1}{3!}(x^2)^3 + \frac{1}{5!}(x^2)^5 - \frac{1}{7!}(x^2)^7 + \ldots$

$x^2 - \frac{1}{3!}x^6 + \frac{1}{5!}x^{10} - \frac{1}{7!}x^{14} + \ldots$

$= \sum_{n=0}^{\infty} (-1)^n \frac{1}{(2n+1)!}x^{4n+2}$

T13. $1000 + 999 + \ldots$ converges, since $r = 0.999 < 1$.
(It converges to $1000/(1 - 0.999) = 1{,}000{,}000$.)
$0.0001 + 0.0002 + \ldots$ diverges since $r = 2 \ge 1$.

T14. $\sum_{n=1}^{\infty} \frac{(2x-5)^n}{3n}$

$L = \lim_{n\to\infty} \left| \frac{(2x-5)^{n+1}}{3n+3} \cdot \frac{3n}{(2x-5)^n} \right|$

$= |2x-5| \lim_{n\to\infty} \frac{n}{n+1} = |2x-5| \cdot 1$

$L < 1 \Leftrightarrow |2x-5| < 1 \Leftrightarrow -1 < 2x-5 < 1$

$\Leftrightarrow 4 < 2x < 6 \Leftrightarrow 2 < x < 3$

Open interval of convergence is (2, 3).
Radius of convergence is 0.5.

T15. At $x = 2$ the series is
$-\frac{1}{3} + \frac{1}{6} - \frac{1}{9} + \frac{1}{12} - \ldots$, which converges by the alternating series test.
At $x = 3$ the series is
$\frac{1}{3} + \frac{1}{6} + \frac{1}{9} + \frac{1}{12} + \ldots$, which is a divergent harmonic series (or 1/3 of p-series with $p = 1$).
Converges at $x = 2$, diverges at $x = 3$

Cumulative Review Number 1—The Dam Problem

1. Limit: See Sections 1-5, 2-2, 2-5, and 2-7.
Derivative: See Sections 3-2 and 3-4.
Indefinite integral: See Section 3-9.
Definite integral: See Section 5-4.
2. a. Continuity at a point: See Section 2-4.
b. Continuity on an interval: See Section 2-4.
c. Convergence of a sequence: A sequence converges if and only if $\lim_{n\to\infty} t_n$ exists.
d. Convergence of a series: A series converges if and only if the sequence of partial sums converges.
e. Natural logarithm: See Section 6-3.
f. Exponential: $a^x = e^{x \ln a}$.
3. a. Mean value theorem: See Section 5-6.
b. Intermediate value theorem: See Section 2-6.
c. Squeeze theorem: See Section 3-8.
d. Uniqueness theorem for derivatives: See Section 6-4.
e. Limit of a product property: See Section 2-3.
f. Integration by parts formula: See Section 9-2.
g. Fundamental theorem of calculus: See Section 5-8.
h. Lagrange form of the remainder: See Section 12-8.
i. Parametric chain rule: See Section 4-7.
j. Polar differential of arc length: See Section 8-9.
4. a. $f(x) = \int_3^x \sqrt{1 + \operatorname{sech} t}\, dt$, $f'(x) = \sqrt{1 + \operatorname{sech} x}$
b. $f(x) = a^x$, $f'(x) = a^x \ln a$
c. $f(x) = x^a$, $f'(x) = ax^{a-1}$
d. $f(x) = x^x$, $\ln f(x) = x \ln x$,
$1/f(x) \cdot f'(x) = \ln x + x \cdot (1/x)$,
$f'(x) = x^x \ln x + x^x$
e. $\int e^{6x} \cos 3x\, dx$

u	dv
e^{6x} (+)	$\cos 3x$
$6e^{6x}$ (−)	$\frac{1}{3}\sin 3x$
$36e^{6x}$ (+)	$-\frac{1}{9}\cos 3x$

$= \frac{1}{3} e^{6x} \sin 3x + \frac{2}{3} e^{6x} \cos 3x - 4 \int e^{6x} \cos 3x\, dx$

$5 \int e^{6x} \cos 3x\, dx = \frac{1}{3} e^{6x} \sin 3x + \frac{2}{3} e^{6x} \cos 3x + C_1$

$\int e^{6x} \cos 3x\, dx = \frac{1}{15} e^{6x} \sin 3x + \frac{2}{15} e^{6x} \cos 3x + C$

f. $\int \cosh^5 x \sinh x\, dx = \frac{1}{6} \cosh^6 x + C$

g. $\int \sec^3 x\, dx = \frac{1}{2} \sec x \tan x + \frac{1}{2} \ln |\sec x + \tan x| + C$

h. $\int (\sin 5x)^{-1} \cos 5x\, dx = \frac{1}{5} \ln |\sin 5x| + C$

i. $\lim_{x\to 0} \frac{\cos 7x - 1}{13x^2} = \lim_{x\to 0} \frac{-7 \sin 7x}{26x}$
$= \lim_{x\to 0} \frac{-49 \cos 7x}{26} = -\frac{49}{26}$

j. $L = \lim_{x\to 0} (1 - x)^{3/x}$
$\ln L = \lim_{x\to 0} \frac{3 \ln (1 - x)}{x} = \lim_{x\to 0} \frac{-3}{1 - x} = -3$
$L = e^{-3} = 0.04978\ldots$

5. a. $\frac{dy}{dx} = 0.2x - 0.3y + 0.3$, (1, 8). Graph.

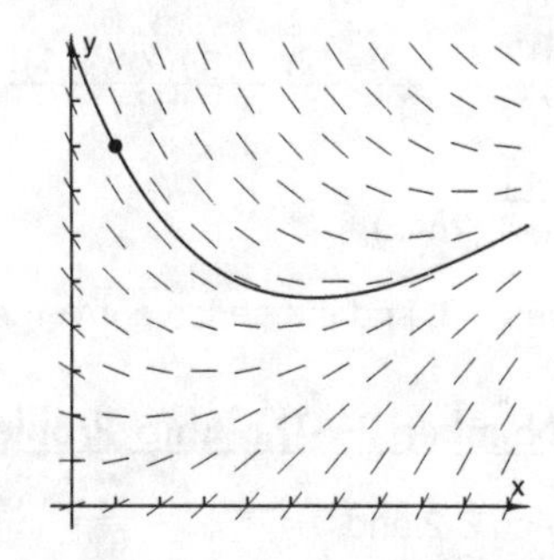

b. If $x = 9$, $y \approx 5.413\ldots$, which agrees with the graph.
6. a. $p = k(40 - y)$
b. $y = 0.1x^2$, $x = (10y)^{1/2}$
$dA = 2x\, dy = 2(10y)^{1/2}\, dy$
$A = \int_0^{40} 2(10y)^{1/2}\, dy = \frac{2}{10} \cdot \frac{2}{3} (10y)^{3/2} \Big|_0^{40}$
$= 3200/3 = 1066.6\ldots\ yd^2$
(Or: Area = 2/3 of circumscribed rectangle $= (2/3)(1600) = 3200/3$, etc.)
c. $dF = p\, dA = k(40 - y) \cdot 2(10y)^{1/2}\, dy$
$F = \int_0^{40} dF = 17066.6\ldots k$ lb (Exactly $256{,}000k/15$)
d. $dM = y\, dF = y \cdot k(40 - y) \cdot 2(10y)^{1/2}\, dy$
$M = \int_0^{40} dM = 292{,}571.4\ldots k$ lb-yd
(Exactly $10{,}240{,}000k/35$)
e. $F \cdot \bar{y} = M$, $\bar{y} = \frac{M}{F} = \frac{10240000k/35}{256000k/15} = 17\frac{1}{7}$ yd
By symmetry, $\bar{x} = 0$.
Center of pressure is at $(0, 17\frac{1}{7})$.

7. a. $z = 30 - 0.5y$

b. For cross section, $A = 2xz = 2(10y)^{1/2}(30 - 0.5y)$.

$A = 10^{1/2}(60y^{1/2} - y^{3/2})$

$A' = 10^{1/2}(30y^{-1/2} - 1.5y^{1/2})$

$= (10^{1/2})(y^{-1/2})(30 - 1.5y)$

$A' = 0 \Leftrightarrow 30 - 1.5y = 0 \Leftrightarrow y = 20$

A' is infinite $\Leftrightarrow y = 0$.

$A(0) = 0$

$A(20) = 565.6854...$ (Exactly $400\sqrt{2}$)

$A(40) = 400$

Max. at $y = 20$; min. at $y = 0$.

c. $dV = 2xz\,dy = 10^{1/2}(60y^{1/2} - y^{3/2})\,dy$

$V = \int_0^{40} dV = 19200$ (exactly)

Use $19200/5 = 3840$ truckloads.

d. $dL = \sqrt{dx^2 + dy^2} = \sqrt{1 + 0.04x^2}\,dx$

$L = \int_{-20}^{20} dL = 92.9356... \approx 92.9$ yd

8. $\vec{r} = (100 \cos 0.03t)\vec{i} + (50 \sin 0.03t)\vec{j}$

$\vec{v} = (-3 \sin 0.03t)\vec{i} + (1.5 \cos 0.03t)\vec{j}$

Speed $= |\vec{v}| = \sqrt{(-3 \sin 1.5)^2 + (1.5 \cos 1.5)^2}$

$= 2.9943... \approx 2.99$ ft/sec

9. $\text{Si } t = \int_0^t \frac{\sin u}{u}\,du$

$= \int_0^t \frac{1}{u}\left(u - \frac{1}{3!}u^3 + \frac{1}{5!}u^5 - \frac{1}{7!}u^7 + ...\right) du$

$= \int_0^t \left(1 - \frac{1}{3!}u^2 + \frac{1}{5!}u^4 - \frac{1}{7!}u^6 + ...\right) du$

$= t - \frac{1}{3 \cdot 3!}t^3 + \frac{1}{5 \cdot 5!}t^5 - \frac{1}{7 \cdot 7!}t^7 + ... + \frac{(-1)^n}{(2n+1)(2n+1)!}t^{2n+1}$

$+ ...$

$L = \lim_{n \to \infty} \left| \frac{t^{2n+3}}{(2n+3)(2n+3)!} \cdot \frac{(2n+1)(2n+1)!}{t^{2n+1}} \right|$

$= t^2 \lim_{n \to \infty} \frac{(2n+1)}{(2n+3)(2n+3)(2n+2)} = t^2 \cdot 0$

$\therefore L < 1$ for all values of t, and the series converges for all values of t.

Third partial sum is

$S_2(0.6) = 0.6 - \frac{1}{3 \cdot 3!}(0.6^3) + \frac{1}{5 \cdot 5!}(0.6^5) = 0.5881296$

$|R_2| < |t_3| = \frac{1}{7 \cdot 7!}(0.6^7) = 0.0000007934...$

Answer is correct within ± 1 in the sixth decimal place.

$\text{Si } 0.6 = \int_0^{0.6} \frac{\sin u}{u}\,du \approx 0.588128809...$

Note that this answer agrees with the third partial sum to within 1 in the sixth decimal place.

10. $r = 5 + 4 \cos \theta$ (changed 5/15/96]

$dA = \frac{1}{2}(5 + 4 \cos \theta)^2\,d\theta$

$A = \int_0^{2\pi} dA \approx 103.6725... \approx 103.7$ ft^2 (exactly 33π)

11. $\frac{dV}{dt} = kV \Rightarrow \frac{dV}{V} = k\,dt$

$\ln |V| = kt + C$

$V = C_1 e^{kt}$

At $t = 0$, $V = 300$.

$300 = C_1$

$\frac{dV}{dt} = -5$ when $V = 300$

$-5 = 300k \Rightarrow k = -\frac{1}{60}$

$\therefore V = 300 e^{-(1/60)t}$

At $t = 10$, $V = 300 e^{-1/6} = 253.9445...$

≈ 253.9 million gal.

Cumulative Review Number 2—The Ship Problem

1. Derivative: See Sect. 3-2 and 3-4
2. Definite integral: See Sect. 5-4.
3. Mean value theorem: See Sect. 5-6.
4. $f(x) = \int_3^x g(t)\,dt \Rightarrow f'(x) = g(x)$
5. $\int \tanh^5 x \operatorname{sech}^2 x\,dx = \frac{1}{6}\tanh^6 x + C$
6. $\int x \sinh 2x\,dx$

u		dv
x	+	sinh 2x
1	−	$\frac{1}{2}$cosh 2x
0	+	$\frac{1}{4}$sinh 2x

$= \frac{1}{2}x \cosh 2x - \frac{1}{4}\sinh 2x + C$

7. $\int \frac{3x + 14}{(x + 3)(x - 2)}\,dx = \int \left(\frac{-1}{x + 3} + \frac{4}{x - 2}\right) dx$

$= -\ln|x + 3| + 4\ln|x - 2| + C$

8. $\int \frac{\sinh x}{x}\,dx = \int \frac{1}{x}\left(x + \frac{1}{3!}x^3 + \frac{1}{5!}x^5 + \frac{1}{7!}x^7 + ...\right) dx$

$= \int \left(1 + \frac{1}{3!}x^2 + \frac{1}{5!}x^5 + \frac{1}{7!}x^6 + ...\right) dx$

$= x + \frac{1}{3 \cdot 3!}x^3 + \frac{1}{5 \cdot 5!}x^5 + \frac{1}{7 \cdot 7!}x^7 + ... + C$

9. $\sum_{n=1}^{\infty} \frac{n(x - 5)^n}{3^n}$

$L = \lim_{n \to \infty} \left| \frac{(n + 1)(x - 5)^{n+1}}{3^{n+1}} \cdot \frac{3^n}{n(x - 5)^n} \right|$

$= \frac{1}{3}|x - 5| \lim_{n \to \infty} \frac{n + 1}{n} = \frac{1}{3}|x - 5| \cdot 1 = \frac{1}{3}|x - 5|$

$L < 1 \Leftrightarrow \frac{1}{3}|x - 5| < 1 \Leftrightarrow -3 < x - 5 < 3$

Open interval of convergence is $2 < x < 8$.

10. $\int_0^1 x^{-0.998}\,dx = \lim_{a \to 0^+} \int_a^1 x^{-0.998}\,dx$

$= \lim_{a \to 0^+} \frac{1}{0.002}x^{0.002}\Big|_a^1 = \lim_{a \to 0^+} (500 - 500a^{0.002})$

$= 500$

11. $y = x^2$

$$\bar{y} = \frac{\int_3^9 x^2\,dx}{9-3} = \frac{1}{6}\cdot\frac{1}{3}x^3\Big|_3^9 = 39$$

12. $f(x) = x^2$

$f(4) = 16$

$f(3.99) = 15.9201$, which is within 0.08 unit of 16.

$f(4.01) = 16.0801$, which is not within 0.08 unit of 16.

Thus, $\delta = 0.01$ is not small enough to keep f(x) within 0.08 unit of 4.

13. $V = \int_2^{10} A\,dx$

$\approx \frac{2}{3}(153 + 4(217) + 2(285) + 4(319) + 343)$

$= 2140\text{ ft}^3$

14. $r = 4\sin 2\theta$

$dA = \frac{1}{2}r^2\,d\theta = 8\sin^2 2\theta\,d\theta$

$A = \int_0^{\pi/2} 8\sin^2 2\theta\,d\theta \approx 6.2831 \approx 6.28\text{ ft}^2$

(Exactly 2π)

15. $(x/5)^2 + (y/3)^2 = 1$

$y = \pm 0.6\sqrt{25 - x^2}$ (Use +)

$dA = 2y\,dx = 1.2\sqrt{25 - x^2}\,dx$

$A = \int_1^5 dA \approx 17.6021... \approx 17.6$ square units

(Exactly $15(\sin^{-1} 1 - \sin^{-1} 0.2) - 1.2\sqrt{6}$)

16. $y = 0.0016x^4$

$dA = (16 - 0.0016x^4)\,dx$

$A = \int_{-10}^{10} (16 - 0.0016x^4)\,dx = 256\text{ ft}^2$

17. $dL = \sqrt{dx^2 + dy^2} = \sqrt{1 + (0.0064x^3)^2}\,dx$

$L = \int_{-10}^{10} dL \approx 42.5483... \approx 42.55$ ft.

18. $p = 62.4(16 - y)$

$dA = 2x\,dy = 10y^{1/4}\,dy$

$dF = p\,dA = 62.4(16 - y)\cdot 10y^{1/4}\,dy$

$F = \int_0^{16} dF \approx 113595.73... \approx 113{,}600$ lb

(Exact: $113595\frac{11}{15}$)

19. $\lim_{x\to\infty} y = \lim_{x\to\infty} \frac{\ln x}{x} \to \frac{\infty}{\infty}$

$= \lim_{x\to\infty} \frac{1/x}{1} = 0$

20. $y' = \frac{(1/x)(x) - (\ln x)(1)}{x^2} = \frac{1 - \ln x}{x^2}$

$y' = 0 \Leftrightarrow \ln x = 1 \Leftrightarrow x = e = 2.718...$ ft.

There is a maximum at x = e since y' goes from positive to negative there.

21. $y'' = \frac{(-1/x)(x^2) - (1 - \ln x)(2x)}{x^4} = \frac{-3 + 2\ln x}{x^3}$

$y'' = 0 \Leftrightarrow \ln x = 1.5 \Leftrightarrow x = e^{1.5} = 4.4816... \approx 4.48$ ft.

There is a point of inflection at $x \approx 4.48$ ft since y'' changes sign there.

22. Graph, $y = (\ln x)/x$.

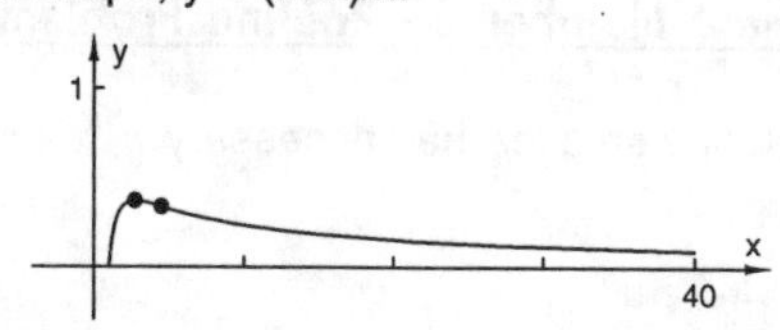

23. $\ln x = (x-1) - \frac{1}{2}(x-1)^2 + \frac{1}{3}(x-1)^3 - ...$

$+ \frac{(-1)^{n+1}}{n}(x-1)^n + ...$

$L = \lim_{n\to\infty} \left|\frac{(x-1)^{n+1}}{(n+1)}\cdot\frac{n}{(x-1)^n}\right|$

$= |x-1| \lim_{n\to\infty} \frac{n}{n+1} = |x-1|\cdot 1 = |x-1|$

$L < 1 \Leftrightarrow |x-1| < 1 \Leftrightarrow -1 < x-1 < 1 \Leftrightarrow 0 < x < 2$

At x = 0 the series is $-1 - \frac{1}{2} - \frac{1}{3} - \frac{1}{4} - ...$, which is a divergent harmonic series.

At x = 2, the series is $1 - \frac{1}{2} + \frac{1}{3} - \frac{1}{4} + ...$, which converges since it meets the three hypotheses of the alternating series test.

$\therefore$ interval of convergence is $0 < x \le 2$, Q.E.D.

24. $|R_n| < |t_{n+1}| = \frac{1}{n+1}(x-1)^{n+1}$

For ln 1.4 to 20 places, make $\frac{0.4^{n+1}}{n+1} < 0.5 \times 10^{-20}$

Solving numerically gives n > 45.817... .

Use 46 terms.

25. If the velocity is 0 ft/sec at time t = 0, the ship speeds up, approaching approximately 34 ft/sec asymptotically as t increases.

If the velocity is 50 ft/sec at time t = 0, the ship slows down, again approaching 34 ft/sec asymptotically as t increases.

(The graphs are shown below. The differential equation is $dv/dt = 0.7(34 - v)$.)

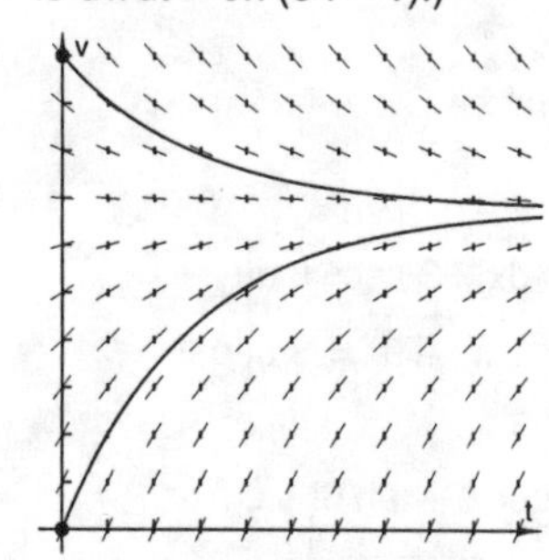

26. $\vec{r} = (\ln t)\,\vec{i} + (\sin 2t)\,\vec{j}$

$\vec{v} = (1/t)\,\vec{i} + (2\cos 2t)\,\vec{j}$

$\vec{a} = (-1/t^2)\,\vec{i} + (-4\sin 2t)\,\vec{j}$

Cumulative Review Number 3—Routine Problems

1. Graph. δ is clearly smaller than necessary

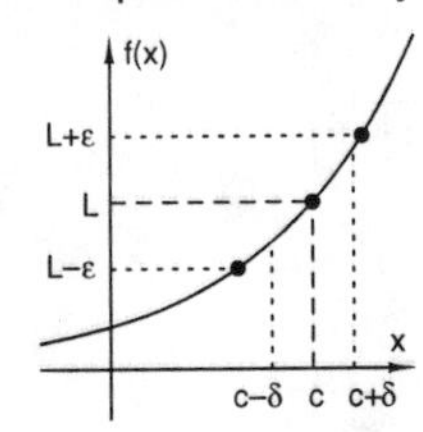

2. See Sections 3-2 and 3-4 for definitions of derivative.
Graphical meaning: Slope of tangent line.
Physical meaning: Instantaneous rate of change.

3. $g(x) = \int f(x)\,dx$ if and only if $g'(x) = f(x)$.

4. $\int_r^s f(t)\,dt = \lim_{\Delta t \to 0} L_n = \lim_{\Delta t \to 0} U_n$, where L_n and U_n are lower and upper Riemann sums, respectively, provided the two limits are equal.

5. l'Hospital's rule.
$$\lim_{x\to 0} \frac{x \cos x}{1 - e^{5x}} \to \frac{0}{0}$$
$$= \lim_{x\to 0} \frac{\cos x - x \sin x}{-5e^{5x}} \to \frac{1}{-5}$$
$= -0.2$

6. $y = \tan(\sin 5x)$
$y' = \sec^2(\sin 5x)\cdot 5\cos 5x$. Chain rule.

7. $y = (5x - 3)(2x + 7)^4(x - 9)$
$\ln y = \ln(5x - 3) + 4\ln(2x + 7) + \ln(x - 9)$
$$y' = y\left(\frac{5}{5x - 3} + \frac{8}{2x + 7} + \frac{1}{x - 9}\right)$$

8. $y = \tan^{-1} x$
$\tan y = x,\ \sec^2 y\, y' = 1$
$$y' = \frac{1}{\sec^2 y} = \frac{1}{1 + \tan^{-1} y}$$
$$y' = \frac{1}{1 + x^2}$$

9. $\int \sin^7 x \cos x\,dx = \frac{1}{8}\sin^8 x + C$

10. $\int \sqrt{x^2 + 9}\,dx$ $\quad x = 3\tan\theta$
$dx = 3\sec^2\theta\,d\theta$
$\sqrt{x^2 + 9} = 3\sec\theta$
$= \int 9\sec^3\theta\,d\theta$
$$= \frac{9}{2}\sec\theta\tan\theta + \frac{9}{2}\ln|\sec\theta + \tan\theta| + C_1$$
$$= \frac{9}{2}\frac{\sqrt{x^2 + 9}}{3}\cdot\frac{x}{3} + \frac{9}{2}\ln\left|\frac{\sqrt{x^2 + 9}}{3} + \frac{x}{3}\right| + C_1$$
$$= \frac{1}{2}x\sqrt{x^2 + 9} + \frac{9}{2}\ln|\sqrt{x^2 + 9} + x| + C$$

11. $$\int \frac{3x - 11}{x^2 + 2x - 3}\,dx = \int \left(\frac{5}{x + 3} + \frac{-2}{x - 1}\right)dx$$
$= 5\ln|x + 3| - 2\ln|x - 1| + C$

12. $\int \sin^{-1} x\,dx$

u	dv
$\sin^{-1} x$ (+)	1
$\frac{1}{\sqrt{1 - x^2}}$ (−)	x

$= x\sin^{-1} x - \int (1 - x^2)^{-1/2}(x\,dx)$
$= x\sin^{-1} x + \frac{1}{2}\int (1 - x^2)^{-1/2}(-2x\,dx)$
$= x\sin^{-1} x + \sqrt{1 - x^2} + C$

13. Fundamental theorem of calculus.
See Section 5-8 for statement.

14. See Figure 5-6a.

15. $f(x) = \int_3^x h(t)\,dt \Rightarrow f'(x) = h(x)$

16. $f(x) = xe^{-x}$
$f'(x) = e^{-x} - xe^{-x}$
$f''(x) = -e^{-x} - e^{-x} + xe^{-x} = e^{-x}(x - 2)$
$f''(x) = 0 \Leftrightarrow x = 2$
$f''(x)$ changes sign at $x = 2$.
$\therefore$ only point of inflection is at $x = 2$.

17. $y = \sin x$ from $x = 0$ to $x = 2$
$dL = \sqrt{dx^2 + dy^2} = \sqrt{1 + \cos^2 x}\,dx$
$L = \int_0^2 dL \approx 2.3516...$

18. a. $\int_0^{16} x^{-3/4}\,dx = \lim_{a\to 0^+} 4x^{1/4}\Big|_a^{16} = \lim_{a\to 0^+}(8 - 4a^{1/4}) = 8$

b. Average value $= \frac{8}{16 - 0} = \frac{1}{2}$

19. $r = 10\cos\theta$
$dA = 50\cos^2\theta\,d\theta$
$A = \int_{0.5}^{1} 50\cos^2\theta\,d\theta \approx 13.3478...$
(Exactly $12.5(1 + \sin 2 - \sin 1)$)

20. $\vec{r} = t^2\vec{i} + 3t^{-1}\vec{j}$
$\vec{v} = 2t\,\vec{i} - 3t^{-2}\vec{j}$
$\vec{v}(1) = 2\vec{i} - 3\vec{j}$
Speed $= \sqrt{13} = 3.6055...$
Distance from origin is $|\vec{r}| = \sqrt{t^4 + 9t^{-2}}$
$$\frac{d|\vec{r}|}{dt} = \frac{1}{2}(t^4 + 9t^{-2})^{-1/2}(4t^3 - 18t^{-3}) = -7/\sqrt{10} \text{ at } t = 1$$
Distance is decreasing at 2.2135... .

21. $y = \cos x$
$dV = 2\pi x\cdot y\cdot dx =$
$V = \int_0^{\pi/2} 2\pi x\cos x\,dx \approx 3.5864...$
(exactly $2\pi(\pi/2 - 1)$)

22. a. $y = -1.5x + 6$
$A = xy = -1.5x^2 + 6x$
$A' = -3x + 6$
$A' = 0 \Leftrightarrow -3x + 6 = 0 \Leftrightarrow x = 2.$
$A(0) = 0,\ A(4) = 0,\ A(2) > 0.$
Thus, maximum area is at $x = 2$, Q.E.D.

b. $V = \pi x^2 y = \pi(-1.5x^3 + 6x^2)$
$V' = \pi(-4.5x^2 + 12x)$
$V' = 0 \Leftrightarrow x = 0 \text{ or } x = 2\frac{2}{3}$
$V(0) = V(4) = 0$ and $V(2\frac{2}{3}) > 0.$
Thus, maximum volume is at $x = 2\frac{2}{3}$.

23. $V \approx \frac{1}{3}(2)(51 + 4(37) + 2(41) + 4(63) + 59) = 394\frac{2}{3}\ \text{ft}^3$

24. a. $\text{erf } x = (2\pi^{-1/2}) \int_0^x e^{-t^2}\,dt$
$f(x) = \int_0^x e^{-t^2}\,dt$
$= \int_0^x (1 - t^2 + \frac{1}{2!}t^4 - \frac{1}{3!}t^6 + \frac{1}{4!}t^8 - \ldots)\,dt$
$= x - \frac{1}{3}x^3 + \frac{1}{5\cdot 2!}x^5 - \frac{1}{7\cdot 3!}x^7 + \frac{1}{9\cdot 4!}x^9 - \ldots$

b. $f(x) = \sum_{n=0}^{\infty} (-1)^n \frac{1}{(2n+1)n!} x^{2n+1}$
$L = \lim_{n\to\infty} \left| \frac{x^{2n+3}}{(2n+3)(n+1)!} \cdot \frac{(2n+1)n!}{x^{2n+1}} \right|$
$= x^2 \lim_{n\to\infty} \frac{(2n+1)}{(2n+3)(n+1)} = x^2 \cdot 0$
$L < 1$ for all values of x, and thus the series converges for all values of x, Q.E.D.

Final Examination, pages 661 to 664

1. $\frac{\sin 1.1 - \sin 1}{0.1} = 0.497363752\ldots$
$\frac{\sin 1.01 - \sin 1}{0.01} = 0.536085981\ldots$
$\frac{\sin 1.001 - \sin 1}{0.001} = 0.539881480\ldots$

2. $f'(1) = \cos 1 = 0.540302305\ldots$
The quotients in Problem 1 are converging to cos 1.

3. $f'(x) = \lim_{h\to 0} \frac{f(x+h) - f(x)}{h}$
$f'(c) = \lim_{x\to c} \frac{f(x) - f(c)}{x - c}$

4. $f(x) = e^x$
$\lim_{x\to 2} f(x) = e^2$
If $f(x) = e^2 + 0.1$, $x = \ln(e^2 + 0.1) = 2.01344\ldots$
If $f(x) = e^2 - 0.1$, $x = \ln(e^2 - 0.1) = 1.98637\ldots$
On the left, keep x within 0.01362... unit of 2.
On the right, keep x within 0.01344... unit of 2.
So you must keep x within 0.01344... unit of 2.

5. $L = \lim_{x\to c} f(x)$ if and only if for any $\varepsilon > 0$ there is a $\delta > 0$ such that if x is within δ units of c but not equal to c, then f(x) is within ε units of L.

6. $\varepsilon = 0.1,\ \delta = 0.01344\ldots$

7. See Figure 1-3a.

8. Graph. Distance ≈ 17.4

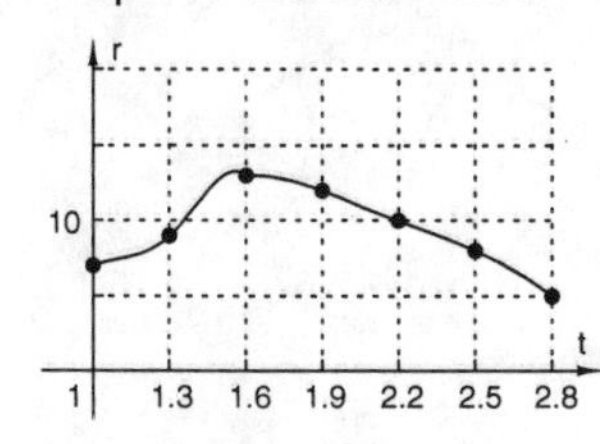

9. Distance $\approx \frac{1}{3}(0.3)(7 + 4(9) + 2(13) + 4(12) + 2(10) + 4(8) + 5)$
$= 17.4$, which agrees with Problem 8.

10. $v(t) = t\,e^{-t}$
Dist. $\approx 0.4(v(0.2) + v(0.6) + v(1) + v(1.4) + v(1.8))$
$= 0.601474\ldots$

11. Dist. $= \int_0^2 t\,e^{-t}\,dt = -t\,e^{-t} - e^{-t} \Big|_0^2$
$= -2e^{-2} - e^{-2} + 0 + 1 = 1 - 3e^{-2} = 0.593994\ldots$
Difference is 0.00748... , which is about 1.26%.

12. If f is integrable on [a, b] and $g(x) = \int f(x)\,dx$, then $\int_a^b f(x)\,dx = g(b) - g(a)$.

13. $f(x) = x^{2/3}$
$f'(x) = \frac{2}{3}x^{-1/3}$
f is differentiable everywhere except at x = 0.
But f is continuous at x = 0, since the limit of f(x) as x approaches 0 is 0, the same as f(0). Thus, f meets the hypotheses of the mean value theorem, since it is differentiable on (0, 1) and continuous at 0 and 1.
Slope of the secant line from (0, 0) to (1, 1) is 1.
$f'(c) = \frac{2}{3}c^{-1/3} = 1 \Leftrightarrow c = \frac{8}{27}$.
Graph. Tangent at x = 8/27 is parallel to secant.

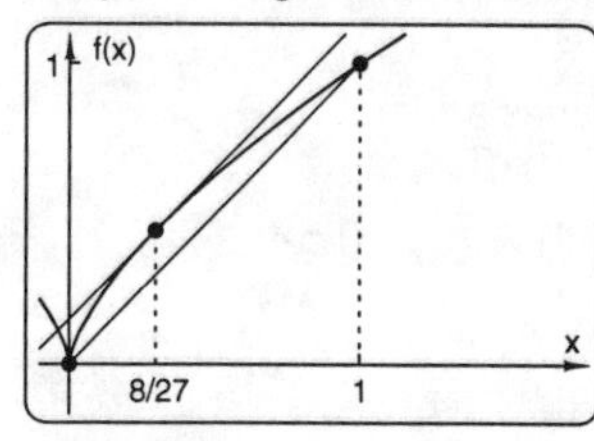

14. a. Example: $\int \frac{5x - 3}{(x-2)(x+3)}\,dx$
$= \int \left(\frac{1}{x-2} + \frac{4}{x+3}\right) dx$
$= \ln|x - 2| + 4\ln|x + 3| + C$

b. Example: $\int \sqrt{9 - x^2}\,dx$ $\quad x = 3\sin\theta$
$dx = 3\cos\theta\,d\theta$
$\sqrt{9 - x^2} = 3\cos\theta$
$= \int 9\cos^2\theta\,d\theta = \frac{9}{2}\int (1 + \cos 2\theta)\,d\theta$
$= \frac{9}{2}\theta + \frac{9}{4}\sin 2\theta + C = \frac{9}{2}\theta + \frac{9}{2}\sin\theta\cos\theta + C$
$= \frac{9}{2}\sin^{-1}\frac{x}{3} + \frac{1}{2}x\sqrt{9 - x^2} + C$

15. $\int \sec^3 x\,dx$

u	dv
sec x	$\sec^2 x$ (+)
sec x tan x	tan x (−)

$= \sec x \tan x - \int \sec x \tan^2 x\,dx$

$= \sec x \tan x - \int \sec^3 x\,dx + \int \sec x\,dx$

$2\int \sec^3 x\,dx = \sec x \tan x + \int \sec x\,dx$

$\int \sec^3 x\,dx = \frac{1}{2}\sec x \tan x + \frac{1}{2}\ln|\sec x + \tan x| + C$

16. $\frac{dy}{dx} = ky \Rightarrow \int \frac{dy}{y} = \int k\,dx \Rightarrow \ln|y| = kx + C \Rightarrow$

$|y| = e^{kx+C} = e^{kx}e^C \Rightarrow y = C_1 e^{kx}$

17. Graph. Cross section of solid at any point in the slice is essentially the same as at the sample point.

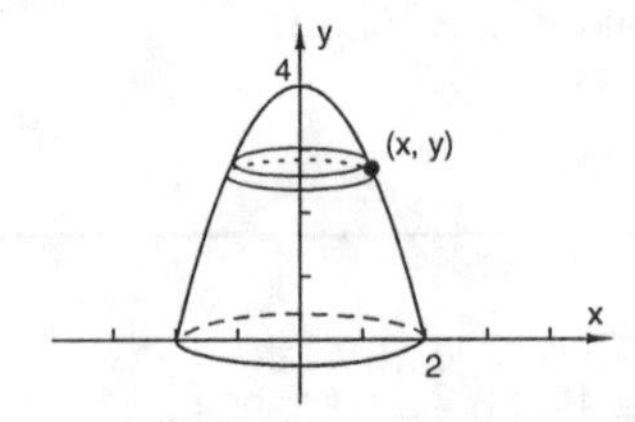

18. Graph. Height at any point in the slice is essentially the same as at the sample point.

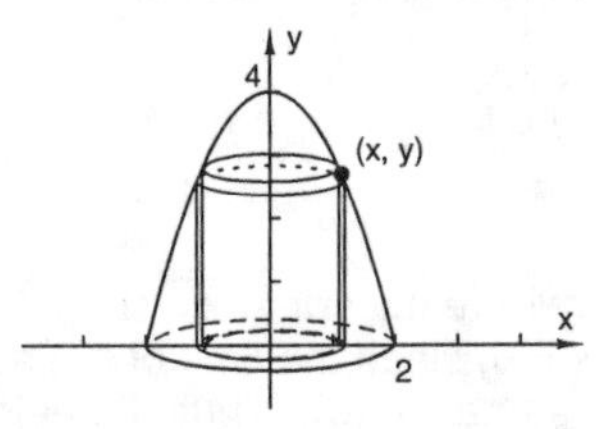

19. $dM_y = x\,dA = x(4 - x^2)\,dx$

$M_y = \int_0^2 x(4 - x^2)\,dx = 4$

$A = \int_0^2 (4 - x^2)\,dx = \frac{16}{3}$

$\bar{x}A = M_y \Rightarrow \bar{x} = \frac{4}{16/3} = \frac{3}{4}$

20. Let H = number of calories added.

$dH = C\,dT = (10 + 0.3T^{1/2})\,dT$

$H = \int_{100}^{900} (10 + 0.3T^{1/2})\,dT = 13{,}200$ cal.

21. a. $\text{Si } x = \int_0^x \frac{\sin u}{u}\,du \Rightarrow \text{Si}'\,x = \frac{\sin x}{x}$

b. $\text{Si } x = \int_0^t (1 - \frac{1}{3!}u^2 + \frac{1}{5!}u^4 - \frac{1}{7!}u^6 + \ldots)\,du$

$= t - \frac{1}{3\cdot3!}t^3 + \frac{1}{5\cdot5!}t^5 - \frac{1}{7\cdot7!}t^7 + \ldots$

c. $\text{Si } 0.7 \approx S_1(0.7) = 0.7 - \frac{1}{3\cdot3!}(0.7^3) = 0.68094444\ldots$

d. $|R_1(0.7)| < |t_2(0.7)| = \frac{1}{5\cdot5!}(0.7^5) = 0.0002801\ldots$

$S_1(0.7)$ equals Si 0.7 correct to 3 decimal places, and is within ±0.3 in the fourth decimal place.

e. See Cumulative Review Number 1, Problem 9.

22. $\vec{r} = (t^3)\vec{i} + (t^2)\vec{j}$

Graph, below.

$\vec{v} = (3t^2)\vec{i} + (2t)\vec{j} \Rightarrow \vec{v}(0.5) = 0.75\vec{i} + 1\vec{j}$

$\vec{a} = (6t)\vec{i} + (2)\vec{j} \Rightarrow \vec{a}(0.5) = 3\vec{i} + 2\vec{j}$

Graph, below.

The object is speeding up at t = 0.5 because the angle between the velocity and acceleration vectors is acute, indicating that the tangential component of acceleration acts in the same direction as the velocity.

(Algebraically, $\vec{v}\cdot\vec{a} = 4.25$, which is positive, again indicating an acute angle)

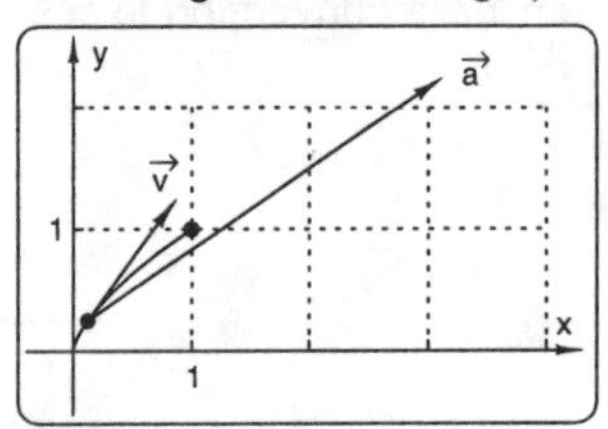

23. $r = \cos\theta$

$dA = \frac{1}{2}r^2\,d\theta = \frac{1}{2}\cos^2\theta\,d\theta$

$A = \int_0^{\pi/6} \frac{1}{2}\cos^2\theta\,d\theta \approx 0.2391\ldots$

(exactly $\frac{\pi}{24} + \frac{\sqrt{3}}{16}$)

Calculus: Concepts and Applications

Correction/Comment Form

Please help us correct and improve *Calculus: Concepts and Applications.* If you find mistakes in the text or the teacher support materials, use this form to let us know. If you have general comments or suggestions about the materials, we'd like to hear those as well. Once you've filled out this form, all you have to do is fold it and drop it in the mail. We'll pay the postage. Thank you!

Your name ____
School ____
School address ____
City/State/Zip ____
Phone ____

Calculus: Concepts and Applications student text

Page ____ Comment ____
Page ____ Comment ____
Page ____ Comment ____
Page ____ Comment ____

Instructor's Guide

Section ______________ Page ____ Comment ________________________________
Section ______________ Page ____ Comment ________________________________
Section ______________ Page ____ Comment ________________________________
Section ______________ Page ____ Comment ________________________________

Instructor's Resource Book

Section ______________ Page ____ Comment ________________________________
Section ______________ Page ____ Comment ________________________________
Section ______________ Page ____ Comment ________________________________
Section ______________ Page ____ Comment ________________________________

Solutions Manual

Section ______________ Page ____ Comment ________________________________
Section ______________ Page ____ Comment ________________________________
Section ______________ Page ____ Comment ________________________________
Section ______________ Page ____ Comment ________________________________

Do you have any other comments about *Calculus: Concepts and Applications* or any suggestions for improving the student text or the teacher's material? ________________________________

____
____
____

Fold carefully along this line.

NO POSTAGE
NECESSARY
IF MAILED
IN THE
UNITED STATES

BUSINESS REPLY MAIL
FIRST CLASS PERMIT NO. 338 EMERYVILLE, CA

POSTAGE WILL BE PAID BY ADDRESSEE

KEY CURRICULUM PRESS
1150 65th Street
Emeryville, CA 94608-9740

Attention Editorial—Foerster, *Calculus*

Fold carefully along this line.

Calculus: Concepts and Applications

Correction/Comment Form

Please help us correct and improve *Calculus: Concepts and Applications.* If you find mistakes in the text or the teacher support materials, use this form to let us know. If you have general comments or suggestions about the materials, we'd like to hear those as well. Once you've filled out this form, all you have to do is fold it and drop it in the mail. We'll pay the postage. Thank you!

Your name ______________________________
School ______________________________
School address ______________________________
City/State/Zip ______________________________
Phone ______________________________

Calculus: Concepts and Applications student text

Page ____ Comment ______________________________
Page ____ Comment ______________________________
Page ____ Comment ______________________________
Page ____ Comment ______________________________

Instructor's Guide

Section __________ Page ____ Comment ______________________________
Section __________ Page ____ Comment ______________________________
Section __________ Page ____ Comment ______________________________
Section __________ Page ____ Comment ______________________________

Instructor's Resource Book

Section __________ Page ____ Comment ______________________________
Section __________ Page ____ Comment ______________________________
Section __________ Page ____ Comment ______________________________
Section __________ Page ____ Comment ______________________________

Solutions Manual

Section __________ Page ____ Comment ______________________________
Section __________ Page ____ Comment ______________________________
Section __________ Page ____ Comment ______________________________
Section __________ Page ____ Comment ______________________________

Do you have any other comments about *Calculus: Concepts and Applications* or any suggestions for improving the student text or the teacher's material? ______________________________

____

____

____

Fold carefully along this line.

NO POSTAGE NECESSARY IF MAILED IN THE UNITED STATES

BUSINESS REPLY MAIL

FIRST CLASS PERMIT NO. 338 EMERYVILLE, CA

POSTAGE WILL BE PAID BY ADDRESSEE

1150 65th Street
Emeryville, CA 94608-9740

Attention Editorial—Foerster, *Calculus*

Fold carefully along this line.